ENCYCLOPEDIA OF
FOREST
SCIENCES

ENCYCLOPEDIA OF
FOREST
SCIENCES

Editor-in-Chief
JEFFERY BURLEY

Editors
JULIAN EVANS
JOHN A YOUNGQUIST

ELSEVIER
ACADEMIC
PRESS

Amsterdam   Boston   Heidelberg   London   New York   Oxford
Paris   San Diego   San Francisco   Singapore   Sydney   Tokyo

Elsevier Ltd., The Boulevard, Langford Lane, Kidlington, Oxford, OX5 1GB, UK

Elsevier Inc., 525 B Street, Suite 1900, San Diego, CA 92101-4495, USA

© 2004 Elsevier Ltd.

FOREWORD

This is a most timely publication because of the vast amount of new information on forest sciences that has been produced over the last few years and because of the growing realization of the vital importance of forests to the world. Fortunately for our future, the world is beginning to realize that forests are both vital for our survival and that they offer many benefits. These benefits vary from the more obvious ones such as timber and fibers for paper pulp, to the environmental aspects such as the sequestration of carbon, the protection of watersheds and the prevention of flooding in many areas. Also there is a growing emphasis on the production of non-timber forest products because of their role in sustainable management of forests.

Since forests are so crucial to our future their sustainable management is essential and this requires a great amount of expertise and information. As I look at the list of the authors and the advisory board of this Encyclopedia, it reads like a who's who of forest science. These experts have put together a collection of information and up-to-date contributions that will be an invaluable resource for anyone involved with forests in any way. I am sure that students at all levels, their teachers and lecturers, professional researchers, policy makers, and even the interested layman or amateur forester will find these volumes of great use.

As I look through the coverage I find it most comprehensive and contemporary. It includes such important modern topics as the molecular biology of forest trees, the role of forests in the carbon cycle, computer modeling and the use of recently developed methods such as geographic information systems. More traditional aspects such as forest biology and ecology, the processing of forest resources into a wide range of products, forestry management and practice and the economic and social aspects of forestry are brought up-to-date here. Not only are the contributions themselves useful, but they also direct the serious investigator to more in-depth or advanced material on each topic. It is also most useful that this fine work will be available in an electronic version that will facilitate cross-referencing to related topics and references.

I know that I will find these volumes most useful and frequently used and I am sure that they will be a standard reference work on forest sciences for at least the next decade. How timely at a period of human history when there is a desperate need to stop deforestation, re-forest many destroyed areas and develop better methods for sustainable use of forests and to conserve the many species of plants and animals which they hold.

Prof. Sir Ghillean Prance FRS
School of Plant Sciences, University of Reading,
Reading, UK

INTRODUCTION

At the start of the Third Millennium the levels of public and political attention to forests, their benefits to mankind, and their management are at their highest. National and international institutions, governmental and non-governmental organizations, all forms of media and representatives of civil society are searching for socially equitable methods of managing forests to obtain all their multiple benefits. Underlying this search is the need for precise and relevant information about the forests, their uses and management together with the political and social institutions that can best effect sustainable management.

Our audience for this reference work includes libraries, governmental and non-governmental organizations, universities and individuals involved in research on forests, forest products and services, and relevant topics, local, national and international decision-making authorities and administrations, forest land-owners and other forest-dependent individuals.

The ranges of biophysical and socio-economic aspects of forests, forestry, forest products and forest services are extremely large; correspondingly, past and current research cover large numbers of scientific disciplines and policy issues. Systematic research has been undertaken for over a century in some forest sciences such as silviculture and forest management; in other topics newly emerging techniques, such as those of molecular genetics, are being developed to aid understanding of physiological and environmental characteristics of trees and forests or to assist selective breeding of trees for plantations. An Encyclopedia of Forest Science therefore has to encompass a broad spectrum of pure and applied sciences, ancient and modern technologies, and old and recent knowledge.

In this Encyclopedia we have obtained outstanding contributions of some 200 specialists covering 250 topics that have wide implications for forest conservation, management and use worldwide. Of course, it is not possible to cover every possible subject of relevance to forests but the ones selected are generally of global interest; and even if they are of local, national or regional character, they are important to all those concerned with forest management, research, education, training, policy-making or public information.

Because of the great breadth of expected readership we asked a wide range of contributing experts to produce up to approximately 4000 words summarizing current views of their topic. The contributions are not written in the traditional form of a scientific journal article with detailed bibliographic references for all major statements. Rather each is a continuous, highly readable description based on an author's personal view of the state of knowledge in her/his area of expertise. Selected major references are given at the end of each contribution to facilitate and encourage further reading on the subject. Wherever possible photographs, other graphical illustrations and tables are used to make the material more concise and visualized. Cross-referencing between contributions and the provision of dummy entries in the table of contents facilitate a full coverage of material relevant to each topic.

Some contributions are short because it proved difficult to identify an author with the appropriate experience and willingness to write full articles. However, these may be enlarged in future editions of the Encyclopedia and in the web-based version of it. The availability of modern information technology facilitates not only the preparation of such a work but also the maintenance of its timeliness, the spreading of its availability and the ease of searching and downloading selected material.

As Editors we thank the authors for their contributions, the editorial advisors for their specialist support, and the staff of Elsevier for their prompt and effective actions that have allowed the four volumes of the Encyclopedia to be published within two years of the initial commissioning of this reference work. We hope that the Encyclopedia will prove to be a valuable tool and source of information for many years to come. In particular we hope it will encourage a growing public and a dedicated profession to understand the facts and institutions necessary for wise management, use and conservation of the world's forest resources for the equitable benefit of all mankind.

Jeffery Burley
Julian Evans
John A. Youngquist

GUIDE TO USE OF THE ENCYCLOPEDIA

Structure of the Encyclopedia

The material in the Encyclopedia is arranged as a series of entries in alphabetical order. Most entries consist of several articles that deal with various aspects of a topic and are arranged in a logical sequence within an entry. Some entries comprise a single article.

To help you realize the full potential of the material in the Encyclopedia we have provided three features to help you find the topic of your choice: a Contents List, Cross-References and an Index.

1. Contents List

Your first point of reference will probably be the contents list. The complete contents list will provide you with both the volume number and the page number of the entry. On the opening page of an entry a contents list is provided so that the full details of the articles within the entry are immediately available.

Alternatively you may choose to browse through a volume using the alphabetical order of the entries as your guide. To assist you in identifying your location within the Encyclopedia a running headline indicates the current entry and the current article within that entry.

You will find 'dummy entries' where obvious synonyms exist for entries or where we have grouped together related topics. Dummy entries appear in both the contents list and the body of the text.

Example
If you were attempting to locate material on yield tables and forecasting via the contents list:

YIELD TABLES *see* MENSURATION: Forest Measurements; Growth and Yield; Timber and Tree Measurements; Yield Tables, Forecasting, Modeling and Simulation.

The dummy entry directs you to the Yield Tables, Forecasting and Simulation article, in the MENSURATION entry. At the appropriate location in the contents list, the page numbers for articles under Mensuration are given.

If you were trying to locate the material by browsing through the text and you looked up Yield Tables then the following information would be provided in the dummy entry:

> **Yield Tables** *see* **Mensuration**: Forest Measurements; Growth and Yield; Timber and Tree Measurements; Yield Tables, Forecasting, Modeling and Simulation.

Alternatively, if you were looking up Mensuration the following information could be provided:

MENSURATION

Contents
Forest Measurements
Timber and Tree Measurements
Growth and Yield
Yield Tables, Forecasting, Modeling and Simulation
Tree-Ring Analysis

2. Cross-References

All of the articles in the Encyclopedia have been extensively cross-referenced.

The cross-references, which appear at the end of an article, serve three different functions. For example, at the end of the PATHOLOGY/Diseases of Forest Trees article, cross-references are used:

i. To indicate if a topic is discussed in greater detail elsewhere.

> PATHOLOGY/Diseases of Forest Trees.
> *See also*: **Ecology**: Plant–Animal Interactions in Forest Ecosystems. **Pathology**: Diseases Affecting Exotic Plantation Species; Heart Rot and Wood Decay; Insect Associated Tree Diseases; Leaf and Needle Diseases; *Phytophthora* Root Rot of Forest Trees; Pine Wilt and the Pine Wood Nematode; Root and Butt Rot Diseases; Rust Diseases; Stem Canker Diseases; Vascular Wilt Diseases. **Soil Biology and Tree Growth**: Soil and its Relationship to Forest Productivity and Health. **Tree Breeding, Practices**: Breeding for Disease and Insect Resistance.

ii. To draw the reader's attention to parallel discussions in other articles.

> PATHOLOGY/Diseases of Forest Trees.
> *See also*: **Ecology**: Plant–Animal Interactions in Forest Ecosystems. **Pathology**: Diseases Affecting Exotic Plantation Species; Heart Rot and Wood Decay; Insect Associated Tree Diseases; Leaf and Needle Diseases; *Phytophthora* Root Rot of Forest Trees; Pine Wilt and the Pine Wood Nematode; Root and Butt Rot Diseases; Rust Diseases; Stem Canker Diseases; Vascular Wilt Diseases. **Soil Biology and Tree Growth**: Soil and its Relationship to Forest Productivity and Health. **Tree Breeding, Practices**: Breeding for Disease and Insect Resistance.

iii. To indicate material that broadens the discussion.

> PATHOLOGY/Diseases of Forest Trees.
> *See also*: **Ecology**: Plant–Animal Interactions in Forest Ecosystems. **Pathology**: Diseases Affecting Exotic Plantation Species; Heart Rot and Wood Decay; Insect Associated Tree Diseases; Leaf and Needle Diseases; *Phytophthora* Root Rot of Forest Trees; Pine Wilt and the Pine Wood Nematode; Root and Butt Rot Diseases; Rust Diseases; Stem Canker Diseases; Vascular Wilt Diseases. **Soil Biology and Tree Growth**: Soil and its Relationship to Forest Productivity and Health. **Tree Breeding, Practices**: Breeding for Disease and Insect Resistance.

3. Index

The index will provide you with the page number where the material is located, and the index entries differentiate between material that is a whole article, is part of an article or is data presented in a figure or table. Detailed notes are provided on the opening page of the index.

4. Glossary

A glossary of terms used within the Encyclopedia appears in Volume 4, before the index. This is organised alphabetically and features explanations of many of the specialist terms used throughout this publication.

5. Contributors

A full list of contributors appears at the begining of each volume.

CONTRIBUTORS

S AbuBakr
Western Michigan University
Kalamazoo, MI, USA

C M Achiam
University of British Columbia
Vancouver, BC, Canada

B J Aegerter
University of California
Davis, CA, USA

S N Aitken
University of British Columbia
Vancouver, Canada

A E Akay
Kahramanmaras Sutcu Imam University
Kahramanmaras, Turkey

W Alfaro
Corporación Nacional Forestal
Santiago, Chile

P W Allen
Harpenden, UK

A Alonso
Smithsonian Institution
Washington, DC, USA

E Apud
University of Concepción, Chile

R G Aravamuthan
Western Michigan University
Kalamazoo, MI, USA

N A Aravind
Ashoka Trust for Research in Ecology and the
   Environment
Hebbal, Bangalore, India

J E M Arnold
Oxford, UK

U Arzberger
Food and Agriculture Organization
Rome, Italy

R H Atalla
USDA
Madison, WI, USA

S Avramidis
University of British Columbia
Vancouver, Canada

A Baldini
Corporación Nacional Forestal
Santiago, Chile

N A Balliet
University of Northern British Columbia
Prince George, BC, Canada

J C G Banks
Australian National University
Canberra, Australia

J Barbour
US Department of Agriculture Forest Service
Portland, OR, USA

J Barlow
University of East Anglia
Norwich, UK

R D Barnes
University of Oxford
Oxford, UK

J R Barnett
University of Reading
Reading, UK

T M Barrett
USDA Forest Service PNW Research Station
Forest Inventory and Analysis
Portland, OR, USA

S Bass
Department for International Development
London, UK

C Beadle
CSIRO Forestry and Forest Products
Hobart, Tasmania, Australia

P Bebi
WSL Swiss Federal Institute for Snow and
    Avalanche Research
Davos, Switzerland

S Bell
Edinburgh College of Art
Edinburgh, UK

N Bhattarai
Government of Nepal
Kathmandu, Nepal

P P Bhojvaid
Forest Research Institute
Dehradun, India

A Blum
Wageningen University
Wageningen, The Netherlands

B Bonnell
Canadian Forest Service
Ottawa, Canada

T H Booth
CSIRO Forestry and Forest Products
Canberra, ACT, Australia

N M G Borralho
Forest and Paper Research Institute (RAIZ)
Alcoentre, Portugal

Ž Borzan
University of Zagreb
Zagreb, Croatia

J L Bowyer
University of Minnesota
St Paul, MN, USA

C L Brack
Australian National University
Canberra, Australia

P Brang
Swiss Federal Research Institute WSL
Birmensdorf, Switzerland

B V Bredenkamp
Department of Forest Science
University of Stellenbosch
South Africa

J L Brewbaker
University of Hawaii
Honolulu, Hawaii, USA

R D Briggs
State University of New York
Syracuse, NY, USA

N Brown
Oxford Forestry Institute
Oxford, UK

L A Bruijnzeel
Vrije Universiteit
Amsterdam, The Netherlands

E M Bruna
University of Florida
Gainesville, FL, USA

R D Burdon
New Zealand Forest Research Institute
Rotorua, New Zealand

J A Burger
Virginia Polytechnic Institute and State University
Blacksburg, VA, USA

J Burley
University of Oxford
Oxford, UK

D F R P Burslem
University of Aberdeen
Aberdeen, UK

Alexander Buttler
University of Franche-Comté
Besançon, France

T D Byram
Texas A&M University
College Station
TX, USA

N Bystriakova
International Network for Bamboo and Rattan
Beijing, China

I R Calder
University of Newcastle upon
Tyne, UK

J H Cameron
Western Michigan University
Kalamazoo, MI, USA

A E Camp
Yale University
New Haven, CT, USA

M G R Cannell
Centre for Ecology and Hydrology
Penicuik, Scotland, UK

R Ceulemans
University of Antwerp
Wilrijk, Belgium

J L Chamberlain
US Department of Agriculture Forest Service
Blacksburg, VA, USA

D C Chaudhari
Forest Research Institute, Dehradun
Uttaranchal, India

J P Cornelius
World Agroforestry Centre
Lima, Peru

J Croke
University of New South Wales
Canberra, Australia

B Dahlin
Swedish University of Agricultural Sciences
Alnarp, Sweden

F Dallmeier
Smithsonian Institution
Washington, DC, USA

C Danks
University of Vermont
Burlington, VT, USA

R K Didham
University of Canterbury
Christchurch, New Zealand

A F G Dixon
University of East Anglia
Norwich, UK

J R dos Santos
National Institute for Space Research
São José dos Campos, Brazil

M R Doshi
Progress in Paper Recycling
Appleton, WI, USA

A Ducousso
INRA, UMR Biodiversité Gènes et Ecosystèmes
Cestas, France

J M Dyer
Weyanwega, WI, USA

O Eckmüllner
Institute for Forest Growth and Yield Research
Vienna, Austria

T Elder
USDA – Forest Service
Pineville, LA, USA

H F Evans
Forestry Commission
Farnham, UK

J Evans
Imperial College London
Ascot, UK

B Fady
Institut National de la Recherche Agronomique
Avignon, France

L L Fagan
Landcare Research
Lincoln, New Zealand

W C Feist
Middleton, WI, USA

M Ferretti
LINNÆA ambiente
Florence, Italy

D Fjeld
Swedish University of Agricultural Sciences
Umeå, Sweden

P D Fleming III
Western Michigan University
Kalamazoo, MI, USA

E M Flores
Academia Nacional de Ciencias
San José, Costa Rica
US Department of Agriculture Forest Service
Starkville, MS, USA

L Fortmann
University of California–Berkeley
Berkeley, CA, USA

J K Francis
Jardín Botánico Sur, San Juan
Puerto Rico, USA

C E Frazier
Virginia Technical Institute
Blacksburg, VA, USA

J S Fried
USDA Forest Service PNW Research Station
Forest Inventory and Analysis
Portland, OR, USA

C J Friel
University of California
Davis, CA, USA

W S Fuller
FRM Consulting
Federal Way, WA, USA

K N Ganeshaiah
Ashoka Trust for Research in Ecology and
   the Environment
Hebbal, Bangalore, India

M Garbelotto
University of California – Berkeley
Berkeley, CA, USA

R García
St Louis, MO, USA

B Gardiner
Forest Research
Roslin, UK

J Ghazoul
Imperial College London
Ascot, UK

J N Gibbs
Aberyail, Llangynidr
Wales, UK

S Gillett
University of Oxford
Oxford, UK

D L Godbold
University of Wales
Bangor, UK

H Goldemund
GeoSyntec Consultants
Atlanta, GA, USA

I S Goldstein
North Carolina State University
Raleigh, NC, USA

T R Gordon
University of California
Davis, CA, USA

J Grace
Edinburgh University
Edinburgh, UK

J E Grogan
Yale University
New Haven, CT, USA

J B Hall
University of Wales
Bangor, UK

J E Hall
Canadian Forest Service
Ottawa, Canada

S W Hallgren
Oklahoma State University
Stillwater, OK, USA

A L Hammett
Virginia State University and Technical Institute
Blacksburg, VA, USA

W E Hammitt
Clemson University
Clemson, SC, USA

G E St J Hardy
Murdoch University
Murdoch, Western Australia

R Harmer
Forest Research
Farnham, UK

S Harris
University of Oxford
Oxford, UK

C D B Hawkins
University of Northern British Columbia
Prince George, BC, Canada

H R Heinimann
Swiss Federal Institute of Technology
Zurich, Switzerland

R Heinrich
Food and Agriculture Organization
Rome, Italy

R Helliwell
West End, Wirksworth
Derbyshire, UK

T L Highley
Henderson, NV, USA

T M Hinckley
University of Washington
Seattle, WA, USA

P Hogarth
University of York
York, UK

C J Houtman
USDA
Madison, WI, USA

M A Hubbe
North Carolina State University
Raleigh, NC, USA

I R Hunter
International Network for Bamboo and Rattan
Beijing, China

J Huss
University of Freiburg
Freiburg, Germany

P Hyttinen
Regional Council of North Karelia
Joensuu, Finland

P J Ince
USDA Forest Service
Madison, WI, USA

J L Innes
University of British Columbia
Vancouver, BC, Canada

G E Jackson
Edinburgh University
Edinburgh, UK

K Jacobs
University of Pretoria
Pretoria, South Africa

R James
Australian National University
Canberra, Australia

J P Janovec
Botanical Research Institute of Texas
Fort Worth, TX, USA

M K Joyce
Western Michigan University
Kalamazoo, MI, USA

M Jurvélius
Forestry Department, FAO
Rome, Italy

F A Kamke
Virginia Polytechnic Institute and State University
Blacksburg, VA, USA

A Kangas
University of Helsinki
Helsinki, Finland

J Kangas
Finnish Forest Research Institute
Joensuu, Finland

P J Kanowski
Australian National University
Canberra, Australia

M Kappelle
Utrecht University
Utrecht, The Netherlands

K Kärkkäinen
Finnish Forest Research Institute
Vantaa, Finland

M Karki
Medicinal and Aromatic Plants Program in Asia
New Delhi, India

D F Karnosky
Michigan Technological University
Houghton, MI, USA

B Kasal
North Carolina State University
Raleigh, NC, USA

S N Kee
University of California
Riverside, CA, USA

G Kerr
Forestry Commission Research Agency
Farnham, UK

B B Kinloch
Institute of Forest Genetics
Berkeley, CA, USA

E D Kjaer
The Royal Agriculture and Veterinary University
Hoersholm, Denmark

M Köhl
Dresden University of Technology
Dresden, Germany

C C Konijnendijk
Danish Forest and Landscape Research Institute
Hoersholm, Denmark

A V Korotkov
UN Economic Commission for Europe Timber Section
Geneva, Switzerland

V Koski
Vantaa, Finland

M V Kozlov
University of Turku
Turku, Finland

A Kremer
INRA, UMR Biodiversité Gènes et Ecosystèmes
Cestas, France

B Krishnapillay
Forest Research Institute Malaysia
Kepong, Malaysia

T Krug
National Institute for Space Research
São José dos Campos, Brazil

S A Laird
University College London
Ascot, UK

D Lamb
University of Queensland
Brisbane, Australia

A Lawrence
University of Oxford
Oxford, UK

R R B Leakey
James Cook University
Cairns, Queensland, Australia

S R Leather
Imperial College London
Ascot, UK

V LeMay
University of British Columbia
Vancouver, BC, Canada

W J Libby
University of California Forest Products Laboratory
Berkeley, CA, USA

K H Ludovici
US Department of Agriculture Forest Service
Research Triangle Park, USA

A E Lugo
US Department of Agriculture Forestry Service
Río Piedras, Puerto Rico, USA

H G Lund
Forest Information Services
Gainesville, VA, USA

E Mackie
Forest Research
Farnham, UK

P Maclaren
Piers Maclaren & Associates
Rangiora, New Zealand

P Maiteny
South Bank University
London, UK

K M Martin-Smith
University of Tasmania
Hobart, Tasmania, Australia

W L Mason
Northern Research Station
Roslin, UK

R Matthews
Forest Research
Farnham, UK

C Mátyás
University of West Hungary
Sopron, Hungary

D G McCullough
Michigan State University
East Lansing, MI, USA

J J McDonnell
Oregon State University
Corvallis, OR, USA

T J McDonough
Institute of Paper Science and Technology
Atlanta, GA, USA

C R McIntyre
McIntyre Associates
Walls, MS, USA

K McNabb
Auburn University
Auburn, AL, USA

R E McRoberts
US Department of Agriculture Forest Service
St Paul, MN, USA

F Médail
Université d'Aix–Marseille III
Aix-en-Provence, France

R Meilan
Oregon State University
Corvallis, OR, USA

M J Meitner
University of British Columbia
Vancouver, BC, Canada

F Meyer
University of Concepción
Chile

E Mikkonen
University of Helsinki
Helsinki, Finland

H G Miller
University of Aberdeen
Aberdeen, UK

M R Milota
Oregon State University
Corvallis, OR, USA

A J Moffat
Forest Research
Farnham, UK

S A Mori
New York Botanical Garden
New York, USA

L A Morris
University of Georgia
Athens, GA, USA

M A Murphy
Virginia State University and Technical Institute
Blacksburg, VA, USA

P G Murphy
Michigan State University
East Lansing, MI, USA

K K N Nair
Kerala Forest Research Institute
Peechi, Kerala State, India

G Newcombe
University of Idaho
Moscow, ID, USA

D D Nicholas
Mississippi State University
MS, USA

W L Nutter
Nutter & Associates, Inc.
Athens, GA, USA

T Nuutinen
Finnish Forest Research Institute
Joensuu Research Center
Joensuu, Finland

C D Oliver
Yale University
New Haven, CT, USA

P M O Owende
Institute of Technology Blanchardstown
Dublin, Ireland

P E Padgett
USDA Forest Service
Riverside, CA, USA

P Parker
Western Michigan University
Kalamazoo, MI, USA

D Parry
State University of New York
Syracuse, NY, USA

T Peck
European Forest Institute
Vaud, Switzerland

H Pereira
Instituto Superior de Agronomia
Lisbon, Portugal

C A Peres
University of East Anglia
Norwich, UK

D Peterson
Western Michigan University
Kalamazoo, MI, USA

B M Potts
University of Tasmania
Hobart, Tasmania, Australia

G T Prance
University of Reading
Reading, UK

M Predny
Virginia Polytechnic Institute and State University
Blacksburg, VA, USA

M L Putnam
Oregon State University
Corvallis, OR, USA

F E Putz
Center for International Forestry Research
Jakarta, Indonesia

A K Rai
Forest Research Institute
Dehradun, India

I V Ramanuja Rao
International Network for Bamboo and Rattan (INBAR)
Beijing, China

T B Randrup
Danish Forest and Landscape Research Institute
Hoersholm, Denmark

S Rani
North-Eastern Hill University
Shillong, India

R B S Rawat
National Medicinal Plants Board
New Delhi, India

M Rebetez
Swiss Federal Institute for Snow and
  Landscape Research
Lausanne, Switzerland

M L Reid
University of Calgary
Calgary, AB, Canada

R S Reiner
USDA
Madison, WI, USA

M Reinhard
Swiss Federal Institute for Snow and
  Landscape Research
Lausanne, Switzerland

D M Richardson
University of Cape Town
Cape Town, South Africa

G J F Ring
University of Wisconsin–Stevens Point
Stevens Point, WI, USA

A Robinson
University of Idaho
Moscow, ID, USA

R Rogers
University of Wisconsin–Stevens Point
Stevens Point, WI, USA

R M Rowell
University of Wisconsin–Madison
Madison, WI, USA

P W Rundel
University of California
Los Angeles, CA, USA

J D Salter
University of British Columbia
Vancouver, BC, Canada

R Sands
University of Canterbury
Christchurch, New Zealand

P S Savill
University of Oxford
Oxford, UK

O Savolainen
University of Oulu
Oulu, Finland

L G Saw
Forest Research Institute Malaysia
Kepong, Kuala Lumpur, Malaysia

H Schanz
Wageningen University
Wageningen, The Netherlands

S E Schlarbaum
University of Tennessee
Knoxville, TN, USA

M Schneebeli
WSL Swiss Federal Institute for Snow and
    Avalanche Research
Davos, Switzerland

S H Schoenholtz
Oregon State University
Corvallis, OR, USA

W Schönenberger
Swiss Federal Research Institute WSL
Birmensdorf, Switzerland

H T Schreuder
USDA Forest Service
Fort Collins, CO, USA

T P Schultz
Mississippi State University
MS, USA

F W M R Schwarze
EMPA, St. Gallen, Germany

D F Scott
Okanagan University College
Kelowna, Canada

G M Scott
State University of New York
Syracuse, NY, USA

W E Scott
Miami University
Oxford, OH, USA

R A Sedjo
Resources for the Future
Washington, DC, USA

E-H M Sène
Food and Agriculture Organization
Rome, Italy

J Sessions
Oregon State University
Corvallis, OR, USA

R Uma Shaanker
Ashoka Trust for Research in Ecology and the
    Environment
Hebbal, Bangalore, India

S R J Sheppard
University of British Columbia
Vancouver, BC, Canada

T Sievänen
Finnish Forest Research Institute
Helsinki, Finland

E A Simmons
National School of Forestry
University of Central Lancashire
Penrith, Cumbria, UK

F L Sinclair
University of Wales
Bangor, UK

J P Skovsgaard
Royal Veterinary and Agricultural University
Forest & Landscape Denmark
Coperhagen, Denmark

P Smethurst
CSIRO Forestry and Forest Products and Corperative
Research Centre for Sustainable Production
Hobart, Tasmania, Australia

I R Smith
University of Queensland
St Lucia, Australia

S Smulski
Wood Science Specialists Inc.
Shutesbury, MA, USA

M Spalding
UNEP World Conservation Monitoring Centre
Cambridge, UK

M R Speight
University of Oxford
Oxford, UK

R Spinelli
National Council for Research – Timber and Tree Institute
Florence, Italy

E L Springer
University of Wisconsin
Madison, WI, USA

B Stanton
GreenWood Resources
Clatskanie, OR, USA

J K Stone
Oregon State University
Corvallis, OR, USA

K Suzuki
The University of Tokyo
Tokyo, Japan

R Szymani
Wood Machining Institute
Berkeley, CA, USA

K ten Kate
Insight Investment
London, UK

R O Teskey
University of Georgia
Athens, GA, USA

R C Thakur
Michigan Technological University
Houghton, MI, USA

K Theron
Department of Forest Science
University of Stellenbosch
South Africa

J R Thompson
Talo Analytic International, Inc.
Duluth, GA 30096, USA

B K Tiwari
North-Eastern Hill University
Shillong, India

T Tokola
University of Helsinki
Helsinki, Finland

M Tomé
Instituto Superior de Agronomia
Lisbon, Portugal

E Tomppo
Finnish Forest Research Institute
Helsinki, Finland

M A Topa
Boyce Thompson Institute for Plant Research
Ithaca, NY, USA

S Torreano
The University of the South
Sewanee, TN, USA

H Tynsong
North-Eastern Hill University
Shillong, India

S J Van Bloem
Michigan State University
East Lansing, MI, USA

J P van Buijtenen
Texas A&M University
College Station, TX, USA

S Vedavathy
Herbal Folklore Research Centre
Tirupati, India

R A Vertessy
CSIRO Land and Water
Canberra, Australia

J A Vozzo
US Department of Agriculture Forest Service
Starkville, MS, USA

F G Wagner
University of Idaho
Moscow, ID, USA

C Ward Thompson
OPENspace Research Centre
Edinburgh, UK

S E Ward
Mahogany for the Future, Puerto Rico

R H Waring
Oregon State University
Corvallis, OR, USA

J Webber (Retired)
Ministry of Forests, Research Branch
Victoria, BC, Canada

J F Webber
Forestry Commission Research Agency
Farnham, UK

M Weiler
University of British Columbia
Vancouver, BC, Canada

L T West
University of Georgia
Athens, GA, USA

C J Weston
University of Melbourne
Creswick, Victoria, Australia

T L White
University of Florida
Gainesville, FL, USA

K L Whittaker
University of Melbourne
Creswick, Victoria, Australia

K F Wiersum
Wageningen University
Wageningen, The Netherlands

K E Wightman
Purdue University
West Lafayette, IN, USA

R J E Wiltshire
University of Tasmania
Tasmania, Australia

M J Wingfield
University of Pretoria
Pretoria, Republic of South Africa

H Wolf
State Board for Forestry (Saxony)
Pirna, Germany

J L G Wong
Wild Resources Ltd
Bangor, UK

P J Wood
Commonwealth Forestry Association
Oxford, UK

M Worbes
University of Göttingen
Göttingen, Germany

M A Wulder
Canadian Forest Service
Victoria, BC, Canada

L A Xu
Nanjing Forestry University
Nanjing, Jiangsu, China

A D Yanchuk
British Columbia Ministry of Forests
Victoria, BC, Canada

J A Youngquist
Forest Products Consultant
Verona, WI, USA

R L Youngs
Virginia Polytechnic Institute and State University
Blacksburg, VA, USA

J I Zerbe
USDA Forest Products Laboratory
Madison, WI, USA

A Zink-Sharp
Virginia Polytechnic Institute and State University
Blacksburg, VA, USA

B Zobel
North Carolina State University
Raleigh, NC, USA

CONTENTS

VOLUME 1

a

I

L

VOLUME 2

M

N

NON-WOOD PRODUCTS

O

OPERATIONS

P

PACKAGING, RECYCLING AND PRINTING

PAPERMAKING

PATHOLOGY

PLANTATION SILVICULTURE

Q

R

VOLUME 3

S

VOLUME 4

U

W

Y

S

Sawn Timber *see* **Solid Wood Products**: Glued Structural Members; Lumber Production, Properties and Uses; Structural Use of Wood.

SILVICULTURE

Contents

Silvicultural Systems

P Savill, Oxford Forestry Institute, Oxford, UK

Introduction

A silvicultural system is a planned series of treatments for tending, harvesting, and reestablishing a stand. The main systems, their variations, and applications are described in this article. There is no fundamental difference between the systems practiced in tropical and temperate parts of the world. Variations often have to be introduced in both, for example in the wet tropics to accommodate the species-rich nature of the forests, and the relatively small number of species with timber that is commercial by current standards.

Classification of Systems

The classification of silvicultural systems, which are by their nature often flexible and imprecisely defined, is not easy. They differ, and can therefore be classified in three major ways. First, the method of regeneration used can be from coppice or root suckers, or by planting, direct seeding, or natural regeneration. Although coppice systems are clearly distinguished, most others can use any of the other three techniques. Secondly, the even-agedness of a stand puts selection systems at one extreme, and clear-cutting and coppice systems at the other. Other systems have two or more age classes for at least part of the rotation. Finally, systems can also differ in the size of the silvicultural unit. This ranges from the compartment in shelterwood and clear-cutting systems to progressively smaller areas in strip and group systems. The place of the selection system in this hierarchy is debatable, depending on whether one considers that each felling is applied to the stand as a whole, or whether each tree is treated individually.

A consideration of these three axes of variation suggests the following classification:

1. (a) Stands originating from stool shoots or suckers of vegetative origin: coppice systems.
   (b) Stands predominantly of seedling origin: high forest systems—**2.**

2. (a) Felling and regeneration are distributed continuously over the whole area, giving rise to an uneven-aged (irregular) stand: selection or polycyclic systems.

   (b) Felling and regeneration are concentrated on one part of the forest area only at any one time—3.

3. (a) Systems of successive regeneration fellings such that the old stand is removed by several fellings over a period of years. This gives rise to an approximately two-aged stand for a period in the regeneration cycle: shelterwood systems.

   (b) Old stand is cleared by a single felling, giving rise to an even-aged stand: clear-cutting (or clear-felling) system.

There are also various group, strip, wedge, and edge systems that are considered here (but not by all authors) as variants of the three basic high forest systems, as determined by the age structure within each. These are discussed later.

Coppice System

Coppice shoots arise primarily from concealed dormant buds that grow from the stump of a tree following cutting (**Figure 1**). They can also develop from buds on roots in some species, to give rise to root suckers, and a few reproduce by both methods.

The coppice system relies upon these methods of vegetative production after each stand of trees has been felled to provide the next generation. Coppice regeneration has an advantage over seedlings in that ample supplies of carbohydrates are available from the parent stool and its root system, so new shoots grow very vigorously from the start. However, coppice shoots of most species seldom grow to the dimensions of trees grown from seed, so the system is used to produce small-sized material. The ability to coppice is far more common in broad-leaved trees than in conifers. Species also vary greatly in their vigor of coppicing: poplars, willows, and eucalypts are generally very good. The longevity of a stool varies with its health, species, and site. Some are relatively short-lived, lasting only two or three rotations, while others, such as *Tilia cordata*, are almost indestructible. Among suitable species, no method of regeneration has a greater certainty of such rapid and complete success, and in the rather rare circumstances today where coppicing is profitable, no other method of regeneration is cheaper. The system can be attractive financially because coppice rotations are much shorter than those in high forest where trees are grown from seed.

Variants of coppicing include coppice-with-standards, pollarding, and shredding, the latter two being mostly associated with wood pasture and isolated trees rather than woodland.

- Woodlands managed as coppice-with-standards usually consist of simple even-aged coppice as the underwood, and an overwood of standards which are normally trees of seedling rather than coppice origin (**Figure 2**). The latter are uneven-aged and the two components have quite different rotation lengths. The system provides both large and small stems from the same piece of land, and is the oldest of all deliberately adopted systems of forest treatment. Cuttings are made in both the overwood and underwood at the same time. When the coppice underwood has reached the end of its rotation and is cleared, standards which have reached the end of theirs are also removed and new ones introduced.

Figure 1 Coppice shoots growing from a sweet chestnut (*Castanea sativa*) stump in Sussex, UK.

Figure 2   Oak coppice with standards in Germany. In this picture, the coppice has recently been cut for fuel wood, after growing for about 25 years, and has been stacked ready for removal. Most of the standards, which are trees of seedling origin, are left and a good indication of the range of ages (sizes) can be obtained.

Figure 3   *Eucalyptus globulus* grown on a 7–10-year coppice cycle for paper pulp production in Portugal.

- In pollarding the trees are cut 1.5–3.5 m above the ground, rather than at ground level, and allowed to grow again. This puts the regrowth out of reach of cattle and other browsing animals. Any tree that can be coppiced will respond to pollarding, except those where suckers are depended upon. Today, pollarding is mostly done for ornament.
- Shredding involves the repeated removal of side branches on a short cycle, leaving just a tuft at the top of the tree. It was practiced in Europe to feed cattle on the leafy shoots removed from trees, especially elm on land where there was little grass. Today it is sometimes carried out in countries with Mediterranean or monsoon climates, such as parts of Nepal, where there is a long, dry, grassless season, while deeper-rooting trees can provide ample fodder from their leaves.

Coppicing is one of the oldest forms of forest management, but it has been in decline in many temperate regions since at least the mid-1800s as a result of industrialization. Plastic, metal, and other alternatives are now available to replace the many objects and implements formerly made of wood of small dimensions. Improvements in infrastructure for distributing gas, electricity, and coal also means that wood is seldom required as a fuel outside the tropics.

In its modern form, coppice is extensively used for the production of pulpwood (e.g., from *Eucalyptus*; **Figure 3**), and for short-rotation energy crops (from

Salix and *Populus*), as well as for fuelwood, mostly in the tropics (e.g., *Leucaena leucocephala*). It is normally worked on a clear cutting system.

High Forest Systems

Selection System

Selection systems involve the manipulation of a forest to maintain a continuous cover, to provide for the regeneration of the desired species and controlled growth and development of trees through a range of diameter classes which are mixed singly (in single-tree selection systems) or in groups (group selection systems). Successful management can be very complex. It depends on a sound ecological knowledge, experience, in which considerable intuition may be involved, and silvicultural judgment. It aims for the maintenance of a stable and relatively unchanging forest environment.

Stands managed on a selection system are, at all times, an intimate mixture of trees of all age classes (**Figure 4**). There is no concept of a rotation length, or of a regeneration period, as both harvesting and reestablishment take place regularly and simultaneously throughout the stand. The only silvicultural interventions are selection fellings, which are typically carried out every 5–10 years throughout the stand. These fellings are a combination of regeneration tending, cleaning, thinning, final felling, and regeneration felling. This can be difficult as the needs of each of the age classes must be taken into account and trees of all sizes are removed. An important feature of selection felling is that it concentrates on improving the quality of the stand rather than felling to remove the largest and best stems, which may result in impoverishment.

Without careful intervention there is usually a tendency for a more even-aged structure to evolve, and also for the different age classes to become spatially separated, so that a group structure develops. In an extreme case, this would result in even-aged, single-storied groups. This occurs with light-demanding species, and such a group selection system is the only form of the selection system which is appropriate to them.

The length of the period between successive selection fellings varies. Short periods (less than 5 years) allow better stand management, particularly of young trees. Long periods result in larger volumes of timber being removed at each visit, making them more economical. They also improve the success of regeneration of light-demanders because the canopy is opened up more.

Selection or polycyclic systems are appropriate for the management of tropical high forests in, for example, West Africa. The best European examples are in the silver fir (with beech and Norway spruce) forests of central Europe. In temperate regions, selection systems are largely confined to mountainous areas where a continuous protection of the soil against erosion and often against avalanches is of great importance. They also protect the soil against leaching and are suitable for regeneration of frost-sensitive species. Selection forests are probably the ideal for conserving landscapes, and appropriate for forests around towns where an apparently unchanging view is important, but contrary to popular belief they do not necessarily even approximate to natural forests in many places where they are applied.

The term 'group selection' is widely used and loosely applied to any irregular or group system. It should strictly refer only to systems in which a stand

Figure 4 A selection forest of predominantly Norway spruce (*Picea abies*) and European silver fir (*Abies alba*), with some beech (*Fagus sylvatica* L.) in the Jura mountains, France.

is subdivided into groups, each of which is, for a large part of its life, uneven-aged, and has more than one storey. They are also referred as 'irregular shelterwood' systems. In practice, group selection closely resembles the selection system, as there is usually no fixed rotation length or regeneration period. It differs in that a time eventually comes when all remaining old trees must be removed, whereas in true selection working no such time ever arrives. There is, therefore, a shelterwood notion: an older stand providing protection for a younger one which is replacing it, but the period of shelter is often over 50 years. It also differs from a selection system in that more emphasis is placed on obtaining and developing regeneration in groups rather than uniformly through the stand.

Shelterwood System

The essential feature of the system is that even-aged stands are established, normally by natural regeneration, under a thinned overstory that produces sufficient shade and a moderated environment for young trees to establish. It is removed as soon as establishment is complete. Treatments usually include the following (**Figure 5**):

1. Preparatory felling: essentially a late thinning to encourage the development of the crowns of future seed bearers.

2. Seeding felling: once it is clear that there is going to be a good seed crop, a third to a half of the stems are removed. The understory and any regeneration already present are also removed. Cultivation may be carried out to assist seedling establishment (**Figure 6**).

3. Secondary fellings: usually two to four fellings, at 3–5-year intervals, with timing and intensity carefully regulated to allow seedlings to grow, but also to prevent rank weed growth (**Figure 7**).

4. Final felling: the last secondary felling in which the remaining overstory is removed. The damage done to regeneration in later fellings is not usually serious, especially if the regeneration is young and supple, dense and even-aged.

The whole series of operations normally takes 5–20 years. Infrequent mast years and frost-sensitive seedlings both necessitate long regeneration periods. The secondary fellings for a light-demanding species must be few and rapid and the whole process may be completed in 5 years.

If seed production is infrequent, then it may take 20 years to obtain adequate regeneration. The stand will then be somewhat uneven-aged and patchily distributed, in which case the system grades into the group shelterwood. Some authors state that one of the main advantages of this system is its simplicity, but in areas where mast years are infrequent,

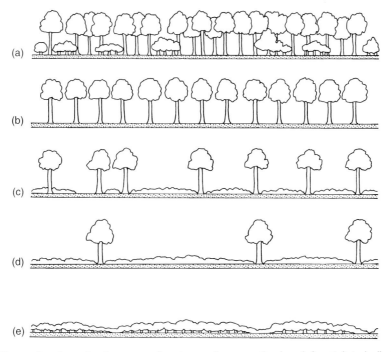

Figure 5 Uniform shelterwood system, showing successive stages of regeneration in oak forest. It typically takes 5–8 years from a successful seed fall to removing the last of the adult trees. (a) The forest before regeneration begins, with understory trees and shrubs; (b) after the seeding felling; (c) a secondary stage where adult trees have been removed around successfully established regeneration; (d) a late secondary stage where very few adult trees remain; (e) the young regenerated stand with all the previous generation of trees removed.

Figure 6 Shelterwood system with oak (*Quercus petraea*). A seeding felling has just been carried out, removing a third to a half of the trees. The understory and any regeneration already present have also been removed and the ground has been cultivated to assist seedling establishment. Bellême forest, Normandy, France.

Figure 7 Shelterwood system with oak (*Quercus petraea*). A late secondary felling, at an intensity and time to allow the prolifically produced seedlings to grow, but also to prevent excessive weed growth. Bellême forest, Normandy, France.

obtaining a fully stocked, even-aged regeneration is a major managerial problem. The shelterwood system can also be used with planted stock where natural seeding is insufficient or irregular, where a change of species is required, and where seed-bearers are insufficient in number or quality.

Variants to the system include both group and strip systems that consist of shelterwood regeneration fellings carried out in a strip ahead of the advancing edge of the final felling. They are sometimes considered more suitable than the shelterwood systems for light-demanding species.

Group shelterwood systems involve retaining an overstory for a short period to provide shelter for the new stand, which is approximately even-aged. The main difference from the shelterwood system, apart from the small size of the areas worked, is the fact that if advance or existing regeneration is present, it is used as the focus of a regeneration felling. (In a strict shelterwood system, existing regeneration would be removed with the understory.) Groups are gradually enlarged by carrying out regeneration fellings (seeding, secondary, and final fellings successively) around the edges until eventually they meet and merge. The regeneration period is generally longer (15–40 years) than with the shelterwood system, and the resulting stand is therefore somewhat more uneven-aged.

Stands managed under a shelterwood system have many features in common with those established by planting under a clear-cutting system. They can be pure, even-aged, and uniform in structure and density over large areas.

Clear-cutting System

This system is universally applied and is likely to remain the predominant silvicultural system in forests managed primarily for profitable wood production. Its main advantages include simplicity, uniformity, and, in particular, the ease of felling and extraction. The use of clear-cutting does not necessarily preclude the use of natural regeneration (as is done in a variant, the 'seed tree' system, where a small number of widely spaced adult trees are retained for seed production), but the system almost always operates with establishment by planting (**Figure 8**). The main advantages of planting arise from its artificiality and minimum reliance on unpredictable natural events. Enough plants can be ordered for the desired year and can then be evenly distributed across the whole area, in rows, to facilitate subsequent tending. This makes reliance on natural regeneration seem like a technique inherited from a primitive 'hunter–gatherer' technology, whereby the time of arrival and dissemination of seed, the genetic quality, and even the species of the regeneration are largely outside the control of the manager.

However, planting is expensive, losses may be high, especially through drought, and since stocking is usually orders of magnitude lower than with good natural regeneration, the resulting stand may be of lower quality. Disadvantages of clear-cutting, rather than of planting, largely arise from the lack of protection, leading to a rise in the water table, extremes of temperature including frost, leaching and soil acidification, and rank weed growth. Clear-cutting is widely regarded as the least desirable system for both landscape and conservation but these disadvantages can be reduced by the use of small coupe-fellings (0.2–2 ha).

Clear-cutting is based strongly upon principles of economics and finance. It provides good opportunities for using labor-saving equipment and machinery efficiently; management is simple and work can be carried out with little skilled supervision. Management can, in fact, be intensive, and hence cost-effective. For production systems where profit is a major motive, clear-cutting is invariably the choice, unless some biological or environmental factor of the locality rules it out.

Group clear-cutting involves felling all the trees in a group prior to restocking. The stand within each group will always be even-aged, but the stand as a whole will contain groups of a wide range of ages, and possibly of all ages. The individual groups may be pure or mixed in species composition, and may be established by natural regeneration, or planting, or a combination. Group clear-cutting is particularly appropriate to strong light-demanders as the only protection given to the young trees is from side shelter. Group sizes commonly range from coupes of about 50 m in diameter (0.2 ha) to areas of a hectare in extent.

Group, Strip, Wedge, and Edge Systems

The various group systems are considered here to be variants of the three main high forest systems, giving group clear-cutting, group shelterwood, and group selection systems. A whole compartment of a group clear-cutting system may therefore be uneven-aged, but each individual group will be even-aged and managed on a clear-cutting system. Similarly, strip,

Figure 8 Extensive even-aged plantations of Sitka spruce (*Picea sitchensis*) in Scotland.

wedge, and edge systems can be considered as variants of each of the three basic high forest systems, depending on the type of stand treatment that is carried out ahead of the advancing felling edge. This gives strip-felling, and strip-shelterwood systems, and also strip variants of the group systems, such as strip-group shelterwood.

In all group systems, the size of the group is a critical characteristic. Large groups are easier to manage, and are essential for light-demanders. The most useful range is probably 0.1–0.5 ha; larger groups are needed in taller and more uneven-aged stands. The shape and orientation of the groups can have a major influence on the variation of microclimate within them, and considerable emphasis is laid on this in central Europe. General observations are that a north–south orientation of an elliptical or rectangular group provides a good compromise between wind and sun, and that light-demanders should be near the north edge, and frost-tender species near the south.

The layout of groups is vital in facilitating management of the stands. Wherever possible, the first groups to be regenerated are those located furthest from the road, thereby minimizing the amount of timber that has to be extracted through a young stand. Fencing costs for small groups are inordinately high and this has always been considered a major disadvantage of any group system.

Group systems come closest to imitating the structure of a natural stand, at least in many temperate regions, and are therefore increasingly recommended for use.

Choice of Silvicultural System

Foresters continually have to choose between different silvicultural and management systems to achieve different mixes of products and benefits from specific forest areas. No single system is ideal for all situations. The choice is most often between even-aged monocultures that are usually, but not always, based on planting and clear-cutting and various uneven-aged systems based on natural regeneration.

The factors that govern the choice of a silvicultural system are silvicultural, economic, and socioeconomic, and include:

- the reproductive requirements and habits of the desired tree species
- the site itself may indicate, or at least rule out certain systems. Where conditions are particularly suitable for seeding and germination, systems for regenerating large coupes can be used, but where they are less certain, much smaller coupes are preferable

- constraints and requirements imposed by wildlife
- likelihood of problems arising from insect pests, fungal diseases, fire or climatic hazards, such as frequent high winds. The latter usually necessitate use of the clear-cutting system, and put the shelterwood system at extreme risk
- the size, age, and vigour of the existing trees may dictate the system
- the introduction of a new species to a site, or genetically improved strains, usually requires planting and even-aged systems
- the nature of the topography and soil may dictate the system
- constraints on manpower, money, equipment, and markets all have considerable influence on the choice of system.

Woodland management can be thought of as grading from intensive through to extensive. The former implies careful and expensive tending to produce valuable high-quality timber and the latter a lower-input approach, accepting mixed and uneven-aged stands, and producing, cheaply, rather lower-quality timber. Intensive management is normally associated with clear-cutting and shelterwood systems. The less intensive approach is more appropriate to selection and group systems, which need careful, but not capital-intensive, management to run well.

The same distinctions apply to the strategy adopted for obtaining and using natural regeneration: one could either invest time and money in trying to get a full stocking from any one seed year (i.e., a shelterwood system with careful preparatory thinnings, cultivation, and weed control) or one could operate a group, or selection, system with minimum preparation for seed, but accepting and using the steady trickle that establishes itself, largely unaided. Both approaches have their merits and the high-input one is not always the most profitable. The low-input approach is particularly appropriate to owners of small woodlands who do not have large sums to invest or where the forest is composed of many species, few of which are merchantable, as in many tropical forests.

Stands of irregular structure and tolerant (shade-bearing) species are best suited to uneven-aged silviculture, and it is also best practiced on fragile sites, steep slopes, sites with high water tables, and very dry sites that would be adversely affected by complete removal of the forest cover, even for short periods. Even-aged systems are most appropriate in stands of intolerant (light-demanding) species and should be used to return over mature, decadent, diseased, or insect-infested stands to productivity.

See also: **Afforestation**: Species Choice. **Plantation Silviculture**: Multiple-use Silviculture in Temperate Plantation Forestry; Rotations; Sustainability of Forest Plantations. **Silviculture**: Coppice Silviculture Practiced in Temperate Regions; Natural Stand Regeneration; Unevenaged Silviculture. **Windbreaks and Shelterbelts**.

Further Reading

Burns RM (1983) *Silviculture Systems for the Major Forest Types of the United States. Agriculture Handbook No. 445*. Washington, DC: US Department of Agriculture.

Dawkins HC and Philip MS (1998) *Tropical Moist Forest Silviculture and Management*. Wallingford, UK: CAB International.

Lamprecht H (1986) *Waldbau in den Tropen (Silviculture in the Tropics)*. Hamburg, Germany: Verlag Paul Parey.

Matthews JD (1989) *Silvicultural Systems*. Oxford: Clarendon Press.

Palmer J and Synnott TJ (1992) The management of natural forests. In: Sharma NP (ed.) *Managing the World's Forests: Looking for a Balance Between Conservation and Development*, pp. 337–373. Iowa, USA: Kendall/Hunt.

Parren MPE (1991) *Silviculture with Natural Regeneration: A Comparison Between Ghana, Cote d'Ivoire and Liberia*. AV. no. 90/50. Wageningen Agricultural University, The Netherlands: Department of Forestry.

Poore D (ed.) (1989) *No Timber Without Trees – Sustainability in the Tropical Forest*. London: Earthscan Publications.

Smith DM (1986) *The Practice of Silviculture*, 8th edn. New York: John Wiley.

Troup RS (1955) *Silvicultural Systems*. Oxford: Clarendon Press.

Whitmore TC (1990) *An Introduction to Tropical Rainforest*. Oxford: Clarendon Press.

Bamboos and their Role in Ecosystem Rehabilitation

I V Ramanuja Rao, International Network for Bamboo and Rattan (INBAR), Beijing, China

Introduction

Bamboos are a treelike, 'woody' plant of the grass family and botanically, one of the closest relatives to rice. It thus combines the best of both worlds – it grows speedily like a grass and in much the same way, while at the same time, it produces a considerable amount of high-strength and easily processed woody material with similar properties. It can grow in very poor soils, but also responds admirably to fertilization and irrigation, much like the modern rices, resulting in a doubling or more of size and annual biomass production.

Within the area of their natural distribution, bamboos are the plant equivalent of the domesticated animal like the cow, sheep, and goat. The high strength-to-weight ratio of the poles, and the absence of cross-fibers that lends bamboo to easy linear splitting, are characteristics that have made rural communities choose bamboo over other trees when it comes to structural as well as diverse subsistence uses. Over 1 billion people on earth live in houses that are reinforced with bamboo, even where wood is available nearby.

There are hundreds of traditional uses of bamboo, from food, construction material, housing, and bridges to household articles, and use in agriculture, fisheries, transportation, and in village industry. Bamboo also finds use today as a structural material, as a wood substitute, food, fuel, and a filtration medium.

Diversity

Bamboos are the most diverse group in the grass family, and the most primitive subfamily. The taxonomy of bamboos remains poorly understood, though the general consensus seems to be that the subfamily Bambusoideae has between 60 and 90 genera with 1100 to 1500 species, with the vast majority being tropical. The main reason for this large variation in diversity estimates is that flowering bamboos are few and far between. Most bamboos flower once in several years (and die thereafter), with the vegetative period extending up to several decades, but commonly 30–60 years for the more useful species. Hence taxonomists have to contend with having to do species determination mainly on the basis of vegetative material, which results in open-ended results that need a flowering specimen for confirmation.

Propagation

Bamboos are commonly propagated using vegetative (clonal) means and, when available, by seeds. The latter method is more common in tropical areas where the bamboos flower and set seed more frequently. Most bamboos produce copious quantities of seed (botanically termed caryopses that are technically fruits); these are called 'bamboo rice' and are even used as such. The rare exceptions are species such as *Melocanna baccifera* that produce large fruits, often the size of small mangoes. In some bamboos, infertility is rampant, with few viable seeds being produced.

More commonly, vegetative propagation methods are used. The methods primarily use (1) rhizome cuttings (or with attached culms (stems)), (2) culm (main stem) cuttings, and (3) branch cuttings. It is observed that the success rate commonly considerably decreases from rhizome cuttings to branch cuttings, but this needs to be considered against the larger number of cuttings available from branches as against the few rhizome cuttings (often one to two from a plant), and the damage the parent plant suffers on removal of material for propagation, which is significantly greater with rhizome removal.

Tissue culture has also been used to propagate bamboos, and has been widely employed where facilities, and availability of seeds that easier starting materials for culture, are available. Fewer bamboos have been mass-propagated by tissue culture from mature adult plants.

Production and Characteristics

The annual incremental biomass production on air-dry basis for a bamboo plantation can range from 10 to 40 tonnes ha^{-1} depending on the species, planting density, soil, and climate, including slope and aspect of a hill. An increase in strength is reported to occur until about 3–4 years and thereafter it decreases. Therefore the maturity period of bamboo is commonly considered 3–4 years with respect to density and strength, although for other applications, younger bamboos from ages 1–2 are used.

The mechanical properties of bamboo differ with species, age, climatic factors, moisture content, and different heights of the culm. Because of its hollowness, the effectiveness of bamboo as a beam is 2.9 times better than a wood beam. Bamboo possesses excellent strength properties especially tensile strength. It is as strong as wood and some species even exceed the strength of timbers such as *Shorea robusta* and *Tectona grandis*.

The density of bamboo varies from 500 to 800 kg m^{-3}. The general mechanical properties of bamboo are:

- tensile strength = 1000–4000 kg cm^{-2}
- compression strength = 250–1000 kg cm^{-2}
- bending strength = 700–3000 kg cm^{-2}
- modulus of elasticity = 100 000–300 000 kg cm^{-2}.

Ecological Requirements and Distribution

Bamboos are important ecologically because of the vast area over which they are distributed, the total quantum of the resource, and the diversity of species and the ecological habitats they occupy. According to an estimate, bamboo accounts for one-quarter of the biomass in tropical regions and one-fifth in subtropical regions. Bamboos occur in latitudes as far north as 46°N and as far south as 47°S, and at elevations from sea level to as high as 4000 m in the Himalayas. Most bamboo is found in the area between the Tropic of Cancer and the Tropic of Capricorn, and its principal distribution completely girdles the world like a belt around the equatorial region, with extensions both to the north and the south into the subtemperate areas.

Bamboos thrive in a semi-evergreen and moist deciduous forest, with the wet evergreen and dry deciduous types as its two extreme limits. The controlling factors for its abundance, distribution of species, growth, and development within these typical limits are mainly annual precipitation, relative humidity, and the nature of the soil. Bamboos can grow as an understory in almost all the forests excepting mangrove vegetation and form a rich belt of vegetation in well-drained parts of tropical and subtropical habitats.

Most clump-forming (or pachymorph) bamboos grow at temperatures ranging from 7°C (sometimes 2–3°C) to 40°C and can tolerate higher temperatures for short periods. Altitude affects the distribution of bamboo even in the tropical region. The clump-forming type is observed to predominate in low and medium altitudes, while the nonclump-forming running (or leptomorph) type occurs more abundantly at high elevations. Altitude and temperature are closely related and it is difficult to separate one from the other, for example, some species of *Phyllostachys* are cultivated at high elevations in India and Nepal but also occur at low elevations in countries of the temperate zone.

Bamboo commonly grows well in areas with an annual rainfall of 1000–6000 mm, but is also found in areas with lower (800 mm) and higher annual rainfall levels.

Role in Ecosystems

Bamboos grow in a vast diversity of ecosystems, both natural and human-made. In general, bamboos are one of the first members to colonize a new site in a seed year and perhaps the last to leave it. Once established on a site, it is relatively difficult to eradicate, with the rhizomes being found throughout the forest area. Even if the bamboos are felled with the trees, the underground rhizomes remain alive and give out new shoots in the following growing season. In the absence of tree regeneration the site would become a pure bamboo forest; with tree regeneration the bamboo comes up as undergrowth.

Generally, one bamboo species will grow in a pure condition. It is rare to encounter a mixture of two or more species.

Their unique biological properties have enabled the bamboos to adapt to diverse situations. Their role in ecosystem rehabilitation is best understood in terms of (1) their role in various natural and human-made ecosystems, and (2) the unique combination of characteristics and properties of this plant that increase the comparative advantage of the plant, and have enabled it to survive and spread around the globe. Principal amongst these are its treelike stature, the aggressive spreading underground rhizome, the strong adventitious root system, the rapid shooting of the pointed and leafless new culms, the production of leaves and branches from the tip downwards, the considerable tensile strength of the culms, the often several decades-long lifespan, and the gregarious flowering of bamboo, all of which together enable the remarkable adaptability of bamboo to diverse ecological conditions.

Treelike Stature and Dense Canopy

Bamboos commonly grow to 15 m; some species are diminutive, some are climbers, while others reach a height of up to 40 m. Bamboos have a dense canopy. A bamboo produces considerable biomass, and a significant part of this is in the form of foliage. For example, in *Gigantochloa scortechnii*, the amount of biomass is 50–100 tonnes ha^{-1}, divided into 60–70% for culms, 10–15% for branches, and 15–20% for the leaves.

Bamboos are not purely evergreen plants. Most of the clump-forming types in the tropical regions shed their leaves in winter when it is dry and renew the leaves simultaneously in a short time. The amount of leaf fall from *Melocanna baccifera*, *Oxytenanthera nigrociliata*, *Bambusa tulda*, and *Dendrocalamus giganteus* is 6.0, 5.6, 5.8, and 7.0 tonnes ha^{-1}, respectively. Bamboos contribute approximately 20 kg tonne^{-1} of organic matter to the soil, which is largely similar to that of other broadleaved species. The abundant leaf fall and rhizome growth in the topsoil layer serves to ameliorate soils.

The spreading foliage takes the impact of the fierce tropical rains and softens their impact on the ground. Leaves that fall up to 10 cm thickness per year also help absorb the impact of rain. A project in China conclusively proved that the canopy and leaf litter of temperate bamboo stands can intercept rainfalls much higher than those for conifers and pines.

Strong Adventitious Root System

The strong and solid underground rhizome of bamboos produce copious roots. Eighty-three percent of the roots of a well-grown clump of *Bambusa tulda* were reported to be present in the upper 33 cm of the soil; 12% between 33 and 66 cm, 4% between 66 and 100 cm, and only 1% between 100 and 135 cm below the surface. Bamboos are thus a superficial grower and feeder, and this characteristic gives them the ability to bind soils and prevent erosion. A study estimated that a single bamboo plant could bind up to 6 m^3 of soil. The weight of the soil bound is considerably more than the weight of the over-ground light tubular, cross-reinforced plant – the considerable dead-weight prevents it from being easily uprooted.

Underground Rhizome

The complex branched and robust underground rhizome system and infrequent flowering also distinguish the bamboo from common trees. The rhizome system spreads horizontally and produces culms from new rhizome growth. Even if a bamboo species is 30 m or more in height, the rhizome seldom grows more than 75 cm deep within the soil, mostly occurring within the top 20–50 cm.

There are two principal categories of bamboos – the clumping type (pachymorph bamboos) and the running type (leptomorph bamboos). The extent of spread of the former is dependent on the length of the rhizome neck, while in the latter, the running rhizome produces buds that grow up into culms. Bamboos can well be called the 'walking tree.' A bamboo can thus quickly expand and consolidate its 'territory' compared to most trees. In more dense wet tropical forests, climbing bamboos are not uncommon.

The underground rhizome network is a function of the type of bamboo. Clumping or pachymorph bamboos would have a clustered set of rhizomes under the clumps with limited spread outwards. Pachymorph bamboos like *Melocanna baccifera* but having an open and diffuse type of rhizome system with long rhizome necks of 1–2 m, form a complete underground network over the entire area that gridlocks the soil and do not give way even under considerable pressure from liquefied soils under strong monsoonal rains. Running or leptomorph bamboos have rhizomes that criss-cross the ground. This kind of rhizome system is stronger than the clumping bamboos but not as strong as that of the diffuse pachymorph type.

Importantly, the underground rhizomes enable bamboo to survive forest fires, including fires set for clearing land for slash-and-burn agriculture. Thus they are fairly tenacious, and difficult to kill or eradicate. In burnt lands that previously had growth of bamboo, it is often the first plant to regenerate.

Once established, the early formation of rhizome protects seedlings from grazing. Even if the tops get eaten, new shoots are produced from the rhizome.

Rapid Shooting of New Culms

The new shoots grow to full height within 2–4 months which is the total time taken from when the newly forming bamboo culm (pole) starts to break ground as a new bamboo shoot to the attaining of full height. This period is the same for a short-stature bamboo and one whose culms reach up to 40 m with a diameter of up to 30 cm. During this period the bamboo shoots can grow 1.2 m in 24 h. The pointed, leafless culms reach full height before branches and leaves are produced on the naked culm from the apex downward. The culms can therefore fully occupy even small open spaces in the forest before spreading their branches.

Annual Production of Culms

Bamboo produces several new full length culms each year. Thus a clump ordinarily produces several kilometers of culms during its lifetime. Since culms are produced each year, annual harvests are possible and recommended. Bamboo therefore combines characteristics of an annual and a perennial, and hence can span agriculture and forestry. Given that there is no secondary growth in bamboo (it being a grass), but that several tonnes of new woody biomass are produced *de novo* each year as new culms, bamboo offers the opportunity to sequester considerable carbon throughout its lifetime. *Guadua* in Costa Rica has been calculated to sequester 17 tonnes ha^{-1} of carbon each year throughout its lifetime.

Considerable Tensile Strength of the Culms

Bamboos poles have a remarkably high tensile strength – weight for weight, this is greater than that of steel. It therefore can withstand very high winds and typhoons.

Bamboo poles mostly attain full strength by the third year, while trees take a considerably longer time to mature. Yet another very important characteristic is that the total quantum of bamboo wood is produced in the very first year of growth, although its composition undergoes a change from year to year.

Gregarious Flowering of Bamboo

Depending on the periodicity of flowering, bamboos fall into three groups: (1) annual flowering (or nearly so), (2) irregular flowering, and (3) gregarious and periodical flowering. Many species that flower gregariously also flower sporadically. Gregariously flowering clumping species generally have vegetative periods of around 25–35 years within a larger range of 15–60 years, while many running bamboos flower after 60–120 years. There are also bamboos such as *Bambusa vulgaris* that have not been known to flower, or do so rarely without seed set and concomitant death, but never gregariously. Gregariously flowering species from the same cohort will flower at the same time even if separated geographically across the globe.

More recently, bamboo hybridization has become possible through an ingenious nutrition control means that seeks to physically bring together naturally flowering bamboos and maintain them in a flowering state. Interspecific and intergeneric hybrids have been produced. The flowering of bamboos *in vitro* has also been demonstrated. Once *in vitro* flowering is established, the bamboo can be alternated between the flowering and vegetative states.

Most species of bamboo die after gregarious flowering at the end of a long vegetative period of growth, often three decades and more, depending on the species. This event with catastrophic economic and social effects (because of the suddenness and scale) has a major impact on the local ecosystem, and affects the vegetation with which it is associated. There is also the possibility of increased soil erosion, effects on wildlife, and also significant social and food security effects. The latter is mostly due to its nutritious seeds and fruits that form food for field rats (commonly called bamboo rats) which increases the number of litters and the live pups per litter. When the bamboo seeds/fruits are exhausted, the ferocious rats turn to household grain stocks. In Mizoram, which is a state in the northeastern part of India, a revolution was spawned as a result. In Thailand, the flowering of *Dendrocalamus asper* brought a flourishing edible shoots export industry to its knees. In Zambia, whole communities were uprooted when the bamboo that was the mainstay of their life and livelihood flowered and died.

The natural regeneration of bamboos occurs profusely after each gregarious flowering. Masses of seedlings form and there is intense competition with consequent natural thinning. By around 6 years, the area again has fairly uniformly spaced clumps, unless there is human intervention, intense grazing or fire. The first year or two are critical since there is little protection, except for refuges in the dead clumps.

Much learning is rapidly taking place in this area, with the result that where prior data of flowering is known, advance steps can be taken to reduce its impact. Mapping of flowered areas on to the geographical information system (GIS) with dates and species/cohorts have started in some areas.

Preventing Soil Erosion in Uplands and Lowlands

The extensive underground root-and-rhizome system makes bamboo a good instrument for arresting the ravages of water erosion in areas prone to it (such as slopes and lowlands). Researchers in Puerto Rico, who experimented with several plant species, found bamboo to be one of the most effective in controlling landslides. It is reported that the *Guadua* bamboo in Colombia has effectively prevented millions of tonnes of mountain soil from being washed down into the ocean. In China it has been observed that the mixed bamboo stands that adorn the southwest mountainous area are instrumental in ensuring that the quantity of soil that reaches Yangtze River through sheet erosion is just half that of the quantity washed out into the Huang River (Yellow River). The plant is so effective in binding soil on steep slopes that Malaysia has planted bamboos on hillsides to block mud and stones sliding on to roads.

Watersheds

Bamboo is commonly used in watersheds for increasing rain interception, reducing impact on the ground of heavy rain, reducing soil erosion, increasing water recharge, and for increasing postmonsoonal flow. In Ecuador, it is common for farmers to plant *Guadua* on the slope above farms since it increases water availability.

Riverbanks, Dam Sites, Lakes, and Ponds

As a plant that, unlike trees, spreads horizontally because of its rapidly growing rhizome and its pronounced ability to bind soil, bamboo is excellent for protecting riverbanks, dam sites, lakes, and ponds. It is also able to tolerate intermittent flooding which helps in this function. For this reason, bamboo cultivation in Japan has been recommended since the sixteenth century.

Bamboo's efficacy as a soil binder has been successfully used in Puerto Rico, Costa Rica, Nepal, the Philippines, and China. Bamboo planted at certain strategic points along the course of a river, especially at points where the river curves, have solved the problem of damage to the riverbank and also flooding. Not only is this due to the soil-binding capacity, but also the clumping bamboos often tend to 'mound,' leading to an increase in the height of banks as well. In Dayingjiang River in Yunnan Province and Jiulongjang River in Fujian Province in China, bamboo succeeded in protecting riverbanks after soil-rock engineering efforts and the planting of other trees had failed to yield results. It was shown that each clump can protect up to $12 \, m^3$ of river embankment.

Windbreaks

Bamboos, particularly the clumping type, are an effective shield against the onslaught of wind. The flexibility of the culms (for green culms the modulus of elasticity is about $9000–10\,000 \, N \, mm^{-2}$ and the modulus of rupture $84–120 \, N \, mm^2$) helps them to bend but not break even in relatively strong winds. Bamboo can bend even until it touches the ground in very strong winds, cyclones, and typhoons without getting uprooted like trees. Because of this bamboo is commonly used as a wind barrier along boundaries of farms, and to protect agricultural land from wind erosion during fallow periods.

Bamboo is also now being planted as an inner line plantation behind coastal mangrove and casuarinas to shield the interior from the effects of strong winds and cyclones.

Inundated Areas and Saline Environments

Bamboo does not grow naturally under saline coastal inundation. However, in Bangladesh, it is common practice for people in coastal areas to cultivate bamboo in homesteads and farmlands. The most successful species is *Bambusa vulgaris*. Another such bamboo is *B. atra* (*B. lineata*) which is found in the tidal swamp forest of the Andaman Islands (India).

Species such as *Ochlandra scriptoria*, *O. stridula*, and *O. travancorica* that are indigenous to the states of Kerala and Tamilnadu in India are mostly found in marshy areas and riverbanks that get flooded in the monsoons. *Phyllostachys purpurata* (*P. heteroclada*) and *P. atrovaginata* are monopodial species that can grow in wet soils and waterlogged areas. Interestingly, the rhizomes of these monopodial species have air canals.

Most bamboos can tolerate a period of inundation. With longer periods of inundation there is death of a considerable number of culms, especially if this occurs during the growing season (up to 60% death of new culms), but the plant usually recovers in the subsequent growing season.

Fish and Shrimp Farming in Water Bodies

Bamboos growing on the banks of water bodies contribute to an increase in aquatic life, including algae, fish, and shrimps. In Puerto Rico, despite the fact that bamboo litter is different from riparian inputs of the indigenous forest species bamboo displaces, the leaves decompose at similarly fast rates. There is also significant increases of filter-feeders (*Atya* spp.) and predators (*Macrobrachium* spp.) in bamboo pools. Data from experiments suggest a structural consideration in shrimp preference for bamboo substrata, in addition to the relative qualities of the leaves as food.

In India, villagers increasingly plant bamboo on water body margins. Even in new ponds established in degraded agricultural land from which the topsoil has been dug out for brickmaking, bamboo planted on the pond banks results in an increase in the fish population because of the leaf fall into the pond (which also reduces the amount of additional feed required). In Bangladesh, bottom mud from the ponds is dug out and used as a fertilizer for the bamboo clumps.

Wastelands

Bamboo is especially useful in converting wastelands, previously used only for grazing based on natural grass growth, to productive agriculture. Such lands after planting with bamboo have been successfully intercropped with soybean, groundnut, and maize, and the results have prompted several farmers to adopt this approach.

Because of the ability of bamboo to grow in poor soils, it has been used in dense plantations at close intervals to build up considerable woody and leafy biomass over ground, considerable leaf litter, and an extensive rhizome system. Together these contribute to a substantial build-up of organic carbon in the soil, an increase in soil microflora, increase in water holding capacity, and amelioration of soil pH from acidic towards neutrality. Bamboo soil is a commodity in some countries because of its fertility.

Agroforestry Systems

A variety of agroforestry systems exists for bamboo. It is common to see bamboo interplanted in fruit orchards in Thailand, and in tea estates in Bangladesh. Agricultural crops are mostly interplanted in the first 4 years of establishment of a bamboo plantation before canopy closure takes place. A diversity of crops are grown depending on the local agroclimatic condition, such as watermelon, soybean, sweet potato, sugar cane, and vegetables in the initial years. Within adult bamboo stands, the raising of pineapple, ginger, turmeric, and shade-tolerant varieties of sweet potato, etc. is undertaken in places where land is scarce. Continued agriculture is possible in situations where bamboo is the interplant.

A large number of mushrooms are also raised in China in bamboo stands which satisfy the fungi's need for humidity, shade, and a fertile bed. Key

amongst these are *Dictyophonra tomentose*, *Plenrotus ostreatus*, and *Auricularia auricular-judoe*.

Medicinal plants are also interplanted with bamboo.

Interplanting with Trees

Bamboo is interplanted with conifers and broadleaf timber trees; in the latter case this is especially successful with trees with deciduous light crowns rather than heavy canopies. Interplanting of bamboo plantations and even dense bamboo plantations with casuarinas (and with eucalyptus) has been done successfully over the past two decades in western India.

Degraded Lands

Bamboo has proved to be ideal for making productive land degraded by removal of the clayey topsoil down to 3 m for producing bricks, down to the sandy layer. The bamboo that is grown interspersed and also on boundaries of farms acts as a shelterbelt. It prevents further soil erosion due to wind action, improves the microclimate at the crop level, improves moisture retention, and contributes to soil rebuilding by increasing organic carbon content from leaf fall, including an increase in water holding capacity. Increases in groundwater levels have been recorded using this method.

The method is increasingly being used following the initial successes, and has significant implications for the over 3 million ha of land that are degraded in India, and similar lands elsewhere.

Ecological Role of Bamboos in Forests

Bamboos grow naturally as a component of forests, often as the understory. Their role in deciduous forests in areas with a pronounced dry season appears to be more significant in that the understory bamboo results in a reduction in soil erosion. The association of teak with bamboo is a common one, with significant benefits in controlling soil erosion.

The gregarious flowering of bamboo has been said to be the reason for development of bamboo brakes and pure bamboo stands; it probably occurs when there is complete death of all tree saplings growing in the understory of the closed bamboo canopy.

Bamboo also appears to play a role in the protection and regeneration of forests. Detailed studies in Asiatic old-growth forests with a bamboo understory have also noted the influence of the life cycle of the bamboos on the age structure of tree populations, and the tendency of synchronization of tree regeneration following bamboo dieback following flowering.

In Costa Rica, oak (*Quercus*) forest regeneration is pulsed as a consequence of the synchronous life cycle of the *Chusquea* bamboos due to gregarious flowering. The *Chusquea* bamboo normally grows as the understory in the oak forests. In the steady state, the understory *Chusquea* clumps are small because of limited light conditions. If there are fires or gap creation through tree fall, the *Chusquea* rapidly responds to the increased availability of light, and grows up to become the local dominant species with a closed canopy under which saplings of trees now grow in a suppressed state because of the low light conditions under the bamboo canopy. When the *Chusquea* flowers gregariously and dies, the forest floor is more illuminated, and the already established suppressed saplings shoot up. The new generation of bamboo then grows under the newly formed tree canopy.

Bamboos in Fire-Disturbed Lands

Bamboos are one community that colonizes disturbed lands in the tropics especially after fire, because of its well-developed underground rhizome system. The widespread distribution of *Melocanna baccifera* throughout eastern India, Bangladesh, northern Myanmar, and Thailand and of species of *Thyrsostachys* in Thailand and *Schizostachyum* in Vietnam mainly occurs as secondary vegetation due to the destruction of tropical rainforest by fire, shifting cultivation, and logging.

As a result of shifting agriculture, huge expanses of bamboo forests have been established in Asia. In northeast India, bamboos constitute the major vegetation after slash-and-burn agriculture, and due to their adaptability and nutrient conservational role, they play a special role in succession. Shortening of the cycle when the bamboos are still the dominant species largely results in the reduction and often elimination of tree species, such that the fire-tolerant bamboos that survive through the underground rhizomes become the permanent dominant species. Repeated firing over short cycles results in almost pure stands of bamboo over vast areas in the hills. While shrubs and trees tend to grow more slowly, the competitive bamboos have rapid rates of dry matter production, continuous stem extension and leaf production during the growing period, and rapid phenotypic adjustments in leaf area and shoot morphology in response to shade. The competitive bamboos also store more nitrogen, phosphorus, and potassium than stress-tolerant shrubs and trees while the reverse is true for calcium and magnesium. Overall it is seen that bamboos follow a strategy of faster uptake and storage of essential elements and a quicker turnover to supplement the soil fluxes, thus

efficiently dominating the stress-tolerant shrubs and tree species for a long duration. Overall, bamboos promote stability in the ecosystem through regulation of its functions like other competitive early successional species.

See also: **Tropical Ecosystems**: Bamboos, Palms and Rattans. **Tropical Forests**: Tropical Dry Forests; Tropical Moist Forests; Tropical Montane Forests.

Further Reading

Banik RL (2000) *Silviculture and Field Guide to Priority Bamboos of Bangladesh and South Asia*. Chittagong, Bangladesh: Bangladesh Forest Research Institute.

Farelly D (2003) *The Book of Bamboo: A Comprehensive Guide to this Remarkable Plant, its Uses and its History*. San Francisco, CA: Sierra Club Books.

Kumar A, Rao Ramanuja IV, and Sastry CB (eds) (2002) *Bamboo for Sustainable Development*, Proceedings of the 5th International Bamboo Congress and the 6th International Bamboo Workshop, Bali, Indonesia. Utrecht, The Netherlands: VSP.

Rao Ramanuja IV, Gnanaharan R, and Sastry CB (eds) (1990) *Bamboos: Current Research*, Proceedings of the International Bamboo Workshop, Cochin, India. Peechi, India: Kerala Forest Research Institute.

Rao Ramanuja IV, Rao IU, and Roohi FN (1992) Bamboo propagation through conventional and *in vitro* technologies. In: Baker FWG (ed.) *Rapid Propagation of Fast-Growing Woody Species*, pp. 41–56. Wallingford, UK: CAB International.

Rao Ramanuja IV and Sastry CB (eds) (1996) *Bamboo, People and Environment*, Proceedings of the 5th International Bamboo Workshop and the 4th International Bamboo Congress, Bali, Indonesia. New Delhi, India: International Network for Bamboo and Rattan.

Natural Stand Regeneration

J Huss, University of Freiburg, Freiburg, Germany

Introduction

There are two possible methods of forest stand establishment, namely natural and artificial regeneration. The process of natural regeneration involves the renewal of forests by means of self-sown seeds, root suckers, or coppicing. In natural forests, conifers rely almost entirely on regeneration through seed. Most of the broadleaves, however, are able to regenerate by means of the emergence of shoots from stumps (coppice) and broken stems. This type of forest reestablishment has obviously been important in temperate natural forests, as well as in tropical forests. A few broadleaves, such as aspen (*Populus tremula)*, Oriental plane (*Platanus orientalis)*, and Oriental beech (*Fagus orientalis)*, can regenerate from root suckers, if their roots have been injured. Vegetative reproduction by means of sprouts and suckers merely renews the aboveground parts of plants and the old roots remain. Strictly speaking only sexual reproduction from seeds that results in a total natural renewal of the stand can be defined as regeneration.

In Europe regeneration by natural distribution of seeds was the standard means of forest renewal for thousands of years until overexploitation, in combination with intensive grazing, which has taken place since the late Middle Ages, led to a gradual depletion of the forests and severely inhibited regrowth. At the beginning of the nineteenth century, extensive afforestation took place in Central Europe by means of sowing and planting, predominantly with conifers. Since then, natural regeneration has been limited to the renewal of beech (*Fagus sylvatica)* and its main associates, such as ash *(Fraxinus excelsior)*, sycamore (*Acer pseudoplatanus*), and wild cherry (*Prunus avium)*.

At the end of the nineteenth century, however, an early back-to-nature movement brought about an increasing interest in the natural regeneration of managed forests, and the creation of a variety of silvicultural systems such as shelterwood strip, strip and group, and wedge system. Most of these systems were geared towards the creation of favorable ecological conditions for the production and germination of seeds, as well as adequate growing conditions for seedlings and saplings. The new ecological movement towards nature-orientated, nature-based, or seminatural silviculture and forestry, which began in the 1980s, has once again revived an interest in natural regeneration.

Planting nevertheless will remain the dominant regeneration method for various reasons, such as the conversion of species, the need for suitable provenances and ease of operation.

Nature-orientated forestry is based on the adaptation of natural dynamics as much as possible, and mimics natural regeneration processes in particular.

Therefore, it is necessary to highlight some of the ecological factors essential to the regeneration process in natural forests, before natural regeneration in naturally managed forests can be discussed.

Natural Regeneration in Natural Forests

Regeneration in natural forests is very much influenced by abiotic stress conditions, such as drought, or catastrophic events like fires, storms, snow, and ice (**Figures 1** and **2**).

On sites with medium to good nutrient and water supplies, the following situations are possible:

- Landslides, fires, and floods create large bare areas, which are colonized by the seeds of pioneer species distributed by the wind, including poplars, willows, and birches. According to succession models, this initial forest cover acts as a nurse crop, improving soil and ecological conditions, paving the way for intermediate successional stage species such as Norway spruce (*Picea abies)* and sycamore (**Figures 3** and **4**). These intermediate species will in turn gradually be replaced by shade tolerant species such as hornbeam (*Carpinus betulus)*, beech, and silver fir (*Abies alba)*.
- On storm-felled stands, a mixture of pioneer and late successional species may develop together, if advance regeneration already exists beneath the original stand, which is usually the case.

Figure 1 Small-scale storm damage from 1999 in the natural beech dominated forest Suserup, Denmark, which has not been managed since about 1850.

Figure 2 Large-scale storm damage from 1990 in beech/Norway spruce stands (Sobernheim, Germany).

Figure 4 Birch acting as a nurse crop for Norway spruce (South Sweden).

Figure 3 Natural regeneration of birch, Scots pine and a few oaks in a 1985 storm-damaged area which does not need much enrichment (Hesse, Germany).

- In the absence of the above situations, smaller gaps are created by individual old trees gradually dying. These smaller gaps provide conditions under which shade-tolerant species, such as beech, silver fir (*Abies alba*), and yew (*Taxus baccata*) can develop, rising up through the canopy and eventually filling the gaps.

On extreme sites (very dry, wet, or cold), however, these general successional trends do not reach any definitive climax stage, as only stress tolerant species are able to grow on them.

Tree species employ different strategies in order to colonize ground effectively. Some of the more important characteristics of a number of selected species are illustrated in **Table 1**.

Flowering

Flowering begins early in the very light demanding pioneers and decades later for most of the shade-tolerant species. Not all species, however, follow this strategy, e.g., hornbeam flowers relatively early. Pioneers usually flower on an almost annual basis. In the case of intermediate and late successional species in particular, flowering is induced by the weather conditions of the preceding summer, and possibly even two growing seasons earlier. This has only recently been discovered for beech. Dominant individuals with large crowns begin flowering earlier and flower more abundantly.

Seed Production

Seed production requires favorable weather conditions during flowering and the development of seeds, as well as the absence of damaging insects. Pioneers, in general, produce more and lighter seeds. Only the oaks (*Quercus* spp.) do not follow this rule. Storage conditions become important immediately after ripening of the seeds. These are usually released from the tree, distributed by wind or animals and deposited on the ground, where they can germinate. Once on the ground, seeds are subject to predation by mammals, birds and insects, as well as fungal attack. Seed survival rates are higher on mineral soils after uprooting of trees by storm. Survival rates are even higher when seeds are buried in the soil, for example by wild boars (*Sus scofra*), 'sown' by jays (*Garrulus glandarius*) or stored in the soil by mice. Therefore, storage conditions are important in determining the proportion of seeds that eventually germinate.

Germination

Germination of the seeds of pioneer species begins immediately upon deposition on the ground. Pioneer seeds have no nutrient reserves and require subsoil conditions that permit easy penetration and access to water, such as mineral soils. The seeds of most other species have a chilling requirement and only germinate after winter has ended and the conditions are again suitable for seedlings to grow. Such seeds exhibit a period of dormancy, which is broken by a change of temperature. Oak again is an exception. Provided that temperatures are adequate in late autumn, the acorns generally develop a radicle, in order to secure a supply of water.

Germination is induced by an adequate temperature and humidity. In contrast to some species in the tropics light is not necessary for the first phases of germination of the species in the temperate zones. Direct light becomes essential once the cotyledons have spread and photosynthesis starts.

Following germination, the further development of the seedlings is very much dependant on the following ecological conditions:

- The water supply becomes a vital factor shortly after germination. Seeds that have germinated in

Table 1 Seed production strategies of some representative tree species

Species	Light requirement	Succession type	Beginning of seed production (age in years)	Weight of seeds (mg)	Agent of seed dispersal
Populus tremula		Pioneer	10–15	<0.2	Wind
Betula pendula	Very light demanding		10–15	0.2	
Pinus sylvestris			15–20	6	
Fraxinus excelsior			20–30	56	
Quercus petraea		Long-lived pioneer	40–50	3030	Birds, rodents
Acer pseudoplatanus	Light demanding		15–25	125	Wind
Picea abies	Intermediate		30–40	8	
Carpinus betulus	Shade-tolerant	Late successional species	15–20	33	
Fagus sylvatica	Very shade tolerant		40–50	192	Birds, rodents
Abies alba			40–60	44	Wind

leaf litter or needles regularly die during dry periods, which are particularly frequent in European regions with a continentally influenced climate. In mountainous areas, a maritime climate usually prevails and regeneration tends to be more successful. Seedlings on mineral soils tend to suffer fewer losses, as their roots can extend into the lower soil horizons and the water supply. Decayed coarse woody debris acts as a sponge, making it a perfect substrate for seedlings to grow on and is of great relevance in natural forests. Norway spruce, in particular, profits from the presence of dead wood (**Figure 5**).

- The further development of the young trees is subject to the light conditions. In open areas, light-demanding pioneers are highly competitive in the early decades because of their fast growth and will dominate the stands at the establishment stage. Under the shelter of old trees, however, the shade tolerance of the seedlings will determine their ability to survive. Even young shade-tolerant plants die if the canopy remains closed, however.

The greater the nutrient reserves stored in the seed, the longer a seedling will be able to endure in a waiting position.

- Various biotic stress factors may decimate the seedlings from the moment of germination. They can become infected by fungi. Mice, birds, and snails often reduce the numbers sharply (**Figure 6**). Saplings are very susceptible to browsing and bark peeling by larger mammals, such as roe deer (*Capreolus capreolus*) and red deer (*Cervus elaphus*) (**Figures** 7 and 8). Under the natural conditions prevalent in times past, the density of these animals was probably not very high and browsing pressure not too severe. There is, however, intense debate over the ecological impact of megaherbivores on the forest cover prior to large-scale interference by humans.

As a general conclusion the natural regeneration of natural forests is steered by a great variety of abiotic and biotic factors, and their interactions. Undoubtedly, natural forests exhibit a high degree of site adaptation. The characteristics of a forest type will mirror the prevailing site factors, such as climate and soils. Additionally, the soil mosaic often leads to a further differentiation of the tree species distribution. The aforementioned 'catastrophes' may pave the way for the early stages of pioneer forests, which will evolve towards later successional stages over the course of centuries. In many cases, a form of climax forest may never be achieved, as the process is set back by further catastrophes. Even in the climax phases the species composition may vary purely as a result of chance, depending on, for example, which species produces seed in a given year and develops on a certain spot in the forest, whereas in another year a different species may have regenerated and conquered the available space.

Figure 5 Regeneration of Norway spruce seedlings on coarse woody debris (North Sweden).

Figure 6 Bark peeling by voles destroying beech seedlings and saplings (Zwiefalten, Southwest Germany).

Figure 7 Browsing by red deer heavily affecting the growth of young beech (Kempfeld, Germany).

All successional models, therefore, only show a general direction leading to later stages of development.

Natural Regeneration in Managed Forests

The management of forests generally aims towards production and/or service goals. This is never the case for purely natural forests, however. Nature-based silviculture seeks to make use of natural forest dynamics to as great a degree as possible, to meet both ecological and economic targets, yet aims to avoid or minimize the disadvantages.

There are several reasons both for and against the practical application of natural regeneration as a means of stand establishment (**Table 2**).

Although some of the advantages of natural regeneration are very appealing, many of the disadvantages provide serious practical obstacles to large-scale natural regeneration (**Figure 9**). Included in the disadvantages are a lack of experience, shortage of qualified and motivated personnel and, of course, impatience – the greatest problem in forestry.

Preconditions

Apart from the sociological and organizational constraints mentioned above, some preconditions must also be met in order to make use of natural regeneration processes.

During the afforestation period of the last two centuries in Europe, which continues to this day,

Figure 8 Browsing of Norway spruce by roe deer. The saplings start to grow normally as soon as they exceed the browsing height (Grafing, Germany).

Table 2 Arguments for and against using natural regeneration in practice

	Comments
Arguments for	
Preservation of site-adapted autochthonous populations	Reduced risk of receiving the wrong provenances from private nurseries.
High degree of adaptation of young plants to the site mosaic	Effective use of microsite differences by the species in mixed stands.
Undisturbed growth of young plants	Development of a regular root system; no deformations following planting, a particular problem on heavy soils.
Saving on high investment costs of plant material and planting procedures	Remarkable savings can be made in the establishment phase. Natural regeneration may require spending on site preparation and fencing, however.
Possible production of wildlings	Uses of site adapted wildlings for: • filling in incomplete young stands • transfer of plants to other regeneration areas • production of transplants in the nursery.
Increased number of potential crop trees for selection at later tending phases	Good sapling quality due to the high density of individuals and the intensive natural differentiation in the young stands; often results in savings on tending costs.
Arguments against	
Dependence on seed production and volume of seeds produced	Requires economic flexibility on the part of forest enterprises because of the irregularity of mast years
Irregular densities of natural regrowth and additional costs of filling in	Risk of reduced sapling quality, especially bordering on gaps. Necessity of filling in gaps in certain areas and of lowering the densities at other places. Difficulties of surveying naturally regenerated young stands, resulting in improper tending measures.
Greater risk to seedlings and saplings	Extended period of exposure to fungi, insects, birds, rodents, and game, especially in the seedling phase, not to mention increased competition with ground vegetation.
Technical problems involved in felling old trees over regrowth	Natural regeneration mainly takes place under the shelter of old trees. The several cuttings necessary to remove the old trees result in damage during harvesting and extraction procedures. Removal of damaged individuals is necessary.
Extended tending efforts/expenditure in the thicket/pole stage	The following measures, not required in the case of plantations, are necessary for the: • reduction of high plant densities • correction of stocking irregularities • elimination of excessively vigorous and coarse trees (wolves) • elimination of unwanted mixture trees.
Extended duration of the regeneration period	The length of time between seed production and the end of the tending process is normally much longer than in plantations. This presents problems of continuity for forest enterprises.

Figure 9 Natural regeneration of different species often early needs tending procedures.

conifers, in particular, have often been planted on the wrong sites. Unfortunately, some of them now regenerate freely and have to be removed at great expense. One of the most important examples of this is the natural regeneration of Norway spruce on compacted soils, with anaerobic subsoil conditions, for example, pseudogleys. Such stands are often prone to storm damage (**Figures 10** and **11**). To avoid further species selection mistakes, a site classification survey would prove to be an invaluable source of basic information.

The use of unsuitable provenances in years gone by, due to a lack of knowledge of the importance of genetically adapted plant material, with respect to abiotic and biotic site factors, would appear to be just as serious a problem. Conifer provenances such as Norway spruce from the lowlands have been planted at high elevations, where they are susceptible to ice and snow break (**Figure 12**), and Scots pine (*Pinus sylvestris*) and European larch (*Larix decidua*) transferred from continentally influenced regions into maritime areas suffer from fungal attacks.

Significantly fewer mistakes have been made with broadleaves because of their lower economic value.

Figure 10   Norway spruce with a flat root system on a shallow pseudogley soil after having been uprooted by a storm (Schaidt, Germany).

Figure 12   Norway spruce from the lowlands suffering from storm, ice, and snow at high elevations (Freiburg, Germany).

Figure 11   Beech, also with a flat root system, uprooted by storm on a pseudogley (Schaidt, Germany).

In order to be successful, it is important, therefore, that there is an adequate distribution of site-adapted tree species in the forest stand to be regenerated, or in its vicinity.

Active Promotion of Natural Processes

In order to minimize the disadvantages and the problems associated with natural regeneration, the following procedures may be helpful and are used in practice.

Promoting seed production   As has already been mentioned, some pioneer species flower annually. Most other trees, however, flower irregularly. Their seed production is highly dependent on the prevailing climatic conditions, as well as conditions in the preceding years, and cannot, therefore, be influenced by the forester. However, vigorous dominant trees with large crowns and sufficient growing space begin to flower earlier, and they do so more frequently and more intensively. Early and continued crown thinning will improve seed production effectively and sustainably, but requires continuity and a great deal of staying-power. Often thinnings are neglected, especially in the case of most broadleaves (Figure 13).

It has been shown, however, that dominant individuals of certain species, including beech and oak, increase seed production when their crowns receive more light. This is true even after very late crown thinning. The process of natural regeneration, therefore, normally begins a few years in advance of seed production, with an intensive crown thinning of the dominant individuals in the stand.

Influencing tree species proportion   Tree species distribution and proportion can be influenced using the following procedures.

Choice of an appropriate silvicultural system   Silvicultural systems are geared towards creating favorable ecological conditions for particular species, depending on its demands (Figures 14–16). Ensuring protection against the main wind direction, as well as providing an infrastructure for felling and extraction, with an adequate road and timber extraction line system, are further components.

Some silvicultural systems are listed in Table 3, according to the ecological needs of the respective tree species.

Generally, natural regeneration of intermediate and late successional species is more important in Central Europe. Therefore, stronger emphasis is laid on these systems compared with regeneration of light demanding species on bare land.

Choice of mast year   Flowering and fruit development can be observed and inventoried during the growing season. In a mast year, natural regeneration is usually initiated by opening the canopy slightly and, if necessary, preparing the soil. If the sheltering stands, or those nearby, contain the desired species, the initial procedures can begin once the trees start to produce seed.

Regulating the light regime   In the event of two or more tree species germinating, with each likely to establish themselves, it is possible to manipulate their proportions by regulating the light regime within the

Figure 13   Poorly thinned beech with very small crowns will not be able to produce seeds later on (Tuttlingen, Germany).

Figure 14 A relatively open uniform shelterwood stand enables young Scots pine to grow in the initial years but has to be removed fairly early to allow sufficient light to reach the young growth (North Sweden).

Figure 15 Beech being regenerated in the group shelter system, protected for many years against late frost and drought (Kelheim, Germany).

forest stand. This is done by varying the intensity of cuttings. Under the canopy of old trees the suppression of young growth of light-demanding species is possible. The seedlings may even disappear because of a lack of light. On bare ground or in larger gaps this problem will not arise, however. The mixed montane forests common in Central Europe provide a good example of the way of regulating the light conditions according to the needs of the species. These forests consist mainly of three species: silver fir, beech, and Norway spruce. Very gradual, light shelterwood cuttings will maintain relatively dark conditions within the stand, which results in the dominance of the very shade-tolerant silver fir. Larger openings favor beech. More dramatic openings in the canopy are required in order to promote Norway spruce (**Table 4**). To increase the proportion of sycamore, a further component of these mixed montane forests, gaps must be made and enlarged further after a few years.

Figure 16   Silver fir and Norway spruce saplings naturally regenerated in a group shelterwood stand (Kelheim, Germany).

Table 3   Main silvicultural systems with regard to the ecological requirements of forest tree species

Silvicultural system	Size of opening		Ecological type	Tree species[a] (examples)	Comments
Clear-cut	Large	>5 ha	Pioneer	*Betula* spp., *Populus* spp., *Alnus* spp., *Salix* spp.	No practical importance in Central Europe
	Small–medium	0.5 – 5 ha		*Pinus sylvestris*, *Larix decidua*	Common traditionally
Gap/strip felling	Small	0.05–0.5 ha <100 m wide	Intermediate	*Picea abies*, *Fraxinus excelsior*, *Acer pseudoplatanus*, *A. platanoides*, *A. campestre*, *Quercus petraea*, *Q. robur*, *Prunus avium* (*Pinus sylvestris*)	Shelterwood system important traditionally. Transition to small-scale free mixture of the three adjacent systems becoming increasingly important.
Uniform shelterwood		Regular crown openings in large stands	Intermediate/ late successional	*Fagus sylvatica*, (*Quercus petraea*), *Tilia* spp., *Carpinus betulus*	The speed with which the crown cover is opened can be adapted to suit the demands of the species.
Group shelterwood; combination of shelter and strips		Groups of >30 m in diameter	Late successional	*Abies alba*, *Fagus sylvatica*, *Picea abies*	Beech should be kept under shelter for 15–20 years, oak for only 5 years.
Selection		Single tree removal		*Abies alba* (*Fagus sylvatica*)	Special site conditions necessary, therefore restricted to specific areas.

[a]Tree names in brackets indicate species of minor importance within the system mentioned.

Another important example is beech, with its many potential admixed tree species. Beech will outcompete almost every other species, including oak (*Quercus petraea* and *Q. robur*), ash, and sycamore, if the canopy is not opened following the initial stand establishment phases. The only exceptions are even more shade-tolerant species, such as yew and silver fir. This has proven to be a very common problem.

Of course, it is important to bear in mind that, flexibility with regard to varying the tree species

Table 4 Effect of the rate of opening of canopy on the species distribution of the regrowth. The regeneration period begins when the initial openings of the canopy are made in order to encourage the development of seedlings and ends when the last tree is removed

Rate of progression of shelterwood treatments		Dominance of species	
Very slow	>50 years	Silver fir	*Abies alba*
Slow	~25 years	Beech	*Fagus silvatica*
Frequent and gentle	~15 years	Norway spruce	*Picea abies*
Cutting gaps and enlargement	~5 years	Sycamore	*Acer pseudoplatanus*

Table 5 Silvicultural means of improving conditions for the storage of seeds in the forest floor, for germination, and for the first phases of establishment

Procedure	Specification	Description of procedure	Comments
Conversion of surface layers not conducive to natural regeneration	Opening of the canopy in order to stimulate soil activity by improving the temperature and water supply	Removal of all individuals that create heavy shade and intercept precipitation, i.e., dominant trees with large crowns, as well as intermediate and suppressed trees	Common starting procedure of many silvicultural systems. Slow, long-term response. Possible development of competing ground vegetation if employed too rigidly.
	Soil preparation to promote soil activity	Breaking up the uppermost organic soil layers and mixing with mineral soil	Necessary in areas with thick raw humus layers or inhibited mineralization.
	Mineral fertilization to promote soil activity	Distribution of limestone dust or compound fertilizer across the whole area; occasionally combined with opening of the canopy and soil preparation	On poor or acid soils, this is only to be recommended if carried out several years in advance of the start of regeneration. Promotes the development of nutrient demanding species, as well as increment growth of the old trees.
Removal of surface layers not conducive to natural regeneration	Exposing mineral soil by removing surface layers in strips or patches (Figs 18 + 19)	Use of small tractors with soil preparation fittings	Important means of improving the germination rate, especially of beech and Scots pine. Growing concerns over soil compaction as a result of driving in the stands. Increasing importance as a measure for mitigating soil acidification.
	Burning of surface layers	Mainly the result of accidental forest fires; controlled burning also possible	Improves establishment conditions, especially for pioneers. Mostly in dry areas, with increasing importance worldwide.
Removal of competing ground vegetation	Removal of ground vegetation in strips or patches prior to germination	Use of small tractors with fitted weeding equipment	Gaining importance with increasing problems with the development of grass cover.
	Herbicides		More and more herbicides have been banned as a result of environmental/ecological concerns.

composition is only possible if the desired species have regenerated naturally.

Improving the seed storage, germination and early development conditions of the young plants In managed forests, the soil surface often fails to provide favorable conditions for storage, germination, and plant establishment. This is true of 'normal' conditions, as well as special climatic situations, which arise only periodically. There are frequently neither sufficient volumes of coarse woody debris nor large enough areas of mineral soil to support the regeneration

process. It may, therefore, be necessary to promote it by employing one or a combination of the procedures mentioned in **Table 5**. These measures are very much specific to each site, however (**Figures 17–19**).

The following developments have taken place in Central Europe in the last two to three decades, with regard to the procedures mentioned in **Table 5**:

• The intensification of thinnings has led to better crown development in the stands of a number of forest enterprises. Preparatory fellings have tended to become less important in certain areas.

- During the last two decades, an increase in seed production has been very obvious for most tree species. Therefore, foresters no longer rely on isolated mast years, as in the past.
- Soils have recovered remarkably from centuries of overuse in the production of timber and firewood, as well as litter extraction. Raw humus layers have become rare. To date, nitrogen inputs from pollution (NH_4 from agriculture and NO_X mainly from traffic) have had an advantageous effect, in spite of increasing acidification. The necessity of soil preparation has, therefore, decreased in some areas.
- Compensatory fertilizing has been used widely as a means of combating acidification. A side effect of this is that, more demanding species are favored in the regeneration process.

Figure 19   Mineral soil allows for improved germination of Scots pine (North Sweden).

Figure 17   Scarification of the soil to improve soil activity and promote natural regeneration (Fuhrberg, Germany).

Figure 18   Line plowing to promote Scots pine regeneration (Sellhorn, Germany).

• Ground vegetation has evidently profited greatly from the rehabilitation of soils and nitrogen inputs, seriously impeding natural regeneration in many places. The problematic species include grasses, such as *Calamagrostis epigejos* and *C. villosa*, *Avellana flexuosa*, *Carex brizoides*, as well as climbers and shrubs including *Rubus fruticosus*, *R. idaeus*, *Clematis vitalba* and *Prunus serotina*. This tendency appears set to continue (**Figures** 20 and 21).

Minimizing biotic damage Seeds, seedlings, and young plants are very prone to damage caused by snails, rodents and game. Snails feed on seedlings shortly after germination, but will not harm them after the woody tissue has formed. Snails profit from the humid conditions under the shelter of the canopy.

Mice (Microtinae) live in grass cover and prefer warm open areas. They feed on the bark of hardwood saplings and are able to destroy whole groups of them up to the thicket stage. Regeneration under

Figure 20 Grasses (in this case *Calamagrostis epigeios)* increasingly cover large areas and are a serious obstacle to natural regeneration (Berlin, Germany).

Figure 21 Bramble (*Rubus fruticosus)* profits from nitrogen input as well as the recovery of soils, and increasingly competes with young forest plants (Saxony, Germany).

the canopy normally brings about a decline in the ground vegetation, resulting in the loss of their habitat. Unfortunately, keeping the canopy closed for a longer period of time is not possible in many stands. This also requires long-term planning and will favor shade-tolerant species, such as beech.

Game, the omnipresent roe deer, in particular, but also red deer, fallow deer (*Cervus dama*), and some other locally distributed species, such as mouflon (*Ovis ammon musimon*) and chamois (*Rupicapra rupicapra*), are the greatest hazard to young plants. Broadleaves are especially susceptible. Roe deer, for example, prefers rare species such as occasional hardwoods in conifers as well as specific hardwoods like ash and sycamore in beech. Some of these trees have become almost extinct in certain areas because of the high browsing and debarking pressure, and damage caused by fraying. In general, there has been a widespread decline in the species mix and a tendency towards conifer monocultures. As the hunting lobby in almost all countries of the temperate zones has succeeded in resisting a

Figure 23 Individual tree protection as a possible method for the promotion of a small number of endangered plants.

Figure 22 Fencing in order to promote growth, especially of endangered broadleaves, is often inevitable – and very expensive.

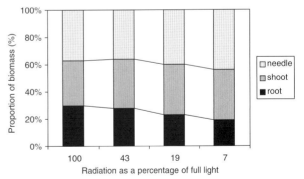

Figure 24 The change in biomass proportion (%) of needles, shoots, and roots of 4-year-old Norway spruce (*Picea abies*), after growing three years in a shading experiment. Apart from the general reduction of biomass, the additional reduction of the root biomass was disproportionately great. Young plants may, therefore, be greatly endangered in the event of water stress and often die in dry periods. (From Huss J 1971 *Untersuchungen über die Wirkung von Beschattung und Düngung auf das Wachstum junger Fichten.* Habilitation thesis, University of Göttingen, Germany.)

reasonable reduction of the high game stocks, fencing or single tree protection is the likely means of protection in many cases (**Figures 22** and **23**).

Securing a species mixture The canopy of an old stand provides shelter against late and early frosts, high temperatures, and desiccation. The regeneration of shade-tolerant tree species susceptible to these climatic stresses therefore normally takes place under the shelter of the old trees. The longer the regrowth is kept under shelter, however, the greater the like-lihood of not only the light-demanding components of the mixture of trees dying or being overgrown, but also the risk of the shade-tolerant species suffering as a result of the low irradiation. Unlike in the tropics, all tree species found in Europe exhibit the greatest biomass production under full light. Under a closed canopy, biomass production and growth in diameter and height are reduced. For instance the biomass production of young Norway spruce was reduced to less than 10% when the global radiation was only 7%. Moreover biomass allocation (**Figure 24**), as well as stem and crown form, may also be affected **Figure 25**. The degree of canopy closure is regulated according to the development phase of the young plants (**Figure 26**).

Combining and optimizing all the different possible effects and goals of management, such as excluding ecological stress conditions on the one hand, and regulating growth and the species mix on the other, is a great challenge for the forester.

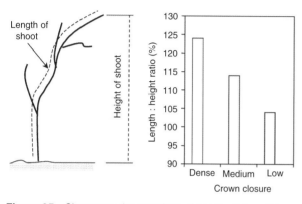

Figure 25 Changes to the stem form of beech wildings (*Fagus sylvatica*) after 9 years growing under the shelter of differentially thinned 55-year-old Norway spruce (*Pinus abies*). The 1–3-m high beech saplings show significant differences in the degree of bending, depending on the density of the canopy, as influenced by the thinning variation. Saplings in deep shade are bent to a much greater extent, and are less stable because their slim stems are more susceptible to snow damage, or even heavy rain.

The Future Role of Natural Regeneration in Forest Practice

It has been shown that the rehabilitation of the soil, as well as increased seed production rates, have improved the potential for natural regeneration over recent decades. The main obstacle to an increase in the use of natural regeneration, however, remains high game densities. There are some examples in Germany where the deer population has been successfully reduced, resulting in an overwhelming

Figure 26 Seedlings and saplings (here Norway spruce) show uneven growth according to varying light conditions in unevenly opened canopy (Gaildorf, Germany).

Figure 27 Rowan and other rare species return when protected by fences or where the deer numbers have been reduced (Hinterzarten, south-west Germany).

recovery of the forest by means of natural regeneration, including species very sensitive to browsing and, consequently, quite rare. Rowan (*Sorbus aucuparia*) is an illustrative example in this regard (**Figure 27**).

Ecological and silvicultural problems aside, sociological and economic factors have, in a way, contributed to the increased acceptance of natural regeneration and its practical application. Three such factors are:

1. The 'green' movement amongst the public, which favors all procedures promoting natural forms of management.
2. Forestry in Central Europe has reached a phase in its development where there is a trend away from afforestation, towards nature-based forestry. Most forests are being reconstructed, and provide the opportunity for more demanding species to regenerate under the shelter of existing stands.
3. Forestry is suffering from the same problems as all other industries within the primary sector: falling

revenues from the production of raw materials and a steady increase in the costs. All forest enterprises have, therefore, been forced to reduce their costs. Natural regeneration is one possible way of achieving this.

See also: **Afforestation**: Stand Establishment, Treatment and Promotion - European Experience. **Ecology**: Natural Disturbance in Forest Environments. **Genetics and Genetic Resources**: Forest Management for Conservation. **Silviculture**: Coppice Silviculture Practiced in Temperate Regions; Natural Regeneration of Tropical Rain Forests. **Sustainable Forest Management**: Overview. **Tree Physiology**: Physiology of Sexual Reproduction in Trees; Physiology of Vegetative Reproduction.

Further Reading

Burschel P and Huss J (1997) *Grundriß des Waldbaus*, 2nd edn. Berlin: Parey Buchverlag.
Huss J 1971 *Untersuchungen über die Wirkung von Beschattung und Düngung auf das Wachstum junger Fichten*. Habilitation thesis, University of Göttingen, Germany.
Matthews JD (1989) *Silvicultural Systems*. Oxford, UK: Clarendon Press.
Smith DM (1986) *The Practice of Silviculture*, 8th edn. New York: John Wiley.

Forest Rehabilitation

D Lamb, University of Queensland, Brisbane, Australia

Introduction

Rehabilitation is a form of reforestation that differs from more traditional approaches because it seeks to achieve outcomes other than just timber production. As well as creating a supply of goods such as timber, many rehabilitation projects aim to achieve functional changes and re-establish the ecological processes that once supported the original forest ecosystems. These changes then increase the supply of ecological services from a forest such as increased topsoil organic matter and fertility, enhanced hillslope stability, or improvements in watershed protection. Most rehabilitation projects try to do this by restoring some, though not necessarily all, of the original biodiversity (unlike ecological restoration which seeks to restore all of the plant and animal communities that were once present in the original forest).

One of the potential advantages of rehabilitation is that it can provide greater benefits for humans living in and around the new forest than most of the more traditional forms of reforestation. This may be through the socioeconomic benefits the forests provide from new goods such as timber, fruit, nuts, or medicinal plants leading to improvements in human livelihoods. Alternatively, it may come from the environmental and cultural benefits generated (Table 1). Finding the right balance between improving human well-being and improving the ecological integrity is difficult. This is because there may be more than one stakeholder involved at a particular site and each may have different priorities. Rehabilitation therefore represents a particularly difficult form of silviculture.

Some say it is too difficult – we should simply separate these different objectives and do each on different parts of the landscape. That is, we should continue to carry out intensive commercial production on those parts of a landscape that are suitable and protect or restore biodiversity in other, residual areas less suited for production. This view ignores the fact that the world's landscapes are being simplified and homogenized as agricultural areas have spread and natural forests are lost. Many now question the sustainability of these agricultural landscapes. Indeed, the provision of ecological services from new forests to ensure the sustainability of some agricultural landscapes may be a far more valuable outcome than any goods these forests may supply.

What is needed, therefore, is a more sophisticated array of silvicultural options to match the range of socioeconomic and ecological dilemmas that land managers are facing. This does not mean that traditional forms of reforestation are superseded. Indeed, in many situations they may continue to be

the predominant method by which cleared land is reforested. What it does mean, however, is that they should not be seen as the only way in which reforestation is undertaken.

This article reviews some of approaches that have been developed to achieve these purposes. It also considers the problems limiting the application of these and some of the issues involving scaling up from these site level interventions to reforesting at a landscape scale.

A Typology of Rehabilitation

Rehabilitation may take place under two circumstances. One is where deforestation is not complete and where logging or agricultural clearing has left some residual forest. This residual forest may consist entirely of remnants of the original forest or it may also include regrowth that has developed since the disturbing event occurred. The other circumstance is where deforestation has been complete and only grassland or shrublands persists. In either situation the prevailing conditions may prevent natural recovery occurring as quickly as is needed meaning that some form of silvicultural intervention is needed. These two conditions generate alternative silvicultural options. These options are summarized by the typology in Table 2. Typologies such as this necessarily disguise the fact that, in practice, these alternatives sometimes merge or overlap.

Some Residual Natural Forest Still Present at Site

Protect residual forest If a significant stocking of trees remains at the site the most obvious silvicultural

Table 1 Goods and services provided by forest rehabilitation

Goods	Ecological services for	
	Individual landowner	Community
Industrial timbers	Hillslope stabilization	Biodiversity
Firewood	Improved soil fertility	Watershed protection
Fruits	Windbreaks and shelter	Hillslope stabilization
Gums and resins	Aesthetic benefits	Clean water
Animal protein	Cultural benefits	Carbon sequestration
Medicinal plants	Recreational benefits	Aesthetic benefits
Other food crops		Cultural benefits
		Recreational benefits

Table 2 A typology of forest rehabilitation approaches

1. Some residual forest still present

- Protect forest and allow natural recovery
- Protect and manage forest to encourage favored species
- Protect forest and enrich with commercially desired species (e.g., timber trees, fruit trees, etc.)

2. No existing forest remains: canopy trees must be replanted
2.1 New plantations with a more or less constant canopy tree composition

- Monoculture of tree species with preference given to native species
- Mosaic of tree monocultures across the landscape using mostly native species
- Tree monoculture with underplantings or inter-row plantings of economically or socially useful agricultural crop plants
- Multispecies tree plantations

2.2 New plantations where the composition of the canopy tree species changes over time (semisuccessional plantings)

- Nurse trees (native or exotic species) used to establish commercial tree species plantations option is to simply protect the site from further disturbances (such as recurrent fires, agricultural clearing, logging, firewood collection, or the harvesting of non-timber forest products) and allow natural successional processes to re-establish the forest. These successional processes might involve regeneration from coppice, seeds, or seedlings already present at the site or from seeds of species dispersed into the site from other nearby forest patches. By providing this protection biodiversity is conserved and forest development occurs without further cost. These species-rich forests are then able to supply a variety of goods and ecological services.

But protection can be difficult. Fire exclusion, for example, can be hard to achieve without a well-established fire suppression organization, particularly if wildfire is unchecked in neighboring lands. Nonetheless, there are many examples of where protection of residual forests has allowed substantial forest recovery over large areas. In time selective harvesting of timber or non-timber species can become possible depending on the density of individuals of these species. The primary advantage of this approach is its low cost while the main disadvantage is that recovery may take some time.

Protect and manage forest to encourage favored species   A variant of this first option is to intervene silviculturally to promote the regeneration and growth of some of the more commercially attractive species present within the protected forest. Possible interventions may take the form of weeding or tending to remove competing species or thinning to reduce competition between trees of commercial species or to remove individuals with poor form or vigor. Pruning of these target species may also be commercially advantageous.

Protect and enrich with commercially favored species   Heavy logging sometimes leaves a residual forest with only a limited stocking of commercially attractive species although many other species may still be present. Under these circumstances the abundance of seedlings or young trees of the more commercially attractive species (e.g., timber trees, fruit trees, medicinal plants in the understory, etc.) may be low. However, it may be possible to accelerate the recovery process by enriching the forest with these species to improve its commercial (or social) value. In tropical forests this usually requires that seedlings of the commercial species are planted as groups in clearings or in lines cut through the forest. In both cases overhead canopy cover must be minimized to avoid seedlings being suppressed. The density of these introduced seedlings is com-

monly less than 100 trees per hectare. This means the cost of treatment is much lower than clearing the residual forest and replanting with a monoculture.

Experience with enrichment planting in the tropics has been mixed because weed control is often difficult to maintain. Nonetheless, the technique remains an important option because of the large areas of logged-over forest that have accumulated that are depleted in commercially attractive species.

No Existing Natural Forest Remains at Site: Canopy Trees Must Be Replanted

The advantages of the techniques described above are that they conserve plant biodiversity and the ecological services provided by these biota. But different approaches are needed where deforestation is more complete.

New plantations with a more or less constant canopy tree composition

Plantation monocultures of tree species with preference given to native species   Most traditional plantation systems are monocultures. Most also involve fast-growing, exotic species chosen because of the attractiveness of their timber properties and their tolerance of a wide range of site conditions. Most of these species also come as a well-developed silvicultural package with seed from seed orchards, a nursery methodology, and a set of postplanting management prescriptions covering fertilizing, thinning, and pruning. These monocultures are highly suited for intensive production and are the favored approach in most large-scale industrial plantation systems.

Some of these monoculture plantations also provide certain ecological services but their capacity to do so may be limited if the species are shallow-rooted or an understory is absent. Some of these disadvantages can be overcome by establishing leguminous groundcovers for nitrogen fixation or to protect surface soils from erosion.

Monocultures of indigenous tree species can offer some advantages over those provided by monocultures of exotic species provided they can still grow at what might have become a rather degraded site. Although they might still make only a minor contribution to regional biodiversity protection compared with, say, a regrowth forest they are still likely to be more attractive to at least some wildlife than plantations of exotic species. This attractiveness may be enhanced by the structural complexity inherent in the different age classes that develop as plantation establishment continues over time. And although native species often grow more slowly than the more common exotic species, they may also have higher market values. This means that timber volume increments may be lower but net value increments may be higher.

Mosaic of tree monocultures across the landscape using mostly native species Additional landscape heterogeneity can be created if a mosaic of monocultures is created across a region using different native species in each plantation wherever this is ecologically possible. In this case, species are matched carefully with their optimal sites. For example, species preferring moist sites are planted in valley floor positions while more hardy species are established on hills or ridges. In this case the silvicultural advantages of monocultures are maintained while landscape diversity is enhanced. Overall productivity may also be enhanced in this way by matching species to their preferred sites. On the other hand, this requires detailed knowledge of the species and their site relationships.

Tree monoculture with inter-row plantings or underplantings of agricultural crops The primary disadvantage of tree crops is the length of the period before any economic benefit is obtained. Rotation lengths for many tree species exceed 30 years. Some landowners or stakeholders need a return before such a time span in order to encourage them to undertake reforestation. One way this might be achieved is by underplanting the tree species with short-lived agricultural crops or medicinal plants. The well-known 'taungya' system that was developed during the colonial period in Burma is just one example of this approach. In this case the crop plants are planted between the rows of trees thereby helping to exclude weeds. Cropping is continued until tree canopy closure occurs and is then abandoned.

This tree-plus-crop combination is commonly referred to as agroforestry and there is a huge number of variants. In some cases, such as the taungya system, the crop is short-lived. In other cases the crop is a more or less permanent component of the plantation system. Many of these systems use only a single species of tree but other agroforestry systems use more than one tree species. The commercial advantages of the system are clear provided the crop species can tolerate their subcanopy position. The system also has some ecological advantages since the more complex canopy structures are likely to provide better ecological services such as watershed protection and wildlife habitats than simple monocultures.

Multispecies tree plantations Plantations involving more than one tree species are more complex silvicultural systems requiring more sophisticated management operations but offering some potential advantages over monocultures. These include the possibility of enhanced productivity, improved nutrition, reduced insect or disease and greater financial security from the spreading of risk (see **Table 3**).

These potential advantages do not invariably occur in every mixture and randomly created mixtures are likely to fail. Great care is needed to ensure that only complementary species are used. Complementary species may be those that minimize competition with their neighbors. Thus they may have differing phenologies (so that their demands on site resources are at different times than their neighbors) or differing root depths (so that roots take resources from different soil horizons). Likewise they may have differing canopy architectures (so that crown and foliar competition is minimized) or differing nutritional requirements (so that resource competition is minimized). Nutritional gains can also occur when nitrogen fixers such as *Acacia* or *Albizzia* are mixed with non nitrogen fixers.

Most mixtures contain only modest numbers of species but these can be planted in various configurations such as in alternate rows of particular species or at random. Alternate rows offer the advantage that a faster-growing species might be removed earlier than a slower-growing species without causing much damage to the residual trees. Random plantings of the trees in the mixture offer the advantage of a more intimate mingling of the species enabling the advantages of complementarity to be more fully expressed.

Table 3 Potential benefits of using more than one species in a plantation

Potential benefit	Reason
Competition between trees reduced	Competitors have differing growth phenologies and use site resources at different times
	Competitors have different root or canopy architectures that partition spatially distributed resources and use them differentially
Tree nutrition is enhanced	One of species is a nitrogen fixer that adds N to soil
	Nutrient decomposition and cycling is faster with more than one litter type
Reduced insect or disease problems	Target species for insects are hidden in space; host plants for particular diseases are more widely distributed
Financial outcome is improved	Provides insurance and spreads risk of markets changing during rotation period

Adapted with permission from Lamb D and Gilmour DA (2003) *Rehabilitation and Restoration of Degraded Forest.* Gland, Switzerland: IUCN.

Mixtures obviously have higher levels of plant biodiversity than plantation monocultures although the extent of any biodiversity gain depends on the number of species included in the mixture. In most cases this will still be modest compared with that in a natural forest. But mixtures are also likely to have a greater structural complexity than any monoculture meaning they are likely to be more attractive to some wildlife species. Any gain in species richness is likely to benefit the restoration of key ecological processes and ecological services. The key disadvantage of mixed species plantations is obviously in their greater silvicultural complexity and need for more intensive management.

New plantations where the composition of the canopy tree species changes over time (semisuccessional plantings)

Nurse trees used to establish plantation tree species Some commercially attractive plantation tree species need an overstory canopy of 'nurse' trees to become established. Once they are established this nurse tree cover can be removed. Thus some temperate tree species need protection from frosts when young. Similarly, some tropical tree species are sensitive to full sunlight when at the seedling stage. Nurse crops such as these are also needed for some agricultural crops (e.g., *Erythrina*, *Cordia*, or *Leuceaena* are often used to provide shelter over coffee or cacoa). A forestry example is the requirement by some of the Dipterocarpaceae of Southeast Asia for a temporary overstory cover. Nurse crops can also benefit certain tree species by reducing insect damage, presumably by altering some element of the microclimate affecting the insect. For example, red cedar (Meliaceae) has been found to have greater survival rates when planted below an established cover than when planted in the open. Likewise nurse trees may act to improve soil conditions allowing more valuable species to be established at the site.

These nurse trees facilitate the development and growth of the target species and add to the biological complexity of the new forest. However, they also pose a series of silvicultural dilemmas. These include the question of how tall the nurse trees must be when the target species is planted and how much cover must they provide? How long should this cover be provided before it begins to reduce the growth rates of the commercially attractive species? If the nurse species are short-lived they may disappear around the time when their disadvantages begin to outweigh their advantages. Otherwise they may need to be removed by poisoning or girdling.

While the focus of this silvicultural sequence is the commercial plantation species the added biological

and structural complexity of the new forest ensures it has some ecological advantages over simple monocultures as well.

Underplant beneath earlier plantation monoculture A variation on the nurse tree model is when circumstances require that an existing monoculture plantation of one species (perhaps an exotic), be replaced by another (perhaps a native species). This may be because the timber value of the original species has declined or because the environmental or ecological benefits of the current plantation are insufficient and need improvement. In such a situation the best option may be to simply clear the original forest and replant with the preferred species. But in some situations it might be preferable to underplant below the original canopy or plant in strips or corridors cleared through the original plantation and manage a more gradual transition. The choice will obviously depend on the shade tolerances of the various species being added to the site as well as the longevity and current market value of the initial plantation species. The new species might be more valuable timber, nut, or fruit trees or they might simply have greater ecological and conservational value.

The advantage of such an approach is that it avoids rapid changes in wildlife habitat and potentially large soil and nutrient losses caused by erosion after clearing. There is also scope for some financial gain from the harvesting process. The disadvantage is that the shade tolerances of the new species and hence the amount of canopy opening needed must be clearly understood to avoid a lengthy period of trial and error during the transition.

Understory development encouraged beneath tree plantation Many plantations located near intact natural forest can gradually acquire an understory of native species because of natural colonization. The rate at which this occurs will depend on the attributes of the plantation species as well as those of the potential colonists and on the dispersal distances involved. In the tropics greater diversity appears to occur beneath broadleaved plantation trees than beneath conifers. Within the time period of a typical plantation rotation, a very species-rich understory can develop, especially in moist tropical regions. In some cases these colonists can grow up and join the canopy layer.

This phenomenon represents both an opportunity as well as a dilemma. The opportunity is that great biological diversity can be acquired for little cash outlay. This means there may be a significant gain in a variety of ecological services such as watershed protection and nutrient cycling and the restoration of many ecological processes. The dilemma is that there may be an indirect cost in the form of increased competition facing the original plantation trees that will slow their growth. The trade-off will necessarily depend on circumstances. If the site is one where enhanced biodiversity is an advantage then it may be appropriate to tolerate a reduction in timber increment caused by increased competition. On the other hand, if production is the predominant objective then careful management of this competition will be needed.

There are four possible alternative management regimes. One is to harvest the plantation as initially envisaged and to treat the enhanced biodiversity as a temporary benefit that will re-establish again when the second rotation of the plantation is re-established. A second is to regard this biodiversity as now being more socially beneficial than any timber harvest and to not fell the trees as was originally planned. A third is to fell the plantation trees at the end of the rotation as originally planned but to try to protect as much of the new biodiversity as possible while doing this. Subsequently, the primary management objective would then become one of fostering and enhancing this biodiversity rather than re-establishing the plantation timber trees. The final option might be to simply manage the plantation species, together with the new timber species that have joined the canopy, as an uneven-aged forest and to manage this on a selection system. This would recognize that some of the new colonists might have also commercial or social values as food or medicinal plants.

This catalytic role of plantations does not occur everywhere and sometimes the only species that colonize beneath the plantation species are exotic weeds. But provided it is carefully managed, the phenomenon is a cheap means by which monoculture plantations can generate a wider range of ecological services.

Problems in Using These Approaches

This variety of potential alternatives might seem to imply that all are equally available. Unfortunately this is not the case and there are two main reasons. One concerns the biology of native species. Much less is usually known about the ecology or silviculture of most native tree species than is known, for example, about the more common industrial forestry species. This means that species–site relationships and nutritional requirements are uncertain and the competitive abilities or tolerances of these species are mostly unknown. This makes it difficult to develop good mosaics of monocultures or design multispecies plantations using complementary species mixes. A second, even more difficult issue is that of managing the

trade-off between production and ecological integrity or authenticity. Different stakeholders will strike different balances because they have differing objectives. This means that reaching a desired balance will probably always involve some degree of trial and error until the basic silviculture and ecology of the several species being used is understood.

The Social–Economic Context for Reforestation

Forest rehabilitation to provide goods and ecological services is more commonly undertaken by farmers and communities rather than by industrial enterprises. This is because of the differing objectives usually being sought by these several groups. But farmers, like industrial enterprises, need some certainty that they will indeed be the ultimate beneficiaries of any reforestation that they undertake. This means that land tenure is a crucial matter. No person is likely to invest time or money in a long-term activity like forestry unless there is some certainty over land ownership or future access. Nor are they likely to protect the young forest from fires or grazing animals unless they can see it to be in their own interest. The irony here, of course, is that many of the most degraded landscapes are also those where rural people's traditional land ownership claims are unrecognized by central governments.

Because ecological services are often distributed far beyond the immediate vicinity of any particular reforestation site there is also the issue of whether these distant beneficiaries of rehabilitation should also contribute to its cost. For example, should a landowner with land affected by salinity contribute to the cost of trees planted in the watershed upstream of his property? These trees will help lower the water table and reduce his salinity problem but will also reduce the area of agricultural land available to his neighbor. If rehabilitation is to be undertaken on a large scale then some way must be found to fund the restoration of these services on degraded lands for the wider public benefit. The current debate over whether the carbon sequestered by tree plantations might be traded in a special market illustrates one approach to this problem.

A related problem is that each forest manager usually makes decisions on a site basis but that many ecological processes operate at a landscape scale. Different land managers will have different goals and therefore use different agricultural and silvicultural approaches. But agricultural sustainability across the landscape as a whole will require collective action by all land managers if optimal outcomes are to be achieved. This will require what might be called forest landscape restoration. Such a landscape may have croplands, patches of remnant forest, and perhaps several of the approaches outlined above. There are few localities where this has been successfully achieved.

See also: **Biological Impacts of Deforestation and Fragmentation. Forest Management for Conservation. Plant Diversity in Forests. Silviculture**: Natural Stand Regeneration; Reclamation of Mining Lands; Sustainability of Forest Plantations. **Sustainable Forest Management**.

Further Reading

Banerjee AK (1995) *Rehabilitation of Degraded Forests in Asia*. World Bank Technical Paper no. 270. Washington, DC: World Bank.

Bradshaw A and Chadwick MJ (1980) *The Restoration of Land: The Ecology and Reclamation of Derelict and Degraded Land*. Berkeley, CA: University of California Press.

Dobson A, Bradshaw A, and Baker A (1997) Hopes for the future: restoration ecology and conservation biology. *Science* 277: 515–522.

ITTO (2002) *ITTO Guidelines for the Restoration, Management and Rehabilitation of Degraded and Secondary Tropical Forests*. ITTO Policy Development Series no. 13, in collaboration with CIFOR, FAO, IUCN, and WWF. Yokohama, Japan: International Tropical Timbers Organization.

Jordan WR, Gilpin ME, and Aber JD (1987) *Restoration Ecology: A Synthetic Approach to Ecological Research*. Cambridge, UK: Cambridge University Press.

Kelty MJ, Larson BC, and Oliver CD (eds) (1992) *The Ecology and Silviculture of Mixed Species Forests*. Dordrecht, The Netherlands: Kluwer Academic Publishers.

Kobayashi S, Turnbull JW, Toma T, Mori T, and Majid NMNA (eds) (1999) *Rehabilitation of Degraded Tropical Forest Ecosystems*, Workshop Proceedings, 2–4 November 1999, Bogor, Indonesia.

Lamb D (1998) Large-scale ecological restoration of degraded tropical forest land: the potential role of timber plantations. *Restoration Ecology* 6: 271–279.

Lamb D and Gilmour DA (2003) *Rehabilitation and Restoration of Degraded Forest*. Gland, Switzerland: IUCN.

Parrotta JA, Turnbull JW, and Jones N (1997) Catalysing native forest regeneration on degraded tropical land. *Forest Ecology and Management* 99: 1–8.

Rodwell J and Patterson G (1994) *Creating New Native Woodlands*. Bulletin no. 112. London: HMSO.

Torquebiau E (1984) Man-made dipterocarp forest in Sumatra. *Agroforestry Systems* 2: 103–127.

Wadsworth F (1997) *Forest Production for Tropical America*. US Department of Agriculture Forest Service Agriculture Handbook no. 710. Washington, DC: Department of Agriculture.

Wormald TJ (1992) *Mixed and Pure Forest Plantations in the Tropics and Subtropics*. Rome: Food and Agricultural Organization.

Treatments in Tropical Silviculture

F E Putz, Center for International Forestry Research, Jakarta, Indonesia

Introduction

Silviculture can be defined as the art and science of controlling the composition, structure, and dynamics of forests. Although the traditional focus of silviculture was on timber production, modern silviculturalists are expected to respond to society's often conflicting demands about forests. Sustained yield of timber is still a common goal, but non-timber forest products (NTFPs) such as medicinal plants and wildlife sometime receive as much or more attention from some important forest stakeholders. Forests providing these products and the jobs and revenues they yield are also expected to serve as recreation areas, watersheds, and effective moderators of local and global climates. Foresters are expected to manage forests for these goods and services in ways that avoid losses of genetic, species-level, and landscape-level diversities; sometimes they are expected to manage without apparent disruption of the pristine nature of old-growth forest. With so broad an agenda, the relevant question seems to become what isn't silviculture rather than what is?

This article has a somewhat traditional focus on plants and plant products, how they grow, and how forests can be silviculturally treated so as to increase production of the desired species. Although reference is made to different silvicultural systems that have been utilized in the tropics, the emphasis is on the ecological reasons behind these different methods for increasing the stocking and growth of commercial species and the conditions under which they are likely to be successful.

Treatments to Improve Stocking

General Approach

Securing adequate natural regeneration for future harvests is a central but often hard-won goal for forest managers. Despite the popular perception of forest management as necessarily involving tree planting in tropical forests, natural regeneration has a number of advantages over artificial regeneration (e.g., hand or machine planting of seeds or seedlings). One of these advantages is that because the seed sources for natural regeneration are individuals that successfully reproduced in the stand, it is reasonable to expect that they are genetically well adapted to local biotic and abiotic conditions. For plantation managers, in contrast, mismatches of species, provenances, and genotypes to local site conditions are commonplace. Furthermore, transplanted seedlings often suffer high mortality rates and, if planted poorly, may grow slowly or develop deformed stems even if they do survive. Natural regeneration is also generally less expensive than artificial regeneration, but it is not always 'free.' In any event, where natural regeneration is relied upon, management interventions are generally less drastic than where seeds or seedlings are planted. Lessening the impacts of stand regeneration operations, in addition to saving money, has the advantage of reducing the effects of forest management on biodiversity and ecosystem functioning (e.g., stream sedimentation and nutrient cycling). This is not to say, however, that methods for securing natural regeneration are always gentle. On the contrary, where natural, stand-regenerating disturbances include fires, hurricanes, or other major perturbations, the appropriate regeneration treatments are also likely to be severe.

Successfully regenerating commercial species without causing unnecessary harm to other species or forest processes requires substantial ecological and more specific silvicultural knowledge. For example, the reactions to harvesting and other stand manipulations of commercial species, weeds, and other taxa need to be known. Forest managers thus need to be aware of the intervals between seed crops (e.g., mast year frequencies), the distances to which seeds are dispersed, the probability of seedling establishment and survival, and the relative growth rates of commercial species and the species with which they compete. Due to a variety of factors including destructive harvesting practices, droughts, intense seed predation, herbivory, and the effects of pathogens, natural regeneration may not result in fully stocked stands.

A major challenge for forest managers is developing sufficient understanding of the regeneration mechanisms of the species for which the area is being managed as well as of the other species that influence forest development. Plants regenerate in a variety of ways, both sexually (i.e., by seed), and vegetatively (e.g., from rhizomes or coppicing from cut stumps). Among sexually reproducing species are those that produce seeds that lack dormancy (i.e., they either germinate or die soon after maturing), and others that produce seeds that may remain dormant in the soil for many years. Species that regenerate vegetatively may simply sprout back after being damaged or spread extensively by root sprouts or stem layering. Extensive vegetative expansion is fairly rare among tropical trees, at least those that grow to be large, but is common among other growth forms such as vines, grasses, and ferns. Sprouting of naturally broken or felled trees, in contrast, is commonplace.

Reducing Logging Damage to Advanced Regeneration

The understories of many forests contain substantial populations of seedlings, saplings, and poles of commercial species, which are collectively referred to as 'advanced regeneration,' and subcanopy trees, which are referred to as 'advanced residuals.' Where harvesting is planned to be carried out before completion of a full rotation (i.e., the time required for a germinated seed to grow into a plant of harvestable size), reducing harvesting damage to the future crop trees is critical. Due to limited knowledge about the capacity of most tropical tree species to respond favorably to canopy opening after suffering prolonged suppression, future crop trees should be selected on the basis of stem and crown form, not just by species and stem diameter. In any event, harvesting should be considered to be an intensive silvicultural intervention and not a forest product mining operation.

Promoting Seed Production and Seedling Establishment

Regeneration from seed can fail at any phase of the process of flower production, pollination, seed set, seed dispersal, and seedling establishment. For species that are poorly represented by advanced regeneration or as buried seeds in the soil, retention of seed-producing individuals is generally of the utmost importance. The minimum density of retained seed-bearers is a function of a large number of factors including both propagule and site characteristics. For example, the required density of retained individuals of a dioecious species (i.e., one with separate sexes) that produces large and poorly dispersed seeds is likely greater than for a species with perfect flowers and small, wind-dispersed seeds. The location of seed trees relative to skid trails, felling gaps, and other canopy openings may also be critical. For example, on the Yucatan Peninsula of Mexico, regeneration of *Swietenia macrophylla* is promoted by retention of seed trees upwind from such openings. The timing of harvesting operations can also be critical if the seed-producing trees are cut before their seeds are dispersed. Setting a minimum diameter limit for harvesting that is close to or less than the minimum size at which trees start to reproduce is another obvious cause of regeneration failures. Unfortunately, diameter limits are all too often determined without regard to the biology of the species being harvested.

There is a wide range of harvesting options designed to promote regeneration, ranging from massive clear-cuts to single tree selection, which results in only small gaps in the canopy. In deciding upon the appropriate harvesting system for the forest and species of concern, the silviculturalist needs to determine the minimum canopy opening that promotes the regeneration of the desired species. Where silvicultural treatments other than harvesting are to be applied, the silviculturalist should also know whether mineral soil needs to be exposed to promote seed germination and seedling establishment.

Seeds may be produced in abundance but regeneration nevertheless fail if seed dispersers are absent or limited in abundance due to over-hunting. Although many of the best-known timber trees in the tropics have wind-dispersed seeds, many other timber-producing species, as well as most understory trees and virtually all palms, shrubs, and herbs, produce seeds that require the services of mammals, birds, reptiles, or even fish for their dispersal. Seeds that are not dispersed mostly fall under the parent plant where they suffer greatly from competition, seed and seedling predation, and the impacts of pathogens.

Pre- and postdispersal seed predation can greatly reduce the numbers of seeds available for germination. In some cases, mammals and birds (e.g., parrots and doves) eat large numbers of immature seeds. Similarly, many insects (e.g., some beetles and flies) lay their eggs on flowers or young fruits; the larvae hatch and bore inside where they are nourished at the expense of developing seeds. Many mature seeds are in a sense sacrificed to animals that serve as both dispersers and seed predators. Squirrels and other rodents that scatter-hoard seeds for future consumption are a familiar example of this dual function; the seeds they fail to recover are the most likely to survive and contribute to the next generation.

Dispersed seeds that escape predation may nevertheless fail to germinate or establish as seedlings if the environmental conditions of the places to which they are dispersed are not suitable. For example, seeds that are stimulated to germinate by high red : far red ratios of light will fail to germinate if they land in the forest understory. More commonly, seedling establishment fails because the seedling root fails to find a reliable source of water. Seedlings from small seeds that germinate on top of leaf litter are particularly prone to desiccation. In deep shade, when the reserves of carbohydrates stored in seeds are exhausted, seedlings die if they are not able to photosynthesize enough to balance their respiratory carbon losses. Herbivory and damage from fallen branches and trampling also result in the death of many seedlings, as do nutrient deficiencies, but desiccation and carbon imbalances (often associated with fungal infection) apparently kill the majority of seedlings.

It perhaps goes without saying that most seeds and seedlings fail to survive to maturity, but detailed and long-term studies of population biology are often required to determine whether apparent 'bottlenecks' at the seed or seedling phases actually threaten population maintenance. Nevertheless, silviculturalists need to be careful to avoid inadvertently jeopardizing sustainability by creating conditions favorable to weeds, seed predators, herbivores, and pathogens, or that are unfavorable to pollinators or seed dispersal agents. In some cases, seedling establishment can be enhanced by removing surface litter and near-ground competition with controlled burns, or exposing mineral soil by mechanical scarification with a tractor-drawn plow. Such intensive site preparation treatments are more commonly used in plantations than in managed natural forests, but they should not be disregarded as silvicultural options.

Although traditional forest-dwelling people have successfully enriched forest with useful species for millenia, industrial-scale 'enrichment planting' has generally proven to be a problematic and costly way to increase the stocking of commercial tree species. Despite numerous expensive failures, enrichment planting of nursery-grown seedlings along lines cleared through the forest or in felling gaps continues to be tried in many forests, particularly where uncontrolled logging has left severely depleted stands. While poor planting technique is sometimes the problem, most seedlings die because they do not receive the postplanting tending operations needed to assure their survival. More successful, from a silvicultural perspective, has been a regeneration system referred to by its Burmese name, 'taungya,' in which commercial tree species are planted among food crops plants by farmers who do the necessary weeding. This system was discredited where it was originally used by colonial foresters because once the planted trees were established, the farmers were displaced and their agricultural practices were criminalized. Given the recent substantial devolution of forest management responsibilities back to rural communities from central governments in many tropical countries, some aspects of 'taungya' might prove useful for forest regeneration where the farmers own the land.

Particularly in seasonally dry forests and woodlands, many tree species can be managed for trees that sprout from stumps (i.e., coppicing) or from trees cut off above the reach of browsing animals (i.e., pollarding). Coppice stems of better quality typically emerge from low stools (i.e., stumps), but even the best coppices seldom yield large logs. Nevertheless, coppicing is an excellent way to produce small-dimension timber, poles, firewood, and fiber. Pollarding, in slight contrast, is generally used to provide seasonal shade over crops in agroforestry systems, to produce forage for animals, and for firewood production.

Treatments to Improve Growth

General Approach

Various stand 'improvement' treatments are available to increase light and soil resource availability to commercial species and thereby increase their productivity. In natural forest management in the tropics, these treatments typically involve competition control. Although we are very aware of aboveground competition for light, belowground competition for water and nutrients can also be intense. In this section, weed control and thinning are considered separately even though they are sometimes hard to distinguish.

Weed Control

A 'weed' can be defined as a plant growing where it is not wanted. Depending on the type of weed to be controlled and the ease to which damage to future crop trees can be avoided, silviculturalists can choose from a wide variety of mechanical and chemical treatments or may opt to perform controlled burns.

Among the mechanical weed control methods available, roller chopping, disking, and other tractor-requiring treatments are generally only useful in young stands regenerating after clear-cutting. More often in managed natural forests, weeds interfering with future crop trees are cut with a machete, brush axe, motor-driven weed whacker, or chainsaw. Although many weeds resprout vigorously after cutting, well-timed mechanical treatments can promote growth of future crop trees that may then shade out light-demanding weeds. Generally, mechanical control is most effective early during the season of most active growth when most carbohydrates and other storage materials have been translocated to the aboveground parts that are removed.

When used properly, modern herbicides can be safe, useful, and cost-effective components of a silviculturalist's toolbox. Chemical weed control methods have improved a great deal during the last decade. Compounds used in the 1960s such as sodium arsenite and 2,4,5-trichlorophenoxyacetic acid (2-4-5T) contaminated with dioxins posed serious environmental and health hazards and are now generally banned. In comparison, herbicides such as glyphosate, tryclopyr, hexazinone, and 2,4-dichlorophenoxyacetic acid (2-4D) have low toxicity to animals, brief residence times in the soil, and apparently safe breakdown products. Modern herbicides are all expensive but vary substantially in their modes of action. For example, some are absorbed by roots (e.g., hexazinone) whereas others penetrate leaf cuticles (e.g., glyphosate).

If after weighing the costs and benefits you decide to use herbicides for weed control, there are a number of choices of commercially available products, tank mixtures, dyes, wetting agents (i.e., surfactants), and modes of application.

Suitable ways to apply herbicides vary with the species and size of the target plants, the number of plants you intend to treat, the season, the type of herbicide, and available equipment. Some herbicides, like glyphosate, are often sprayed or wiped on foliage, whereas others, like Garlon 4, are more often squirted around the inside of the bark (i.e., on the vascular cambium) of fresh-cut stumps or into frill girdles cut with a chainsaw or hatchet. To penetrate the waxy coating (cuticle) on leaves, a surfactant is sometimes needed. Because herbicides disrupt metabolic functions, they are best applied when plants are metabolically active. Late growing season applications are often particularly effective because that is when many plants are moving sugars belowground to store for the winter or dry season. Volatile herbicides should be applied when the air is cool and still, lest the fumes escape and kill plants that you were trying to save. And whether herbicides are being applied to bark, stumps, girdles, or leaves, never apply so much that the chemical runs off the surface.

Woody vines, including climbing bamboos, pose serious silvicultural problems in many tropical forests. Vine infestations are especially common in logged forests, particularly those where logging was uncontrolled and carried out by untrained crews. Because many vines survive when their host trees are felled and sprout vigorously from fallen stems, many of the vines in logged areas propagate vegetatively. Prefelling cutting of vines, therefore, can have substantial postfelling advantages in addition to reducing logging damage. Furthermore, due to easier forest interior access prior to logging, prefelling vine cutting is generally more cost effective than trying to control vines in vine-infested logged forests. Finally, because vine leaves may constitute 25% or more of the total forest leaf area, vine cutting is analogous to carrying out a light shelterwood cut; tree seedling densities and growth rates may increase in response to vine removal. Silviculturalists trying to rescue commercial trees in heavily vine-infested forests are generally advised to focus on liberating the crowns of future crop trees rather than trying to cut all of the vines in the entire management area, which is generally too costly.

Thinning

Where future crop trees are crowded by neighbors, thinning can result in substantial increases in growth due to release of soil resources and increased access to light. Thinning treatments can be applied to entire stands or just in the near vicinities of selected future crop trees. Both commercial thinning, in which the thinned trees are extracted and sold, and precommercial thinning are reasonable options in some stands. But before discussing some of the many types of thinning, a few of the silvicultural costs and benefits of thinning need to be considered.

While diameter or volume increments of selected future crop trees can be improved by removing neighbors, heavy stand thinning can lead to retention and growth of lower branches, formation of epicormic branches, increased stem taper, barkscald, abrupt changes in wood properties, and other changes that lead to reductions in stem or wood quality. Thinning stands can also make the remaining trees susceptible to windthrow and weed encroachment. Finally, thinning does not invariably result in the desired growth response. For example, after long periods of suppression, trees of many species do not respond well to thinning; some previously suppressed trees may even die if they are too rapidly exposed to high light intensities, high temperatures, and the consequent water deficits. Where exposure is less rapid and less extreme, formerly suppressed trees that are released from competition may adjust to the new conditions by replacing their shade-adapted leaves with thicker leaves, with thicker cuticles, and other characteristics of 'sun' leaves. Released individuals also adjust their root : shoot ratios so as to increase their water uptake capacities in the more water-demanding conditions of thinned stands.

In silviculturally managed natural forests in the tropics, perhaps the most common thinning operation is the release of selected future crop trees from competition from immediate neighbors. This treatment, often referred to as 'liberation thinning,' has many silvicultural, financial, and environmental advantages in the poorly stocked stands in which tropical foresters generally work. By restricting thinning operations to the near vicinities of future crop trees, portions of most stands remain untreated, which often makes silvicultural sense, saves money, and avoids needless environmental disruption.

Liberation thinning prescriptions generally call for cutting, frill-girdling, or arboriciding trees with crowns above or within some lateral distance (e.g.,

2–4 m) of the crowns of future crop trees. The appropriate extent of lateral opening varies with the species and size of the tree to be released. For example, tree species that typically develop broad spreading crowns may require large openings for maximum growth, at least after the selected individual has developed the desired length of branch-free bole.

To maximize the likelihood of increased timber volume increments, future crop trees selected should not have been heavily suppressed for long periods of time. Because stand records are seldom available, the silviculturalist must rely on visible characteristics of trees themselves to determine their histories of suppression. Crown form is generally the best indicator of the conditions under which a tree has been growing. Trees with small, sparse, or poorly formed crowns are likely to have been suppressed for a long time and may not respond well when released from competition. Heavily vine-laden trees may also not be good candidates for liberation treatments. Due to the complexity of liberation thinning operations, tree marking should be carried out by trained staff and the silvicultural responses should be monitored in permanent research plots. Repeated liberation may be required for maximum stand production if the benefits of liberation do not persist for the duration of stand retention.

The primary thinning treatment that most natural forests receive is timber harvesting. All too often logging is not considered to be the silvicultural treatment that it actually represents. In stands with substantial advanced regeneration of commercial species and where some trees have been marked for harvesting and others for retention, timber harvesting is equivalent to heavy thinning and results in similar growth responses of future crop trees.

Environmental Impacts of Silvicultural Treatments

Liberation thinning, vine cutting, soil scarification, and other stand 'improvement' treatments are not improvements at all from the perspective of the vines that are cut, the trees that are girdled, or all the various animal species that depend on the plants selected against. Stands that are intensively managed for timber can be essentially converted into plantations, with all the attendant negative impacts on biodiversity. In most of the tropics the problem is too little, not too much management, but silviculturalists nevertheless should be aware of this concern.

Impatience is a common threat to environmentally, silviculturally, and fiscally sound silviculture. Sometimes the best decision is to let a stand recover slowly on its own, without silvicultural intervention. And some silvicultural treatments may be misapplied. For example, an overstory of fast-growing, short-lived, light-demanding trees may serve as a nurse crop for the slower-growing commercial species that grow up in their sparse shade – removing the cover crop would be wasteful and ineffective. Also, dense stands can be left to self-thin, at no direct cost to the forest manager. And heavily thinned stands may suffer excessive windthrow and other damages. The best overall advice when prescribing and applying timber stand improvement treatments is to be gentle unless the forest indicates otherwise. Silviculturalists need to remember that a noncommercial species today may fetch a high price tomorrow and that today's weed may be tomorrow's wonder crop.

Complicating the challenges faced by tropical silviculturalists is increased awareness of the importance of stand history in determining stand structure and composition. Radical differences between old-growth forests and young (<50 years old) secondary forests developing after abandonment of agricultural clearings are well known. Less widely recognized are the persisting influences of agricultural interventions even several centuries after abandonment. Given the drastic declines in Amerindian populations after European colonization and similar demographic and cultural upheavals elsewhere in the tropics, history cannot be ignored when silvicultural options are being investigated. Similarly, major natural perturbations, such as windstorms and fires, even if they occur at intervals of centuries, can have lasting effects on forests in which trees can live for several hundred years.

It is widely known that well-managed monospecific plantations of fast-growing trees generally out-yield natural forests by up to a factor of 10. Some proponents of plantation forestry argue that given their high productivity, plantations should be established to reduce pressure on natural forests. Although plantations have a substantial role to play in many tropical countries, this argument is weakened by the fact that the wood produced by trees in natural forests is of a quality unlikely ever to be matched in plantations. Furthermore, given the many non-timber benefits derived from tropical forests (e.g., biodiversity protection, carbon sequestration, hydrological functions), it is not reasonable to compare plantations and natural forests solely on the basis of volume yields. Finally, it is critical to remember that forests are more than trees and should be managed accordingly.

See also: **Biodiversity**: Plant Diversity in Forests. **Ecology**: Natural Disturbance in Forest Environments. **Harvesting**: Forest Operations in the Tropics, Reduced Impact Logging. **Plantation Silviculture**: Tending. **Silviculture**: Managing for Tropical Non-timber Forest Products; Natural Regeneration of Tropical Rain Forests; Natural Stand Regeneration. **Site-Specific Silviculture**: Ecology and Silviculture of Tropical Wetland Forests. **Sustainable Forest Management**: Overview.

Further Reading

Baur GN (1965) *The Ecological Basis of Rainforest Management.* Sydney: Forestry Commission.

Bruenig EF (1996) *Conservation and Management of Tropical Rainforests: An Integrated Approach to Sustainability.* Wallingford, UK: CAB International.

Dawkins HC and Philip MS (1998) *Tropical Moist Forest Silviculture and Management: A History of Success and Failure.* Wallingford, UK: CAB International.

De Graaf NR (1986) *A Silvicultural System for Natural Regeneration of Tropical Rain Forest In Suriname.* Wageningen, The Netherlands: Agricultural University.

Fox JED (1976) Constraints on the natural regeneration of tropical moist forest. *Forest Ecology and Management* 1: 37–65.

Fredericksen TS and Putz FE (2003) Silvicultural intensification for tropical forest conservation. *Biodiversity and Conservation* 12: 1445–1453.

Guariguata MR and Kattan GH (2002) *Ecología y Conservación de Bosques Neotropicales.* Cartago, Costa Rica: Libro Universitario Regional.

Hutchinson ID (1988) Points of departure for silviculture in humid tropical forests. *Commonwealth Forestry Review* 67: 223–230.

Kellman M and Takaberry R (1997) *Tropical Environments: The Functioning and Management of Tropical Ecosystems.* London: Routledge.

Lamprecht H (1989) *Silviculture in the Tropics.* Eschborn, Germany: Deutsche Gesellschaft fur Technische Zusammenarbeit.

Oliver CD and Larson BC (1990) *Forest Stand Dynamics.* New York: McGraw Hill.

Palmer J and Synnott TJ (1992) The management of natural forests. In: Sharma NP (ed.) *Managing the World's Forests*, pp. 337–373. Dubuque, IA: Kendall/Hunt.

Pinard MA, Putz FE, Jardim T, Rumíz D, and Guzman R (1999) Ecological characterization of tree species to guide forest management decisions: an exercise in species classification in semi-deciduous forests of Lomerio, Bolivia. *Forest Ecology and Management* 113: 201–213.

Putz FE, Blate GM, Redford KH, Fimbel R, and Robinson JG (2001) Biodiversity conservation in the context of tropical forest management. *Conservation Biology* 15: 7–20.

Smith DM, Larson BC, Kelty MJ, and Ashton PMS (1997) *The Practice of Silviculture: Applied Forest Ecology.* New York: John Wiley.

Uhl C, Barreto P, Verissimo A, *et al.* (1997) Natural resource management in the Brazilian Amazon: an integrated approach. *BioScience* 47: 160–168.

Wadsworth FH (1997) *Forest Production for Tropical America.* US Department of Agriculture Forestry Service, Agricultural Handbook no. 710. Washington, DC: US Department of Agriculture Forestry Service.

Coppice Silviculture Practiced in Temperate Regions

R Harmer, Forest Research, Farnham, UK

Published by Elsevier Ltd., 2004

Introduction

Coppice is a word that is used by foresters to cover many things including: a type of woodland consisting of trees that are periodically cut; the multistemmed trees that occur in such woodlands; the process of felling the trees; and the production of new shoots by recently cut stools. The management of woodlands as coppice has a long history and archeological evidence indicates that the process was used in prehistoric times. The basic method is simple and relies on the ability of many trees to regrow from the stumps remaining after felling. At its simplest, woodland comprising single-stemmed trees which have grown from seed are clear-felled and allowed to regrow. Repeated felling produces the multistemmed stools typical of coppice woodland. In the developed world elaborate forms of coppice management to control yield, and provide a sustainable supply of small wood and large timber, reached their zenith prior to industrialization when alternative fuels, building materials, and chemicals became more readily available. However, in these regions the art of coppice management has been in decline for 100–200 years and many woodlands have been transformed to high forest. There are still about 50 million ha of coppice within the industrialized nations but only 60% of this is classified as utilizable (Table 1). However, during the last two to three decades there has been a resurgence of interest in coppice grown on short rotations, primarily for use as a biofuel although longer rotations are used for the production of pulp woods. In contrast coppice has remained an important system of management in tropical areas where demand for fuel and small-diameter wood, for building purposes is still high. In addition to the use of naturally occurring species and woodland, several million hectares of plantation, often comprising species of eucalyptus, have been established.

Silvicultural Systems

Three systems of coppice woodland management are generally recognized: simple coppice, coppice with standards, and the coppice selection system. In many areas these idealized systems are probably impracticable at the present time and *ad hoc* systems of irregular cutting are likely to be more typical. Pollarding, which is similar to coppicing and also relies on the ability of the trunk to sprout new shoots, can be used to manage individual trees.

Simple Coppice

In this method the woodland is managed as an even-aged single-story crop grown for fuelwood and small/medium-sized material. The coppice is cut on a regular rotation, the length of which depends not only on the product required but also on species, location, and rate of growth. Theoretically the coppice is managed by sequential cutting of coupes throughout the woodland, with the woodland divided into a number of coupes equal to the number of years in the rotation; one coupe is then cut each year. Coppice woodlands managed in this way, with coupes cut at the appropriate time are said to be 'in-cycle' or 'in-rotation' (Figure 1).

Short rotation coppice woodlands are a special example of simple coppice in which the lifespans of any shoots or stools are short in comparison to those of traditional coppice woodlands. For example, typical rotations for clonal stands of *Populus* and *Salix* short rotation coppice are 2–4 years, with the expected lifespan of stools being 10–20 years before they are replaced when yield declines – perhaps four to five rotations in total. In contrast, mixed broad-leaved coppice woodlands managed to produce fuel and small-diameter wood, may be cut on 20-year rotations with some stools capable of surviving for centuries.

Coppice with Standards

These woodlands are multistoried with an even-aged lower story of coppice underwood cut regularly to produce small material, and a partial overstory of uneven-aged standard trees which are usually grown

Table 1 Estimated areas (ha $\times$ 10^3) of coppice woodland[a] in industrialized temperate/boreal countries

Region	Utilizable	Non-utilizable[b]
Nordic and Baltic	16	0
Central Europe	7687	64
Southern Europe	13 506	4411
Commonwealth of Independent States	12 643	16 071
USA and Canada	0	0
Australasia and Japan	56	0
Total	33 908	20 546

Data adapted from UN-ECE/FAO report ECE/TIM/SP/17, Geneva Timber and Forest Study Paper no. 17 (2000).
[a] Figures are for both simple coppice and coppice with standards.
[b] Non-utilizable, not available for wood supply for a variety of conservation, protection, or economic reasons.

Figure 1 A recently felled coupe of in-cycle, simple sweet chestnut (*Castanea sativa*) coppice approximately 15 years old (Kent, UK). Reproduced with permission from Harmer R and Howe J (2003) *Silviculture and Management of Coppice Woodlands.* Forestry Commission, UK.

from seed and allowed to grow to a sufficient size to produce large timber. This system is more difficult to manage than simple coppice as it is necessary to manage the number, age class distribution, and location of large overstory trees which affect the growth of the understory crop. The underwood is managed as simple coppice, and after cutting each coupe the number and age class distribution of the standards present is adjusted: it is necessary to remove the oldest, reduce numbers of those of intermediate ages, and recruit new standards. This system is rarely used in the tropics.

Coppice Selection System

This method is similar to that for the selection system in high forests. Within the woods managed using this method the stools have populations of stems that are both of different sizes and ages. A target diameter for the product is set, and the age at which the crop achieves this fixes the length of the rotation: this period is divided into a suitable number of felling cycles and the woodland area is divided into a number of annual coupes which equals the number of years in the felling cycle. Harvesting of stems that have reached the target diameter occurs annually within one of the coupes; all smaller stems remain uncut. This is a special system which is rarely applied and is only likely to work well with shade-bearing species; for example, it has been used with *Fagus sylvatica* on poor ground

in mountainous areas where the remaining canopy can have advantageous effects protecting both the new shoots and soil from damaging environmental factors such as frost, drought, and erosion.

Pollards

A pollard is a tree that is cut like coppice, but the new shoots grow from a trunk that is several meters long and they are not subjected to browsing damage from animals which can be allowed to graze beneath the trees. The branches are harvested periodically, after one or more year's growth, when the crown is partially or totally removed. Although ancient pollards persist and others managed for ornamental purposes are often seen in urban areas, this method of management is generally unimportant in the developed world. However, in arid regions of the tropics pollarding remains an important method of management to provide products such as fuelwood and animal fodder.

Biology of Coppice Shoots

The ability of trees to resprout is an adaptation that promotes survival after damage to the aboveground parts of the tree by a variety of factors such as fire, storm damage, and pathogens. Not all species of tree will produce coppice shoots and the phenomenon is more common in angiosperms than gymnosperms (**Table 2**). Some species regenerate more readily from

Table 2 Illustrative list[a] of angiosperms and gymnosperms that have been reported to regenerate by coppice shoots

Angiosperms	Gymnosperms
Acacia spp.[b]	Araucaria araucana
Acer pseudoplatanus[c]	Cryptomeria japonica
Aesculus hippocastanum[c]	Cunninghamia lanceolata
Albizzia spp.[b]	Pinus echinata
Alnus glutinosa	Pinus rigida
Betula pendula	Pinus serotina
Carpinus betulus[c]	Sequoia sempervirens
Castanea sativa	Taxodium distichum
Cornus florida	
Corylus avellana	
Eucalyptus spp.[b,c]	
Fagus sylvatica[c]	
Fraxinus excelsior	
Gmelina spp.[b]	
Liquidambar styraciflua	
Nothofagus obliqua	
Platanus occidentalis	
Populus spp.[b,c]	
Prunus serotina	
Quercus spp.[b]	
Salix spp.[b,c]	
Sorbus aria	
Tectonia grandis	
Tilia spp[b,c]	
Ulmus spp[b,c]	

[a] This list is not exhaustive.
[b] Many species or clones in this genus are known to produce coppice shoots.
[c] One or more species in this genus is reported to produce coppice shoots from adventitious buds (i.e., stool sprouts).

stumps than others, for example regrowth of *F. sylvatica* is poor relative to that of *Alnus glutinosa* and *Castanea sativa*. The capability of individuals within a species to regenerate from cut stumps varies with a variety of factors such as the age, size, and vigor of the tree prior to felling.

Origins of Coppice Shoots

Two types of coppice shoot are recognized, these develop from either suppressed or adventitious buds on the stump remaining. In the North American literature these are termed stump and stool sprouts respectively. In addition some species produce root suckers which are new shoots that grow from adventitious buds formed on the tree's roots.

Stump sprouts These are the most common type of coppice shoots found on broadleaved trees. As shoots of broadleaved trees grow they produce lateral buds that are associated with both leaves and bud scales. Most of these newly formed buds are suppressed by the apical meristem and do not grow during the season in which they are formed: they become dormant and will not grow into shoots until their

dormancy has been broken by exposure to winter conditions or by other causes. The fates of lateral buds vary: on a typical temperate broadleaved tree some near the shoot tip form branches; many will die; and others, often the smallest, remain suppressed and return to the dormant state growing slowly outwards as the stem increases in diameter. Throughout subsequent annual cycles of growth the suppressed buds remain poorly developed, but they may divide to form large clusters of small buds embedded in the bark. Such suppressed buds are the primary source of most coppice shoots.

Stool sprouts Coppice shoots can also grow from adventitious buds that develop from tissues not closely associated with suppressed buds. Although many woody plants have the potential to form adventitious buds few are formed on stems. When a tree stem is cut adventitious buds and coppice shoots often arise in the ring of callus that develops between the wood and the bark of the stump. Unlike suppressed buds most adventitious buds do not undergo a period of dormancy and they develop into shoots in the season in which they are formed. Whereas suppressed buds are connected to the vascular system via a vascular trace, adventitious buds and shoots must develop a new connection with the plant's vascular system. Adventitious coppice shoots are uncommon, short-lived and generally unimportant in the regeneration of most broadleaved trees (**Figures 2** and **3**).

Silvicultural Factors

The silviculture of traditionally managed coppice woodlands evolved through centuries of practical experience, and there has been relatively little detailed research to investigate and understand the general biology of established coppice stools and shoots. In contrast, considerable effort has been expended during the last 10–20 years studying the growth, physiology, yield, establishment, harvesting, etc., of short rotation coppice crops. Most detailed knowledge on the biology of coppice comes from observations made on regrowth from stumps of single-stemmed trees that have not previously been coppiced, rather than complex multistemmed coppice stools. Many studies have shown that regrowth from such stumps following felling is influenced by age and diameter, but as these are related, their individual effects are difficult to disentangle.

Number and growth of coppice shoots For most species it is not possible to give precise advice about the effect of either stump size, or age, on the probable number of shoots that will be produced

Figure 2 Stump sprouts growing from suppressed buds on an established stool of hazel (*Corylus avellana*). Courtesy of the Forestry Commission.

Figure 3 Stool sprouts growing from adventitious buds formed in the cambium of a recently felled 60-year-old beech tree (*Fagus sylvatica*). Courtesy of the Forestry Commission.

and how they will grow. In general there are relationships between either stump diameter or age, and number of shoots produced and their initial growth. The relationships vary with species and site but overall the number and growth of shoots tend to decline with the size and age of stumps.

Mortality of stumps In general, the mortality of stumps tends to increase with both age and size, but the relationships vary with species. Site quality may influence the success of coppicing by its effect on vigor with slow-growing stools on poor sites regrowing less well than those on good sites. Although several suggestions have been made to explain the decline in shoot numbers and survival of stumps as they become older or larger, there has been little detailed study. The changes may be related to the loss of viable dormant buds from the stem either due to age or reduced vigor; the presence of a thick bark which restricts the growth of deeply embedded buds; and changes that occur when the trees reach the age at which they flower. In productive, managed woodlands dead stools can be replaced by planting or layering (a form of vegetative reproduction using shoots of live stools).

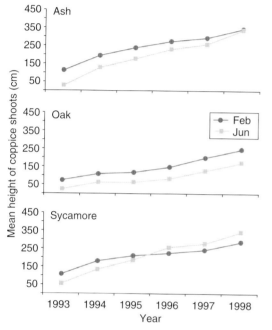

Figure 4 Mean length of the three longest shoots that regrew from stumps of 6-year-old saplings of ash (*Fraxinus excelsior*), oak (*Quercus robur*), and sycamore (*Acer pseudoplatanus*) felled in February or June 1993. The height differences gradually disappeared for *F. excelsior* and *A. pseudoplatanus*, but after six growing seasons the shoots on stumps of *Q. robur* felled in June remained shorter than those cut in February. Reproduced with permisssion from Harmer R and Howe J (2003) *The Silviculture and Management of Coppice Woodlands*. Edinburgh, UK: Forestry Commission.

Seasonal effects Season of felling can influence regrowth and whilst there is some variation between species, it has generally been found that stem survival, and initial numbers and growth of new shoots (**Figure 4**), is usually better when trees are cut during the dormant season. However, this is not necessarily true of all species and in subsequent years the initial differences in numbers and growth of shoots may disappear (**Table 3**). Due to insufficient growth and hardening-off, shoots produced late in the season after summer cutting can suffer more severe winter damage than those that grow early in the season.

Height of the stump The position of the cut and size of the stem remaining can influence subsequent growth. The initial number of shoots produced by some species increases with stump height but differences decline with time. When stumps are cut high the probability of butt rot occurring in the stems that develop is increased. This can have consequences for both the quality of stems in stored coppice, and the longevity of the stool. On some species, the shoots that arise on high-cut stumps develop from buds in areas of thick bark which constricts development of the vascular connection and can affect the stability of the coppice shoot. Shoots that arise at or below ground level can develop their own root systems.

Longevity of Stools

The lifespan of a stool will depend on a variety of factors including species, environment, and management: good growing conditions where soils are fertile, the climate is favorable, and overstory canopy cover is low, will enhance longevity of the stools. Those that are cut on a regular rotation when stems are young and of small diameter will survive longer than those that are cut on less regular, long rotations. Neglected stools can survive for many years with stems attaining large dimensions, but their ability to regrow after cutting will decline with age.

Table 3 Mean number of coppice shoots after 1 and 6 years of regrowth on stumps of three species that were 6-year-old saplings when they were felled in February, April, or June in 1993[a]

	February		April		June	
	1 year	6 years	1 year	6 years	1 year	6 years
Fraxinus excelsior	7.8	3.1	10.4	4.2	7.3	3.8
Quercus robur	8.1	4.5	6.7	4.6	7.8	4.2
Acer pseudoplatanus	6.4	3.2	9.0	3.9	11.6	3.6

Reproduced with permission from Harmer R and Howe J (2003) *The Silviculture and Management of Coppice Woodlands*. Edinburgh, UK: Forestry Commission.
[a]Over the period of observation there were, for all species, a reduction in the number of branches present on the stump, and a decline in the relative differences between months of felling.

Browsing Animals

Although coppice shoots can be used as a source of fodder, the browsing of shoots during the early years of regeneration can have an adverse effect on the re-establishment of canopy cover. Prolonged severe browsing can ruin crops, kill stools, and seriously degrade woodland. Provision of adequate protection to the stools from browsing animals is probably the most important operation necessary to ensure successful regrowth of new shoots. Whether the method used is physical exclusion of animals, or control of population size, it must be of sufficient duration to allow re-establishment of robust shoots on stools throughout the woodland. The length of time for which protection is required will vary with a variety of factors including tree species, growing conditions, and type of animals present. Alternatively browsing damage can be avoided by managing trees as pollards.

Management of Stools and Standards

Woodland management by coppicing can play an important role in maintaining biodiversity by providing a wide range of habitats created by variation in both time and space across a range of factors such as structure, light environment, and age of trees. Relative to high forest, traditionally managed coppice woodlands have a large amount of open space and edge habitats, and a range of tree size and age classes, varying from newly regenerating shoots to mature standards. Consequently, the apparent biological interest in a small area of coppice may be greater than for a similar area of high forest. Although coppice woodlands are traditional and provide a sustainable resource, they are managed and have characteristics that differ significantly from natural woodlands including: the size and rate of gap formation; the age structure of trees and compartments; species mixture; amount of dead wood; size; and the flora and fauna present. Many former coppice woodlands have been transformed to high forest and although this trend is likely to continue there are good reasons, both cultural and biological, for the retention of some woodland under traditional systems of coppice management. However, such woodlands must be managed using best available practice otherwise their value may diminish.

Stool Management

Failure to manage stools within a woodland correctly may lead to their death and changes in a number of woodland characteristics; for example, a reduction in stool density and canopy cover, and a change in the structure and species mixture.

Method of cutting The quality of the cut is more important than the tool used. It is important that cuts are clean with no separation of the bark from the remaining stump. Traditionally coppice was cut manually using hand-tools, and whilst these may still be appropriate for young stems with small diameters (e.g., 7–8-year-old *Corylus avellana* stems for hurdle making, or 2-year-old *Betula pendula* for brooms and horse jumps) a chainsaw is probably the only realistic option for cutting most stools (**Figure 5**). The systematic spacing of stools, uniformity of growth, and the easy terrain of sites with young short rotation coppice allows mechanized harvesting. However, efficient use of harvesters within traditional coppices is difficult due to the variable distribution, growth, size, and structure of stools; the terrain; and the need to avoid damage to stools that will regenerate to produce the next crop.

Angle of cut Tradition suggests that stems should be cut to ensure that water drains from the center of the stool; the cut surface of the stump should have a sloping face to shed water, and be south-facing to dry more quickly. Although there is generally little quantitative evidence to support these logical suggestions, young red alder stumps with a flat surface showed greater mortality than those with cut surfaces having southerly or westerly aspects (**Figure 6**). The structure of many coppice stools will make it difficult to fell stems leaving a cut surface with a generally southerly aspect, but all cuts should be clean and wherever possible slope towards the outside of the stool.

Position of cut Maintain the stool at a level close to the ground. When establishing new coppice stools from single-stemmed trees cut as close to the ground as possible, on existing stools fell just above the height of the last cut leaving short stumps from the most recent stems. It is generally inadvisable to cut into old wood below the level of the last cut as successful resprouting is less likely to occur.

Time of felling The best time to cut coppice is during the dormant period: the bark is less likely to tear from the wood; stump mortality will probably be reduced; and new shoots are likely to grow better and suffer less frost/winter damage than shoots formed after a summer cut.

Conversion to High Forest

Many woods that were traditionally managed as coppice have developed a high forest structure following growth after the cessation of regular

Figure 5 Coppice worker using a billhook for felling and trimming 3-year-old *Castanea sativa* stems that will be made into walking sticks. Courtesy of the Forestry Commission.

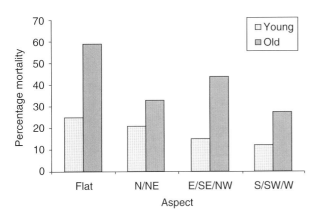

Figure 6 Percentage mortality of young (1–5-year-old) and old (6–16-year-old) red alder stumps in relation to aspect of cut surface. Data adapted from Harrington C (1984) Factors influencing initial sprouting of red alder. *Canadian Journal of Forest Research* 14, 357–361.

cutting. These crops, which comprise trees known as 'stored coppice,' are simple to create but may not be appropriate for all sites or species. This is the situation that currently affects many neglected woodlands with overmature coppice stems, on old coppice stools which, if cut, may neither survive nor produce a suitable crop for the future.

Stored coppice   Although storing coppice is a simple procedure it has a number of drawbacks which may influence the decision on whether it should be used.

In comparison to single-stemmed trees of the same species, growth may be inferior, the stems be of worse form with more butt sweep, and the inclusion of wood from the old stool may cause stem defects. The trees produced are often less stable than single-stemmed trees grown from seed which may cause problems of windthrow after subsequent felling operations. The quality of stored coppice can be improved by thinning to remove from the stool all stems except those which are judged to be the straightest and most vigorous: the stools may be 'singled,' leaving only the best stem. Storing coppice is likely to be most successful where stools are young, vigorous, have been cut close to the ground, and are free from decay.

Managing Standards

Well-defined, systematic procedures to control yield from standards have been developed but these have generally fallen into disuse as most large timber is now grown as high forest. The fundamental principle of the method is that number of standard trees in each age-class should be approximately half of that in the next younger class, with about 50–100 standards per hectare of all age-classes, most of which are young: a possible age-class structure is shown in **Table 4**. When the underwood is felled at the end of each rotation the mature trees (age-class IV) are felled, new standards (age-class I) are

Table 4 Possible age-class structure for standards in coppice cut on a rotation of 20 years. Adapted with permission from Harmer R and Howe J (2003) *Silviculture and Management of Coppice Woodlands*. Forestry Commission, UK

Age class of standard	Rotation number[a]	Number of stems to remain[b] (ha^{-1})
I (young)	1	50
II	2–3	30
III	3–4	13
IV (old)	4–6	7
Total		100

[a]The age of the standards defined by the number of coppice rotations for which they have been retained.
[b]Number of standards retained in each age-class.

recruited and intermediate ages thinned. The number of coppice cycles for which a standard is retained depends on species, length of coppice cycle, growth rate, and size of timber required.

The adverse effect of standards on the growth of coppice is well known, and is related to the canopy cover and crown density which influence light, water, and nutrient availability. Silvicultural systems of coppice with standards describe the management of standards in terms of stem numbers, rather than size of individual tree canopies and the amount of shade cast. Under well-managed coppice with standard woodlands, most standards should be young and small, and cast little shade compared with those that are old, large, and cast a lot of shade. Species differ in the amount of shade that they cast, varying in both size of crown produced and the density of leaf cover within the crown. This affects the density of standards of each species that can be maintained with a woodland, and trees such as *F. sylvatica*, *Tilia cordata*, and to a lesser extent *Quercus* spp., which have very dense crowns that can cast heavy shade, should be avoided.

The Future for Coppice Woodlands

In many areas of the world existing coppice woodlands are relics of a bygone age when there was a much greater demand for the crops produced by this simple method of management. Many woodlands have already been converted from coppice to high forest and this trend is likely to continue as the crops produced are more marketable. In contrast, the amount of short rotation coppice may increase if the promises of cost-effectively producing a long-term sustained yield can be turned into reality, and suitable methods of utilization firmly established.

Well-managed coppice woodlands regenerate quickly and the period of time without canopy cover is short relative to that of some high-forest systems where large gaps are made in the canopy. This will have obvious benefits for protection of the physical environment. Similar benefits may be obtained by use of continuous cover forestry, but the temporal and spatial variation in characteristics such as distribution and age-class of crop, and the light environment within the woodland, will differ to that for coppice. Conversion to such high-forest systems is likely to lead to the loss of species that flourish under the routine system of gap creation produced by regular coppicing. The establishment of short rotation coppice plantations may have positive benefits for a variety of characteristics including biodiversity, nutrient capture, and erosion, especially when established on agricultural land.

As traditional coppice woodlands provide a cultural link with the past and can be of important biological interest they are unlikely to disappear completely, but it seems likely that the area of woodland actively managed as coppice will continue to decline.

See also: **Operations**: Small-scale Forestry. **Plantation Silviculture**: Short Rotation Forestry for Biomass Production; Sustainability of Forest Plantations. **Silviculture**: Silvicultural Systems. **Temperate and Mediterranean Forests**: Temperate Broadleaved Deciduous Forest. **Tree Physiology**: Physiology of Vegetative Reproduction; Shoot Growth and Canopy Development.

Further Reading

Buckley GP (1992) *Ecology and Management of Coppice Woodlands*. London: Chapman & Hall.

Evans J (1992) *Plantation Forestry in the Tropics*, 2nd edn. Oxford, UK: Oxford University Press.

Harmer R and Howe J (2003) *The Silviculture and Management of Coppice Woodlands*. Edinburgh, UK: Forestry Commission.

Harrington C (1984) Factors influencing initial sprouting of red alder. *Canadian Journal of Forest Research* 14: 357–361.

Kozlowski TT (1971) *Growth and Development of Trees*, vol. 1, *Seed Germination, Ontogeny, and Shoot Growth*. New York: Academic Press.

Kramer PJ and Kozlowski TT (1979) *Physiology of Woody Plants*. New York: Academic Press.

Macpherson G (1995) *Home-Grown Energy from Short-Rotation Coppice*. Ipswich, UK: Farming Press.

Matthews JD (1989) *Silvicultural Systems*. Oxford, UK: Oxford University Press.

Peterken GF (1996) *Natural Woodland*. Cambridge, UK: Cambridge University Press.

Rackham O (1980) *Ancient Woodland*. London, UK: Edward Arnold.

Forest Dynamics

A E Camp and C D Oliver, Yale University, New Haven, CT, USA

Introduction

Forest stand dynamics (stand dynamics, forest development, forest succession) integrates plant community and population ecology, silvics, physiology, morphology, and knowledge about biotic and abiotic disturbance events and regimes. Forest stand dynamics informs silviculture since it allows predictions of the pathways along which forests could develop given initial conditions, growth, silvicultural operations, natural disturbances, regeneration, and other natural and human influences on the system. Practicing foresters and applied ecologists require a thorough understanding of stand dynamics to predict how stands will change, to determine what values they will provide and when, and to manipulate them as appropriate to ensure they provide the desired flow of values over time. Forest stand dynamics lays the groundwork for landscape management, in which the changes to many stands are coordinated across the landscape and through time.

The defining scale of forest stand dynamics is the individual stand – a relatively homogeneous area of vegetation, soils, climate, and disturbance history that can be easily discerned from an aerial photograph. The primary foci at this scale are the interactions that occur among individual plants and between plants and abiotic factors. Explicit in the term is that these interactions occur in time; forests are dynamic and can be expected to change, albeit in predictable ways. Despite the variety of climates, soils, and evolutionary backgrounds of forests in different parts of the world, they follow remarkably similar patterns of stand dynamics in those temperate, boreal, and tropical forests where stand dynamics have been studied. These similarities probably arise because their physiological similarities leads trees to follow a 'uniformity of processes' in their interactions.

Stand Structures and Development (Silvicultural) Pathways

A useful conceptualization of forest stand dynamics is that, over time, the structure of a stand changes (**Figure 1**). Stand structure refers to the spatial attributes of the living and dead plants and plant components in the stand: the species, sizes, and spatial distributions of living and dead trees and other plants and their components. These structures are helpful in identifying the suitability of the forest for different values – such as habitats for different species, timber quality, and recreation. Stand structure also contributes to risks of fires, insects, and windstorms. The sequence of structures that a particular stand moves among is described as its 'development pathway' or 'silvicultural pathway' (**Figure 2**). The pathway followed by a stand is determined by a number of factors; stands are not predestined to follow a single, specific pathway. Furthermore, pathways are not unidirectional and do not culminate in a fixed endpoint, although a now outdated ecological paradigm previously described forest succession as a fixed, unidirectional pathway towards a stable condition termed the 'climax' forest.

While it is possible – and perhaps sometimes useful – to differentiate many stand structures for a particular forest type, a relatively small number are sufficient to provide a structural overview of a majority of the world's forests. This article refers to five structures commonly encountered as forests develop. Some structures may not occur in some forest types, and more detailed structural classification systems may better explain certain objectives. The five structures used in this article are termed open, dense, understory, complex, and savanna (**Figure 1**). Subsets of these structures can be used to depict the different pathways a stand can follow. As an example of one pathway, a stand initiating after a major (stand-replacing) disturbance and with abundant regeneration would develop from an open structure to one characterized by density-dependent mortality (dense structure). Eventually the stand might develop an understory. Then, a partial disturbance might leave only a few large trees (savanna). As younger trees establish and grow beneath the sparse overstory, the complex structure could result.

One area of expertise that distinguishes professional foresters, especially silviculturists, is the ability to determine the pathway a stand is currently following, predict alternate pathways the stand could follow given various natural disturbances or silvicultural operations, and prescribe silvicultural operations that direct the stand along a desired pathway. The pathways and structural stages are most easily predicted and managed by first understanding the causes of changes in structures along the different pathways.

Ecological Processes Underlying Stand Dynamics

Stands contain a variety of organisms that happen to occur together at the time of observation. Paleoecological research indicates that different trees and

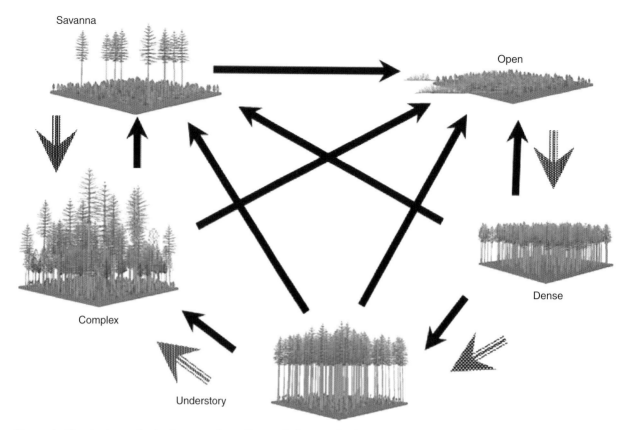

Figure 1 Stands change in structure over time with growth (large, striped arrows) and disturbances (solid black arrows). A robust classification suitable for many forests and purposes are the five structures shown here; however, different structure classifications may be better for certain purposes. © Professor Chadwick Oliver.

other organisms have lived together for only a few hundred or thousand years, have migrated from different locations at different rates, and in many instances are continuing to migrate to new locations. Different organisms evolve at a variety of timescales, with new generations occurring several times each year in insects but only every hundred years or more in trees. Because evolution in trees occurs over very long timescales, trees are slow to evolve mutualistic relationships with their associated species. Most evidence suggests that the dominant interactions among trees are best explained in terms of competition. Trees and other green plants require the same basic factors for survival and growth – light, moisture, nutrients, and warmth. In general, all tree species generally grow best when they receive these factors in the same, relatively narrow ranges of concentration, rather than having diversified into growing best at different ranges. For example, nearly all tree species grow best in full sunlight, under similar soil moisture regimes, and at approximately the same temperatures. A primary difference among species is that various tree species have evolved different abilities to tolerate (survive at) low levels of one or more of these factors. Species that tolerate a wide range of conditions are termed site insensitive and are considered to have wide ecological amplitudes. Species that have a low tolerance for growth factor limitations are termed site sensitive. In general, relative tolerance or intolerance is specified with respect to a particular growth factor, and tolerances such as shade or drought tolerance or intolerance in species are commonly described (**Figure 3**).

Different growth factors, or resources, needed by trees are frequently limited in the natural environment. Trees compete for these limited resources, with different individuals and species gaining a competitive advantage depending on whether they were first to access the growth factors and on whether they can efficiently use the specific range of growth factors found on the site at a given time. Different growth factors become limiting at different times of the day, month, year, and stand development stage. Sometimes it is the interaction of growth factors that determines whether growth is limiting. It is convenient to refer to the net presence of the factors required for growth as the available 'growing space' within a stand. Growing space fluctuates with seasonal variations in rainfall, temperature, and other factors. Growing space is referred to as 'occupied'

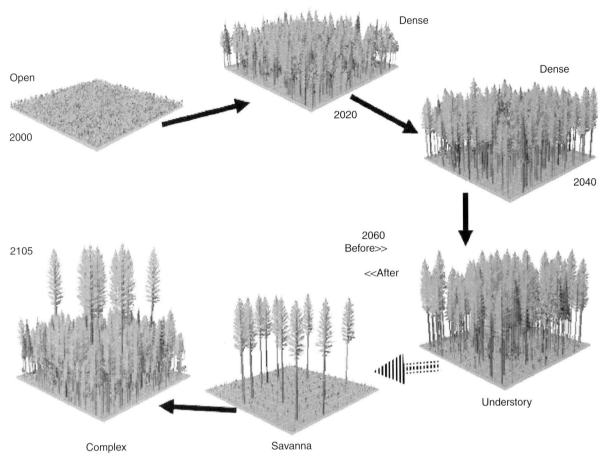

Figure 2   The change in a stand over time caused by growth, natural disturbances, and silvicultural operations is its development pathway or silvicultural pathway. The pathway is depicted here by the stand's changes in structures. This stand modeled here began after a stand-replacing disturbance in 1995, and was shelterwood treated in 2080. A stand can potentially follow many different pathways. © Professor Chadwick Oliver.

when a tree or other plant's roots or leaves are utilizing the moisture or light growing space and excluding other plants from utilizing it. Growing space is available when it is not occupied, such as immediately after a disturbance or during early spring in a field previously occupied by annual plants.

Trees compete with each other over available growing space. The ability to compete successfully is a result of the ability of an individual tree to capture this growing space. Trees that compete successfully become the dominant trees in the stand. Trees that lose the competition for growing space are eliminated or relegated to subordinate positions if they can tolerant less-than-optimal ranges of the growing space. The latter instance is more commonly found where competition for growing space occurs among trees of different species. Competitive ability under a given circumstance integrates species' physiological traits, such as rapid juvenile growth or early germination, with the environment.

Stand dynamics is also concerned with the impacts of natural and human disturbances on the ecological processes, pathways, and structural characteristics of stands. All forests are impacted by disturbances, with different regions of the world characterized by different disturbance regimes. A disturbance regime refers to the integration of the typical kinds, magnitudes, frequencies, and sizes of disturbances impacting a region. In general, disturbances that occur frequently are of less magnitude than disturbances that rarely occur. On one end of the disturbance spectrum are infrequent events such as volcanic eruptions or continental glacial expansions. Other disturbances include hurricanes, landslides, avalanches, fires, ice storms, and insect outbreaks. Some frequent disturbances (at least in some locations) include thunderstorms, windstorms, livestock grazing, and endemic insect and pathogen activity.

Disturbances affect forests by physically deforming or killing trees and other plants and by improving or degrading the soils, depending on specific characteristics of the disturbance. Growing space becomes available when trees are killed; following a disturbance residual and newly initiating trees

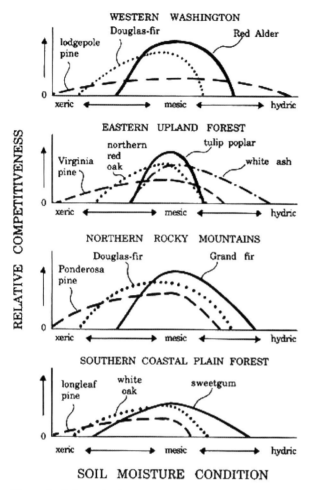

RELATIVE COMPETITIVENESS

WESTERN WASHINGTON

lodgepole pine · Douglas-fir · Red Alder

xeric ←——→ mesic ←——→ hydric

EASTERN UPLAND FOREST

Virginia pine · northern red oak · tulip poplar · white ash

xeric ←——→ mesic ←——→ hydric

NORTHERN ROCKY MOUNTAINS

Ponderosa pine · Douglas-fir · Grand fir

xeric ←——→ mesic ←——→ hydric

SOUTHERN COASTAL PLAIN FOREST

longleaf pine · white oak · sweetgum

xeric ←——→ mesic ←——→ hydric

SOIL MOISTURE CONDITION

Figure 3 Schematic of relative growth (and competitiveness) of selected species growing together in four forest types found in the USA. All species grow most vigorously under optimum (mesic) conditions, but each species is found where it can outcompete other species, or where other species, cannot grow at all. Reprinted from Oliver CD and Larson BC (1996) *Forest Stand Dynamics*, updated edn, Copyright © John Wiley & Sons Inc. Reprinted by permission of John Wiley & Sons Inc.

reoccupy this growing space. The forest that develops following the disturbance could have a similar or very different structure than the preceding one.

Processes, Stand Development, and Development Stages

As a stand develops, many interactions, or processes, occur among trees and between trees and the environment, with different processes becoming more dominant influences as stands change. It is useful, therefore, to divide the processes of stand dynamics into development stages that reflect the dominance of different processes. Not surprisingly, these development stages are similar to, but not identical with, the stand structures. Four development stages are commonly recognized, but like the

stand structures can, if required, be further subdivided. These development stages are shown in **Figure 4** and are discussed below.

Stand initiation Following a stand-replacing (top left, **Figure 4**) or partial (bottom left, **Figure 4**) disturbance, growing space becomes available. Newly initiating trees, other plants, and surviving residual trees can expand to capture this growing space. Where surviving trees are absent, weak, or infrequent, the growing space is primarily occupied by newly initiating plants. Plants, including trees, have a variety of regeneration mechanisms that confer a competitive advantage depending on disturbance type and magnitude. For example, toppling of mature trees by a windstorm can release small advance regeneration of shade-tolerant species growing in the understory. Because this advance regeneration is already established and has a developed root system, species with this regeneration mechanism have a competitive advantage over species that must regenerate from seeds. Fires consume organic matter (and frequently, advance regeneration) on the forest floor, leaving a nutrient-enriched seedbed that favors species with light, windblown seeds or species that can resprout from the root collar or other underground structure. The different regeneration mechanisms can be listed in a gradient according to their relative advantage following disturbances of different magnitudes. This gradient, and examples of species with different regeneration mechanisms, is shown in **Figure 5**. Ages of newly sprouting trees or advance regeneration released by a disturbance are conventionally considered from the time of release (when the stem begins to grow beyond the forest floor level) rather than from the date of germination. Trees that initiate following a specific disturbance are considered a 'cohort,' regardless of whether they initiated from seed germination, sprouts, advance regeneration, or other mechanisms. On very poor sites, or on sites where seedling establishment is slow, there can be a wide range of ages within a single cohort.

Trees and other plants continue to invade during the stand initiation stage until the growing space is refilled with perennial trees, shrubs, and/or herbs. Refilling the growing space can take many decades where the site (soils and climate) is poor and the only regeneration mechanism is primarily from seeds having a distant source. Alternatively, it can take less than 5 years where the site allows rapid growth and preexisting advance regeneration or sprouts are present at the time of the disturbance. During stand initiation, trees compete for growing space with annual and perennial herbs and shrubs, creating a great diversity of potential interactions.

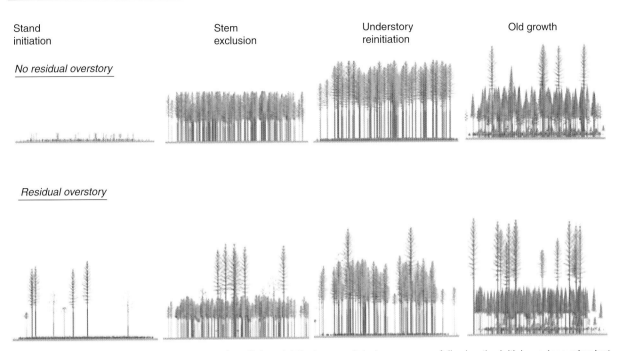

Figure 4 Stages of forest development over time (left to right) when no disturbances occur following the initial one (occurring just before stage at far left). Different ecological processes are dominant during the different stages. Top: the stages when no residual trees were left following the initial disturbance. Bottom: the stages when some residual trees are left following the initial disturbance. © Professor Chadwick Oliver.

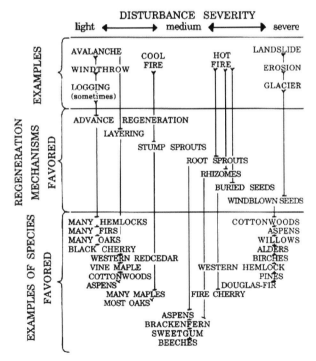

Figure 5 Disturbance 'severity' is here listed as a gradient according to how much of the understory, forest floor, and soil is destroyed. Different forms of sexual and/or asexual regeneration have competitive advantages depending on the severity of the disturbance. Species listed occur in different forest types in the USA. Reprinted from Oliver CD and Larson BC (1996) *Forest Stand Dynamics*, updated edn, Copyright © John Wiley & Sons Inc. Reprinted by permission of John Wiley & Sons Inc.

The species, or groups of species, that gain the competitive advantage during stand initiation can dominate the growing space during the subsequent stem exclusion and understory reinitiation stages, which can last several hundred years. Consequently, a stand can be dominated by a different suite of species than those that previously occupied the site, depending on which species gain a competitive advantage because of regeneration strategies, disturbance type, or stochastic factors such as good seed years.

When no residual trees are present, the stand initiation stage reflects the open structure (**Figure 1**). Because many herbaceous species also initiate following a disturbance, this stage usually contains a high diversity of plants, which attracts a high diversity of animals – butterflies, insects, deer, rabbits, and their predators.

When a partial disturbance leaves residual trees from older cohorts, these trees compete with new regeneration for the released growing space. The influence of the residual trees depends on their vigor and number. If residual trees are numerous and vigorous they can completely reoccupy the growing space, preventing a new cohort from establishing, or outcompeting and eliminating any newly initiating trees. The stand then quickly returns to a dense structure. If a new cohort does establish but is so suppressed that it remains as advance regeneration, the understory structure develops. If the residual trees are few and widely spaced, the savanna structure develops. As in the open structure, the savanna structure contains a great diversity of herbaceous plants and accompanying animals. The savanna structure can also provide habitat for woodpeckers, raptors, and other birds that utilize the relatively isolated trees. In some instances, presence of these trees attracts birds that disseminate the heavy seeds of species that would otherwise have a difficult time moving into open areas.

Partial disturbances during the stand initiation stage can reduce the competitive advantage of established plants, allowing other species to capture and hold growing space. For example, burning newly regenerating conifer forests in arid parts of the United States can convert them to semipermanent brushfields. Frequent surface fires or grazing can maintain a savanna structure by killing new cohorts of trees and promoting the growth of grasses in the growing space between large trees.

Stem exclusion Once growing space is fully occupied, intense competition occurs among existing trees, generally excluding new cohorts. This stage is referred to as the stem exclusion stage and can last between about 40 years for shade-intolerant pine species to over 100 years in mixed species stands that include shade-tolerant species.

Some natural stands and most plantations occur as monocultures of trees that regenerate within relatively short time-frames. Because conspecific trees require an identical set of growth factors, development pathways and resulting structures in monocultures are somewhat limited. Unless moisture or nutrients are limiting, trees will grow vigorously during the stand initiation and early stem exclusion stages until their crowns touch and sunlight becomes limiting. In a uniformly spaced stand with trees of nearly identical ages, the period of vigorous growth will be similar for all trees. In a stand with more irregular spacing and age, some trees will continue to grow vigorously while others will be less competitive, develop small crowns, decline in vigor, and become relegated to subordinant positions. The more vigorous trees in single species stands are generally those that have a competitive advantage because of microsite, age, spacing, and/or genetic makeup. In general, trees in single species stands do not grow well after being relegated to a subordinant position in the stand. Species that are more shade tolerant can sometimes persist, albeit in a condition of low vigor. In a single species, single cohort stand, the canopy will remain as a single layer, with crown differentiation into dominant, codominant, intermediate, and overtopped trees (**Figure 6**).

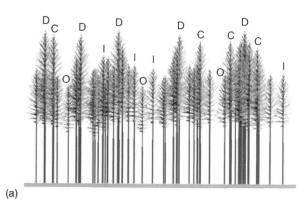

(a)

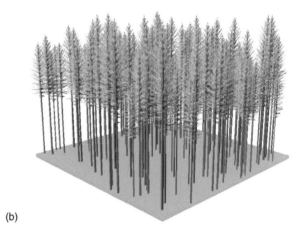

(b)

Figure 6 (a) Single species, single cohort stands usually develop in a single stratum; the trees differentiate into crown classes within this stratum. D, dominant; C, codominant; I, intermediate; O, overtopped. (b) The same stand as above, from perspective view. © Professor Chadwick Oliver.

During the stem exclusion stage, dominant trees continue to grow in height and diameter. Subordinant trees continue to grow in height, but diameter growth as well as insect and disease resistance decline considerably. There is less tendency for trees to differentiate in stands that are uniformly spaced, on poor soils, and/or have limited genetic variability. Trees in such stands simultaneously can decline in diameter growth and insect and disease resistance, with the result that entire stands become highly susceptible to wind damage, ice breakage, and insect attacks. In differentiating stands, the number of trees in the stand decreases over time as the average size of the tree (measured in diameter or total volume) increases. The relationships among tree sizes, numbers, and other measures have been quantified and studied.

Multiple tree species regenerating after a disturbance follow a similar pattern of intense competition during the stem exclusion stage. The primary difference between mixed and single species stands is that the different species in mixed stand have different tolerances for growing under conditions where resources are becoming limited. A slower growing species with greater tolerance for light-limited conditions may survive if overtopped by a faster-growing species. Because of these differences among species, the canopy of a mixed species stand can segregate into different strata representing the variety of species' tolerances for growing in shade (**Figure 7**). Trees in lower strata grow very slowly because of the reduced light environment, and eventually are much smaller than upper stratum trees in the same cohort. Small trees in lower strata have been mistakenly assumed to be younger, with the stand considered the result of an uneven or all-age pattern of development. Mixed species, single cohort stands often produce trees of higher timber quality more economically than in pure species or multiple-cohort (uneven-aged) stands. Trees that are eventually relegated to lower strata surround the trees that will eventually form the B-stratum when the stand is young, acting as 'trainers' and keeping the B-stratum crop trees pruned. The B-stratum tree crowns eventually expand above the trainers avoiding the need for a costly thinning.

Mixed species stands also differentiate into dominance classes within each canopy stratum. Trees in lower strata will express dominance in essentially the same manner as trees in the upper stratum by retaining a full, deep crown of photosynthetically active tissue (leaves or needles). Dominant trees in lower strata usually do not grow rapidly until released. Upon release these lower stratum dominants are likely to grow more rapidly than the less dominant trees in any stratum, providing they can survive the initial 'shock' of release. While it is possible to have shade-tolerant species in all strata in a stratified, mixed species stand, shade-intolerant species will be found only as emergents (the A-stratum) or in the continuous upper canopy (the B-stratum).

Especially in stands of coniferous species, the forest floor is devoid of vegetation during the stem exclusion stage because most herbaceous plants are eliminated by the vigorous occupation of growing space by the trees. In stands dominated by deciduous trees, shrubs and herbaceous plants that can take advantage of trees' dormant season sometimes are able to persist. Single species stands in the stem exclusion structure commonly create the dense structure. There are generally fewer species of plants and animals in the dense structure than in other structures. Mixed species stands in the stem exclusion stage can assume the dense structure, but are sometimes classified as having the complex structure because of the vertical distribution of their canopies. Mixed and pure species stands in the stem exclusion stage that contain some older, residual trees can be classified as having the complex structure. Such stands may be suitable to more wildlife species than single species, stem exclusion stands lacking residual overstory trees.

Upper and lower strata affect each other's growth in both single and multiple cohort stands. These effects are more pronounced in mixed species stands with more than one cohort. Trees growing immediately beneath an intact canopy experience a light regime that alternates between spots of full sunlight (sunflecks) and shade as the sun moves across the sky. With enough periods of full sunlight, trees in lower strata can retain a full crown and their terminals continue to grow upwards, retaining a single-stemmed form. A light environment that alternates between periods of full sun and shade is termed low shade. A high shade environment develops when trees in the upper canopy grow much taller than trees growing beneath them. Sunlight in this environment

A-stratum (emergents)

B-stratum (upper continuous canopy)

C-stratum

Forest floor stratum

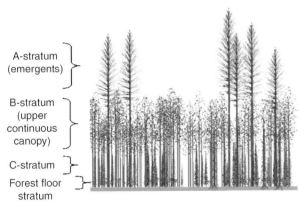

Figure 7 Mixed species, single cohort stands can develop into strata. Nomenclature shown here is common. (a) Within each stratum, the trees can differentiate into crown classes, similar to those in Figure 6. (Multiple cohort stands can develop into similar strata.) (b) The same stand as above, from perspective view. © Professor Chadwick Oliver.

is extremely diffuse, with few, if any, sunflecks reaching the understory. Trees growing in high shade develop characteristically flatter tops as the ratio between terminal and lateral branches decreases. These trees die unless they are extremely tolerant of shade, and once released from the effects of this shade, trees may not retain a single terminal leader. Trees in lower strata trees can sometimes affect overstory trees. Especially on sites limited by moisture or nutrients, lower strata trees in the same or younger cohorts can deplete soil moisture and nutrients to such an extent that overstory trees are weakened and invaded by insects and/or pathogens.

Disturbances affect mixed species stands in more complex ways because species differ in their responses to various kinds of disturbances. A fire may selectively kill trees in lower strata because these trees are smaller, have thinner bark, and commonly consist of species more susceptible to fires. Windstorms will generally topple trees in the emergent or upper continuous canopy. Insects and diseases are usually host specific to varying degrees. In this way, disturbances have the potential of reducing the number of species initially present in a stand. Small disturbances in mixed species, single cohort stands can also result in the establishment of new cohorts.

Residual trees of older cohorts can suppress newly initiating cohorts during the stem exclusion stage, depending on the number and vigor of these residual trees. Extreme suppression can kill the younger cohort or relegate it to advance regeneration, as described earlier. Even less extreme suppression will reduce height growth or eventually kill younger trees, with shade-intolerant species killed first. Recent studies suggest that in some instances surprisingly little overstory shade is required to suppress or kill a younger cohort.

The physical appearance of a mixed species, single cohort stand is quite similar to a multiple cohort stand, and the same stratification classification (and crown classes within strata) of **Figure 7** is used in both stand types. Management of these stand types is also similar, recognizing that dominant trees in each stratum are the potentially more vigorous ones and that lower strata trees can become flat-topped, lose their vigor, and possibly die, especially if shade intolerant.

Understory reinitiation Eventually trees grow so large that the death of an individual tree releases enough growing space that adjacent trees cannot rapidly capture all of it, and a new cohort (often a different species that is more tolerant of shade) establishes. The establishment of a new cohort signals the onset of the understory reinitiation development stage. This stage can last for several

hundred years because trees in the newly regenerating cohort are commonly so suppressed that they remain in a flat-topped condition near the forest floor as advance regeneration or die within a few years. They are then replaced by more newly germinating seedlings that also may die after a few years. Residual trees of an older cohort can suppress the intermediate cohort and any newly regenerating trees, prolonging their suppression.

The understory reinitiation stage can exhibit the understory structure, although in mixed species stands and in stands with residual older trees it more commonly reflects the complex structure. The understory structure can also result from partial disturbances in the stem exclusion stage that created a new cohort that became suppressed as the forest floor stratum.

Old growth The old growth development stage describes what would happen in the event that no external (autogenic) disturbance event impacted a stand during the lifespan of any of the original initiating trees. The old growth development stage is probably not particularly common in many parts of the world, as fire, wind, insect outbreaks, or other disturbances generally impact a stand before it attains this stage. The old growth stage occurs as overstory trees become increasingly weak and die intermittently, allowing the trees existing near the forest floor in the understory reinitiation stage to grow to the overstory, through a series of suppressions and releases. The resulting stand would consist of shade-tolerant trees in a variety of heights as individual gaps created by senescing overstory trees allowed the released trees to grow at different rates.

Because most tree species live for hundreds of years, a true old growth development stage would not occur until a stand was several hundred years old and had not been impacted by an intermediate disturbance. In some instances of shorter-lived species, this stage might occur much sooner.

The old growth stage would generally take on the attributes of the complex structure; however, most stands identified as having the complex structure are not in the old growth development stage. Instead, they are generally in the stem exclusion or understory reinitiation development stages. These stands are generally made complex by the presence of residual trees and multiple strata (bottom line of **Figure 5**).

These phases of stand development have been observed and documented by foresters and scientists in temperate and tropical forests in many parts of the world. The four phases of stand development are sometimes contrasted with 'gap phase' dynamics, which describes forest development as the ongoing process of recolonization of small openings in the forest that occur upon the death of individual or small groups of trees. The two systems differ mainly in terms of temporal and spatial scales. In some tropical and temperate forests, stand-replacing disturbances occur at longer timescales than the lifespans of individual trees. Senescence and death of individual canopy trees create gaps that are regenerated by seedlings or advance regeneration. As the trees in these gaps grow, they compete with each other for resources. The tree that eventually replaces the gap-forming tree is one that can successfully regenerate and compete in the gap environment. Depending on their geographical location, orientation, and size, gaps can have an abundance or dearth of resources required for tree growth. Trees that can capture resources and/or tolerate lower levels of resources will be favored.

Application of Stand Dynamics to Silviculture

By understanding the processes affecting each development stage and the structures created by the different processes, silviculturists can predict the development pathways that each stand could take and the values that each stand might provide at different times in the future. Moving stands along desired development pathways can be achieved using silvicultural operations as surrogates for natural processes such as disturbances and regeneration. An appropriate silvicultural operation can be prescribed by understanding how the stand will respond. Through understanding the dominant processes occurring within a stand at different development stages, silvicultural operations can be implemented when they will be most effective – at appropriate 'windows of opportunity.' Well-timed silvicultural operations will cause the stand to follow a planned development pathway – a silvicultural pathway.

When in each structure, a stand will provide some values, but not others. For example, an open structure will provide deer and butterfly habitat, but not habitat for 'late successional' species and no opportunity for obtaining timber revenue for a long time. Alternatively, an understory structure will provide some late successional habitat and opportunities for obtaining high-quality timber, but no 'early successional' habitats for deer and butterflies. The full spectrum of forest values can only be obtained when individual stands are managed in concert across a landscape.

Stand Dynamics and the Landscape Scale

Although the primary scalar focus of stand dynamics is the forest stand, knowledge of stand-level pro-

cesses readily scale up to the landscape. Landscapes are mosaics of individual stands. Landscape vegetation patterns arise from the interactions between vegetation, soils, climate, and disturbances. At the landscape scale, disturbances vary with climate, geomorphology, topography, soils, and vegetation. Some portions of landscapes are very prone to disturbances such that stand development or silvicultural pathways are constrained. Other areas of the landscape are protected from disturbances such as wind and fire and act as 'disturbance refugia' where developmental pathways and structures may differ markedly from those found in the surrounding matrix. At the landscape level, each stand follows developmental pathways and exhibits characteristic structures that reflect its disturbance history and its structure at the time of the disturbance. Like individual stands, landscapes are dynamic, but landscapes still reflect the developmental pathways and forest structures that are possible given the climate, soils, vegetation, and inherent disturbance regimes of the region. Some landscapes are a mosaic of many different structures and development stages, reflecting a history of small disturbance sizes or an underlying patchwork of geological or soil conditions. Other landscapes are structurally and compositionally more homogeneous, indicating large-scale disturbances, homogeneous substrates, and few species; such landscapes typically exhibit a narrow range of structures and pathways.

See also: **Afforestation**: Stand Establishment, Treatment and Promotion - European Experience. **Ecology**: Natural Disturbance in Forest Environments; Plant-Animal Interactions in Forest Ecosystems. **Health and Protection**: Biochemical and Physiological Aspects; Diagnosis, Monitoring and Evaluation. **Landscape and Planning**: Landscape Ecology, the Concepts; Landscape Ecology, Use and Application in Forestry; Spatial Information. **Mensuration**: Yield Tables, Forecasting, Modeling and Simulation. **Plantation Silviculture**: Forest Plantations; Multiple-use Silviculture in Temperate Plantation Forestry. **Silviculture**: Natural Stand Regeneration; Unevenaged Silviculture. **Soil Development and Properties**: The Forest Floor. **Tree Physiology**: A Whole Tree Perspective; Shoot Growth and Canopy Development.

Further Reading

Camp A, Oliver C, Hessburg P, and Everett R (1997) Predicting late successional fire refugia pre-dating European settlement in the Wenatchee Mountains. *Forest Ecology and Management* 95: 63–77.

Frelich LE (2002) *Forest Dynamics and Disturbance Regimes*. New York: Cambridge University Press.

Harper JL (1977) *Population Biology of Plants*. London: Academic Press.

Hunter ML Jr (1990) *Wildlife, Forests and Forestry.* Englewood Cliffs, NJ: Prentice Hall.

Kelty MJ, Larson BC, and Oliver CD (eds) (1992) *The Ecology and Silviculture of Mixed-Species Forests: A Festschrift for David M. Smith.* Boston, MA: Kluwer Academic Publishers.

Oliver CD and Larson BC (1996) *Forest Stand Dynamics,* updated edn. New York: John Wiley.

Oliver CD and O'Hara KL (2003) Effects of restoration at the stand level. In: JA Stanturf and P Marsden (eds) *Restoration of Boreal and Temperate Forests.* Boca Raton, FL: CRC Press.

Smith DM, Larson BC, Kelty MJ, and Ashton PMS (1997) *The Practice of Silviculture.* New York: John Wiley.

Natural Regeneration of Tropical Rain Forests

N Brown, Oxford Forestry Institute, Oxford, UK

Introduction

Natural regeneration is the process by which juvenile plants and coppice that have established naturally replace plants which have died or have been killed. Over time, following a disturbance, the growth of natural regeneration will reestablish canopy trees. This natural recovery process can be exploited in tropical forest management systems to create a new stand after canopy trees have been harvested. This article provides a review of the advantages and problems associated with natural regeneration. The effects of different silvicultural systems on natural regeneration are examined and the causes of success and failure discussed.

Advantages and Disadvantages of Natural Regeneration

Tropical rainforests are well-known for their extraordinarily high diversity of species, including trees. The use of natural regeneration in forest management helps to reduce logging impacts on biodiversity, since the objective is to ensure that exploited trees are replaced by juveniles of tree species characteristic of the natural forest. The diversity of natural regeneration will generally exceed the diversity of species that could be planted on a commercial scale. For example, in a recent large-scale forest rehabilitation project in Borneo many thousands of hectares of logged rainforest were replanted with only 33 commercial tree species. Some of these were not native to the region. Planting replacement trees in sites that are often remote and inaccessible is an expensive operation. Consequently there is little incentive to use species that are of low commercial value or that are relatively slow-growing. Such species are only likely to remain a component of a sustainably managed forest under a natural regeneration system.

Natural regeneration systems exploit existing seed and seedling banks and circumvent the problem of obtaining healthy planting stock. Seed production in many important tropical tree species is erratic and poorly documented and it is often difficult or impossible to obtain a regular supply. Planting stock cannot therefore be produced on demand. Where planting stock is available it is often collected from a narrow range of sites outside the local area and is likely to be of unknown but probably rather narrow genetic composition. Planted seedlings often suffer an initial period of poor growth and high mortality, termed planting shock. Poor initial growth will often put planted trees at a significant competitive disadvantage relative to the regeneration of other plants in disturbed forest sites. In contrast, natural regeneration will often show enhanced survival and vigorous growth in response to canopy disturbance.

In many parts of the world little is known about the ecology of commercially important tree species, including their tolerance of a range of site conditions or their requirements for successful establishment as seedlings. This can make artificial regeneration problematic. Where new trees have been planted extensively in tropical rainforest (typically, enrichment planting of forests with poor natural regeneration of commercially valuable species), seedling mortality has often been high and growth rates disappointing. This has been attributed to poor site–species matching, poor planting and maintenance techniques. The use of natural regeneration increases the chance that seedlings and saplings are of species capable of growing to maturity under local site conditions because they belong to species (and ecotypes) that are already growing in the immediate vicinity.

Under an appropriate silvicultural system the density of seedlings in a naturally regenerating tropical rainforest can be very high. Densities in excess of 75 000 seedlings ha^{-1} of commercial species have been recorded in forests in Borneo. This gives a broad base for the selection of the fastest-growing, best-formed individuals of the most desirable species. In contrast, the costs of replanting a forest are so great that the forester generally aims to make sure that a large proportion of all individuals survive and grow to maturity regardless of their quality. However, a major disadvantage of natural regeneration systems is that the forester has only indirect control over the composition of future forest stands. Although an aim of natural tropical rainforest silviculture is to increase the regeneration of commercially desirable species and enhance their growth, this is constrained by the species and genotypes that are present in the seed and seedling banks. Genetic improvement is unlikely to occur through natural regeneration systems and little or nothing is known about the relative performances of different provenances of climax tropical rainforest trees.

Concern has often been expressed that the 'creaming' or preferential felling of the largest trees or those with the best form from an area of natural tropical rainforest will leave only trees with undesirable genotypes in the forest. Natural regeneration offers a simple method for reducing the risk of such dysgenic selection. Most climax tropical rainforest tree species have populations which are composed of large numbers of seedlings and saplings and progressively fewer larger-sized trees. The largest commercial-sized trees will therefore constitute only a small fraction of the total population (**Figure 1**).

There is also a strong relationship between tree size and fecundity for many tropical trees. This implies that the largest trees are likely to have made a disproportionate contribution to the genetic structure of the seed and seedling bank. As a consequence, if the forest is well-stocked with natural regeneration, harvesting of only the largest individuals is unlikely to result in an immediate loss of genetic variation.

Environmental Control of Regeneration

Foresters and ecologists have been aware for centuries of the importance of forest canopy gaps in the regeneration dynamics of most tropical rain-

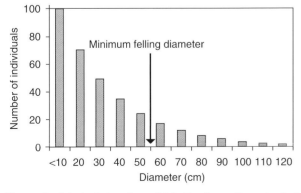

Figure 1 A typical size class distribution for a climax tropical rainforest tree species. Tree size is usually measured as the diameter of the trunk at 1.3 m above the ground.

forest trees. Gaps are formed naturally when canopy trees are damaged or die. They can range in size from a tiny patch of light formed by the loss of a branch to several hectares when many trees are lost in a landslide or major blow-down. Most seedlings require the enhanced light levels found in a gap in order to grow to maturity. Only the most shade-tolerant species can survive and grow in the deep shade of a forest understory.

Measurements of seed germination and rates of photosynthesis by seedlings have shown that species differ in their responses to increasing light levels. Two broad strategies have been described that characterize plant responses to disturbance. Pioneer species show significantly higher levels of seed germination under full sunlight. Their seeds are typically small, widely dispersed, and can remain dormant in the soil seed bank awaiting a disturbance to trigger germination. Once established, pioneer seedlings will grow very rapidly to maturity in a large gap, but they rarely persist for long in the shaded forest understory. In contrast, climax species have the greatest germination success in shade where their seedlings may persist for many years. Even relatively small increases in insolation will increase their growth and survival but they are unable to achieve the very high rates of growth of a pioneer species in the most disturbed conditions. Most species-rich, primary rainforests contain species which fall on a continuum of light response from the most shade-tolerant climax species to the most light-demanding pioneer.

The size of a canopy gap is the principal determinant of the amount and duration of insolation that penetrates the forest, hence different species of tree will find optimum radiation regimes for maximizing their growth in different sizes of gap. As a consequence, forests which are heavily or frequently disturbed will have abundant regeneration of light-demanding species. Pioneer species are often abundant in early successional forest communities such as those found on islands hit by tropical cyclones. Tropical rainforests which are infrequently disturbed are often dominated by more shade-tolerant, slow-growing climax species.

However, competitive superiority is not just determined by which plant has the greatest relative growth rate in response to the ambient light environment. Tall plants are able to capture more light and consequently grow faster and cast shade on the shorter plants beneath them. As the tallest plants in a gap may capture most incoming sunlight they will often dominate the regeneration regardless of their species. When the seedling bank and all advance regeneration is destroyed by a disturbance, the first plants to recolonize a gap will often preempt the light and delay or inhibit further colonization by other species. Furthermore, the species composition of seedling banks and the soil seed bank changes over time, reflecting the fruiting patterns of trees in the vicinity. Only a tiny fraction of the species found in a forest will be represented in the seed or seedling banks at any one place or time. A tree stands a good chance of regenerating if it is simply present as a seed or seedling when a gap forms, irrespective of whether it is well adapted to growing in that particular gap environment. It is salutary to note that in 1930 forest officers in Malaya concluded from practical experience that regeneration was influenced more by chance than by design and that regeneration of any particular species could not be relied on unless it was actually present before or immediately after the felling.

The implication of this for silvicultural systems that depend on natural regeneration is that it is crucial that the forest is already well stocked with abundant seedlings and advance regeneration of desirable species when the forest is logged. It is also important that logging does not destroy these seedlings. If this is not the case then regeneration will be composed primarily of noncommercial species or colonists.

Although many species of tropical rainforest tree have the ability to resprout after damage to the crown, coppicing has rarely, if ever, been used as a means to regenerate tropical rainforest after commercial exploitation. Resprouted stems are known to suffer much higher mortality rates than previously undamaged individuals and resprouts from large-diameter stems are more likely to die than those from small stems. Resprouting has also been found to be more common beneath small canopy gaps than in large ones. This implies that coppicing is unlikely to be a viable silvicultural system in tropical rainforests but may play an important role in forest regeneration after shifting cultivation.

Promoting Seedling Establishment

One of the real challenges in tropical rainforest management is to make sure that there is adequate regeneration before logging. In temperate forest silviculture this can be done by delaying felling operations so that they follow good seed years, by preparing suitable seed beds to enhance seedling establishment and thinning the forest canopy to encourage both seed production and seedling survival. Good seed years can be forecast when production forests consist of only one or a few tree species. However, in tropical rainforests it is much less easy to predict when or where a commercial species is likely

to reproduce. Tree species fruit asynchronously in many tropical forests and their fecundity varies in response to very different climatic conditions. For example, the high-value tree Borneo ironwood (*Eusideroxylon zwageri*) has been noted for very poor regeneration for decades, to the point where, exacerbated by overexploitation, the species has become extremely rare. Recent extreme El Niño events which have caused high levels of seedling mortality in many other climax rainforest species seem to have promoted prolific regeneration of *E. zwageri*. Variation in the environment has different effects on the reproductive success of different species. The diversity of most tropical rainforest militates against efficient application of silvicultural treatments to increase the establishment of seedlings of desirable species to the whole forest block. Experience has shown that this only happens for the small number of species that produce abundant seed when the treatment occurs. Otherwise such treatments can promote dense regeneration of unwanted species that can inhibit the establishment of useful seedlings in the future.

The dipterocarp rainforests of South-East Asia are an important exception. Trees in the family Dipterocarpaceae occur in large numbers in these forests, and most provide valuable timber. A large number of dipterocarp species have supraannual, gregarious fruiting across large regions. As a consequence, at intervals varying typically between 3 and 11 years, there is substantial multispecies recruitment to the dipterocarp seedling bank. The density of seedlings can exceed several million ha^{-1} immediately after such a fruiting event, but declines rapidly with time until the next fruiting. These forests were some of the first tropical rainforests to be exploited extensively for timber. In the first half of the twentieth century regeneration of a forest was seen as one of the most important silvicultural tasks. There was a great deal of experimentation in dipterocarp rainforest, with methods for 'releasing' natural regeneration by thinning the canopy above newly established seedlings. A uniform shelterwood silvicultural system was developed that required the removal of all unwanted trees across the entire forest block, resulting in a drastic increase in understory light levels. An essential rule in this system was that felling should 'follow the seed,' meaning that a regeneration improvement felling could not be instigated until there was a substantial crop of newly established seedlings. The Malaysian Uniform System was found to result in a very large increase in the number of high-quality saplings of light-demanding dipterocarps. The success of the system was, however, attributable to the high density of adult trees of desirable species that simultaneously produced heavy seed crops. Similar tropical shelterwood systems, when applied in forests elsewhere in the humid tropics, have been considerably less successful. Either the systems proved too complex to apply reliably or, when applied indiscriminately to a whole forest block, resulted in dense regeneration of unwanted pioneer and light-demanding species.

Promoting Seedling Survival and Growth

Most tropical rainforests are now managed on a selection system, where no silvicultural operations are carried out at all. Some success has been achieved in improving the growth and survival of selected seedlings and saplings by opening the canopy directly above them and cutting back competitors. This type of treatment, known as liberation thinning, is relatively inexpensive and has been shown to increase the number of high-quality crop trees without impacting large areas of forest. Trees of unwanted species that are not impeding the growth of future crop trees are left alone. Concern has often been expressed that older saplings may become moribund and fail to respond to release. However, detailed long-term monitoring of advance regeneration has shown little evidence to endorse this concern. A positive relationship has been found between the height of advance regeneration and its growth response to artificial canopy gaps. Furthermore, it would appear that many canopy trees have experienced repeated periods of rapid growth interspersed with shade suppression in their passage to maturity.

Regrettably, as the costs of silviculture have increased, a view has developed among tropical foresters that logging alone would be sufficient to stimulate adequate regeneration and that silvicultural intervention is expensive and unnecessary. Extraction, rather than regeneration, has become the most important operation. Unlike lowland dipterocarp rainforest, many tropical rainforests have relatively low densities of commercially valuable species and sparse regeneration. Although selective logging has often stimulated vigorous regrowth, it has not been of valuable species. As a result of 'logging and leaving' there are now significant areas of secondary forest which have little or no productive potential. The only chance of rehabilitating such forests is through costly and unreliable enrichment planting. Many of these areas are now being converted to more productive nonforest uses, with serious consequences for conservation. An area of logged rainforest of more than 200 000 ha in the Ulu Segama area of Sabah, Malaysia, has recently been cleared and converted to pulpwood plantation because it was judged to be poorly stocked and devoid of natural regeneration and potential crop trees.

Why Does Natural Regeneration Fail?

Some of the most important causes of failure for natural regeneration include:

- Inadequate stocking of seedlings and saplings of desirable species at the time of harvesting. Many species of commercially valuable tropical rainforest tree do not have persistent seed or seedling banks. This is commonly true of more light-demanding climax species, including a number of important timber trees. In the Brazilian Amazon, species such as mahogany (*Swietenia macrophylla*) do produce seedling banks irregularly but these suffer very high rates of mortality in closed forest. Such species are problematic because the logging of large adults removes a significant proportion of the total population and the potential for future seed production. One possible solution is the retention of seed trees; however, experimental studies suggest that seed predation and poor germination limit successful seedling establishment in secondary forest. For many tropical rainforests the period during which recruitment can occur following a disturbance is short, because light and other resources are rapidly preempted by competing vegetation. Consequently the retention of seed trees is unlikely to result in regeneration of these species.
- Excessive damage to natural regeneration caused by harvesting operations. Surveys of logged tropical rainforest frequently report between 30% and 70% of the residual stand damaged. The majority of damage to natural regeneration is caused by careless and unplanned skidding rather than felling. Regeneration in badly damaged areas is either from the soil seed bank or from seed rain and is dominated by pioneer species. Some felling damage is inevitable when harvesting natural tropical rainforest but strict reduced-impact logging guidelines have shown that with care this can be substantially reduced.
- Poor maintenance of the forest following harvesting, resulting in poor growth and high mortality in existing seedlings. Scrambling bamboo and vines such as *Merremia* spp. can infest heavily damaged forest and smother young trees. Surveys in a logged forest in Borneo have shown over three-quarters of all trees to be infested with bamboo or vines. Little is yet known about the ecology of these climbers and the most effective methods for their control.

Long-Term Sustainability of Natural Regeneration

Sustainable use relies on the forest retaining its capacity to regenerate after harvesting. A very large proportion of tropical rainforest trees are dependent on animals for pollination and seed dispersal. Logging can disrupt animal communities in ways which have an impact on tree regeneration. Reduced pollination may lead to reduced seed-set or greater prevalence of inbreeding. Seeds which fall close to a parent tree are often found to suffer greater predation losses than those that are well dispersed. Similarly, seedling survival increases away from the pests and pathogens associated with a parent. Although there are indications that both pollination and dispersal may limit regeneration in forest fragments, there is as yet no clear evidence of impacts on seedling populations in large-production forests. However, seed predation rates have been found to be sufficiently high in logged forest to prevent regeneration of some tree species. Logging removes a significant proportion of the large seed-producing adults of commercial species and the residual seed trees become the focus of all predation.

Fire is becoming an increasing problem in many logged tropical rainforests and has a particularly severe impact on seedling populations. Almost no climax rainforest tree species have fire-tolerant seedlings and even lightly burned forests have been shown to be devoid of natural regeneration of anything other than pioneer species.

See also: **Harvesting**: Forest Operations in the Tropics, Reduced Impact Logging. **Silviculture**: Forest Dynamics; Forest Rehabilitation; Natural Stand Regeneration; Treatments in Tropical Silviculture. **Tropical Ecosystems**: Dipterocarps; Swietenia (American mahogany); Tropical Moist Forests,

Further Reading

de Graaf NR, Poels RLH, and van Rompaey RSAR (1999) Effect of silvicultural treatment on growth and mortality of rainforest in Surinam over long periods. *Forest Ecology and Management* 124: 123–135.

Fox JED (1976) Constraints on the natural regeneration of tropical moist forest. *Forest Ecology and Management* 1: 37–65.

Hutchinson ID (1987) Improvement thinning in natural tropical forests: aspects and institutionalization. In: Mergen F and Vincent JR (eds) *Natural Management of Tropical Moist Forests – Silvicultural and Management Prospects of Sustained Utilization*, pp. 113–133. New Haven, Connecticut: Yale University, School of Forestry and Environmental Studies.

Kuusipalo J, Hadengganan S, Adjers G, and Sagala APS (1997) Effect of gap liberation on the performance and growth of dipterocarp trees in a logged-over rainforest. *Forest Ecology and Management* 92: 209–219.

Lowe RG (1978) Experience with the shelterwood system of regeneration in natural forest in Nigeria. *Forest Ecology and Management* 1(3): 193–212.

Nicholson DI (1979) *The Effects of Logging and Treatment on the Mixed Dipterocarp Forests of Southeast Asia*. Report FO: MISC/79/8. Rome: Food and Agriculture Organization of the United Nations.

Webb EL (1998) Gap-phase regeneration in selectively logged lowland swamp forest, northeastern Costa Rica. *Journal of Tropical Ecology* 14: 247–260.

Wyatt-Smith J (1963) *Manual of Malayan Silviculture for Inland Forests*. Malayan Forest Records No. 23. Kepong, Malaysia: Forest Research Institute Malaysia.

Managing for Tropical Non-timber Forest Products

J L G Wong, Wild Resources Ltd, Bangor, UK
J B Hall, University of Wales, Bangor, UK

Introduction

Interest in the management of non-timber forest products (NTFPs) in the tropics has increased dramatically over the past 20 years. This process reflects observations that:

1. Some economically or culturally significant NTFP resources are being overexploited.
2. NTFPs can provide a raw material resource for local enterprise and income development.
3. NTFPs may be the only harvestable commodities left in degraded forests.
4. NTFPs have significant subsistence and cultural values to local peoples.

Although these concerns are most commonly associated with development forestry in the tropics, all of them are increasingly recognized as present and significant in temperate forests and rural economies (e.g., in the Pacific Northwest of the USA, Eastern Europe, and the UK).

Increasing interest in the poverty and development relevance of NTFPs has engendered work on the promotion of income generating enterprises based on them. Because this has a social focus much of this work has been undertaken by socially orientated advisors and hence on management systems based on participatory rural appraisal and other social science techniques. The development of the ecological or autecological basis for species management has only recently become of more concern and suitable protocols for ecological investigation of the multifarious species of NTFPs are only now being developed. Good management should be based on sound ecological knowledge whether this is the result of extended observation and encapsulated in local knowledge or the result of biometric investigations. This article considers how this knowledge has been used to develop NTFP management or silvicultural systems in the tropics.

What is a Non-Timber Forest Product?

For millennia people have used forests as a source of sustenance, raw materials for craft and industry, and as a home. Ethnological surveys demonstrate that roughly 60–70% of any flora and a lower percentage of the fauna are utilized by traditional forest-dwelling societies as food, clothing, shelter, tools, and medicines (**Figure 1**). The advent of sedentary farming, industrialization, and colonialism removed

Figure 1 Many NTFPs are used as medicines. This lady is a wholesaler of medicinal plants in the Durban herb market. She is selling parts of wild plants collected from indigenous forest and montane land in South Africa and neighboring countries. Many of these plants are becoming threatened by this trade. Shortages may compromise access to healthcare by poorer members of society. There is an urgent need to institute sustainable management for these resources. Photograph courtesy of Jenny Wong.

people from the forest, made them less reliant on wild resources and focused attention on the exploitation of forests for timber primarily for export. However, this did not mean that the other products were entirely disregarded. Harvesting of several wild products developed into large-scale export enterprises (e.g., cocoa, coffee, rubber, chicle, and palm oil) though many of the plants from which these were derived were eventually brought into plantation cultivation. By the middle of the twentieth century, the majority of managed tropical forests were a focus for the production of export quality timber. The continued reliance of local people on other products was considered to be insignificant and largely irrelevant and they were termed 'minor,' 'non-timber,' and 'non-wood' and all lumped together – often with less tangible forest 'benefits' and 'services.'

Although these terms are in common usage among foresters they do not have currency outside the profession. There is no accepted term for non-timber forest products that is recognized by all disciplines interested in managing forests. This is unfortunate as the successful management of NTFPs by foresters would benefit greatly from cross-disciplinary exchange with wildlife managers (especially as wildlife is considered an NTFP), ethnobotanists, human ecologists, and conservation biologists, none of whom use or recognize the term NTFP.

An examination of the NTFP literature reveals that the term is used to describe wild and semicultivated plants from natural, managed, and modified forests and also semidomesticated forest plants (e.g., trees for fruit or understory plants such as Marantaceae) even where these are not in a forest environment (e.g., in agroforestry systems). Furthermore, some NTFPs are wild products taken from artificial forest environments (e.g., mushrooms from pine plantations in southern Africa and snails from oil palm plantations in Cameroon). The NTFPs themselves may also be cultivated using artificial techniques such as *in vitro* propagation. Careful examination of the actual products and environments covered in the NTFP literature suggests that we can map the area of interest as shown as the shaded areas in **Figure 2**.

Although the rhetoric suggests that animals should be considered as NTFPs there is very little evidence that foresters have done much work in this area. However, there is substantial work on sustainable management of animals in the conservation world especially in Latin America which is not often referenced in the forestry literature.

In a further complication, the term NTFP has been more literally interpreted as including products made from wood but which cannot be classed as 'timber' including the derivation of chemical feedstock from

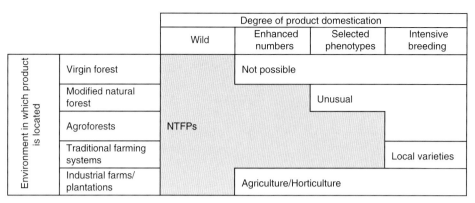

Figure 2   Map of products termed NTFPs.

wood. This latter interpretation is ignored for the remainder of this article as silviculture for wood-based products is the same as for maximizing wood volume which is dealt with elsewhere (*see* **Silviculture**: Silvicultural Systems).

What is NTFP Silviculture?

Before answering this question we have first to consider what is meant by silviculture. Silviculture is the art and science of controlling the establishment, growth, composition, health, and quality of forests and woodlands. Silviculture entails the manipulation of forest and woodland vegetation in stands and landscapes to meet the diverse needs and values of landowners and society on a sustainable basis.

In principle this definition includes the proactive management of NTFPs. However, silvics is the study of the life history and dynamics of forest trees. Although including other forest plants seems reasonable, stretching it to include animals seems unreasonable. However, the principle of developing an understanding of a species and then manipulating its environment to produce desirable products is one that applies to sustainable management of any NTFPs.

Proactive manipulation of a species to increase the quantity or quality of a product often begins with harvesting regulations and ends in the domestication of the species with production in monoculture far from the forests which were its original home. Cocoa and oil palm were both once harvested from the wild and ended as highly modified plants in monocultures. Other products such as locust bean (*Parkia biglobosa*) are halfway along this road and although not yet extensively modified by selective breeding are hardly present in the wild. Yet others, such as Brazil nuts (*Bertholettia excelsa*), are closer to the beginning and have properties that make them difficult to domesticate. Once a species has been recognized as an NTFP it seems to retain this title as it becomes

progressively domesticated and increasingly characteristic of farmland. The line between NTFP silviculture and horticulture is indistinct.

Identifying a product as an NTFPs depends on the plant or animal being found in a forest or being produced by a tree more or less regardless of location. The only exceptions are orchards or fruit tree plantations. This means that wild-harvested products from different habitats, such as veld or desert, are not included. However, the similarities between the management systems required by these products are such that they are increasingly classed as NTFPs in the literature even though they have little to do with 'forests' (e.g., devil's claw (*Harpagophytum procumbens*) in Botswana).

So a pragmatic definition of NTFP silviculture would need to include the development of cultural systems for all wild and semidomesticated non-timber tree products, regardless of where they are located, and anything found in a forest environment.

Although the issues included in NTFP silviculture represent a continuum which is rather poorly defined, it is possible to recognize three areas that have distinct silvicultural and management features. The regulation of harvesting from wild populations has a very long history and is known in the Americas as 'extractivism.' The semidomestication of trees in traditional farming systems across the tropics likewise has a long history, and has resulted in distinct anthropogenic landscapes such as the African savanna parklands, the agroforests of Indonesia, and the home gardens of Nigeria. A third trend is for cultivation of wild products leading eventually to full domestication, this being a more recent phenomenon.

Harvesting Natural Forests

This section describes the silvicultural systems that are used to harvest 'wild' products, i.e., those in the third column of **Figure 1**. Most silviculture for wild products in natural forest takes the form of harvesting rules. These are most often concerned with one or more of the following:

- prescribed harvesting methods
- exploitation of only a portion of the species range in any year (coupes)
- a fixed harvesting interval.

Wild products are also exploited from farm and plantation habitats where they often occur as weeds or by serendipity. Silviculture in such environments may be the same as for natural forests but, in these anthropogenic situations, there is much more scope for proactive intervention such as the tending of plants and the promotion of suitable habitats for wildlife.

Traditional Systems

Local people who have depended on NTFPs for many generations have a vast repository of knowledge of the plants, animals, and ecosystems in their locales. This experience is very often encoded into myths, taboos, rules, and decision-making processes which maintain a balance between exploitation and productivity.

NTFP protection and harvesting restrictions feature in many cultures. In some African parklands, for example, anyone felling the soil-improving *Faidherbia albida* could traditionally face execution! In other instances, all a community's trees of a key species might be owned by the chief, regardless of who farmed beneath them (*Parkia biglobosa*), or the community could harvest fruit only when the chief declared the season open (*Sclerocarya birrea*).

The use of traditional management practices has in many cases provided a sustainable resource for local use for many generations. However, as the market economy takes hold, favored products enter commercial trade and the equilibrium between traditional rules, expectations, and market demand is disrupted. Almost inevitably unchecked, these processes lead to either overexploitation or the domestication of the species, both to the detriment of the local economy.

The advent of participatory forest management initiatives such as Joint Forest Management in Nepal has provided a basis for the integration of traditional knowledge with modern forest management planning. The silvicultural elements of this exchange are exemplified in Oaxaca in Mexcio with the development of what has been termed 'barefoot silviculture.' The origins of such systems is indigenous knowledge which can give rise to systems which can be recognized as conforming to single and multicohort stand management. Within such systems NTFPs are managed alongside the trees as an integral part of the silvicultural system.

Extractivism

Extractivism is a term used, mostly in the Americas, to describe any gathering of natural products, whether of mineral (mining), animal (skins, meat, fats), or plant (woods, leaves, fruits etc.) origin. In the forests of Amazonia, large stocks of nuts and rubber resulted in the establishment of a harvesting system based on wild collection using indentured labor. In time this system collapsed but the nut collectors and tappers remained and have found themselves in conflict with forest clearance for large-scale ranching. The outcome has been the formal recognition of extractive reserves in Brazilian law. By April 1994, nine extractive reserves had been established for harvesting of babaçu (*Orbignya phalerata* – fruit), açai (*Euterpe oleracea* – fruit), rubber (*Hevea brasiliensis* – latex), Brazil nuts (*Bertholletia excelsa*), and copaiba (*Copaifera langsdorffii* – oil) though each reserve is managed for multiple use.

An example of the type of silviculture proposed in the utilization plans is that for babaçu in the Frexal Extractive Reserve. Babaçu is a palm which grows in dense monospecific stands in which fruit productivity can be restricted by overcrowding. It is therefore suggested that unproductive trees should be removed and the density of immature plants controlled by thinning. It is also suggested that the babaçu forests could be combined with perennial crops adapted to the region. In effect, this is a move towards a more managed landscape with the wild trees treated as a plantation crop.

The management planning and social elements of extractive reserves make them uniquely suitable for the Forest Strewardship Council type of certification. Recently Brazil nuts and chicle (edible tree latex) have been successfully certified as being derived from sustainably managed forests.

Sustainable Harvesting Plans

The development of a management system for NTFPs is basically the same as that for timber with the following recommended sequence of activities:

- inventory
- growth and yield determination
- determination of harvesting methods and yields (perhaps using some form of growth modeling)
- monitoring.

Although much of this information is often available as local knowledge, there is increasing interest in the scientific appraisal of such knowledge and biometric approaches to data collection. A review of the available biometric methods for NTFPs revealed a dearth of tried and tested protocols. However, in many cases the use of conventional forest inventory techniques is prohibitively expensive for use with NTFPs. There is a need to develop cheaper, statistically efficient means of inventoring NTFPs.

The scarcity of good resource and growth data for many NTFPs means that taking an adaptive management approach is desirable. Adaptive management accepts that decisions have to be based on imperfect information. Management prescriptions are therefore based on the precautionary principle and monitoring systems put in place to learn from experience. The monitoring itself therefore becomes both an instrument for research and feedback to ensure that management improves with each reiteration which should therefore take place at regular intervals.

Wild Products from Farmed Landscapes

Farmed landscapes with trees retained from the natural ecosystems originally cleared, sometimes as much as 200 years earlier, cover millions of square kilometers of the tropics. They support tens of millions of people in Africa alone and supply a wide range of NTFPs produced under varying degrees of management. These environments constitute an outstanding example of the way that NTFPs are integrated into the daily life and vital needs of rural communities on an extensive scale, primarily from indigenous trees.

Parkland Systems

Since the 1960s the farmed landscapes of the savanna regions of sub-Saharan Africa, especially, have been described and studied in some detail. The farmed landscape with trees (widely called 'parkland') is a refinement of the natural vegetation of the area. Tree removal is effected to enable annual crops to be grown but the removal is highly selective. Impact is less on the populations of species valued for NTFPs and, favored by measures taken to tend crops, the individual trees retained commonly display enhanced growth and vigor. Products sought from the trees have significance as dietary essentials (e.g., vitamin C in the fruit flesh of *Sclerocarya birrea* and *Ziziphus mauritiana*), positive seasonal impact as nutrient rich fruit pulp and seeds in the mid- and late dry season when alternatives are few (e.g., *Adansonia digitata*), and options for making cash income (e.g., tapped sap from the palm *Borassus aethiopum* or the fresh fruits of *Lannea microcarpa*). Complementing these rewarding but routine uses of the most highly regarded species is the availability of others with food security

roles exploited when circumstances dictate. Among these 'famine' foods are proteinaceous meal from the kernels of *Balanites aegyptiaca*, palm kernels (*Hyphaene thebaica*), foliage of *Ficus* spp., and young shoots of *Borassus aethiopum*.

Keystone Species

Particularly significant NTFP tree species retained in farmed landscapes are the keystone species – those which are so abundant that the ecosystems are named from them. Parklands of *Faidherbia albida* (fodder, including fruit for livestock), *Vitellaria paradoxa* (edible oil from fruit), *Parkia biglobosa* (seeds for seasoning), and *Adansonia digitata* (leaves as a vegetable) are examples (**Figure 3**). Tendencies towards gregariousness are reinforced by selective removal of unwanted species, and a high proportion of the trees left may be of the keystone species. Thus, *Vitellaria paradoxa* (the shea butter tree) commonly accounts for 70–90% of the mature trees in large areas of farmed landscapes but under 20% of those in natural woodland.

Because of their significant nutritional values, dominant among the NTFP tree species of farmed landscapes are the fruit trees. Some of these are the basis of considerable specialized activity involving restricted sections of the local communities, generally defined by gender and/or age. Those NTFPs of outstanding local importance ultimately result in processed output. The cooking oil (shea butter) extracted from the seeds of *Vitellaria paradoxa* and the fermented seed meal (soumbala) of *Parkia biglobosa* are the best-known West African examples, and in many parts of southern Africa fermented drinks are processed from the fruit pulp of *Sclerocarya birrea*.

Management

In an established farming setting, the tree cover is the product of considerable conscious selection when individuals for retention are identified, as well as management actions at system and tree level. Selection goes well beyond choice of species and removal of moribund or unhealthy individuals. Over a period of several years as the farming system is introduced, the farmer also applies a wealth of indigenous knowledge equivalent to infraspecific taxonomy, with varieties recognized within the local culture being valued differently and individuals of the less attractive ones likely to be removed. In central Burkina Faso, for example, several varieties of *Parkia biglobosa* are locally distinguished, the so-called 'black' type (dark bark; black seed coat) being favored as superior for seeds used in cooking.

Figure 3 The dry season aspect of typical agroforestry parkland in northern Nigeria. Prominent in the foreground is the spreading, heavily branched crown of a large *Parkia biglobosa* tree. To the right, further back, is a baobab tree (*Adansonia digitata*), the pale bole a consequence of bark removal for fiber. Photograph courtesy of Fergus Sinclair.

Other than undertaking selection, the principle thrust of the management of farmed landscape NTFPs is the imposition of pruning practices. Despite the impression of stability given by scattered large trees in crop land the system is highly dynamic. The enhanced growth rates arising in the favorable environment of a well-tended crop brings a need to prune trees which progress to a widely spreading form in old age (such as *Ficus* spp. and *Parkia biglobosa*), which would otherwise cast excessive shade. An alternative, used more to compensate for the growth in species with more compact crowns (e.g., *Vitellaria paradoxa*) is thinning of the tree population. With increasing demand for fodder and wood products, particularly fuelwood, poles, and wood for tool handles, pruning tends to meet more than one need. Nevertheless unless pruning intensity is modest (with half or more of the crown left in place) fruit production may be severely depressed for several seasons – to a mere 5–10% of a mature tree's full fruit crop in *Faidherbia albida* (typical yield 125 kg), *Parkia biglobosa* (typical yield 70 kg), and *Vitellaria paradoxa* (typical yield 50 kg).

Whilst presently minor elements of management, two further measures, fire protection and planting, merit comment. Fire protection is mainly achieved opportunistically because after crops are harvested, and livestock brought to feed on the residues, there is no fuel bed at the period when fire risk is high. However, in many farmed landscapes fallow phases remain an integral part of the land use system and are associated with increasing frequencies and intensities of wildfire. It is traditionally recognized that NTFP yields from trees exposed to intense fire are lowered (e.g., with *Parkia biglobosa*), and that smoke and other particulate matter released in an untimely fire will reduce pollination efficiency in species with dry season flowering (e.g., *Vitellaria paradoxa*). Individual trees considered of exceptional value may be protected with a firebreak, usually an area of cleared ground. Assuming wildfires will become increasingly problematic, active fire protection will be routinely needed in farmed landscapes for efficient NTFP production.

Much attention has been drawn to the lack of planting of indigenous NTFP trees in farmed areas and the population structures of NTFP tree species emphasizes this and has prompted forestry extension services to address the problem. There are two main difficulties. The first is complacency, since in most tree populations there is a vigorous core of mature trees with a projected productive life of decades. Nevertheless, the combined impact of natural mortality, removal of trees of declining productivity and of further trees to create crop space and emergency fellings for fuelwood indicate accelerating change and a need for the reinvigoration of the populations. The second difficulty is opposition to planting indigenous trees based on cultural beliefs which have been reported for various societies. It does not apply everywhere, nor to all species, however, and there are also traditions which encourage planting, as with

Adansonia digitata. The *Sclerocarya birrea* population in Namibia has also been attributed to planting germplasm brought from what is now Angola, and suggestions have also been made that planting and introduction could explain aspects of the regional variation of *Vitellaria paradoxa*.

Commerce

There has been a long history of trade in more easily handled NTFPs from farmed landscapes, where processing is relatively simple and storage difficulties are minor. Foremost among these are exudates tapped directly from the trees (e.g., gum arabic, *Acacia senegal*) or collected from insects, such as lac, from, for example, *Butea monosperma* in India. Another significant NTFP from farmed landscapes is the leaf of *Diospyros melanoxylon*, used to wrap cheroots, through which upwards of 1 million people find employment even though serving the internal market of India rather than international consumers.

Today, commercial interests based on NTFPs from farmed landscapes are expanding and diversifying as technological advance has created opportunities to utilize the qualities of fruit products in the cosmetics and food sectors, notably with *Sclerocarya birrea* and *Vitellaria paradoxa*. There is also growing willingness to support processed and packaged products from these species released in local markets, together with those from other keystone species (e.g., food seasoning cubes from *Parkia biglobosa*; cosmetics and drinks based on *Adansonia digitata*).

The Road to Domestication

All domesticated plants and animals were at one time wild. Presumably some proved so useful or amenable that they were domesticated and eventually rendered dependent on cultivation. This process of taming, and later modifying, species for more intimate use by humans is a continuous one and there are many species presently in the process of being domesticated. However, there are several forms that such a transformation can take as shown in columns four and five of **Figure 1**, a few of these are described below.

Farming the Forest

The first stage in domestication is often the manipulation of a wild species *in situ* to improve productivity. This often involves an increase in the number and density of the target species either by protecting juveniles, creating conditions for enhance recruitment or transplanting wild plants to create gardens of the species. In America this process of 'farming' wild plants *in situ* is termed 'woods grown'

and is applied to understory herbs such as American ginseng and goldenseal. In Japan similar techniques are used to grow indigenous saprophytic mushrooms (e.g., shi-take) using stacks of cut logs as a substrate within the forest.

Rescue from Extinction

For a great variety of reasons many NTFP species end up being overharvested to the extent that they are at risk of becoming locally extirpated and perhaps even threatened with extinction. In these circumstances the only option is to undertake *ex situ* conservation and if market demand remains high to proactively domesticate the species. An example of such a process for a tropical species is that for eru (*Gnetum africanum*) in Cameroon. This is a climbing plant from which the leaves are harvested, for use as a vegetable. It is becoming increasingly rare in the wild and has been the subject of intensive cultivation trials at the Limbe Botantical Gardens in Cameroon.

Figure 4 This is a wild coffee (*Coffea* sp.) that grows in the forests of Uganda. In the past young plants were collected and used to establish coffee farms outside the forest. Since the introduction of cultivars this practice has all but ceased. The world coffee market is swamped with large volumes of cultivated coffee but the speciality market is always receptive to additional varieties. Wild coffee could potentially be sold to the speciality market and its reintroduction into coffee farms in Uganda could bolster farm incomes. Photograph courtesy of Jenny Wong.

Trials have been successful and local communities and farmers' groups are now successfully cultivating the plant and obtaining a good income from sales locally and export to Nigeria. Silviculture in these cases is synonymous with horticulture.

The Market Takes Over

When market demand is for consistent quality, reliable large volumes, and a product which is a profitable export, it is often only a matter of time before production becomes industrialized (**Figure 4**). At this point market forces take over and capital is invested in large-scale or at least farm-scale production which almost inevitably takes the production process away from small-scale farmers, gatherers, and the poor. This is the end of the road to domestication; from this point onwards agriculture and horticulture take over. However, through long association, the tag NTFP may still remain as evidenced by articles in the *Journal of Non-Timber Forest Products* covering *in vitro* propagation of trees and provenance trials for common farm trees (e.g., neem).

Although often advocated, and in many instances necessary, captive production or cultivation (*ex situ*) is not without its conservation risks. Domestication can lead to environmental degradation, pollution, and reduction in genetic diversity as well as loss of incentives to conserve wild populations.

See also: **Biodiversity**: Plant Diversity in Forests. **Ecology**: Human Influences on Tropical Forest Wildlife. **Medicinal, Food and Aromatic Plants**: Edible Products from the Forest; Forest Biodiversity Prospecting; Medicinal and Aromatic Plants: Ethnobotany and Conservation Status; Medicinal Plants and Human Health; Tribal Medicine and Medicinal Plants. **Non-wood Products**: Resins, Latex and Palm Oil; Rubber Trees. **Sustainable Forest Management**: Definitions, Good Practices and Certification.

Further Reading

Boffa J-M (1999) *Agroforestry Parklands in Sub-Saharan Africa*. Rome: FAO.

Booth FEM and Wickens GE (1988) *Non-Timber Uses of Selected Arid Zone Trees and Shrubs in Africa*. Rome: FAO.

Cunningham A (2000) *Applied Ethnobotany*. London: Earthscan.

Falconer J (1990) *The Major Significance of 'Minor' Forest Products*. Rome: FAO.

Murrieta JR and Rueda RP (1995) *Extractive Reserves*. Gland, Switzerland: IUCN.

Oyen LPA and Lemmens RHMJ (2002) *Plant Resources of Tropical Africa: Precursor*. Wageningen, The Netherlands: Plant Resources of Tropical Africa.

Robinson JG and Bennett EL (1999) *Hunting for Sustainability in Tropical Forests*. New York: Columbia University Press.

Russo L, Vantomme P, Ndeckere-Ziangba F, and Walter S (2001) Non-wood forest products. *FAO Forestry Paper* 140: 81–98.

Sequeira V and Bezkorowajnyj PG (1998) Improved management of *Butea monosperma* (Lam.) Taub. for lac production. *Forest Ecology and Management* 102: 225–234.

Verheij EWM and Coronel RE (1991) *Plant Resources of Southeast Asia: Edible Fruits and Nuts*. Wageningen, The Netherlands: Pudoc.

Wong JLG, Thornber K, and Baker N (2001) *Resource Assessment of Non-Wood Forest Products*. Rome: FAO.

Unevenaged Silviculture

R Helliwell, West End, Wirksworth, Derbyshire, UK

Introduction

Uneven-aged silviculture may be defined as the tending and regeneration of woodlands or forests which contain trees of several age classes in intimate mixture. In terms of silvicultural systems (*see* **Silviculture**: Silvicultural Systems) this would, strictly speaking, include only selection and group selection systems. A looser interpretation might include stands of trees with only two or three age classes, such as coppice-with-standards or even-aged crops which have been underplanted with younger trees. However, these will either be managed as overlapping even-aged crops, which will be maintained as such, or as the first stage towards a truly multiaged stand.

Stands of trees which are basically even-aged may also go through a period when some of the older trees are retained while younger trees become established, as in shelterwood systems, so that the stand will be temporarily uneven-aged to some degree, but the silviculture which is involved will remain essentially even-aged. Similarly, areas of forest may, for various reasons, be divided into smaller units, but the silviculture of these units would still be described as even-aged if each is managed with reference to its age and area, even if each unit is very small. The essential difference, in silvicultural terms, between even- and uneven-aged silviculture is that the latter does not take any direct account of the age of the trees or the area which is occupied by each age class. Age and area, as such, are ignored. This involves a fundamentally different approach, both in theory and in practice.

History of Uneven-Aged Silviculture

In many parts of the world there have been periods when forests have been managed on an uneven-aged basis. Often, this was carried out without sufficient understanding, consistency, or care, and led to the removal of the best timber trees and/or inadequate regeneration of young trees, leaving the forest inadequately stocked or containing few trees of value. This led to a desire to adopt more organized forms of silviculture, and even-aged silvicultural systems with clearfelling came to be regarded as the best way to manage forests. This was most notably so in Germany in the latter part of the eighteenth century, and forests managed in that way were certainly easier to organize and control.

Towards the end of the nineteenth century a few foresters, most notably in Switzerland, became unhappy with the even-aged approach and developed systems of selection, whereby individual trees or small groups of trees were selected for removal and the forest was never subjected to clearfelling. Recording and management of the growing stock were by periodic measurement of all trees above a minimum size, enabling productivity and changes in growing stock to be assessed over time. These forests typically included spruce (*Picea abies*), silver fir (*Abies alba*), and beech (*Fagus sylvatica*) growing in their natural habitat, and management in this way was seen as being fairly natural or 'close to nature.' Other advantages were perceived, including reduced risk of soil erosion and avalanches of snow, greater emphasis on the production of large stems, and reduced costs of planting. This approach became more widespread in some areas and, from early in the twentieth century, Swiss law has forbidden felling of any areas greater than 2 ha without special consent. Slovenia followed suit in 1950, and state-owned forests in a number of German provinces have been managed without clearfelling since the 1980s.

Elsewhere, experience was less satisfactory. Methods which may have been successful in spruce/silver fir/beech forests in Switzerland did not always transfer readily to conditions in Scandinavia, North America, or other parts of the world, and uneven-aged silviculture fell out of favor in such countries during most of the second half of the twentieth century.

In Germany, an organization called Arbeitsgemeinschaft Naturgemässe Waldwirtschaft (Working Group on Woodland Management Using Natural Methods) was formed around 1950 to promote forestry which utilized natural processes as far as possible, and this eventually provided a catalyst for the creation of Pro Silva (a pan-European organization with similar objectives) in 1989. This now has national groups in most European countries, and there has been a considerable resurgence of interest in uneven-aged silviculture or 'continuous cover' forestry in many parts of Europe and North America. Elsewhere in the world, in places such as New Zealand and many tropical countries, there has in recent years been a dichotomy of silviculture, with even-aged plantations of timber species on the one hand and conservation of what remains of the natural forest, in the form of nature reserves, on the other. Harvesting of timber on a sustainable basis from natural tropical forests has been attempted in a number of places, but has not had a generally good track record. This has often been due to a combination of political, social, and economic problems rather than to any intrinsic silvicultural difficulties.

Felling and Regeneration

For management purposes, forests are usually divided into compartments (typically between 5 and 50 ha in temperate forests, but often much larger in tropical regions) which are relatively uniform in terms of physical attributes such as soil type and slope, and which are of a convenient size to be dealt with as part of an annual program of thinning or felling. In uneven-aged forest, each compartment will be visited every few years (usually between 5 and 12 years, depending mainly on the rate of growth) and selected trees removed.

The selection of trees for removal needs to be undertaken with several objectives in mind, and demands a degree of skill and experience. Where timber production is a main object of management there will be an emphasis on favoring trees of good form and growth potential by the removal of trees which are coarsely branched or which have already reached their maximum potential value. The removal of any one tree should, in theory, maximize the value of the forest, in terms of current and future income combined. The forester will be constantly striving to improve the quality of the trees and the overall value of the forest at minimum cost.

At the same time, the removal of trees should not be carried out in such a way as to cause instability of the forest. In particular, in places where there is a high risk of damage from wind, only a limited proportion of the timber volume should be removed at any one time and it may be necessary to leave some big trees to provide stability, if their removal would leave other trees vulnerable to being uprooted or broken by the wind. However, uneven-aged forests are, in general, less likely to suffer catastrophic damage from wind than vulnerable stages of even-aged forests. In vulnerable areas, removal of more than about one-sixth (15–17%) of the standing volume of timber at any one time might be inadvisable. If, on a highly productive site in a vulnerable area, annual increment were equal to 5% of the standing volume, that would imply a felling cycle of only 3 years in such areas, whereas if increment is equal to only 2% of the growing stock a felling cycle of 8 years would be appropriate.

There is a viewpoint which considers that the best way to manage forests in areas where gale-force winds are frequent and soils are wet and anaerobic is to grow trees with an even-aged unthinned canopy and then to clearfell them before they start to be blown down. If conditions are not so severe, then it is likely that an irregular structure will be less subject to catastrophic windthrow than an even-aged structure and will, in the long term, be more sustainable and more economic.

If a greater proportion of the standing volume can be removed without causing instability or other problems, a longer felling cycle may be appropriate. This will improve the economics of the harvesting operation, and may favor the regeneration of light-demanding species, but shorter felling cycles will allow better stand management and will tend to favor shade-tolerant species. In some instances removal of more than 50% of the standing volume may be possible. However, such heavy felling is likely to reduce the range of size classes and the productivity of the stand for several years and removal of more than 30% at any one time would be unusual.

Trees of unwanted species will be preferentially removed, while maintaining a reasonable diversity of species, and mature trees of desired tree species may be retained for longer than normal in order to ensure an adequate supply of seed.

In uneven-aged stands, a mixture of tree species is nearly always easier to manage than a single species, and also tends to have greater biodiversity and fewer problems with pest species.

Wherever possible, regeneration will be by natural seeding rather than planting, as this will be cheaper and easier to manage on an extensive basis. The selection of trees for felling will take into account the need to allow space for some seedlings and saplings of desired tree species to survive and grow, although these will not normally occupy more than 15% of the forest area at any one time. Too many saplings can be a problem, as they may require costly thinning or respacing to prevent them becoming overcrowded and spindly. With shade-tolerant species, in particular, there will often be seedlings present which are growing very slowly in shaded conditions and are 'waiting' for an opportunity to grow. If some of the

mature trees are removed in that area, these established seedlings are then likely to make more rapid growth, due to the additional light and a reduction in competition for soil moisture and nutrients, even if there is some increase in the growth of herbs and shrubs, or other tree species. Ideally, individuals or small groups of saplings should then be able to grow rapidly into the upper canopy; and, ideally, these should require little or no tending until they reach a useful size and thinning can be done at no net cost.

The balance between the various factors can be critical, and obtaining natural regeneration is not always easy. However, it should be only one of several considerations in the mind of the person who is deciding which trees to remove, and should not be allowed to dominate the system.

Other factors (**Figure 1**) also influence the success or failure of natural regeneration, including the numbers of grazing or browsing animals such as deer, sheep, goats, cattle, rabbits, and hares. If these are too numerous there may be no successful regeneration, either planted or natural, unless fencing or other methods of control or protection are implemented.

Structure of the Growing Stock

The growing stock of uneven-aged forests often tends to follow a negative exponential curve, when numbers of trees are plotted against their stem diameters (**Figure 2**). This curve is frequently referred to as a reverse-J or simply a J-curve. It can be expressed mathematically, and an 'ideal' curve can be produced for any particular area of forest, but the mathematical formula requires the input of data on the required ratio between the numbers of trees in one diameter class and the next, and the 'ideal' basal

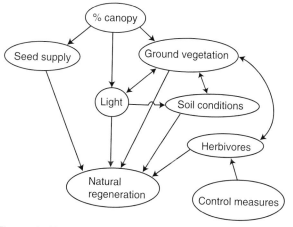

Figure 1 Factors affecting natural regeneration. © R Helliwell.

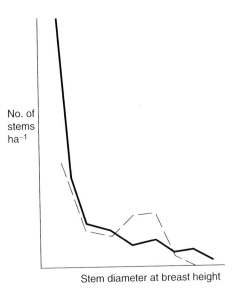

Figure 2 Typical distribution of stem sizes and numbers. (The dashed line indicates an abnormal distribution.)

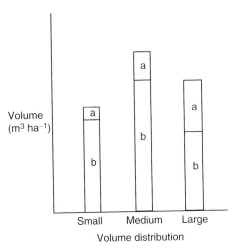

Figure 3 Typical distribution of size classes, by volume. a = species a; b = other species.

area of the stand. Neither of these can be known until a period of management experience has been obtained and data collected from several periodic measurements. It tends, therefore, to be something of a circular process, and it is probably better to regard the J-curve simply as an expression of what is happening, rather than as a prescriptive tool. Its exact form is probably not important, although any major difference from the general negative exponential form (such as a large hump in the middle: **Figure 2**) may indicate that all is not as it should be. Slavish attempts to make the forest conform to such a curve are not likely to be necessary, and may result in unnecessary expense.

One alternative to plotting stem numbers against diameters is to plot the volume of different size classes of tree, usually in three classes: small, medium, and large. The relative volumes in each class will depend to some extent on the size categories which are selected, but this method can provide a better visual impression, as significant changes in the volume of large trees may scarcely be visible on a J-curve, but will be quite clear if presented as volumes (**Figure 3**). As with J-curves, however, there is no easy way to determine the 'ideal' distribution of size classes.

Yield Prediction

Under even-aged systems there will usually be published yield tables available, which tabulate the rate of growth of trees of a given species against volume production, based on data from sample plots. If the age of the trees is known and the height of the dominant trees is measured, such yield tables can then be applied to predict future timber production by establishing a site index or yield class.

There are no such yield tables for uneven-aged stands, as the age of the trees is not known (and younger trees can sometimes spend several decades 'waiting' to grow, so their actual age is not of any particular relevance). The volume of timber which is likely to be produced from an uneven-aged stand can only be assessed by reference to the site type (i.e., the soil and climate) and tree species, or to previous records of production from the site or similar sites in the locality.

Control of the Growing Stock

If periodic measurements are taken of the growing trees (usually by the use of sample plots) and of any trees that are blown down or harvested, a picture will be built up of the growth of the forest and any changes in the growing stock. It is usual for managers to adopt tentative targets for the appropriate volume or basal area of the standing crop, which they think will give optimum timber production and regeneration. If the volume of the growing stock becomes too large, there is likely to be inadequate recruitment of smaller trees and it is possible that the larger trees will be so overcrowded that useful timber increment will stagnate and the individual trees lack stability and vigor, and they may even suffer outbreaks of diseases or pests as a result of the stresses which result from this. On the other hand, if the growing stock is too small, there may be an excess growth of troublesome herbs, shrubs, or climbers, and timber volume production will be reduced, as there will be fewer trees on which volume can accrue.

Control of regeneration by measuring the size of gaps or the amount of daylight at ground level is not a part of normal practice in uneven-aged silviculture. Reliance is placed on adjusting the intensity of felling according to the perceived response to previous fellings. This is more a matter of judgment than following a set formula.

Shade-Intolerant Species

Uneven-aged silviculture is particularly well suited to shade-tolerant tree species, such as beech and silver fir, which can regenerate in the relatively shaded conditions which are created by the removal of a small percentage of the standing volume. Other species, such as pines and oak in north temperate countries, or the various species of mahogany (e.g., *Swietenia* and *Khaya*) in the tropics, which require more light for regeneration and growth, are sometimes perceived as being less well suited. It is, however, possible to manage such species on an uneven-aged basis if they are well matched to the site and if there are no other more shade-tolerant species that would tend to replace them. In marginal cases, a shift from single stem selection to a group selection system may allow sufficient regeneration of the less shade-tolerant species to maintain an adequate percentage of those species in the stand.

Nature Conservation

There appear to have been few direct studies of the relative merits of different forms of silviculture for nature conservation. Uneven-aged silviculture may not provide suitable conditions for mobile or ephemeral species that utilize clear-felled areas, and if all the forest in a region is managed in this way it may be necessary to have some clear-felled areas (which would include any coppiced areas) or permanent open space, in order to allow such species to survive. However, uneven-aged forest provides a much greater degree of stability and continuity for the many species which require this. It is also easier to leave some trees to grow to senescence, and to provide a continuity of deadwood for species of fungi, insects, and birds which make use of this. The greater structural complexity of uneven-aged forest provides a greater variety of ecological niches at a local scale than do even-aged stands (and should be more ecologically stable as a result).

See also: **Biodiversity**: Biodiversity in Forests. **Plantation Silviculture**: Sustainability of Forest Plantations. **Silviculture**: Coppice Silviculture Practiced in Temperate Regions; Silvicultural Systems.

Further Reading

Dawkins HC and Philip MS (1998) *Tropical Moist Forest Silviculture and Management*. Wallingford, UK: CAB International.

Hagner M (ed.) (1992) *Silvicultural Alternatives. Proceedings from an Internordic Workshop*, June 22–25, 1992. Report 35. Umeå, Sweden: Sveriges Lantbruksuniversitet, Institutionen för Skogsskötsel.

Hart C (1995) *Alternative Silvicultural Systems to Clear-Cutting in Britain: A Review*. Forestry Commission bulletin no. 115. London, UK: HMSO.

Kelty MJ, Lawson BC, and Oliver CD (eds) (1992) *The ecology of mixed-species forests. dordrecht*. The Netherlands: Kluwer Academic Publishers.

Kuper JH and Maessen PPThM (eds) (1998) *Proceedings of the Second International Congress of Pro Silva (1997) Apeldoorn, The Netherlands* (in English, French, or German). Apeldoorn, The Netherlands: Dutch Pro Silva Congress Foundation.

Matthews JD (1989) *Silvicultural Systems*. Oxford, UK: Clarendon Press.

O'Hara KL (1998) Silviculture for structural diversity. A new look at multiaged systems. *Journal of Forestry* 96(7): 4–10.

O'Hara KL (2001) The silviculture of transformation – a commentary. *Forest Ecology and Management* 151: 81–86.

O'Hara KL (2002) The historical development of uneven-aged silviculture in North America. *Forestry* 75: 339–346.

Otto H-J (ed.) (2000) *Third International Congress of Pro Silva, Fallingbostel, Germany* (in English, French, or German). Langenhagen, (Hanover), Germany: Poppdruck.

Peterken GF (1996) *Natural Woodland. Ecology and Conservation in Northern Temperate Regions*. Cambridge, UK: Cambridge University Press.

Pro Silva (1993) *Proceedings of First European Congress, Besançon, France* (in English, French, or German). Besançon, France: Centre Régional de la Propriété Forestière de Franche Comté.

SITE-SPECIFIC SILVICULTURE

Contents
Reclamation of Mining Lands
Silviculture in Mountain Forests
Ecology and Silviculture of Tropical Wetland Forests
Silviculture and Management in Arid and Semi-arid Regions
Silviculture in Polluted Areas

Reclamation of Mining Lands

A J Moffat, Forest Research, Farnham, UK

Introduction

Worldwide, land has been significantly, and in some areas drastically, affected by mineral extraction. Societal pressures in most parts of the world now demand that after mining has ceased, someone (usually the mineral companies) should restore the affected land back to beneficial use, and this is controlled by legislation of various kinds and severity. Depending on a variety of factors including geology and landform, regional land use and ecology, climate and the views of community and landowner, the post-mining landscape may take a number of forms. Increasingly, the disturbance to the land caused by mining is used to advantage to regenerate the economic potential of the region or locality, increase the diversity of the landscape, and to enhance bio-diversity and recreational value. In many parts of the world, trees, woodland, and forests are an essential part of this new landscape, following mining for materials that include lignite and coal, bauxite and other metal ores, aggregates, clays, and limestones.

The success of forestry schemes has not been assured – there has been considerable effort to improve reclamation standards by a growing understanding of the environmental and silvicultural issues involved. Even today, after several decades of modern research, forestry schemes can and do fail. This article will examine the main factors that must be considered in order to achieve the aims and objectives set for a woodland or forest planted on land previously used for mining.

Basic Principles

Trees have similar requirements on a post-mining site as they do in a forest: below ground, the provision of a nontoxic soil (or soillike) substrate to provide water, nutrients, air and anchorage, together with adequate climatic conditions above ground. The main issue for silviculturalists is that mined land often fails to meet these basic needs, so it is necessary for reclamation to take place according to their advocacy of the tree's requirements. Thus, the silviculturalist must have a reasonable understanding of basic biological tree needs, coupled with an appreciation of proper site and substrate characterization, and the ability to find a 'best fit' solution given inevitable constraints on substrate and site improvement. It can also be an advantage to think laterally in order to secure the best reclamation solution that will suit forestry planting. In addition to basic silvicultural concerns, forest establishment on often unstable and certainly fragile sites will require particular attention to the risk of soil erosion and surface water pollution. These needs usually require a team approach to land reclamation and tree establishment, and may include civil engineering and soil science in addition to silviculture. Other inputs may involve landscape architects and wildlife ecologists, as well as community consultation.

Reclamation of mined land is very dependent upon the manner of site preparation for mineral extraction, and subsequent site management (**Figure 1**). The most important factor determining the success of the forest re-established on the site is whether soil resources are identified, stripped, and stored sensitively. For sites to be mined, there should be no reason why soils are not stored for future re-use, but unfortunately many mined sites suffer from a paucity of soil or its damaged state through misuse. It is therefore vital that the silviculturalist gets involved in the process that will lead to forest establishment, preferably before any mineral has been extracted from the site.

Plans for the reclamation of the site should ideally be drawn up and agreed before mineral extraction. A soil resource survey and plans for final topography should enable an evaluation of the potential for the site. The actual plans for the site will be adjusted by the needs and wishes of the landowner, as modified

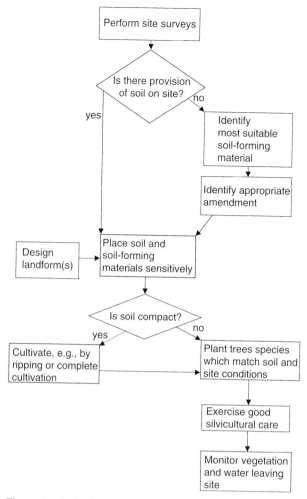

Figure 1 Basic stages of reclamation of mining land to forestry.

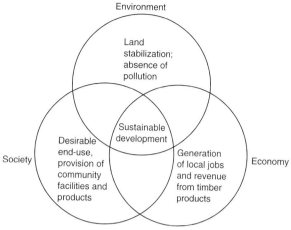

Figure 2 Mining reclamation to forestry and sustainable development.

by community expectations, usually expressed through the planning process. In all these deliberations, it is important that the aims and objectives for any woodland established on the reclaimed site should marry with natural soil and ecological processes. In other words, the direction of reclamation and tree establishment should be similar to that which naturally occurs, or might be predicted to occur. In addition, it is desirable to trim expectations for the forest according to realistic assessment of the resources available to support it, and not to strive for forestry objectives, for example an expectation of high wood quality, that cannot be met without inordinate inputs of engineering, raw materials, and continual site maintenance.

Mineral extraction per se will pose a certain risk of environmental pollution, but technologies at the mining site for mineral concentration and processing and mineral waste disposal usually pose far greater risks which must be managed upon reclamation. Mineral tailings are a particular type of waste which results from mineral processing, and may form a significant area of the site, usually in lagoons of mineral material of small particle size (e.g., fine sand, silt, and clay). Depending on mineral industry, tailings can contain elevated concentrations of heavy metals or potentially toxic elements (PTEs) and are often very acidic due to the presence of pyrites (FeS_2). Such areas may require significant remediation (see below) if they are to support forest, though trees may be amongst the most suitable vegetation types as they are generally relatively tolerant of elevated metal concentrations. Furthermore, forests and woodland can act to phytostabilize these areas, significantly reducing both wind and water transport and redistribution of pollutants. Phytoremediation, the abstraction or destruction of pollutants, may also be a realistic goal in some cases, because tree metal uptake and rhizosphere activity can both help to decontaminate some sites. For example, some poplars and willows enjoy a reputation for metal uptake, and in intensive silvicultural systems such as short rotation coppice, site pollutant remediation may be possible in the long term. Nevertheless, decontamination will only occur within the depth of the root zone.

An important principle is to plan a reclamation solution which is genuinely sustainable (**Figure 2**). From an environmental viewpoint, this is one that does not require repeated inputs of fertilizer, or continuing remedial attention to prevent water pollution. After trees are planted, it is difficult and cost-ineffective to right wrongs, and these should be scoped, predicted, and dealt with during the reclamation phase when earth-moving equipment is on site. From an economic point of view, the forest, if successful, should fully meet the aims set for it, and preferably generate income to support the silvicultural management inevitably required. Finally, the forest should meet societal aspirations and needs, whether for timber production, wildlife habitat, landscape stabilization or improvement, sport and recreation, or some or all of these. Forestry schemes that fail in some of these are likely to falter before they reach maturity. The management needs of the forest must be built into the plans for site reclamation, even though the responsibility for these may fall to agencies other than those responsible for the actual engineered reclamation solution.

Although satisfying the demands briefly described above may be a complex task, many examples worldwide indicate that successful woodland and forest reclamation can take place, testifying to the ability to avoid the weakest links in the reclamation chain.

Because mining technologies vary considerably according to geological circumstance and economic ability, there is a large range in the type of site and substrate presented for the silviculturalist to consider establishing forest on. It is therefore difficult to generalize effectively with broad reclamation guidance so that risk of failure is reduced adequately. It is essential that scientific (and other) literature relating to a particular mineral extraction and physiographic region is used effectively to build understanding of the local problems to be overcome. Nevertheless, there are some issues common to most mine sites which should be addressed, and these are discussed in broad terms below.

Landform and Drainage

The final landform of the mined site is usually partly determined by the nature of the geological obstacles to be overcome, and the original topography. Nevertheless, there are usually opportunities to input design into the final landform, and silvicultural needs should be included. For all sites, slope plays a part in affecting soil water drainage, and may be used to advantage in slowly permeable soil materials to reduce the likelihood of waterlogging. Slope angle, length, and form are also important in the control of soil erosion, and this should be dealt with by suitable engineering input. For relatively large sites where mechanical timber harvesting is in prospect, landform should be planned to facilitate this, and drainage located with due regard for the need for vehicular access. Roads should be designed at the same time as surface drainage, again by an appropriate engineering authority.

Surface water features are often sought on reclaimed sites. From an engineering viewpoint, these may serve as settling facilities to remove sediment before discharge of site waters into the main land drains and surface water system off-site. Suitably vegetated, e.g., with willows (*Salix* spp.) or reeds (*Phagmites* spp.), they may also help to remove water contaminants such as sulfates from the oxidation of pyrites. Water features can be attractive components of a reclaimed forest site, and will usually enrich its biodiversity and recreation potential.

Soil

Soil Selection

If soil materials are inadequate for forest establishment because of loss or degradation, there are two main options: (1) importation of substitute soil, or (2) soil manufacture using geological and/or waste materials. Option 1 is likely to be comparatively expensive if materials require purchasing, and there remains a need for strict quality control to prevent accidental importation of unsuitable (e.g., toxic) materials. For forestry schemes around the world, option 2 has been a mainstay in the absence of soil provision, and through considerable experience there is now strong guidance on this aspect of reclamation. There are usually good opportunities to select quarry wastes or reject materials, and possibilities to mix and blend to produce a desirable particle size range of soil-forming material. Reclamation of some mineral sites, e.g., after opencast coaling, will allow a wide choice of material due to the range of overburden materials, and it is important to characterize these fully with chemical and physical laboratory tests in order to select the most suitable for use. Here, the silviculturalist has a vital part to play by stipulating the kind of soil-forming material that will support the proposed forest. Sometimes, geological prospecting cores can be used to establish the range of possibilities before mineral extraction begins, but usually soil-forming materials will be identified during mineral extraction. It is important to have prepared guidance for machine operators so that they can select and store appropriate materials.

Some mineral substrates are intrinsically toxic and will not support satisfactory tree survival and growth without considerable treatment, for example some metalliferous mine tailings. If possible, such materials should be rejected as potential soil-forming materials in favor of less hostile materials rather than attempt to treat them. If there is little alternative but to attempt to establish vegetation, opportunities should be taken to cover these materials with whatever benign materials are available, even if these will not provide the full rooting depth of the trees and other vegetation types chosen. Of course, the underlying materials should be treated to minimize phytotoxicity before covering them, usually by controlling pH with lime or organic materials (see below).

Soil Placement

If original soil materials exist or can be saved before mineral extraction, reclamation can proceed routinely once final landform has been engineered. In hard rock quarries where a large void is created with steep sides, there will be limited opportunities for tree planting except in the bottom of the quarry. In soft rock quarries or opencast quarries where the product to overburden ratio is small, restoration to final landform involves the manipulation of overburden materials. Soils are then simply spread over them, provided slopes have been suitably engineered to allow this to take place and erosion risk has been assessed.

Soil (and soil-forming material) placement is at the center of good reclamation practice. Tree performance is severely hindered by soil compaction, which is often caused during reclamation by careless or misguided placement, or subsequent trafficking over newly laid soil. Compaction prevents deep rooting and therefore restricts the tree's ability to abstract moisture and nutrients. It can also cause surface waterlogging and ultimately lead to premature death or windthrow. Prevention is more certain than cure, and methods that spread soil without trafficking such as loose tipping are infinitely preferable to methods using earthscrapers or dozer tractors. The final configuration of the ground surface should be influenced by the climatic limitations of the site, and whether moisture retention against drought, or water shedding against waterlogging is the most important issue.

Soil Amendment

The principal difference between soil and soil-forming materials is the presence of soil organic matter in the former. This is the substrate which allows biological soil processes which in turn support and sustain plant life. In the absence of organic matter, soil-forming materials usually struggle to provide adequate nutrients to planted trees, especially nitrogen but also usually phosphorus. Soil materials put in storage often suffer from a loss of organic matter and a reduction in biological activity, but they generally recover if spread sensitively. In contrast, soil-forming materials may take decades or centuries to acquire organic matter levels comparable to those of normal soil. Research around the world has shown conclusively that it is extremely beneficial to amend soil-forming materials with organic matter at the time they are placed on the reclaimed land

Table 1 Examples of organic rich materials used as amendments in land reclamation to woodland

Raw sewage sludge
Digested sewage sludge
Thermally dried sewage sludge
Farmyard manure
Sugar mill waste
Paper mill sludge
Fish mort compost
Spent mushroom compost
Green (yard) waste compost
Municipal solid waste (MSW) compost
Wood residue

surface and awaits vegetation establishment. Materials such as sewage sludges or composted wastes are often used for this purpose, and **Table 1** gives more examples. Organic amendment can significantly improve the physical, hydrological, and nutritional qualities of the soil materials to be used. It may also reduce effects of acidity and metal toxicity, for example produced by the oxidation of pyrites. Soil placement methodologies using loose tipping can easily be developed to include the placement and incorporation of organic amendments, though for other technologies it may be necessary to consider premixing before the amended soil-forming material is finally placed on site.

The size of organic material addition will depend on its chemistry, physical, and hydrological behavior, the evaluation of the amount required to produce a sustained supply of nutrients to the growing plantation, and the degree of risk posed to other receptors such as water bodies or humans who may visit the reclaimed site. It has been proposed that as a general rule, a reclaimed site requires between 1000 to 1500 kg N ha^{-1}, and this can usually be supplied by a manageable amount of organic material. It is desirable to achieve the addition of an amount that will supply tree nutrient needs until nutrient cycling via leaf fall and litter mineralization can provide the major source. A balance may have to be struck between this aim and managing the risk of water pollution from leaching and runoff. In some cases, it may be necessary to consider mixing more than one material, e.g., sewage sludge and papermill sludge, in order to achieve a more controlled nutrient supply.

Cultivation

It is still commonplace to require remedial cultivation in order to decompact soil (or soil-forming) materials prior to planting. This can be avoided completely if soils are loose tipped, but this may not be possible. Nevertheless, decompaction remains a vital operation – the comparative failure or poor performance of many tree planting schemes on land reclaimed after mineral extraction is due to lack of effort in achieving this. Techniques for decompaction will vary depending on available technology, ground conditions, and climate. In temperate countries, 'ripping' is commonly deployed, using a set of tines pulled by a crawler tractor. Fitted with 'wings,' these can be effective in loosening the ground, and ripping to depths of 1.5 m has been achieved in Australia, though depths of about 0.75 m are more common. Ripping is comparatively inexpensive, but it is prone to abuse by poor operator control, and loosened soil can recompact quite quickly. It must take place when the soil is dryer than the liquid limit to be effective in creating fissures and porosity. Ripping has been carried out both parallel and perpendicular to the contour.

Ripping is most suitable when a full soil sequence has been replaced on site because the operation generally keeps the soil horizons unmixed. It is not effective for mixing and incorporating organic amendments. Here, soil loosening with an excavator bucket also allows the incorporation process to take place with the same machinery, and 'complete cultivation' has proved very successful, if a little expensive.

It is obvious that, once decompacted, the ground so treated should not be trafficked by machinery if possible. Ripping can cause large stones to emerge at the soil surface, but stone picking and removal should only take place if such material will form a genuine impediment to tree planting.

Silvicultural Issues

Tree Stock and Planting

It is difficult to give useful generalizations because decisions about tree stock size, species, and density of planting will depend to a large extent on local environmental limitations and the particular objectives for the forest when mature. Experience in the UK has shown that it is important to be flexible in approach. There is a widespread belief that 'native' or 'indigenous' species are the most suitable for newly created sites such as those coming out of mineral reclamation, but this is challenged by considerable research. It seems sensible to choose species from those known to perform well on such substrates (including nonnatives), and to consider removing the least desirable species as thinnings when the forest matures, or to replant with more desirable species in a following rotation once the site has stabilized and nutrient cycling has commenced. Certainly, it is useful insurance to plant several

species in group mixtures, so that some failures will not cause instability in the plantation as a whole. So-called pioneer species, such as willows (*Salix* spp.), poplars (*Populus* spp.), and alders (*Alnus* spp.) in the UK, tend to do well in the early stages of forest growth, and it is wise to use a significant proportion of these unless the site has been restored with original soil resources. These pioneers can tolerate the relative infertility that is usually associated with reclamation using soil-forming materials, and some are also able to withstand elevated concentrations of potentially toxic elements such as heavy metals.

Establishing forest blocks on post-mining land by application of tree seed is increasing in popularity. Seemingly ecologically more acceptable, especially if local seed sources are used, this technique has a place if carried out with due regard to seed dormancy (and seed is duly treated), and animal predation. The degree of silvicultural input is probably larger than with conventional planting, and the risk of failure is greater, but the results may look more naturalistic. Nevertheless, attention must still be given to the preparation of a suitable thickness of soil or soil-forming material during the engineering phase of reclamation.

Mycorrhizae and *Frankia* Inoculation

Initially, mineral sites restored using soil-forming materials can be almost microbiologically sterile unless organic amendments have been added. There has been considerable interest in the potential for purposefully introducing mycorrhizal fungi with tree stock in order to encourage survival and early performance on mined land. Several outlets now exist for the supply of material supposedly suitable for this purpose, but tree response is by no means assured, and local advice should be taken before embarking on a program of inoculation as a matter of course. In contrast, there is good evidence that when planting actinorhizal species such as *Acacia* spp., *Casuarina* spp., *Alnus* spp., *Elaeagnus* spp. or *Shepherdia* spp., only plants with Mycorrhizae and *Frankia* inoculation should be used.

Ground Vegetation

Although the importance of weed control is obvious, it is also the case that reclaimed post-mining sites often benefit from the establishment of a ground vegetation cover at the same time that trees are planted. For sites restored using soil-forming materials this vegetation will act immediately to facilitate the processes of soil formation which will benefit the site and the trees planted on it. While the trees are small, it will also 'green up' the site, improving its visual appearance and demonstrating commitment to the reclamation process. For sites restored using original topsoil, or amended with organic wastes, the correct choice of vegetation will permit effective control using selective herbicides – the alternative is to see a wide spectrum of weeds establish themselves that can be very difficult or expensive to control. For example, nonvigorous grass species are often chosen on reclamation sites in the UK, in order to hinder broadleaved weed germination while being susceptible to graminocide weedkillers. There has been considerable interest in the use of leguminous or actinorhizal plants as a significant component of a low ground cover, in order to provide or enrich the nitrogen capital of the site, and thus of the trees established on it. Choice will depend upon circumstance. However, it is important to ensure that such types of vegetation are truly infected with the requisite microorganism (usually confirmed visually by the presence of nodules on the plant roots).

Forestry objectives to increase biodiversity may demand that a ground flora of native plants be established, or vegetation similar to that which would be found under mature, seminatural woodland on neighboring undisturbed land. Nevertheless, these objectives should not obstruct the need to protect the tree seedlings from weed competition. In addition, the risk of fire should always be considered in the choice of ground vegetation cover.

Tree Protection

Tree protection is an important issue in all forest establishment, but imperative for forest planted on post-mining land. Unless reclamation operations have been exemplary, the site will still pose considerable problems for the newly planted tree, and silvicultural care must be first class. Weed control is usually vital but practice will depend on available technology and the size of the problem. Droughty sites, for example where stone content is high and organic matter content is low, should be given particular attention. So, too, should sites where organic amendment has taken place. Such materials usually promote rapid and large weed growth which can outcompete the planted trees for moisture, space, and light. Weed control may be necessary for several years on sites where tree growth is comparatively slow. Protection from animal browsing can also be important on reclaimed sites, and again, the form of protection will depend on the particular threat or threats. It may include fencing or individual tree protection; animal culling or control may also be necessary. Illegal grazing can be a significant problem in some parts of the world, requiring more severe measures if it is to be kept to tolerable levels.

Fertilizer Application

Infertility will require attention, and is commonplace when soil materials are not used for reclamation. Nevertheless, if organic amendments are used to improve both the physical and nutritional behavior of the soil-forming material, the use of mineral fertilizers may be unnecessary. And because funding for reclamation is usually more certain than that for maintenance, this approach is preferable to a reliance on one (or more) fertilizer applications during tree establishment. Fertilizers should be used with care, especially if soil materials contain little organic matter, because risk of leaching can be high. Fertilizer prescription should be based on soil or foliar analysis, or both. Local experience will guide interpretation, and, if limited, nursery or field experimentation may be warranted.

Site Monitoring and Maintenance

A forest established on sites reclaimed after mineral extraction is usually more susceptible to destructive agents such as drought, insect attack, or infertility than that on undisturbed land. It is therefore vital that attention be paid to the performance of the forest as it develops, especially in its early years. Regular site visits are necessary to check protective measures and the efficacy of operations such as weed control. Tree failure should be investigated and remedies put in place in case of significant loss. In addition, monitoring of water quality may be necessary for those sites where there is a risk of degradation of water quality, and consequent pollution to surface or groundwaters supplied from the site.

Conclusions

The principles of sustainability demand that land used for mineral extraction is brought back to beneficial use, and legislation around the world has been progressively tightened to ensure that this occurs. The largest responsibility for reclamation usually falls on the mineral operator. From an ecological viewpoint, a forestry after-use is often a serious candidate following mineral reclamation, though economic and social issues must also be taken into account. There is sufficient known about the science behind land reclamation to forest to suggest that high standards of reclamation practice are realistically attainable, and **Figure 3** shows examples of some successful schemes. Reclamation methodology is not overdemanding intellectually or economically. However, it is important for silvicultural issues to be put forward at the beginning of any

Figure 3 Examples of successful reclamation practice. (a) Bauxite mine in Australia during mineral extraction and about 15 years after reclamation (photographs by P. Garside). (b) China clay waste tip in Cornwall, UK before and 10 years after woodland establishment (photographs by A. Moffat). (c) Afan Argoed Country Park, Wales, UK during coal extraction and after reclamation (Forestry Commission). (d) Sand and gravel workings in southern UK before and after reclamation to woodland and wildlife habitat (photographs by A. Moffat).

reclamation project, understood, and then adhered to. There are many stages in the reclamation process, and failure at any of them will compromise forest performance. Effective management is therefore essential.

See also: **Afforestation**: Species Choice. **Landscape and Planning**: Forest Amenity Planning Approaches. **Site-Specific Silviculture**: Silviculture in Polluted Areas. **Social and Collaborative Forestry**: Social and Community Forestry. **Soil Development and Properties**: Nutrient Cycling. **Temperate Ecosystems**: Alders, Birches and Willows. **Tree Physiology**: A Whole Tree Perspective.

Further Reading

Ashby WC and Vogel WG (1993) *Tree Planting on Minelands in the Midwest: A Handbook*. Carbondale, IL: Coal Research Center, Southern Illinois University.

Barnhisel RI, Darmody RG, and Daniels WL (2000) *Reclamation of Drastically Disturbed Lands*. Madison, WI: American Society of Agronomy.

Bending NAD, McRae SG, and Moffat AJ (1999) *Soil-Forming Materials: Their Use in Land Reclamation*. London: Stationery Office.

Bradshaw AD (1983) The reconstruction of ecosystems. *Journal of Applied Ecology* 20: 1–17.

Bradshaw AD and Chadwick MJ (1980) *The Restoration of Land: The Ecology and Reclamation of Derelict and Degraded Land*. Oxford: Blackwell Scientific Publications.

Cooke JA and Johnson MS (2002) Ecological restoration of land with particular reference to the mining of metals and industrial minerals: a review of theory and practice. *Environmental Reviews* 10: 41–71.

Gardner J (2001) Rehabilitating mines to meet land use objectives: bauxite mining in the jarrah forest of Western Australia. *Unasylva 207* 52: 3–8.

Griffith JJ and Toy TJ (2001) Evolution in revegetation of iron-ore mines in Minas Gerais State, Brazil. *Unasylva 207* 52: 9–15.

Hüttl RF, Heinkele T, and Wisniewski J (eds) (1996) *Minesite Recultivation, International Symposium*, 6–8 June 1994, Cottbus, Germany. Dordrecht, The Netherlands: Kluwer Academic Publishers.

Kendle AD (1997) Natural versus artificial methods of woodland establishment. In: Moffat AJ (ed.) *Recycling Land for Forestry*, pp. 26–35. Edinburgh: Forestry Commission.

Malajczuk N, Reddell P, and Brundrett M (1994) Role of ectomycorrhizal fungi in minesite reclamation. In: Pfleger FL and Linderman RG (eds) *Mycorrhizae and Plant Health*, pp. 83–100. St. Paul, MN: American Phytopathological Society Press.

Sarrailh JM and Ayrault N (2001) Rehabilitation of nickel mining sites in New Caledonia. *Unasylva 207* 52: 16–20.

Sopper WE (1993) *Municipal Sludge Use in Land Reclamation*. Boca Raton, FL: Lewis Publishers.

Torbert JL and Burger JA (2000) Forest land reclamation. In: Barnhisel RI, Darmody RG, and Daniels WL (eds) *Reclamation of Drastically Disturbed Lands*, pp. 371–398. Madison, WI: American Society of Agronomy.

Silviculture in Mountain Forests

W Schönenberger and P Brang, Swiss Federal Research Institute WSL, Birmensdorf, Switzerland

Mountain Forests are of Global Importance

What is a mountain forest? Definitions are, to a certain extent, arbitrary. Defining criteria usually include altitude, slope, and local elevation range (**Table 1**). Thus, steep mountain forests can also occur in the lowlands. Mountain regions cover 24% of the earth's land surface and contain 28% of the world's closed forests. Fifty-five percent of these mountain forests occur below altitudes of 1000 m above sea level. Mountain forests are found in areas with tropical, subtropical, temperate, and boreal climates. While only one in 10 people live in mountain regions, what happens in these regions affects many more people living in the lowlands. For example, deforestation in mountain forests may have an impact on climates and contribute to flooding in lower regions. Mountain forests are therefore globally important.

Rather than adopting a definition based on arbitrarily chosen ranges of altitude and slope, we take a silvicultural perspective in this article. Our focus is on those forests that require specific silvicultural treatments due to particular characteristics, or because they provide forest products and services associated with high altitudes and/or steep slopes. We therefore exclude, e.g., forests on flat highlands that are primarily used for timber production. We also exclude mountain forests in nature reserves since these are not silviculturally treated.

We first describe the characteristics of mountain forests, and then outline the silvicultural systems used in them. Since our areas of expertise focus on temperate mountain forests of the northern hemisphere, this article makes most reference to this forest type.

Mountain Forests are Different from Lowland Forests

Mountain forests of the montane and subalpine zones differ from lowland forests with regard to physical

Table 1 Areas (km^2) of mountain forest types in different mountain classes

Forest type according to altitude, slope, and elevation range	≥ 4500 m	3500–4500 m	2500–3500 m	1500–2500 m and slope ≥ 2°	1000–1500 m and slope ≥ 5° or local elevation range > 300 m	300–1000 m and local elevation range > 300 m	Total	%
Tropical (and subtropical) moist forests	19 359	83 597	139 607	399 656	482 061	1 197 610	2 321 890	24.5
Tropical (and subtropical) dry forests	183	15 054	35 293	50 565	107 267	343 390	551 752	5.8
Temperate and boreal evergreen conifer forests	2008	22 954	151 809	547 984	788 684	1 377 105	2 890 544	30.5
Temperate and boreal deciduous conifer forests			1241	76 209	313 908	985 600	1 376 958	14.5
Temperate and boreal deciduous broadleaf and mixed forests	1713	19 832	122 858	476 865	441 055	1 275 723	2 338 046	24.7
Total	23 263	141 437	450 808	1 551 279	2 132 975	5 179 428	9 479 190	100
%	0.2	1.5	4.8	16.4	22.5	54.6	100	

Reproduced with permission from Kapos V, Rhind J, Edwards M, et al. (2000) In: Price MN and Butt N (eds) *Forests in Sustainable Mountain Development. A State of Knowledge Report for 2000.* IUFRO Research Series 5. Oxford, UK: CABI Publishing http://www.wcmc.org.uk/habitats/mountains/statistics/htm.

conditions, species composition, stand structure, disturbance regimes, and the products and services they provide. Forest management must take into account the characteristics of mountain forests and the fact that the range of silvicultural options becomes smaller with increasing altitude or steepness.

Physical Environment of Mountain Forests

Many mountain forests at lower elevations are among the most productive in the world. However, the physical conditions of mountains change and usually deteriorate with increasing altitude. Mountains are exposed to excessive solar radiation. At 1800 m above sea level solar radiation is doubled compared to sea level. In contrast to lower altitudes, soil and vegetation absorb most heat from direct insolation, not from warm air currents. Wind speeds increase, and between 500 and 2500 m above sea level precipitations increase by about 100 mm per 100 m. Moreover, soil and air temperatures decrease, in the case of air temperature by about 0.55°C per 100 m in the free atmosphere. Precipitations fall partly as snow, and the duration of the snow cover increases by about 10 days per 100 m. Correspondingly, the growing seasons are shorter (about 1 week per 100 m), especially for young trees covered by snow. Tree growth is slow, seed production rare, and seedling establishment threatened by browsing ungulates, pathogenic fungi, snow movement, and climatic injuries. A unique feature of mountains is the Foehn, a frequent strong, warm, dry, falling wind, which in some regions can raise the temperature considerably above the usual values, but also cause severe windthrows.

On steep terrain in higher altitudes pronounced variations in slope and aspect give rise to steep gradients in site factors and a high variability in mesoclimate and small-scale microhabitat patterns. Here surface erosion and rockfalls may have considerable impact on the forest and vice versa.

The harsher climate at higher altitudes affects tree growth and forest dynamics. Snow cover and snow movements, ranging from creeping and gliding to avalanches, damage trees mechanically, and can uproot and kill seedlings. The growth and regeneration dynamics of trees are slowed down, reducing productivity and tree size. Regeneration is often scarce since seed years are infrequent; the harsh climate impedes the reestablishment of trees after logging or natural disturbances, and successful establishment is confined to favorable microsites. Moreover, established seedlings at high altitudes grow slowly and may therefore be potentially affected by competing vegetation, pathogenic fungi, and browsing ungulates for several years or decades.

Timberline

With increasing altitude the trees become gradually smaller. Finally, above the upper or alpine timberline (treeline), regeneration and growth of trees are no longer possible. The timberline can vary from sea level in polar up to about 4500 m in tropical regions. The current location of the timberline can have climatic, orographic, edaphic, or anthropogenic causes. In many parts of the world it has been considerably lowered by human activities, mainly by livestock grazing over the centuries. A variety of factors may locally be responsible for the timberline: low air and soil temperatures, negative CO_2 balance, frost damage, winter desiccation, wind abrasion, short growing season due to long-lasting snow cover, pathogenic fungi, or mechanical damage by moving snow. The transition between the forest and alpine meadows is often not a line but a zigzag ecotone. Trees growing in the timberline ecotone are often restricted to the most favorable microsites and are forced to adjust their growth forms to the respective conditions (e.g., tree islands, flag shape, carpets). Near the timberline many tree species almost exclusively regenerate by layering. In some arid regions of the world, mountain forests not only have an upper, but also a lower timberline, which grades into grasslands.

Species Composition of Mountain Forests

The number of tree species that are able to cope with the increasingly harsh environment at higher altitudes decreases from the montane to the subalpine zone. The lower elevations of the wet tropics are often covered with very complex montane rainforests, whereas the upper parts carry cloud forests, which are extremely rich in endemic species. On the medium and high mountains of the temperate zone and on the high mountains of the tropics needle-bearing genera such as *Abies*, *Cedrus*, *Juniperus*, *Larix*, *Picea*, *Pinus*, *Tsuga*, and *Dacrycarpus* prevail, often accompanied by *Betula* and *Alnus*. In the southern hemisphere the genera *Nothofagus*, *Libocedrus*, *Podocarpus*, *Dacrydium*, and *Eucalyptus* are prominent. Important timberline species in the tropics are *Senecio*, *Polylepis*, and many others. In the subalpine zone, the resulting stands are typically rather poor in species, sometimes even almost monospecific.

Structure of Mountain Forests

The northern coniferous mountain forests at lower and medium altitudes usually have a rather homogeneous stand structure, similar to many lowland forests. Towards the subalpine zone near the timberline, the horizontal stand structure is increasingly open, with single trees or tree clusters alternating with gaps of different sizes (**Figure 1**). The open texture is often accentuated by human activities, such as livestock pasturing or tree cuttings. The upper parts of these forests grade into tree islands and then into the alpine environment above the timberline. Avalanche tracks or screes often interrupt the forest canopy. Open stands have extensive internal margins and green crowns reaching close to the ground. Such forests are referred to as 'mountain selection forests' or 'group selection forests.' However, not all subalpine forests are open. *Nothofagus* forests in the southern hemisphere can form completely closed canopies near the timberline.

Disturbance Regimes in Mountain Forests

Mountain forests are subject to most of the well-known natural disturbance agents, such as fires, wind storms, droughts, insect and pathogen outbreaks (**Figure 2**). Human disturbance occurs as a result of road construction, timber harvesting, fire, or livestock grazing. Some disturbance agents are specific features of high-altitude mountain environments: for example, snow gliding can cause stem deformations, avalanches are capable of destroying whole stands, while rock and ice fall often injure stems or break trees.

The establishment and growth of seedlings and saplings may be hampered by livestock or browsing wild ungulates, by pathogenic fungi developing in the snow pack, or by frost injuries and winter desiccation. These agents may reduce growth or sometimes even kill regeneration established over decades. While mountain forests are not generally less resistant to most disturbance agents than lowland forests, their recovery after disturbance (resilience) becomes increasingly slow the closer the timberline is. This special feature of mountain forests must be considered in any silvicultural operations.

The Value of Mountain Forests

People use forest products and services in a variety of ways: for protection, for cultural and leisure activities, and as sources of timber and food. Some of these are specific to mountain forests.

The protection of the human environment against natural hazards is nowadays often regarded as the most important economic value of forests in mountain regions with high population densities. Most such hazards primarily pose risks on steep slopes, and some occur only at high altitudes. Steep slopes are prone to all sorts of mass movements, such as soil erosion, debris flows, mud- and landslides, rockfall, torrents, and snow avalanches (**Figure 3**). Many mountain forests provide the people or objects of value beneath them with direct protection. The

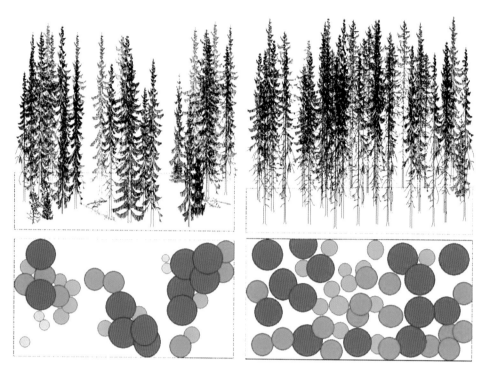

Figure 1   Cluster structure in a natural spruce mountain forest (left) in contrast to the typical uniform and homogeneous structure of a forest originating from afforestation (right). The clustered stand allows enough light and warmth to penetrate to the ground, thus creating good microsites for regeneration. The trees within a cluster maintain a common crown reaching almost to the ground. In the uniform stand there is not enough light for long crowns and forest regeneration. Reproduced with permission from Price MF and Butt (eds) (2000) *Forests in Sustainable Mountain Development. A State of Knowledge Report for 2000.* IUFRO Research Series 5. CABI Publishing.

Figure 2   Windthrow is an important disturbance agent in mountain forests. In protection forests natural hazards, such as rockfall, avalanches, and surface erosion, are matters of concern. Windthrow area near Disentis, Switzerland, caused by the winterstorm Vivian in 1990.

protective effect must be maintained continuously at the stand level, and not just at the landscape scale. If such a stand is destroyed, it must be replaced by expensive technical defense constructions. In direct protection forests the silvicultural options are therefore limited. Other protection forests provide only indirect protection, i.e., their effect is regional or at the scale of a whole landscape. Examples of indirect protection are forests that help to mitigate floods, or forested water catchments that ensure continuing

Figure 3 Mountain forests are capable of preventing natural hazards, in this case avalanche release, and of protecting people and assets. Andermatt, Swiss Alps.

Figure 4 Steep slopes hamper timber harvesting. Cable crane logging is a suitable technology developed for mountain forests. Photo courtesy of F Frutig.

supply of clean water and protect against soil erosion. In such cases, the exact location of the protection forest is not the important factor, but rather the proportion of the area stocked. In indirect protection forests more silvicultural options are available.

Timber production is not easy in mountain forests. Steep slopes and high altitude complicate timber harvesting operations (**Figure 4**). Access to the forests is usually difficult, so that logging is expensive and may be impossible in winter. Road construction is often costly if the roads are not to lead to more landslides. The potential for rationalization is limited in mountain forests. Most harvesting and planting technologies have been developed for lowland forests and cannot be used on steep terrain. But cable crane logging is one technological development that is suitable for harvesting in mountain forests. Another factor is that slow tree growth at high altitudes also means low forest productivity. This makes investing in a permanent infrastructure in mountain forests unattractive. It will only pay off if large enough quantities of timber are harvested; this may be excessive and unsustainable.

In less developed regions mountain people still depend directly on their local forests to satisfy many needs. However, timber production for fuel and construction wood has lost much of its former importance in industrialized regions during recent decades because cheaper fuel and imported timber mean it is no longer economically competitive.

With regard to nontimber products and uses mountain forests perform important functions as wildlife habitats, hunting areas, and livestock pastures. Forest products include fodder from forest trees, forest litter, fruits, mushrooms, fibers, resins, gums, medicinal plants, and agricultural crops in agroforests. These products are of variable importance over the world. In addition, the social, ecological, and amenity functions of forests are becoming increasingly valuable. For example, forests are essential for preserving biodiversity, for nature and soil conservation, for storing CO_2, as sources of fresh water, as recreation areas, and as areas of scenic beauty with spiritual or sacred values. Mountain regions play a special role in providing areas where these services can be performed because many mountain forests are still relatively uninfluenced by human activities.

While all mountain forests are multifunctional and provide several products and services, one function often dominates and guides silvicultural decision-making in a particular case. In some stands, silvicultural operations may not be required since either there is no specific local requirement for forest products or services, or a natural forest development is unlikely to impair the forest's ability to fulfill existing demands.

Silvicultural Systems for Mountain Forests

Historically, many mountain forests have been subject to severe degradation followed by erosion, which has caused loss of soil and site productivity. Large parts of the European Alps, for instance, were destroyed by excessive felling, burning, and grazing, before their restoration during the last 150 years. Most of the bushlands that cover the eroded mountains surrounding the Mediterranean today were once forest. Such silvicultural treatments – or maltreatments – have shaped many forests ('silvae' in Latin), but certainly not in the sense of a 'culture.' And the degradation continues today: silvicultural practices in mountain forests still deviate greatly, in some regions of the world, from recommended practice. Silviculture as a scientific discipline and wide-ranging practice only has a history of about 200 years. During this time several silvicultural systems, i.e., planned series of treatments for tending, harvesting, and reestablishing stands, have been developed for managing forests in a sustainable way.

Silvicultural systems vary in their ability to handle the management constraints in mountain forests. These constraints are related to the steep terrain, difficult forest access, harsh climate, slow tree growth, and natural hazards. Taking these constraints into account is part of a preventive silvicultural practice which strives to avoid costly restoration measures, regardless of whether they are biological (e.g., planting) or technical (e.g., erosion control).

Below we describe those silvicultural systems that are especially important and useful for managing mountain forests and make recommendations for how they should be applied. They include clearcutting, shelterwood, border cutting, selection, and coppice systems. Other systems that can be successfully practiced in mountain forests are agroforestry and variable retention systems (*see* **Silviculture: Silvicultural Systems**).

Clear-Cutting

Clear-cutting is a silvicultural system that removes an entire stand of trees from an area of 1 ha or more, and greater than two tree heights in width, in a single harvesting operation (**Figure 5**). It can be highly profitable. However, its application in mountain forests often involves unacceptable risks, or impairs landscape values.

Clear-cutting mountain forests can initiate erosion processes which may result in a complete loss of the soil. On a regional scale, higher altitudes in mountain areas usually receive higher precipitation. Steep slopes are prone to surface erosion (gullying, rill erosion),

Figure 5 A clear-cut and subsequent planting in Austria. On steep slopes clearcutting may lead to serious erosion problems.

nutrient leaching, landslides, and debris flows. Clear-cutting often contributes to reductions in root strength and soil water-holding capacity, due to soil compaction and reduced transpiration. Moreover, the removal of the forest cover exposes the soil surface to heavy precipitation and large variations in temperature. If natural hazards are to be prevented, the size of clear-cut areas in protection forests must be kept small. Thus, clear-cutting is often not an option.

Unstocked, even slopes steeper than about 30° at high altitudes are prone to avalanche release. If a slope exceeds 45°, snow avalanches can start in canopy gaps exceeding 30 m perpendicular to the contour line. Any rough surface structure, such as a rock, trunk, or tree, reduces the risk of snow movement by creating heterogeneity in the snow layer and 'nailing' the snow to the ground. While forests can rarely stop flowing snow avalanches, they are highly effective in preventing avalanche release. Surface roughness is also important for impeding rockfalls. However, in this case, forests serve not to prevent rockfall starting, but rather stop falling rocks.

If clear-cutting is not properly applied as a silvicultural system and is the first step to permanent deforestation, it usually has a negative impact on the fresh water supply. More than half of the world's population relies on clean water from mountains. While the demand is increasing, the supply is endangered. Mountains are the sources of most rivers, and mountain forests help to ensure that the water supply is seasonally balanced and that the water is of high quality. Clear-cutting large mountain forests without restoration cannot, therefore, be considered at all sustainable.

The impact of clear-cutting will obviously depend on the size of the clear-cut area. Large clear cuts in environments with pronounced climatic extremes, where tree regeneration depends on the beneficial effects of adult trees, must be avoided. This means that clear-cutting is not appropriate on very dry, very cold, or very wet sites, as it can lead to failures in stand renewal, even with repeated plantings. A system of small patch cuts is similar to the selection system, whereas leaving seed-dispersing trees to facilitate natural regeneration (the seed tree system) is comparable to the shelterwood system.

Not all damage attributed to clear-cutting is caused by the unwanted side-effects of the silvicultural system itself. The damage may actually be the result of inadequate road construction, of inappropriate site preparation treatments such as burning, or of careless logging practices, which damage the advance regeneration. However, even careful clear-cutting should not be used in those mountain forests where protection from natural hazards is needed, where erosion is a matter of major concern, and where the sites do not restock easily.

Shelterwood System

The shelterwood system is a silvicultural system in which trees are removed in a series of cuts designed to achieve a new stand under the shelter of remaining trees (**Figure 6**). In contrast to clear-cutting, it avoids having time periods where there are no trees to give shelter and to protect the soil, and thus reduces the associated risks. This system, therefore, has potential in mountain forests. However, it involves more costly

Figure 6 A shelterwood area with larch (*Larix occidentalis*) retained to provide seeds and to shade the regeneration. British Columbia, Canada.

timber harvesting than the clear-cutting system, and careful logging is required to avoid damage to the remaining stand and to the regeneration, particularly on steep slopes. If the individual trees in a protection forest are vulnerable to wind damage, shelterwood cuts will destabilize the stand and are therefore not advisable. The final cut can only be carried out when the regeneration has grown up sufficiently to ensure the protective effect is maintained.

Border-Cutting System

The border-cutting system (or strip-cut system) may also be appropriate in mountain forests (**Figure 7**). It involves successive cuttings in narrow strips, which combine the advantages of concentrated harvesting operations (one cut in one area) with limited harvesting damage. It does not create an open-land climate that impedes natural regeneration. In avalanche protection forests, the borders need to be sufficiently narrow to prevent avalanche release and must not be parallel to the slope. The borders can be laid out in the direction of cable crane lines.

Selection System

Selection systems remove mature timber either as single scattered trees or small groups at short, repeated intervals. Selection systems can be applied in a highly variable manner. They can range from small-scale patch cuts, shelterwood cuts and border cuts, to the single-tree selection system where only single trees are harvested. Selection systems are based on a heterogeneous stand structure and are therefore most suitable for ensuring continuous cover on steep

slopes. A patchwork of tree groups of variable sizes and gaps is most efficient in structuring snow deposition, and can thus prevent, or at least reduce, avalanche release. Natural disturbance regimes can create this structural diversity, in particular in forests in extreme edaphic or climatic environments. However, on more productive sites, natural disturbances often lead to rather uniform stands, which then require conversion treatments.

Limited accessibility often makes the selection system too costly since the timber to be harvested is distributed over large areas, and very careful logging practices are required to avoid damage to the remaining stand. In some cases, cable cranes or even helicopters need to be used.

Group selection (or patch-cut) systems create openings narrower than twice the height of mature trees in the stand, and leave groups of up to about 20 trees in a cluster (**Figure 8**). They can be flexibly designed to fulfill potentially conflicting requirements in protection forests, namely high stand density in tree groups to ensure effective protection against avalanches and rockfall, and open canopy patches to allow sufficient regeneration and thus ensure continuous protection. Group selection, with special focus on the retention of small tree clusters and gaps, is referred to as 'mountain group selection.'

Selection systems also facilitate advance regeneration and thus ensure high resilience after disturbances. In subalpine forests, the gaps created with single-tree selection systems may be too small to ensure sufficient regeneration. Examples are the numerous dense, uniform Norway spruce stands in the European Alps, which are often the result of

Figure 7 An example of a border cutting in a Norway spruce–larch forest with narrow strips and replanting in Austria.

Figure 8 Tending in a regular thicket of Norway spruce to create clusters and gaps in Switzerland.

Figure 9 An example of a slit opening in a Norway spruce stand to stimulate forest regeneration in Switzerland.

Coppice System

Coppice systems lead to a high stem density and can therefore be recommended for rockfall protection forests if the areas cut are sufficiently small. This system is highly appropriate if there is need for fuel wood. Collecting fuel wood does not require heavy machinery and therefore is less of an erosion hazard than commercial timber harvesting.

Afforestation

The restoration of degraded mountain forests on pastures by means of afforestation is not a silvicultural system, but requires great silvicultural expertise. For afforestation at high altitudes, suitable species and provenances from similar environments need to be carefully selected. Damage due to grazing by wild or domestic animals needs to be limited to acceptable levels. In environments with extreme climates, planted seedlings may need further management interventions for decades, e.g., planting a forest of pioneer trees to reduce frost damage, watering during drought periods, or setting up temporary barriers to prevent snow gliding.

In contrast to the open structure of natural stands described above, many planted stands tend to become single-storyed, even-aged, uniform, mono-specific, and short-crowned. In protection forests, new plantings should be arranged in an irregular, grouped pattern over the terrain, corresponding to the distinct microsite variations found at this altitude. Favorable microsites, such as locally raised areas, are planted, while unfavorable ones, such as gullies or patches with well-established tall forbs, are left unplanted. This minimizes losses among planted

untended regular plantings or of natural regeneration after large-scale disturbance. They can be opened up with slit-shaped openings to stimulate natural regeneration (**Figure 9**). Leaving 'nurse logs' is a good long-term means of encouraging future regeneration on decaying wood.

trees and prevents the formation of uniform thickets. Planting should take place over a long time span to create uneven-aged structures of different sizes.

Conclusions

Mountain forests provide goods and services that are vital for people's well-being throughout the globe. They are, however, notoriously difficult to manage: their special topographic and climatic features mean that they are highly susceptible to degradation. To sustain mountain forests, careful and sometimes very sophisticated silvicultural approaches are required.

Careful silvicultural practices alone, however, will not ensure a sustainable future for the mountain forests of the world. A silvicultural system might be biologically perfect, but totally inappropriate if it fails to take into account the wider social context. Moreover, attempts must be made to anticipate the effects of changes in human demand, economic constraints, and ecological changes, such as global climate warming. Existing silvicultural systems must then be refined accordingly, or new innovative systems developed. Approaches such as the mountain group selection system, and their use on a large scale, are quite recent. Testing the real merits of these systems on an operational scale is a challenge that forest managers and scientists will have to face.

See also: **Harvesting**: Forest Operations in the Tropics, Reduced Impact Logging; Forest Operations under Mountainous Conditions. **Plantation Silviculture**: Multiple-use Silviculture in Temperate Plantation Forestry. **Silviculture**: Coppice Silviculture Practiced in Temperate Regions; Forest Rehabilitation; Silvicultural Systems. **Windbreaks and Shelterbelts**.

Further Reading

Brang P, Schönenberger W, Ott E, and Gardner B (2001) Forests as protection from natural hazards. In: Evans J (ed.) The Forests Handbook, vol. 2, pp. 53–81. Oxford: Blackwell Science.

Evans J (ed.) (2001) The Forests Handbook. Oxford: Blackwell Science.

Garfitt JE (1995) Natural Management of Woods – Continuous Cover Forestry. Taunton, UK: Research Studies Press.

Glück P and Weber M (eds) (1998) Mountain Forestry in Europe–Evaluation of Silvicultural and Political Means. Publication Series of the Institute for Forest Sector Policy and Economics. Vienna: Universität für Bodenkultur.

Hamilton LS, Gilmour DA, and Cassells DS (1997) Montane forests and forestry. In: Messerli B and Ives JD (eds) Mountains of the World. A Global Priority, pp. 281–311. New York: Parthenon.

Helms JA (ed.) (1998) The Dictionary of Forestry. Bethesda, MD: The Society of American Foresters, CABI Publishing.

Holtmeier FK (2003) Mountain Timberlines. Ecology, Patchiness, and Dynamics. Dordrecht: Kluwer Academic.

Matthews JD (1989) Silvicultural Systems. Oxford: Oxford Science Publications.

Messerli B and Ives JD (eds) (1997) Mountains of the World. A Global Priority, pp. 281–311. New York: Parthenon.

Ott E, Frehener M, Frey H-U, and Lüscher P (1997) Gebirgsnadelwälder. Haupt, 287 S. Bern, Switzerland: Verlag Paul Haupt.

Peterken GF (1996) Natural Woodland. Ecology and Conservation in Northern Temperate Regions. Cambridge: Cambridge University Press.

Price MF and Butt N (eds) (2000) Forests in Sustainable Mountain Development. A State of Knowledge Report for 2000. IUFRO Research Series 5. Oxford, UK: CABI Publishing.

Ecology and Silviculture of Tropical Wetland Forests

P Hogarth, University of York, York, UK

Introduction

Tropical wetland forests comprise a highly diverse group of habitats scattered throughout the humid or coastal tropical regions of Africa, Asia, the Americas, and Australia. They include inland riverine and swamp forests and coastal mangroves. Depending on definition, the total area of tropical wetland forest is probably in the range $160–180 \times 10^6$ ha worldwide. The tree species of inland forests are often of poor quality as timber, and are difficult to extract: forest management and silviculture are therefore often rudimentary. Nevertheless, some trees, and many secondary products, are of economic value. Mangroves, or tidal forests, in contrast are often of high value, and may be intensively and efficiently managed for timber, as well as providing a range of other goods and services.

The defining character of a tropical wetland forest is that the soil in which the trees stand is submerged or waterlogged, either permanently or intermittently. Intermittent flooding may be seasonal, for months at a stretch or for shorter periods, with the forest sometimes reverting to virtually dry land conditions between inundations. In the case of coastal mangrove forests, flooding is tidal and typically occurs twice daily for hours at a time, with the soil remaining waterlogged between high tides.

The topology and hydrology of wetland forests profoundly affect their ecology and relationship with adjoining ecosystems. Basin forests, with net inflow of water into a depression, are net accumulators of silt, nutrients, and suspended organic matter. Forests fringing rivers may trap sediment, hence may also be net accumulators, or, depending on flow patterns and other factors, they may be net exporters. Tidal forests are exposed in addition to fluctuating salinity as well as to fluctuating water levels, and have special adaptations to cope with salt as well as with water-logging.

Adaptations to the Wetland Environment

Waterlogged ecosystems present particular challenges to plants growing in them. The underground roots must acquire oxygen for respiration and eliminate carbon dioxide. In a normal soil, gas exchange presents few problems. The atmosphere comprises 20% O_2, and, since much of the soil volume consists of air space, rapid diffusion is possible. In contrast, diffusion of O_2 and CO_2 through water occurs at a fraction of the rate through air. Moreover, even at saturation the concentration of O_2 in water is low: in the richly organic waters of many wetland forests microbial action is likely to reduce it further, creating virtually anoxic conditions.

Wetland forest trees have therefore evolved adaptations to their waterlogged environment. The ratio of root-to-shoot biomass is often lower in wetland trees: relatively less of the tree structure is in the anoxic waterlogged soil, and underground roots are in general restricted to the upper, partially aerated layers of the soil. The relatively high stem density of some basin wetland forests, a response to poor soil aeration, may also result in a relatively increased stem surface area available for gas exchange. In many species, the roots themselves leave the main trunk well above ground (or water) level. Such aerial roots take many forms, and are often described as buttress or knee roots. They have numerous lenticels to allow gas exchange with the atmosphere, and spongy aerenchyma tissue to allow gas movement by diffusion within the root mass. The most striking forms of aerial or buttress root occur in mangrove trees, such as *Rhizophora* species, where the roots may separate from the trunk several meters above ground level (**Figure 1**). Freshwater wetland trees such as *Pterocarpus* (**Figure 2**), *Casuarina*, and *Myristica* produce similar aerial roots, and are sometimes known as freshwater mangrove.

Aerial roots supply adequate anchorage and support. The absorptive function of roots is carried out by the reduced underground components: as these lie

Figure 1 A mature mangrove (*Rhizophora*) with aerial roots (Merbok, Malaysia).

Figure 2 The bloodwood or freshwater mangrove, *Pterocarpus officinalis*, in Dominica. Photograph courtesy of Lance Leonhardt.

close to the soil surface they benefit from close proximity to the leaf litter layer in which inorganic nutrients are released by microbial decomposition.

Mangroves (*Avicennia* and *Sonneratia* species) and some freshwater wetland trees (*Dactylocladus* in

Southeast Asia, *Mitragina* in Africa) facultatively produce another specialized respiratory structure, the pneumatophore. Pneumatophores are vertical peg-like columns of aerenchyma that grow from horizontal underground roots and protrude from the soil surface. One tree may be served by many thousands. In *Avicennia*, these are typically 10–15 cm in height, but in *Sonneratia* may be more than 3 m, suggesting that their role is to maintain contact with the atmosphere even at high tide, rather than merely to avoid anoxic soil.

Tidally inundated mangroves are also exposed to high and fluctuating salinity: significantly raised salinity also occurs in some other wetland forests in coastal plains. Several methods of coping with high salinity have evolved. The proximity of horizontal roots to the surface enables them selectively to exploit less saline water in the surface layers of soil, avoiding the sea water itself and the deeper soil water, which may be of higher salinity. In some mangrove species, such as *Aegiceras* and *Avicennia*, up to 90% of salt is excluded at the root surface, by a poorly understood selective physical process.

Inevitably, some salt does accompany water uptake. *Avicennia* and other mangrove species (*Rhizophora*, *Sonneratia*) tolerate high internal salt levels by sequestration within vacuoles and exclusion from cell cytoplasm. Finally, salt may be either deposited in bark or in senescent leaves that are then shed (*Xylocarpus*, *Excoecaria*) or actively secreted from leaf salt glands (*Avicennia*, *Aegiceras*, *Sonneratia*).

Reproduction in a flooded environment presents particular problems. Mangroves typically show vivipary, and the release of large floating propagules. Those of *Rhizophora*, for example, may be 0.5 m long (**Figure 3**). Flotation provides a means of dispersal, with the size and robustness of the propagule conferring resistance to current and wave damage, and its

advanced stage and the lack of a quiescent stage and the need to germinate enhancing its prospects of successful settlement. Freshwater wetland trees show fewer obvious reproductive adaptations, but the Central American *Pterocarpus officinalis* has a buoyant fruit 5 cm in diameter which can be dispersed by water currents.

Meaningful comparisons between wetland and dry tropical forests are not easy, and there are exceptions to all generalizations, but in general wetland forests are slower-growing and lower in above-ground biomass, and show simpler physical structure and reduced understorey vegetation. Tree species diversity is generally lower than in dry forests, decreasing with increasing frequency or duration of inundation: wetland forests have a tendency towards domination by a small number of tree species. In mangroves, and some fresh or brackish water coastal plain forests, there may be virtually monospecific zones within a forest. Offsetting relatively low tree species diversity, canopy epiphytes may be abundant. Riverine wetland forests tend to have greater productivity than those with stagnant water. Within the mangroves, increasing salinity is associated with lower growth rates and biomass, and towards the northern limits of mangrove distribution the combination of adverse physical circumstances results in dwarf forests, where the maximum height attained by mature trees may be as little as 1 m.

Wetland Forest Communities

The fauna of wetland forests falls into two more or less distinct categories: the terrestrial or arboreal, and the aquatic. Animals associated with the trunk, leaves, and canopy of wetland forests are in general similar to those in dry forests and other adjacent habitats. They are usually highly mobile, and individuals may move freely between the wetland forest and its surroundings. Most ground-living vertebrates such as deer, rodents, and lizards retreat from seasonal or tidal wetland forests as the water rises, and reenter as it falls: flying animals such as many bird, bat, and insect species can exploit wetland forests even when the ground is submerged, and may even benefit from the scarcity of predators.

Few species of bird, mammal, or insect are restricted to wetland forests: in Australia, for instance, of more than 200 species of passerine bird recorded from mangroves, only 14 are virtually confined to this habitat. The relatively small number of mangrove-specific bird species may reflect the simplified physical structure of the forest, with little scope for niche specialization. Similarly, although many monkey species forage within Southeast Asian mangrove

Figure 3 Propagules of *Rhizophora*. Reprinted from Encyclopedia of Biodiversity, Vol. 3, P. Hogarth, Mangrove ecosystems, pp. 853–870, 2001, with permission from Elsevier.

forests, only the proboscis monkey (*Nasalis*) is found exclusively in mangroves and adjacent riverine forests. Among the invertebrates, many insect species occur in mangroves – any mangrove biologist can testify to the abundance of biting midges and mosquitoes – but only a single truly mangrove-specific species of ant has been reported, the Australian *Polyrachis sokolova*, which lives intertidally under the mud surface.

The aquatic components of wetland forest faunas are also largely the same as in adjoining habitats with few endemic species. In freshwater forests the dominant aquatic groups are mollusks (gastropod and bivalve mollusks) and fish. Mangrove faunas are dominated by marine fish and crustaceans. Among the fish, mudskippers are largely restricted to mangroves: the remaining species, often commuters, also occur in other habitats. The most abundant and diverse crustacea in Indo-Pacific mangroves are crabs, most notably fiddler crabs (*Uca*: family Ocypodidae) and leaf- or detritus-eating sesarmids (family Grapsidae). Fiddler crabs are deposit feeders, favoring sandy and muddy habitats which often coincide with mangroves. Sesarmids are more strongly associated with mangroves, at least in the Indo-Pacific region where some species have been recorded only from mangrove habitats: in the neotropics the association is less exclusive.

Freshwater forests are less well understood, but the general situation is likely to be similar to mangroves, with the majority of the forest fauna derived from adjacent terrestrial and aquatic habitats. The lack of a characteristic fauna does not, however, mean that the fauna is not important in the distinctive ecosystems of tropical wetland forests. In mangroves the role of sesarmid crabs, for example, is often crucial: by selectively predating seedlings, they influence the distribution of mangrove species, hence forest structure; by eating fallen leaves they facilitate energy flow through the ecosystem; by burying leaves they retain primary production locally; and by their labyrinthine burrows they aerate the soil and increase productivity of the trees. Fish that enter mangrove forests to forage at high tide represent a major channel of energy flow between mangroves and other habitats.

Similarly, in the freshwater forests of Amazonia, many species of fish seasonally occupy flooded forests. Amazonia has the most diverse freshwater fish fauna in the world: more than 1300 species have been described, and perhaps around 2500–3000 species exist, representing one of the most extreme cases of evolutionary radiation known. With the seasonal rise in river level, the adjacent forests are flooded for several months at a time, to a depth of up to 15 m. During this period many fish invade the forest. These range from predators such as piranhas (family Characidae) and small blood-sucking siluroid catfish to leaf-, fruit-, and seed-eating fish which have no clear ecological parallel elsewhere in the world. The characid *Colossoma macropomum*, for instance, has molar- and incisor-like teeth which have evolved to crush hard nuts. The gut of a single fish can contain up to 1 kg of seeds of the rubber tree *Seringa*, comprising a total of about 150 seeds. A single tree may carry only 100–200 seeds at a time. Many other fish species (including, despite their reputation, species of piranha) also eat seeds and fruit. Although it is hard to evaluate the importance of seed-eating fish, it is likely that, among other impacts, they contribute to the maintenance of tree diversity within the forest. They may also assist in seed dispersal.

Tropical wetland forests are therefore ecologically diverse, notwithstanding the common features of trees adapted to inundated habitats, and contain a fauna that comprises both aquatic and terrestrial components.

Silviculture and Management of Tropical Wetland Forests

Freshwater Wetland Forests

In the neotropics, wetland forests are often inaccessible for much of the year, and inhospitable because of the hosts of biting insects. Many of the tree species are of little commercial value, and the species richness that delights biologists means that, to foresters, the few economically valuable species tend to be sparsely distributed. Exploitation of neotropical wetland forests is generally minimal and management virtually nonexistent. Secondary forest products, such as fisheries, may be significant, but timber extraction is sporadic.

Pterocarpus forests   An example is the *Pterocarpus* forested wetlands of Central America and islands of the Caribbean (**Figure 2**). These are dominated by *P. officinalis* (Leguminosae), the bloodwood or dragon's blood tree. In coastal forests, for example in Puerto Rico, *Pterocarpus* forms monospecific stands, but it is more typical for it to comprise perhaps 70% of the basal area in a mixed forest which may contain scores, or even hundreds, of other tree species.

Pterocarpus is a species well adapted to the swamp environment. It grows to a height of 30 m, with buttress roots arising from up to 5 m above soil level. The subterranean roots are shallow, with nodules of symbiotic nitrogen-fixing bacteria, giving an advantage in a (presumably) nitrogen-depleted environment. A further, probably major, factor contributing to its dominance is the propensity to develop secondary sprouts (suckers) from the roots following damage or rotting of the primary trunk. This may enable reproduction in permanently flooded conditions, as the floating seeds of *Pterocarpus* cannot root in water deeper than 3–4 cm, but it is also highly advantageous in recovery following hurricane damage. Much of Central America and the Caribbean is subject to frequent hurricanes.

Unfortunately, given the relative abundance of the species, *Pterocarpus* wood is of poor quality, being weak, light (with a specific gravity of 0.3–0.6), and lacking resistance to termite and fungal attack. It is therefore of use chiefly for the manufacture of boxes and plywood, in the production of charcoal, and as fuelwood. More than 90% of the rural population of Central America depend on fuelwood for cooking. The blood-red resin that seeps out when the bark is damaged, and which gave the tree its common names, was formerly exported as an astringent and hemostatic, but is now of very limited pharmacological interest. Harvesting involves much waste, because *Pterocarpus* must be cut above the buttress roots: this further reduces its economic value.

Most attention is currently being given to enhancing the economic value of the swamp ecosystem so that *Pterocarpus* and other low-value species are replaced, where appropriate, by more valuable species. In Guyana and Surinam, for instance, swamp forests include the decay-resistant *Triplaris surinamensis*, the very hard *Eschweilera longipes* and *Ceiba pentandra*, and species of medicinal interest such as *Bonafousia tetratstachya*; other favored species in the region include *Symphonia globulifera*, *Calophyllum calaba*, *Carapa guianensis*, and *Virola surinamensis*.

In Guadeloupe, there are plans to cultivate *Calophyllum* and *Symphonia* at the expense of *Pterocarpus* where these species are already well established, to maintain monospecific *Pterocarpus* plantations where this species has virtual dominance, and to introduce, on an experimental basis, valuable nonnative species such as *Carapa* and *Virola*. Cultivation of economically desirable tree species will depend on successful harvesting and germination of seeds, and mastering effective planting techniques.

The Acai palm (*Euterpe*) One of the most successful manipulations of forest composition is of the multistemmed Acai palm *Euterpe oleracea* (**Figure 4**). This is widespread throughout parts of Latin America in *Pterocarpus* and other wetland forests, and is the source of several products of major economic importance. The fruits, of which a single

Figure 4 The palm *Euterpe oleracea*, near Belem, Brazil Photograph courtesy of Rolf Kyburz.

tree produces about 20 kg per year, are used to produce a refreshing drink (acai) which is the most important nonwood product of the Amazon river delta, amounting to more than $100\,000\,t\,year^{-1}$, valued at more than US$40 million.

The other major *Euterpe* product is palm heart, a popular gourmet food in North America and Europe. In one region of Amazonian Brazil, harvesting of palm hearts employs 30 000 people and generates US$300 million annually. As the palm heart or 'cabbage' is the terminal bud of the palm, its removal kills the stem, and traditionally, Acai palm trees were simply cut down to harvest hearts. The relative ease of replanting in the middle of the forest and rapid growth, made this a reasonably viable process. A recent and more sustainable approach is to harvest stems from an individual palm by rotation, so new stems continually appear and a single tree can be cropped for decades. Regular cropping in this way also increases fruit yield.

Euterpe depends on the organic matter supplied by trees of the surrounding forest, so its successful cultivation depends on a balance being maintained with other species. Manipulation of wetland forest ecosystems, rather than single-species cultivation, can undoubtedly enhance the economic value of the forest resource. The success of this strategy depends on an understanding of the interactions between species. Due regard must also be had to other goods and services supplied by wetland forests, such as fishing, hunting, and ecotourism.

Mangroves

In contrast to the situation with freshwater wetland forests, mangrove forests are often intensively and efficiently exploited, using relatively sophisticated management strategies and techniques. This is particularly true in Asia, where large numbers of people depend directly or indirectly on mangrove forests. In addition to the use of mangrove wood as timber, fuelwood, and in charcoal production, mangrove leaves are used in fodder and medicinally, and the forests are the basis of local and nearshore finfish and shrimp fisheries and a productivity base for aquaculture; the protective value of mangroves against typhoons and coastal erosion generally is increasingly recognized.

There are many reasons why the exploitation and management of mangrove forests is so different from that of freshwater swamp forests. Mangroves almost always occur on the coast, or in the estuaries of large rivers. They are thus intrinsically more accessible than inland swamp forests. The number of species of mangrove tree is low: only around 50 true mangrove species are recognized worldwide, and an individual forest may be dominated by only two or three species. These generally grow in more or less single-specific zones, rather than being intermingled, so efficient extraction of a preferred species is relatively straightforward. And, finally, several mangrove species provide valuable timber which is resistant to insect attack and fungal decay.

An important factor in the management of mangrove forests is the typical mode of mangrove reproduction: vivipary, with the release of large, robust propagules. These can be collected either from the tree or after release, and either used directly or reared in nurseries for subsequent replanting (**Figure 5**).

The potential for ecosystem modification, and the effective management of the mangrove forest resource, is therefore greater than for freshwater forests. In countries such as Thailand and Malaysia, recognition of the economic importance has led to the development of long-term strategies for the sustainable management of mangrove forests, which in some cases have been in place for many decades.

The Matang forest, Malaysia One of the best examples of intense exploitation of a mangrove forest is that of the Matang forest of western peninsular Malaysia. The present sustainable management regime, accommodating timber extraction and other uses, has been running in more or less its present form for around a century.

The managed area of the Matang comprises an estuarine complex of streams, creeks, and inlets, amounting to more than 40 000 hectares. Around 2000 hectares are left untouched as virgin jungle reserve, a biodiversity reservoir which helps to sustain the surrounding managed area. Further patches are set aside for research, or protected as archeological, ecotourism, educational, or bird sanctuary forests.

The principal harvest from the Matang is wood for charcoal, the major domestic fuel of the local rural population. The management routine currently operates on the basis of a 30-year rotation period. The exploited forest is divided into blocks of a few hectares, allocated to charcoal companies by the Forestry Department, which manages the whole forest. Each block is clear-felled: workers move in by boat and demolish every tree with chainsaws, cutting the timber into logs of standard length. Where a cleared area abuts a river or tidal creek, a band of trees 3 m wide is left on the shoreward side of the block to prevent erosion of the bank. The logs are ferried to charcoal kilns in a nearby village.

No two adjacent blocks are cleared simultaneously, so that the forest is a mosaic of patches of different ages and newly cleared areas are always surrounded by mature trees. Spontaneous colonization and repopulation with incoming mangrove propagules are therefore rapid. The debris from the clearing operation takes about 2 years to decompose. A year after clearance, each site is inspected. If the area then covered by natural regeneration is less than 90%, repopulation is assisted by artificial planting, mainly with the dominant, and preferred, species *Rhizophora apiculata*. Local villagers rear seedlings in small nurseries for this purpose. At this time, weed species can also be removed by hand, or with weedkillers. The mangrove fern *Acrostichum* can be a particular problem (**Figure 6**). It is well adapted to occupying sunlit spaces in the forest, so rapidly occupies a cleared site, and prevents successful rooting of mangrove propagules. Destruction of seedlings by crabs and monkeys can also be a problem. The following year, the site is again inspected, and any parts where seedling survival has been less than 75% successful are again replanted.

Figure 5 Replanted mangrove, *Rhizophora mucronata* in the Indus delta, Pakistan (Korangi creek). The established trees are mixed *Avicennia marina* and *Rhizophora*.

Figure 6 *Rhizophora* in the intensively managed mangroves of Matang, Malaysia. All trees shown are of the same age, hence similar diameter. Much of the understorey vegetation is the mangrove fern *Acrostichum*, a significant weed species that may prevent the establishment of mangrove propagules.

Some 15 years later, the site is revisited, and the young trees thinned out to a distance of 1.2 m apart (based on a premetric distance of 4 feet, unchanged since). The thinnings – all the same age, hence a standard thickness – are valuable as fishing poles. When the stand is 20 years old, it is again thinned, this time to a distance between trees of 1.8 m (6 feet): this time the thinnings (still of uniform thickness) are of a size suitable for the construction of village houses. Because the previous thinning means that the trees are not crowded, these grow straight and are ideal for their purpose. Finally, after 30 years, the block is again clear-felled for charcoal.

Since management began, there has been a trend towards virtual monoculture of *Rhizophora apiculata* in the intensively managed areas of the Matang. During this time, there is some equivocal evidence of a slight decline in productivity, but overall the Matang is a model of sustainable management of a natural resource – a depressingly rare situation.

In 1992, wood extraction amounted to more than 450 000 t and was worth a little over US$4 300 000. In recent years, declining demand for charcoal, and a shortage of workers for the labor-intensive business of timber extraction and charcoal-burning suggest that the future value of the Matang may lie in other products. Although the management is largely directed towards timber extraction, this accounts for only around 12% of the total economic value. The area supports thriving fisheries: the offshore waters annually yield more than 50 000 tonnes of fish, valued at US$29 million, and supporting nearly 2000 people. Much of this probably depends on the productivity of the mangroves. Farming of the blood cockle (*Anadara*) currently runs at more than 34 000

tonnes a year, worth US$3 million, and could be further developed. The Matang also has considerable potential for tourism, being rich in wildlife, including otters, monitor lizards, and a wide range of birds, including the rare milky stork (*Mycteria cinerea*). At present, with virtually no infrastructure, tourism probably brings in around US$430 000 annually to the local economy.

Sustainable forest management is therefore of importance beyond the production of wood and other direct forest products. Even if the market for charcoal disappears, managed mangrove forests such as the Matang should therefore have good long-term prospects, provided the connections between mangrove production and other activities are fully recognized.

See also: **Plantation Silviculture**: Multiple-use Silviculture in Temperate Plantation Forestry; Sustainability of Forest Plantations. **Silviculture**: Managing for Tropical Non-timber Forest Products; Treatments in Tropical Silviculture. **Tropical Ecosystems**: Mangroves.

Further Reading

Beadle LC (1974) *The Inland Waters of Tropical Africa: An Introduction to Tropical Limnology*. Harlow, UK: Longman.

Field C (1995) *Journey Amongst Mangroves*. Okinawa: International Tropical Timber Organization, and Institute for the Study of Mangrove Ecosystems.

Goulding M (1980) *The Fishes and the Forest: Explorations in Amazonian Natural History*. Berkeley: University of California Press.

Hogarth PJ (1999) *The Biology of Mangroves*. Oxford: Oxford University Press.

Hunter ML (ed.) (1999) *Maintaining Biodiversity in Forested Wetlands*. Cambridge: Cambridge University Press.

Kathiresan K and Bingham BL (2001) Biology of mangroves and mangrove ecosystems. *Advances in Marine Biology* 40: 85–254.

Lacerda LD (ed.) (1993) Conservation and sustainable utilization of mangrove forests in Latin America and Africa regions. *ISME/ITTO: ITTO Technical Series* 13.1: 1–42.

Lacerda LD de (ed.) (2002) *Mangrove Ecosystems. Function and Management*. Berlin: Springer.

Lugo AE and Bayle B (eds) *Wetlands Management in the Caribbean and the Role of Forestry and Wetlands in the Economy*. Puerto Rico: USDA Forest Service.

Lugo AE, Brinson M, and Brown S (eds) *Ecosystems of the World*, vol. 15, *Forested Wetlands*. Amsterdam: Elsevier.

Whigham D, Dykyjová D, and Hejný S (eds) (1992) *Wetlands of the World: Inventory, Ecology and Management*, vol. 1. *Handbook of Vegetation Science*, vol. 15/2. New York: Kluwer.

Silviculture and Management in Arid and Semi-arid Regions

E-H M Sène, Food and Agriculture Organization, Rome, Italy

Introduction

Drylands cover 41% of the earth and are represented in all the continents. Insufficient water quantity and in particular inadequate moisture to support plant growth during most of the year characterize these drylands.

Forests and tree formations play important economic, social, and environmental roles in these regions through a variety of functions including:

1. Conservation of soils through the buffering of erosion processes and land degradation control.
2. Conservation and improvement of the quality of water and regulation of the water regime.
3. Reduction of wind velocity, control of wind erosion, and buffering of water and moisture depletion.
4. Influencing local rainfall and condensation.

All these functions are essential and of high value in drylands and for the communities living therein.

The management and silviculture techniques and other human activities essential to the conservation and sustainable development of forests and trees are important but insufficiently documented in drylands. They promote efficient ecological and environmental buffering, and help to mitigate the harsh climatic conditions that characterize drylands. Biological diversity of forests and woodlands in drylands and the physiological functioning that allows their survival under the harsh conditions are conducive to a number of adaptations and processes. These need to be understood so that they may be used as tools underpinning sound silvicultural practices and good management of dry forests.

Arid and Semi-Arid Regions

Drylands 'experience during all or part of the year a period when evaporation exceeds precipitation, a period when all life in such lands must adapt in some way to reduced supplies of water or face death from dehydration.' They are understood generally as being in regions of the earth where the availability of water is deemed unsufficient to respond to the needs of living organisms. In particular, the water supply is insufficient to respond to the needs of human development including all the production activities that transform natural resources into goods and services. Drylands are generally marked by seasonality of rainfall, translating into an unsatisfactory distribution of water and moisture through the year. These elements affect the nature, quality, and distribution of plant life and of forests in particular.

Drylands are defined in terms of water related stress where mean annual rainfall (P) over potential evapotranspiration (PET) is less that the unity: P/PET < 1. Drylands are divided into various categories depending on the value of this equation. The greater the difference from 1, the greater the saturation deficit and the greater the stress plant communities are submitted to. The various subdivisions are shown in **Table 1**.

The Food and Agriculture Organization of the United Nations, with concerns mostly related to an effective growth period of vegetation used definitions based on the length of growing period (LGP). The growing period starts once rainfall exceeds half of the potential evapotranspiration. Areas are classified as follows:

- hyperarid (true deserts): LGP less than 1 day
- arid lands LGP less than 75 days,
- (dry) semi-arid LGP 75 to 120 days,
- (moist) semi-arid 120 to less than 180 days.

Overall, drylands cover 61 million km^2 or 40.7% of the total land area of the earth.

Forest Resources in Arid and Semi-Arid Regions: Categories, Location, Extent, State, and Evolution

The *Forest Resources Assessment 2000* estimated the extent of dry forests, mostly in arid and semi-arid areas, at 676 million ha, or 17% of the world's forested area. This covers a variety of formations from woodlands to steppe formations of various

Table 1 Subdivisions of the drylands of the world

Category	P/PET	Percentage of global land area
Hyperarid lands (usually known as deserts where vegetation is absent or discrete)	< 0.05	8%
Arid lands	0.05–0.20	12%
Semi-arid lands	0.20–0.50	18%
Dry subhumid lands	> 0.50	10%

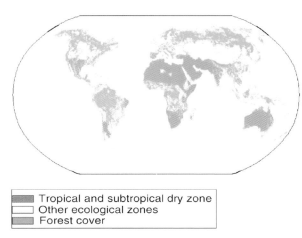

Tropical and subtropical dry zone
Other ecological zones
Forest cover

Figure 1   World distribution of dry zones and forest cover. From *Forest Resources Assessment 2000.*

structures and composition, but they occur mostly in the intertropical zones and subtropics (**Figure 1**). (Forests that are dry owing to the unavailability of water because of frost processes are not covered in this section.) Subtropical or Mediterranean forests have the same main characteristics as tropical arid and semi-arid forests: seasonal rainfall with frequent drought periods; structuring and biological influences of forest/bush fires; strong interactions with and mutual influences of agriculture and livestock raising; and the multifarious social and human functions they fulfil.

Categories of Forests and other Wooded Lands in Arid and Semi-Arid Areas

Most of the intertropical dry forests change according to rain and temperature/ecological gradients that run parallel to the equator. Although they share a number of characteristics due to the adaptation of local vegetation (vegetative cycles around and in the warmer and rainy seasons, presence of spines in arid areas, brilliant or velvety foliage, staged and deep rooting, stunted shapes under extreme conditions), these forests differ according to regions and continents. In general, tree presence, cover, and density decrease while grass cover increases regularly from higher to lower rainfall areas and increasing areas of stress. The typological gradient goes from dry deciduous forests to thickets, to open woodlands and savanna woodlands and then to tree savanna, shrub savanna with mixed trees, to thorny shrub steppes. **Figure 2** gives an overview of the arid and semi-arid woody plant formations of the world.

In the forest or woodland formations of arid and semi-arid areas, woody species play important and various functions. They produce small-dimensioned

timber of specific and valued characteristics in density, grain, coloration, and resistance, suitable for various uses and applications from luxury wood handicrafts, saw timber to fuelwood and charcoal. Such forests also produce a great amount and diversity of non-wood goods including material for handicrafts, food, gums, resins, honey and wax, feed and fodder which help in the livelihoods of the local communities. Thus they provide vital support, directly or indirectly, for food production, security, health, and amenity.

Extent of Arid and Semi-Arid Forests in the World

Forests of arid and semi-arid areas are designated dry forests in this section. Dry forests occur in the dry, semi-arid, and arid ecological zones in tropical and subtropical regions. Most of them are found in the dry tropics and subtropics (83%). A low percentage of dry forest (17%) is found in the areas characterized by shrubs, steppes and desert formations (**Table 2**).

Economic and Social Importance of Forests in Arid and Semi-Arid Areas

The importance and central role of forest and tree formations in the well-being of populations in dry areas and specifically in arid and semi-arid areas cannot be overemphasized. Populations in arid and semi-arid areas have technologies and practices that use tree and forest resources in many aspects of their livelihoods: dwelling, food supply, clothing, comfort and amenity. In this, timber is a secondary product compared to non-wood forest products.

Direct Food Production

Shrubs and trees provide many food items. These include fruits, nuts, gums, roots and more rarely tubers, an innumerable array of leaves, and flowers. A number of species of particular interest have become internationally traded products such as gum arabic from *Acacia senegal*, setigera gum from the mbep tree *Sterculia setigera* occurring in the African Sudano-Sahelian woodlands and tree savannas, tamarind from *Tamarindus indica* of the tree savannas and woodlands of Africa, Southern America and tropical Asia, the butter from the renowned shea butter tree *Vitellaria paradoxa*, and the various products from the genus *Prosopis* particularly *Prosopis juliflora* of Central and South America. Flowers in dry forests yield excellent honey, pollen, and wax. A host of beverages are brewed from leaves and grasses, e.g., *Combretum* spp., *Vitex*, *Lippia*, and *Vetiveria*.

Dry deciduous forests These formations are at the fringe of semi-arid forests. They derive from subhumid forests with trees around 20 m tall over an understory of smaller trees and shrubs. The grass layer is discontinuous except in openings or clearings.

Thickets These are low formations of shrubs and small trees of 8 m or less. Generally they include shrubby acacias other stunted evergreen species.

Open woodlands As rainfall decreases formations of tall trees (around 20 m) scattered over an understory of smaller trees and shrubs appear in the landscapes of open woodlands. These are strongly wooded formations neither as tall nor as densely populated as forests but whose overall multistory stands cover the soil.

Savannas Dry forests and woodlands generally respond to the agreed definition of forest: 'land with tree crown cover (or equivalent stocking level) of more than 10% and area of more than 0.5 ha. The trees should be able to reach a minimum height of 5 m at maturity.' When woodlands evolve to savannas, grass cover becomes nearly dominant to exclusive. These formations are common in Africa and in the Brazilian *cerrados* and *campos* in South America.

Steppes The steppes have an even more modest tree cover and a discontinuous grass cover. They are however the domain of some woody species of high ecological, economic, and social relevance.

Figure 2 An overview of dry forest and tree formations. After Tropical Forest Botany, CTFT, Tome I, p. 135–139.

Table 2 Extent and distribution of dry forests

Region	Tropical dry forest (ha × 10⁶)	Subtropical dry forest (ha × 10⁶)	Total dry forest (ha × 10⁶)	Percentage of total regional forest	Percentage of total world dry forest
Africa	215 560	7 176	222 736	34	33
Asia	98 178	5 938	104 116	19	15
Oceania	78 535	47 881	126 416	64	19
Europe	0	41 748	41 748	4	6
North and Central America	8 861	15 267	24 129	4	4
South America	147 404	9 850	157 254	18	23
Total	548 539	127 861	676 399	17	100

Data from Forest Resources Assessment 2000 (FAO).

Medicinal and Related Products

Some of the species mentioned above provide medicinal preparations, but many other species of the arid and semi-arid lands produce the active ingredients for medical and cosmetic uses. These products bring cash income into the communities living in the forest and savanna. Many countries in the dry zones of Africa have organized the traditional practitioners and their activities in the formulation and presentation of local medicines. Cooperation has been established with modern medical and health institutions. Species such as *Vitellaria paradoxa*, *Jatropha curcas*, the jojoba (*Schimondsia chinensis*), and many other species exemplify the contribution of plants of dry areas to the production of medicinal ingredients.

Timber, Fuelwood, and Charcoal

Forests and trees of dry areas yield important timber resources but only in limited quantities; hence their sustainable management is important. Due to the heat and water stresses, growth of timber is usually slow. This results in high-value timber in terms of texture, grain, and coloration. Most of the timber is of precious wood for cabinet-making or art handicrafts. Examples include the *Pterocarpus* species such P. *erinaceus* producing the precious Venn timber, the dry-area mahogany (*Khaya senegalensis*), and the ironwood produced by *Dalbergia melanoxylon*.

Wood for various local services (poles, building materials) is also important. But the most pressing use of wood is for energy. In all arid and semi-arid areas the processing and transport of fuelwood or charcoal is an active sector of the local and national economies. The first initiatives in the management of dry forests are aimed at organizing and regulating the supply of fuelwood to consumers, mostly in cities.

Miscellaneous Products for Small Industry Opportunities

Dry forests and other wooded lands of arid and semi-arid areas are sources of various products which play

Figure 3 Various locally manufactured products from non-wood forest products in a dry region of West Africa. Courtesy of FAO.

key roles in the livelihoods of local communities. A rich and diversified set of traditional technologies have made use of them. Today they are often the basis of small family enterprises contributing to fighting poverty. Processing of nuts, drupes, and beans (e.g. of *Balanites*, *Ziziphus*, *Parinari*, *Parkia*, and *Borassus*, to note some examples from dry West Africa), provides trade opportunities beyond village consumption to medium and large cities and to regional and international markets (**Figure 3**).

Wildlife, Game, and Recreation

Arid and semi-arid zones are rich in wildlife and spectacular landscapes. This is an interesting area that forest management cannot ignore but which has not up till now been appropriately taken into account. It has been dealt with in protected areas and game reserves, but in terms of international tourism and hunting. However, in the African woodlands and savannas antelopes and gazelles, (e.g., *Tragelaphus scriptus*, *Gazella rufifrons*, and *Cephalophus* spp.), as well as many small rodents, can provide protein for the diet of the local population. Warthogs and larger antelopes in the more subhumid areas offer opportunities for hunting and tourism. The spectacles of myriad of birds local or migratory in wet areas and water points are also excellent features, which benefit conservation and tourism activities. The criteria for sustainable forest management developed in all dry forest zones include conservation of biological diversity and it is expected that greater attention will be devoted to this in future.

Support for Agriculture

Dry forests are areas of major human development. Agriculture has had maximum development in semi-arid tropical and subtropical regions and at present they continue to play major roles in providing food in these areas. Forests and tree formations are a ready source of agricultural lands, and countries where rates of deforestation have remained high have lost these forests to agriculture. In the Sudan, hundreds of thousands of hectares of *Acacia seyal* forests have been lost to extensive sorghum cultivation; most of the annual loss of 900 000 ha of forest and other wooded land in this country between 1990 and 2000 was from the semi-arid and arid areas. The same situation prevails in all dry tropical countries. In the Mediterranean region pressures on forests for agriculture are very limited, except where irrigation systems can be extended. Indeed most suitable dry lands have been already occupied. Pressures may remain high in Asia and Latin America.

Fodder Production and Animal Husbandry in Pastoral Communities

Arid and semi-arid lands provide range areas *par excellence*. Throughout the world, people in these areas have built their livelihoods on the intimate knowledge and use of plant communities. A substantial corpus of traditional knowledge on the multifaceted role of the woody and grass vegetation of drylands has been developed. Very specialized

modes of utilization have been developed, as shown in the example in **Table 3**.

Amenity

Species of arid and semi-arid areas are usually slender, with symmetrical canopies and often beautiful flowers. Some offer much needed shade in hot areas or may constitute efficient windbreaks to buffer heat and check dust. Some *Acacia* species, *Bauhinia*, *Cassia*, *Combretum*, and *Prosopis* are beautiful trees with magnificent flowers (**Figure 4**). Some species of worldwide importance include *Dichrostachys* spp., *Bauhinia*, some *Cassia* (e.g., *C. sieberiana*); and a number of *Cactus* species. The development of urban and peri-urban forestry has used species such as

Figure 4   A blooming *Combretum lecardii* in the dry season in the Sudano–Sahelian zone. Photograph by E Sène.

Table 3   Species utilization in the livelihood systems of dryland communities in the Sahel of Senegal

Objective	Species used
Animal nutrition	
For lactation	*Grewia bicolor, Acacia radiana, Acacia albida, Adansonia digitata*
For fattening	*Acacia radiana, Acacia albida, Acacia senegal*
Medicinal/veterinarian purposes	*Adansonia digitata, Adenium obesum, Acacia nilotica, Combretum glutinosum, Combretum micranthum, Combretum aculeatum, Crataeva religiosa, Bauhinia rufescens, Grewia bicolor, Dichrostachys cinerea, Cadaba farinosa, Balanites aegyptiaca, Sclerocarya birrea, Salvadora persica*
Construction	*Balanites aegyptiaca, Acacia nilotica, Prosopis africana, Hyphaena thebaica, Borassus aethiopum*

Parkinsonia spp., *Prosopis*, *Tamarindus indica*, and a number of Australian species including dry-area eucalyptus and acacias (e.g., *Acacia bivenosa*, *A. holosericea*, and *A. tumida*), *Prosopis*, in particular *P. juliflora* and *P. chilensis*, *Tamarix* spp., etc.

Biology of Dry Forests, and their Silviculture

Ecology of Arid and Semi-Arid Areas

The biological and physiological characteristics of the vegetation of arid and semi-arid areas guarantee adaptation to great heat and light, the inadequate availability of water, and, in a number of cases, salinity. In many cases the highest temperatures correspond to periods when availability of water is lowest which significantly increases stress in plant communities. A number of characteristics and attributes of these plant communities will be strong tools for the silvicultural treatment of forest and tree formations. The following should be particularly retained:

1. Protection and mobility of seeds. Most seeds are efficiently protected either by a long dormancy or a physical barrier to moisture, comprising a cuticle which needs to be altered chemically or mechanically before germination. Thus, seeds eaten by animals may benefit from partial modification of the cuticle, which later facilitates germination far from their origin. Other seeds (e.g., *Pterocarpus*) have wings or light tufts that facilitates transportation by wind.
2. Structure and functioning of the root system. The root systems of plants in arid and semi-arid areas are the strongest tools for their adaptation, survival, and regeneration. Most of them are deep with a taproot, which can extend to more than 10 m below ground. They have, in addition, extremely well-developed superficial horizontal roots (**Figure 5**), which can explore both for nutrients and moisture from the upper layers of the soil. Often roots develop suckers when they are slightly damaged or after fires.
3. Sprouting and protection of shoots. Many arid area species sprout vigorously and abundantly. The initial vitality of the shoots may facilitate survival through part of the dry season. These shoots have a number of adaptive options (stunting, early formation of thick bark, survival through shedding the aboveground part of the stem, and strengthening of underground organs) that guarantee final survival.
4. Reduction of leaf surface area. A relatively small leaf surface area helps dry-zone species overcome

Figure 5 Rooting system of *Acacia*. Photograph by E Sène.

stress and maintain limited functions during the dry season.
5. Other flexible biological adaptations. Grasses and some shrubs develop a number of other adaptations, producing, e.g., bulbs, voluminous rootstock (*Guiera senegalensis*, *Icacina* spp.) which not only guarantee survival but also facilitate dissemination.
6. Adaptation to salinity. Many species are able to grow on saline soils or resist rising salinity. They adapt through evaporation and deposition of the salt on the leaves which are protected by leaves becoming succulent (*Dodonea* spp.) or very thin (*Tamarix* spp.).

It is only through these various adaptive strategies that plant formations succeed in living nearly unnoticed during dry periods and indeed are able to bounce back with speed and vigor as soon as rains occur. The silviculturist will use these adaptative strategies to trigger and manage regeneration.

Silviculture and Dry Forests

The corpus of knowledge supporting silviculture in arid and semi-arid forests is still to be largely completed. Some of the elements on which silviculture of these ecosystems are based are reviewed below.

Climate and seasonality The general pattern in drylands features the existence of strongly marked seasons. The dry season, of variable length according to the region, subjects living organisms to strong stresses. They are usually accompanied by the loss of foliage, to reduce evapotranspiration. Species adapt in a number of ways: spines, coated or velvety leaves, thick bark. This period is also marked by fires which debilitate the forests, kill seedlings, and when occurring late in the cycle destroy flowers and fruits. This may influence the livelihoods of populations as their strategy includes the use of fruits that mature in dry seasons (e.g., *Cordyla*, *Parkia*, *Ziziphus*) for lean periods. It may, by contrast, facilitate germination when the rainy season comes. Managing forest fires is then a potent tool in the management of dryland forests.

The unpredictability of the onset of the rains, the occurrence of large spells of drought during the rainy season itself or its precocious end are factors that strongly affect the growth and vitality of the forest in drylands and which make more difficult the silviculture of these forests. Fire hazards and the spread of insects will be highly dependent on such factors.

Heat and moisture are other important factors affecting the vitality of the forest. Temperatures in drylands may reach very high levels. In the Africa Sudano-Sahelian and Sahelian zones they are over 30°C for most of the year. In some periods high temperature and low humidity combine to produce high stress. These periods are the ones that most influence survival and the physiognomy of arid and semi-arid formations. When biological activity is at its lowest logging and other silvicultural operations may best be carried out.

Land and soils In most semi-arid regions, the most valuable land is devoted to agriculture. Forestry is reserved for poorer lands. In arid areas livestock rearing is dominant. But forests and tree formations have other important roles to play. Organic matter is in short supply in dryland soils. In forests and other wooded lands, which should play important roles in producing organic matter, mineralization is extremely quick. The grass biomass, however, contributes much to the process and should be incorporated into soils as early as possible. This prevents the export of much of the moisture when the climate dries up. Plantation silviculture needs to take this into account through well-planned seedling production campaigns, thorough soil preparation practices optimizing the relatively small amount of rainfall, adequate timing of planting operations, and weeding.

Human and social environment The dependence of local communities on the forest and tree resources is very high in arid and semi-arid areas. Stabilized agriculture takes place mostly in valleys and other topographically suitable areas with a high water table. Rain-fed agriculture is linked to the removal of the forests where some organic material has been accumulated under fallow or as new land. Pastoral land use is pervasive and forests and other wooded lands are the main resources supporting livestock. Silviculture as well as agriculture withstands competition with animal husbandry, but the control of livestock movements will be an important prerequisite in any forest management option. The utilization of a host of non-wood forest products is characteristic of dry forest use. This entails an intimate interaction of people and forests which can have a strong impact on silviculture and forest management.

Options for Silvicultural Models in Arid and Semi-Arid Forests

Silvicultural operations have a number of major functions, including structuring the stands; boosting growth and favoring selected stems; enhancing non-wood production, in particular fodder; securing health and vitality; and assisting regeneration. Generally, dry formations include separate or combined grass layers, bush and thicket, and intermediate small trees between taller trees. Silvicultural operations will aim at:

- controlling grass for proper use and avoiding its unplanned burning
- clearing or structuring the thicket to make it 'user friendly' and easy to enter
- maintaining the intermediate trees as a balanced filling to respond to needs for wood for fuel and service (usually by coppicing)
- dealing with biotic interferences, especially protecting regeneration from browsing by livestock or wild animals
- maintaining at long rotations the 'high forest' component often made up of species of high value.

Objectives usually cover (1) conservation and protection; (2) multipurpose production; (3) fuel-wood production; and (4) timber production. As in all silvicultural regimes the regeneration methods and objectives govern options in dry forest silviculture. Dry forest formations can be regenerated through seeding and planting and through a series of vegetative regeneration practices. The regeneration methods are summarized below.

Natural regeneration Natural regeneration is constrained by many factors. Most fruits and seeds mature at the end of the rainy season or just before it. Seeds are very difficult to conserve when they are fleshy or if they are difficult to germinate. Fleshy seeds germinate very easily with the rains (e.g., *Sclerocarya birrea*, *Cordyla africana*) provided the soil is not hard or glazed. Unfortunately the seedlings have to face immediate competition from grass and other plants and the difficult survival conditions of the dry season. The risk of fire is high and most probably with no particular protection a very limited number of seedlings survives. There is also the risk of seedlings being eaten by wild or domesticated animals. Seeds with hard coats may lie dormant and resistant to mild natural processes and germinate only under particular natural processes or guided assistance provided by the silviculturist. The ingestion of fruits and seeds by animals including birds is important in the natural regeneration process. The digestion process alters the seed coat and facilitates germination (this explains the clustered nature of trees in *Acacia* savannas and steppes.)

Assisted natural regeneration   Silvicultural interventions to assist and enhance natural regeneration are indispensable. They will aim at (1) easing water percolation and storage through subsoiling, ridging, and creation of structures where seeds and water preferentially accumulate; (2) reducing competition from grasses and shrubs with timely weeding; and (3) protection from fire either through complete weeding, partial weeding around the seedlings, and establishment of fire breaks.

Vegetative regeneration   Usually species of dry areas react well to vegetative stimuli through sprouting, layering, cutting, and suckering. Vegetative regeneration is the most common basis of silviculture. Stands are regenerated after logging as most species sprout very strongly, thus providing stems that are appropriate for fuelwood or for making posts. Medium to superficial subsoiling may be used to scar roots and enhance regeneration through sucker inducement (e.g., most *Acacia* species, *Balanites aegyptica*, *Daniella olivieri*, *Cordyla pinnata*, and a number of miombo species).

Silvicultural Regimes

The coppice system   Production of fuelwood and posts is the major objective of dry forest management. In West Africa it is in the production of fuelwood from the mix of Combretaceae and Leguminosae (mostly *Acacia*), with a filling of *Detarium macrocarpum* that management has evolved. These constitute the bulk of woodland stands. Pure stands sprout after logging. Cases in point are stands of *Combretum* and *Anogeissus*; pure stands of *Acacia seyal*; and partially inundated valley stands of *Acacia nilotica*.

Coppice and standard system   In many types of dry forests and woodlands dominant trees are species of high value that are not used for fuel but for timber (*Khaya senegalensis*, *Pterocarpus erinaceus*, *Detarium* spp.) or fruit production (*Parkia biglobosa*, *Cola cordifolia*, *Sclerocarya birrea*). The same approach is valid for the miombo woodlands. Smaller trees and shrubs are periodically clear-cut, mostly for fuelwood and charcoal. This treatment is a coppice-with-standard system with different objectives pursued through the two components.

High forest system   Pure high forests originating from seedlings are seldom established in dry regions. However under some special stand conditions pure stands can exist and naturally regenerate. A number of *Acacia* species are gregarious and may develop sizeable pure stands. Examples are *A. seyal*, *A. senegal*, and *A. nilotica* associated with floodplains or low-lying lands. In Central and southern America, *Prosopis juliflora* and *P. tamarugo* grow usually in thick pure stands, naturally regenerated. With the potential of abundantly producing suckers, some species produce pure stands with the appearance of seedling originated natural regeneration. *Daniella oliveri* in West Africa is an example. Silvicultural operations may choose to take advantage of these special situations, but then sprouts and suckers may overtake seedlings and most of apparently seed generated communities may well have derived from vegetative propagation.

Plantations   Plantations in arid lands raise many problems but may be the only option when needs are urgent, or when rehabilitation and restoration are essential. Considerable efforts have been made in creating new forest plantations in some countries. There are 14 countries in the dry zones that have large planted forests. They include India, Thailand, Iran, Turkey, South Africa, Australia, Pakistan, Algeria, Sudan, Argentina, Chile, and Spain. These countries account for around one-third of the world's planted forests as estimated in the FAO's *Forest Resources Assessment 2000*.

Economic considerations   Silviculture and management of forests succeed only if the operations engaged are sustained throughout the cycle of the forests. The initial investment in partitioning the forest and the subsequent operations of maintenance, thinning, and intermediate cutting call for financial resources. These are not always readily available with neither national forestry institutions nor local or private entities and individuals as investors. Options should be low in external and capital inputs and reasonably labor intensive. Foresters in many dry areas have promoted community-driven forest management and efforts on efficient marketing of products from managed forests (*see* **Social and Collaborative Forestry**: Joint and Collaborative Forest Management).

Managing Dry Forests for Various Objectives

Specificity and General Objectives of the Management of Dry Forests

Dry forests have to meet diversified economic, social, and ecological needs. The management of dry forests aims at (1) assessing societal needs; (2) measuring the resources and their potential, and (3) prescribing programs and operations to satisfy the needs, while securing conservation of the major characteristics of the resources. This is common to all types of forests, but dry forests are strongly constrained by low water availability, drought spells, forest fires, and strong human needs and expectations. Managing dry forests will respond to the needs for timber, wood for energy, a host of non-wood forest products, conservation and utilization of wildlife, recreation and overall conservation of the unique genetic and biological diversity present in them. Management includes a range of options corresponding to: (1) conserving and using sustainably naturally occurring formations; (2) cultivating coppice and high forest trees for differentiated production; (3) planning, organizing, and effecting active renovation of stands through reforestation; and (4) planning and effecting afforestation on bare land. A number of activities where trees are mixed with other land uses can be associated with forest.

History in the Management of Dry Forests

Until the early 1950s in many dry areas forestry was focused on conservation. Then initiatives for plantations started to grow, initially with no clear set objectives. Forest management started with very simple goals in many cases, aiming at securing fuelwood supplies for rail companies or for small industries such as brickmaking or cane alcohol distillation. But by the early 1980s, overconsumption of fuelwood and initiatives concerning renewable energy resources had brought attention to the potential of forest management to secure sustained supplies and conservation of resources. Programs of management of native forests instead of plantations were later promoted by aid donors, and by the early 1990s a number of demonstration projects had been completed allowing lessons to be drawn and targeted extension work to be developed. Countries such as Burkina Faso, Niger, and Madagascar in Africa began to develop national programs of forest management.

Promoting Sustainable Management of Dry Forests

The Intergovernmental Panel on Forests/Intergovernmental Forum on Forests program of action has addressed the issue of criteria and indicators for sustainable management of dry forests in Africa, Asia, and Latin America. A set of internationally accepted thematic areas corresponding to the following seven criteria for sustainable forest management have been agreed upon:

1. The extent of forest resources.
2. Biological diversity of the forests.
3. Forest health and vitality.
4. Productive functions of forests.
5. Protective functions of forests.
6. Socioeconomic functions of forests.
7. Legal, policy and institutional framework.

Forest management and silviculture should aim for the realization of these criteria that cater for the new paradigms of sustainable development.

Defining and protecting forest status/extent in arid and semi-arid areas At international level, FAO estimated that in developing countries dry forests, which covered 238.3 million ha in 1990, were being lost at the rate of 2.2 million ha per year in the period 1980–1990. This represented 1.1 million ha in Africa, 0.5 million ha in Asia, and 0.6 million ha in Latin America. *Forest Resource Assessment 2000*, estimated dry (tropical and subtropical) forests at 374 million ha. At national level maintaining the forests is a great challenge for dryland countries with growing populations and rampant poverty. Many countries now encourage the populace to get organized and engage in forest management as full partners.

Conserving the biological diversity of dry forests The multifunctional characters of vegetation from arid and semi-arid areas underlines the need for the conservation of the genetic resources they contain. Many efforts have been devoted to this and the multipurpose woody species of arid and semi-arid regions have been the subject of many projects on forest genetic resources. The Convention on Biological Diversity has reserved particular efforts to defining a program on the biological diversity of drylands, Mediterranean, arid, semi-arid, grassland, and savanna ecosystems. FAO has promoted national and regional projects for the conservation and use of the genetic resources of woody species of arid and semi-arid zones in Africa, Asia, and South America. A number of countries from the arid and semi-arid regions have recently developed national forest seed centers supporting growing afforestation programs. Ecosystem conservation is active in arid and semi-arid regions in response to their rich animal biological diversity, but more efforts are certainly needed.

Health and vitality of semi-arid and arid forests   The greatest challenge to the management and protection of forests and woodlands of arid and semi-arid areas is the prevention and control of forest fires. Forest and/or range management should intimately encompass fire management. This will entail where possible methods of early burning in semi-arid forests, forest protection work in areas with high asset values, and population sensitization, training, and organization. The most efficient measures are those that create assets for people in and close to the forests through sustainable use of pasture, wood, bee-keeping operations, etc. Pests and diseases may cyclically break out and careful monitoring is essential.

Maintaining and heightening the protective functions of forests in arid and semi-arid areas   It is essential that the management models of forests enhance the role of forests, trees, and grass formations in controlling land degradation, especially through limiting water loss, controlling wind erosion, and improving nutrient intake in soils. A number of species such as *Acacia albida* and *Prosopis procera* are known to improve and maintain soil fertility and moisture content of soils. The ability of, e.g., *A. albida* to conserve its foliage during the dry season and hence attract livestock and other animals under its shade is used in the agroforestry parklands and farming systems in dry regions. Efforts are being made to manage woodlands in watersheds (Guinea, Fouta Djallon, the Volta watershed in Ghana, etc.) to protect headwaters and secure steady flow to the major rivers in West Africa.

Productive and socioeconomic functions of forests   The productive and socioeconomic functions of dry forests are closely linked (**Figure 6**). Silviculture and forest management should enhance them. The productive capacity of the resource is however limited. While some woodland and wooded savanna could yield wood products up to $8\,m^3\,ha^{-1}\,year^{-1}$, dry shrub savanna and steppes yield less $1\,m^3\,ha^{-1}\,year^{-1}$. Information on yield is fragmented and of various reliability; it needs to be further documented.

Legal, policy, and institutional framework of dry forest management   Forest management needs continuity and monitoring to learn the lessons of experience and to consolidate options, techniques, and practices. In most arid and semi-arid areas the institutional framework for forestry is weak or strongly dependent on other sectors. Laws and regulations may be obsolete. During the last decade, however, sustained efforts have been made to strengthen national institutions and to update legislation and regulations. Efforts to involve local communities in forest management and the work of a number of networks have advanced decentralized models of participatory forest management, mostly in dry areas. The post-Rio Conventions, in particular the Convention to Combat Desertification, have provided new opportunities for institutional strengthening for overall natural resources management in dry areas.

Figure 6   A women's cooperative group in Nazinon forest, Burkina Faso.

Practical Experience

Experiences at country level have closely followed international developments in incorporating progressively current and emerging paradigms in forest management. Among those most important are (1) the devolution of the resources to people and putting forest at the service of local community development; (2) developing and disseminating the concept around the link of forests, trees, and people; (3) managing forest to enhance the multiple functions they support and following agreed-upon criteria and indicators for sustainable forest management in dry areas.

At the start of the twenty-first century, it is difficult to assess overall progress in effective forest management. The *Forest Resources Assessment 2000* of the FAO showed that for developing countries engaged in forest management, out of a total of 2139 millions ha, at least 123 millions ha or about 6% were covered by 'a formal, nationally approved forest management plan.' This shows that efforts are still inadequate. The situation is not much worse in arid and semi-arid areas taking into account the greater involvement of populations in participatory forest management in those areas. In Africa 4% of the dry forests of countries covered by the *Forest Resources Assessment 2000* study on forest management are under some management plan; in South America only 2% are under a management plan.

Challenges Ahead

There are daunting challenges in the management of forests in arid and semi-arid areas which will need to be faced in a sustained and continued way. They include, among others, the following:

1. Raising awareness on the many functions goods and services provided by dry forest resources, to communities that are among the poorest in the world.
2. Strengthening institutions that deal with dryland ecosystems, in particular research and policy institutions at national and regional levels.
3. Increasing knowledge and expanding technologies about assessment, management, conservation, and use of arid and semi-arid forest and tree resources.
4. Continuing work and strengthening cooperation on the assessment of the social, economic, and environmental services of dry forests.
5. Further focusing work on criteria and indicators for sustainable management of dry forests towards effective application and development on the field including considerations of wood and non-wood products of forests of arid and semi-arid zones.
6. Supporting effective action on the field so as to apply the wealth of knowledge acquired and

paradigms developed to the sustainable management of forest and tree resources of dry areas.

See also: **Genetics and Genetic Resources**: Forest Management for Conservation. **Medicinal, Food and Aromatic Plants**: Medicinal and Aromatic Plants: Ethnobotany and Conservation Status. **Silviculture**: Managing for Tropical Non-timber Forest Products. **Social and Collaborative Forestry**: Common Property Forest Management; Forest and Tree Tenure and Ownership; Joint and Collaborative Forest Management; Public Participation in Forest Decision Making; Social and Community Forestry; Social Values of Forests. **Tree Physiology**: Stress. **Tropical Forests**: Tropical Dry Forests.

Further Reading

Arnold JEM (1991) *Community Forestry: Ten Years in Review.* Rome, Italy: Food and Agriculture Organization.

Association Internationale Forêt Méditerranéenne (2002) Problématique de la forêt méditerranéenne. *Journal Forêt Méditerranéenne* 1: (Special Issue).

Bellefontaine R, Petit S, Pain-Orcet M, Deleporte P, and Bertault J-G (2002) *Trees outside Forests: Towards Better Awareness.* Conservation Guide no. 35. Rome, Italy: Food and Agriculture Organization.

Boffa JM (1999) *Agroforestry Parklands in Sub-Saharan Africa.* Conservation Guide no. 34. Rome, Italy: Food and Agriculture Organization.

Booth FEM and Wickens GE (1988) *Non Timber Uses of Selected Arid Zone Trees and Shrubs in Africa.* Conservation Guide no. 19. Rome, Italy: Food and Agriculture Organization.

Center for International Forestry Research (2002) Africa's tropical dry forests: time to re-engage an agenda for priority research. CIFOR & SIDA.

De Montgolfier J (2002) *Les Espaces Boisés Méditerranéens: Situation et Perspectives.* Montpellier, France: UNEP.

FAO (1984) *Études sur les Volumes et la Productivité des Peuplements Forestiers Tropicaux*, vol. 1, *Formations forestières sèches.* Rome, Italy: Food and Agriculture Organization.

FAO (1989) *Role of Forestry in Combating Desertification.* Conservation Guide no. 21. Rome, Italy: Food and Agriculture Organization.

FAO (1992) *Forestry in Arid Zones: A Guide for Field Technicians.* Conservation Guide no. 20. Rome, Italy: Food and Agriculture Organization.

FAO (1993) *The Challenge of Sustainable Forest Management: What Future for the World's Forests.* Rome, Italy: Food and Agriculture Organization.

FAO (2000a) *Fodder Shrub Development in Arid and Semi-Arid Zones.* Rome, Italy: Food and Agriculture Organization.

FAO (2000b) *Management of Natural Forests in Dry Zones.* Conservation Guide no. 32. Rome, Italy: Food and Agriculture Organization.

Hopkins ST and Jones DE (1983) *Research Guide to the Arid Lands of the World*. Phoenix, AZ: Onyx Press.

UNESCO (1961) *Histoire de l'Utilisation des Terres des Regions Arides*. Nancy, France: Berger-Levrault.

Silviculture in Polluted Areas

M V Kozlov, University of Turku, Turku, Finland

Introduction

The influence of industrial pollution on forest health has long been recognized as a serious applied and scientific problem. Although numerous field experiments have been established to determine practical measures for both the alleviation of pollution impacts on stand vitality and the rehabilitation of damaged forests, a general strategy has not emerged, and 'silviculture in polluted areas' is still in the incipient stages of development. Maintenance of forests in polluted areas requires more intensive management than in unpolluted areas, involving 'soft' techniques and highly skilled manual labor.

The prescriptions that form the basis of silviculture in polluted areas should be preventive, aimed at improving the ecological stability of stands in such a way that they will better resist pollution impacts. In many cases the vitality and productivity of forests affected by chronic acidification and heavy-metal contamination can be maintained by chemical amelioration. However, to be successful, the revitalization strategy should first aim at identification of nutritional disturbances and then apply diagnostic fertilization to alleviate these disturbances, balancing the anticipated beneficial and adverse effects. Suggested silvicultural measures include the creation of substitute stands, maintenance of stand integrity, a decrease in rotation time, avoidance of monocultures, and replacement of clear-cuts by selective logging and gap-oriented regeneration. The practical application of silvicultural measures, with successful amelioration of pollution impacts, is still limited to a very few areas of boreal and temperate forests.

Polluted Forests: Past, Present, and Future

Pollution, Polluters, and Pollutants

Historically, sulfur dioxide was the first pollutant to cause local but severe forest deterioration. This is the best-studied pollutant, under both experimental and natural conditions. In high concentrations it causes acute foliar damage, which weakens and then kills the trees; in low concentrations it contributes to regional acidification. Conifers are generally more sensitive to SO_2 than broadleaved species.

Fluorine emissions to the atmosphere started to increase in the late 1930s, reaching peak values in the late 1960s. These emissions were primarily associated with aluminum production, and they caused severe but local forest damage. However, fluorine emissions strongly decreased between 1970 and 1980 due to effective measures taken to minimize the release of fluoride from aluminum smelters to the atmosphere.

Heavy metals are very common pollutants but in general do not spread far from smelters. Only some of the largest polluters have caused detectable contamination of soils and vegetation at distances exceeding 50 km from the emission source. Heavy metals emitted by Monchegorsk and Norilsk can be detected (in atmospheric aerosols) and identified (e.g., attributed to the specific polluter) at distances up to 2000 km from the polluter. However, these long-transported metals have never been said to cause any biotic effects, especially in forests. Although most heavy metals are extremely toxic, they have rarely been reported as a cause of forest death. However, heavy metals adversely affect seedling establishment, thus hampering the natural revegetation of contaminated areas long after any decline in atmospheric pollution levels.

Increased deposition of nitrogen started to play an important role in European forests several decades ago. Although this pollutant does not create the dramatic landscapes of some other pollutants, its effects are insidious and long-lasting. In some countries, such as the Netherlands, annual deposition of nitrogen in the late 1980s reached $200 \, Kg \, N \, ha^{-1}$, making eutrophication more important than the impact of 'traditional' pollutants. Increases in N deposition are also a big issue in some parts of North America, such as the San Bernardino Mountains of California.

Finally, ozone was recently identified as a possible contributor to forest damage in Europe and North America. Although unequivocal evidence for O_3-induced foliar injury on woody species under field conditions has only been found in a few places, mostly in regions with a warm and sunny climate (the Mediterranean, south California), and in alpine areas, including Sierra Nevada and the Appalachian mountain chains, ozone obviously weakens the trees leaving them vulnerable to other assaults and stresses. Overall, the quantitative risk assessment of O_3 impact on mature trees and forests is uncertain at the

European scale. Research suggests that risks exist, but these need to be validated for stand conditions.

Extent and Severity of Impacts

Local scale Extensive forest mortality around large sources of pollution has sometimes transformed forests to barren 'industrial deserts', and – despite the relatively small areas affected – has attracted considerable public and scientific attention in recent decades. The most striking examples of severe local pollution have long been associated with the Canadian smelters (Trail, Sudbury, Wawa). However, after implementation of strong emission controls in most industrial countries during the 1970s, the largest individual polluters are now located in Western Europe and Russia, with the Norilsk smelter in Northern Siberia being the largest globally: forest damage had been observed at distances over 150 km from this smelter. The largest point sources of fluorine-containing emissions are also situated in Siberia (Bratsk, Shelekhov, Irkutsk). The most extensive scientific information concerning both severe pollution impact on forest ecosystems and experimental remediation measures has been collected around the Monchegorsk smelter (Kola Peninsula, northwest Russia).

Regional scale Large areas of forest require rehabilitation as a result of the impacts of acidic deposition and other forms of pollution. The problem is particularly apparent in central Europe, with the most striking example being the 'Black Triangle,' an area along the German–Czech–Polish border. This region has been heavily affected by industrial pollution over the past 50 years, with severe consequences for the forests, landscapes, environment, and public health. Model calculations demonstrate that by 2050 severe regional problems will also occur in Southeast Asia, South Africa, Central America, and along the Atlantic coast of South America. However, almost no relevant research had been conducted in these regions, which may pose a serious problem for sustainable silviculture in the near future, when local foresters are faced with the need to mitigate pollution impacts.

Global scale In 1985, 8% of the forested areas of the world received annually >1 kg H^+ ha^{-1} as sulfur, and it is estimated that 17% of the forested areas of the world will receive this pollution load by 2050 (**Figure 1**). Similarly, 24% of the global forest was exposed to O_3 concentrations exceeding 60 ppb in 1990, and this proportion is expected to increase to 50% of global forest by 2100. These model calculations, however, should be treated with cau-tion, as they are based on a number of assumptions and simplifications; however, it seems more likely that more and more extensive areas will require specific management that accounts for pollution impacts. Moreover, current predictions of forest responses to global climate change do not consider important physiological changes induced by air pollutants that may amplify climatic stress.

Forestry Facing Pollution: History, Theory, and Practice

Silviculture in Polluted Areas: An Operational Field

The impact of pollutants in concentrations exceeding critical levels (or permissible loads) results in the deterioration of forest ecosystems, and they move from their original state towards industrial barrens (secondary open landscapes with $<10\%$ vegetation cover and extensive soil erosion) with the rate proportional to both the severity and the longevity of the pollution impacts.

In two-dimensional space, with canopy closure along the horizontal axis and pollution load along the vertical axis (**Figure 2**), industrial barrens occupy the upper left-hand corner (low canopy closure, intolerable pollution load) as opposed to undisturbed forests in the lower right-hand corner (high canopy closure, low pollution load). Clear-cuts occupy the space along the left vertical axis (low to zero canopy closure, low to intolerable pollution load).

The costly measures aimed at changing the landscape appearance in areas affected by very high levels of pollution are called 'regreening'; these changes do not lead to forest formation. Forest restoration can be attempted only following a decrease in pollution loads; it results in the formation of semistable forests on previously deforested contaminated (acidified) landscapes. Restored forests, as well as existing forests subjected to pollution, need to be managed differently from unpolluted forests. This practice, accounting for environmental changes caused by pollution, can be called 'silviculture in polluted areas.' The lower part of **Figure 2** represents traditional silviculture, or 'silviculture in unpolluted areas.'

As forest regeneration is very sensitive to pollution, and dense forests better sustain pollution impacts than sparse forests, silvicultural practices involving clear-cutting should be adjusted at lower pollution loads than practices based on selective logging and gap-oriented regeneration.

Silviculture in Polluted Areas: Myth or Reality?

The practical measures applied in some of polluted forests are still too intuitive to be called 'silviculture';

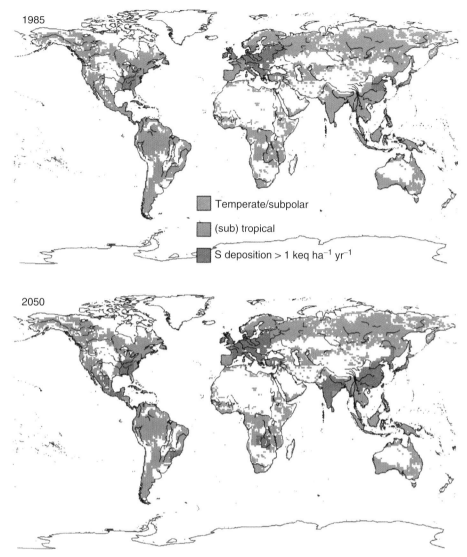

Figure 1 The global distribution of forest cover where total sulfur deposition exceeds $1\,keq\,ha^{-1}\,year^{-1}$, for 1985 and 2050. Reproduced with permission from Fowler D, Cape JN, Coyle M, *et al.* (1999) The global exposure of forests to air pollutants. *Water Air Soil Pollution* 116: 5–32.

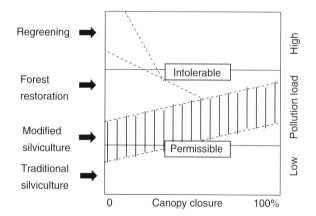

Figure 2 The operational field of silviculture in polluted areas in relation to traditional silviculture, forest restoration, and regreening of heavily contaminated barren landscapes.

optimistically, the silviculture in polluted areas, which can be seen as a specific branch of silviculture, is now *in statu nascendi*. It will need to develop for several decades at least to become 'the science of managing a polluted forest,' and even more time is necessary before 'the art of managing a polluted forest' is evident. This delay is partly related to the long time, measured in decades, that is necessary to evaluate the consequences of modified forestry practices and hence recommend (or not recommend) these practices for wide-scale application.

The International Union of Forest Research Organizations (IUFRO) Working Group on silviculture in polluted areas was established in 1951, and existed in the IUFRO structure until 1996. Activities of this group were mainly experimental, but they steadily declined in the mid-1990s due to a loss of scientific interest and (presumably) an absence of social or industrial demands for results. Not surprisingly, publications in this field are scarce and mainly restricted to reports on small-scale and usually short-term experiments. No general overview has ever been attempted, and silvicultural textbooks usually ignore the existence of polluted areas.

On a few occasions, specific silvicultural practices have not only been developed but also applied in polluted areas. These practices have resulted from the extensive and long-term efforts of scientists, and are largely based on site-specific information. Adjustment of these practices for other polluted areas would require extensive research; direct application of existing methods could easily result in adverse consequences.

What Can Be Done with a Polluted Forest?

The decision on what to do with a polluted forest naturally depends on the primary objectives of a stand at a given site. Any decisions will obviously differ between commercial forests and ecologically important forests that have a role in, for example, watershed regulation, erosion control, or nature protection.

When commercial forests started to die due to pollution impact, the first reaction of foresters was often to cut down the damaged stands in order to prevent further losses of timber. This practice was widely applied in central Europe until at least the mid-1970s, when it became obvious that the cost of harvested timber was minor in relation to the costs of rehabilitation measures required after clear-cutting.

Despite this knowledge, some local regulations (such as in Russia) still require the immediate felling of pollution-damaged forest in order to make use of the timber, regardless of what happens after the clearcutting. This emphasis on short-term economic values of the forest can be highly detrimental to longer-term values, as illustrated by the difficulties in reforesting areas such as the Ore Mountains of the Czech Republic.

The polluted forest never dies completely, and even the dead trees maintain some climatic and biotic stability for the contaminated habitats, in particular preventing soil erosion. The old clear-cuts under severe pollution impact can be rapidly transformed into industrial barrens, while some vegetation in the adjacent uncut areas remains alive (**Figure 3**). Therefore stand integrity should be maintained as long as possible, allowing some time for the development of pollution control technologies and the application of rehabilitation strategies.

It might sometimes be possible to plan different forms of timber production for different levels of pollution, but in practice this has been done only exceptionally. If a pollution impact had not been expected when a forest was established, or no preventive measures had been taken despite an obvious danger of pollution impact, the forestry practices are best modified when the process of forest degradation is at its initial stages. Whenever possible, the modified management strategy should allow an optimal balance between timber production and long-term sustainability of forest ecosystems. In some countries, modification of silvicultural practice in polluted areas is obligatory, but in most cases the

Figure 3 The former Scots pine forest 1.5 km north of the nickel–copper smelter at Nikel, Russia. Pictures are taken from the same position: uncut area (left) and former clear-cutting (right). Photographs by M. Kozlov.

recommendations developed by scientists are implemented only rarely, either because of the high cost of the suggested measures or through ignorance or negligence. In many areas, there is a recognition that severely polluted forests should not be used for timber production, especially in the ecosystems that have been badly damaged. Instead, the emphasis is on regaining ecosystem stability and integrity, and preventing any further deterioration of the forest. This is the approach often adopted in North America, with the reforestation of slopes around the Trail smelter in British Columbia, Canada, being an example.

Suggested Silvicultural Measures

Maintenance of Existing Forests

General strategy   As the visible symptoms of forest damage appear long after ecosystem stability has become affected, and after a long period of invisible or latent damage, emergency measures are needed to help declining stands. Regular restorative measures, forming the basis of silviculture in polluted areas, should be preventive, aimed at an improvement of the ecological stability of stands in such a way that they will better resist future pollution impacts. The maintenance of forests in polluted areas requires more intensive management than in unpolluted areas, involving 'soft' techniques and highly skilled manual labor.

The health of forests depends not only on pollutant toxicity or soil nutritional quality but also on a number of other environmental factors, including climate, water supply, stand density and composition, weeds, pests, and pathogens. Therefore, the direct mitigation of pollution effects is only one of several options; any technically possible and economically feasible measure to improve forest growth could be used to maintain and improve the stability of forests suffering from pollution.

This article describes restorative measures that are likely to prevent or at least slow down forest deterioration in polluted areas. For commercial forests it is also important to promote the vigor of stands as well as to attempt to produce larger trees in a shorter time, as the stands may need to be cut prematurely. Shortening the rotation time is recommended so that trees are cut before they start to die from pollution, and also to minimize soil acidification, which increases with stand age; the latter is especially important for stands of Norway spruce (*Picea abies*). In the most polluted temperate forests, rotation times may be reduced by 20–40 years, and in moderately polluted forests by 10–20 years; forests subjected to low pollution load can be cut at the same interval as unpolluted forests. Large-scale curative measure should only be applied if they are likely to mitigate the expected adverse consequences of pollution impact for at least 20 years.

Stand integrity management   The maintenance of continuous canopy (closure >80%) is especially important in polluted boreal forests, because it not only maintains a favorable microclimate near the ground but also provides some shelter for individual trees. Intentional or accidental increases in crown exposure of healthy trees often results in severe crown damage. In nitrogen-polluted forests, any disturbance of stand structure may have even more dramatic consequences, because it leads to nitrate mobilization, implying high risks of water contamination. Disturbances caused by silvicultural management should therefore be minimized, and a gap-oriented natural regeneration is preferable to clear-cuts.

Silvicultural systems based on the maintenance of diverse forests (both in terms of species composition and distribution of age classes) often need almost no adjustment when pollution increases. The continuous cover method prescribes the removal of individual trees and tree groups weakened or damaged by pollution, thereby maintaining integrity of the stand. This approach is ecologically sound, although in the long term it can result in the conversion of a predominantly coniferous forest to one dominated by broadleaved trees, simply due to the higher sensitivity of conifers to pollution.

If cutting is considered in polluted areas, the forest should not be felled until adequate regeneration is established. This is especially true of mountain areas, where the forests have important soil and climate protective roles. Large, uninterrupted clear-cuts should be avoided; instead, a two-pass system with initial cuts of 15–30 m wide strips has been recommended as facilitating the reconstruction of damaged forests. The remaining forest strips can be harvested in a second pass after 7–10 years, when young forest has established in the cleared strips.

Liming   No other silvicultural method is so debatable as the liming of polluted forests. Its principle is based on the idea that soil acidification due to the uptake of weak acids not only results in modification of nutrient availability but may cause toxic damage of fine roots of trees. An alternative theory attributes some forms of forest decline primarily to the leaching of magnesium and calcium directly from needles, giving less importance to nutrient deficiency in soil.

The main objective of older liming trials and practices was to enhance the mobilization of nutritional elements in acidic forest soils and thus increase stand productivity. However, the majority of German liming trials indicate either insignificant or no growth increase. In both Finland and Sweden, liming of Norway spruce and Scots pine (*Pinus sylvestris*) stands actually resulted in slight growth reductions. As expectations of increased tree growth were not met, and important questions about the ecological side effects of liming arose, widespread liming was discontinued in the mid-1970s. However, with the appearance of symptoms of magnesium deficiency in many forests, liming was reconsidered as a means of stabilizing stands affected by acidic deposition. Over the past two decades, dolomite lime or easily soluble neutral salts such as magnesium sulfate have been applied to many forests in central and northern Europe, the United Kingdom and the USA.

Diagnostic liming trials conducted in Germany suggest that Mg-containing lime improves the Mg status of soils, although the effect is considerably slower compared with rapidly soluble Mg fertilizers. Some of the trials conducted in the Bohemian Mountains have demonstrated a positive effect of Mg-containing lime on the growth of Norway spruce. More recently, the application of granulated magnesium-rich limestone to Scots pine stands growing on soils heavily contaminated with Ni and Cu in southwest Finland enhanced both the aboveground volume increment and the fine root production. However, the stimulation of fine root growth in the uppermost soil layers may not always be beneficial to the stand as it increases the risk of damage by drought, frost, and windthrow.

Fertilization Fertilization has long been used in forestry both to improve forest health and to enhance the productivity of stands, including forests suffering from excesses of sulfur dioxide and fluorine. As many forest ecosystems developed under conditions in which nitrogen supply is the limiting factor for tree growth, N-containing mineral fertilizers were widely applied between 1950 and the 1970s, also to aid the recovery of degraded forests.

A change has occurred in recent decades, as N inputs in polluted areas now exceed the demand of some forest ecosystems. As a result, elements such as Mg have become limiting factors for tree growth on acidic substrates. In such circumstances, application of rapidly soluble mineral NPK fertilizers in acidified stands, even those with a high soil Mg content, induced Mg deficiencies and led to nutritional imbalances in Norway spruce, as well as to NO_3^- contamination of seepage water. Conversely, an organic slow-release fertilizer amended with magnesite-derived fertilizers led to balanced nutrition and a fast recovery of tree health.

Following the widespread appearance of Mg deficiency in central Europe in the 1980s, a large number of diagnostic Mg fertilizer trials were established. These trials demonstrated that Mg deficiency in Norway spruce, silver fir (*Abies alba*), Scots pine, Douglas-fir (*Pseudotsuga menziesii*), and beech (*Fagus sylvatica*) could be corrected through the application of soluble Mg fertilizers. Although nearly any source of Mg is able to improve the nutrition of trees, in some cases an improvement in stand vitality and growth was only recorded following the application of dolomite lime or magnesite; for example, the fertilization of forests on acidified soils was particularly efficient when the supply of nutrients was combined with pH stabilization measures. Site- and stand-specific K and Mg fertilization led to the successful recovery of affected deciduous and coniferous stands of all ages (**Figure 4**) and resulted in a long-lasting improvement in soil nutritional status, aboveground biomass production and fine root vitality.

Figure 4 Scots pine in a heavily polluted site, 10 km south of Monchegorsk smelter, 3 years after application of dolomite and NPK fertilizer. Note the condition of control trees in the background. Photograph courtesy of N. Lukina.

Removal of excess nutrients In northern boreal forests, growing on infertile soils, increases in nitrogen deposition have increased forest growth. This effect may appear beneficial for commercial forests in a short-term perspective, but it can be damaging for ecologically important forests, mainly due to changes in species composition and general loss of biodiversity. Moreover, from a long-term perspective the increased N availability may lead to the economically undesirable replacement of coniferous stands by broadleaved forests.

Reduction of the accumulated nutrients can be achieved by removal of the litter and humus layer, usually by mechanical sod-cutting; the experimental removal of litter in oak forests was once carried out by a powerful litter-blower. Grass mowing with subsequent removal, intensive grazing, and prescribed burning have also been suggested, although such techniques have rarely been applied, even at the experimental scale. Mechanical removal of litter and humus should be combined with intensive thinning, which reduces the litter production and increases the decomposition rate by changing the microclimate near the forest floor. As a palliative, measures enhancing the medium-term storage capacity of forest ecosystems for nitrogen should be applied before the nitrogen deposition levels are reduced, and nitrogen-releasing disturbances should be strongly avoided.

Protection against co-occurring stressors Forests damaged by pollution may be subjected to increased attacks of pests and pathogens, implying a need for careful monitoring and possibly for the application of protective measures at lower levels of infestations than recommended for unpolluted forests. Moreover, silvicultural measures, especially the application of N-containing fertilizers, may enhance forest damage by some herbivores.

Regeneration of Polluted Forests

General strategy The regeneration procedure that is adopted will obviously depend on the scale of disturbance and the site conditions, primarily microclimate, soil toxicity, and soil nutritional quality. If neighboring stands ameliorate the microclimate sufficiently, target forest stands with the original or an adjusted species composition can be established directly. On large clear-cuts, where the forest microclimate has been severely disrupted, substitute forest stands should first be established. This may be with a nurse crop of trees that will not necessarily be a component of the final forest, mainly due to change in species composition and general loss of biodiversity. For example, in the Ore Mountains, rowan (*Sorbus aucuparia*) has been used as a nurse crop for

beech, enabling the beech seedlings to become established.

In the most severely affected areas, where soil toxicity inhibits the growth of seedlings, soil detoxification by liming should be undertaken, followed by the establishment of a herbaceous grass cover before trees and shrubs can be successfully established. Monospecific stands should be avoided, as these are unstable.

Site preparation Soil ploughing after clear-cutting is a common forestry practice, which has positive effects on the first phases of forest regeneration. In the Upper Silesian Industrial Region, full tillage of the sandy soil promoted better growth of nearly all tree species in their juvenile period than other methods of soil preparation (plowing or disk cultivation). Full tillage decreased soil acidity, reduced metal contents, enhanced microbiological activity, and decreased infections of young trees by root-rot fungi (*Heterobasidion annosum*). However, plowing also decreased mycorrhyzal infestation of Scots pine roots and the soil content of N, K, and Mg, requiring compensatory measures.

During the reforestation of clear-cuts exposed to acidic deposition, diagnostic fertilization and liming were applied in the same way as for the revitalization of damaged stands in Germany and the Czech Republic. Current recommendations are that liming be conducted at least twice, before the mechanical preparation of soils and after planting of seedlings. Fertilization should be restricted to planting holes or planting rows so as to minimize competition from weeds. Herbicide application may enhance seedling establishment in habitats covered by grasses (*Calamagrostis villosa* or *Agropyron repens*) but others recommend that herbicides be avoided during site preparation in polluted regions. Bulldozing of areas covered by *C. villosa*, the grass species that makes the replanting of forest trees extremely difficult or even impossible, promoted the establishment of pioneer trees and therefore accelerated the natural succession leading to the establishment of a full forest cover.

Selection of tree species In some cases, forest stands that are unable to fulfil their production, protection, or recreation functions as a result of recent or expected damage by pollution should be gradually converted. In particular, dense stands of Norway spruce trap more pollutants than broadleaved forests, and therefore a change to beech stands has a potential to reduce the impact of further deposition on forest soil to about half the value in spruce stands. Conversion may also be unintentional, resulting from subjective (partially economic) reasons, when trees requiring greater cultivation skills and continuous care, such as beech and silver fir (*Abies alba*), are replaced by less demanding tree species, primarily birches (*Betula pendula* Roth and *B. pubescens* Ehrh.) and mountain ash (*Sorbus aucuparia* L.), which simply occupy the clear-cuts when recultivation measures are insufficient or neglected. After 10–20 years, these substitute forests can be gradually converted by planting the seedlings of target species.

Substitute tree species should assure the environmental and, to a certain extent, also the production functions of forest ecosystems. The choice of tree species for the conversion depends primarily on the site conditions, but it is always advisable to allow the development of a forest with a tree composition typical for the region, and seed material should preferably represent a local ecotype.

Selection of resistant genotypes Conspecific plant individuals differ greatly in their sensitivities to both pollutant toxicity and the impact of co-occurring stressors. Some individuals of generally sensitive species, such as Scots pine and Norway spruce, can sustain extreme pollution loads for decades after their neighbors have been killed by pollution. Selection for pollution resistance has been demonstrated for trembling aspen (*Populus tremuloides*), birches, and willows, and several researchers have recommended the planting of the progenies of the resistant individuals in polluted areas. However, it seems that this recommendation had never been applied, nor have recommendations arising from several provenance experiments that demonstrated different pollution tolerances amongst geographical strains.

In view of the co-occurrence of numerous stressors in polluted areas, as well as the long production time of trees, it seems inadvisable to select genotypes on the basis of their resistance to a single stressor, even if this stressor is currently believed to be the most important. Sufficient genetic variation should therefore be maintained in the cultivated populations to allow for the distribution of risks.

Planting, tending, and thinning The reforestation measures to be adopted in clearcuts subjected to acidic deposition do not differ from those applied under normal forestry practices. Direct sowing is mostly used for birches (*Betula pendula* and *B. pubescens*) and *rowan*, provided that conditions permit. When using the seedlings, container-grown plants (normally with a bigger root-ball volume) are preferable to bare-root stock because they increase the chances of successful establishment. The best-growing seedlings and saplings should be selected with the assumption that their vigor will potentially assure relatively higher performance in contaminated habitats.

Stand density is linked to tree health via competition with neighbors, resistance to wind and snow, and the ability to regulate microclimate. It has long been suggested that young stands in areas affected by acidic deposition should be established with a low density, which would allow plants to develop large symmetrical crowns. However, recent recommendations have been to the effect that the number of seedlings planted in the polluted areas should be 15–20% higher than in unpolluted areas. This compensates for higher mortality and also offers more opportunities for selecting the trees with the best crown vitality during precommercial and commercial thinning.

Silvicultural measures in young stands growing in polluted areas should begin earlier and be more frequent but less intensive than in unpolluted areas. From the earliest stages of the stand, i.e., from the thicket stage onwards, care should be taken to ensure the optimal development of crowns but at the same time avoid disruption of the canopy. An additional problem is stand resistance to wind breakage, which is generally lowered by pollution; it can be increased by manipulation of the crown cover, specifically encouraging the growth of long crowns.

Forest Restoration

The full restoration of forests differs from the restoration of other types of vegetation, mostly in relation to the time required to complete the process, and there is no known example of a successfully completed restoration (*sensu stricto*) of the forest communities on lands contaminated by industrial pollution. The land reclamation program in Sudbury, Canada, the only practical example of a large-scale restoration of an area impacted by an extreme pollution conditions, has only been in operation for a relatively short period compared to the time required for successional processes to form forest ecosystems. However, this example (**Figure 5**) shows that it is possible to convert heavily contaminated barrens into forests over a period of about two decades, assuming that there is the social demand for such a conversion and sufficient financial support is granted.

Forest restoration in Sudbury started with liming and seeding of barren land, followed by planting tree seedlings, mostly of species that were dominant in the previous forest. The original motivation was to improve Sudbury's image as a treeless wasteland, but gradually the revegetation philosophy became increasingly based on landscape and ecosystem. New perspectives include assistance in the establishment

Figure 5 Revegetation of the Camberian Heights site in Sudbury, Canada. (a) 29 July 1981; (b) 20 May 1982, following liming and grass sowing; (c) 6 July 1988; (d) 28 April 2003. (a, b, c – reproduced with permission from Winterhalder K (1995) Natural recovery of vascular plant communities on the industrial barrens of the Sudbury area. In: Gunn J (ed.) *Environmental Restoration and Recovery of an Industrial Region*, pp. 93–102. New York: Springer-Verlag. d, photograph courtesy of K Winterhalder.)

of an appropriate understory in the re-established pine 'forests.'

When the Sudbury Environmental Enhancement program started in 1969, it was specifically stated that the intention was not to create a commercial forest. The main motive was aesthetic, which means that there was no plan to harvest these forests in the future, although they are not formally protected like a nature reserve.

Conclusion

As forests cover some 30% of the earth's land surface, account for some 70% of terrestrial net primary production, and are being bartered for carbon mitigation, it is critically important that we continue to develop the strategies aimed at sustainable forestry in the industrialized world. Forests were disturbed or destroyed by pollution for a quite long time, as an inevitable part of civilization. We inherit a large area from the past and the destruction continues to the present, in spite of efficient pollution control and advanced mitigation measures.

The key to the sustainable management of forests under pollution stress is the knowledge of the biological processes that are affected by pollution, as well as on basic forest ecology, and substantial progress in obtaining relevant knowledge was achieved during recent decades. However, the knowledge that a certain input may stress certain type of forests is of little use unless those forests can be identified reliably and treated accordingly. Identification of forest damage is progressing better than the mechanisms for making management decisions, most of which are currently based on empirical field trial results. More generally, silviculture in polluted areas, seen as a specific branch of silviculture, is still in the process of development. However, in spite of the limited theoretical framework, silviculture in polluted areas has already produced valuable practical results, showing that both forest restoration and sustainable forest management in polluted areas are possible – although costly – as they usually require highly skilled manual labor and intensive application of lime and fertilizers.

See also: **Afforestation**: Stand Establishment, Treatment and Promotion - European Experience. **Environment**: Environmental Impacts; Impacts of Air Pollution on Forest Ecosystems. **Genetics and Genetic Resources**: Genetic Aspects of Air Pollution and Climate Change. **Silviculture**: Forest Rehabilitation.

Further Reading

Evers FH and Hüttl RF (1990) A new fertilization strategy in declining forests. *Water Air Soil Pollution* 54: 495–508.

Gunn J (ed.) (1995) *Environmental Restoration and Recovery of an Industrial Region*. New York: Springer-Verlag.

Hüttl RF and Schneider BU (1998) Forest ecosystem degradation and rehabilitation. *Ecological Engineering* 10: 19–31.

Hüttl RF and Wisniewski J (1987) Fertilization as a tool to mitigate forest decline associated with nutrient deficiencies. *Water Air Soil Pollution* 33: 265–276.

Kozlov MV, Haukioja E, Niemelä P, Zvereva E, and Kytö M (1999) Revitalization and restoration of boreal and temperate forests damaged by aerial pollution. In: Innes JL and Oleksyn J (eds) *Forest Dynamics in Heavily Polluted Regions*, (IUFRO Research Series no. 1), pp. 193–218. Wallingford, UK: CAB International.

Malkonen E, Derome J, Fritze H, *et al.* (1999) Compensatory fertilization of Scots pine stands polluted by heavy metals. *Nutrient Cycling in Agroecosystems* 55: 239–268.

Schütz J-Ph (1985) Forest decay in a continental-wide polluted environment: control by silvicultural measures. *Experientia* 41: 320–325.

Sheppard LJ and Cape JN (eds) (1999) *Forest Growth Responses to the Pollution Climate of the 21st Century*. Dordrecht, The Netherlands: Kluwer.

Slodičák M and Novák J (eds) (2002) *Results of Forestry Research in the Ore Mountains in 2001*, Proceedings from the National Workshop, 14 March 2002, Teplice, Czech Republic. Prague: Forestry and Game Management Research Institute.

Tesař V (ed.) (1994) *Management of Forests Damaged by Air Pollution*, Proceedings of 'Silviculture in Polluted Areas' Working Party, 5–9 June 1994, Trutnov, Czech Republic, Brno, Czech Republic: University of Agriculture.

SOCIAL AND COLLABORATIVE FORESTRY

Contents

Forest Functions

A Blum, Wageningen University Wageningen, The Netherlands

Introduction

The term 'forest functions' is often used to describe a set of functional relations between forest and humans. Despite its descriptive and pragmatic advantages, the term offers some analytical shortcomings: these can be overcome, if the functional relations are separated into two classes: the effects of forests and the specific performance of forestry. This can offer a sound analytical base for forest policy and forest management.

Functions

A Descriptive and Pragmatic Concept

Trees and forests have always provided goods and services for individual or societal use. The term 'function' refers to the relation between forest and humans that is constituted by the process of offering and obtaining goods and services. Similar to the way in which the term is used in mathematics, forestry tries to encapsulate human–forest relationships by means of the term 'forest function.' It is not known when the term 'function' was used first in forestry but in 1953 Viktor Dieterich stated in his forest policy textbook a system of functional relations and described a so-called theory of forest functions (*Funktionentheorie*). Since the second half of the twentieth century forestry has been, and still is, influenced by this theory of forest functions, but the triad of Dieterich's forest functions, namely 'use,' 'protection,' and 'recreation' (in German: *Nutz-, Schutz-, Erholungsfunktion*) has been extended and modified over several decades. One example for a list of forest functions is shown in **Table 1**.

Whether developed by practitioners or scientists, most of the tables enumerating functions have been pragmatically constructed after seeking the existing or potential use of forests. Intuitive answers or empirical findings were then transformed into abstract classification systems, which in general can be seen as groupings according to the main types of forest use. Main functional categories refer to 'commodity functions' for timber and nontimber forest products, 'protective functions' against natural hazards, 'social functions,' which are mainly related to recreational use of forest areas, and 'conservation and cultural functions.' Nowadays the various classification schemes for forest functions, which are described in literature or used in forestry practice, are innumerable.

Multifunctional Forestry

There is constant debate about whether a separation or an integration principle for the management of the various forest functions should be used as a guiding principle. A central European perspective, developed on the basis of the natural potentials of temperate zone forests, favors the multifunctional integration of different forest uses in the same forest area. The Anglo-Saxon and American management approach seems to favor a separation of uses, thus defining areas mainly to be used for wood production, while dedicating other forest areas for nature conservation purposes or recreational use. For both of the approaches some good arguments from the natural sciences do exist. However, in essence, the main reason for accepting or rejecting separation or integration can be traced back to some ideological and normative aspects, rooted in the realm of social sciences.

The separation or integration of forest uses is directly related to the political and economic question of what type of ownership should be responsible for guaranteeing appropriate levels of function provision. The separation approach allows private forest owners to concentrate on the production function, while community- or state-owned forest land is to be used to provide recreational or conservation functions.

In contrast, the integration approach served for a long time as the standard for good central European forest stewardship and led, irrespective of ownership, to a concept of multifunctional forestry. This option for a harmonious coexistence of different uses on the same forest land is based on the assumption that sustainable timber production and all other nonproductive functions could be supplied at suitable levels. Statements that all other functions of forest follow in the wake of the production function have been used in forest policy debates especially since the 1970s in order to avoid restrictions on forest management, potentially imposed by societal concerns for the recreational and natural protection functions.

Currently, new approaches to nature conservation, in particular to the protection of evolutionary and self-regulated processes, increasingly pose questions about the multifunctional concept. The separation concept also increasingly comes under pressure as acceptance of pure production from at least parts of the forest area is vanishing. Regardless of whether the ongoing developments will lead to forest management concepts beyond separation or integration, the central European idea of being able to perform simultaneously various, if not all, forest functions at the same place and time generated the term multifunctional forestry, which has a striking appeal and has become accepted worldwide.

Political Merits of the Term Functions

The forest functions offer exceptional potential as container terms in political debates. On the agendas of these debates forestry communities seek to legitimize their claims in a changing society and to be approved for using existing forest resources according to their own needs as free as possible from unwanted outside influences. A 'functions' perspective always ranks the forest first and somewhat overshadows the user: forests offer functions that can be obtained provided forest management is appropriate. The ideology of forest-centrism (*Silvazentrismus*) therefore can restrict societal attempts to misuse forests and to restrain forest community infighting, which undoubtedly exist, if only subliminally, as the respective forest managers represent different types of forest ownership.

Be it a standard functional or a more sophisticated multifunctional perspective the term 'function' can be used to emphasize the societal importance of the interconnected unit of both forests and foresters. According to traditional self-perception and external communications there is a cooperative supply chain, as forestry transmits and administers forest functions to society. Forestry is located in the center of the exchange system between forest functions and contributes to societal welfare (**Figure 1**).

Table 1 Example of a classification scheme for forest function: reference model for variety, importance and interactions of forest functions of the European Parliament (1997)

Social functions				Economic functions		Ecological functions					
Cultural	Education	Recreation	Landscape	Activities and services	Production	Preservation		Protection		Regulation	
History	Information and sensitizing	Leisure (relaxation, culture)	Rural landscape	Environment for recreation	Wood (industrial wood, fuelwood)	Biological diversity	Maintenance of current diversity	Against natural risks	Avalanches	Climate	Temperature
Myths	Ecocitizenship education	Eco-tourism	Urban landscape (Trees and green areas)	Reserve of land	Game/fowl		Preservation of future diversity at local level		Rock-slides		Humidity
Aesthetic and spiritual values				Hunting	Cork and bark		Preservation of future diversity in land-use planning	Against noise			Atmospheric composition
				Leisure activities and tourism	Decorative plants						Rainfall
				Land use planning							Wind
										Air quality	Refinement
											Purification
										Water systems	Controlling rising water levels
											Maintenance of low levels
										Water quality	Purification
											Protecting water-catchments and supply areas
											Reduction of sediment content in water flows
										Soil maintenance	Reduction of diffuse erosion
											Reduction of erosion in fragile areas
											Soil reconstitution

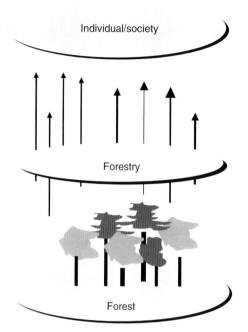

Figure 1 A classical perspective on the various functions of forests and multifunctional forestry as a transmitter of forest functions to society.

Analytical Shortcomings

Regardless of the merits of the functions term in political discussions, there are some basic analytical shortcomings that need to be mentioned. From a scientific point of view, the quality of all descriptive approaches to collecting and enumerating existing or potential forest functions is restricted by the completeness of the enumeration of individual functions and the logical consistency of the ordering system employed. A collection, enumeration, or classificatory system can itself never serve as a sound explanatory system, which provides deeper insights or better understanding of the object of interest. For example, the German discussion on the intrinsic content of the term use-function (*Nutzfunktion*) can be mentioned; is there reason to distinguish the mainly timber-related use-function from the nature protection-function, as both are inevitable of societal use? A pure classification system, offering definitions only, was mistaken for an explanatory system to be employed for directing processes and influencing actual political developments.

Nowadays, forest policy research therefore rejects the uncritical use of the concept of forest functions, which never met the demands of a theory. Instead the interest approach of the social sciences is employed in order to describe, analyze, and explain processes in forestry and activities of forest-related stakeholders.

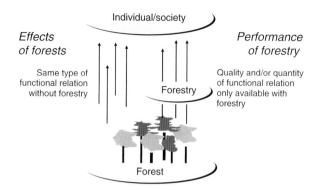

Figure 2 Distinction between effects of forests and the performance of forestry.

Beyond Functions

Effects of Forests vs. Performance of Forestry

Traditional forest economics has some problems with the concept of forest functions; this can be linked to the fact that the concept fails to describe forestry adequately, as the main object of interest of forest economics, in its role as a transmitter of benefits between forest and humans (**Figure 2**).

Analyzing the list of forest functions shown in **Table 1** it must acknowledged that only parts of the beneficial stream of goods and services from forest to humans can be improved or even influenced by forestry. At least for some of the functions of forests, there is no need for forestry (by means of any kind of human influence on natural processes) to safeguard given levels of individual or societal well-being. One can make a thought-experiment to envisage the future development of existing forests or even bare land in the absence of any kind of forestry and to analyze the hypothetical outcome, for all ecotypes and geographic zones that are naturally covered with forests. There is evidence that for all regional conditions a distinction can be made between functions or forest–human relations, which will remain unchanged or continue to exist only slightly changed without forestry, while other functions immediately or in the mid-term will cease to exist, if forestry activities should be stopped.

Managing for Performance

According to a standard definition, sustainable forest management aims to ensure that the goods and services derived from the forest meet present-day needs while at the same time securing their continued availability and contribution to long-term development. The clear distinction between effects and performances will help forestry to focus its activities efficiently. Some of the functional relations deserve and require intensive forest management, while other functional relations between forest and humans do exist, even without any kind of forestry intervention. Forestry activities therefore may be ordered according to a tripartite classification system (see **Figure 3**):

I. Functional relations are described as the effects of forests that exist without human interaction through forest management. There is no way to manage forests efficiently to improve the benefit. All forestry resources dedicated to influence these pure effects of forests may result, at best, in an alteration, but not in an improvement of the respective functional relation.

II. The performance of forestry can be understood as the ability to alter quality and quantity of existing functional relations between forest and humans through forest management. Pristine forests may provide a base level of goods and services that will meet present-day individual or societal needs, but there is an option to increase the quantitative or qualitative level of these 'functional flows' by active management (IIa). Some other functional flows may not be provided by nature herself and so do inevitably require forestry to be practiced (IIb).

III. A basic precondition for the clear distinction between effects and performance is the assumption of an enduring existence of forests. All over the world situations may be found where forests naturally could exist and even could recover easily from disturbances, but are currently threatened by destructive human influences. All forestry activities that result in a reduction of harmful human influence and increase the preservation of natural forests and their effects must be acknowledged as important measures of the

performance of forestry in safeguarding the functional relations between forest and humans. This is true even if the intrinsic relation must be classified as a pure effect of forests.

Social Conditionality of Forest Effects and Forestry Performance

At first glance, the distinction between the effects of forests and the performance of forestry seems to be a straightforward result of a thorough analysis employing data and information mainly of natural sciences.

The amount of, e.g., carbon sequestered in trees may completely be described on the basis of information delivered by the natural sciences. However, the question of whether or not carbon sequestration is an effect of forests or a specific performance of forestry has to be seen in direct relation to its social conditionality.

The property rights of forest management are a direct result of the social conditions and legal framework in which forest management takes place. If, for example, the property right of forest management includes the explicit right to permanently eradicate forest cover, all functional relations between forest and humans inevitably must be classified as in the forestry performance category. The permission to decide freely whether a forest is kept or cleared offers the broadest set of options for forest management, while, in contrast, strict standards of forest stewardship, including obligations to safeguard specific functional relations, will reduce the options available for forest management.

Implications and Outlook

As the functions of forests often justify financial and other public support of forestry, there is good reason for the intensity of debates on the meaning of functions, effects, and performances. The term forest functions offers a nebulous concept, which might be of specific value in political debates. In contrast, the terms effects and performance require a clear statement of whether something is delivered by nature without additional need to spend forestry resources, or whether something has to be delivered by forestry under given legal conditions, or, lastly, something can be offered as beneficial good or service by forestry. Under given societal and market conditions, for most countries the distinction will result accordingly in no financial streams, in compensatory payments, which at best will cover the related expenses, or in the option to actively market and sell functional relations and to gain profits, if expected income exceeds related expenses.

The term forest functions (as well as its predecessors and its successors) served and will serve an

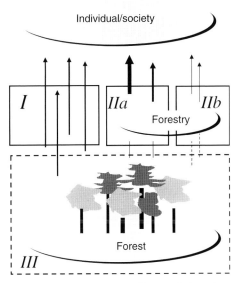

Figure 3 Distinction between effects of forests and the performance of forestry.

important function itself, as it enables foresters and society to discuss forestry in a broader perspective than primary production alone. The constant change of relative dominance of particular functional relations (production, recreation, conservation) has characterized the history of forestry and probably will characterize its future development; time will show, for which functional relations societies will appreciate forests in future.

See also: **Landscape and Planning**: Perceptions of Forest Landscapes; Perceptions of Nature by Indigenous Communities. **Social and Collaborative Forestry**: Canadian Model Forest Experience; Common Property Forest Management; Forest and Tree Tenure and Ownership; Joint and Collaborative Forest Management; Social and Community Forestry; Social Values of Forests.

Further Reading

Blum A and Schanz H (2002) From input-oriented to output-oriented subsidies and beyond–theoretical implications of subsidy schemes in forestry. In: Ottitsch A, Tikkanen I, and Rieva P (eds) *Financial Instruments of Forestry Policy, Rovaniemi, Finland 2001*. Joensuu, Finland: European Forest Institute.

Blum A, Brandl H, Oesten G, *et al.* (1996) Wohlfahrtsökonomische Betrachtungen zu den Wirkungen des Waldes und den Leistungen der Forstwirtschaft. *Allgemeine Forst- und Jagdzeitung* 167(5): 89–95. (English and French summaries.)

Dieterich V (1953) *Forstwirtschaftspolitik*. Hamburg, Germany: Parey Verlag.

European Parliament (1997) *Europe and the Forest/ L'Europe et la Fôret*, vol. 3. DG IV Publication, Series AGRI. www.europarl.eu.int/workingpapers/forest/eurfo_en.htm.

Ferguson IS (1996) *Sustainable Forest Management*. Melbourne, Australia: Oxford University Press.

Göttle A and Séne E-HM (1997) Protective and environmental functions of forests. In *Proceedings of the 11th World Forestry Congress*, 13–22 October 1997, Antalya, Turkey, vol. 2, pp. 233–243.

Leibundgut H (1985) *Der Wald in der Kulturlandschaft*. Bem, Switzerland: Haupt-Verlag.

Social Values of Forests

A Lawrence, University of Oxford, Oxford, UK

Introduction

Amongst all the environmental sciences, forestry is perhaps the one that has to recognize and work with the values of the widest range of social groups. Forests affect the interests of everyone, but are often the property or responsibility of a few. Even the definition of a forest is a value-laden exercise, in what has been termed the 'social construction of forests.' There is however a difference between the postmodernist view that forests are the projections of each observer, and the more pragmatic philosophy that forests are real systems with definite contents and boundaries – but that the importance of the contents, boundaries, and whole varies according to the observer. The last consideration has been much discussed during the last 20 years, following the famous statement by Jack Westoby in 1968 that 'Forestry is not about trees, it is about people'.

This article explores the many ways in which social values have been defined and applied, and looks at how such values are formed, recognized by forest managers, and incorporated into forest management – and what happens when they are not. Issues of consensus and conflict are considered, and the article concludes with a discussion of the evolving demands on the modern forester who needs to be able to balance social sensitivity with technical and management skills.

Definitions

The value of a forest refers to its 'worth, desirability or utility,' while the values held by people regarding the forest refer to their principles, or judgments about what is important in life. Values are implicitly subjective, and forestry, which has always held itself to be a science, sits uneasily with subjectivity. Economics has evolved its own ways of dealing with the economic value of a forest in the face of environmental concerns. However, forestry is not only about environmental values, but also about social values, a phrase which has come to be used frequently in relation to forests, but often only in passing and without explanation.

The term 'social values of forests' can best be understood as referring to the basic worth and utility of forests as are experienced by people. A distinction can be made between material utilitarian values, nonmaterial utilitarian values (such as soil conservation, climate regulation), cultural and spiritual values, and aesthetic values. These terms all relate to values of forest with respect to human use and perception. In addition, the term 'intrinsic value' is used, to denote that value related not specifically to human use and benefit, but an unchanging value outside the human sphere of influence and perception.

Another approach towards defining social values of forests is derived from environmental economics. Here a distinction is made between direct use values, indirect use values, option values (options for use in the future), bequest values (value of leaving use values for coming generations), and existence values (value from knowledge of continued existence).

Both the social values of forests and the environmental economics approach basically focus on the role of forests for human benefits. Such values do not include all forest–people relations. For instance, social values regarding forests may also include perspectives on the appropriate relation of people to forests, with, for instance, a distinction between dominion or guardianship.

The term social values has a more general connotation, referring implicitly to 'values held by people other than foresters.' In democratic, post-industrial countries the phrase might perhaps be synonymous with public values but the notion of a public that is unanimous in its desires and behavior, is transparently a problematic one.

Whilst in industrialized countries the social values of forests can seem largely related to enhancing the quality of life, in developing countries the phrase can refer to much more tangible benefits. Poor rural communities are often highly dependent on forests as part of their resource use system, for animal fodder, fuelwood, soil nutrients, medicinal supplies, and also in emergencies (times of famine, drought, war) as their sole source of food. Where forests are so essential to livelihoods, their use is often controlled by other social values as well, such as the need to maintain good social relations or one's place in the social hierarchy; and in the expression of cultural values which hold the community together. For example, the presence of sacred groves in India, Laos, and Ghana continue (to varying extents) to represent persistence of culture and to symbolize a nonutilitarian importance of the forest.

Other values held by society, or groups of people, affect their attitude to forest less directly. Spiritual beliefs, or an ecocentric philosophy, can affect people's stance on whether a forest and its species have intrinsic value, or whether aspects that benefit only humans should be valued. In the same way, some social values also have a negative impact on forests. The spiraling desire to consume, and the search for satisfaction in material goods, which underpins so much deforestation, urbanization and environmental degradation, is a much more powerful force than that based on conservation and aesthetic values.

One definition cannot cover all of these uses. 'Social' refers to society, its organization, and the relationships between groups of people. We might summarize by describing social values of forests as those that are beneficial to society as a whole, or to particular sections of society, or that are held dear in particular cultures, or that contribute to the development of human organization in a sustainable way. They may or may not be freely available, measurable, and/or accessible to all who desire them. Furthermore, they do not exist independently of people, so they evolve as society evolves – and forest management that takes account of social values will therefore be a dynamic, adaptive enterprise.

The Evolution of Social Values in Forestry

Both society, and forestry, have changed radically over the centuries of forest management, and both have affected ways in which social values are recognized. Social values change as society's organization, beliefs, affluence, level of education, and spare time change. The rise of pluralistic forestry is often attributed to the surplus income and spare time of people in post-industrial parts of the world, and it is true that the social value of forests is referred to increasingly in industrialized countries. But there has always been a social value or function of forests, in that forests have always provided benefits for people other than foresters or forest owners; and it is interesting to note that much of the early discussion of social values in forestry publications comes from Romania, Bulgaria, Poland, Hungary, and (the then) Czechoslovakia, while donors and policy-makers emphasize the value of forests for the poor, in developing countries.

There is an element of positive feedback here, in that the recognition of social values stimulates study of them, leading to further recognition. Some of the stimulus has come from within forestry: the rise of approaches such as community forestry, urban forestry, and adaptive management, and the recognition of non-timber forest products in rural communities' lives has opened the way to foresters listening to a wider range of people. But these approaches have in turn been prompted by wider movements: the global sustainability debate, and the rise of interdisciplinarity. To foresters, sustainability has in the past meant sustainable timber production, but the enormous amount of global discussion, while sometimes appearing inconclusive, at least highlights the need for attention to social as well as ecological and economic factors.

Attempts to bridge the natural and social sciences have also affected forestry. The door has opened to anthropology, which has provided a number of insights into the cultural construction of nature, the recognition of a conservation ethic among some cultures, and the documentation of indigenous knowledge and practices with potential importance for forest management. Environmental psychology has also contributed understanding of the meaning of nature, wilderness, and beauty, among other factors, to forest management. At the same time, science itself is increasingly recognized as a political and value-laden activity, where conservation values are not objective. These changes are affecting the way in which the relationship between society and nature is mediated by policy and research, and forestry is not alone in having to adapt to the new agenda.

Social values, or the values held by society, are particularly evident in the choice of species to be planted, for example on farms and common land, as well as in more conventional plantations. In making such choices, foresters, farmers, and planners reveal and reflect a wider set of values. In particular, the importance attached to the use of native or exotic species varies widely. In postindustrial society, there is often a strong public demand for native trees, resulting from awareness of threats to wildlife depending on those species, as well as perhaps a nostalgia for wilderness and more 'natural' appearance of the landscape. By contrast, foresters in many countries continue to favor exotics which grow fast and reliably, and have established markets. Exotic species can also have social value. In Ghana, rural people can associate foreign with modern and successful, and hence favor exotic trees; in contrast, in India, introduced species represent colonialism and can inspire political protests and moves to uproot plantations. A sense of aesthetic in forestry is also affected by society's stage of 'development'; in Cameroon the forest landscapes considered most beautiful include modern houses and electricity wires, a view which provides a sharp contrast to the aesthetic sense of the overurbanized, jaded, European.

Values and Stakeholders

Value Formation

In order to understand the wide range of perspectives held by society in relation to forests, we must look at the process by which values are formed. Values are strongly linked to culture, or the set of practices and beliefs which holds a community together; but they are also affected by individual circumstances, education, and experience.

Forests feature in the mythology of many cultures, and have deep-rooted associations with nature, magic, religion, safety, or evil. Consequently, they mean something to almost everyone. Religious beliefs can also influence value formation with respect to the environment, though in a wide range of ways: there are numerous studies of the proto-environmentalist messages in religious texts, but Christianity at least has in the past nurtured a view of humankind as lord of creation, which arguably has supported the exploitation and destruction of nature.

Societal change obviously affects such values, and disillusionment with consumer culture is reportedly causing a decline in materialist values among the young, in Western Europe. The global debate about biodiversity has brought a new term, and arguably a new concept, into the forest debate: to a wide range of people, forests are no longer just utilitarian storehouses of trees and forest products, but the embodiment of biodiversity, a more holistic, intangible concept. And of course the changing environment, loss of forests, and loss of contact with wilderness, as society becomes more urbanized, leads to greater interest in nature as it becomes scarcer. But the increasing emphasis placed on social choice means the public often have influence over decisions for which they are not equipped to understand the ecological consequences.

At a more individual level, education and personal experience deeply affect values. People who have experience of the negative effects of deforestation are more cautious about further damage to forests, and value forest more highly. Contact with nature is also relevant; longstanding visitors to national parks often have stronger conservation values than short-term and new visitors.

Stakeholders, Conflict, and Consensus

The existence of different values for forests among different sectors of society requires an approach that analyzes the perspectives of stakeholders. 'Stakeholders' are defined as groups and organizations that have an interest or are active players in a system, such as a forest. A methodology known as stakeholder analysis for exploring the goals, values, and influence of such groups has become widely used since the early 1990s. Stakeholder analysis begins by defining the system boundaries, in order to then define groups of people who may have an interest. Direct and indirect research methods are then used to analyze the perspectives of each stakeholder. The tool is a powerful one for pointing to potential conflicts of interest, based on conflicting goals, beliefs, or values; and also for providing a starting point for building consensus or trade-off of costs and benefits between different stakeholders.

Some differences of values are broadly predictable. For example, communities living close to forests are likely to be more economically dependent on them and to value the products accordingly, while those traveling from further away tend to be seeking the 'wilderness experience' or landscape beauty values. Forests with high economic value may have low social and ecological value; and conversely, wild, wet, irregular and twisted trees may fill the imaginations of myth-starved urbanites and provide them with the high social value that the foresters' forest fails to. At a global level, those with most influence over international policy-making may value the rarity of particular kinds of forests or species (e.g., montane cloud forest in Costa Rica, or elephants in Namibia) which contrast directly with the values of local people who depend on alternative ecosystems or species for their livelihoods.

Hence, pluralistic, democratic decision-making needs to take into account not only the different values of different stakeholders, but also the potential for distortion by the greater power and louder voices of some stakeholders. A new and challenging role for foresters requires them to see through this clamor and balance the multiple desires and goals of forest users, with the need to maintain an ecologically healthy forest.

Eliciting and Measuring Social Values

Defining the stakeholders is one important step in understanding social values, but the most challenging methodologically is that of finding out (or eliciting) and comparing the values held by the different stakeholders. Economists are expert in comparing values, particularly where a financial value can be attached to them, and their expertise has certainly provided a starting point for the measurement of social values for forests. Many of the values termed 'social' are what economists would consider to be externalities, i.e., not values accounted for within the forest production system, and not accruing to the forest owner. Many are also 'intangibles,' in other words not directly amenable to measurement. Both provide a challenge in terms of observation and measurement – because the stakeholders need first to be accessed, and then indirect methods need to be used to measure their values. Still worse, as we have seen, social values can be strongly affected by personal experience, and hence be subjective, highly variable between individuals, and even unmeasurable.

Many clever methods have been devised to measure social values indirectly, under what is generally termed 'contingent valuation' using indicators such as 'willingness-to-pay.' Such values are then added or subtracted, in a process known as cost–benefit analysis, which produces an overall value for the forest. Criticism of such approaches has focused on the hypothetical nature of such responses, their vulnerability to the phrasing of the questions, and the essentially consumerist assumptions underlying such approaches. The reaction against the economist's desire to quantify all values has asked questions such

as, 'How are we to attach a number to the beauty, uniqueness, or spiritual importance of a forest or a place in a forest? How are we to account for the subjectivity of personal experience, and how do we add together the variety of personal experience?' And to some stakeholders, values of nature are absolute and cannot be discussed; for example, the Paiute Indians of Michigan, USA, cannot rank one species over another, because they consider them all to be sacred.

Experience suggests that quantitative valuation may in any case be fallacious because the resulting numbers do not represent 'reality.' The value of valuation may lie more in the process, i.e., in the scope that the activity provides for helping different stakeholders to understand each others' goals and objectives. The use of participatory methods, semi-structured interviews, focus group discussions, and storytelling may help people to express their values in ways that they can later communicate to foresters and forest planners, so that they are taken into account.

Combining the quantitative and qualitative approaches, a range of visualization tools has been developed recently that helps stakeholders interact in discussing their preferences for forest management. An approach known as multicriteria analysis (MCA) can be used to define a set of criteria that are weighted after consultation with experts, after which stakeholders are invited to score each criterion. The quantification process can itself provoke questions about the meaningfulness of such numbers, and stimulate reflection on the usefulness of instead making values explicit in debate amongst stakeholders.

A similar approach is used in the many attempts to define criteria and indicators for sustainable forest management, epitomized by a large research program conducted throughout the 1990s by the Centre for International Forestry Research (CIFOR). This enterprise has recognized that indicators of social values need to be more widely developed and applied than they currently are, and must be able to respond to change in those values. Attempts so far have proved particularly difficult – largely because the results are so different in different cultures, ecosystems, and stakeholder groups.

A different approach may be taken by psychologists, who seek to understand the attitudes and values that affect people's behavior, both in order to understand what 'the public' wants, and to consider effective communication methods to encourage the public to interact with forests in a sustainable way. Psychologists may use both quantitative and qualitative approaches in their research, but conduct their analysis and communicate their results on their own behalf. They can also help foresters to understand how they are perceived, and to change their public image.

Implications

Implications for Forest-Based Trade and Certification

The values that consumers hold in relation to forests can be powerfully expressed through their purchasing behavior. The ethics of consumption choices has increasingly been expressed through various certification schemes, in the case of forestry since the early 1990s. Most certification schemes allow consumers to choose timber which has been sourced from forests deemed to be managed sustainably – a definition which in the last few years has sought to include social sustainability by responding to the concerns of forest-dwelling communities. In so choosing, the consumer rarely knows the forest in question and is in fact expressing a value for the forest's existence and for the philosophy of ethical consumption; he or she is valuing an idea as much as a product. The premium for certified forest products might be held to represent the social value of sustainability, and reflect the increasing concern about sustainability in general.

The timber certification movement has taken off surprisingly quickly, but its representation of social concerns responds more to the beliefs of consumers about how forests should be managed, than to their knowledge.

Implications for Forest Training and Practice

The rise of pluralistic and adaptive forest management requires a revolution in forestry planning, management, and evaluation. The forester can no longer be the manager of a biological resource with economic value, but must acquire skills in communication, consultation, facilitation, and conflict-management participation. The forester has evolved from regulator to facilitator, from harvest planner to intermediary, channeling communication and perspectives between community and government.

Foresters continue to be on the receiving end of criticism that they fail to understand the values and needs of the urbanized or forest-dependent communities that they serve, both in postindustrial countries and in developing countries. Several studies and surveys indicate contrasts between the values of foresters (favoring nature conservation and/or timber production) and their constituency (villagers needing sustainable production of food and medicine; urban public wanting landscape beauty and recreation, or a wilderness experience). To a large extent, diplomas and undergraduate training in forestry tend to be a biological and industry-based education, focusing on timber production; the social skills are acquired (if at all) during MSc courses and vocational or in-service training programs.

Foresters can feel threatened by the changes in values and expectation, but on the other hand there is little currency in the argument that there is no longer room for professional foresters who can ensure biological sustainability. Instead, foresters need their ecological training, and must also be able to listen to the public and balance publicly defined goals with the demands of biology.

Implications for Policy and Governance

Amongst forest users, the single factor that most directly affects values for the forest is tenure; and in industrialized countries, recreational access. It is widely recognized that the forest with highest value to society is not private forest. Both ownership and access rights are factors which are directly affected by policy and its implementation.

Finally of course the vast range of social values and stakeholders in forestry require attention to the processes by which forest-related decisions are taken. Deliberative, inclusive, and reflective policy-making processes help people to recognize and develop their values. The fact that pluralistic, values-based forest management involves moral and political questions, has in many countries moved forestry decisions out of the relevant department of the civil service, to a higher, or more intersectoral, or more participatory, arena.

See also: **Landscape and Planning**: Perceptions of Forest Landscapes; Perceptions of Nature by Indigenous Communities; Visual Resource Management Approaches. **Social and Collaborative Forestry**: Canadian Model Forest Experience; Common Property Forest Management; Joint and Collaborative Forest Management; Social and Community Forestry

Further Reading

Adamowicz WL (ed.) (1996) *Forestry, economics and the environment*. Wallingford, UK: CAB International.

Buckles D (ed.) (1999) *Cultivating Peace: Conflict and Collaboration in Natural Resource Management*. Ottawa, Canada: International Development Research Centre and World Bank.

Colfer CJP and Byron Y (eds) (2001) *People Managing Forests: The Links Between Human Well-Being and Sustainability*. Washington, DC: Resources for the Future.

List PC (ed.) (2000) *Environmental Ethics and Forestry: A Reader*. Radnor, PA: Temple University Press.

Lockwood M (1999) Humans valuing nature: synthesising insights from philosophy, psychology and economics. *Environmental Values* 8(3): 381–401.

Raison RJ, Brown AG, and Flinn DW (eds) (2001) *Criteria and Indicators for Sustainable Forest Management*. Wallingford, UK: CAB International.

Richards M, Davies J, and Yaron G (2003) *Stakeholder Incentives in Participatory Forest Management: A Manual for Economic Analysis*. London, UK: Immediate Technology Publishing.

Sheil D and Wunder S (2002) The value of tropical forest to local communities: complications, caveats and cautions. *Conservation Ecology* 6(2).

Sheppard SRJ and Harshaw HW (eds) (2000) *Forests and Landscapes: Linking Ecology, Sustainability and Aesthetics*. Vancouver, Canada: University of British Columbia.

Vermeulen S and Koziell I (2002) *Integrating Global and Local Biodiversity Values: A Review of Biodiversity Assessment*. London, UK: IIED.

Westoby J (1989) *Introduction to World Forestry*. Oxford, UK: Blackwell.

Common Property Forest Management

J E M Arnold, Oxford, UK

Concepts, Definitions, and Terms

A 'common-property' regime is a regulated form of joint control and management of a resource by a group of users, with powers to define membership of the group, to exclude those who are not members, and to set rules governing use of the resource. It contrasts with unregulated 'open access' use of such resources when they are available to all and consequently not owned or managed by anyone, or with private or state control.

In the past a resource used in this manner has often been termed a 'common-property resource.' However, the use of the term 'common property' for both a resource that can be used in a managed or unmanaged fashion, and for a form of management regime that is limited to a specific group that holds rights in common, has proved to be confusing. A resource used in common is therefore now termed a 'common-pool resource.' Such a resource is usually characterized as one where exclusion of users from the resource is costly, one person's use subtracts from what is available to others, and overuse leads to degradation.

A common-pool forest resource may be the forest as a whole, or part of it. Or it may relate just to the product flows from that resource, or to individual product flows, such as timber, or fuelwood, or grazing. It is thus necessary to distinguish between rights to use a resource and the rights related to the resource itself. A common-property regime does not necessarily require ownership of the forest resource, just rights to control usage.

This is particularly important in understanding uses in forests, where much of the resource is owned by the state, but most usage is by individual, collective or industrial entities, frequently with multiple users exercising rights to different products or to use at different times of the year. There can therefore be several different common-property regimes governing different outputs of a particular forest, and involving different groups of users. Similarly, the institutional arrangements for producing and selling forest products (flow units) are quite likely to be different from those controlling and managing the forest itself (the stock). Common-property use of particular forest products can also be found on private property.

Most management of forest resources as common property involves extractive outputs such as wood, nonwood products, and forage. However, it can also involve nonextractive uses, such as flood control.

Common-Property Versus Alternative Forms of Forest Tenure

Historically, common-property regimes have evolved where the demand on a resource has become too great to tolerate open access use any longer, so that property rights in the resource have to be created, and other factors make it impossible or undesirable to allocate the resource to individuals, or to the state. A common-property regime can also emerge as a way of securing control over a territory or a resource, to exclude outsiders, or to regulate the individual use by members of the community. Collective management has historically been particularly prevalent where forests have provided critically important inputs into agriculture (e.g., providing replenishment of soil nutrients through green mulch or tree fallow), where livestock management depends on access to woodland or forest (as in arid Africa and Asia), or where forests provide important dietary inputs (e.g., in high forest regions without livestock).

As pressures on the resource increase over time, common-property regimes may be replaced by private property or state management, or revert to unregulated open access use, or, as is found in many forest situations, to some combination of rights and regimes. However, forest resources can continue to be managed as common property for long periods, where this continues to be the most appropriate form of management. For instance, it is still an active system of forest management in parts of the European Alps.

Historically, however, common-property forest management regimes have been widely reduced. Much of the decline has come about because of economic, demographic and social change, e.g., increasing pressures to privatize a resource or product in order to benefit from new market opportunities, the option of purchasing rather than producing certain goods earlier sourced from a common-pool resource, and changes in rural labor availability and allocation. The share of forest resources controlled as common property has also been much reduced by expropriation by governments of forest and woodland as forest or nature reserves or some other form of state property, or as part of moves by colonial and postcolonial governments to increase their control over local activities.

Government policies and strategies that eroded common property have been widely influenced by arguments that it is inefficient, and unsustainable, by comparison with private property or state ownership. Such arguments stem from an assumption that, as user pressures build up, the cohesion and discipline necessary for effective collective management cannot be sustained and will break down, and that it will become increasingly difficult to exclude outsiders, resulting in unregulated, open access overuse of the resource. This thesis, given prominence through a very influential 1968 article by G. Hardin in *Science* entitled 'The tragedy of the commons,' contributed to pursuit of land distribution policies that favored individual private land holdings, and state control of forest resources.

Since the mid-1980s, evidence has accumulated to show that, while this thesis can and often does apply, it should not be held to be of general application. In appropriate situations users often prove to be able to create and sustain collective arrangements that avoid overuse. In addition, it has been demonstrated that private and state alternatives to common-property management can also fail to prevent overuse of forest resources.

Recently there have been major shifts in development thinking and policy that have begun to reverse some of the tendencies to centralize control. Structural adjustment policies in favor of devolution and decentralization, and greater local participation, have seen the emergence in forestry of a much greater focus on local forest management. Much of social or community forestry has been taking forms that are derived to some extent from concepts and practices of common-property management.

Conditions Favoring Common-Property Forest Management

A considerable amount of research attention has been directed towards identifying the conditions in which common property is likely to be viable and stable. **Table 1** summarizes the main variables that have been identified as being critical to the sustainable functioning of common-property systems across

Table 1 Critical enabling conditions for sustainability on the commons

(1) Resource system characteristics
- Small size
- Well-defined boundaries
- Low levels of mobility
- Possibilities of storage of benefits from the resource
- Predictability

(2) Group characteristics
- Small size
- Clearly defined boundaries
- Past successful experiences – social capital
- Appropriate leadership – young, familiar with changing external environments, connected to local traditional elite
- Interdependence among group members
- Heterogeneity of endowments, homogeneity of identity and interests
- Low levels of poverty

(1 and 2) Relationship between resource system characteristics and group characteristics
- Overlap between user group residential location and resource location
- High levels of dependence by group members on resource system
- Fairness in allocation of benefits from common resources
- Low levels of user demand
- Gradual changes in levels of demand

(3) Institutional arrangements
- Rules are simple and easy to understand
- Locally devised access and management rules
- Ease in enforcement of rules
- Graduated sanctions
- Availability of low-cost adjudication
- Accountability of monitors and other officials to users

(1 and 3) Relationship between resource system and institutional arrangements
- Match restrictions on harvests to regeneration of resources

(4) External environment
- Technology
  - Low-cost exclusion technology
  - Time for adaptation to new technologies related to the commons
- Low levels of articulation with external markets
- Gradual change in articulation with external markets
- State:
  - Central governments should not undermine local authority
  - Supportive external sanctioning institutions
  - Appropriate levels of external aid to compensate local users for conservation activities
  - Nested levels of appropriation, provision, enforcement, governance

Adapted with permission from Agrawal A (2002) Common resources and institutional sustainability. In: Ostrom E *et al.* (eds) National Research Council, *The Drama of the Commons*, pp. 62–63. Washington, DC: National Academics Press.

a range of different common-pool resources. All four of the areas identified – characteristics of the resource, characteristics of the user group, institutional arrangements, and external factors – have application to common-pool forest resources.

Characteristics of the Resource

Physical characteristics   Collective management is more likely to succeed if the resource has definable boundaries and can be shown to be linked with the user community. For instance, proximity to the user community facilitates protection of the resource for the exclusive use of the controlling group, and monitoring of its use by its members.

A forest resource that needs to be managed in its entirety, in order to maintain the interactive environment necessary to maintain some of the desired outputs, is more likely to induce collective management than tree stocks that could be split up into individually managed units. This is also the case with some large resource systems, such as woodland in arid areas, where the location of productive zones can vary from year to year. Group management will also be favored where there are multiple uses and users, and coordination among them is necessary.

Productivity and capacity to meet user needs   The incentive for users to invest in collective management is likely to be greater if the resource is capable of meeting a substantial part of users' needs, and if these benefits can be obtained rapidly and regularly. An existing forest that is already producing is consequently more likely to be suited to local management than one that has to be planted up and will yield benefits only after several years.

The resource also needs to have the potential to yield benefits commensurate with the costs the group are likely to incur in bringing it under management. Failure of common-property forest management can often be linked to the shrinking size or degraded nature of the available local resources. Similarly, if only low-grade forest or low-value components of a forest are made available for local use, the incentive for users to manage them as common property is likely to be weak.

Ease of management   The ease with which the resource can be managed by the user group is also important. Most functioning local collective systems in practice involve easily managed products such as fodder and fuel (which are also products from which members of the user group are likely to be able to benefit in an equitable manner). Managing a wider range of forest products, or more intensive use, can introduce levels of complexity and skills that groups may find difficult to take on.

This reflects the high costs of obtaining information on which to establish more intensive management and use practices, and the risk that lack of knowledge or skills could lead to overuse of the resource on which they depend. Ease of enforcement of rules governing use by members can also be an important factor.

Characteristics of the Group of Users

A number of group characteristics may affect the capacity of a group of users to collaborate effectively in the control and management of a local forest resource.

Shared or conflicting interests   One is the presence of more than one set of users, each with different interests and objectives. While some among multiple demands on a forest may be complementary (e.g., for products obtained from different component species, or for using the forest at different times of the year), others may be more competitive or incompatible. For instance, the continued dependence of the poor on local common-pool forest resources for outputs to meet their subsistence needs frequently conflicts with the interest of the wealthier within the community in privatizing the resource, or some of its product flows, in order to take advantage of growing market demand for forest products. A consequence of such competing pressures is likely to be a need for more complex control and management measures. This increases the transaction costs associated with maintaining a common-property system, sometimes to the point where such management is no longer possible without external support.

Creation of a common-property system, by excluding those who are not members of the group from further use of the resource, can also lead to conflict between the group and outsiders who previously had access to it. In addition, there can be disputes within a group over collective choice processes, or over rules for resource management and enforcement of these rules on members.

Size and composition   It has been widely argued that some of these difficulties and constraints can best be minimized by organizing collective management around small homogeneous groups, with membership of each confined just to those with similar views about the use of the resource. There is considerable evidence that such small uniform groups do find it easier to establish and maintain collective control.

However, the thesis that smallness is invariably desirable is being increasingly challenged. Although the task of dividing responsibilities and benefits may favor small and cohesive user groups, the task of managing and exercising control over the resource may call for a larger body that encompasses all those with a claim on the resource. Larger bodies are likely to be able to generate more funds with which to hire watchers to protect the resource, or to buy in outside advice or assistance. Bigger groups are also likely to have more leverage in accessing public support services, and in other dealings with government departments.

Similarly, though homogeneity of interest, needs, etc., among users can have obvious benefits in terms of internal cohesion, the thesis that this is necessary in order to manage collectively is also being questioned. Although cultural differences, or differences in the nature of the interests of participants, can make collaboration difficult, differences in economic endowment need not necessarily be an impediment, for instance if rich and poor in communities have common use patterns, and consequently a shared interest in how local forest areas should be managed. Alternatively, component subgroups may have complementary interests, e.g., with poorer members able to draw on the subsistence goods they need, and wealthier members able to generate income from other parts of the resource.

Active involvement of the more powerful within the community can also provide it with effective leadership, and increase the chances that the common-property regime will work. Lack of trust in their leaders has proved to be one of the main reasons for failure of common-property systems.

Local Institutional Arrangements

The rules relating to control and management of common property, and the local institutions to develop, apply, and enforce these rules, lie at the heart of any common-property management system. It is only a self-governed form of forest management if it rests primarily on the decisions and actions of the user group. This in turn requires that it encompass a mechanism that enables members to communicate with each other about its functioning.

Freedom to set, modify, and enforce group rules Few common-property forest management regimes are governed entirely by participants. In most situations local and central government regulations also affect what can be done. Some measure of external regulation is usually also necessary in order to establish the rights of the group to control and use the resource, to protect it against unauthorized uses

by those who are not members of the group, and to enable it to access government support services.

However, overly tightly formulated government rules for the operation of common-property systems can create problems. The very process of imposing rules itself undermines a basic principle of self-governance – namely, that the local body needs to be able to create rules appropriate to its own situation, and to modify these rules as the need to do so arises. Rules that cannot be altered by a group can freeze a constantly evolving relationship between people and the resource they draw upon at a particular point in time, preventing its adaptation to further change.

If the ability to determine and implement its own rules becomes undermined to the point that the user group is no longer the principal source of decisions and enforcement, the system is likely to have become one that is more accurately categorized as a form of shared management with the state, or industry, or whatever other entity has also acquired rights or authority to participate in the control and use of the forest resource.

For rules to be effective they need to apportion benefits in proportion to the costs that participants incur through participation in the common-property regime, which can vary across a user group. Groups in the middle hills of Nepal, for instance, recognize that households living further away from the resource are less able to benefit from it and should therefore not be expected to bear as much of the burden of protecting and tending it as those living nearer to it. There need to be incentives to cooperate, and an effective system for monitoring to ensure adherence to the rules, with agreed sanctions to be imposed on offenders, and a mechanism for resolving conflicts among users. Rules need to be accepted as being fair and legitimate by all participants.

Functional and representative institutions A wide variety of different forms of local institution, both informal and formal, can take responsibility for a common-property forest management regime. Some comprise just the group of users themselves, acting as an independent body. These will usually need to be recognized by formal government bodies in order to get access to government resources, services, and authority. Many user group institutions are in practice affiliated to, or are a subbody of, a higher-echelon community or local government institution. However, issues arise when such parent bodies, with predominantly political and bureaucratic agendas, have priorities that conflict with the interests of the forest user group.

Difficulties can also arise for long-established local common-property institutions, which reflect social values and practices from an earlier period when they came into existence, in accommodating to changes in the broader framework of local governance, for instance male-dominated forest management groups that may not adequately reflect current requirements for equitable participation by women.

External Environment

The capacity of common-property forest management regimes to function, and their continued relevance by comparison with alternative forms of tenure and management, can be affected by change in a number of external factors, for instance introduction of new technology that permits agricultural use of land previously left as commons. However, the two most important factors are usually increasing exposure to market forces, and the impact of actions by the state.

Articulation with external markets As households become more integrated into the market economy, and seek to generate more income with which to purchase goods, the task of managing forest as common property becomes more complex. Wage employment becomes more rewarding than gathering activities. The potential to sell products of the forest is likely to increase pressures to privatize the resource, and to overharvest. If the interests of those within a user group able to exploit such market opportunities, and those needing continued access to it to meet their subsistence needs, diverge, the potential for dispute and conflict is increased. Exposure to market forces can therefore put pressures on existing mechanisms for exclusion and control, and increase the costs of maintaining a resource as common property. This can be a major factor in moving management from common property to shared control involving other categories of stakeholder as well.

It has consequently been argued that management of forests as common property is usually better suited to meeting subsistence demand rather than production for the market. Though there are many instances where this form of management has handled commercial production successfully, one factor that may need to be taken into account in assessing whether a resource is suited to management as common property can therefore be the extent to which its output is likely to attract commercial rather than local use.

Interactions with the state The environment within which local common-property forest management systems are located is likely to be shaped by broader government actions in a number of ways. For the rights of a user community to control and manage a local forest resource to be recognized outside that community, they need to be supported in a manner that records this transfer of rights from the state. Ideally, there need to be legislation and regulations that provide authority both to communities and government agencies to generate the necessary rules, regulations, and operational measures, and that give them authority to implement and enforce them.

Lack of enabling legislation does not necessarily mean that local self-governance of forest resources cannot happen. In its absence, forest departments can still arrive at extralegal working arrangements with communities that enable them to continue to manage the forest areas from which they draw supplies. However, without a legal base, community-based rights can be challenged in terms of national law, and local groups can encounter difficulty in using the law to assert their rights. Without secure legal backing, local people are also left in a weak position in negotiating change with government, and can be left exposed to risk by even the best-intentioned initiatives introduced by the government.

Such problems are often aggravated because the legal base is weak and confused. In most developing countries western tenure, and more recent systems designed to transfer control over land to the new political elites, coexist with community systems, undermining the latter systems but seldom providing a satisfactory alternative because they are not enforced. This causes confusion, because the legal status of land and forest resources becomes unclear, and people can be faced with different fora for settling a dispute under the different legal systems.

The other main way in which the state impacts on common-property forest management is through broader national policies and strategies, and in the way these are implemented by government agencies. Recent trends towards liberalization and privatization, and towards structural adjustment and downsizing of the presence of central governments, have had a number of profound impacts. Liberalization has tended to reinforce pressures to privatize land and other resources, to the detriment of the often informal common-property practices that provided the poor in many places with their fuelwood, grazing, and other forest products. Structural adjustment, on the other hand, has given impetus to policies to devolve and decentralize control over forest resources, thereby encouraging local participation in forest governance and management. This has been reinforced by the growing focus of development policies on poverty alleviation.

With community forestry having become a major component of forestry over the past quarter-century, forms of local management which contain elements of common-property management have become widespread, particularly in developing countries. However, this has often evolved in ways that entail quite close involvement of government forest departments in their organization and operation. Local forest management institutions frequently have to operate within a framework of quite restrictive regulations laid down by forest departments. Forest departments often also have a presence in local management structures, and retain rights over some of the income-generating components of the forest, such as commercial timber. In practice, though there is no clearly defined border between them, many of these systems have more of the character of forms of control that are jointly managed by local people and the state, than of common-property regimes governed exclusively or primarily by the group of users.

See also: **Landscape and Planning**: Perceptions of Nature by Indigenous Communities. **Social and Collaborative Forestry**: Canadian Model Forest Experience; Forest and Tree Tenure and Ownership; Joint and Collaborative Forest Management; Public Participation in Forest Decision Making; Social and Community Forestry.

Further Reading

Arnold JEM (1998) *Managing Forests as Common Property*. Forestry Paper no. 136. Rome: FAO.

Baland J-M and Platteau J-P (1996) *Halting Degradation of Natural Resources: Is There a Role for Rural Communities?*. Oxford: Clarendon Press.

Hardin G (1968) The tragedy of the commons. *Science* 162(3859): 1243–1248.

McKean MA (2000) Common property: what is it, what is it good for, and what makes it work? In: Gibson CC, McKean MA, and Ostrom E (eds) *People and Forests: Communities, Institutions, and Governance*, pp. 27–55. Cambridge, MA: MIT Press.

Messerschmidt DA (ed.) (1993) *Common Forest Resource Management: annotated Bibliography of Asia, Africa and Latin America*. Community Forestry Note no. 11. Rome: FAO.

Ostrom E (1999) *Self-Governance and Forest Resources*. Occasional Paper no. 20. Bogor, Indonesia: CIFOR.

Ostrom E, Dietz T, Dolsak N, Stern PC, Stonich S, and Weber EU (eds) (2002) *The Drama of the Commons*. Committee on the Human Dimensions of Global Change. Division of Behavioral and Social Sciences and Education. National Research Council. Washington, DC: National Academy Press.

Social and Community Forestry

K F Wiersum, Wageningen University, Wageningen, The Netherlands

Introduction

Traditionally, in tropical countries forest management strategies have been based on the premise that sustainable forest management is best secured by state custody over forests, with management being the responsibility of a professional forest service, and by focusing forest production measures predominantly on commercial timber production. In the mid-1970s it became recognized that this strategy was too top-down-oriented and that it focused predominantly on national interests rather than on the needs of local communities. Therefore it did not contribute much towards improving the welfare and well-being of large segments of the population living in or near forests. Consequently, a new strategy for forest management was proposed, in which explicit attention was given to the forest-related needs of rural communities and to community participation in the sustainable management of forest resources. This new strategy was termed social forestry or community forestry. This strategy has become widely accepted, and in the last decades of the twentieth century much experience has been gained about how to involve local communities actively in forest management. Although many local interpretations of the meaning of the terms social forestry and community forestry exist, at present often a conceptual differentiation between the terms is made. Social forestry relates to the planning and implementation by professional foresters and other development organizations of programs to stimulate the active involvement of local people in small-scale, diversified forest management activities as a means to improve the livelihood conditions of these people. Community forestry refers to the forest conservation and management activities that are carried out by people living within rural communities, who are not trained as professional foresters, and who carry out management activities on the basis of local norms and interests. In contrast to the traditional professional approach to forest management, community forestry is not based on standard models, but on adaptation to site-specific conditions in respect to both type and conditions of forests, local livelihood strategies, and community institutions. Two main community-based forest management systems exist: community forestry in the form of the management of forest resources on any lands within a local territory by the community inhabitants, and collaborative management in the form of the collaboration of community groups in the management of state forest lands as the result of (partial) delegation of the management responsibility by professional forestry organizations. By the beginning of the twenty-first century community-based forest management had reached a significant scale, and has been accepted as a genuine strategy for forest management in tropical countries. Gradually this approach to forest management is also gaining prominence in the more economically advanced countries in Europe, northern America and Australia.

History

Changes in Thinking on Forestry and Development

In the second half of the 1970s changes in thinking about the concept of rural development as well as increasing concerns about the ongoing process of deforestation contributed to a reappraisal of traditional forestry policies and a search for new forest management systems, which would contribute better towards rural development.

Changing concepts of rural development Since the start of international programs to assist the development of the newly independent tropical countries in the 1950s, concepts of development have changed. In the early development strategies, economic growth through the creation of a modern economic sector was a major objective. Subsequently, it was realized that an increase in production does not automatically result in a proper distribution of the products. In several cases the one-sided attention to the creation of a modern economic sector resulted in a growing gap between the modern and traditional economic sectors and marginalization of various groups of people. To counter the effects of this growing inequality, more attention was then given to the distribution of economic assets, focusing specifically on provision of basic human needs and poverty alleviation. The main objective of this basic needs strategy was to fulfill the needs of underdeveloped groups of the population for food, clothing, education, and health. This strategy was based not only on humanitarian objectives, but also on the theory that economic growth will be stimulated once basic needs are met. Later still, a third aspect received attention, i.e., the possibility for rural people to participate actively in their own development process rather than being a subject of development. The objective of such local participation is to stimulate the emancipation and self-reliance of the local people. Self-reliance is not only a development objective in itself, but it also enables a more efficient use of development efforts and funds.

This evolution in thinking on the meaning of development has influenced ideas about the role of forestry in rural development in several ways:

- In line with the critical assessment of the results of the modernization approach, it was recognized that the traditional approach to forestry development, in which it was supposed that forestry would contribute to economic development through the creation of employment and income from timber plantations and wood-working industries, is often not effective. The supposed forward and backward linkages of such enterprises were mostly smaller than originally anticipated. Too often, local people hardly profited from such enterprises and, if realized, profits were siphoned off to urban elites and/or foreign investors.
- In conformity with the basic needs development strategy, it was recognized that wood products such as fuelwood for cooking and heating and timber for house construction are essential for human survival. The concerns in the early 1970s about an energy crisis contributed towards increased attention for the critical fuelwood situation in many tropical regions.
- The growing interest in providing basic needs for rural people increased awareness about the need to improve food production on marginal lands. On these lands forests and/or trees have important protective functions in moderating climatic and soil conditions. They also provide a wide range of forest products which are essential for the livelihoods of local people, not only fuelwood and timber for construction, but also wood for agricultural implements, fodder, and a multitude of non-wood forest products such as edible leaves and fruits, edible and oil-bearing seeds and nuts, honey, medicinal plants, gums and tannins, and bark products.
- As a result of the growing interest in stimulating participation, it was recognized that, rather than restricting local people's access to the forest resources, their involvement in forest management should be stimulated. Forest benefits for local people can best be assured when they can manage the forests themselves.

Impacts of deforestation, desertification, and forest degradation Simultaneously with the changes in thinking about the role of forests in rural development, concern also grew about the rate of uncontrolled deforestation and forest degradation in tropical countries. The loss of forest resources results in many undesirable ecological and environmental effects and influences the livelihood of many rural people in a negative way. In the humid tropics deforestation has resulted in land degradation and the advent of waste lands, in mountainous areas in erosion and increasing flood damage, and in the arid tropics in desertification. Especially after the disastrous drought years of the 1960s in the Sahel, these degradation processes received increasing international attention. It was recognized that the prevailing forestry policies had not been able to control the process of deforestation, and that the state forest services had often been unable to deal with the various pressures on forest which induce over-exploitation or conversion to other types of (often marginal) land use. In many tropical regions the local population is dependent on forests for their livelihoods, and consequently they often bore the brunt of deforestation. It was suggested that, in view of their forest-related needs, local communities should have a stake in maintaining forest resources and could contribute towards forest conservation.

Reappraisal of forestry policies The new insights on alternative approaches to rural development and forest conservation reinforced each other as regards the development of forest policy. Increasingly it was recognized that important discrepancies exist between the claims for sustainable forest management for multiple human benefits and the actual situation with respect to the conservation and utilization of tropical forest resources. Consequently, during the 1970s a reevaluation of the relation of forestry to rural development took place. The assumption that forest protection and management should be based on central policy and planning within an authoritative and hierarchical forest service, having im-

portant territorial and policing functions, was reappraised. A need was identified to complement the strategy of forestry development based on national interest and industrial growth with new strategies focusing on basic needs, equity, and popular participation. It was proposed that a dualistic forestry development strategy should be pursued, in which the emphasis on developing modern forest industries with their related industrial wood production areas is matched by efforts to develop forestry for rural development by focusing on the needs of the local communities and their active involvement in forest management. The new approach for forestry serving rural development was labeled as social forestry.

Gaining Practical Experience

Since the identification of the need for a new social forestry strategy, much attention has been given to formulating and implementing social forestry programs. In 1978 both the Food and Agriculture Organization and the World Bank indicated their intent to stimulate such programs. An important stimulus was also provided by the deliberations at the Eighth World Forestry Congress held in 1978 at Jakarta under the theme 'forests for people.' Many international donor agencies quickly accepted the new strategy and, since the early 1980s, an increasing number of social forestry projects have been implemented. Three phases in social forestry development can be distinguished: an experimental phase, a consolidation phase, and a diversification phase. During this evolution a gradual diversification in approach took place (**Table 1**).

The diversification in social forestry strategies concerned both technical and organizational aspects. Regarding the technical aspects, at first most attention was directed at reforestation of degraded lands,

Table 1 Phases in social forestry development

Period	Social forestry development approach
Experimental phase (late 1970s to mid-1980s)	Emphasis on establishing village woodlots and individual tree growing based on scaling-down of conventional forestry practices as a means to address fuelwood and desertification problems
Consolidation phase (second part of 1980s)	Increased understanding about the role of trees in livelihood strategies of villagers
	Less emphasis on firewood, more on multiproduct systems and integration of tree-growing with agriculture
	Increased recognition of significance of indigenous forestry practices
	Growing attention to village-level manufacturing of forest/tree products
Diversification phase (early 1990s)	Increased emphasis on conservation and management of existing forests, including controlled utilization of nonwood forest products
	New understanding about the role of common property
	Recognition of the need to conserve the cultural integrity of tribal forest dwellers
	Development of joint and collaborative forest management

but increasingly the focus became enlarged to involve natural forest conservation and management as well as agroforestry development. Several social forestry programs still focus on rehabilitating degraded lands, but increasingly also well-stocked forests are brought under community management. Concurrently, a change in product orientation took place. At first most attention was focused on the provision of products for subsistence needs. However, gradually it was recognized that appropriate forms of commercial production are also of importance for improving rural livelihoods, and that communities should have access to increased benefits from markets rather than focus on subsistence production only. Also regarding the local organization of forest management a gradual change in policy took place. Originally, social forestry projects were mainly based on the involvement of village organizations in managing village lands. In the first instance, this approach was not very effective, and consequently the emphasis changed to schemes on private lands. However, with increased understanding of the nature of common pool resources, a renewed interest in involving user-group organizations in forest management developed. Moreover, the scope of social forestry projects gradually became enlarged from either communal or private village lands to officially gazetted state forest lands. Whereas on village lands, management is under the authority of the local organizations, on the public lands the final authority still rests with the official forestry service. In this case, local organizations and professional forestry organizations enter into a collaborative program. This collaborative forestry strategy has gained prominence since the mid-1990s.

Thus, during the first phases of social forestry development it was considered that forestry development should be based on a dualistic model in which professional forest management on state lands and community forest management on village and private lands should coexist. As demonstrated by the advent of collaborative forest management schemes, at the start of the twenty-first century increased attention is given to the integration of professional and community-based forest management.

By the beginning of the twenty-first century community forest management had reached a significant scale. In tropical countries 23% of forests are either owned or managed by indigenous people and local communities. In several tropical countries an impressive number of local communities have become involved in community-based forest management. For instance, in India 63 000 village forest committees have been formed under the Joint Forest Management program, and in Nepal over 4 million people are represented in the Federation of Forest User Groups. In Mexico in less than 15 years between 7000 and 9000 communities have moved from merely owning land to community-based timber production and have started local manufacturing of wood products.

Definitions of Social and Community Forestry

During the advent of the social forestry strategy, various terms were used to represent it: not only 'social forestry' but also 'community forestry.' Originally, these terms were often considered as synonyms. Both terms were used to refer to any forestry policies and activities that closely involved local people in forest management and tree-growing, for which rural people assumed (part of) the management responsibility, and from which they derived a direct benefit. Gradually, however, the terms were differentiated on the basis of either normative commitments or management systems. In respect to normative commitments it has been suggested that the term social forestry should primarily be understood as a reaction to the conventional approaches to forestry, which were dominated by the ideology of forest conservation and production forestry under state stewardship, which legitimized forest service control over forest lands and tree species. It was suggested that social forestry involves the development of new forestry professionals who can work within a rural development context rather than a bureaucratic context. The motives of local people for being involved in forest management are not related to such considerations regarding the nature of professional activities. Rather, the community interests are to maintain forest resources as part of the local livelihood strategies. Community forestry can best be used in relation to such local interests. Alternatively, it was also suggested that the term social forestry is often used in an implicitly narrower sense than community forestry. Social forestry would refer to activities that aim at the fulfillment of subsistence needs of the poor people, and thus refer predominantly to a basic welfare function of forests, whereas community forestry would refer to a more diversified set of activities, including more commercially oriented ones.

In respect to management arrangements, it was suggested that the term social forestry could be defined as an umbrella term for various schemes aiming at forest and tree management on private and village lands aimed to produce local needs. Community forestry could be used as a broad term which includes indigenous forest management systems and government-initiated programs in which specific community forest users protect and manage state forests in some form of partnership with the government.

Thus, the term social forestry has a strong policy connotation, and is mainly related to activities of professional foresters. In contrast, the term community forestry has a more descriptive connotation, and is mainly related to activities of rural communities. The two terms can logically be differentiated on the basis of whether the terms relate to policy development activities or forest management practices and whether these activities are carried out by professional foresters or local communities.

Social forestry can be defined as a development strategy of professional foresters and other development organizations with the aim of stimulating active involvement of local people in small-scale, diversified forest management activities as a means to improve the livelihood conditions of these people.

Community forestry can be defined as any forest management activities undertaken by rural people as part of their livelihood strategies. Such activities may be self-initiated or proposed by external development programs.

The differentiation between social forestry and community forestry can further be clarified by the identification of social forestry as a development strategy aimed at the stimulation of more effective community forestry.

Social Forestry as Development Strategy

Social forestry policies encompass the process of formulation and implementation of measures to stimulate community involvement in the management of forest resources. It refers on the one hand to activities of professional foresters or development organizations aimed at stimulating the forest and tree management activities that are under the control of local people. On the other hand it refers to activities aimed at adapting the professional management practices in official (public) forest reserves, in order that this management becomes more explicitly directed towards an improvement of the welfare of rural communities. The development measures to stimulate local communities to intensify forest management may consist of the provision of external inputs, such as secure access to land, financial incentives, technical support, or extension. Also they may include arrangements for proper institutional and organizational frameworks, including legal codes, tenure policies, forestry extension organization, in order that community forestry can proceed.

Organizations which plan and implement social forestry programs do so for different reasons. The rationale for social forestry development is based either on assumptions regarding the contribution of social forestry measures to improved forest conservation and management, or on assumptions concerning its contribution to socioeconomic development (Table 2). Due to the different assumptions regarding how social forestry can contribute to solving either forest management or rural development problems, there is not just one objective for stimulating social forestry, but rather a group of objectives:

- To improve livelihoods of rural people by linking rural development and environmental conservation by ensuring that rural people can produce, or have better access to, certain basic needs in the form of essential forest and tree products and

Table 2 Assumptions on the rationale for social forestry development

Assumptions with respect to forest conservation and management

- Small-scale forest exploitation by local community groups better ensures sustainable forest management and forest conservation than large-scale commercial timber exploitation by concessionaries, because of the lower ecological impact of such small-scale activities and because, in contrast to large companies, local people cannot shift their activities to other areas in case of forest degradation resulting from overexploitation
- Allowing local forest utilization in certain concentrated areas can take the utilization pressure away from essential conservation areas, and therefore ensures better forest and nature conservation
- Ensures optimal use of human resources in forest management and therefore provides better prevention of forest degradation and improved rates of forest rehabilitation
- Changing open-access forest exploitation to community-controlled forest exploitation ensures more effective forest conservation
- Active participation of local communities in forest management lowers the costs of the state for forest conservation

Assumptions with respect to social development

- Local people should be legitimized to use and manage forest resources for their own needs and encouraged to apply their own indigenous knowledge in doing so
- Community forest management contributes towards the increased self-reliance of local people in producing valuable forest products, and allows equitable distribution of those products
- Community management of natural forests allows the preservation of the cultural integrity of tribal people and contributes to the empowerment of tribal communities to gain control over their own traditional resources
- Underprivileged rural groups should be empowered to gain control over the resources needed to improve their livelihood

services, and by promoting sustainable use of natural resource, employment generation and local institution building

- To honor the principles of democracy and social justice by devolving power and authority from state bureaucracies to local groups, increasing the participation of rural people in the management of forest and tree resources as a means of stimulating their self-reliance, and by addressing the needs and aspirations of specific underprivileged groups within the rural population, such as subsistence farmers, landless families, or other sectors of the rural poor
- To make forest conservation and management more efficient by involving local communities in the management of forest and the rehabilitation of degraded and marginal lands, thus reducing the state's costs for forest conservation

Some of these objectives may be congruent or may reinforce each other. Others are broadly divergent:

- Much attention has been given to the role of social forestry for meeting subsistence needs of poor people. However, activities to optimize subsistence production for poor people do not contribute towards the economic development of rural households which are incorporated in a commercial economy. For such households attention should be given towards improved options for production, local manufacturing, and marketing of commercially valuable forest products.
- In schemes to stimulate farmers to grow trees to meet specific market demands, it may be difficult to achieve democratic participation, especially of poor, landless people. In this case, equity objectives and distributive benefits may have inconsistent impacts among different sectors of the rural population.
- The provision of specific tree products (such as wood, fodder, or fruits) to local people may be assured by individual trees, even if standing alone or scattered in backyards or agricultural lands. These needs could be met by stimulating agroforestry practices on private lands. However, for securing other forest-related benefits (e.g., environmental services) it is often necessary to maintain forest reserves as complete and well-functioning ecosystems.

Thus, when formulating social forestry programs it is essential to specify what the precise objectives of the program are and to relate those objectives to the specific characteristics of different community forestry management schemes.

Community Forest Management

Variation in Community Forestry Arrangements

Community forestry refers to forest and tree management activities undertaken either individually or cooperatively by the local people, either on their own or on leased private lands, on communal lands or on state lands. It involves the process of making and implementing decisions with regard to the use and conservation of forest resources within a local community, with the organization of the activities being based on shared norms and the interests of the people living in that local community. Community forestry is a generic term as different forms of community forest management exist. This variation reflects the various meanings of the term 'community.' A community may be either a locality in the sense of a human settlement with a fixed and bounded local territory, a local social system involving interrelationships among people living in the same geographic area, or a type of relationship characterized by a sense of shared identity. Consequently, different community forestry arrangements are possible depending on the type of territory and the type of social relations being considered. In respect of such institutional arrangements, three main types of community forestry may be distinguished:

1. Management of any woody resources on lands which are located within a local territory, irrespective of whether these resources are privately, communally or *de facto* state-owned
2. Management of common pool resources, such as communal forest or grazing lands, which are shared or held in common and jointly used by people who are formally or informally organized in a forest user group
3. Collaborative management of state forest lands under cooperative arrangements with a public forest administration

The term community forestry is often used in reference to any local arrangements for managing forest resources within a village territory, irrespective of the land tenure conditions. In this case community forestry involves both forest or tree management on private lands (often labeled as farm forestry), on village lands, or on state lands which are used by local people. However, the term is also used in reference to specific forest management arrangements on either communal or public lands.

Community forest management arrangements may also be differentiated on the basis of the type of the community organization which bears responsibility for forest management. Such organizations may range from specific user groups and family lineages, to village organizations or tribal organizations. Thus, community forestry is not restricted to village territories, but may also involve the ancestral territories of indigenous tribal groups.

Community Forestry Activities

In community forest management the main responsibility for making arrangements for forest management rests primarily with rural people. The local people do so on the basis of their own specific management objectives, rather than on the basis of the policy objectives of forestry development organizations. The local objectives for forest management involve not only fulfillment of basic household needs and the provision of marketable products, but also include the provision of forest products to be used as inputs for agricultural and livestock production. Moreover, forests may also be maintained because of cultural and religious values. Community forest management is not a specialized activity, as in the case of professional forest management, but rather forms an integrated component of the local land-use strategies. Local communities often not only attribute utilitarian values to forests, but also cultural and spiritual values. Their multiple values concerning forests may be reflected in location-specific indigenous forest management systems. Such indigenous forest-related practices include not only regeneration and maintenance of trees in either forests or agroforestry systems, but also conscious conservation of forests, controlled harvesting of forest products, and local manufacturing of these products. In many rural communities such indigenous management activities have existed for a long time. Due to the advent of modern state bureaucracy and the belief in the progressive value of professional forest management, these practices have often been overlooked in traditional forestry development programs, and have even been marginalized. However, the advent of interest in community forestry development has brought renewed interest in using such indigenous systems as a starting point for further community forest management. Thus, regarding the evolution of community forestry, a distinction can be made between indigenously evolved systems and externally sponsored systems.

Conclusion

In the late 1970s the concepts of social and community forestry emerged as a focus for addressing the linkages between forestry and rural development. Different interest groups stimulated community forest management for different reasons:

- As a component of strategies to enhance rural livelihoods, in particular the livelihoods of the poor, and/or to maintain the cultural integrity of tribal people
- As a means to manage forest resources sustainably so as to conserve both forests and their biodiversity
- As a component of government strategies to devolve and decentralize responsibilities, and to reduce the budgetary costs of state governments for forest management

Since the advent of social and community forestry considerable experience has been gained with these strategies. Experience has shown that it is not always possible to fulfill all different expectations regarding the outcomes of social and community forestry at the same time. It was also found that the original approach to social and community forestry was rather limited; consequently the approaches became gradually more diversified. At the start of the twenty-first century it is clear that social forestry policies and project approaches should be carefully harmonized with the realities of local communities. In view of the various interpretations regarding the scope of community forest management, the objectives for social forestry development should be clearly specified and related to the specific characteristics of different community forestry schemes.

Another important lesson learned is the need not to limit social forestry to a strategy for meeting subsistence needs and alleviating poverty of the poor. Rather, social forestry should be focused on a large array of social development issues, notably aspects of provision of land rights, reclaiming of indigenous territories, and access to markets. Gradually also collaborative management schemes are developing between local communities and commercial forestry enterprises. To stimulate such trends, attention also needs to be given to networking of community forestry organizations and improvement of the skills of community organizations to negotiate with external organizations. As a result of such developments, community forestry will increasingly become a multifaceted component of a pluriform system of forest management rather than a complement to professional forest management.

See also: **Landscape and Planning**: Perceptions of Nature by Indigenous Communities. **Operations**: Small-scale Forestry. **Silviculture**: Managing for Tropical Non-timber Forest Products. **Social and Collaborative**

Forestry: Canadian Model Forest Experience; Common Property Forest Management; Forest and Tree Tenure and Ownership; Joint and Collaborative Forest Management; Public Participation in Forest Decision Making; Social Values of Forests.

Further Reading

Arnold JEM (2001) *Forests and People: 25 Years of Community Forestry*. Rome: Food and Agriculture Organization of the United Nations.

Fisher RJ (1995) *Collaborative Management of Forests for Conservation and Development*. Gland, Switzerland: IUCN/World Wide Fund for Nature (WWF). Issues in Forest Conservation.

Hobley M (1996) *Participatory Forestry: The Process of Change in India and Nepal*. Rural Development Forestry Study Guide no. 3. London: Overseas Development Institute.

Mayers J and Bass S (1999) *Policy that Works for Forest and People*. London: International Institute for Environment and Development.

Peluso NL, Turner M, and Fortmann L (1994) Introducing community forestry; annotated listing of topics and readings. Community Forestry Note no. 12. Rome: FAO.

Wiersum KF (1999) *Social Forestry: Changing Perspectives in Forestry Science or Practice?*. Wageningen, The Netherlands: Wageningen Agricultural University.

Working Group on Community Involvement in Forest Management (1999–2002). *Communities and Forest Management*. Regional profiles series. Gland, Switzerland: IUCN World Conservation Union.

Joint and Collaborative Forest Management

A Lawrence and S Gillett, University of Oxford, Oxford, UK

Introduction

With the increasing recognition over the last 30 years that forestry is a pluralistic enterprise with a wide range of legitimate stakeholders, new arrangements for sharing management decisions among local forest users and professional forestry services are emerging under various titles including 'participatory forest management,' 'collaborative forest management' (CFM), and 'joint forest management' (JFM).

In many parts of the world CFM is a relatively new idea. Despite widespread use of the term, and 20 years since its inauguration in India and Nepal, CFM in many ways remains an experimental process.

Consequently, CFM often takes the form of adaptive management with objectives and activities gradually being adjusted to both the experiences learned as well as the evolving needs of the resource and the stakeholders.

Since the 1990s many countries have introduced CFM programs and policies (**Table 1**), usually with strong donor support, and encouraged by international post-Rio forest dialog supporting National Forest Programs. There are high expectations for CFM. Different stakeholders hope that it will:

- benefit the rural poor who depend on forests for their livelihoods
- contribute to sustainable resource use and reduced forest degradation (through strengthened ownership)
- reduce the cost of forest management by the state.

The diversity of CFM models, stakeholders, objectives, forms of community organization, and partnerships with professional forestry organizations makes it hard to generalize about the impact of CFM, particularly in relation to forest conservation and social aspects factors. Similarly, the factors contributing to success are open to interpretation. Whilst tenure, institutional arrangements, and local organizational strengthening have often been highlighted, the effects as experienced by forest users are rarely considered.

In this article we first look more closely at the various terms used, and take an overview of the way CFM has developed around the world, before discussing the issues that are implicated in its success or failure.

Definitions and Main Characteristics

The involvement of nonforesters in forest management has taken off to such an extent that there is now a plethora of terms to describe it (**Table 2**).

'Collaborative forest management' refers to an explicit partnership between professional forestry organizations and communities or defined groups of local forest users. The objective of this strategy is to manage forests to provide sustainable benefits for a range of stakeholders. It has been emphasized that CFM is an intervention by outsiders (public forest services, donors, and nongovernmental organizations (NGOs)), and therefore contrasts with traditional forest management practices.

The term 'participatory' has become so widely used that there is a risk of its being misunderstood. Participatory is understood to refer to a range of relationships between professionals and local people,

Table 1 Examples of countries implementing CFM to a significant level

Region/country	Policy and date introduced (with amendments in parentheses)	Type of partnership	Estimated numbers of communities involved	Area of forest under CFM (ha)
South Asia				
Nepal	**1976 – National Forestry Plan.** Allowed land to be handed over to local users, with technical assistance provided by the forest department.[b,o] **1978 – Panchayat Forest and Panchayat Protected Forest Regulations.** (1980) CFM enacted.[o,u] (1988 – Adopted concept of Forest User Group, 1990 – Panchayats replaced by Village Development Committees.[o]) **1982 – Decentralization Act.**[o,u] Formalized duties and responsibilities of village panchayats and ward committees, empowering them to form people committees for forest conservation and management.[u] (1984) **1987 – Decentralization Act.**[u] Introduced the concept of User Groups for local administration. **1988 – Community Forestry By-Laws.**[o] (1989) **1989 – Master Plan for Forestry Sector.**[b,o] **1993 – Forest Act.**[b] FUGs clearly defined, and clear implementation guidelines produced. Provides the legal basis for CFM implementation.[u] (1999 – provisions for FD to impose penalties on offenders at request of FUG if they are unable to enforce themselves.) **1995 – Forest Regulations.**[b] Procedural guidelines for implementing the Forest Act of 1993. **2001 – Forest (Second Amendments) Bill.**[u]	Forest User Groups supported by District Forest Office	6022[b] to 13 000[a] Forest User Groups	400 719[b]–850 000[a] ~ 12% of Nepal's forest lands
India	**1988 – Forest Policy.** The launch of JFM. Followed by State JFM Resolutions.[e] **1990 – Guidelines for JFM** issued by Ministry of Environment and Forests.[e,o] **1994 – Draft Forest Act.**[e] **1998 –** Formation of **JFM Standing Committee** by the Ministry of Environment and Forests.[o] **2000 – Guidelines for JFM revised** to include forests with over 40% canopy cover.[v] **2002 – Guidelines for JFM revised.**[v]	State forest department with village forest committees or forest protection committees	30 000–35 000[o] (2000)	10.24 million ha in 22 states[d]
Pakistan	**1996 – Hazara Protected Forests Rules**[o] (modification of the Forest Act of 1927). Mandates the formation of JFM committees, including operational guidelines and production sharing arrangements with provincial FD.[o]	Provincial Forest Departments with Forest Management Committees		

Southeast Asia Philippines	1982 – **Integrated Social Forestry Programme** established.[p] 1987 – **Constitution**. Recognized the importance of the environment and rights of indigenous people.[p] 1990 – Indigenous people's rights to ancestral lands and domains recognized.[p] 1994 – **Social Reform Agenda**.[p] 1996 – **Community Based Forest Management Program** formulated.[c,p] Guidelines included community mapping. 1997 – **Indigenous Peoples' Rights Act**. Gave indigenous communities title to ancestral domain and land claims.[c,p] 1999 – CBFM program put on hold.[p]	Villagers and local government representatives work together.[p]	700 000 ha (potential area 1.5 million ha)[c]
Laos	1994 – **National Leading Committee** for Decentralized Rural Development (1996, 1998).[c] Village forestry is a key element in the **National Forestry Action Plan**, and policies are being adopted that foster local people's participation in forest management, including the allocation of access and use rights of forest resources.[c]	Forest departments and villages	550[c]
Thailand	1993 – **Forestry Master Plan**.[p] Extends forest areas under conservation. 1992 – **Tambon Administration Organization Act (TAO)**. Strengthens role of village governments in forest use and planning decision-making.[p] 1997 – **Constitution**. Traditional communities granted the right and duty to manage resources where they live. However, without enabling CFM laws, current conservation policies are at odds with the community rights provisions listed in the Constitution.[p] **Pending** – New **Ministry of Natural Resources Bill**, formalizing CFM. Deferred for approval to 2003.[f]		
Vietnam	1991 – **Tropical Forestry Action Plan**, the Forest Resources Protection Act, the National Forest Policy. Private households replace state forest enterprises as new units for forest management, with appropriate guidance from the state.[p] 1993 – **Land Law** gives local inhabitants extensive user rights over agricultural and forest land.[p] Recent amendments restrict rights and limit role of local people as forest custodians.[p]	Private households with state guidance.[p]	1203 communes[c]
Meso-America			Over 2 602 425 ha (14.5% of forest cover)[g]

continued

Table 1 Continued

Region/country	Policy and date introduced (with amendments in parentheses)	Type of partnership	Estimated numbers of communities involved	Area of forest under CFM (ha)
Mexico	**1917 – Constitution.** Ancient land use customs clarified and applied to land tenure. The reforms enabled indigenous communities to obtain property titles for their lands via presidential decree, and to reclaim usurped land if they could legally show when and how it was taken.[s] **1992 – Ejido property laws** were reformed. Allow lands to be rented by ejidos to anyone from farmers to multinationals. Ownership assigned to ejidos already managed communally, allowing them to be sold for the first time.[s] The National Forest Commission developed the **New Community Forestry Plans.** This provides loans for development and management of non-timber resources in Community and Ejido Forests.[s]		Approximately 8 000 ejido village communities.[s]	80% of Mexican forests owned by ejidos.[s]
South America				
Bolivia	**1996 – Forestry Law** recognizes that communities may be better stewards of the land than large, private concessionaires. Communities given preferential rights to use forest areas on properties that they possess.[h]	State forest department and communities		
Brazil	**1965 – Forestry Code,** Law No. 4.771/65 (the Code). Establishes woodland zones that are subject to 'permanent preservation management.'[r] **1988 – Federal Constitution** clearly recognizes indigenous rights over lands that they have traditionally occupied. Extraction is allowed, but only after zoning and an inventory of exploitable land has been done.[r]			
Africa				
Cameroon	**1994 –** Community forests can be formed from National Forests by a community official entering into an agreement with the Ministry of Environment and Forests. Forest products from those forests are the exclusive property of the community for the duration of the agreement, but the forest is not owned by the community.[j]	State forest department and communities[i] Ministry of Environment and Forests and communities	45 000 rural communities in 30 countries[i] 35[k] to 40[i] community forests allocated	At least 3 million, 1% of forest area of Africa.[i] 1 000 000[i]
Tanzania	**1998 Changes in Forest Policy.** Include Guidelines on the development of CBFM and JFM.[l]	Forest departments and villages or communities	500 village forest reserves; 100 community forest reserves (groups); 30 pilot comanagement of forest reserves[l]	500 000[l]

continued

Country/Region	Policy/Description	Partners	Villages	Number
The Gambia	**1990 – The Forest Department introduce Community Forestry** **1994 – The Gambian Forest Management Concept.**[m] Forest park management and CFM merged into one framework. **1995–2005 – New Forest Policy.** Aims to transfer ownership thus encouraging local participation for sustainable forest management as well as advancing decentralization within the country.	Between the local community and the forest department on behalf of the government.[m]	300[m] to 500[i] villages involved	39 000[i] to 50 000[n]
Europe	International policy frameworks supporting CFM in Europe: **1992 – Agenda 21** **1992 (in force 1995) – Convention on Biological Diversity** **1992 – The UNCED Forest Principles** **1999 – The Forest Stewardship Council's Principles and Criteria** **1998 (in force 2001) – European Aarhus Convention on Access to Information, Public Participation in Decision Making and Access to Justice in Environmental Matters.**[q]			
Belgium	**1990 (1999) – The Government of Flanders Act on Forest.** Requires local forest managers to consult the local people when drafting management plans.[q]	Forest Department and local stakeholders		
Finland	**1997 – new Forest Act.** Requires public participation in forest planning and management. Usufruct rights of the Saami people have not been recognized.[q]	Forest Service and local stakeholders		
Ireland	**1996 – Strategic Plan for Forestry.** Involves a broadly based consultation procedure.[q]	Forest Service and forest owners, farmers and local communities		
Portugal	**1996 – new National Forest Act.** Participatory planning required at regional levels.[q]	National Forest Service and forest owners, local community-owned forests, forest industries, and hunters		
Spain	**2000 – National Forest Strategy.** Based on a public participation process lasting several years.[q]			
UK	Clear policy statement on multiple use forestry. **1995 – Rural White Paper.** The government wish to enhance the contribution forestry can make to sustainable communities	Forest Commission and rural communities		

Table 1 Continued

Region/country	Policy and date introduced (with amendments in parentheses)	Type of partnership	Estimated numbers of communities involved	Area of forest under CFM (ha)
North America				
USA	**1994 – Federal Advisory Committee Act.** This law has thwarted many CFM initiatives, and remains a barrier.			
Canada	**1992 – Canada Model Forest Programme.** Funds given to local communities, and all rights devolved to them as a pilot study.[t]	Between Forest Industry and local communities, environmental NGOs and First Nations Groups		
	Different provinces have different laws. Quebec has the richest history of CFM in Canada.[t]			

[a] Ojha ZW and Bhattarai B (2003) Learning to manage a complex resource: a case of NTFP assessment in Nepal. International Forestry Review 5(2).

[b] http://www.panasia.org.sg/nepalnet/forestry/comm.forestry.htm

[c] http://www.recoftc.org/01country/home.html

[d] Sharma RC (2000) *Indian Forester* 126(5): 463–476.

[e] Hobley M (1996) *Participatory Forestry: The Process of Change in India and Nepal.* London: Overseas Development Institute.

[f] Daniel R (2002) Thailand: Forests communities to renew struggle for rights. *World Rainforest Movement Bulletin* 63: 24–25.

[g] http://www.forestsandcommunities.org/central-south-america.html

[h] http://www.forestsandcommunities.org/Country-Profiles/bolivia.html

[i] Alden Wiley L (2002) The political economy of community forestry in Africa: getting the power relations right. *Forests, Trees and People Newsletter* 46: 4–12.

[j] Watts J (1994) Developments towards participatory forest management on Mount Cameroon (The Limbe Botanic Garden and Rainforest Genetic Conservation Project 1988–1994). *Rural Development Network Paper* 17(d): 1–19.

[k] Research and Action Centre for Sustainable Development in Central Africa (2002) Cameroon: developments of community forests. *World Rainforest Movement Bulletin* 63: 14–16.

[l] Moshi E, Burgess N, Enos E, *et al.* (2002) Tanzania: joint and community-based forest management in the Uluguru Mountains. *World Rainforest Movement Bulletin* 63: 16–17.

[m] http://www.dfs-online.de/cfo.htm

[n] http://www.statehouse.gm/budget2002/9.htm

[o] Poffenberger M (ed.) (2000) *Communities and Forest Management in South Asia.* Gland, Switzerland: IUCN.

[p] Poffenberger M (ed.) (1999) *Communities and Forest Management in South East Asia.* Gland, Switzerland: IUCN.

[q] Jeanrenaud S (2001) *Communities and Forest Management in Western Europe.* Gland, Switzerland: IUCN.

[r] http://www.forestsandcommunities.org/Country_Profiles/brasil.html

[s] http://www.forestsandcommunities.org/Country_Profiles/mexico.html

[t] http://www.forestsandcommunities.org/Country_Profiles/canada.html

[u] Springate-Baginski O, Blaikie P, Dev O, *et al.* (2001) Community forestry in Nepal: a policy review. http://www.york.ac.uk/inst/sei/prp/pdfdocs/nepalpolicy.pdf

[v] http://www.rupfor.org/jfm-india.htm

Table 2 Different terms for joint and collaborative forest management

Abbreviation	Term in full
CBF(R)M	Community-based forest (resource) management
CF	Community forestry
CFM	Community forest management or collaborative forest management or collective forest management or community involvement in forest management
JFM	Joint forest management
PFM	Participatory forest management
VJFM	Village joint forest management

Table 3 Typology of meanings of 'participation'

Type of participation	Characteristics
1. Passive	Participants are treated as sources of information, and/or are told about decisions already taken. Information being shared belongs only to external professionals.
2. Consultative	Participants are consulted about their opinion, but does not necessarily lead to those views being taken into account when decisions are made, usually by non-participants.
3. Functional	Participants contribute knowledge and skills to meet predetermined objectives (such as forest management goals). Often seen as helping to reduce costs of outside agents.
4. Collaborative	Although the initiative is usually taken from outside, participants share goal-setting and analysis, development of action plans and any follow-up activities.
5. Active (self-mobilization)	Participants take the initiative, and develop contacts with external institutions for resources and technical advice they need, but retain control over goals and resource-use.

Source: Adapted from Biggs (1989) and Pretty *et al.* (1995).

from consultation to joint decision-making and power-sharing (**Table 3**). Within the context of CFM participation refers to the active involvement of local people in goal-setting, planning, implementation, and monitoring of forest management activities on forest lands that are legally under public authority.

Although CFM is based on the principle of active participation of local people in managing state forest lands, the public forest services have the final authority over the forest lands. Through CFM, they delegate management authority to local people under the proviso that the management activities are in

Table 4 Forest User Group (FUG) formation, Nepal

1. Forest Department (FD) officials identify forest area and users.
2. FD conducts meetings with community leaders and key informants.
3. Forest User Group (FUG) assemblies are called to discuss rules for the management of the community forest and of conflicts.
4. A committee is formed. This is generally between eight and 13 people, and has representatives from all groups (including women and low caste groups).
5. The FUG constitution is prepared.
6. The FUG is approved by the District Forest Office (DFO).
7. The FD and FUG survey the forest, and produce an operational plan (OP) (management plan). This usually focuses on timber value only.
8. The OP is approved by the DFO.
9. The FUG implements the OP with monitoring, support, and strengthening activities by the field staff of the FD.

Source: Hobley M and Ojha H, personal communication.

accordance with the general forest management policy. Thus, CFM is in essence based on an approach of decentralization and collaboration rather than an approach of devolution as is the case in the legal recognition of common property management regimes.

Schemes may be differentiated according to the type of forest lands involved (e.g., any forest lands of interest to local communities, only degraded lands but no commercial forest lands, or buffer zones around conservation areas). They can also be differentiated according to the level of involvement of the defined forest users in planning and implementing management. The management plan is always approved by the state forestry department or its equivalent, but in different contexts may be drawn up by the forest user group and submitted for approval, or drawn up by the foresters and approved by the forest users.

Global Overview

This section discusses CFM as it has developed around the world.

Nepal

Nepal has been heralded as a world leader of CFM. In the process termed 'community forestry,' the Forest Department (FD) retains some control over forest management (**Table 4**). Management plans, known as Operational Plans (OPs) in Nepal are developed with advice from the FD, in line with national legislation. Once the OP is approved, the forest is formally handed over to the Forest User Group (FUG), which then carries out the activities with advice from the FD only if sought. OPs generally span a 5-year period, and any alterations to them within this time require further approval from the FD.

CFM in Nepal has been strongly supported by donor organizations, and in the 1990s, the newly democratic government supported the devolution of management rights to FUGs. Transfer of rights has accelerated since then.

The relatively long history of CFM in Nepal has provided some important lessons regarding equity and benefit distribution. Wealthier members of communities are favored by a strong focus on timber species; women, scheduled castes, and poor people are marginalized when communities 'manage' forest solely by protecting it. Probably only 30% of FUGs are functioning according to democratic principles in decision-making. Claims that CFM is intended to support poverty alleviation are undermined by the slow expansion of CFM to the forest-rich Terai lowlands, where 50% of the country's population is underrepresented by only 2% of the country's FUGs.

Nevertheless Nepal continues to develop CFM by acting on lessons learnt, leading to continuing policy and implementation challenges such as the Forest Regulations (1995) requiring a detailed forest inventory by the FD before handover to the FUG. However, the FD is underequipped to meet the demand for inventory, and both new and established FUGs are suffering as a consequence.

India

CFM in India is known as Joint Forest Management (JFM) (**Table 5**), under a model whereby the forest is not handed over to the community, but is jointly managed by a Village Forest Committee (VFC) and the state Forest Department (**Table 6**). The earliest recorded case of JFM was in Arabari, West Bengal in 1972. Earlier attempts such as the 1948 and 1956 Industrial Policy Resolutions, which introduced the need for participatory management, were unsuccessful due to conflicting priorities and historical antagonism between local communities and the government. In 1988, the National Forest Policy explicitly emphasized the participation of local

Table 6 Village Forest (Management) Committee (VF(M)C) or Forest Protection Committee (FPC) formation, India

1. The FD hold a preliminary meeting in the village to explain the concept of JFM.
2. A VFC/FPC will be constituted if a minimum of 50% of adults pass the resolution for its formation.[a]
3. The VFC may be made up of all voting adults in the village, but more generally is made up of a certain percentage of them. Different resolutions have rules about the number of women and lower caste people that need to be in the VFC.
4. An executive committee of the VFC/FPC is elected (seven to 15 members), and generally must contain specified numbers of women, lower castes, and landless people.
5. A microplan is suggested by the FD after a survey conducted by them. This will set levels for harvesting firewood, etc.
6. The VFC/FPC can ask to be registered and boundaries to be demarcated.

[a]The different States of India have different JFM Resolutions; accordingly while some form VFCs, others form FPCs. The formation of VFC or FPC depends on the state, due to the differences in JFM Resolutions. Generally the formation follows the pattern above.
Source: Hobley M (1996) *Participatory Forestry: The Process of Change in India and Nepal*. London: Overseas Development Institute and Kinhal G, personal communication.

Table 5 Definition of Joint Forest Management

Definition	Structure	Products	Purpose
Joint Forest Management (JFM) is a forest management strategy under which the Forest Department and the village community enter into an agreement to jointly protect and manage forest land adjoining villages and to share responsibilities and benefits.	The village community is represented through an institution specifically formed for the purpose. This institution is known by different names in different states (e.g., Vana Samaraksha Samitis in Andhra Pradesh and Hill Resource Management Societies in Haryana) but most commonly referred to as Forest Protection Committee or FPC. In some states, panchayats can also enter into JFM agreement with the Forest Department.	Under JFM, the village community gets a greater access to a number of Non Timber Forest Products (NTFPs) and a share in timber revenue in return for increased responsibility for its protection from fire, grazing and illicit harvesting. The details vary from state to state as each state has issued its own JFM resolution/rules.	The essential difference between 'social forestry' and JFM is that while the former sought to keep people out of forests, the latter seeks to involve them in the management of forest lands. JFM also emphasises joint management by the Forest Department and the local community.

Reproduced from: Resource Unit for Participatory Forestry (http://www.rupfor.org/jfm_india.htm)

people in the management and protection of forests, signifying the birth of JFM, later interpreted at state level where each state forest department has control over forest policy (**Table 5**).

JFM in India was, until recently, reserved for degraded forest lands. Guidelines passed in 2000 allow JFM to be implemented in forests with over 40% crown cover. The 1988 National Forest Policy is federal law, but is adapted by each state, so that the exact arrangements of JFM Resolutions differ between states. Twenty-two of India's 26 states have implemented JFM resolutions, and both the minutiae of the Resolution and the motivational levels of each state forest department influence its success.

JFM has been criticized for transferring too little power to community members. The language of many JFM resolutions is seen to reflect continuing control of VFC by FDs. Due to historical exclusion from forest reserves, and the state enforcement of their lack of rights to land, rural people have deep-founded mistrust of the state forest department and regional forest offices. In some cases, JFM is seen as a means for the FDs to organize local labor to improve public lands. Others note a tendency for JFM to be imposed on tribal people without consultation or consideration of their rights. Although results vary between states, JFM has achieved many of its goals, and has succeeded in increasing awareness about resource fragility, arresting depletion of forests, and the regeneration of degraded forests.

Elsewhere in Asia

Because of the wealth of many of the remaining forests in Southeast Asia, forest legislation still favors commercial logging. However, communal systems of forest management have existed for centuries, and an emerging peoples' movement forms the context for community-based resource management, whether of forests, national parks, or coasts. For example, Community Based Forest Management is a promising approach in the Philippines, but critics point to heavy dependence on donor support with little financial or political support from central government. Despite the enormous popularity of participatory methods among development organizations, by trying to build on incipient civil society initiative before any supportive national institutional change had been instated, at times the donor agenda has swamped the national reform process and, it is sometimes suggested, left indigenous people less empowered than before. The region is particularly supported in CFM by the presence of the Centre for International Forestry Research (CIFOR) (which has its international headquarters in Indonesia) and their

innovative work on adaptive collaborative management, in developing the social learning processes essential for successful CFM.

Central Asia has recently undergone radical change with the collapse of Soviet rule in 1990. Kyrgyzstan is the only republic that has adopted democracy and decentralized administration, and with this new form of governance, has also embraced the system of CFM. The Swiss government has facilitated the introduction of CFM in Kyrgyzstan, and its influence has been high due to the decrease of state funding for forestry. One condition that may promote the success of CFM in this republic is the strong preference of the government for long-term leases of state forest land, with tenants managing the forests, and receiving the benefits of nontimber forest products (NTFPs) from their plots.

Africa

Despite its short history in Africa (less than 10 years), CFM policies exist in over 30 countries, with forestry administrations preferring collaborative arrangements to more devolutionary regimes such as community forestry. As in other parts of the world, the reluctance of governments to review forest tenure arrangements is one important reason for slow progress.

Different countries within Africa have adopted different strategies of CFM. Some, including Zambia, Cameroon, and Burkina Faso, have followed India and Nepal in only allowing CFM in 'poorer' forest areas. Other countries (e.g., Uganda, Guinea, and Ethiopia) support CFM within National Forest Reserves. Most other countries have no restrictions on the type of forest eligible for CFM activities.

As in the Philippines, critics warn against the dependency on community forest policy formulated by external organizations (donors or NGOs), with little knowledge of local social and environmental conditions. It has been argued that policies made in this way have a tendency to benefit Western donors and NGOs more than the rural communities who have to deal with the consequences. Most argue that sincere governmental support is essential for the success of CFM.

Latin America

Latin American nations are currently witnessing a high level of grassroots mobilization, and are calling for forest resources to be used for the benefit of local communities. However, policies remain centralized, and communities lack the capital and capacity to develop economically sustainable forest management models.

Land tenure is a key issue in Latin America. Failure of the state to uphold secure tenure management systems limits the potential for community management models, and many Latin American nations are in the midst of an ongoing debate over the nature of land ownership. Many indigenous common property management regimes are being eroded through central tenure legislation, the reality being that most state models do not recognize indigenous land use systems. Agrarian reforms have attempted to return land to campesinos (peasants, or rural farmers), but the late twentieth century has seen a state- and industry-led desire to privatize land in order to promote foreign investment. However, some innovative and exemplary policy changes in Bolivia and Colombia have created new opportunities for recognized indigenous groups to manage their land and forest collectively.

Latin America is characterized by the distinctiveness of indigenous people and their association with tropical forest communities, and the role of forest-dwelling communities in conservation is beginning to be valued. A number of countries in South America have CFM policies, but contradictory policy and legislation in other sectors is delaying implementation.

North America

Forest management in North America has been influenced strongly by the environmental movement of the 1980s. Most initiatives and developments arising from this influence emphasize the need for more collaborative and participatory approaches to forest ecosystem management. Both the USA and Canada are gradually developing policies that provide a framework for small forest-dependent communities and civil society at large to participate in public forest land management decision-making. Critics are concerned that if local communities are empowered with public forest decision-making responsibilities, they may not reflect the values of more distant stakeholders. Others point out that NGOs and policy-makers tend to be city-based, so the views of city-dwellers are more often represented, with rural communities marginalized in the decision-making processes.

In the USA, the CFM movement is still in its infancy, but it is growing in numbers and in its ability to influence forest policy and management. Forest policy-makers and public forest managers are increasingly drafting laws and management prescriptions that are sensitive to the needs of forest-based communities. Forest organization personnel show strong support for collaborative planning, but in some cases the public feel that their participation is inadequate in decision-making processes, and are unwilling to engage in the process, often choosing to meet their objectives through a reactive, conflict-based means.

In Canada, 96% of the forest area is state owned. The state leases its forest land-base to timber companies who manage the area under agreed provincial regulations. The federal government is limited to influencing forest policy indirectly, with the 13 provincial governments controlling their own legislation concerning forest management. Many jurisdictions have now passed regulations that require public and local community input to forest operations through structured committees that provide advice during the planning stages and/or comanagement during the implementation and operational stages. In general, current forest enterprise responses to the environmental movement and to indigenous peoples' issues have been proactive, and companies are aware of the need for a 'social licence to operate' (i.e., public acceptance of their management strategies). Both of these have contributed to the frequency with which public consultations are made before forest operations are carried out.

Europe

In Europe, as in the USA and Canada, governments are moving towards more pluralistic forms of planning and management, but in a context of forest decline and recovery, the changing values of a largely urbanized society, and declining rural social institutions. The governments of most countries in Western Europe support multiple-use forestry, and, as in North America, many new CFM initiatives have been motivated by environmental concerns. Two types of participation prevail: with the public, concerning state forest lands, and private forest owners in processes organized by themselves. The few European indigenous groups are also significant players in some European countries, although they too have had to prove their customary rights in judicial courts.

The high proportion of privately owned forests in Western Europe provides a special context for CFM. In most cases private ownership limits public access and influence over the land. However, it has provided opportunities for new patterns of collaboration such as the evolution of associations of small forest owners, e.g., in Austria or Finland. These have often been supported by governments through subsidies and tax reductions, and by providing technical support via the state forest agencies. Owners also benefit from overcoming the disadvantages of small size, and in addition, the Pan European Forest

Certification (PEFC) scheme is tailored towards all the private forest owners in an area working in collaboration.

The Impact of CFM

In general CFM is considered a promising forest management strategy, as it is believed to be able to contribute on the one hand to forest conservation and sustainable forest use, and on the other hand to livelihood improvement of local communities. Much aid, and aid-related research, is linked to the search for compatibility between conservation and sustainable livelihoods, or poverty alleviation, and CFM is one of its principle vehicles. In reality, different stakeholders often have their own distinctive aims for being involved in or stimulating such strategies (**Table 7**). These aims and aspirations may not be made explicit to all stakeholders, and may in fact be incompatible (see 'Social Aspects' below).

Potentially conflicting goals complicate the evaluation of 'successful' or 'sustainable' CFM, and leave supporters and skeptics alike with confusing evidence. Notably, the evaluations and impact assessments that are published tend to reflect the views of the institutional stakeholders and the voices of the local forest users are little heard. There is also very little documented evidence of the impact of CFM on biodiversity or livelihoods. Given the

Table 7 Summary of the different achievement goals that different stakeholders expect from CFM

Stakeholder	Goal
Donors	Poverty alleviation
Policy-makers	Reduced deforestation
	Poverty alleviation
Forest Departments/ governments	Reduced pressure on forest resource
	Reduced pressure on Forest Department
	Improved regeneration
	Improved quality of forest resource
	Devolution of decision-making
	Transition in roles and power
NGOs	Empowerment of rural poor/ forest-dwelling communities
	Equitable distribution of benefits
Local communities/rural poor	Securing livelihood resource
	Stabilization and improvement of livelihoods
	Development of income
	Control over culturally important resource
	Decreased vulnerability to shocks
	Increased control over life

propensity for donor funding it is essential not to confuse inputs, or management outputs, with successful outcomes.

It is beginning to be recognized that more participatory approaches must be developed to make sure that local stakeholders have a say in how impact is achieved and measured.

Factors Contributing to Success

This lack of evidence of the success of CFM does not negate emerging patterns of factors contributing to successful CFM, as judged by the participating stakeholders themselves. The case study approach taken by the World Conservation Union (IUCN) series on CFM is particularly valuable in this regard. For example, the very different approaches in Bangladesh (lowest forest cover, high population density, distinction between tribal and lowland communities, and the rise of private nurseries) contrast with Sri Lanka (long tradition of agroforestry management in home gardens, recent history of conflict). These summaries are given credibility by drawing on interviews and on government, NGO, and academic sources to present a realistic view, pointing to ecological, social, economic, political, and institutional factors.

Ecological Factors

Ecological factors include the original forest type, as well as its condition when CFM is initiated. While it is widely accepted that CFM improves ecosystem functioning and the quality and quantity of forest area and products, this remains to be demonstrated on a general scale. Studies in India have shown that CFM can improve diversity of tree species, although general impacts on biodiversity conservation have yet to be proved. More CFM has worked in sub-humid and semi-arid forests than in high tropical forest. The widespread tendency to hand over poorer-quality forest for local management is currently being addressed by advances in forest policy in Nepal and India (see above).

Social Aspects

Stakeholder analysis CFM often assumes the ideal of a 'community.' Contrary to idealized assumptions, communities are often culturally heterogeneous, governed by top–down approaches rather than historical customs and traditions, and have few or no regulations relating to resource use. Stakeholder analysis is essential for successful CFM, as rapid and participatory rural appraisals (RRAs and PRAs) often do not identify the most vulnerable and poorest members of the community, or understand local political dynamics. For example, women are often the most regular forest users, but, due to cultural barriers and traditions, are often not consulted on forest management decisions.

Indigenous or 'tribal' people are often culturally more closely linked to forests than their immigrant neighbors, and are (often correctly) perceived as more likely to conserve their ancestral lands. However, the breakdown of respect for traditional social structures and resource management techniques heralds the need for more CFM, social learning, and adaptive management.

Conflict management Inevitably, working with such an array of stakeholders, the goals, ideas, and values of forest management often vary considerably between (and within) groups. This plurality often requires high levels of conflict management, a technique that has developed in synchronization with CFM. In general, experiences with CFM have increased respect for indigenous forest management systems, knowledge systems, and modes of organization, although the often-traditional forestry sector is at times slow to accept and initiate change. Foresters may feel that CFM initiatives are a reallocation of their former powers and, despite training programs, may remain unconvinced by CFM.

Civil society The emergence of civil society can add support to CFM, as shown by the effect of campaigning by the educated middle classes in the Philippines and Indonesia, and the increasing popularity of CFM in Kyrgyzstan in post-Soviet rule. Nevertheless, while quality timber still exists in these forests, the power of logging companies and corrupt officials is enough to frustrate many attempts at CFM.

Economics

In order to become established, CFM needs short-term benefits for local participants as the rural poor are unable to invest labor or funds into long-term management. Interest and motivational levels decline markedly if financial rewards are not seen within the first few years of CFM. Benefits depend on local markets for products that can be harvested regularly and to an acceptable quality. Information about markets and good access to them are important factors of successful CFM, and many local groups say that these are the biggest constraint to success. However, financial aspirations can also undermine sustainability, although a management plan can help to prevent overharvesting for instant monetary gain.

Organizations and Institutions

Local organization and power structures Experience particularly highlights the importance of incorporating existing local organization and power structures, with or without NGO support, and of forming partnerships and coalitions. Success in individual cases can be linked to the attitude of individual professionals, and to local people with strong leadership qualities.

In both India and Nepal, success of CFM has often been attributed to the formation and functioning of the core management team (VFC/FUG). Guidelines suggest that for these groups to be effective, numbers should be limited to 30–40 participants, members should be as socially homogeneous as possible, and membership should include representatives of all user groups (including women, landless poor, and lower caste members).

Sometimes community structures that appear to be 'participatory' can in fact be very top–down, with decision-making rights unfairly distributed to the elites of the group. However, if existing rules in the user groups are strong and fair, and methods for dealing with common problems and rule-breaking are in place, the rate of success tends to be higher.

Government As mentioned above, government forest departments can be reticent in their acceptance of CFM approaches. Often successful CFM is dependent upon one key official with undivided support for the venture. Even if extensive training is provided, the remit of foresters changes considerably with the introduction of CFM.

In most cases the government is responsible for providing technical support for the CFM ventures. The amount of technical support for management activities varies depending on the needs of the user group, and respect for local knowledge of how to manage the resource; recognition of when scientific knowledge is needed and appropriate is a key determinant. For example in severely degraded forests, the government will most likely be needed to play a major role in forest regeneration activities before user groups can be given more power.

Developmental agencies and NGOs The influence of international development agencies and/or NGOs in pioneering CFM systems is evident particularly in countries such as Pakistan, that have no policy mechanisms to support CFM. However, strong interest and availability of funding from these agencies may reduce support of the CFM process by national government.

Networks   A key to successful CFM development is the learning-by-doing approach, which engages user groups in forest management activities, creates a sense of ownership of the process, and can empower users through their new knowledge. Regular formal and informal meetings between forest officials and locals can help to create trust and understanding among stakeholders. Study tours enable horizontal exchange of experience (farmer to farmer, forester to forester). NGOs, networks, and collaborations between user groups provide useful routes for information exchange (**Table 8**). The more links between communities, NGOs, and governments that exist, the more likely it is that CFM will be successful. Links are particularly beneficial for mutual learning, encouraging synergistic relationships with respect to resource management, and

enhancing efficiency and effectiveness of the CFM program.

Policy and Governance

Flexibility of policy processes are an important aspect of successful CFM; India and Nepal, having the longest experience in CFM, have demonstrated the value of adapting forest policy in response to experience. Policy factors affecting success can be seen as external and internal constraints. External aspects are under the control of national and local governments, and global markets: forest tenure, tax burdens, and market development for forest products. Factors internal to the community of forest users include organization, transparency of resource management, participation by the community (or

Table 8   CFM networks and organizations

International organizations	*Area-specific organizations*
The International Network of Forests and Communities. Works internationally to provide and enhance networking between stakeholders. network@forestsandcommunities.org	Asia RECOFTC (The Regional Community forestry training center for Asia and the Pacific) Supports work in Cambodia, China, India, Indonesia, Laos, Nepal, Philippines, Thailand, Vietnam. http://www.recoftc.org/index.htm
The UN FAO Forestry Program. Addresses how to use forests to improve people's economic, environmental, social, and cultural conditions while ensuring that the resource is conserved to meet the needs of future generations. There is an exhaustive list of links on the programs website, including government agencies, nongovernmental organizations, and research projects. www.fao.org/waicent/faoinfo/forestry/forestry.htm	Members of RECOFTC include: Nepal–UK Community Forestry Project (NUKCFP), Nepal–Swiss Community Forestry Project (NSCFP), and Nepal–Australia Community Resource Management Project (NACRMP). Resource Unit for Participatory Forestry (RUPFOR). A neutral stakeholders' forum promoting interaction among various stakeholders in participatory forestry in India. http://www.rupfor.org/jfm_india.htm
The UN FAO Community Forestry Program. Provides information including topics covering communal management, decentralization and devolution, gender, market analysis and development, participatory processes, rural learning networks. www.fao.org/waicent/faoinfo/forestry/FON/FONP/cfu/cfu-e.stm	Federation of Community Forest Users of Nepal (FECOFUN) Europe Confederation of European Forest Owners (CEPF) http://www.cepf-eu.org/
Forests, Trees and People Program. This is designed to share information about improving community forestry activities and about initiatives of interest to its members. Links CFM initiatives throughout the world.	South America Central American Community Agroforestry Network (Agroforesteria comunitaria en Centroamericana) Indigenous and Peasantry Coordinator for Community Agroforestry in Central America (CICAFOC)
Rural Development Forestry Network (Overseas Development Institute's Forest Policy and Environment outreach group). Disseminates information to over 2000 members around the world. http://www.odifpeg.org.uk/network/index.html	North America National Network of Forest Practitioners (NNFP). Aims to strengthen the efforts of individual groups to achieve a common vision of sustainable economies and healthy ecosystems. http://www.nationalcommunityforestrycenter.org/presearch.html
The Community-Based Natural Resource Management Network (CBNRM). Aims to enhance and provide networking opportunities worldwide. http://www.cbnrm.net/	Canada's Model Forest Programme. http://www.nrcan.gc.ca/cfs-scf/national/what-quoi/modelforest_e.html

user group) as a whole, and attention to equity issues.

CFM illustrates the importance of looking beyond explicit policy objectives to examine implicit policy, and requires the mixing of different policy disciplines. For example, rural development policy bears on the traditionally separate domain of forest administration.

Tenure   Perhaps the most effective policy tool is change in tenure. Most CFM is initiated in state or community forests, and is most successful when the tenants or owners have long-term leases or secure land rights. In countries where communities have no access rights to forest land or products, encroachment and conflict is common; in contrast CFM in Nepal has created a legislative process whereby communities can acquire the right to manage their forests, and across Southeast Asia legislation to recognize ancestral lands of indigenous groups has encouraged those groups to formulate management plans. Little CFM has been recorded on private land, and the incidence of CFM on 'open access' land is low.

Devolution of rights and responsibilities   In the devolution of rights and responsibilities to the user group, it is essential that customary rights as well as legal rights be recognized. There is often confusion as to whether the community is being involved as a forest user or a forest manager, and for success, rights and responsibilities need to be clearly defined. Case studies show that motivation of communities for management is highest when power-sharing is most complete and implemented within management regimes that define the community as a whole as the source of decision-making. For community interest and participation to be maintained, it is important to ensure they feel a sense of 'ownership' of the process.

Reduction of poverty   Development advisers question whether CFM can be successfully implemented with the rural poor if their basic development needs are not met first. Interest and motivation levels decline if local people have to wait several years to see any returns, and success is related to markets and benefits linked to labor inputs. Donor-funded CFM ventures often include the double and difficult remit of improved livelihoods and conservation.

Governance   A number of international, pan-European, and national policies and treaties are beginning to support sustainable forest management and to provide a more enabling context for CFM. The Convention on Biological Diversity addresses forests through its work program on forest biological diversity, implemented by the United Nations Food and Agricultural Organization, the UN Environment Programme, the Global Environment Facility, the UN Framework Convention on Climate Change, the UN Forum on Forests, and the Centre for International Forestry Research. The program emphasizes the ecosystem approach, socioeconomic considerations, conservation and sustainable use. Objective 3: Goal 4 in the Forest Work Programme approved at the 6th meeting of the parties to the Convention on Biological Diversity reads:

> Enable indigenous and local communities to develop and implement adaptive community-management systems to conserve and sustainably use forest biological diversity.

The Aarhus Convention on 'Access to Information, Public Participation in Decision Making and Access to Justice in Environmental Matters' also supports CFM initiatives.

Future Directions

For CFM to continue its success, supportive legislation and policy need to be developed and enacted at institutional, organizational, and ground levels. Foresters need to be trained in how to impart technical knowledge to forest users about forest management. With regular contact and trust-building exercises, there should be a reduction of the exploitation of communities. Forest departments should clarify the benefits for them of the devolution of forest management responsibilities, to make it easier for professional foresters to accept and advocate the new CFM approach.

Many practitioners and planners do not have access to information because of poor dissemination or because it is presented without lessons being sufficiently distilled to convey general principles across cultural boundaries. There is also a strong sense that 'knowledge cannot be transported directly' but that there is a need to create the conditions in which knowledge can be generated. Thus more and more detailed case studies, with particular attention applied to documentation of community experience, should be encouraged, along with greater dissemination and information exchange.

CFM has great potential in linking with participatory monitoring and evaluation (PM&E) and adaptive management. By personally assessing their impact on the forest, communities become more aware of the need for sustainable management, and motivation levels increase as a sense of ownership of the process develops.

See also: **Landscape and Planning**: Perceptions of Nature by Indigenous Communities. **Social and Collaborative Forestry**: Canadian Model Forest Experience; Common Property Forest Management; Forest and Tree Tenure and Ownership; Social and Community Forestry; Social Values of Forests.

Further Reading

Carter J, Steenhoff B, Haldimann E, and Akenshaev N (2003) Collaborative forest management in Kyrgyzstan: moving from top-down to bottom-up decision-making. http://www.iied.org/docs/gatekeep/GK108.pdf.

Dubois O and Lowore J (2000) *The 'journey towards' collaborative forest management in Africa: Lessons learned and some 'navigational aids' – An overview.* London, UK: International Institute for Environment and Development.

Fisher RJ (1995) *Collaborative management of forests for conservation and development.* Gland, Switzerland: IUCN, WWF International.

Hobley M (1996) *Participatory Forestry: The Process of Change in India and Nepal.* London: Overseas Development Institute.

Jeanrenaud S (2001) *Communities and Forest Management in Western Europe.* Gland, Switzerland: IUCN.

Kant S and Cooke R (1999) Jabalpur District, Madhya Pradesh, India: minimizing conflict in joint forest management. In: Buckles D (ed.) *Cultivating Peace: Conflict and Collaboration in Natural Resource Management,* pp. 81–97. Ottawa, Canada: International Development Research Centre and World Bank.

Khare A, Sarin M, Saxena NC, Palit S, Bathla S, Vania F, and Satyanarayana M (2000) *Joint Forest Management: Policy, Practice and Prospects.* India: IIED Forestry and Land Use, WWF.

Lawrence A (ed.) (2000) *Forestry, forest users and research: new ways of learning.* ETFRN, Netherlands. Individual chapters can be downloaded from: http://www.etfrn.org/etfrn/workshop/users/index.html.

Poffenberger M (1999) *Communities and Forest Management in Southeast Asia.* Gland, Switzerland: IUCN.

Poffenberger M (2000) *Communities and Forest Management in South Asia.* Gland, Switzerland: IUCN.

Poffenberger M and McGean B (eds) (1996) *Village voices, forest choices: joint forest management in India. 356.* Delhi, India: Oxford University Press.

Pretty JN, Guijt I, Thompson J, and Scoones I (1995) *Participatory Learning and Action: A Trainer's Guide.* London: IIED.

Richards M (1997) *Tragedy of the Commons for Community-Based Forest Management in Latin America.* London: Overseas Development Institute.

Richards M, Davies J, and Yaron G (2003) *Stakeholder incentives in participatory forest management: a manual for economic analysis.* London, UK: ITDG Publishing.

Forest and Tree Tenure and Ownership

C Danks, University of Vermont, Burlington, VT, USA
L Fortmann, University of California–Berkeley, Berkeley, CA, USA

What is Social and Community Forestry?

Community forestry is a set of institutional arrangements in which communities are involved wholly or in part in decision-making and benefits and contribute knowledge and labor to achieve healthy forests and social well-being. Social forestry encompasses both multiple forms of locally initiated and implemented forest management as well as externally initiated social forestry projects. It ranges from formal, legally recognized arrangements such as comanagement agreements between communities or individual citizens and government forest bureaucracies, to:

- community management of government forest land
- the cumulative effect of tree planting and management on individual parcels
- forest commons
- communities that without government sanction management government forest land as a *de facto* commons.

Social forestry is a development strategy to stimulate community forestry. Analysis of property and land and tree tenure arrangements enable us to understand the distribution of costs and benefits of social forestry as well as the pitfalls that may befall it.

Basic Concepts in Property and in Land and Tree Tenure

Although people often think of property as a thing or the possession of a thing by someone, it is better understood as social relations between people regarding the possession and use of things, that is, as a claim to some use or benefit of something that will be enforced by society or the government. Lawyers make a distinction between real property (that is, land in particular but also trees, water, and minerals) and personal property (clothing, copyrights, goodwill, and so forth). Lawyers are, as a general rule, interested only in property rights recognized by the government. They ask the question: what does the law say?

In contrast, social scientists are also interested in the interface between rights and reality often referred to as tenure. They ask the question: How do claimants to rights actually behave regardless of the law? Tenure is a term borrowed from archaic English property law and refers only to real property. The doctrine of tenures which dates to eleventh-century England established the terms on which rights to land were granted. The doctrine of estates determined how long a person had the right to hold land. The present-day study of land and tree tenure encompasses both the doctrine of tenures and the doctrine of estates.

Legal Pluralism

When land tenure differs from formal property rights in land, scholars use the analytical concept of legal pluralism. Legal pluralism encompasses situations in which at least two legal systems coexist. In addition to national statutory and case law, legal pluralism takes into account legal regimes such as customary or traditional law codified and recognized by colonial regimes, religious law, and law created and enforced by smaller social groups. An example of legal pluralism can be found in the differentiation of property recognized under government law (*de jure* property) from property not recognized under government law but recognized by other social groups (*de facto* property). Depending on the circumstances, *de facto* property may be more important than *de jure* property in determining who may be where, when, and doing what. Legal pluralism may be especially relevant to social forestry in a forest area where an indigenous system of customary law coexists with government statutory law. Social forestry may be used to legitimate, and thereby strengthen, indigenous tenure and management.

Property as a Bundle of Rights

Property rights to trees and tree products on a parcel of land may be held by someone other than the landowner. The complexity such property relations introduce to understanding the role of property in social forestry can be analyzed with the concept of property as a bundle of rights (e.g., rights to use, sell, loan, give away, lease, destroy, bequeath) which may be held separately by different people at different times. While useful in revealing what kind of rights a particular property relation may entail, the bundle of rights concept has been criticized for not recognizing the interconnections and interdependence among different rights. The bundle of rights is often portrayed as a bundle of sticks in which removing one stick from the bundle has no effect on other sticks. Other images such as interconnected strings of genes have been suggested but have not achieved much currency in the literature.

Usufructuary rights   Usufructuary rights, the rights to use something, add complexity to the bundle of rights. Different and overlapping usufructuary rights may be asserted simultaneously against the same forest or same tree. This is discussed below in the example of palm trees in the Dominican Republic. The rights to the trees on a parcel of land may be held by different people or institutions. For example, the rights to the fruit of date palms in Sudan were divided among the man (and they were all men) who obtained the shoot and planted it, the man who owned the land where it was planted, and the man who watered the young palm. Since these rights were inheritable, the number of right-holders grew in subsequent generations. Multiple claimants of this sort can make social forestry extremely complicated.

Different types of rights   Types of rights included in a bundle of rights could include any combination of a variety of rights. One general cluster includes the rights to sell, loan, lease out, mortgage, or bequeath the tree itself or any or all of its products. A farmer might mortgage her cocoa trees or sell an entire mango crop before it is ripe to get immediately needed cash. The right to plant perennials such as trees is often constrained. Consumptive uses such as chopping down a tree for timber or poles constitute another set of rights.

Usufructuary rights may differ depending on where the tree or the product is located. Anyone may pick up fruit from the ground but taking fruit from the tree may constitute theft. Harvesting from a tree growing inside a compound (particularly if it is fenced) usually requires permission of the owner. Using trees growing elsewhere may not require permission. There may be differences in the rights to use different parts of or attachments to a tree such as leaves, flowers, needles, bark, roots, twigs, branches, nests, fruit, seed pods, and cones. Similarly within a forest rights to (among others) grazing or browsing, thatching grass, medicinal plants, water for human use, water for livestock use, water for irrigation, mushrooms, berries, dead and downed wood, green wood, or wildlife may vary widely.

Security of Tenure

Security of tenure consists of three elements: breadth, duration, and assurance. Breadth refers to the composition of rights such as usufructuary rights, the right to sell, the right to bequeath, and the right to destroy. Larger numbers of rights are associated with more secure tenure. Duration is the length of time a right is legally valid. Longer duration is associated with more secure tenure. Assurance is the certainty with which a right is held. It reflects the predictability and enforcement ability of the tenure-granting regime. Security of tenure does not require private property rights. Rather secure tenure can be found in every form of property regime whether or not it is sanctioned by the government. It is often assumed that the greater the security of his/her/their tenure, the more likely a person or group will be to invest in the maintenance and enhancement of property. This relationship does not always hold. For example, forest owners with secure tenure might clear-cut and not replant because they have an urgent need for capital from the sale of timber.

Access

Access is the ability to benefit from things. A step beyond property-rights-based focus on 'who may' benefit, the ability-based focus of access is on 'who actually' benefits and how. The property question is who has rights to this resource. The access question is who actually uses and/or controls this resource. That is, it asks who does (or does not) get to use what, in what ways, when.

Mechanisms of access fall into three general categories.

Rights-based access   Access may depend on rights defined by law or custom, encompassing both property and tenure.

Illegal access   Illegal access involves the ability to benefit without the sanction of the government or society. It may involve stealth, violence, or establishing relations with people who control access. Illegal access differs from *de facto* rights in that *de facto* rights are sanctioned by a local community or group. In illegal access we see people who are not officially recognized beneficiaries helping themselves to the benefits of social forestry.

Structural and relational mechanisms of access   Property rights in or access to forest land and trees are not the only kind of property or access that matters in community forestry. Access to technology, capital, labor, knowledge, and markets can affect the ability of people to benefit from social forestry. For example, the value of timber harvested from a community forest may depend on access to processing machinery such as a sawmill. If that machinery is owned by others, then the size of the benefits received by social foresters depends on the terms of access to the machinery.

Gendered Property and Tenure

There is no entry on women and forestry in this Encyclopedia. This is indicative of a general problem of which gendered property rights in forests and trees is only one manifestation. Women and their knowledge about and their uses of trees and forest resources are often invisible to forest agency staff, foresters, forest project planners, and implementers, and even to their own husbands.

Three aspects of gendered property and tenure are related to social forestry.

Gender and security of tenure   When the household is assumed to be a homogeneous unit, women's property rights (or the lack of them) are made invisible, often with adverse consequences for women. Even in households with secure tenure, women's property rights are often insecure. In most of Africa, for example, the breadth of women's security of land tenure is narrower than men's since it significantly less frequently than men's includes the ability to rent, give away, loan, lease, sell, or bequeath. In many places women acquire access to land not in their own right but through their fathers, husbands, and brothers. Daughters may have no rights of inheritance from their parents or may be unable to exercise their inheritance rights. The corollary to this principle of access to land is that the fruits of a woman's labor on the land often belong to her husband or his relatives, not to her. Security of duration of tenure is a matter of particular concern for women living under a gendered property regime in which changes in marital status can be catastrophic for them. It is not uncommon in the case of divorce for property acquired by a woman during marriage to become her husband's property, leaving her destitute. Widows may have limited property rights. They may have no right to inherit their husband's property, including trees that they themselves have planted and tended. In central Zimbabwe such insecurity of land and tree tenure for women appears to have resulted in significantly less tree planting by women than by men.

Women's usufructuary rights may be even less secure. In the Dominican Republic, palm trees owned by the men were subject to two sets of usufructuary rights. Women had usufructuary rights to the fronds while men had usufructuary rights to the fruit which they fed to their pigs. After their pigs were destroyed in a national campaign to contain an outbreak of swine flu, the men simply cut down the now useless (to them) palms, leaving their wives without access to a source of fronds.

Gender and title   Governments may undertake land titling programs in the hopes that it will increase security of tenure and, therefore, will increase productivity of agricultural or forest land. Generally the title is put in the name of the male head of household, although in some cases widows and/or divorcees may receive the title in their own name. Wives, however, may lose land that is theirs by right as well as long-standing usufructuary rights. For example, in the current land titling under way in Laos, the title to all household land (including land that came from the wife's family) is put in the name of the husband. If the title includes the right of the titleholder to sell the land, the wife is in a precarious position. Thus, if social forestry includes land titling, women may end up worse off in terms of their rights to land and trees.

Gender and access   Women may have secure property rights in land or trees but lack access to or control of their own property due to gendered power relations. Intrahousehold power relations may lead to men controlling the use of and the distribution of benefits from forest land and trees that their wives, mothers, sisters, or daughters legally own. Women may acquiesce in such arrangements either because they have no choice or as a conscious investment in long-term social capital.

Property and Social Forestry

The outcome of social forestry can be affected by property and tenure relations in a number of ways. The relationship of tree planting and harvesting to the creation of property rights can be a key factor. Under some circumstances clearing forest creates rights to the land on which the trees grew, while in others planting trees creates rights to the land on which the trees are planted. People's willingness to plant trees or harvest trees or allow others to do so may depend on the property outcomes of these acts. Social forestry may include a wide variety of usufructuary rights such as collecting fire-wood, moss, leaves, or pine needles, cutting poles or timber, grazing domestic animals, hunting, gathering wild foods and medicines, as well as religious practices.

Social Forestry on Private Land

Private property (also called freehold property) is owned by an individual or group of individuals or legal persons such as partnerships or corporations. Within the limits set by the government (in such forms as taxation and zoning) or social practice, the owner has the right to use the land or trees as s/he sees fit. Social forestry programs may take the form of sponsoring the planting and maintaining of trees on private property. When tree planting creates property rights or when the closing canopy will make other uses impossible, tree planting for a social forestry project may also be used as a weapon in property struggles. This use of tree planting to seize control of land is sometimes called the 'green machete.' For example, in The Gambia, men used tree planting sponsored by an agroforestry project to drive women off the land they had been using for lucrative vegetable production.

Social forestry may involve privatizing public forest land on the grounds that this will lead to better management. This is not necessarily so. Both large and small holders of privatized parcels may be under financial pressure to harvest their parcel or sell it to speculators. In either case, privatization may lead to conflicts between the new private *de jure* right holders and pre-existing *de facto* right-holders.

Social Forestry on Forested Commons

Joint ownership, management, and use of forest and tree resources by a designated group of users, often all or part of a community, is known as the commons or a common pool resource. In contrast to private property, the resource can not be sold, mortgaged, leased, or bequeathed outside the group. Common pool resources are sometimes confused with open access resources that anyone may use. Garrett Hardin's 'tragedy of the commons' argument that common property is inevitably degraded actually describes an open access resource, not a commons. Contrary to the 'tragedy of the commons' argument, when it is difficult to exclude users from resources such as forests that are subject to degradation, a commons system often constitutes the most effective property regime. One reason for this is that common property regimes generally include specific responsibilities as well as rights.

Elinor Ostrom's 'design principles' regarding the sustainability of common property resources are discussed in detail elsewhere (*see* **Social and**

Collaborative Forestry: Common Property Forest Management). The importance of each principle differs under different circumstances; however, monitoring has been found in many systems to be the most crucial component.

A clearly defined user group is an important component of effective common property regimes. Since local communities are rarely socially or economically homogeneous, it would be erroneous to assume that local user groups represent all community inhabitants. Externally initiated projects on forest commons may attract the interest of village elites and hence have the potential to harm women, the poor, and migratory users unless careful attention is paid to access, property, and tenure.

Women In social forestry systems on common property, if the decision-makers are male, women's uses of forest and tree products may not be incorporated into the management plan. The loss of access to these resources may create serious hardship for women.

The poor An initially widely praised social forestry project of tree planting on a common turned out to have been a successful move by village elites to seize the common land by planting trees on it. In another case, poor villagers begged visiting agroforestry experts not to replace the crooked thorny trees on the commons which only they used with productive multipurpose trees which would attract the attention of the rich and reduce their access to the resource.

Migratory users Nomadic pastoralists who have seasonal usufructuary rights, for example to graze their animals on a forest commons, are frequently overlooked when a social forestry project introduces a new management system with the result that they lose their access to the common resource.

Social Forestry Undertaken by a Community on Government Land that is not Effectively Controlled by the Government

Not every government controls every inch of its territory. In places where central government control is weak, local systems of rules may have a far greater effect on behavior than the government legal system. For example, in Teri Garhwal, India local communities managed parts of oak forest that was *de jure* government forest. A community's *de facto* rights to clearly defined areas of the forest were recognized and respected by other communities. The government's *de jure* property claim was simply irrelevant to local practice.

Social Forestry Undertaken in Collaboration by the Government and Local Communities on Government Controlled Forest Land

One of the earliest and probably the best-known example of social forestry undertaken in collaboration by the government and local communities on government controlled forest land is Joint Forest Management (JFM) initiated by the Indian Forest Service. This kind of social forestry in which the government forest is protected and/or managed by local people in return for usufructuary rights to forest and tree products or the right to farm in the forest is common throughout South and Southeast Asia and parts of Africa. In a related model, the government may give local people rights to harvest subsistence goods from individual trees such as trees on roadsides.

In a different kind of social forestry in the USA, the government allows local people to participate in decision-making about and/or implementation of forest management of government forest land as a means of reducing legal challenges to its management decisions. It also benefits from local expertise and sometimes labor.

Although they may be interested in access to forest resources, local citizens may also participate in such social forestry out of personal commitments to forest health, hope of employment, or a desire to protect or enhance their private property adjacent to a forest. For example, residents of mountain forest communities in California participate in fire management planning and implementation on adjacent government forest land in order to ensure effective forest fire management to protect their privately owned homes. This is another example of the point that property rights in or access to forest land and trees are not the only kind of property or access that matters in social forestry.

The Butter Creek Watershed Analysis in California is another example of this sort of social forestry. The US Forest Service hoped to get buy-in from local citizens holding diverse, often opposing views about government forest management by involving them in identifying desired future outcomes, analyzing current conditions, and choosing suitable management activities to achieve their goal. A long and sometimes contentious process of consultation and analysis resulted in what was widely viewed as a higher-quality watershed analysis than usual, increased understanding of the new forest management policy, improved relations between the US Forest Service personnel and the community, support for later projects, and a total absence of legal appeals against the plan.

In both of these cases, property rights remained unchanged but citizens gained access to the decision-making process affecting adjacent forest resources and, in theory, to the benefits of a healthy forest.

See also: **Landscape and Planning**: Perceptions of Nature by Indigenous Communities. **Social and Collaborative Forestry**: Canadian Model Forest Experience; Common Property Forest Management; Joint and Collaborative Forest Management; Social and Community Forestry; Social Values of Forests.

Further Reading

Agarwal B (1994) *A Field of One's Own: Gender and Land Rights in South Asia*. Cambridge, UK: Cambridge University Press.

Baker M and Kusel J (2003) *Community Forestry in the United States: Learning from the Past, Crafting the Future*. Washington, DC: Island Press.

Bruce JW (1989) *Community Forestry: Rapid Appraisal of Tree and Land Tenure*. Rome: FAO.

Fortmann L and Bruce JW (1988) *Whose Trees? Proprietary Dimensions of Forestry*. Boulder, CO: Westview Press.

Fortmann L and Rocheleau D (1985) Women and agroforestry: four myths and three case studies. *Agroforestry Systems* 2: 253–272.

Hulme D and Murphree M (eds) (2001) *African Wildlife and Livelihoods: the Promise and Performance of Community Conservation*. Portsmouth, NH: D. Philip and Heinemann.

Leach M (1994) *Rainforest Relations: Gender and Resource Use among the Mende of Gola, Sierra Leone*. Washington, DC: Smithsonian Institution Press.

Macpherson CB (ed.) (1978) *Property: Mainstream and Critical Positions*. Oxford, UK: Basil Blackwell.

Merry SE (1988) Legal pluralism. *Law and Society Review* 22(5): 869–896.

Ostrom E (1990) *Governing the Commons: The Evolution of Institutions for Collective Action*. Cambridge, UK: Cambridge University Press.

Peluso NL (1992) *Rich Forests, Poor People: Resource Control and Resistance in Java*. Berkeley, CA: University of California Press.

Poffenberger M (ed.) (1990) *Keepers of the Forest: Land Management Alternatives in Southeast Asia*. West Hartford, CT: Kumarian Press.

Ribot JC and Peluso NL (eds) (2003) A theory of access. *Rural Sociology* 68(2): 153–181.

Rocheleau D, Thomas-Slayter B, and Wangari E (eds) (1996) *Feminist Political Ecology: Global Issues and Local Experiences*. London: Routledge.

Rose C (1994) *Property and Persuasion: Essays on the History, Theory and Rhetoric of Ownership*. Boulder, CO: Westview Press.

Schroeder R (1999) *Shady Practices: Agroforestry and Gender Politics in the Gambia*. Berkeley, CA: University of California Press.

Canadian Model Forest Experience

J E Hall and B Bonnell, Canadian Forest Service, Ottawa, Canada

Introduction

As a partnership-based strategy, Canada's Model Forest Program (CMFP) provides an excellent case study of collaborative forest management (CFM). In model forests, the partnerships and their goals are expanded beyond the relationships usually associated with CFM that are between industry or government professional forest managers and local communities. Model forest partnerships include a broad array of participants from all levels of government, industry, academia, Aboriginal communities, and other groups representing a wide diversity of timber and non-timber forest values. Canada, through the Canadian Forest Service (CFS) and the Canadian Council of Forest Ministers (CCFM) initiated this approach in 1991 as part of a long-term, nationwide experiment in developing approaches to sustainable development in forestry. The scale of CMFP is representative of Canada's forest sector, its diversity of socioeconomic circumstances, and its variety of forest types; it is the largest such undertaking in the world.

Origins of Canada's Model Forest Program

After the concept of sustainable development was introduced by the Brundtland Commission Report of 1987, it was clear that maximizing social, economic, or ecological goals independently through conventional management systems would not lead to sustainable development. To incorporate the concept of sustainable development, managers must integrate the goals of all three elements of development (social, economic, and ecological) and optimize these goals as a suite where balance is sought among all over time.

In developing an approach to sustainable development in forestry, Canada recognized the strengths demonstrated by CFM partnerships in integrating the goals of different partners, increasing awareness of forest values, improving knowledge to create potential solutions, and broadening the type of benefits derived from the forest and their distribution. By building on these strengths and increasing the constituency of participants in the partnerships beyond that of conventional CFM (which is generally characterized by industry – community or government – community partnerships), Canada designed model forests to provide Canadians with an opportunity to participate in developing and demonstrating approaches to sustainable development in forestry, otherwise termed sustainable forest management (SFM). To date, model forests continue to be very active in Canada and have since expanded to many countries around the world.

Purpose of Canada's Model Forest Program

Canada's Model Forest Program was developed to support Canadians interested in participating in partnerships that represent a broad array of interests for the development of approaches to sustainable development for the forest area of their choice.

In 1991, the Canadian Forest Service invited interested groups or individuals across Canada to form partnerships and to compete to become one of 11 model forests that would form a national network and receive federal government funding to support their work. Successful proposals would describe comprehensive and innovative approaches to SFM that would include the production of timber as well as other forest-based values as determined by the partnership. The partnership would focus its efforts on an area of forest of their choice that would reflect the scale of Canada's forest sector and be no less than 100 000 ha. **Figure 1** illustrates the forest type and location of Canada's model forests.

What Is a Model Forest?

A model forest is a partnership of individuals and groups representing diverse forest values working together to develop and demonstrate approaches to SFM that are locally acceptable and nationally relevant. Model forests are designed as large-scale, living laboratories where people with an interest in the forest participate in decisions about how to manage the forest sustainably. They provide a process that helps participants recognize the impact of their activities on the land base, develop a shared understanding of SFM, and demonstrate this in operational terms. A model forest is of a size that includes the full range of forest uses and needs that are considered in the surrounding geographic region and which is representative of a broad ecosystem. In Canada, model forests are of a scale that is representative of the country's vast forest and range from 100 000 ha up to 7.7 million ha. The basic elements that describe Canada's model forests are provided in **Table 1** including forest type, tenure, participants, governance, and objectives.

Figure 1 Major forest regions of Canada and the Canadian Model Forest Network.

Table 1 Summary of model forest characteristics including forest type, tenure, participants, governance, and objectives

Model forest	Forest type	Size ($ha \times 10^3$)	Tenure	Number of partners[a]	Key partner types	Governance	Objectives
Western Newfoundland	Boreal	923	Public, industry license, national park	17	Forest industry; federal and provincial government; communities; NGO; national park; trapper association; academia/research; education	Not-for-profit corporation; small Board of Directors; Management (Partnership) Committee; Scientific Advisory Committee; Executive Committee; two activity committees; issue-oriented working groups; consensus-based decision-making	1. Develop SFM systems and tools, and increase capacity for partners to implement approaches to SFM; 2. Communicate national, provincial, and local SFM priorities through the dissemination of acquired results and knowledge; 3. Increase public understanding of SFM and provide opportunities for effective participation.
Nova Forest Alliance	Acadian	458	Public, private (small land holdings), industry license	40	Large and small forest industry; federal and provincial government; First Nations; small landowner associations; NGOs; ENGOs; academia/ research; education	Not-for-profit corporation; Partnership Committee; sector-based Executive Committee; standing committees; project working groups; consensus-based decision-making	1. Develop and test a landscape-level SFM system; 2. Generate and transfer new knowledge on key SFM issues; 3. Design and test model processes to assist in forest certification; 4. Increase capacity of landowners to implement best management practices; 5. Facilitate transfer of SFM practices; 6. Increasing understanding of SFM; 7. Nurture local involvement in model forest.
Fundy	Acadian	419	Public, industry license and private, national park, private (small land holdings)	34	Forest industry; federal and provincial government; communities; First Nation; small landowner associations; NGOs; ENGOs; national park; academia/ research	Not-for-profit corporation; Partnership Committee; Executive Committee; Working Groups; consensus-based decision-making	1. Develop knowledge of ecosystem integrity and impacts; 2. Develop cooperative approach to research, monitoring, and planning; 3. Technology transfer of SFM tools and processes; 4. Provide education and training to forest professionals; 5. Collect and report on SFM and ecosystem information; 6. Provide a forum for discussion of SFM issues; 7. Increase public awareness.

Bas-Saint-Laurent	Boreal	113	Industry private, private (small land holdings)	40	Forest industry; federal and provincial government; small landowner associations; academia	Not-for-profit corporation; small Board of Directors; Partner Committee; Advisory Committees; consensus-based decision-making	1. Promote development and adoption of forest management models; 2. Help improve SFM systems; 3. Foster the development and application of new forest management techniques; 4. Communicate and disseminate results.
Waswanipi Cree	Boreal	3300	Public, industry license	18	First Nation; forest industry; federal and provincial government; academica/research; communities; NGOs	Administered under First Nation Band Council; Board of Directors (proponents); consensus	1. Develop and adopt SFM systems and tools based on Western science and Cree values and principles; 2. Disseminate results and knowledge at local, regional and national levels; 3. Increase local level (Cree) participation in SFM decision-making and implementation.
Eastern Ontario	Great Lakes-St Lawrence	1530	Public, industry license and private, national park, private (small land holdings)	>200 members	Forest industry; First Nation; federal and provincial government; small landowners and landowner associations; NGOs; ENGOs; academia, conservation organizations; communities	Not-for-profit corporation; open membership structure; 10-member Board with four permanent members; five standing committees; working groups; consensus-based decision-making	1. Increase quality and health of existing forests of eastern Ontario; 2. Increase forest cover to improve forest sustainability and biodiversity; 3. Increase awareness and understanding of SFM; 4. Increase transfer of SFM principles and practices; 5. Strengthen SFM efforts through equity generation, partnership building, and program evaluation.
Lake Abitibi	Boreal, claybelt	1100	Public, industry license	19	Forest industry; federal and provincial government; communities; NGOs; community groups; academia; First Nations	Not-for-profit corporation; Board of Directors; Executive Committee; Strategic Advisory Committee; standing committees; consensus-based decision-making	1. Effect positive change by building a legacy of SFM knowledge; 2. Effectively promote the adoption of model forest technical knowledge to forest practitioners; 3. Enhance local involvement in SFM; 4. Expand web of influence.

continued

Table 1 Continued

Model forest	Forest type	Size ($ha \times 10^3$)	Tenure	Number of partners[a]	Key partner types	Governance	Objectives
Manitoba	Boreal	1050	Public, industry license	26	Forest industry; Aboriginals; federal and provincial government; communities; academia; ENGOs	Not-for-profit corporation; Board of Directors (full partnership representation); Executive Committee; Advisory Committee; consensus-based decision-making	1. Facilitate opportunities for local level participation in SFM with emphasis on Aboriginal involvement, planning, and diverse economic opportunities; 2. Ensure that the value of forests and the results and knowledge gained were communicated to practitioners, forest users, and general public; 3. Increase development and adoption of innovative forest stewardship practices, systems, and tools; 4. Share knowledge and participate in joint ventures with other model forests and organizations.
Prince Albert	Boreal, parkland	360	Public, industry license, national park	11	Forest industry; federal and provincial government; First Nations; Metis; academia; NGOs; research institutions; national park; communities	Not-for-profit corporation; Board of Directors (full partner representation); Executive Committee; standing committees; consensus-based decision-making	1. Increase the development and adoption of SFM systems and tools among the partners; 2. Extend the Prince Albert Model Forest program through mentoring and partnerships; 3. Increase public awareness of results and knowledge gained through the practice of SFM; 4. Ensure that results and knowledge are disseminated broadly; 5. Increase opportunities for local level participation in the development of SFM systems and tools; 6. Strengthen model forest network activities in support of Canada's SFM priorities.

| Foothills | Boreal, montane, subalpine | 2750 | Public, industry license, national park | 81 | Forest industry; federal and provincial government; mining, and oil and gas sectors; NGOs; communities; First Nations; national park; academia | Not-for-profit corporation; Board of Directors; Executive Committee; Program Implementation Team; Activity Teams; Scientific/Technical Committee; partner categories (sponsoring, management, program, project, other) consensus-based decision-making | 1. Demonstrate SFM; 2. Develop and implement mechanisms that result in wider understanding and application of SFM; 3. Deliver communications and outreach programs that improve understanding of and support for SFM; 4. Support and influence policy that improves the practice of SFM. |
| McGregor | Boreal, montane, subalpine | 7700 | Public, industry license | 41 | Forest industry; federal and provincial government; communities; First Nations; academia; NGOs; consultants | Not-for-profit corporation; Board of Directors (based on membership classes); Technical Steering Committee; consensus-based decision-making | 1. Build a legacy of ecological knowledge and management expertise applicable to SFM; 2. Foster the implementation of knowledge and expertise to SFM planning and decision-making, improving forest practices, and maintaining environmental values; 3. Enhance local understanding of, participation in, and support for SFM; 4. Expand influence through local, provincial, national and international networks, organizations, associations, and institutions. |

ENGOs, Environmental Non-Governmental Organizations; NGOs, nongovernmental organizations; SFM, sustainable forest management.
[a] Some partnerships have increased since the time of writing of the Action Plans.
Source: Information derived from the 2002–2007 5-Year Action Plans developed by each model forest.

Introduction to Stages of the Collaborative Partnership Process: Form, Storm, Norm, Perform, Reform

Collaborative forest management is both a process and a learning environment. Experience shows that the process of CFM consists of recognizable stages through which participating groups continually journey. To effectively participate and support the collaborative process, all stakeholders must be aware of the purpose and the role of the partners in each stage. The group begins with the 'Form' stage where it agrees on who will be involved, how they will be selected, and the purpose for which they will work. After the group is formed it then faces the 'Storm' stage where the participants explore their limits and boundaries and agree in how they will operate the partnership and work together. Storm is followed by the 'Norm' stage where the group comes to agreement on what it can and will do. Next is the 'Perform' stage where the group's ideas are actually put into action. After performing, the partnership goes through a 'Reform' stage that has two aspects. One is where their performance is evaluated, the circumstances are revisited, and based on the new information and experience gained in the preceding round(s), the partners undertake to return to the appropriate stage and continue the process at the point deemed necessary. The other aspect is where a partner changes its practices based on the lessons learned from the 'model' developed by the partnership. **Figure 2** provides an outline of the various stages.

The stages of CFM will be used as a framework to present the model forest approach. Where applicable, specific examples from model forests will be included to illustrate the change in practice brought about as a result of collaborative forest management.

Stage 1: Form

In this stage, usually catalyzed by an individual or small group, the potential partners are brought together to determine who should and who is able to participate, what forest tenure(s) will be involved, and the ground rules governing involvement.

Initiators of model forests seek to establish a voluntary, broadly based group open to views of interested parties who can identify an area of forest land of mutual interest and who ensure that their group includes, on a voluntary basis, those having land management authority and others with an interest in the SFM of that forest area. Typically model forest partnerships include stakeholders such as land users, land managers, industry, community groups, government agencies, nongovernmental environmental and forestry groups, academic and

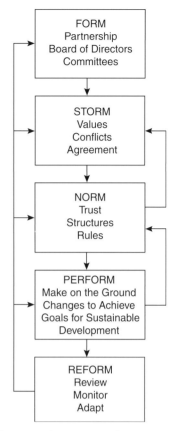

Figure 2 Overview of the stages of the collaborative partnership process.

educational institutions, national parks, Aboriginal groups, private landowners, and others as appropriate. The character of each model forest partnership is a function of the local conditions including who is present, who is interested in participating and is available, and local issues. The number of partners can change over time but has generally increased.

Model forests are managed in an integrated manner for all forest values identified as important by the partnership. Model forest management is a transparent, democratic, and usually consensus-based process where the ground rules for the group are defined by all the participants. The governance structure is designed to reflect the cultural, social, political, and economic realities of the region, allow for greater empowerment of people who often have little or no say in the decision-making processes, and ensure consideration of each identified value in the management planning process. Typically, model forests have an 'open seat' policy to provide for and encourage new perspectives at the table. It is not uncommon for new members to be invited to participate and contribute their expertise as the model forest explores additional and more complex SFM issues. The fundamental challenge of the partnership is to discover how they can continue to move forward together which often requires extensive discussion.

Because each model forest organization is founded on collaboration and establishes a self-governance structure, according to the standards and norms that apply in the model forest's region their management structures create unique relational frameworks that promote vertical, horizontal, and cross-sectoral linkages over time. In general, a model forest partnership will constitute itself as a legal, not-for-profit public association where overall accountability rests with the Board of Directors who seek input from the broader partnership, management committee, staff, technical committees and advisory boards.

The partnership group At the center of each model forest is the partnership group. It is composed of key land users and other stakeholders of the region who volunteer to work together towards the common goal of SFM. Generally there is a core group of partners who manage model forest activities; typically these include the tenure holders (forest industries), government, environmental specialists, Aboriginal and other local communities, nongovernmental organizations, and academia.

The board of directors Each model forest has a body to which model forest staff report and receive direction and authorization on substantive issues. The partnership generally elects a president or chair, and board of management (directors) from among its members, who are charged with ongoing program oversight and ensuring implementation of annual plans as endorsed by the partnership group. The size of the body is highly varied and ranges from as few as four members to nine or more. In the case of the Manitoba Model Forest in Canada, the Board of Directors comprises over 30 members – one representative for each partner. In that instance, the Board and the Partnership Group are the same.

Technical committees Model forests attract a wealth of professional expertise and benefit greatly from the input and guidance of these specialists. Expert input is often structured around formal or informal technical or advisory committees. Generally, there is at least one permanent technical committee that operates in an advisory capacity to both the board and management.

Demonstrating Diversity in Governance Model forest structures depend on local circumstances and choices. For example, the Eastern Ontario Model Forest (EOMF) has a population base of over 1 million people and 88% of its 1.5 million ha land base is made up of small, privately owned land holdings. To provide access to the EOMF organization, the EOMF established a membership program whereby individuals can join the model forest for a small annual fee. Membership provides regular newsletters, access to special events, and the right to stand for election and to cast a vote for members of the Board of Directors over and above the four 'seats' on the board that are reserved for the founding organizations (Canadian Forest Service, Ontario Ministry of Natural Resources, Domtar Communication Papers, and the Mohawk Council of Akwesasne).

Stage 2: Storm to Norm

During the 'storm' stage, model forest participants generate ideas, express values, bring knowledge and science into play to support decision-making, and enhance their understanding of each other and local SFM issues. Agreement is reached on how the partnership will operate and the activities to be undertaken – the 'norm' stage.

The common goal of the new partnership is also decided at this stage. For model forests, while this is sustainable forest management, the partnership must define their vision for SFM for the area selected within which they will operate. This can take time as the participants must begin to understand each other and each other's perspectives before a common vision can be articulated and agreed upon.

Inherent within model forest partnerships is the ability for the participants to have access to a wide range of expertise, technology, and information. Scientists have participated on various committees and brought their scientific perspectives, knowledge, and other capacities to activities within the model forest governance. Model forests and their partners develop computerized decision-support systems which greatly strengthened the ability of planners and managers to analyze information accurately and quickly along both spatial and temporal scales. They also engage in research activities that lead to a greater understanding of ecological processes, the impacts of various anthropogenic and natural disturbances on forest ecosystems, wildlife habitat and population dynamics, sivicultural applications, biological control mechanisms, and the socioeconomic dimensions of SFM.

Activities that will assist in achieving the vision are also discussed and decided upon during the 'storm' stage. A model forest's objectives include a range of sociocultural, economic, and environmental needs that are considered in an integrated manner by all partners with respect to the overall goal of SFM. Therefore, as the partners identify, develop, and test activities that reflect the values and needs at the community, regional, and national levels, they are supported by a combination of pure and applied research, and undertake to report formally on outcomes, assess impacts, and modify new approaches to SFM. Activities are wide ranging and have included: research on riparian buffers, natural disturbance regimes, and wildlife habitat; development of best management practices; production of guidelines on minimizing soil disturbance; development and implementation of local level indicators of SFM; examining certification schemes and their applicability to small landholders; and thousands of others.

Creating new norms of local involvement in integrated resource planning at the provincial level Starting in 1998, the Prince Albert Model Forest (PAMF) initiated development of an ecosystem-based integrated resource management plan for the PAMF region. The entire PAMF partnership, including three levels of Aboriginal government and three levels of non-Aboriginal government, participated in the process. The interests and diverse values of First Nations, industry, government, area residents, and others were weighed over a 2-year period. The development of the initial plan has resulted in a planning process that is currently being implemented in six additional areas in the province by the Saskatchewan government.

Stage 3: Perform

In this stage, the partnership takes the ideas it has generated, conducts any research needed to confirm the ideas, and tests the ideas on the ground to create its 'models' of practice. It undertakes technology transfer and outreach to inform its partners and others of the results of the partnership's work.

An important characteristic of model forests is that the model forest organization itself does not and can not exercise decision-making authority over the land base. Instead, the model forest includes in their partnership those with legal tenure and management responsibilities over the land. Without jurisdictional responsibility, a model forest becomes a forum within which the partners can feel free to discuss a wide range of issues and approaches to solutions without feeling either powerless to do something (those without responsibilities) or under intense pressure to make immediate changes on the ground (those with jurisdictional responsibilities). Changes occur because those with management authority see the benefit to initiate such changes. The model forest provides the information on alternatives that is created through the joint effort of the partners working within their shared commitment to SFM.

Sustaining rural infrastructures through forest employment The forest tenant farmer system of the Bas-Saint-Laurent Model Forest exemplifies an innovative approach to collaborative forest management. Forest tenant farming is a land leasing system defined as: 'Allocation of a unit of land to an individual, called a forest tenant farmer, who agrees to manage it in a sustainable manner and to share the ensuing revenues with the landowner.' Abitibi Consolidated Inc., a major forest industry, is providing the land and the model forest has hired staff to assist the landowners with both direct technical assistance and in building linkages with others. Planning of forest management activities is based on a multi-resource management plan developed by consensus among the diverse model forest partners. In addition, forest tenant farmers cooperate on a landscape level with respect to joint management of hunting, fishing, and recreational and tourism activities. An evaluation concluded that tenant farms are viable enterprises and that the socioeconomic impacts are tangible and concentrated at the local and regional levels.

Stage 4: Reform

This stage refers to the decisions that are made based on the wisdom gained by the partners and the group as a whole as a result of going through the previous stages in the process. There are two aspects to this stage. One is a change in practice by a given partner as a result of the model forest's demonstrations. In addition, the partnership decides to re-examine their outputs and, based on new knowledge and experiences, return to any one of the previous stages and redo the process.

Successfully managing endangered species within an industrial forest landscape The pine marten is an endangered mammal in Canada's eastern province of Newfoundland and Labrador. The majority of the estimated 300 animals left on the island of Newfoundland are mainly found on the west coast in an area that has important timber resources for the island's pulp and paper industry. The area was the site of the longest environmentally based conflict in the province and was a key factor in selecting the area as a model forest. The Western Newfoundland Model Forest (WNMF) was instrumental in bringing together 22 organizations, including government departments, forest industry, mining interests, environmental groups, national parks, trappers, and others, to discuss the issue and develop a unified strategy for the protection of the marten. The WNMF supported research and facilitated an exchange of views which finally led to the establishment of a reserve area to protect the marten's critical habitat by provincial authorities.

Networking: A Defining Activity of Canada's Model Forests

Local model forest participation in a broader, national network was part of the original design of Canada's Model Forest Program. The premise for the need for a network came from the realization that each participant and model forest group would be breaking new ground and, being in such a unique situation, would benefit from having a 'peer group.' The network is a structure within which the individual model forests collaborate and share information and experiences and, by learning from each other, reduce duplication of efforts, and create synergies that can be applied to larger challenges. The network facilitates communication of ideas and cooperative efforts among the model forests, development of linkages with other organizations at the national level, and engagement in projects to further accelerate the advancement of SFM at each site and throughout Canada. The network and its activities are supported by a national Secretariat within the Canadian Forest Service.

Where the network identifies issues or needs of major importance to SFM in Canada and to model forests, a network strategic initiative is developed. To date strategic initiatives have been created to enhance Aboriginal involvement in SFM, to develop local level indicators of SFM (or measures of progress towards SFM), carbon accounting, and managing private woodlots for SFM.

The International Model Forest Network

The International Model Forest Network (IMFN) was announced by Canada at the UNCED Summit in Rio in 1992 to pilot the model forest concept outside of Canada. The IMFN has since grown from three sites in two countries (outside of Canada) in 1994 to 19 sites in 11 countries, in addition to numerous additional sites proposed and at early stages of development. The IMFN is supported by a Secretariat established in 1995 and housed with the International Development Research Center located in Ottawa, Canada. In 2002, a Regional Model Forest

Center for Latin America and the Caribbean was established to provide additional support for the establishment of model forests throughout that region. A similar regional center is under development for Asia.

Lessons Learned

Based on Experiences with the Model Forest Concept to Date in Canada, the Following Key Lessons can be Suggested

1. Collaborative forest management as manifested through the model forest concept has proven to be well suited to address a wide range of SFM and development issues in a broad range of circumstances that are important to participants as well as observers interested in emulating the approach. These issues include governance, environment, biodiversity, natural resource management and conservation, and economic development.
2. The collaborative approach adopted by model forests has been beneficial in successfully providing an open forum through which all interested parties, in particular marginalized and indigenous peoples, are able to become involved in the forest management decision-making process and generate tangible benefits to improve and sustain the forests upon which their livelihoods depend.
3. Inherent in the model forest concept is the recognition that there was no one solution to SFM. By facilitating the development of bottom-up approaches, the model forest concept, by design, allows for the development of local solutions within broader contexts that are innovative in the design of sites and in approaches undertaken to advance SFM.
4. A model forest is not a project, rather it is a process. Both individual model forests and national and international model forest networks and programs are continually in a learning phase within which participants learn to adapt as conditions and issues change and evolve and as challenges emerge or fade.
5. If forests are to be managed in a sustainable fashion then real benefits must be apparent for the full range of values that forests offer (e.g., water, biodiversity as well as forest products both timber and non-timber in nature). Model forests and the networks that have developed have demonstrated that real benefits are accrued that far exceed individual partner inputs and that duplication is reduced by collaborating in the

exchange of information and focusing efforts and resources on common goals.

6. Through local partnerships and national and international networking, model forests facilitate both global to local and local to global linkages that are important to creating effective SFM strategies.

7. The combination of broad-based partnerships working together in a respectful forum towards common goals, the use of science and technology to aid in decision-making within increasingly complex issues, and enhancement of participant capacities allows model forests to be highly adaptable to situations and issues beyond just forests.

8. By collaboratively addressing the identified issues and sharing information, the education and expertise of both individual partners and the partnership as a whole is substantially increased contributing to the long-term sustainability of the partnership. Over time, an integrated process of decision-making develops within which participants cannot only envision how their interest or value fits into the framework but also where others fit in. The mutual learning and understanding which take place within this process (and partnership) builds a synergy between the participants allowing the development of a much broader vision than the individual visions of the participants. SFM requires this broader vision that cannot be achieved through an isolated, individualistic sectoral approach.

9. Partnerships may create new challenges and increase the complexity of current ones, but they also offer the chance to create a learning environment rather than conflict to share information, to make trade-offs between conflicting objectives, and to develop better and more effective solutions to resource management issues. Model forests illustrate that the partnership (collaborative forest management) approach, although demanding of time and patience, leads to better and more sustainable decisions.

10. Successful collaborative relationships for SFM developed within the model forest partnerships creates the springboard for continued collaborative approaches in other sectors and spheres of activity.

11. Not having the capacity to ensure that each element of collaboration (i.e., full participation; the consideration of multiple values and a scientific basis for decision-making) are at play within the model forest has been shown to compromise their long-term success. Despite having done much valuable work, one model forest in Canada did not continue beyond the second 5-year phase as it was unable to demonstrate its capacity to fulfill each of these elements.

12. One very important role in collaborative forest management is that of the interventionist or champion. The interventionist is defined as any individual or group that undertakes to initiate change. In getting CFM started, the interventionist must fill two roles: first as the facilitator of the collaborative process, and second as a stakeholder in that resource management system. To do this the interventionist must establish a role of 'honest broker' with interests that accord with the provision of SFM. The interventionist must also be able to both understand and solve problems and be able to negotiate effectively with the full spectrum of stakeholders. Once the initial interventionist has established the collaborative group it is crucial for the success of the process that all participants take on interventionist characteristics.

13. Perhaps the most important lesson to be learned from the model forest experience is that collaborative forest management as a process must become the 'norm' to achieve SFM rather than just a series of individual projects.

14. Model forests are tackling the complex issue of SFM through a partnership process that is based on an expanded approach to CFM. The successful establishment of model forests around the globe further demonstrates the flexibility, versatility and utility of the model forest concept in helping interested individuals and organizations participate in the challenge of SFM. However, there are a number of factors that frustrate success in working towards SFM. These include and are not restricted to circumstances where there is insufficient political support, there is a history of unresolved conflict, there is a lack of clear purpose, goals or deadlines are unrealistic, the distribution of benefits is unsatisfactory, and partnerships are not managed in an equitable, respectful, and transparent manner.

Concluding Remarks

Resource managers are dealing with increasingly complex issues in sustainable forest management such as endangered species, landscape-level forest values, and an increasing demand for forest products. These complex issues require both diverse information and cooperation among a wide range of interests, organizations, and agencies. Collaborative forest management aptly provides for these needs.

Since its inception in 1992, the model forest concept has grown from an original 10 sites in Canada to over 30 sites in 11 countries (in 2003) with more sites in the planning stages. Clearly this demonstrates that collaborative forest management can be applied and can often flourish in a wide range of geographic, institutional, and cultural settings where the model forest approach is taken. This growth also attests to the relevance and still unrealized potential of collaborative forest management to make lasting and significant contributions to critical internationally shared challenges to achieving SFM in practice.

From the experience of the model forests, resource managers should, with confidence, apply CFM elsewhere in order that CFM increasingly becomes a normal operating procedure rather than the exception.

See also: **Social and Collaborative Forestry**: Forest and Tree Tenure and Ownership; Joint and Collaborative Forest Management; Social and Community Forestry; Social Values of Forests.

Further Reading

Besseau P, Dansou K, and Johnson F (2002) The International Model Forest Network (IMFN): elements of success. *Forestry Chronicle* 78(5): 648–654.

Canadian Model Forest Network (2003) http://www.modelforest.net

Carter J (2002) *Recent Experience in Collaborative Forest Management Approaches: A Review of Key Issues.* Geneva, Switzerland: SDC, Intercooperation.

Hall JE (1996) Canada's Model Forest Program: an experiment in the application of sustainable development in forest management. A paper presented at the *Integrated Application of Sustainable Forest Management Practices International Workshop*, 22–25 November 1996, Kochi, Japan.

Hall JE (1997) Canada's Model Forest Program: a participatory approach to sustainable forest management in Canada. *Commonwealth Forestry Review* 76(4): 261–263.

Ingles AW, Musch A, and Qwist-Hoffmann H (1999) *The Participatory Process for Supporting Collaborative Management of Natural Resources: An Overview.* Rome: Food and Agriculture Organization.

International Model Forest Network (2003) http://www.imfn.net

LaPierre L (2002) Canada's Model Forest Program. *Forestry Chronicle* 78(5): 613–617.

Mayers J and Vermeulen S (2002) *Company–Community Partnerships: From Raw Deal to Mutual Gains.* London: International Institute for Environment and Development (IIED).

Public Participation in Forest Decision Making

S R J Sheppard and C M Achiam, University of British Columbia, Vancouver, BC, Canada

Introduction

Over the last few decades, the formal practice and supporting science of public participation have emerged as key components of forest management and decision-making in many countries. The Montreal Process and virtually all certification systems call for appropriate public participation in decisions on forest management. Some cultures and traditional practices have incorporated what we would now term participatory decision-making for centuries. The formal methods and structures used more recently to make decisions in forestry, particularly in western nations, have evolved considerably, with a trend towards more public involvement in decision-making. This can be seen at both the local level (increasing control over use of local resources) and the global level (in terms of public opinion affecting policies and practices at the level of the global marketplace).

This article briefly describes potential benefits of applying public participation in forestry, and identifies some key theoretical concepts and broad empirical reviews of practice which inform the field. General findings and emerging principles for public participation are summarized, and criteria for assessing the performance of public participatory techniques and processes are identified. Selected techniques in use in forest decision-making are described briefly, together with indications of their performance where information is available. The article concludes with general guidance from current knowledge on the design of good processes for public involvement in forestry.

This article focuses on the scientifically documented aspects of public participation in forest planning, rather than in the broader arenas of public education and governance. Much of the literature reviewed comes from the democratized and more industrially developed nations, especially applying to the public forests of temperate countries. Many of the principles apply more broadly, however, including to private lands in western nations and forest management in developing countries or nations in transition. Readers should also consult the related articles on community forestry and collaborative management (*see* **Social and Collaborative Forestry**: Canadian

Model Forest Experience; Joint and Collaborative Forest Management; Social and Community Forestry) for more on participatory mechanisms in tropical regions worldwide. It should not be assumed that methods of community involvement in less industrialized nations are necessarily less effective or equitable than those in Europe or North America.

Public participation has been defined by the FAO/ECE/ILO Joint Committee Team of Specialists on Participation in Forestry as:

> various forms of direct public involvement where people, individually or through organized groups, can exchange information, express opinions and articulate interests, and have the potential to influence decisions or the outcome of specific forestry issues.

Public participation is an inherently two-way process, and should not be confused with public relations which attempts to convey information in one direction in a manner favorable to the disseminator of the information.

Stakeholders have been defined as all individuals or organized groups interested in the issue or opportunity driving the participatory process. This includes both recognized 'interest groups' and other, sometimes less visible, sectors of society affected by or concerned with some aspect of forest management.

Potential Benefits of Public Participation

Why is public participation important, and what good does it do? The potential benefits often described include:

- increasing public awareness of forests and forestry among the public through interaction and collaborative learning
- increasing the overall flow of benefits to society by contributing to better decisions and outcomes for multiple forest uses and products, and more equitable sharing of costs and benefits
- improving social acceptance of sustainable forestry through better information and involvement in the decision-making process
- building trust in institutions.

Other practical benefits include gaining information from stakeholders that would otherwise be ignored (e.g., traditional ecological knowledge), and streamlining the process of plan and project implementation by avoiding delays, resolving conflicts among competing interests, and reducing risks of legal action. However, increasingly, there is seen to be an overarching moral purpose in incorporating public values into forestry decisions.

Theoretical Concepts and Broad Empirical Reviews

The scientific background to public participation stems from various sources, many of them outside the field of forestry. Most notably, the science of sociology and the discipline of community and regional planning have contributed to our understanding of participatory mechanisms, though influenced by various social sciences and professions. In less industrialized countries, much knowledge on effective processes has been gained from the broad application of participatory rural appraisal methods for assessing local resources and development options with local community involvement. Public participation in forestry is now conducted by public participation specialists, foresters, planners, and land managers, in addition to social scientists.

The concept of public involvement in forestry has changed considerably since Gifford Pinchot's 'scientific forestry' ethos in the early 1900s, where the public interest was to be served by having experts apply conservation policies that produced the greatest good for the greatest number for the longest time. More recently the public has become increasingly adamant about accountability in government and has begun to demand more direct involvement in the decision-making process. The role of government has evolved from decision-maker based on expert knowledge to that of arbiter among different interests within a pluralist public.

Sociologists have identified two normative models of participation in a democratic political framework where public participation is encouraged: participatory democracy and representative democracy. In a participatory model, the broadest cross-sections possible would be involved in decision-making to be representative of the widest majority in the society. Several challenges face this model, including the reality that individual citizens may not have the time, knowledge, or interest to participate in resource decision-making. The alternative normative model is representative democracy, which suggests that to compensate for the lack of capacity to participate in multiple decision-making activities, individuals join together in forming or supporting various interest groups which, in combination, can fairly represent the balance of individual interests in society.

Specific theoretical frameworks have been developed which attempt to explain or structure the range of participatory processes, in various settings. Sherry Arnstein in 1969 developed a ladder of public participation (**Figure 1**) which described the role of citizens in decision-making, ranging from nonparticipation, through token participation, to degrees of

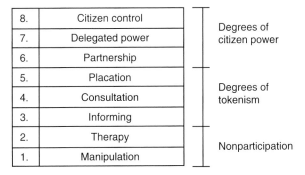

8.	Citizen control	⎤ Degrees of
7.	Delegated power	citizen power
6.	Partnership	⎦
5.	Placation	⎤ Degrees of
4.	Consultation	tokenism
3.	Informing	⎦
2.	Therapy	⎤ Nonparticipation
1.	Manipulation	⎦

Figure 1 Arnstein's ladder of public participation. (Reproduced with permission from Arnstein SR (1969) A ladder of citizen participation. *American Institute of Planning Journal* 35(4): 216–234.)

citizen power. While this typology has been criticized for creating unrealistic expectations that citizens could or should make public policy decisions, it has also been praised for its simplicity, and continues to be one of the most widely cited references in public participation literature.

Another model, developed in the 1970s, was the widely tested Vroom–Yetton Model, originally designed to assist business managers to determine what level of participation by subordinates (on a scale similar to Arnstein's ladder) would improve the effectiveness of decision-making in the corporate business setting. Attempts have been made to adapt the Vroom–Yetton Model to the needs of natural resource management; in one such application, R Lawrence and D Deagen developed a scheme for managers to determine whether and how public consultation should be used, using a hierarchy of questions addressing the likelihood of public acceptance of management actions, the manager's knowledge of salient public preferences, the likely benefits of public learning on the issue, and other aspects relating to efficiency of the process.

Beierle and colleagues have developed a framework for evaluating public participation in environmental decision-making which can be directly applied to forestry. This framework recognizes three major components: context, process, and results. Context refers to all the conditions or features of a given situation that a public participation process should address, such as the institutional setting and history of prior participation or conflict. Process encompasses what actually happens in a participatory program of exercise, including the kind of participation mechanisms used and various associated factors which influence their effectiveness, such as responsiveness of the lead agency. Results refer to the outcomes of the context and process, in terms of the decisions or actions enabled, the

relationships built among the participants, and capacity-building achieved through the process.

Empirical reviews have also sought to develop classification systems for participatory mechanisms. Thomas Beierle and Jerry Cayford recognized four categories of participatory mechanisms to address environmental issues: public meetings and hearings; advisory committees not seeking consensus; advisory committees seeking consensus; and negotiations and mediations (seeking consensus). They described these mechanisms by relating the number of participants to be involved with the level or intensity of involvement desired. The FAO/ECE/ILO Joint Committee Team considered public participation that was specific to forestry in 13 countries, and identified several types of participation at various levels from national to local; types of public involvement processes included (1) those addressing forest policies, programs, and plans, (2) those promoting specific forest projects, (3) those used in audits of forestry projects or practices, and (4) those involving advisory boards or permanent councils. Max Hislop and Mark Twery, working at the UK Forestry Commission, produced a menu of participatory techniques, with matrices that arrayed appropriate techniques against the various stages of the decision-making process and the number of stakeholders to be involved.

A simple classification that has been suggested by various authors and researchers to describe participatory methods recognizes three typical levels of involvement: information exchange or directive participation (where information is communicated primarily in one direction); consultation, where public opinions are sought and considered in expert or managerial decision-making; and collaboration, where representatives of the public are involved actively in developing solutions and directly influencing decisions. **Figure 2** presents a simple scheme using this classification, and listing various techniques (some of which are described below) under each level of involvement. In addition, mechanisms providing fuller control of decisions to public groups (such as Community Forests) are described in articles (**Social and Collaborative Forestry**: Joint and Collaborative Forest Management) and (**Social and Collaborative Forestry**: Social and Community Forestry).

Many examples of particular participatory techniques have been documented in various ways in the scientific and professional literature. Apart from occasional illustrative examples, this article draws primarily on the broad reviews mentioned above, as well as a recent review of public processes conducted by the author and other researchers in British Columbia. These sources include empirical studies, normative papers, and professional practice.

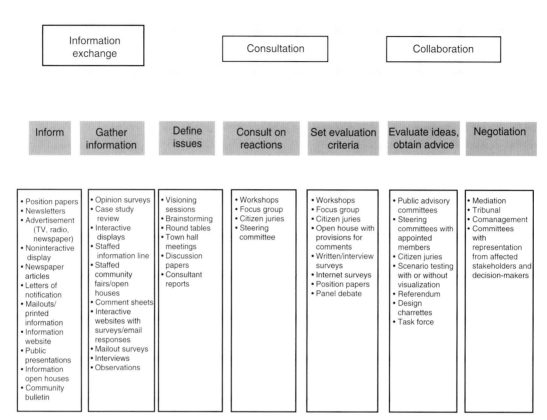

Figure 2 The public participation continuum. Courtesy of Forest Investment Account and Slocan Forest Products. Derived in part from Hislop M and Twery M (2001) *A Decision Framework for Public Involvement in Forest Design Planning.* Final Report Prepared for Policy and Practice Division. Roslin, UK: Forestry Commission.

The concepts and methods applied to public participation in forestry also relate strongly to other allied regulatory processes in certain jurisdictions, e.g., environmental and social impact assessment, land use and resource planning, and sustainability assessment, certification, and monitoring.

General Findings and Principles

This section describes some of the patterns of use of participatory approaches in forestry, general findings on the performance and quality of participation, and principles for successful participation which emerge from the current state of our knowledge.

The FAO/ECE/ILO review of studies from various nations suggested that participatory processes in forestry occur at all levels from national to local, but most commonly at the regional and local levels. These processes appear to be affecting decisions in most cases. Public participation applies both to public and private forestry, though often with different purposes and constraints: not surprisingly, more effort is expended in public involvement on public forest land than on private land. Public

processes range from the formal to the informal. They may be part of the statutory process, e.g., more formal/procedural and institutionalized processes, such as the public process under the National Environmental Protection Act governing the US Forest Service Forest Resource Management Plans; they may be scientifically procedural but discretionary, as in the use of social science/research tools such as surveys to inform the process; and they may be procedurally informal but built into ongoing management or governance structures such as community forest initiatives (*see* **Social and Collaborative Forestry**: Common Property Forest Management; Joint and Collaborative Forest Management; Social and Community Forestry) or voluntary comanagement agreements with First Nation aboriginal groups.

In terms of the range of participatory mechanisms on the scale of Arnstein's ladder or the simpler three-category classification described above (see **Figure 2**), the more collaborative mechanisms are least common. They tend to be more difficult to introduce and implement and require considerable flexibility on the part of participants and enlightened attitudes on the part of the agencies or vested interests; they can consume more time than other methods, although it is argued that they may save time in the long run by improving understanding and reducing conflict.

Empirical research shows that many public participation processes in practice to-date have not lived up to their potential or public and agency expectations. The FAO/ECE/ILO study found that project-oriented processes tended to address certain sectors of the public and not others. Many researchers have commented on the failure of processes to engage the silent majority. Some have suggested that environmental groups, for example, have successfully used the process to shift the focus on to environmental interests at the expense of other values, thereby distorting the real public interest, although there are also many instances of apparent domination of the public agenda by industry, landowners, or government. As an example, the US Department of Agriculture Forest Service conducted a public participation process in the Nantahala National Forest and researchers evaluated the representativeness of the public involvement. The research indicated that the socioeconomic characteristics of participants in the public process did not reflect the make-up of the local public: participants tended to have more general education, more formal education about forests, greater incomes, and a higher proportion with occupations related to natural resources, as compared with the general public. State government, environmental, and timber interests were overrepresented. Nonetheless, the research concluded in this case that the preferences of the participants, on balance, broadly reflected the general public's values.

Various barriers commonly prevent or discourage voluntary participation by some groups. These can include:

- lack of information, either explaining the process itself or why the issue is important
- lack of access to the participatory process due to cultural or psychological factors, such as inexperience or perceived repercussions; women, young people, and aboriginal groups are often under-represented in conventional processes, as well as other groups who lack organizational capacity, such as small-scale forest owners or less affluent social classes
- belief that participants have little or no ability to influence the process/decision
- tactical behavior, whereby some interest groups perceive they can be more influential by staying outside the process
- lack of interest, often compounded by the cost or time commitment required to sustain a participatory effort; people choose to participate only as

long as they perceive the benefits outweigh the costs of their participation.

Public participation in forestry land use planning has met with mixed success, often leading to low public satisfaction with the processes concerned. Many processes are institutionalized, and not agreed to or influenced by the participants. Recent Canadian research indicates that some conventional techniques for eliciting public input such as noninteractive public displays and open houses with highly technical material have generated less than useful results. Recurring problems in some political climates include long and acrimonious processes that appear to favor certain lobby groups while marginalizing other values. The links between the public process and final decisions or implementation of forest plans are often not transparent. Evaluation of the success of processes, to gauge effectiveness and satisfaction of participants, is seldom conducted routinely in practice. In this article, some more specific evaluations of the performance of particular public involvement mechanisms are provided with the descriptions of key techniques below.

According to some researchers, successful public involvement may be more affected by the specific context of the geographic area and issues such as the available time, budget, and pre-existing relationships between the stakeholders, than by the specific public involvement techniques employed. Even the most sophisticated public involvement processes can sometimes be unsuccessful due to internal and external contextual factors; however, there is some evidence in recent research that innovative processes facilitated by neutral third parties can influence the pre-existing stakeholder or institutional dynamics and revitalize productive participation (**Figure 3**).

The growing body of research evaluating public participation in forestry leads to some emerging general principles. The UK Forestry Commission has concluded that the process of community participation is as important as the product (management decisions), if public support for decision-making is to be maintained. This process is iterative, cyclical, and woven into other aspects of management and decision-making; it should not be thought of as a single event or the application of a single technique; it continues after the planning process is 'complete.'

The process needs to recognize multiple publics, not just the extreme interests. Consensus among stakeholders is not necessarily a realistic outcome for an effective process, even though many processes are designed to achieve this; sometimes, providing inclusive and balanced information to the decision-makers for use in a structured and controlled

Figure 3 Workshops facilitated by researchers with separate stakeholder groups to assess forest management alternatives, using model-based time-lapse maps and visualizations, were deemed more effective than conventional public processes in the politically charged atmosphere of British Columbia's Slocan Valley.

decision process may be enough, and better than the alternative of a simplistic majority vote process. Not all participatory processes need to involve all stakeholder groups in the same venue at the same time; more constructive results may be obtained by granting equal access to each stakeholder group separately. Researchers have found that using a small group of stakeholder representatives can be more efficient in reaching solutions than processes that directly involve large numbers of people, but risks divorcing the participants from the groups they are intended to represent.

The context of political and cultural norms and traditions is important, as is building trust. This can take a long time, especially if cultural and communication barriers between scientists or managers and indigenous groups (for example) need to be overcome. The skill and capacity of participants to engage with a public process may need to be enhanced for an equitable process to occur.

Belief in the fairness of the decision-making process is key. However, merely increasing participation in the decision-making process does not always enhance satisfaction with the perceived fairness of either the process or the decision. Besides conducting procedurally fair public involvement processes, it is necessary to demonstrate that the decision-makers acted in good faith by impartially considering the views of participants in the decision-making process.

Evaluating the Effectiveness of Participatory Processes

How is a good public involvement process determined? This section goes beyond the general principles outlined above, to describe criteria for evaluating the effectiveness of participatory processes. The following criteria have been proposed by or derived from various authors and researchers.

1. Logistical effectiveness. The process should be appropriate to the scope, financial resources available, and the time limitations of the project requirement.
2. Clearly structured and integrative decision-making framework. The nature and scope of the participatory process should be articulated at the outset and used throughout the process as a guide to keep the tasks on track; mechanisms for structuring and

working through the decision-making process should be clear and well coordinated.

3. Representation. The process should provide inclusive representation of all interests concerned by the issue driving the participatory process, including administrators, actual and potential users, and people whose livelihoods or other interests are affected by the decisions. Participants should have an equal right to express their opinion and a fair chance to assert their interests and rights.

4. Open communication and access. Steps should be taken to ensure that participants have multiple opportunities or choices for involvement e.g., different event times, length of time and format involved, and intensity of involvement in a culturally appropriate manner. In addition, all participants should have access to needed resources and should be involved in the process as early as possible and as need arises.

5. Participants' agreement. The process should be based on participants acting in good faith, and agreeing not to use shared information to abuse or sabotage the process. Participants should be included in the design of the process, agreeing to ground rules for the process; participants in collaborative processes should ensure good communication with their respective interest group.

6. Transparency. The process should be transparent to participants and the broader public, and the information understandable and readily available.

7. Independence and neutrality. The process should be conducted in an independent, unbiased manner. Participants should be free to conduct themselves in a voluntary and self-directed manner without coercion, and process management should be neutral. The process should seek the common good, not just accommodating specific interests.

8. Influence and accountability. It should be clear that the process and recommendations are capable of genuine impact on decisions. The process should not guarantee or predetermine the outcome, and should be open to consideration of reasonable alternatives and choices, including at a minimum a 'do nothing' alternative to the proposed action. Action should follow decisions and designated parties should ensure their follow-through. Participant satisfaction with the process should be documented.

Individual Participatory Techniques

This section reviews selected participatory techniques applicable to forest planning, as examples of the methods and tools in use or available. Methods range from the highly scientific to the pragmatic: some can be submitted to rigorous statistical analysis consistent with the high standards of social science research methods (utilizing techniques such as random sampling and adequate sample size calculation to ensure validity, reliability, and generalizability of results); others apply simple descriptive statistics to characterize findings from available participants, or yield only qualitative discussion of general preferences and decisions, as with many public advisory groups.

A menu of some key techniques follows, loosely arranged on a scale from informational through consultative to collaborative; results of empirical studies on these techniques are summarized where these are available and pertinent.

1. Information open house. The public is invited to visit a specific venue during a specified time period where information on a project or issue is displayed and a presentation may be made. There are usually opportunities for comments to be received. This can represent an easy form of public participation to manage, and is useful early in the process, but may not secure input from various affected stakeholder groups; it is often inadequate as the primary mechanism to support decisions.

2. Surveys (e.g., mail-out questionnaires and person-to-person or telephone interviews). These are a means to gather information using a representative sample that reflects the opinions of the larger population. Return rates are sometimes quite low, and participants may be skewed demographically, but surveys usually expand significantly the range of opinion gathered, as compared with meeting-based techniques. They do not enable dialogue.

3. Interactive websites with surveys/email responses. Use of the World Wide Web can provide information to the public as well as gather responses. This promises broad and open participation to local and global interests alike, is cost effective in relation to the breadth of outreach, and allows updating of information and some dialogue; however, its weaknesses include only being open to people connected to the Web, and experience has demonstrated the risk of overuse/distortion of the system by certain motivated interest groups.

4. Citizen advisory committee or public advisory group (PAG). This is a public involvement forum which advises forest managers on issues and initiatives as an ongoing mechanism for public consultation. The level of responsibility and influence of the group can vary. The PAG is intended to provide an avenue for local constituencies to represent their interests and views regarding forest management; however, the

Canadian Forest Service has found that PAG members can differ systemically from the general public in sociodemographic characteristics and values and attitudes to forest management, suggesting that the process for selecting community representatives is critical.

5. Focus groups. These are small groups of people, formally or informally organized, and randomly selected or carefully chosen to represent various interests, for the purpose of interactive and spontaneous discussions of one particular topic or plan. Focus groups can be used at any stage of the public involvement process to accomplish tasks ranging from gathering information, or defining issues or criteria, to providing perceptual data (*see* **Landscape and Planning**: Perceptions of Forest Landscapes). As with other methods, representation of the wider public interests is key. A variant of the focus group technique is to hold structured workshops with various stakeholder groups to assess alternative forest plan scenarios, against multiple agreed criteria. The scenarios can then be compared and the results tabulated to quantify commonalities or differences in preference between each stakeholder group (**Figure 4**). Workshops can also be used to generate new or preferred solutions collaboratively.

Various new participatory techniques are emerging to expand the tools available to researchers and forest managers; examples include self-directed photosurveys of community values by local participants; cable TV channels providing opportunities for community dialogue and instant opinion polling; and decision support tools using real-time integrated resource-forecasting models linked to forest visualizations (*see* **Landscape and Planning**: The Role of Visualization in Forest Planning).

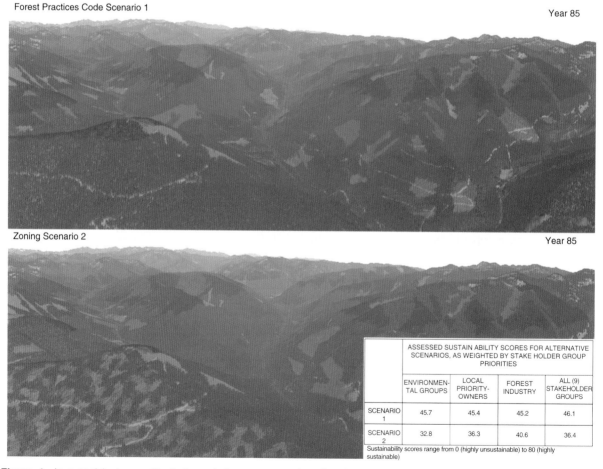

Figure 4 In a participatory multi-criteria analysis process conducted under the Arrow Forest District IFPA pilot study in British Columbia, different stakeholder groups weighted sustainability criteria and generally agreed on preferred forest management scenarios, as shown here in landscape visualizations. Visualizations by J Salter and D Cavens, Collaborative for Advanced Landscape Planning; reproduced with permission from Sheppard SRJ and Meitner MJ (2003) Using multi-criteria analysis and visualization for sustainable forest management planning with stakeholder groups. In: *IUFRO Decision Support for Multiple Purpose Forestry Conference Proceedings*, Vienna, Austria.

Towards Best Practices in Participatory Forest Decision-Making

Public participation is more than just a set of tools or a mechanical process: it has been called 'a way of thinking and acting.' Nonetheless, research and practical experience suggests some ways to design and structure an appropriate public participatory process. Beierle and colleagues have suggested five steps in designing public participation processes: (1) determine the need for public participation; (2) identify goals in the process; (3) determine key design decisions on appropriate participants, level of engagement, degree of public influence desired, and governmental role; (4) select and modify appropriate process; and (5) carry out a post-process evaluation. The FAO/ECE/ILO outline three stages and nine steps to consider when planning a participation process (**Table 1**). The overall decision-making process into which the public involvement fits, generally involves the selection of stakeholders, identification of issues, establishment of goals and objectives, agreement on evaluation criteria, generation of options, assessment of alternatives, and, finally, the selection of a course of action to achieve the plan.

In any public process, an analysis of stakeholders early on is essential: omissions or misrepresentation at this stage can hamper success throughout the remaining process. Stakeholder analysis requires a thorough search of stakeholder groups and contact details, including affected individuals, nonorganized stakeholder types (whether involved in or excluded from the usual processes), and a sample of the wider public. A typical range of stakeholders in western countries might include:

- indigenous communities if present
- other neighbors, local residents, and the community at large
- industry, labor, and local economy interests
- special-interest groups representing other forest users, such as tourism providers, recreation user groups (including visitors), environmental groups, and nontimber forest products users
- government agencies
- experts (to provide technical knowledge).

Stakeholders can be characterized in terms of the degree to which they are affected, their level of organization and influence over planning processes, and their capacity to participate meaningfully. Some attempts have been made to identify primary, secondary, and tertiary stakeholders, based on issues such as proximity to the area and how salient a forest resource is to them, but there is disagreement on how this classification should be used, for example, to influence levels of access to the participatory process. The stage of the decision-making process along with the level of involvement and the purpose of the public consultation will influence the selection of the type of stakeholders to be engaged. Within stakeholder interests, some researchers recommend leaving the choice of representatives to the stakeholders themselves wherever possible. Different levels of planning may require different skills and knowledge from the participants. The public involvement process may have to include capacity-building in order to achieve meaningful responses.

In terms of selecting appropriate participatory techniques (such as those described above) as part of the larger designed process, some researchers such as Hislop and Twery at the UK Forestry Commission have provided menus and selection guidance. However, it is generally accepted that multiple approaches are generally required: one technique is usually not enough to address the different publics, cultures and contexts identified through stakeholder analysis and

Table 1 Stages in planning a public participation process (adapted from FAO/ECE/ILO Joint Committee, 2000)

Stage		Steps
Define the context	1	Identify issue (e.g., proposed forest management activities), geographic scope, and potential stakeholders (stakeholder analysis)
	2	Define objectives, needs and budget for public participation, and possible approaches/mechanisms
	3	Commit to conducting a participatory process (or opt for another type of decision-making)
	4	Disseminate information about the issues and public process, and collect initial reactions/concerns
Plan the process	5	Develop a participation plan with participants, including goals, timetable, scope, rules and responsibilities, information management, techniques to be used, needs for training/capacity building, internal and external communications, and evaluation.
Implement the process	6	Implement the participation plan, and adapt if necessary
	7	Evaluate the participation plan and outcomes with stakeholders
	8	Communicate the outcomes of the public process to all stakeholders and wider interests
	9	Implement the outcomes (e.g., forest management activities) and provide feedback on progress

Source: FAO/ECE/ILO Joint Committee (2000) *Public Participation in Forestry in Europe and North America*. Geneva, Switzerland: International Labour Office.

scoping. The selection of the appropriate processes to match the given time, budgetary, and staffing constraints, and other external influences, is key. Clarification of the intent and intensity of the public involvement required will help differentiate between ongoing techniques, such as PAGs, versus more occasional major efforts at regular intervals, such as participatory forest management plan development.

Transparent documentation and monitoring of the process over time is important in helping to demonstrate social sustainability. Feedback to participants is critical to building trust over the longer term, together with evaluation of the effectiveness of processes and the level of public satisfaction achieved, as part of adaptive management of the public process itself. Beyond decision-making processes, constructive public involvement can be extended to include participation in implementing management actions, forest protection, and monitoring of sustainability criteria and indicators.

See also: **Landscape and Planning**: Forest Amenity Planning Approaches; The Role of Visualization in Forest Planning. **Social and Collaborative Forestry**: Canadian Model Forest Experience; Common Property Forest Management; Joint and Collaborative Forest Management; Social and Community Forestry; Social Values of Forests.

Further Reading

Arnstein SR (1969) A ladder of citizen participation. *American Institute of Planning Journal* 35(4): 216–234.

Beckley TM, Boxall PC, Just LK, and Wellstead AM (1999) *Forest Stakeholder Attitudes and Values: An Annotated Bibliography*. Northern Forestry Centre Information Report no. NOR-X-365. Edmonton, Canada: Natural Resources. Canada, Canadian Forest Service.

Beierle TC and Cayford J (2002) *Democracy in Practice: Public Participation in Environmental Decisions*. Washington, DC: RFF Press.

Brown K, Adger WN, Tompkin E, *et al.* (2001) Trade-off analysis for marine protected area management. *Ecological Economics* 37: 417–434.

FAO/ECE/ILO Committee on Forest Technology, Management, and Training (2000) *Public Participation in Forestry in Europe and North America*. Report of the Team of Specialists on Participation in Forestry. Geneva, Switzerland: International Labour Office.

Hamersley Chambers F and Beckley T (2003) Public involvement in sustainable boreal forest management. In: Burton PJ, Messier C, Smith DW, and Adamowicz WL (eds) *Towards Sustainable Management of the Boreal Forest*, Chapter 4, pp. 113–154. Ottawa, Canada: NRC Research Press.

Hislop M and Twery M (2001) *A Decision Framework for Public Involvement in Forest Design Planning*. Final Report Prepared for Policy and Practice Division. Roslin, UK: Forestry Commission.

Lawrence RL and Deagen DA (2001) Choosing public participation methods for natural resources: a context-specific guide. *Society and Natural Resources* 14: 857–872.

Overdevest C (2000) Participatory democracy, representative democracy, and the nature of diffuse and concentrated interests: a case study of public involvement on a National Forest District. *Society and Natural Resources* 13: 685–696.

Parkins J (2002) Forest management and advisory groups in Alberta: an empirical critique of an emergent public sphere. *Canadian Journal of Sociology* 27(2): 163–184.

Sheppard SRJ and Lewis JL (2002) Democratising the SFM planning process: the potential of landscape visualization as a community involvement tool for First Nations. In: Veeman TS, Duinker P, MacNab B, *et al.* (eds) *Advances in Forest Management: From Knowledge to Practice*, Proceedings 2002 Sustainable Forest Management Network Conference, pp. 304–309. Edmonton, Canada: Sustainable Forest Management Network.

Shindler B and Neburka J (1997) Public participation in forest planning: eight attributes of success. *Journal of Forestry* 95(1): 17–19.

Susskind L and Cruickshank J (1987) *Breaking the Impasse: Consensual Approaches to Resolving Public Disputes*. New York: Basic Books.

SOIL BIOLOGY AND TREE GROWTH

Contents
Soil Biology
Soil and its Relationship to Forest Productivity and Health
Tree Roots and their Interaction with Soil
Soil Organic Matter Forms and Functions

Soil Biology

C J Weston and K L Whittaker, University
of Melbourne, Creswick, Victoria, Australia

Introduction

Forest soils harbor an enormous variety of life forms that principally derive their energy from organic matter produced by photosynthesis and shed from plant structures and from animals. The major biological components of forest soils are plant roots, microbes, and soil animals. As other articles deal with tree roots (*see* **Soils and Site**: Tree Roots and their Interaction with Soil) and the mycorrhizal and rhizosphere organisms associated with them (*see* **Soils and Site**: Soil Organic Matter), this article will concentrate on the freeliving microbial and faunal components of the soil biota. Together these organisms play a critical part in the function of forest ecosystems through their role in organic matter breakdown, decomposition, and release of materials to the soil environment and atmosphere. Through these processes they have a positive influence on the availability of nutrients for plant growth and on soil structure.

Forest Soil Biota

The structure of cells and the way they obtain energy gives rise to the fundamental classification of all life forms. Two domains, prokaryotes and eukaryotes, and six kingdoms are recognized. There are two kingdoms within the prokaryotes, bacteria and archaea; within the eukaryotes are the four kingdoms – protoctista (under revision), plantae, fungi, and animalia (**Table 1**). Viruses are less than 0.3 μm in size and make a negligible contribution to microbial biomass and ecology in forest soils; they are not discussed further here. All these life forms have representatives in forest soils; indeed it is thought that soils provide habitat for the majority of earth's biodiversity. The extent of microbial diversity in soil remains largely unknown (**Table 2**), mainly due to the difficulties of studying such small organisms that have simple morphology. Furthermore, only a small percentage of the soil microbial community responds to cultivation in laboratory media, so that only a small fraction of them has been isolated and cultured. The best evidence for the vast biodiversity among soil biota is derived from molecular techniques, some of which are listed in **Table 3**. Overall, there is an extremely high diversity of decomposer species in forest soils that is undoubtedly related to the heterogeneity of the forest soil environment. This diversity ensures the maintenance of matter and energy fluxes and it confers resistance against disturbances to decomposition. For example, both fungi and heterotrophic bacteria play a role in nitrification, particularly in acid forest soils.

Despite recent advances in our knowledge of the range of bacteria occurring in soils, we have little knowledge of the ecology and biogeography of most microorganisms in forest soils. The relatively recent application of rRNA sequence analyses in determining the phylogenetic relationships between organisms has led to some reclassification within and among microbial groups.

Prokaryotes

From an evolutionary point of view the prokaryotes were the first life form to appear, evolving about 3.5 billion years ago. Prokaryotes are molecules surrounded by a membrane and cell wall; they lack subcellular membrane-enclosed organelles.

Bacteria

The bacteria are single-celled prokaryotic organisms that lack a true nucleus, and at between 0.2 and 1 μm in length they are among the smallest forms of life in forest soils. They have rigid cell walls and, where motile, move by means of a flagellum. There are three basic cell shapes among the bacteria: cocci, rods, and spirals. Among the 12 or so phyla of bacteria, three are generally associated with forest soils: the purple bacteria, the Gram-positive bacteria,

Table 1 Overview of the major biota found in forest soils. The dashed line shows the division of biota according to size

Size group	Cell type	Kingdom or domain	Important groups found in forest soils	Example subgroup or genus
Microflora (0.1 μm– 10 μm)	Prokaryotes	Archaea	Methanogenic archaea	*Methanobacterium, Methanococcus*
		Bacteria	Purple bacteria	Nitrifying bacteria
			Sporogenic bacilli	Bacillales
			Cyanobacteria	Nostocales
			Actinomycetes	Thermomonosporas
		Mycota or fungi	Zygomycota	Zygomycetes, *Mucor*
			Ascomycota	Ascomycetes, *Aspergillus*
			Basidiomycota	Mushrooms, *Agaricus, Gloeophyllum*
			Deuteromycota	Deuteromycetes, *Arthrobotrys*
			Algae	Chlorophyta, *Chlorella*
			Oomycetes	Saprolegionales, *Phythium*
Microfauna (body width< 100 μm)		Protoctista	Ciliophora	Ciliates, *Paramecium*
			Sarcomastigophora	Naked and testate amoebae
			Mycetozoa	*Dictyostellium, Acrasis*
Mesofauna (body width 100 μm to 2 μm)	Eukaryotes	Animalia	Nematodes	Nematodes
			Rotifers	Rotifers
			Microarthropods	Acari (mites)
				Collembola (springtails)
			Annelids	Enchytraeidae (enchytraeids)
Macrofauna (body size generally ranges from 2 mm to 20 mm, but may be greater)			Macroarthropods	Lumbricidae (earthworms)
				Megascolecidae (earthworms)
				Hymenoptera (ants)
				Isoptera (termites)
				Chilopoda (centipedes)
				Diplopoda (millipedes)
				Pauropoda (pauropods)
				Isopoda (crustaceans)
				Coleoptera (beetles/weevils)
				Mollusca (mollusks)
Macroflora		Plantae	Plant roots	

Adapted from Coleman DC and Crossley DA (1996) *Fundamentals of Soil Ecology*. London: Academic Press and Lavelle P and Spain AV (2001) *Soil Ecology*. London: Kluwer.

Table 2 Known and estimated total species numbers

Group	Known species	Estimated total species	Percentage known
Vascular plants	220 000	270 000	81
Bryophytes	17 000	25 000	68
Algae	40 000	60 000	67
Fungi	69 000	1 500 000	5
Bacteria	3 000	30 000	10
Viruses	5 000	130 000	4

Adapted from Coleman DC and Crossley DA (1996) *Fundamentals of Soil Ecology*. London: Academic Press.

and the cyanobacteria. These bacterial groups are capable of exploiting a wide range of energy sources – a trait that is important in the functional processes of forest ecosystems. Overall, because bacteria are not able to penetrate organic material their progress as cellulose decomposers is limited to the surface erosion of substrates; their rate of substrate breakdown is proportional to the rate at which exoenzymes are produced and diffuse out from the bacterial colonies. The purple bacteria cover a diverse range of metabolism including aerobes, anaerobes, chemoautotrophs, chemoheterotrophs, and chemophototrophs. The Gram-positive bacteria include the actinomycetes and the sporogenic bacilli. Members of both these groups (including the free-living *Clostridium*) are able to fix atmospheric nitrogen. The cyanobacterial group comprises obligate photoautotrophs that occur in unicellular, colonial, and filamentous forms with cell diameters usually within 1.0 to 10 μm. The relatively recent development of 16S ribosomal RNA (rRNA) gene sequence studies has revealed evidence in soil of bacterial divisions not usually associated with soil, including green nonsulfur bacteria, planctomycetes, spirochaetes, and novel methane-producing archaea.

Table 3 Examples of current methods for analyzing microbial diversity in soils and their application

Method	Comments
Culturing of microbes	Generally not representative of biota present
16S rRNA gene sequence analysis with polymerase chain reaction amplification	Provides identification of members of a community
In situ hybridization	Can be used to identify metabolically active microorganisms
Substrate utilization	Measures metabolic diversity
Flow cytometry	Enumeration of microorganisms
Terminal restriction fragment length polymorphisms	Comparative analysis
Polymerase chain reaction amplification or expression cloning	Functional diversity targeted
RNA dot or slot block	Representation of metabolically active members of a community

Reproduced with permission from Rondon MR, Goodman RM, and Handelsman J (1999) The Earth's bounty: assessing and accessing soil microbial diversity. *Trends in Biotechnology* 17(10): 403–409.

Archaea

This group has generally been known as the archaeabacteria, with recent studies preferring to call them archaea because of significant differences in their cell structure compared with bacteria. Members of this classification are subdivided into a range of groups on the basis of photosynthetic ability, means of locomotion, and nature of the cell wall where one is present. The archaea lack a muramic acid component in their cell walls, which contain branch-chained, ether-linked lipids that differ greatly from cell walls in eukaryotes. This radically different cell wall structure has led some taxonomists to claim that, in evolutionary terms, archaeans are more distant from the bacteria than are animals. Although the group includes organisms capable of flourishing in extreme conditions not usually associated with forests (e.g., the extreme halophytes and extreme thermophiles), there are a few reports of archaea occurring in nonextreme environments in forest soils. In addition, a number of groups may be important under certain conditions in forest soils; among these are the methane-producing archaea (methanogens; e.g., *Methanobacterium, Methanococcus*) and the thermoacidophiles (*Sulpholobus, Acidothermus*). The latter group are chemoautotrophic sulfur archaea capable of transforming sulfur forms in soil. In boreal forest soils the first reports of the genetic diversity among archaea have begun appearing in the literature over the last 5 years.

Eukaryotes

The eukaryotes appeared about 1.5 billion years ago. The basic eukaryote cell consists of a plasma membrane, glycocalyx, cytoplasm, cytoskeleton, and membrane-enclosed subcellular organelles. All of the soil animals and fungi are eukaryotes.

Fungi

The fungi (Mycota) are eukaryotic organisms that have a mycelial structure formed from slender filaments or hyphae (2–10 μm in diameter) that may be unbranched or branched, septate or nonseptate and which are commonly multinucleate. The fungi are subdivided on differences in mycelium structure and method of reproduction. Some of the main classes common in forest soils include the chytridiomycetes, the zygomycetes, the ascomycetes, and the basidiomycetes. Despite the wide range of fungi they are all chemoheterotrophic and in forest soils most are aerobic. None of the fungi is capable of fixing nitrogen from the atmosphere. Fungi are particularly prevalent in forest soils because of their ability to decompose lignin, which is a major component of wood, and to tolerate a wide range of soil pH. Fungi use exoenzymes to decompose substrates and their filamentous habit allows them to invade and ramify through substrates, applying mechanical pressure with their elongating hyphae. In this way fungi are able to import nutrients to enable them to break down substrates. These life-form advantages of fungi in decomposition mean that only in anaerobic habitats, such as waterlogged soils, do the bacteria predominate over the fungi. Fungi are the most abundant decomposing organisms in aerated forest soils, with typical biomass ranges of 500–5000 kg ha^{-1}. In the forest floor the fungi can represent between 10% and 60% of the total biomass; only plant roots exceed them in terms of biomass in soil.

Soil Fauna

Based on body size, habitat preference, and food consumed, soil fauna are generally assigned to one of three functional groups – microfauna, mesofauna or macrofauna (**Table 1**). In forests, approximately 90% of the soil faunal biomass is usually found in the top 10 cm of humus and soil. The relative abundance of soil fauna changes among forests at different latitudes; macrofauna tend to be more abundant in the tropics than they are in temperate regions, while microfauna are often more common in temperate regions than in the tropics. The microfauna, of which nematodes and protozoa are the major taxa, are single-celled fauna with a body width of < 100 μm; they lack mitochondria and live in water-filled pores and water films around soil particles. Some are motile. Most are heterotrophic and feed by engulfing their prey, usually other soil microbes. They are predominantly restricted to the topsoil for this reason. Among the protozoa are a number of groups that are common in forest soils – the ciliates, the amoebae, and the slime molds. Ciliates (Phylum Ciliaphora) are mostly freeliving in water films in soil; they feed by grazing on bacteria and particulate organic matter. Amoebas (Subphylum Sarcodina) are either naked or shelled, with the encased or testate amoebae largely inhabiting freshwater and moist soils. Slime molds (Phylum Mycetozoa) are divided into cellular and true slime molds, both of which are found in moist soils where they feed on live bacteria. The mesofauna, including the microarthropods, such as mites, collembolans (wingless insects), and enchytraeid worms, have a body width of 100 μm to 2 mm. The mesofauna are litter-transformers that produce organic structures in the form of faecal pellets that act as incubators for microbial digestion; their effect on soil structure is minimal.

The macrofauna, often termed ecosystem engineers, include earthworms, ants, termites, myriapods (centipedes and millipedes), snails, and slugs. Their body size generally ranges from 2 to 20 mm but may be much greater, particularly in the case of earthworms. The macrofauna directly or indirectly modulate the availability of resources and microhabitats for other soil biota by causing physical changes to the soil environment and biotic materials. While the role of the larger soil animals such as earthworms in litter mixing with other soil components is accepted, their role in decomposition is largely unknown. We know that earthworms ingest and move organic material but the extent of direct decomposition by soil animals is relatively unknown.

Energy Sources and Modes of Nutrition of Soil Biota

Soil microorganisms in forest ecosystems function through control of decomposition and the release of materials from organic substrates. In particular, they mediate carbon (C), phosphorus (P), nitrogen (N) and sulfur (S) biogeochemical cycling. The way in which soil microorganisms satisfy their demands for energy and nutrients is a guide to their particular role in the flow of energy and nutrients in forests and, more broadly, to their role in ecosystem function. A useful functional classification of these organisms is based on the nature of their principal carbon sources and energy. On the basis of principal carbon source organisms are classified as either autotrophic (inorganic C source; mostly CO_2; also referred to as lithotrophic) or heterotrophic (organic C source; diverse range of compounds; also referred to as organotrophic). In a similar way, organisms are classified based on their energy source; those using radiant energy (phototrophs) and those dependent on energy released during chemical oxidation (chemotrophs) (**Table 4**). Microorganisms regulate a wide range of processes critical to forest ecosystem function including denitrification, sulfate reduction, methanogenesis, and manganese reduction (see **Table 5** for a comprehensive listing of chemoautotrophic transformations).

Heterotrophs and Autotrophs

The vast majority (>90% biomass) of bacteria and fungi in forest soils are chemoheterotrophic (derive

Table 4 Energy and carbon sources for classes of soil organisms

Class of soil organism	Energy source for generating ATP	Source of carbon for the cell	Example of organisms
Photoautotroph	Light	CO_2	Cyanobacteria, plants
Chemoautotroph	Inorganic compounds	CO_2	Non-purple sulfur bacteria
Photoheterotroph	Light	CO_2, organic matter	Bacteria
Chemoheterotroph	Organic matter	Organic matter	Most bacteria, fungi

Table 5 Physiological groups of soil chemoautotrophs

Physiological group	Life form	Energy source	Oxidized end product	Organism
Hydrogen bacteria	Bacteria	H_2	H_2O	Alcaligenes, Pseudomonas
Methanogens	Archaea	H_2	H_2O	Methanococcus
Carboxydobacteria	Bacteria	CO	CO_2	Rhodospirillum, Azotobacter
Ammonium oxidizing bacteria	Bacteria	NH_3	NO_2^-	Nitrosomonas
Nitrite oxidizing bacteria	Bacteria	NO_2^-	NO_3^-	Nitrobacter
Sulfur oxidizers	Bacteria	H_2S or S	SO_4^{2-}	Thiobacillus
	Archaea	H_2S or S		Sulfolobus
Iron bacteria	Bacteria	Fe^{2+}	Fe^{3+}	Gallionella, Thiobacillus

both energy and materials for cell growth from an organic substrate). Because of the dominance of this group in most soil conditions they are often simply referred to as the heterotrophs. In well-aerated forest soils, aerobic heterotrophic respiration dominates, but fermentation and anaerobic respiration take over as soils become waterlogged. Among the bacteria two groups of heterotrophic nitrifiers exist, one oxidizing ammonium and the other the various organic forms of N including hydroxylamine, amino acids, peptones, oximes, and some aromatic compounds. Autotrophic microflora carry out a wide range of transformations and also play a critical role in ecosystem functioning. **Table 5** summarizes the major groups and end products of these organisms. Foremost in forest soils are the chemoautotrophic nitrifying bacteria that are responsible for the transformation of ammonium (NH_4^+) into nitrite (NO_2^-) and nitrate (NO_3^-). Autotrophs grow more slowly and are less abundant in soil than heterotrophs, due to their lower energy yield. Despite this there is good evidence to show that chemoautotrophic bacteria are the main nitrifying agents in most acid forest soils.

Activities and Impacts of Soil Biota in Forest Ecosystems

Forest floor litter type provides evidence of differences in composition and activity of forest soil biota. The activity of soil biota is directly related to the three humus forms generally recognized in forests (see **Table 6**). A mull humus results from the rapid disappearance of leaf litter under the influence of a wide range of faunal groups (macro-, meso-, and microfauna). Mull is typical of grasslands and deciduous forests and is associated with rapid litter decomposition and relatively nutrient-rich soils. A mor humus is characterized by the accumulation of undecomposed plant remains that form a distinct organic horizon overlying the mineral soil. Compared with mull humus, biological activity is low in a mor with minimal animal and lignin-decomposing

fungal activity. This humus type is associated with acidic surface soils, cool to cold climates and relatively nutrient-poor soils. Typically, mor humus is associated with coniferous forests where decomposition of the acidic litter is dominated by saprophytic fungi; and the 'ecosystem engineer' functional group is dominated by ants rather than deep-burrowing earthworms, which tend to be acid-sensitive. Moder humus is intermediate between mull and mor, with reduced macrofaunal activity compared with a mull and a microflora dominated by fungi due to the predominantly acid conditions. Moder humus forms are mainly found in deciduous and coniferous forests.

Functional Groups Among Forest Soil Biota

Each group of soil organisms contributes either directly or indirectly to the breakdown of organic matter, decomposition and the release of nutrients back into the soil environment for plant growth (**Table 7**). The following section outlines the roles of microbial and faunal organisms in the process of decomposition. In forest ecosystems only about 1.5–5% of primary production is consumed by herbivores. A very large portion of primary production is consumed by the soil organisms. The microbial component of the soil biota is the main consumer of this organic matter in forest soils, being responsible for over 90% of decomposition and mineralization. The soil fauna play an important role in the physical breakdown or comminution of litter that a exposes a surface area for subsequent microbial attack.

The Decomposers

Bacteria and fungi drive the decomposition and release of nutrient ions from organic substrates; they are central to the functioning of forest ecosystems and more broadly to the functioning of the biosphere. Soil microorganisms are unable directly to ingest the often large and complex range of

Table 6 Summary of biological features associated with the three main humus forms found in forests

Characteristic	Mull	Moder	Mor
Biodiversity and productivity	High	Medium	Low
Phenolic content of litter	Low	Medium	High
Humification rate	Rapid	Slow	Very slow
Mycorrhizal partners	Zygomycetes	Basidiomycetes	Ascomycetes
Faunal group dominant in biomass	Earthworms	Enchytraeids	None
Microbial group dominant in biomass	Bacteria	Fungi	None

Reproduced with permission from Ponge J-F (2003) Humus forms in terrestrial ecosystems: a framework to biodiversity. *Soil Biology and Biochemistry* 35: 935–945.

Table 7 Influences of soil biota on soil processes in forest ecosystems

Group	Nutrient cycling	Soil structure
Microflora (fungi, bacteria, actinomycetes)	Catabolize organic matter; mineralize and immobilize nutrients	Produce organic compounds that bind aggregates; hyphae entangle particles into aggregates
Microfauna (e.g., protozoa, nematodes)	Regulate bacterial and fungal populations; alter nutrient turnover	May affect aggregate structure through interactions with microflora
Mesofauna (e.g., Acarina, Collembola, enchytraeids)	Regulate fungal and microfaunal populations; alter nutrient turnover; fragment plant residues	Produce fecal pellets; create biopores; promote humification
Macrofauna (e.g., isopods, centipedes, millipedes, earthworms)	Fragment plant residues; stimulate microbial activity	Mix organic and mineral particles; redistribute organic matter and microorganisms; create biopores; promote humification; produce fecal pellets

Adapted from Hendrix PF, Crossley DA Jr, Blair JM, and Coleman DC (1990) Soil biota as components of sustainable ecosystems. In: Edwards CA *et al.* (eds) *Sustainable Agricultural Systems*, pp. 637–654. IA: Soil and Water Conservation Society.

molecules that comprise soil organic matter; instead they secrete enzymes that digest organic matter outside the cell and they accumulate nutrients – either from the decomposing substrate or the surrounding soil solution – against a concentration gradient; most are aerobic. Overall, fungi are a crucial link in terrestrial nutrient cycling as they are involved in decomposition, in mycorrhizal associations, and in predatory and pathogenic activities. The activity and abundance of fungi in forest soils can be assessed by a number of means including analysis for ergosterol (a major sterol found in most fungi but not in higher plants) that can be used to measure fungal penetration of plant material. Another relatively recent and promising line of investigation is analysis for C and N stable isotope abundance in fungal sporocarps, a technique that can differentiate between ectomycorrhizal and saprotrophic forest fungi. For example, forest basidiomycetes become enriched in ^{13}C relative to their bulk C source, and either enriched or depleted in ^{15}N relative to atmospheric N. The coupling of molecular marker methods with stable isotope abundance in biomarkers offers considerable promise in linking bacterial identity with function in the environment. These molecular and isotope techniques are likely to become important diagnostic tools and will help elucidate ecological roles of various fungi and bacteria in the field.

The Ecosystem Engineers

Soil fauna play an indirect role in decomposition and mineralization through regulation and stimulation of microbial populations, fragmentation of plant residue and alteration of the physical soil environment. From a functional perspective, organisms that regulate the availability of resources to other species by physically rearranging biotic materials – to modify, maintain and/or create habitats – have become known as ecosystem engineers. Foremost among ecosystem engineers in forest soils are earthworms and termites. The natural tilling effect of earthworms in soils has been long known; they may pass up to 30 tonnes ha^{-1} of soil through their bodies, some of which is excreted as casts which may be enriched in nutrients relative to bulk soil.

Climate Change, Forest Management, and Soil Biota

Impact on Soil Processes

There is considerable interest in fluxes of CO_2, N_2O, and CH_4 from forest soils because of the potential for climate change to alter emission rates of these greenhouse gases. Soil organic matter (SOM) is a major pool of carbon and its magnitude and dynamics are largely controlled by soil microbial activity. For this reason, there is interest in improving our understanding of humus formation and degradation as controlled by soil microorganisms; however, research into the direct effects of increased atmospheric CO_2 on the soil microbial community is not sufficient to predict outcomes. Where nitrogen deposition or inputs to forests are high there is concern for increased N_2O emissions through either heterotrophic denitrification or, possibly, through leakage from autotrophic nitrification. For example, N_2O emissions of the order of 1–4 kg N ha^{-1} year^{-1} occur from spruce forests in southern Germany, where N deposition is around 30 kg N ha^{-1} year^{-1}. These N_2O emissions are thought to result mainly from the activities of facultative anaerobic heterotrophs, such as *Pseudomonas*, that switch to NO_3^- as

Table 8 Denitrifying bacteria in soil, and their metabolism and energy source – an example of the diverse range of organisms potentially involved in converting nitrate to gaseous N in forest soils

Denitrifying organism	Metabolism	Energy source
Pseudomonas	Chemoheterotroph	Soil organic matter
Paracoccus denitrificans	Chemoautotroph	H_2
Thiobacillus denitrificans	Chemoautotroph	Reduced S
Rhodopseudomonas	Photoautotroph	Light

a terminal electron acceptor when O_2 diffusion is limited by high soil moisture. There is also some evidence of N_2O production in woodland soils by heterotrophic fungi, where NO_3^- is used as an alternative for O_2 in respiration, and denitrification occurs simultaneously. Because of the broad range of processes with potential to produce N_2O in forest soils (summarized in **Table 8**), further studies are required to determine the impacts of forest management and climate change on N_2O emissions. There has been considerable interest in the impacts of forest management on methane (CH_4)-oxidizing bacteria because temperate forests are major sinks for atmospheric CH_4. For example, forest clear-cutting can reduce the activity of methane-oxidizing bacteria and therefore the net CH_4 consumption in forest soils; changes that apparently result from the inhibition of CH_4 oxidation by elevated soil inorganic N. Less invasive forms of management such as thinning have been associated with increased CH_4 consumption.

Impact on Species Composition and Abundance

Determining the impact of climate change and forest management on soil biota and the critical processes they mediate in forest soils remains a significant challenge for the future. For example, the current literature indicates that there is not enough information to predict the impact of increased atmospheric CO_2 on the soil microbial community. Progress towards this task will rely on linking, through empirical testing, functional groups and key species among the soil biota with key processes maintaining ecosystem stability, such as decomposition and nitrogen fixation. In this way the contributions of the huge diversity of soil biota may be simplified to allow a better understanding of changes in the soil environment on ecosystem processes and stability.

Further Reading

Blondel J (2003) Guilds or functional groups: does it matter? *Oikos* 100: 223–231.
Coleman DC and Crossley DA (1996) *Fundamentals of Soil Ecology*. London: Academic Press.
Hendrix PF, Crossley DA Jr, Blair JM, and Coleman DC (1990) Soil biota as components of sustainable ecosystems. In: Edwards CA *et al.* (eds) *Sustainable Agricultural Systems*, pp. 637–654. IA: Soil and Water Conservation Society.
Jones CG, Lawton JH, and Shachak M (1994) Organisms as ecosystem engineers. *Oikos* 69: 373–386.
Killham K (1994) *Soil Ecology*. Cambridge, UK: Cambridge University Press.
Lavelle P (2002) Functional domains in soils. *Ecological Research* 17: 441–450.
Lavelle P and Spain AV (2001) *Soil Ecology*. London: Kluwer.
Paul EA and Clark FE (1996) *Soil Microbiology and Biochemistry*, 2nd edn. London: Academic Press.
Ponge J-F (2003) Humus forms in terrestrial ecosystems: a framework to biodiversity. *Soil Biology and Biochemistry* 35: 935–945.
Richards BN (1987) *The Microbiology of Terrestrial Ecosystems*. New York: John Wiley.
Rondon MR, Goodman RM, and Handelsman J (1999) The Earth's bounty: assessing and accessing soil microbial diversity. *Trends in Biotechnology* 17(10): 403–409.
Swift MJ, Heal OW, and Anderson GM (1979) *Decomposition in Terrestrial Ecosystems*. Oxford, UK: Blackwell Scientific Publications.
Woese CR (1987) Bacterial evolution. *Microbiology Reviews* 51: 221–271.

Soil and its Relationship to Forest Productivity and Health

J A Burger, Virginia Polytechnic Institute and State University, Blacksburg, VA, USA

Forest Soil and its Functions

Soil is a mixture of mineral materials, organic matter, water, air, and plant and animal life. It varies in depth from a few centimeters to several meters across most of the earth's terrestrial surface. Its rock, sand, silt, clay, and organic matter physical composition varies in texture and structure, which controls the infiltration, percolation, and storage of water and the balance between water and air in its pore space. The amount and nature of clay and organic matter and the influence of parent material and vegetation largely control its chemistry and level of fertility. Soil also contains and is made up of myriad macro-, meso-, and microorganisms, both plant and animal, essential for organic matter decomposition, nutrient cycling, energy conversion, and soil formation processes. Soils vary greatly across the landscape due to soil forming factors, including the nature of parent rocks and minerals from which they are derived, the amount of relief in the local topography, the types of plants and animals in and on the soil, the nature of the local climate, and the amount of time a soil has been in place. Soils can vary in age from a few years to millions of years.

Soils serve a variety of functions in forest ecosystems. They serve as a medium for tree growth; they anchor the tree physically and supply water and nutrients for uptake by tree roots; and they serve as water-transmitting layers on the earth's surface. During rain events or snowmelt, water moves into soil, percolates to a saturated zone or water table, and remerges downslope in streams and rivers. Absorption of water into soil regulates the flow and controls the quality of water in watersheds. Finally, soil serves as an ecosystem component. It controls the flow of energy, the cycling of chemical elements, the rate of organic matter decomposition, carbon sequestration, and biodiversity. The interaction of soil properties and processes determines forest health and productivity.

Forest Health and Productivity

Forest Health

Forest health is a qualitative term that refers to the general condition of a forest. A healthy forest is one that is relatively free of insect infestations, diseases, exotic weeds, and air pollution. All species making up the forest are able to grow at rates commensurate with the local climate, geographic position, and soil resource to complete their life cycles. A healthy forest can resist damage from catastrophic events like acute insect and disease attacks, fire, wind, and flooding, and fully recover from these perturbations to continue its life history functions over decades, centuries, or millennia. Soil influences forest health by securely anchoring trees' roots, by regulating energy flow among ecosystem components, and by controlling water and nutrient availability for the benefit of the entire forest system. The habitat of soil organisms that play a role in decomposition and nutrient cycling processes is also controlled by the presence and nature of the soil. During dry periods, droughty soils may predispose forests to insect and disease attack, but if the forest can recover normally, natural, periodic stress caused by soil-induced limits on water or nutrients is not considered unhealthy over the long term.

Forest Productivity Definition and Concepts

Forests that grow quickly and produce large amounts of biomass in a short period of time are said to be highly productive. For example, a mixed tropical forest in the Amazon basin of Brazil is more productive than a black spruce forest in Canada. Forest productivity is the rate of accumulation of forest dry matter per unit area per unit time. It is commonly expressed as net primary productivity (NPP). NPP includes the biomass accumulation of all plants' stems, leaves, roots, and reproductive structures, and it includes litterfall, root sloughing, and the plant biomass consumed by herbivores and plant and animal decomposers. NPP is expressed in units of dry mass accumulation per square meter per year $(g\,m^{-2}\,year^{-1})$, or dry mass per hectare per year $(Mg\,ha^{-1}\,year^{-1})$. The belowground component of NPP is difficult to measure. Most measures of NPP are for the more easily determined aboveground component only (ANPP).

Forest productivity can be depicted and defined as a logistic curve of production as a function of time (solid line in **Figure 1**). Just after forest establishment, when light, water, and nutrient resources are in ample supply, biomass increases exponentially until a point in time (inflection point) when resources are fully exploited by the forest. This usually coincides with stand closure and maximum leaf area development. After this point of inflection on the curve, production decreases exponentially due to light, water or nutrient limitations. Biomass accumulation reaches a maximum when light, water, or nutrient

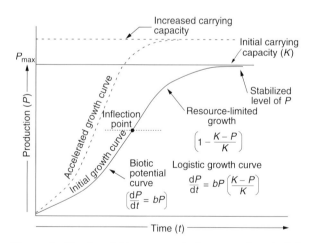

Figure 1 The forest biomass production curve is a logistic function based on the relative availability of light, water, and nutrient resources through time. Dashed lines show the potential for increasing productivity with site treatment over that of a nontreated condition (solid lines). Increasing soil quality (carrying capacity) increases productive potential (P_{max}), and alleviating water and nutrient limitations shortens the time required to reach carrying capacity. Reproduced with permission from Burger JA (2002) Soil and long-term site productivity values. In: Richardson J, Bjorheden R, Hakkila P, Lowe AT, and Smith CT (eds) *Bioenergy from Sustainable Forestry: Guiding Principles and Practice*, pp. 165–189. Dordrecht, The Netherlands: Kluwer.

resources limit the rate of photosynthetic carbon fixation to the level of carbon depletion via respiration; this is called the compensation point. This level of maximum production is the site's carrying capacity or potential.

Measuring Forest and Site Productivity

Historical production records from multiple harvests of fully stocked stands growing on the same site would provide the best and most direct measure of forest and site productivity; however, records for multiple growth cycles are not available for most forest sites. Foresters estimate forest productivity by measuring the rate of growth, or the volume accumulation of live, standing, aboveground woody biomass ($m^3 ha^{-1} year^{-1}$) contained in the stems of desired crop trees. The mean, or average annual growth, is determined by dividing the total stand volume of live, standing tree stems by the total age of the tree stand; this is also called mean annual increment (MAI).

Forest sites that have the potential to produce biomass at a rapid rate are said to have high site quality. Site quality is the sum of the effect of all site factors on the capacity of a forest to produce biomass. MAI can be used for a relative measure of site quality. To estimate site quality, MAI is determined at the culmination of the increase in mean annual increment, the age at which mean annual increment peaks.

A faster, easier, but indirect measure of site quality is a tree's height relative to its age. Trees grow faster on good sites and slower on poor sites, while height remains well correlated to tree volume. As the quantity and quality of soil improves, trees grow at faster rates and will be taller at a given age (**Figure 2**). Their height growth is sensitive to site factors, but relatively independent of stand density. This height/age relationship is called the site index and is usually defined as the height of dominant and codominant trees in well-stocked, even-aged stands at a preselected or index age. Index ages of 25, 50, and 100 years are commonly used for fast-growing pines and eucalypts, hardwoods, and slow-growing northern conifers, respectively.

For the purpose of spatially mapping forest land and prescribing silvicultural treatments to areas based on site potential, site quality is commonly ranked by class, depicted by Roman numerals I through V, with site quality class I being the most productive and class V the least. **Table 1** shows the relationship between site quality, volume, product class, and value. As trees grow, diameter increases exponentially; therefore, volume and value increase exponentially. Wood in large tree stems is disproportionately more valuable than wood in small tree stems due to the products associated with each. For example, sawtimber is more valuable than firewood and results in a much greater return on investment from forest stands managed as a business enterprise.

Site and Soil and their Relationship to Forest Productivity

Overall, tropical rainforests have the greatest ANPP, followed by temperate and boreal forests. This gradient in productivity with latitude is mostly due to length of growing season, temperature, and amount of available water. ANPP increases as

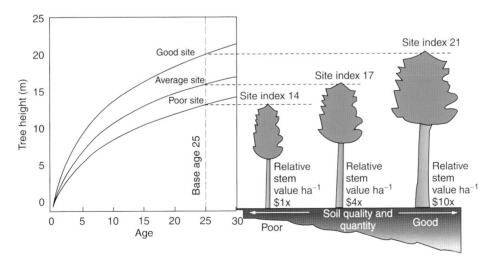

Figure 2   The depth and quality of soil influences the rate at which trees grow and accumulate biomass. Site index, the height of dominant and codominant trees in stands at an index age (e.g., age 50), is the most common method used by foresters to estimate site quality.

Table 1 The influence of site quality on wood production, product class, and return on investment; Appalachian oak is used for this example

Site quality class	I	II	III	IV	V
Oak site index (m)	26	23	20	17	14
Stem volume MAI ($m^3 ha^{-1} year^{-1}$)	8.0	6.2	4.6	3.0	1.8
Commercial use and value	Furniture, veneer	Sawtimber	Railroad ties	Firewood	None
Return on investment (%)[a]	10	7	3	0	−5

[a] Return on investment estimates were based on average stumpage values and management costs for the Appalachian region during 2001. Emphasis is on the relative difference in values among site quality classes; absolute values vary with regional economic conditions.

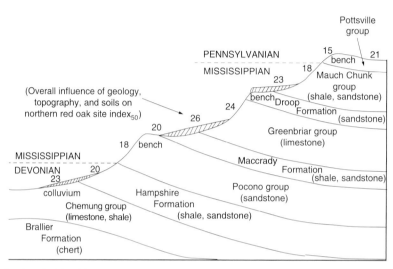

Figure 3 Hillslope in the Appalachian Mountains region of West Virginia. Site quality varies greatly on this hillslope gradient due to geologic, topographic, and soil features.

growing season, temperature, and available water increase. Across this gradient, ANPP varies by more than an order of magnitude, from more than $20 \, Mg \, ha^{-1} \, year^{-1}$ for tropical rainforests to less than $2 \, Mg \, ha^{-1} \, year^{-1}$ for boreal forests. Within a region of relatively uniform temperature and rainfall, ANPP can vary tenfold due to topographic position, geology, and soil quality. These site and soil factors influence tree growth primarily through water and nutrient availability.

Geologic and Topographic Site Factors

Soils are formed from residual material or from material transported and deposited by water, wind, ice, or gravity. The productivity of residual soils is influenced by rock and mineral type and the rate at which they weather. Limestones and shales weather faster than most sandstones creating deeper, more fertile soils. Common igneous and metamorphic soil-forming rocks are generally more resistant to weathering, although most are rich in minerals required by plants. Soils derived from transported materials are generally very productive, as they are found in low landscape positions and consist of existing soil

materials transported from higher elevations. The position, orientation, and layering of geologic materials also influences soil weathering rates, soil water movement and storage, and depth of rooting. In the northern hemisphere, steep, mid-slope positions with southwest aspects have the shallowest soils and highest evaporative demand. The deepest, most productive soils are found on northeast-facing slopes at slope bottoms. Topographic features influence productivity predominantly by controlling plant available water and controlling the harmful effects of fire, wind, snow, and ice. On flatter terrain, slight changes of only a few centimeters in elevation can influence the depth to a water table and the effective soil depth that trees can exploit. In the case of soils with high water table, productivity is more often nutrient limited due to insufficient aerated soil volume.

Figure 3, a not-to-scale drawing of an actual hillslope in the Appalachian Mountains of the USA, illustrates the interaction of geologic, topographic, and soil factors influencing site productivity. The site index of northern red oak (*Quercus rubra*), a native species that occurs naturally across the entire hillslope gradient, ranges from 15 to 26 meters as a function of these interacting factors. It is most productive at mid-slope, growing in colluvium and residuum of a limestone-derived soil. It is least productive growing on bench positions above weathering-resistant, quartzitic meta-sandstone layers (Pocono and Pottsville formations). Its productivity is intermediate on soils derived from shale formations. Productivity is intermediate (higher than expected due to site factors alone) at the top of the mountain due to higher rainfall caused by orographic precipitation.

Soil Factors

Soils have basic physical, chemical, and biologic properties that influence soil climate and fertility, the two general conditions that influence forest productivity and health. The complex structural and functional components of soil climate and fertility are conceptualized in the drawing in **Figure 4**. Soil depth, horizonation, texture, structure, and porosity determine the rate of flow and storage of heat, water, and air that in turn influence rates of metabolic activity in roots and their growth. Soil fertility and nutrient availability is determined, in part, by organic matter decomposition and mineralization, and the weathering of soil parent materials. The extent to which soil climate and fertility processes are optimized determines the availability of water, oxygen, and nutrients for uptake by forest plants.

Measurable soil factors influencing tree growth include total depth or depth of certain layers, organic matter content, nutrient content, air/water balance, and depth to a water table or restricting layer. There are dozens of studies in the literature that correlate ANPP with soil properties. Different soil properties are more influential than others in different regions. For example, numerous correlation studies have shown that, in the Atlantic coastal plain region of the USA, southern pine growth is most influenced, in order of listing, by thickness of the subsoil, depth of the surface soil, drainage, depth to mottling, nutrient content, and organic matter content. In the northwest region of the USA, mixed conifers are most influenced by soil depth, surface soil texture, water-holding capacity, nutrient content, subsoil texture, and coarse fragment content.

Increasing Forest Productivity by Increasing Soil Quality

Forest productivity is determined by tree genetic potential, soil and site factors, and silvicultural inputs. Therefore, forest productivity can be increased (dashed line in **Figure 1**) by improving the genetic make-up of the trees, and by temporarily alleviating deficiencies in water and nitrogen by irrigating or fertilizing. These silvicultural inputs usually shorten the length of time required for biomass to reach the site's carrying capacity, which is one way to increase forest productivity (shorter rotations). A second way of increasing productivity is to increase site carrying capacity for additional

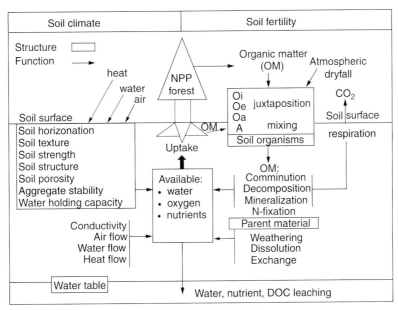

Figure 4   Conceptual model of soil properties and processes influencing forest productivity. DOC, dissolved organic carbon; NPP, net primary productivity. Reproduced with permission from Burger JA (2002) Soil and long-term site productivity values. In: Richardson J, Bjorheden R, Hakkila P, Lowe AT, and Smith CT (eds) *Bioenergy from Sustainable Forestry: Guiding Principles and Practice*, pp. 165–189. Dordrecht, The Netherlands: Kluwer.

production potential. Carrying capacity can be increased with site treatments that cause a more or less permanent change in site carrying capacity, such as increasing effective rooting depth by eliminating barriers to root growth, by draining wet soils, by adjusting soil acidity or alkalinity, or by adding phosphorus to deficient soils. These modifications of the soil resource raise the P_{max} on the y axis in **Figure 1**. The dashed production curve depicts an increase in forest productivity due to an increase in site quality or carrying capacity, and a further increase due to a shorter growth cycle.

In most cases it is not practical to irrigate forest stands. Instead, foresters shift limiting water resources to crop trees by eliminating competing vegetation and by thinning crop trees at appropriate times during the growth cycle. ANPP is not increased, but the amount of merchantable wood is increased by shifting resources to fewer, merchantable trees at the expense of nonmerchantable vegetation. Nitrogen is often growth limiting in both managed and nonmanaged forests throughout the world. In managed forests, deficiencies can be aggravated by removing harvest slash and soil organic matter in the process of preparing the site for planting, and by accelerating nitrogen mineralization through soil tillage. Deficiencies usually occur in managed, even-aged forests during or just after canopy closure. Adding nitrogen at midrotation temporarily fertilizes the trees, but usually has little long-term effect on soil fertility. Multiple additions of nitrogen through time are usually needed to completely alleviate deficiencies. Because nitrogen additions fertilize the trees with little permanent effect on the soil, forest productivity increases, but site quality remains unchanged.

Phosphorus limits forest productivity in some forested regions of the world where total soil phosphorus levels are inherently low, or where phosphorus is chemically or physically bound and unavailable to plants. Deficiencies are alleviated by applying phosphorus at time of planting or site preparation. Because of the unique chemistry of soil phosphorus, it remains for long periods of time, increasing fertility for the length of the growth cycle and beyond. This long-lasting effect improves soil quality and increases site carrying capacity.

High soil strength and soil air and water imbalances are physical problems that can be addressed with site treatments. In all cases, forest practices that improve soil physical properties increase the amount and quality of the rooting environment. The amount of soil available for rooting is usually a function of depth, but can be a function of physical impedance or the inability of roots to physically penetrate soil,

especially when dry. The physical quality of soil is mostly a function of soil structure and consistence that allows water and air to flow and be stored at optimum amounts. Naturally compacted soils, or soils compacted by machine trafficking, can be subsoiled, bedded, or harrowed to create better rooting environments. Poorly drained soils can be ditched to lower the water table, and sites can be bedded to elevate planted seedlings above water-saturated soil.

Forest productivity can also decrease if soil quality is damaged by forestry practice. Soil damage is usually an unintended side effect of forest harvesting, with the exception of chronic air pollution causing soil acidification and base leaching in forest soils of some industrialized regions of the world. Forest harvesting on wet soils compacts and puddles soils, which can restrict root growth and impede normal soil drainage. Site clearing after harvest, either mechanically or with intense fire, can remove significant amounts of organic matter and nitrogen, causing nutrient deficiencies at some point in the growth cycle. Forest practices and site treatments invariably change a variety of soil properties and processes, with both positive and negative effects. Sustainable forestry practices will ensure that the net effect is positive for sustainable forest productivity and health.

Human communities throughout the world desire forests that sustain plant and animal productivity, maintain balanced hydrologic, carbon, and mineral nutrient cycles, and maintain protective and environmental forest functions. Forest soils play an important role in each of these functions. Research for a better understanding of soil and its relationship to forest productivity and health is ongoing. Given that soils have complex properties and processes and are highly variable across the landscape, carefully prescribed soil- and site-specific forest management practices and treatments should ensure the maintenance of soil quality in both extensive and intensively managed forests.

Summary

Forest health is the condition of a forest relative to being free of insect, disease, water, and nutrient stresses, and to its ability to survive and recover from catastrophic events like fire, tornadic winds, and floods. Forest productivity is the rate of forest biomass accumulation per unit area per unit time. Forest productivity is controlled by the genetics of the species and individuals that make up the forest, and site and soil factors that include local climate, geology, topography, and soil properties that control water and nutrient availability and a tree's ability to root and anchor itself. Forest productivity can be increased by silvicultural site treatments that mitigate naturally compacted soils and those compacted by trafficking of heavy equipment. Improving drainage of wet soils, and reducing evaporative demand of dry soils by conserving organic matter and harvest debris, increase forest productivity by optimizing the balance of air and water in soils. Conservation of soil organic matter and harvest slash during forest operations conserves essential nutrients and helps regulate their availability, especially nitrogen, phosphorus, and calcium that are found limiting in some forest soils. Careful management of all site and soil resources will ensure sustainable forest productivity and health for the production of products and ecosystem services such as water control, carbon sequestration, wildlife habitat, and biodiversity.

See also: **Health and Protection**: Biochemical and Physiological Aspects. **Soil Biology and Tree Growth**: Soil Biology; Soil Organic Matter Forms and Functions; Tree Roots and their Interaction with Soil. **Soil Development and Properties**: Forests and Soil Development; Landscape and Soil Classification for Forest Management; Nutrient Cycling; Nutrient Limitations and Fertilization; Soil Contamination and Amelioration; The Forest Floor; Waste Treatment and Recycling; Water Storage and Movement. **Tree Physiology**: A Whole Tree Perspective. **Wood Formation and Properties**: Wood Quality.

Further Reading

Adams MB, Ramakrishna K, and Davidson EA (eds) (1998) *The Contribution of Soil Science to the Development of and Implementation of Criteria and Indicators of Sustainable Forest Management*. Madison, WI: Soil Science Society of America.

Boyle JR and Powers RF (eds) (2001) *Forest Soils and Ecosystem Sustainability*. Amsterdam, The Netherlands: Elsevier.

Burger JA (2002) Soil and long-term site productivity values. In: Richardson J, Bjorheden R, Hakkila P, Lowe AT, and Smith CT (eds) *Bioenergy from Sustainable Forestry: Guiding Principles and Practice*, pp. 165–189. Dordrecht, The Netherlands: Kluwer.

Doran JW, Coleman DC, Bezdicek DF, and Stewart BA (eds) (1994) *Defining Soil Quality for a Sustainable Environment*. Madison, WI: Soil Science Society of America.

Dyck WJ, Cole DW, and Comerford NB (eds) (1994) *Impacts of Forest Harvesting on Long-Term Site Productivity*. London: Chapman & Hall.

Gessel SP, Lacate DS, Weetman GF, and Powers RF (eds) (1990) *Sustained Productivity of Forest Soils*. Vancouver, Canada: University of British Columbia, Faculty of Forestry.

Greenland DJ and Szabolcs I (eds) (1994) *Soil Resilience and Sustainable Land Use*. Wallingford, UK: CAB International.

Proe M, Smith CT, and Lowe AT (eds) (1999) *Indicators of Sustainable Forest Management*. Amsterdam, The Netherlands: Elsevier.

Raison RJ, Brown AG, and Flinn DW (eds) (2001) *Criteria and Indicators for sustainable Forest Management*. Wallingford, UK: CAB International.

Stone EL (ed.) (1984) *Forest Soils and Treatment Impacts*. Knoxville, TN: University of Tennessee.

Tree Roots and their Interaction with Soil

K H Ludovici, US Department of Agriculture Forest Service, Research Triangle Park, USA

Introduction

Root systems provide three key elements for the establishment and productivity of a tree: stability, uptake, and storage. Site characteristics such as slope, aspect, drainage, and land use history will directly and indirectly impact the success of these elements. Many species use the plasticity of their root system to adapt to site conditions, but others simply do not occur on sites incompatible with their normal root system. Edaphic factors such as temperature, soil water potential, oxygen concentration, mechanical resistance, and the content of nutrient ions will influence the growth and function of the roots themselves. At the same time, root systems have a profound effect on the physical and chemical characteristics of the multiple soil horizons. As roots grow, they stabilize, penetrate, enlarge cracks and crevices, and lower water and nutrient contents. Finally, root decay allows infiltration of water and surface materials downward through old root channels and organic material is concentrated within the soil profile.

Root System Characteristics

Root Mass and Configuration

Root systems provide stability or anchoring to trees and are most often characterized as one of three principle forms: taproot, heart root, or sinker root (**Figure 1**). Although site conditions will influence root growth and the array of diameter size classes, root form tends to be under a degree of genetic control. The taproot form is characterized by one

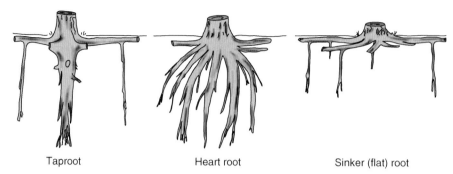

Taproot   Heart root   Sinker (flat) root

Figure 1   Principal tree root forms. Reproduced with permission from Fisher RF and Binkly D (2000) *Ecology and Management of Forest Soils,* Third Edition, Wiley.

primary, deeply penetrating taproot. Such root systems occur in species of *Carya, Juglans, Quercus, Pinus,* and *Abies.* Many taprooted species have extensive laterals and sinkers that allow them to survive on shallow soils or soils with seasonally high water tables. Species of *Larix, Betula, Carpinus,* and *Tilia* develop the heart root form which is characterized by numerous lateral and oblique roots radiating from the tree base. This form grows best on deep permeable soils and is more capable of exploiting fractures in bedrock than other root forms. The sinker or flat root form has an advantage on shallow soils and is characterized by shallow laterals from which vertical sinkers grow downward. This form is seen in species of *Populus, Fraxinus,* and *Picea* and can be found on a wide range of soil conditions.

Root structure   Root diameter is commonly used to differentiate function and often correlates with degree of suberization and longevity. Taproots primarily function as physical support, but also provide valuable storage. They comprise 10–30% of mature tree biomass and as much as 90% of total root biomass. Even though taproots have been documented to extend >20 m, the bulk of most root systems is 1.5 m from the surface and within the canopy drip line. Larger primary lateral roots emanate from the taproot in patterns influenced by genetics and site. Secondary laterals extend from primary laterals and combine to represent the bulk of the coarse root fraction. Coarse roots are >15 mm, generally have a well-developed bark, which is marked by lenticels and cracks which facilitate their contribution to water and nutrient uptake. These roots are perennial and contribute 5–20% of mature tree biomass and as much as 40% of the total root biomass. Fine roots are commonly referred to as the absorbing roots and in many species include any roots <15 mm. Roots 5–15 mm provide continuity of nutrient and water flow. Roots 2–5 mm are generally suberized roots that provide extension, uptake, and transport, but are not observably infected with mycorrhizae.

Roots <2 mm are often termed feeder roots, as they principally function to absorb water and nutrients. Feeder roots are not suberized, can exhibit root hairs and may be noticeably infected by mycorrhizae. In some species, roots <1 mm diameter provide much greater surface area to dry weight correlation than do roots 1–2 mm, and are more accurately termed very fine feeder roots.

Root hairs and mycorrhizae are the smallest root features but are responsible for measurable increases in water and nutrient uptake. Root hairs are microscopic extensions of root epidermal cells which greatly increase the surface area of the root. They are delicate and easily ruptured when the soil is disturbed, suggesting why newly transplanted seedlings and plants need to be protected from water loss for the first few days after transplantation. Mycorrhizal fungi infect roots and can develop extensive hyphal networks which increase the uptake capacity of the system. The amount of ectomycorrhizal fungal mycelium can be so extensive that its total mass is comparable to the mass of fine roots themselves; however, the endomycorrhizae make up only a small mass of fungal material and are unlikely to exceed 10% of the fine root weight.

Root function   Plant roots grow continuously, but their proliferation depends on the availability of water and minerals in their microenvironment. At the same time, the ability of plants to absorb both water and mineral nutrients from the soil is related to their capacity to develop an extensive root system.

Solute absorption occurs in a zone behind the root tip, where the processes of cell elongation and root hair formation occur (**Figure 2**). Within this zone of elongation, the pathway of least resistance occurs in the apoplast of the cortex up to the endodermis. Older root surfaces can absorb soil solution through cracks and breaks in cortical tissues, creating discontinuous zones of absorption along the root length. In roots of woody angiosperms and gymnosperms, a periderm arises and the epidermal and

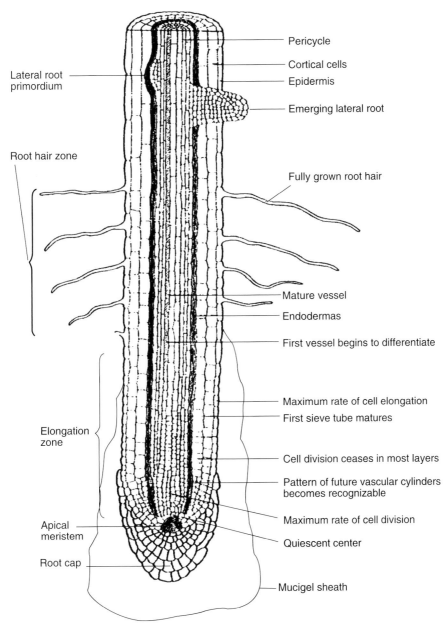

- Pericycle
- Cortical cells
- Epidermis
- Emerging lateral root
- Fully grown root hair
- Mature vessel
- Endodermas
- First vessel begins to differentiate
- Maximum rate of cell elongation
- First sieve tube matures
- Cell division ceases in most layers
- Pattern of future vascular cylinders becomes recognizable
- Maximum rate of cell division
- Quiescent center
- Mucigel sheath

Lateral root primordium

Root hair zone

Elongation zone

Apical meristem

Root cap

Figure 2 Schematic of root thin section. Reproduced with permission from Lake JV, Gregory PJ and Rose DA (1987) *SEBS 30 Root Development Function*. Cambridge University Press.

cortical tissues exterior to it are shed leaving a highly variable, but appreciably permeable layer of cork cells. Because these roots dominate the root system in mature plants, this contribution to the water supply of the plant must outweigh that of the younger unsuberized tissues.

Water contacts roots in two ways: (1) mass flow of water (Darcy's law) to the root, or (2) interception of water as roots grow through moist soil. The rate of water flow through soils depends on the size of the pressure gradient and on the hydraulic conductivity of the soil which will vary with soil texture. As water is absorbed from the soil near the rhizosphere, the water potential of the soil decreases and a gradient toward the root is created. As more of the soil spaces become filled with air, there are fewer contiguous channels through which water can easily flow. Root hairs may traverse air gaps between the root and moist soil particles. When a soil dries out enough, the water potential can fall below what is called the permanent wilting point. This is the point at which the water potential of the soil is so low that plants could not regain turgor even if all transpiration were stopped. The permanent wilting point is not a unique property of the soil, but depends on the plant species.

Roots absorb mineral nutrients at low concentrations from the soil solution and translocate them to various parts of the plant for utilization. Uptake can be active (as is the case of phosphorus) or passive (as is the cases for calcium, magnesium, and other cations). Experimental evidence supports nutrient absorption at the apical region of the root axes, and along the entire root surface, depending on the nutrient being investigated. Soil chemistry and parent material will greatly influence the bonding and binding of anions and cations to clay lattices and soil colloids, thereby determining the degree of availability. Rainfall and soil texture will also impact uptake capacity, as tortuosity and pore size distribution impact mass flow and desorbtion characteristics.

Tree root systems are vital in their capacity to store water, nutrients, and carbohydrates. It is well documented that tree boles shrink and swell within a day in response to water use patterns, and studies have observed a similar pattern in large lateral roots. However, the degree of elasticity and propensity for deep water recharge remain important study points. The tremendous reservoir of nutrients in root systems is not retranslocated from roots before they die, thus they are returned to the soil where they can be utilized by other plants. At the same time, tree roots are an immediate source of labile and stored carbohydrates. Starch storage in mid-rotation loblolly pine (*Pinus taeda*) has been documented to contribute >14% of the total carbon needed for annual tree growth.

Root systems also produce hormones that function to regulate whole tree growth. Roots are known to produce and export cytokinins and abscicic acid (ABA) to the xylem sap. When dehydration of the root medium occurs, the cytokinin content in the xylem decreases and a large increase in ABA concentrations can be measured in the roots. The ABA content of the leaf epidermis is closely related to the degree of stomatal closure even without a change in leaf water potential, and stomatal closure can occur even if only part of the root system is dehydrated. In addition, while the absolute magnitude of osmotic adjustment is less in roots than in leaves, as a percentage of the original tissue potential it can be greater in roots than in leaves. These adjustments may only slightly increase water extraction from previously explored soil, but they also enhance turgor and maintain root growth.

Root longevity There is little disagreement that taproots and coarse roots can be as old as the bole itself, and generally root diameters increase with age. The common misconception is that fine roots live only a very short time. In fact, research has shown that fine roots of pine can live 8 years or more. Evidence suggests that fine roots of other species also have a substantially longer lifespan than previously believed.

The anatomy and morphology in parts of the root system vary greatly according to the age of the tissue and the soil environment. In the apical zone of the root, cells are thin-walled, rich in cytoplasm, and have a high rate of respiration. However, relatively old tissues with thick-walled suberized endodermis and few passage cells can be effective in transport of phosphorus and potassium. The movement of calcium and magnesium into the xylem is, by contrast, greatly restricted by the development of suberized lamellae in the endodermis, suggesting normal transport across the plasma membrane of young endodermal cells.

Mycorrhizal Infection

Mycorrhizae are widespread in natural conditions and extensively infect tree species, creating mutualistic relationships through which the fungi receive sugars from the host plant, in exchange for increasing mineral uptake efficiency. Mycorrhizae occur in two major classes: ectotrophic and endotrophic. The ectotrophic mycorrhizal fungi typically form a thick sheath or mantle of fungal mycelium around the roots, with some of the mycelium penetrating between cortical cells. This network of internal hyphae is called the Hartig net. Endotrophic or vesicular–arbuscular (VA) mycorrhizal fungi do not produce a fungal mantle around the root, but form ovoid structures called vesicles and branched structures call arbuscules within plant root cells.

Fungal mycelia extend into the soil, forming hyphal rhizomorphs and hyphal strands supporting fruiting bodies. This extension of fungal hyphae beyond the nutrient-depleted soil zones near roots increases the capacity of the root system to absorb nutrients. Ectotrophic mycorrhizae may also proliferate in the organic layer of the soil and hydrolyze organic phosphorus for the root. Studies have shown that mycorrhizal fungi can transport phosphate at a rate more than four times higher than that of an uninfected root.

A key factor in the extent of mycelial development is the nutrient status of the host plant and site. Deficiency of a nutrient such as phosphorus tends to promote mycorrhizal infection, whereas, infection tends to be suppressed in well-fertilized soil. A correlation also exists between volume of root surface fungi and bacteria (closely related to biomass), and shoot nitrogen. Although such a correlation could be caused by the microorganisms increasing the plant's nitrogen uptake, it is more likely that increased nitrogen in the plant causes increased microbial growth through increased exudation. This interaction has significant application in forest systems where species competition, spacing, and site preparation continue to impact site productivity.

Tree Allometry

Allometry is an empirical expression of the distribution of biomass between aboveground and belowground tissues. In general this relationship will be species specific and it will shift as a stand develops. Trees generally shift from a predominance of belowground tissue to aboveground tissues with age and stand development; however, it may be difficult to separate this pattern from seasonal effects. Site conditions including temperature, planting density, and competition do not usually change the root to shoot ratio (R/S), but may impact the rate of growth and the absolute root density.

It is frequently reported that the relative allocation of carbon for root growth decreases drastically with fertilization, and that trees respond to improved site fertility by shifting the allocation of tree mass belowground on infertile sites and aboveground on fertile sites. Research also shows shifts in root size distribution toward fewer fine roots in response to increased site fertility. However, roots proliferate in microsites with high nutrient contents and it is most likely that total tree growth changes rather than the allometry of that growth changing. Similar arguments can be made for impacts of competition. In any event, even insignificant shifts in allometry may be biologically important to stand productivity and longer-term carbon storage.

Soil Conditions and Root Growth

Soil Texture

Root form is closely associated with tree species, but the mixture of sand, silt, and clay in a soil will impact water availability and resistance to root penetration, thereby influencing the expression of that form. Higher clay contents increase resistance to penetration, may restrict vertical and horizontal root growth, and can result in thinner roots and slower growth. Sandy soils provide lower resistance to penetration, allow extension through large pore spaces, and can contain roots that are on average of greater diameter.

Bulk density is the representation of mass of soil per unit volume. The lower a bulk density reading, the lower the resistance to root penetration, while the higher the bulk density, the greater the resistance to root penetration. Within a range of values, root growth is possible regardless of soil texture or water availability, but beyond a value of approximately $2.65 \, \mathrm{g \, cm^3}$, root penetration is restricted.

Impeded roots are known to develop a layer of suberized lamellae close to the root tip which greatly increase resistance to the radial flow of water, and delay re-establishment of continuous films of water when roots are moistened after a period of desiccation. Uptake of potassium would not be affected in impeded roots, but transfer of calcium and magnesium across the root would be hindered.

Historically it has been accepted that roots will grow unrestricted only in pores of diameter greater than their own, and only enter those of at least a similar size to the root tip. While this growth strategy may be predominantly true, advancement of root and mycorrhizal research has shown that a root tip needs only a single cell to pass through a pore space before it continues to extend through unrestricted media. Extension of root tips and hyphae through restricted pore sizes in many soil structures leads to the physical breakdown of organic and inorganic impediments.

Soil Moisture

Clearly there are tree species better adapted at living on wetter sites than drier sites, and vice versa. A large portion of this adaptation is in how plant roots adjust to and thrive in conditions of low oxygen. The supply of oxygen to the roots is essential for cellular respiration, the source of metabolic energy that drives mineral uptake processes. In general, roots require a minimum oxygen level and will cease to elongate when water levels are high. Unsuberized roots may become thicker in response to high water levels, but whether the cause for this is expansion of individual cells, or growth of additional cells is not known.

Soils at field capacity have 10–30% of the volume composed of air-filled spaces, and this percentage decreases as water content increases. Under most conditions, the oxygen supply in air-filled pore spaces is in the range of 15–20% but plant roots cannot obtain oxygen when soils are flooded, and anaerobic environments are created. In wetlands and along the shores of oceans, lakes, rivers, and ponds, pore spaces become saturated with water, the rates of water and nutrient absorption are suppressed, and death of roots can occur. While some woody species are tolerant to flooding during dormancy, formation of adventitious roots and aerenchyma after flooding (linked to increased ethylene production) has been shown to alleviate the effects of root injury to some species.

In contrast to flood-sensitive species, wetland vegetation is well adapted to growth for extended periods in saturated soil. Even when shoots are partially submerged, they grow vigorously and show no signs of stress. In these plants, the stem and roots develop longitudinally interconnected, gas-filled channels, known as aerenchyma, which provide a low-resistant pathway for diffusion of oxygen and other gases. Hypoxia stimulates greater production of ACC and ethylene, and the latter promotes the breakdown (lysis) of cells in the root cortex. As roots extend into oxygen deficient soil, continuous formation of aerenchymas just behind the tip allows oxygen movement within the root to supply the apical zone. This retained oxygen aerates the apical meristem and allows growth to continue 50 cm or more into anaerobic soil.

Under adverse soil conditions the extension of roots is retarded and differentiation is slowed less than extension. In this way, cell maturation occurs much closer to the apex than in rapidly extending roots. Suberization of roots in response to dry soil conditions corresponds to a cessation of root extension and formation of a continuous suberized layer just beneath the root cap. Thus the hypodermis and endodermis are found to develop closer to the apex when soil conditions are unfavorable. As long as desiccation does not cause cortex cells to collapse, the root apices are able to rupture the suberized layer and extension resumes within a few days of soil rehydration.

Temperature

Soil temperature influences both adsorption of water and nutrients by existing roots and affects future root growth. As soil temperature increases, root carbohydrate demands increase due to increased respiration and as the carbon sink strength of the roots increases. In the long term, shoot biomass production is decreased at the expense of root maintenance and growth. Conversely, changes in phospholipids in the roots, as a response to gradual shifts in temperature, may influence transport processes across cell membranes by maintaining them in a fluid condition at lower temperatures. This cell membrane level mechanism may serve as a root adaptation to seasonal changes in soil temperature.

The optimum root temperature for shoot growth is a function of the R/S ratio. Optimum root growth occurs at approximately 35°C for subtropical plants, 27.7°C for warm temperate plants, and 20°C for cool temperate plants. There are ranges of temperature within which plants and microorganism can grow and function, but it is important to remember that temperature impacts are not independent for roots and shoots. Increasing root temperature decreases the R/S ratio, just as increasing shoot temperature increases the R/S ratio.

Nutrient Availability

Tree roots usually favor a slightly acidic pH, one in which fungi predominate the rhizosphere. A low pH favors the weathering of rocks, the release of ions such as potassium, magnesium, calcium, and manganese, and the increased solubility of carbonate, sulfate and phosphate salts present in the soil solution. Increasing solubility facilitates absorption by the root.

The inorganic particles of the soil solid phase act as a reservoir of nutrients such as potassium, calcium, magnesium, and iron. Also associated with this solid phase are organic particles containing nitrogen, phosphorus, and sulfur. Nutrient movement to the root surface can occur by mass flow and by diffusion. Mass flow describes movement of nutrients along with the convective flow of water moving through the soil toward the root. The amount of nutrient provided to the root by mass flow will be dependent on the rate of water flow to the plant and the concentration of nutrients in solution. Where water flow is high and nutrient concentrations are high, mass flow can play an important role in nutrient supply.

Diffusion occurs when mineral nutrients move from a region of higher concentration to a region of lower concentration. Because active nutrient uptake by the root will lower nutrient concentrations at the root surface, concentration gradients are created surrounding the root. Diffusion of nutrients can supply nutrients to the root surface from areas of high concentration to areas of lower concentration. When diffusion is too slow, a nutrient depletion zone is formed adjacent to the root surface.

Carbon Dynamics of Tree Roots

Growth

Production and growth of roots require more plant resources and energy than production or growth of aboveground tissues. This idea is largely driven by attempts to complete and balance models with only a black-box understanding of root production and turnover. Research has shown that the carbon compounds used by roots, in order of preference, are carbohydrates > amino acids > soluble proteins > insoluble proteins. Because carbon is fixed during photosynthesis, site properties that are linked to photosynthetic capabilities and sink strength will impact root growth.

Root growth varies seasonally in response to carbon fixation by leaves and demand by various parts of the tree. Deciduous species have wide range in photosynthetic capacity, while evergreen species maintain some photosynthetic capacity all year. Under these two scenarios we understand that an excess of carbohydrates would be available to deciduous species roots only after leaf-out in the spring, whereas evergreen root production would be bimodal, with excess carbohydrates produced in the early spring and autumn.

Root development is critical during seedling establishment. Establishment may be limited by site-specific properties (such as nitrogen or phosphorus availability, or aeration) or by process-limiting situations (such as establishment of a mycorrhizal hyphal network, production of absorbing root surface area, or allocation of resources between sources and sinks).

Exudates

Interest in the rhizosphere effect on microbial activity and plant health did not gain momentum until about 1955. Since that time, researchers have calculated that carbon released from roots growing in soil can amount to approximately 20% of the total plant dry matter. Exudates are produced from carbohydrates which are primarily synthesized in the shoot during photosynthesis and then translocated to the root system. A majority of total root exudates, approximately 60%, are cations and to a lesser extent anions. The carbon components of root exudates are typically composed of 66% organic acids, 29% carbohydrates, and 5% amino acids.

The presence of microorganisms in the rhizosphere increases root exudation, either through physical damage to the root tissues, or through release of metabolites from the microorganisms which affect root physiology. In this way, measuring microbial population in the rhizosphere in response to various factors indirectly assays exudation. Research has generally shown that change in any biological or physical factor that affects plant growth also affects the quantity of exudates released by roots. The principal factors affecting the type and quantity of substances released by roots into the rhizosphere include species and developmental stage of plant, soil physical stress factors, plant nutrition, mechanical or disease injury, microbial activities, and foliar-applied chemicals.

Decomposition

Decomposition of root systems provides a network of continuous root channels, and improves soil porosity. Roots are the principal source of organic matter in the deeper soil layers, and their decomposition directly and indirectly influences nutrient release. Studies of several tree species indicate that decomposition rate decreases as a function of increasing root diameter. Decomposition of large lateral roots and taproots can potentially impact nutrient release over several decades while decomposition of fine roots affects nutrient release on a seasonal basis.

Typically, a 'wet' forest has more living than dead roots, while a 'dry' forest has more dead than living roots. The major influence of increasing soil moisture is to improve decomposition and mineralization of dead roots and their nutrients. Because carbon dioxide, produced as a by-product of decomposition of organic material, equilibrates with the soil water, we can measure changes in respiration and link this to biological activity. Conversely, site disturbances including fire and clear-cuts will affect biological respiration presumably with little change in belowground biomass.

See also: **Soil Biology and Tree Growth**: Soil and its Relationship to Forest Productivity and Health. **Tree Physiology**: Mycorrhizae; Nutritional Physiology of Trees; Root System Physiology.

Further Reading

Harley JL and Russel RS (1979) *The Soil–Root Interface*. London: Academic Press.

Lambers XY (1987) Root development and function. In: Gregory X, Lake Y, and Rose Z (eds) *Root Development and Function*. Society for the Study of Experimental Biology Seminar Series vol. 30. Cambridge, UK: Cambridge University Press.

Taiz L and Zeiger E (1991) *Plant Physiology*. New York: Benjamin/Cummings.

Soil Organic Matter Forms and Functions

L A Morris, University of Georgia, Athens, GA, USA

Introduction

Soil organic matter is important in determining both relatively stable soil properties as well as dynamics of soil systems. This article focuses on the contribution of organic matter to mineral soil horizons dominated by inorganic sand, silt, and clay-sized particles. The role of the organic forest floor is described elsewhere (*see* **Soil Development and Properties**: The Forest

Floor). Within mineral soil horizons, organic matter contributes to soil development through its role as food and nutrient sources for soil fauna and heterotrophic flora that give life to the soil, through production of organic acids and stabilization of structure, through its contribution to relatively stable characteristics such as color, water holding capacity and nutrient retention and release, and as the primary soil reservoir and sources of several plant nutrients. Soil organic matter consists both of relatively simple organic compounds as well as large complex and ill-defined molecules of high molecular weight classified based on chemical solubility or other characteristics. Elemental composition varies, but generally the least soluble and most complex organics have increased concentrations of nitrogen (N) and carbon (C) and decreased concentrations of oxygen (O). Functional groups of alcohol, carboxyl, enol, and phenol impart high capacity to adsorb and exchange nutrients and retain inorganic and organic contaminants. Human activities and forest management can alter the quantity and distribution of organic matter. This has ramifications both for forest productivity and ecosystem functions as well as for global carbon cycles.

Functions

Contributions to Soil Development (Pedogenesis)

Food source   Organic matter created by binding of atmospheric C with water during photosynthesis and incorporated into leaves, roots, and wood is the base of a complex and still partly unknown universe of soil organisms. Beginning with large wood-boring beetles and other organisms that feed on freshly fallen logs or leaves, and ending with microbes that are involved in decomposition of the most recalcitrant organic compounds, organic matter sustains life within the soil. Between 10% and 20% of the CO_2 released from the soil during organic matter decomposition is associated with soil fauna. Fauna play an essential role in breaking down coarse debris with low surface area to weight ratio deposited on the surface soil as litter, or within the soil as roots, into finer particles and mixing these particles with mineral soil fractions where they can be further decomposed by the microbial community. It is through the activity of this microbial community that most of the C fixed through photosynthesis is returned to the atmosphere; however, the portion that remains in the soil is converted to complex, relatively stable compounds through a combination of biological and physiochemical processes.

Acid leaching   Decomposition of organic matter in forests results in formation of soluble organic acids

that, over time, have a major impact on soil formation. Acids produced during decomposition of litter on the surface move down through the soil with percolating water removing base cations such as calcium (Ca^{2+}), magnesium (Mg^{2+}), and potassium (K^+) weathered from minerals. Charge balance is maintained through accumulation of H^+ and concentration of acid forming aluminum (Al) in the process. This acid leaching creates soils that tend to be slightly (pH_w 6.5) to very acidic (pH_w 3.8) in the surface and contributes to development of distinct profile features associated with some forests. For instance, organic subsoil horizons resulting from leaching of organic acids from the surface and subsequent precipitation as organic–metal complexes deeper in the profile are characteristic of conifer stands grown on coarse textured soils throughout the world.

Stabilization of soil structure   Organic matter is important to development of soil structure in two important ways. First, it serves as a food source for soil fauna. Through their movement, soil fauna create large pores that serve as major pathways for water and gas movement thereby increasing the depth of biological activity. Also, soil fauna that ingest organic and mineral material bring surfaces in close proximity where they can react with one another. Second, organic matter can directly bind soil particles together or combine with metals to create bridges that link individual soil particles. The size, shape, and stability of these aggregates are considered an important characteristic affecting water and gas flow, soil strength and suitability for root growth, ease with which the soil can be tilled, and the soil's resistance to erosion.

Contributions to Soil Properties

Color   The dark surface colors of forest soils, particularly soils beneath productive hardwoods, are largely due to particulate organic matter and organic matter coatings of mineral surfaces. Even low concentrations of organic matter can create dark-colored soils, especially where dark colors are associated with organic coatings on mineral surfaces. For example, dark organic subsoil horizons resulting from accumulation of organic matter leached from surface organic layers can contain only 3–5% organic matter (2–3% organic carbon) on a mass basis. Color is important as characteristic for recognizing and describing soil profiles in all soil classification approaches. Additionally, color can affect thermal properties of soils. Dark surface soil colors promote soil warming and biological activity in cool climates.

Available water holding capacity   Soils with high organic matter content generally have improved available water holding capacity. Water holding capacity is affected both directly and indirectly. Increases in organic matter content are associated with improved aggregation of soil particles into structural units. As a consequence of improved aggregation, the volume of large pores that drain under gravitational forces and provide air passages from the soil surface to deeper in the profile is increased. This is particularly important in fine textured (clay and clay–loam) soils. In coarser textured soils, organic matter can increase the volume of fine pores that retain water against gravitational drainage contributing to increased water holding capacity. General relationships between an increase in soil organic matter expressed as organic C and available water holding capacity have been developed and tested by several authors. Increases in available water holding capacity between 1% and 2% for each 1% increase in organic matter content (about 2–4% for each 1% increase in organic C content) are average for mineral soils.

Provision of reactive surfaces for nutrient and element retention In many soils, soil organic matter is responsible for the majority of charged sites that interact and hold nutrients and metals to soil surfaces. For each 1% increase in soil organic matter, there is between a 1–3 cmol kg^{-1} increase in cation exchange capacity (CEC). The charge of organic surfaces results from the presence of various functional groups such as carboxylic, phenolic, alcoholic, and amides (**Figure 1**) from which hydrogen can disassociate creating negative charges that serve as sorption sites. The degree to which disassociation occurs varies as a function of pH of the soil. When pH is low, the abundance of H$^+$ limits disassociation and positive charge can exceed negative charge. When pH is increased, and OH$^-$ concentrations in solution are high relative to H$^+$, then H$^+$ disassociates from the surface creating negative charge than can hold cationic nutrients and metals. Under soil reaction (soil pH) typical of natural field conditions, the CEC of soil organic matter ranges from 60 to 3000 cmol kg^{-1}.

Formation of complexes The variable physical structure and multiple functional groups in organic matter enables it to form complexes with inorganic compounds. These complexes have a number of important effects. Organic matter competes with P for sorption sites on minerals and can displace it from these sites rendering it available for plant uptake. Organic matter can increase availability of trace metals through formation of soluble organic–metal complexes. For example, organic matter forms soluble complexes with Fe that protect it from formation of insoluble inorganic precipitation products and increase its plant availability in near neutral pH soils. Conversely, formation of insoluble products that reduce plant availability can also occur. Formation of insoluble complexes limits copper (Cu) availability in many organic soils. Finally, organic matter plays a critical role in the contaminant retention (*see* **Soil Development and Properties**: Soil Contamination and Amelioration).

Nutrient source Organic matter is the chief reservoir and source of several key plant nutrients. Nitrogen, in particular, does not occur in appreciable quantities in primary minerals or on soil exchange sites. For instance, the surface soil beneath an upland forest may contain from 1500 to over 5000 kg ha^{-1} of total N. Less than 1% of this normally exists in inorganic forms retained on surfaces or in soil solution, a quantity much too small to support forest growth for extended periods. Sufficient supplies of N to support forest growth depend upon release of nutrients from bound organic forms into inorganic forms that are readily available for plant uptake during decomposition, a process termed mineralization. Organic sources of P and sulfur (S) are also important, particularly on sandy forested sites where both primary minerals and soil exchange is low.

Forest Productivity

Many of the soil properties affected by soil organic matter have direct bearing on rooting conditions, water retention and release, and nutrient availability. Thus, a relation between forest productivity and measures of total soil organic matter content or concentration should exist. Attempts to establish such relations have met with various degrees of success. On upland sites with good drainage, a positive relation often exists between soil organic matter in the surface soil or entire soil profile and measures of productivity such as site index (**Figure 2**).

Alcoholic	R–CH$_2$–OH
Amides	R–C=O–NH–R
Amines	R–CH$_2$–NH$_2$
Carboxylic	R–COOH
Enolic	R–CH=CH–OH
Phenolic	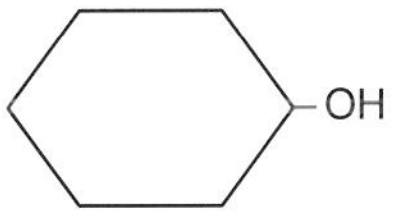

Figure 1 Important functional groups associated with soil organic matter.

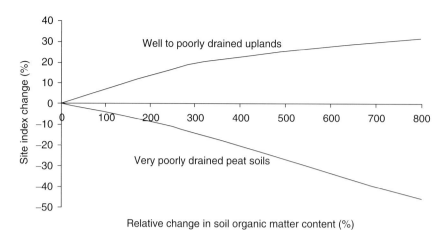

Figure 2 General relation between total soil organic matter content and forest productivity as measured by site index.

On these sites, increases in soil organic matter are associated with reductions in soil density and more favorable rooting conditions, improved moisture holding characteristics, and greater nutrient availability. Productivity increases associated with increased organic matter tend to be greater at low organic matter contents and are particularly important in sandy soils which have low water holding capacity and CEC in the mineral fraction. On very poorly drained bog or peat sites, a negative relation occurs between organic matter content and productivity. Under these very poorly drained conditions, increases in soil organic matter reflect increasingly unfavorable conditions for organic matter decomposition, nutrient mineralization, and root growth (**Figure 2**). For agricultural crops, specific fractions of organic matter (see following section) have been shown to be more closely related to productivity than total soil organic matter. Such relationships are being investigated for forests, but have not yet been established.

Characterization of Organic Matter

Soil organic matter consists of: (1) light fraction and particulate components that are largely recognizable as to chemical composition and consist of primary plant remains and (2) organic compounds called humus that have passed through one or more stages of decomposition and have been recombined into more complex molecules. Separation of the light fraction and particulate components can be accomplished by particle size sieving and density separation. These organics have a density less than $1.0\,g\,cm^{3}$. This fraction of organic matter is largely composed of identifiable organic polysaccharides such as cellulose and hemicelluloses, amino acids,

chitin, waxes, and lignin. This organic fraction is extremely important in forest systems, particularly within the forest floor, because of its high energy content. It is an important source of mineralizable nutrients and is relatively sensitive to changes in the soil environment. In contrast, the humus fraction is less reactive and more important in development of stable characteristics of the mineral soil horizons. Traditional methods of classifying the humus fraction into constituent parts depend upon differences in solubility under alkaline and acidic conditions as illustrated in **Figure 3**. Three major components of soil humus are recognized in this classification approach: humin, which is the portion that is not soluble under alkaline (OH-rich) conditions, humic acid, which is the portion that is soluble under alkaline conditions but insoluble under acidic (H^{+}) conditions, and fulvic acid, which is soluble in both alkali and acid. Molecular weights, N and C concentrations decrease with humin > humic acid > fulvic acid. CEC, acidity and O concentrations decrease in the sequence: fulvic acid > humic acid > humin.

The chemical composition and structure of soil organic matter are not precisely known. Average element composition are about $C_{10}H_{12}O_5N$ and $C_{12}H_{12}O_9N$ for humic and fulvic acids, respectively. Structurally, they are largely comprised of aromatic rings heavily substituted with functional groups (carboxyl, hydroxyl, and carbonyl) and alkyl chains up to 20 C long that include bound proteins and carbohydrates. The molecules are randomly coiled and cross-linked. An example structure for a unit of fulvic acid is illustrated in **Figure 4**. There is a range in structure and the abundance of specific functional groups among humin, humic, and fulvic acids as well as within materials classified within any of these fractions from different locations.

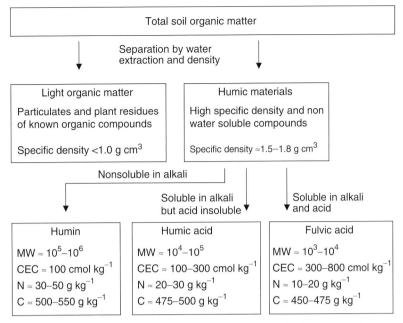

```
                    ┌──────────────────────────────────────────────┐
                    │          Total soil organic matter            │
                    └──────────────────────────────────────────────┘
                              Separation by water
                              extraction and density
```

Light organic matter	Humic materials
Particulates and plant residues of known organic compounds	High specific density and non water soluble compounds
Specific density <1.0 g cm³	Specific density ≈1.5–1.8 g cm³

Nonsoluble in alkali

Soluble in alkali but acid insoluble

Soluble in alkali and acid

Humin	Humic acid	Fulvic acid
MW ≈ 10^5–10^6	MW ≈ 10^4–10^5	MW ≈ 10^3–10^4
CEC ≈ 100 cmol kg^{-1}	CEC ≈ 100–300 cmol kg^{-1}	CEC ≈ 300–800 cmol kg^{-1}
N ≈ 30–50 g kg^{-1}	N ≈ 20–30 g kg^{-1}	N ≈ 10–20 g kg^{-1}
C ≈ 500–550 g kg^{-1}	C ≈ 475–500 g kg^{-1}	C ≈ 450–475 g kg^{-1}

Figure 3 Major fractions of soil organic matter and approximate characteristics. CEC, cation exchange capacity; MW, molecular weight.

Figure 4 Possible structure of humic acid illustrating aromatic rings, peripheral chains, and functional units. Redrawn after Dragunov SS (1948) A comparative study of humic acids from soils and peats: Pochvovedenie 7. In: Kononova MM (1961) *Soil Organic Matter: Its Nature and Role in Soil Formation and in Soil Fertility*, p. 65. New York: Pergamon Press.

Quantity and Distribution

Comparisons among Forest Ecosystems

The quantity of soil organic matter within a given forest ecosystem reflects a balance between annual C inputs and loss through decomposition. In mature undisturbed forests, inputs and losses tend to approach an equilibrium condition determined by site factors such as overall forest productivity, species, soil and rooting depth, and soil physical and chemical properties. Increased precipitation is generally associated with increased soil organic matter, apparently because of its association with increased productivity. Under conditions of similar precipitation, organic matter tends to decline as temperatures are increased. Despite these general relationships, a clear pattern of differences in soil organic matter content does not

exist among ecosystems from different climatic biomes (**Table 1**). Highly productive tropical soils may contain the same quantity of soil organic matter as some low productivity boreal forests. Production and incorporation of organic matter into boreal forest soils is slow, but so is decomposition. Additionally, several factors other than temperature and moisture affect soil organic matter content. Organic matter can adsorb to the surface of clay particles and this adsorption protects organic matter from decomposition; consequently, clay soils tend to have higher concentrations of organic matter than nearby coarser-textured sandy or loamy soils. Chemical composition plays an equally important role. High concentrations of multivalent cations (e.g., Ca^{2+}, Mg^{2+}, Fe^{3+}, or Al^{3+}) can potentially protect organic matter from decomposition in two ways. First, clays tend to

Table 1 Soil organic matter content as a proportion of total organic content (aboveground biomass, forest floor organic matter and soil organic matter to specified depth for several mature forest ecosystems)

Forest Ecosystem	Aboveground biomass $(Mg\,ha^{-1})$	Forest floor biomass $(Mg\,ha^{-1})$	Soil organic matter[1] $(Mg\,ha^{-1})$
Boreal–*Picea mariana*, Alaska[2]	120	119	47
Boreal–*Picea abies*, Sweden[3]	289	19	207
Subalpine–*Picea nobill*[4]	606	53.5	244
Temperate–*Pseudotusuga menziesii* plantation[5]	158	10.9	56
Temperate–*P. taeda*[6]	247	70	192 (6 m)
Temperate–Mixed Hardwoods[7]	207	62	260
Temperate–*Liriodendron tulipifera*, USA[8]	134	6	159
Temperate–Mixed *Quercus*, Belgium[9]	322	5	300
Tropical–*Celtis-Triplochiton*[10]	334	27	106

[1] For rooting zone and exclusive of root mass.
[2] From Cole and Rapp, Stand No 3.
[3] From Cole and Rapp, Stand No 9.
[4] From Turner and Singer 1976, standing dead included with aboveground biomass.
[5] From Harmon *et al.* 1990.
[6] Estimated assuming carbon content of OM is $0.5\,Mg\,Mg^{-1}$ from Richter *et al.* 1995.
[7] Estimated assuming carbon content of OM is $0.5\,Mg\,Mg^{-1}$ from Johnson *et al.* 1995.
[8] From Cole and Rapp, Stand No 22.
[9] From Cole and Rapp, Stand No 28.
[10] Estimated from Greenland and Kowal (1960) and Sanchez (1976).

remain flocculated in soils with high concentrations of multivalent cations. The flocculation protects organic matter adsorbed to surfaces and within aggregates from microbial decomposition. Second, these multivalent cations form complexes with organic matter that, again, protect it from microbial attack.

Forestation and Afforestation

Changes in soil organic matter content resulting from forest removal and conversion to agricultural use are well documented, especially where old-growth forests are replaced by farming that includes regular tillage. Although the amount of reduction varies, the pattern is consistent from cool to tropical climates. Prior to forest removal, organic matter content is high and considered to be in near equilibrium with inputs and outputs. Following forest removal, organic matter content decreases rapidly reaching a new equilibrium determined by the inputs and outputs and the new management regime. On average, soil organic matter declines average from 25–30% of the predisturbance levels; however, on individual sites, declines can be much greater. This is particularly true on sites with coarse-textured (sandy) soils that afford little physical protection of organic matter from decomposition. Increases in soil organic matter similarly occur when areas formerly in agriculture or reclaimed mines are returned to forest; however, the processes of soil organic matter accumulation are much slower than loss and the period for a new equilibrium to be reached is decades or longer.

Harvesting and Management

Forest management affects the amount and composition of soil organic matter in two ways: by changing the quantity and composition of organic inputs and by altering decomposition rates. In the absence of other forest management activities, harvesting trees has only a small impact on soil organic matter content. Most data indicate that changes in soil carbon resulting from harvesting alone are less than 10% with almost an equal change of an increase as a decrease. It is likely that increases in soil organic matter content observed following harvest occur when large amounts of slash are left on site and allowed to decompose and become incorporated with the surface mineral soil. On sites that had initially low amounts of soil organic matter, such as reclaimed mines or degraded agricultural sites, long-term increases in soil organic matter can be expected when forests are managed with normal growth and removal cycles. In contrast, when forest harvest is followed by soil preparation treatments that displace or remove the forest floor and organic rich surface soil, then organic matter may be reduced from 20% to 50%.

Management activities other than harvest can affect soil organic matter. Fertilization can have either a positive or negative affect on organic matter contents depending upon the type of site. Where fertilization increases production without concomitant increases in decomposition rate, soil organic matter can be increased. In contrast, on sandy sites fertilization can decrease soil organic matter content even though forest production is increased. In this case, organic matter is poorly protected against decomposition by structural aggregates or clay–organic complexes and fertilization stimulates decomposition rates of organic matter by lowering the carbon-to-nitrogen ratios and/or carbon-to-phosphorus ratios. Although productivity is stimulated and overall site C content may be increased, the increase is in aboveground forest components and not in soil organic matter. Another management operation that can affect soil organic matter is understory vegetation control. In theory, removal of understory vegetation with a large proportion of production belowground can decrease inputs of soil organic matter. However, the limited research on this management activity tends to suggest it has a relatively small influence on soil C content.

Global Carbon Cycles

Conversion of forests into other land uses results in a release of CO_2 into the atmosphere both as a result of biomass burning or use and eventual decomposition and as a result of mineralization of soil organic matter and CO_2 evolution from the soil. In boreal and temperate regions of the world, little net deforestation is occurring. Most deforestation is occurring in tropical regions where about 17 million-ha of tropical forest are deforested annually and converted to other uses. As a result of this conversion, about 1.6 Pg C are contributed to the atmosphere annually. This represents about 20% of the annual input of CO_2 to the atmosphere from all sources. From 15% to 25% of this contribution can be directly attributed to loss of soil C.

Reforestation of former agricultural lands will increase soil C storage, the increase depending on how badly degraded the soil was prior to reforestation and the productivity of the forest. Projections of C storage potential in the worlds forests based on land availability suggest that between 1 and 2 Pg C could be stored in forests over the next 50 years with 20% of this storage attributable to increases in soil C.

See also: **Soil Development and Properties**: Nutrient Cycling; Soil Contamination and Amelioration; The Forest Floor.

Further Reading

Baldock JA and Nelson PN (2000) Soil organic matter. In: Sumner ME (ed.) *Handbook of Soil Science*, pp. B25–B84. Boca Raton, FL: CRC Press.

Cole DW and Rapp M (1980) Elemental cycling in forest ecosystems. In: Reichle DE (ed.) *Dynamic Processes in Forest Ecosystems*, pp. 341–409. London: Cambridge University Press.

Dragunov SS (1948) A comparative study of humic acids from soils and peats: Pochvovedenie 7. In: Kononova MM (1961) *Soil Organic Matter: Its Nature and Role in Soil Formation and in Soil Fertility*, p. 65. New York: Pergamon Press.

Greenland DJ and Kowal JML (1960) Nutrient content of the moist tropical forests of Ghana. *Plant Soil* 12: 154–173.

Grigal DF and Vance ED (2000) Influence of soil organic matter on forest productivity. *New Zealand Journal of Forest Science* 30: 169–205.

Johnson CE, Dricoll CT, Fahey TJ, Siccama TG, and Hughes JW (1995) Carbon dynamics following clear-cutting of a northern hardwood forest. In: McFee WW and Kelly JM (eds) *Carbon Forms and Functions in Forest Soils*, pp. 463–488. Madison, WI: Soil Science Society of America.

Johnson DW (1992) The effects of forest management on soil carbon change. *Water, Air and Soil Pollution* 64: 83–120.

Orlov DS (1985) *Humic Substances of Soils and General Theory of Humification*. Washington, DC: US Department of Agriculture.

Richter DD, Markewitz DD, Wells CG, *et al.* (1995) Carbon cycling in a loblolly pine forest: implications for the missing carbon sink and for the concept of soil. In: McFee WW and Kelly JM (eds) *Carbon Forms and Functions in Forest Soils*, pp. 233–251. Madison, WI: Soil Science Society of America.

Turner J and Singer MJ (1976) Nutrient distribution and cycling in a sub-alpine forest ecosystem. *Journal of Applied Ecology* 13: 295–301.

SOIL DEVELOPMENT AND PROPERTIES

Contents

Forests and Soil Development

S Torreano, The University of the South, Sewanee, TN, USA

Introduction

Soils are formed by the interaction of five factors: geology (parent material), landscape and topography, climate, animals and vegetation (biotic factors), and time. The interaction of biotic and abiotic factors in the development of soil beneath forest vegetation is highly complex and unique as compared to soils derived under other vegetation types. Because trees dominate forests, their multilayered canopies have a unique and complex effect on environmental conditions at the forest floor. The level of solar radiation, humidity, and effective precipitation under forest canopies vary markedly from nonforest communities. Also, trees are deeply rooted and long-lived, they can access water and nutrients from greater depths compared with other vegetation. Trees extract and cycle nutrients at different rates compared with other vegetation.

Soil genesis and its interaction with forests are complex and do not conform well to generalizations. However, three concepts are crucial to understanding the interaction between forests and soils:

1. Soils and vegetation develop together.
2. Soil includes both the largely mineral material as well as the layers of organic matter (forest floor) that form in undisturbed forests. The presence of this forest floor is a major difference between agricultural and forest soils and is a major reason for differences in characteristics.
3. Many agricultural soils are derived from soils originally developed under forest vegetation; however, removal of the forest canopy and forest floor during conversion to agriculture has such important impacts that they no longer resemble forest soils.

Soil Forming Factors and Forest Vegetation Development

Parent Material

Parent material influences weathering (the breakdown of parent bedrock) rates and, consequently, the stage of soil development and the prevailing vegetation. Although the initial mineralogical composition of the parent material matters, similarities in other soil forming factors, together with time, can result in mature soils of very similar physical and chemical properties from differing parent material. Under forest vegetation, the result is usually a clay-rich, acidic, and relatively infertile soil. These conditions result from specific pedogenic (soil forming) processes as follows:

1. Additions of organic and mineral substances as solids, liquids, or gases.
2. Losses from a portion of the soil, including movement within the profile from one horizon to another.
3. Changes in molecular form among organic and mineral compounds.

Soil physical and chemical properties that result from differences in these processes determine the development of forests. The four primary soil physical factors are texture (the relative proportions of sand, silt, and clay particles), structure (the three-dimensional arrangement of individual soil particles into aggregates such as single-grained, blocky, columnar, prismatic, or massive), size distribution of fines (particles <2 mm) versus stones (mineral solids

>2 mm), and depth available for rooting. Other soil characteristics such as soil bulk density, aeration, and hydraulic conductivity also determine the extent to which root systems and soil organisms will utilize a given soil. Together with climate, time, and parent material, knowledge of the soil physical factors helps predict the successional patterns of vegetation on a landscape. However, these soil physical factors are, in turn, influenced by vegetation dynamics.

Two classifications of soils based on the origin of parent material are generally used:

1. Residual soils result from *in situ* weathering of parent material (the underlying bedrock) on relatively stable landscapes. With time, intense weathering results in fine-textured surface soils, and coarser fragments with depth. Soil development is linked to the zone of biological and chemical weathering.
2. Transported soils tend to be more uniform in textural composition with depth than residual soils but they can vary drastically in texture. They often contain material from soils formed in place at other locations. These soils are further classified by their mode of transport. Alluvial soils are derived from materials transported by water and deposited in the floodplain associated with the watercourse. Waterborne sorting of grain sizes can lead to soils of distinctly textured layers, the finest of which are deposited near the surface. Speed of the transport waters is the greatest influence on sorting. Lacustrine deposits result from suspended sediments in lake water, and tend to be fine-textured. Colluvium is material transported downslope at varying speeds. Textural differences can be large or small with little sorting by size class. Aeolian materials are windborne deposits, usually of particles silt-sized (called loess), or smaller.

There are some general relationships between parent material and vegetation type. Under a given set of climatic conditions, limestone, shale, and similar fine-textured rocks weather into clay-rich, high base nutrient status soils. Acid crystalline rocks (those with high quartz content) such as granites generally form acidic, coarse-textured (sandy) soils of relatively low base nutrient status compared to siltstones and shales. Less moisture- and nutrient-demanding tree species, such as pines, tolerate these conditions better than most angiosperms (hardwoods).

Topography and Landscape Position

Energy from topographic relief, aspect (position of the slope relative to the radiant energy of the sun), and position in the landscape (top, mid-slope, or bottom) drive the formation of soil. Steeper slopes usually experience greater erosion from soil and water movement. These high-energy environments may be so dynamic as to preclude the development of a mature soil no matter how much time passes (see discussion of zonal model of soils, below).

Local topography influences the development of soils and forests through its influence on erosion and drainage. For example, microsite differences in elevation can result in dramatically different dissolved oxygen contents in the soil, which affects soil chemistry. Under anaerobic conditions, metals such as iron, manganese, and aluminum are reduced to more soluble and mobile forms that may leach or be reoxidized to precipitates. The color of a soil, especially in the subsoil, can be used to predict drainage class. Reds and oranges signify oxidized conditions, whilst darker grays and bluish colors indicate reduced conditions typical of impeded drainage.

Climate

Climate and, in particular, the amount and seasonality of available moisture, is important in soil formation and key to the development of vegetation. Moisture and temperature drive chemical reactions. Chemical and physical weathering of parent material leads to the development of soil horizons. Climate also dictates the development of vegetation and can override the influence of parent material by precluding or enabling the establishment of specific types of vegetation, which in turn contributes to the type of soil formed.

Forest growth (biomass production) is usually proportional to available moisture. As litter falls to the forest floor, it decays and is transformed by a series of chemical reactions and biologically mediated decomposition into organic acids and humus (*see* **Soil Biology and Tree Growth**: Soil Organic Matter Forms and Functions. **Soil Development and Properties**: The Forest Floor). Soils high in organic matter are typically dark-colored by humus. Organic acids assist in the weathering of minerals in the uppermost layer of soil (A horizon), the products of which leach (a process called eluviation) into the underlying zone (B horizon). The soil directly above this zone of accumulation is sometimes so highly leached of metals (especially oxides of Al and Fe) and soluble organic matter that a distinctly light-colored horizon develops (E horizon) at the bottom of the A horizon. The products of leaching which have moved out of the E horizon give a darker color to the B horizon. Horizon development beneath a New Zealand forest is illustrated in **Figure 1**.

Organic matter dynamics is largely a function of moisture availability, temperature, and biotic

Figure 1 A soil profile beneath a kauri (*Agathis australis*) forest on old coastal sands (North Island, New Zealand). Note the dark surface horizon (A horizon) beneath the forest floor. Beneath this horizon is a 30-cm thick lighter zone (E horizon) leached by organic acids. Translocated humic and aluminum compounds have accumulated into the reddish-colored B horizon (Bhs horizon). Reproduced with permission of the New Zealand Soil Science Society.

communities. Forest soils are especially diverse compared with agricultural environments. Flora and fauna populate and modify the soil, especially in the rooting zone, an area known as the rhizosphere. Three major impacts of organisms are:

1. The movement of soil particles and organic matter between the surface and subsurface of the soil.
2. The mediation of some chemical reactions and resultant nutrient availability.
3. Forming a significant source of organic matter and nutrient additions to the soil.

The soil food web is a complex community ranging from predatory vertebrates like shrews and moles to tens of thousands of invertebrate species such as worms, arthropods (bugs), and decomposing fungi and bacteria, all which mediate the decomposition of soil organic matter (**Table 1**). Soil organic matter is the source of energy and nutrients used by plants and other organisms. Because they move within the soil, vertebrates, earthworms, and arthropods aerate and mix the soil as they feed. Shredders, such as millipedes, termites, sowbugs, and roaches process tens of tonnes of organic matter yearly derived from the forest floor and plant roots. Soil structure is improved through burrowing and the creation of fecal pellets, rich in readily available nutrients. In terms of biomass and overall activity in the soil, earthworms dominate the invertebrates. Earthworms dramatically enhance the porosity of soil as they burrow, thereby creating conduits for water. Moreover, they move large amounts of mineral soil and organic matter throughout the soil by providing deep cultivation. Compared with other terrestrial ecosystems, forest soil food webs are by far the most complex in the number of separate functional organismal groups.

As organisms consume food, they add to their biomass and they release wastes. Bacteria play a crucial role in mediating the chemical transformation of nutrient elements, like N and P, which are bound in the organic form (unavailable to plants), to elemental (inorganic) forms readily used by plants. This process is known as mineralization. In addition to their crucial role in decomposing organic matter, fungi also enter into a mutually beneficial relationship with tree roots. These fungal–root relationships are known as mycorrhizae (*see* **Tree Physiology: Mycorrhizae**). Roots, and their fungal and bacterial symbionts, have been found to release carbohydrates, vitamins, and amino acids into the rhizosphere, resulting in greatly increased populations of bacteria and fungi. In turn, the increased activity accelerates mineral and organic matter weathering.

activity. As with any chemical reaction, decomposition is fastest when rate limiting factors are at optimum levels. Low concentrations of oxygen, low temperatures, and extremes of moisture content slow decomposition of organic matter.

Biological Factors of Soil Formation

Biological interactions are essential to pedogenesis. The diversity of life in soil, as measured by species, variety, and number, far exceeds that of aboveground

Table 1 Characteristics of organisms in the forest soil food web

Class of soil organism	Important functions	Biomass[a] $(g m^{-2})$
Protozoa	Bacterial feeders	2–20
Bacteria	Decomposition, conversion/release of nutrients to plant available forms	40–500
Fungi	Decomposition, binding soil, enhance root function in uptake of nutrients	100–1500
Nematodes	Feed on fungi, roots, bacteria	1–15
Arthropods	Shred litter; mix soil; feed on bacteria and fungi	2–5
Earthworms	Same as arthropods; enhance soil structure and fertility; most important macrofaunal species	10–150

[a]To a depth of 15 cm.

Perhaps the greatest impact of bacteria in forest soils is their mediation of the chemical transformations of N. Nitrogen availability limits forest productivity globally more than does any other single nutrient. Because the supply of N is so important, nature has developed means to provide that supply, yet to also preserve stocks so that they are not lost from the ecosystem. The ultimate source of N in the soil comes from the abundance of N_2 in the atmosphere. Plants cannot use N_2. In a microbially mediated process, rhizosphere bacteria (and a few other microbes) convert N_2 to ammonium. This is called biological N-fixation. However, most plants require N in the form of NO^{-3} (nitrate), so bacteria must convert ammonium to nitrate. Unused ammonium and nitrate are lost easily from the soil, so conversion back to forms (insoluble) not easily lost is essential to preserving ecosystem productivity.

Tree roots grow where soil conditions are favorable. Thus, the proliferation of fine roots (the growing root tips) is usually greatest in the surface soil, as a result of greatest resource availability. Although roots of some forest species may extend to depths of 10 m or more, 90% of the root length and surface area occurs within the first 1 m of the surface. Together with the biotic activity of other soil flora and fauna, roots occupy and modify the top zone of soil, with activity decreasing exponentially with soil depth. The most important factors are availability of oxygen and moisture, soil temperatures, amounts of available (inorganic) nutrients, and organic matter quality. Turnover (herbivory, and root death and decomposition) of roots accounts for a significant portion of the soil organic matter pool. Studies of root mortality and decomposition have found that as much as 50% of annual biomass production may be invested in root production, with 20–45% of that as annual root turnover.

Observations of changes in a soil following deforestation and afforestation, and the resulting morphological soil traits, indicate that the relationship between forest vegetation and soil is interactive. Students are often introduced to this relationship by considering the influence of forest vegetation on the genesis of podzols (spodosols). The litter from certain tree and shrub species decomposes to an especially acidic form of humus, which results in a lowering of soil pH, especially if the soil is not well buffered (*see* **Soil Biology and Tree Growth**: Soil Organic Matter Forms and Functions). The acidic, nutrient-poor status of these soils results in an edaphic climax. For example, certain conifers, such as the Pinaceae, *Picea*, and *Tsuga* (northern hemisphere), and the broadleaved evergreen *Agathis* (southern hemisphere), commonly form on Spodosols, and under certain conditions, result in a site-specific soil climax. Experts question whether the formation of these morphological features is merely accelerated by certain vegetation or if they are most likely examples of forest vegetation adapting to pre-existing edaphic constraints. Podzolization can occur on pure, relatively sterile sands after a few hundred years under conifer forest, although well over 1000 years is considered usual. It has been noted that successional change to hardwoods can result in changes in nutrient cycling and soil chemistry, leading to a reversal of the podzolization process.

An especially illustrative example of the relationship between forests and soil development are the 'egg-cup' podzols formed under some New Zealand podocarps (in particular old-growth forests of kauri (*Agathis australis*). In this case, moisture, parent material, and vegetation combine to form a unique soil morphology consisting of well-developed E and B horizons. Years of litter fall, and the concomitant leaching from the products of litter decomposition result in a distinct, bleached, egg-cup shaped E horizon beneath the roots of giant, old-growth kauri, underlain by a zone (spodic horizon or Bhs horizon) of accumulated sesquioxides, soluble bases, clays, and colloidal organic compounds, largely from the E horizon beneath the stems of individual trees (**Figure 2**). This process is aided by soil textures dominated by sands of acid crystalline minerals, such as quartz.

Figure 2 An 'egg-cup' podzol formed under the stems of long-lived trees in New Zealand, where extra leaching of water down the stems of Kauri trees results in distinct zones of leaching and accumulation. Reproduced with permission of the New Zealand Soil Science Society.

Figure 3 Example of a fallen tree and the development of pit and mound topography in a hardwood forest in the USA.

Another important forest-mediated soil process is known as desilication, wherein high uniform temperatures and rainfall along with the acidic products of litter decomposition favor loss of silica from the upper soil profile. Simultaneously, iron- and aluminum-rich oxides concentrate and form an oxic horizon. Typically, this is a clay-rich, but lacking in any mineralizable primary minerals (those containing calcium, magnesium, and potassium). This process is characteristic of the intensely red tropical soils known as Oxisols.

The ecology of soil change as forests are cleared and grow back has been studied around the world. The magnitude of change depends on management practices and the differences among sites. It is important to remember that farmed soils are a result of constant human inputs and harvests as opposed to forested soils which, depending on harvest intensity, are largely a product of natural soil-forming factors. Our knowledge of these changes have been aided by research which quantifies the change in soil properties as forests are cleared to make way for farming, followed by reversion to forest.

Another example of the interaction between forest and soil development can be observed in the 'pit and mound' microtopography created by tree falls. Windthrow and uprooting results in a pit at the former root collar and a mound nearby where the displaced surface soil clings to the remaining roots and tree stem (**Figure 3**). Tree falls increase in mature and old-growth forests, and where predisposing environmental conditions such as restricted rooting depth and meteorological conditions exist. The resulting effects on soil formation include: litter accumulation and decomposition, respiration, soil climate (humidity, moisture content, temperature, solar radiation), sequence and thickness of soil horizons, and biotic diversity/activity. Forest floor tends to accumulate in pits due to increased trapping of litter, and reduced decomposition rates resulting from higher moisture contents. Greater moisture in surface soil may facilitate the weathering process unless oxygen is limiting. Horizon differentiation is slowed on mounds due to attenuation of weathering from a decrease in moisture levels and organic matter inputs from litter fall. Pits have the highest amounts of organic matter, nitrogen, and carbon, while mounds have the least, and the surrounding undisturbed (flat) areas are intermediate. Calcium and other soluble bases are often higher in pits, resulting in higher soil pH. The occurrence of pit and mound microtopography varies from as little as 1–2% to as much as 30–40% of the forest floor in especially prone areas.

Pits, when associated with high water tables, can lead to the formation of vernal (ephemeral) pools. These pools remain as long as the water table remains high, or longer when sediments coat and seal the edges of the depression. Microtopography, and the resulting creation of soil microsites, has been found to influence the distribution of understory plants. Animal activity is also tied to the availability of favorable microsites. Variation in earthworm and other invertebrate activity contributes to the fine-scale heterogeneity in forest soils characteristic of pit and mound landscapes.

Time

Changes occur constantly in soils as a result of parent material weathering and vegetation dynamics. Given enough time and a particular set of climatic and vegetative factors, most soils will stratify, developing the characteristic horizons and other features we use to distinguish among them. The concept of soil maturity, or that a predictable type of soil will develop over time, is referred to as the zonal model of soils. Although this concept is manifest under certain conditions, it does not adequately explain the variation in soils under all conditions and the concept does not have universal acceptance. Similarly, the idea of climax vegetation communities in equilibrium with the soil is a largely misleading one based on studies of limited time scales, within relatively few old-growth forests. Thus, it is difficult to predict how long it will take for soil to develop. It may take 100 years to add 1–2 cm of topsoil in residuum under harsh climatic conditions. In contrast, well over 10–20 cm of soil may form on volcanically derived parent material under tropically moist conditions in that same 100 years. Because soil is constantly being lost by erosion on some landscapes, it is probably best to discuss time and forest soil formation in terms of soil profiles and horizons.

Under temperate climatic conditions, such as those found in the continental USA and Western Europe, a well developed A horizon can form in as little as 150–400 years, with full profiles averaging 1500–12 000 years. Extremes in environment such as high moisture content, arid conditions, or dynamic landscapes due to slope or depositional intensity, can slow development dramatically. Ultisols (red–yellow podzolic soils) and Oxisols (Latosols, Ferralsols) are

commonly the most ancient of soils ranging in age from 50 000 to well over 500 000 years. Some clayey soils, especially those rich in aluminum or iron, are particularly resistant to change.

Soil Classification Systems

The most widely used classification systems are the US Department of Agriculture (USDA) *Soil Taxonomy* and the United Nations Food and Agriculture Organization (FAO) *Legend*. *Soil Taxonomy* is an hierarchical system based on morphological variables that are quantitative, and thus easily interpreted. The system groups all soils into 12 soil orders based on their current properties (color, clay content, etc.), similarities in pedogenic factors (climate, presence or absence of diagnostic horizons) and overall profile development (**Figure 4**).

Table 2 provides a comparison of the world distribution of soil, by percentage of land area, for the FAO Legend, and Soil Taxonomy. Entisols and shifting sand or rock constitute the largest categories.

Distribution of Soil among and within Forest Biomes

Past and present differences in climate and landscapes have created the forests we view today. Discounting the role of humans, the species composition of the worlds forests correspond to areas of distinctive landscapes, climates, and biota referred to as biomes. Because the extent of biomes can extend across continents, large differences can occur in the types of soils encountered. Describing this variation is really a matter of the scale chosen. However, three major points are:

1. soils commonly differ as much within regions as around the globe
2. soil types are distributed unevenly around the globe
3. a particular forest biome can occur on a variety of soils.

Patterns of soil properties vary in relation to the five soil-forming factors. However, variation in a given parameter can be as great within a forest stand as among biomes. Variation across a landscape can be as great as among soil types on a continent. Therefore, a given forest type can occur across a range of soils, and a particular soil type can occur in multiple forest regions.

Within the temperate regions, Entisols, Alfisols, Inceptisols, and Ultisols support the majority of forest (**Figure 5**). Other orders, excepting Aridisols and

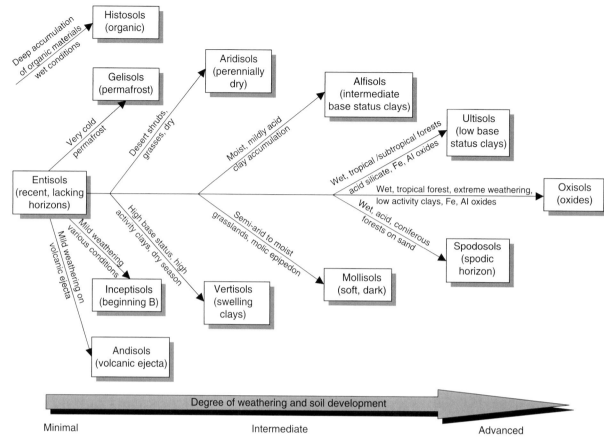

Figure 4 Diagram showing general degree of weathering and soil development in the soil orders within the US Department of Agriculture *Soil Taxonomy*, including the general climatic and vegetative conditions under which the orders are formed. Modified from Brady NC and Weil RR (2002) *The Nature and Properties of Soil*, 13th edn. Upper Saddle River, NJ: Prentice-Hall.

Table 2 World distribution of soil orders by percentage of land area

US Taxonomy Soil Order	Analogous categories in FAO and other widely used classification systems	Percentage of ice-free land
Entisol	Regosols, lithosols, arenosols	16.2
Inceptisol	Acid brown soils, gleysols, cambisols	9.8
Mollisol	Prairie soils, chernozems, rendzinas,	6.9
Histosol	Bog soils, histosols	1.2
Gelisol	Gelic members of gleysols, cambiosols, and others	8.6
Spodosol	Podzols	2.6
Alfisol	Grey wooded soils, luvisols, planosols	9.7
Vertisol	Grumusols, vertisols	2.4
Ultisol	Red–yellow podzols	8.5
Oxisol	Latosols, ferralsols	7.5
Aridisol	Xerosols, solonetz, solochaks, yermosols	12.0
Andisol	Andosols	0.7
Shifting sand or rock		14.0

Source: Modified from US Department of Agriculture Natural Resources Conservation Service.

Gelisols, are also capable of supporting forests, but large portions have been reserved for nonforest uses, particularly agriculture. Aridisols are too dry to support forests, and Gelisols are too cold. Boreal forests occur mostly on Spodosols, Entisols, Incepti-

sols, and Histosols. In most of the world, Alfisols indicate the potential for broadleaved forests. Because of their volcanic origins, Andisols are limited in occurrence, usually near the edges of continental plates, but can support some of the world's most

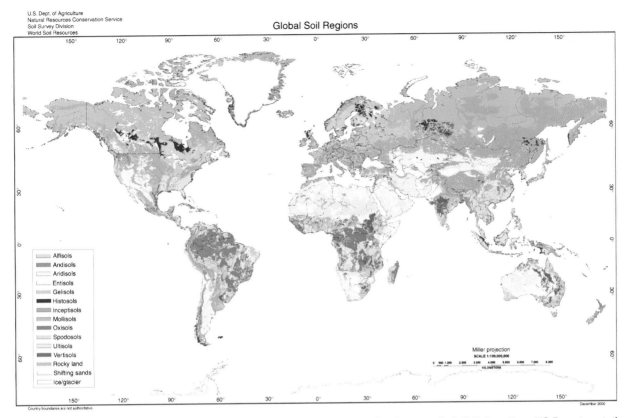

Figure 5 Map of global soil regions using the US Department of Agriculture *Soil Taxonomy's* Soil Orders. From US Department of Agriculture Natural Resources Conservation Service.

productive forests. Ultisols are most common in tropical and near tropical latitudes, and the warmest, moistest regions where soils have been permitted to weather in place for long periods of time. Both broadleaved and conifer species are common, with the broadleaves dominating on the moister and more fertile Ultisols. Oxisols are the worlds most weathered and mature soils, occurring in the tropics. A synopsis of the world's forested communities follows.

Tropical Forests

Tropical forests begin at the equator, and span north to the Tropic of Cancer, south to the Tropic of Capricorn. Approximately 33% of the world's forests occur here amidst considerable variation in climate, elevation, and geology. The major soil orders are Inceptisols, Andisols, Ultisols, and Oxisols.

Tropical rainforest These moist tropical forests comprise about 30% of the tropics. The nutrient cycle between the vegetation and the soil is essentially closed. Rainfall is generally between 2000 and 4000 mm year^{-1}. Constant litter fall and decomposition throughout the year (udic environments) and the virtual absence of leaching permit the development of

luxuriant forest with no nutrient deficiency symptoms in soils of low native fertility. The only marked vegetation differences outside of swamps that can be correlated with soils are the reduced stature of rainforests growing on very sandy Spodosols.

Seasonally dry deciduous and semideciduous tropical forest Deciduous and semideciduous forests occur where the dry season is sufficiently strong to exclude rainforests but grasses are not dominant. Rainfall is between 1200 to 2000 mm year^{-1}. About 15% of the tropics are covered by semideciduous, deciduous, and thorn forests. The nutrient cycle, however, is markedly different from that of the rainforest. With substantial litter fall during the dry season, the solar radiation reaching the soil surface increases drastically, and the litter layer does not decompose during the dry season.

Savanna These are transitional areas between the tropical forests and deserts. Rainfall is in the range of 900 to 1500 mm year^{-1}. Also known as tropical grasslands, savannas have widely scattered trees that are generally deciduous. Fire frequency is important in maintaining these communities as trees are normally excluded when burn frequency and intensity increases.

Temperate Deciduous Forests

These forests reach maximum abundance between the tropics and 45° N latitude. The climate is characterized by relatively cold winters and warm summers with reasonably evenly distributed rainfall (averaging 750 to 2500 mm year^{-1}) throughout the year. Leaf fall corresponds to a period of cold and unavailability of water. Conifers become more prevalent at the drier and colder, and mountainous margins of this biome. Entisols, Inceptisols, Alfisols, Spodosols, and Ultisols are the most common soil orders.

Boreal Forest

The boreal regions of the world are characterized by long, cold, snowy winters. These biomes are the result of a climate found only in the interior of large continental landmasses in the northern hemisphere. Conifers are the most abundant tree species with some cold-tolerant, deciduous broadleaved vegetation occurring at the southern and milder margins. Entisols, Inceptisols, Spodosols, and Histosols are the most common soil orders.

Further detail on the extent and development of the world's forest biomes can be found in the section on Further Reading.

Summary

Forests provide a unique set of environmental factors influencing soil formation. The most important of these is the microclimate at the earth's surface engendered by the canopy of trees and understory vegetation, the role of tree roots in cycling nutrients from great depths, and the large additions to soil organic matter made by tree roots and foliage. Fully one-third of the earth's soils developed under a original cover of forest. Although forests can occupy very fertile soils, much of the world's remaining forest exists on landscapes marginally suited for other human uses.

The two dominant soil-forming processes in forests are podzolization and desilication. These two processes occur in the two forest biomes least influenced by humans, the boreal and tropical forests, respectively.

Some tree genera and species assemblages will thrive on most of the soil orders making it difficult to predict forest composition based solely on soil. Forest composition and productivity depend more on local-scale factors such as topography, soil physical properties, and inherent differences in local climate, than to soil categories.

See also: **Soil Biology and Tree Growth**: Soil and its Relationship to Forest Productivity and Health; Soil Biology; Soil Organic Matter Forms and Functions; Tree Roots and their Interaction with Soil. **Soil Development and Properties**: Landscape and Soil Classification for Forest Management; Nutrient Cycling; Nutrient Limitations and Fertilization; The Forest Floor. **Tree Physiology**: Nutritional Physiology of Trees; Root System Physiology.

Further Reading

Brady NC and Weil RR (2002) *The Nature and Properties of Soils*, 13th edn. Upper Saddle River, NJ: Prentice Hall.

Fisher RF and Binkley D (2000) *Ecology and Management of Forest Soils*, 3rd edn. New York: John Wiley.

Hendricks RL (2001) Forest types and classification. In: Evans J (ed.) *The Forests Handbook*, vol. 1, pp. 23–60. Oxford, UK: Blackwell Science.

Soil Survey Staff, US Department of Agriculture (1976) *Soil Taxonomy*, 2nd edn. Pittsburgh, PA: US Government Printing Office. Available online at http://www.nhq.nrcs.usda.gov/WSR

Soil and Water Conservation Society (2000) *Soil Biology Primer*. Ankeny, IA: Soil and Water Conservation Society.

Landscape and Soil Classification for Forest Management

L T West, University of Georgia, Athens, GA, USA

Soil Classification

Soils vary across the earth's surface, and understanding and managing this variation is key to understanding, managing, and sustaining both natural and anthropogenic ecosystems. Properties of the soil at any point in the landscape are the product of an array of complex processes, tempered by the environmental factors climate, biota, and topography, acting on a parent material over time. Because of the vast numbers of combinations and intensities of these five state factors, the number of different soils is seemingly endless. It is generally agreed, however, that it is possible to group soils into classes having many properties that are similar which is the basis for soil classification.

Properties chosen to form classes vary among soil classification systems, and the choice of properties used as the basis for developing classes and the property limits used to separate classes are often debated. The goal of all systems, however, is to provide classes that have similar properties and/or similar responses to external inputs. In addition, soil classification provides a means for organizing knowledge about soils and for enhanced communication among soil scientists since a few terms can be used to convey a great deal of information. Grouping soils into classes with similar properties also provides a mechanism for identifying appropriate uses of the soil, for estimating production, for extrapolating knowledge gained at one location to other locations, and for determining research needs.

Most national and international soil classification systems, such as *Soil Taxonomy*, are general-purpose natural classification systems. The systems were developed to group soils based on their properties without consideration of any particular use. Thus, these systems use many properties to form classes, and interpretations of soil behavior under any of a broad range of uses can be made from an understanding of how properties that define the class affect the intended use.

This is in contrast to soil classification systems developed and used for more narrow purposes such as forest management. Forest managers are mostly interested in soil properties that influence the occurrence and productive potential of a forest stand such as texture, rooting depth, native fertility, and water supplying capacity. Because only a subset of all possible soil properties are of interest, classes are defined based on combinations of properties thought to affect the narrow purpose of the classification system. Thus, the system will be more precise than natural classification systems in predicting expected behavior for the intended use. If land use or management system changes, however, the use-specific classification system may not include the properties needed to effectively implement the change without major changes to the system.

Soil Taxonomy

This section presents a general overview of the structure, basis for class differentiation, and nomenclature of *Soil Taxonomy* which was developed in the USA. Presentation of *Soil Taxonomy* is not meant to imply that it is the only or the best system of soil classification. The structure and nomenclature used in *Soil Taxonomy* are similar to those used in other classification systems. *Soil Taxonomy* is presented as an example that is intended to provide a basis for

understanding the basis behind and structure of natural soil classification systems. Its use as an example reflects the author's base of knowledge and experience as do other examples presented in this article.

Soil Taxonomy comprises six categorical levels. These are: order, suborder, great group, subgroup, family, and series. The structure of the system is somewhat analogous to the plant and animal taxonomies in that the highest category (order) is the most general and has the fewest classes (12), and the lowest category (series) is the most specific and has the most classes (16 000 +).

Details of criteria used to separate taxa in *Soil Taxonomy* at all categorical levels are beyond the scope of this text. The general criteria used for each category, however, are given below:

- Order: properties resulting from major soil-forming processes that aid in understanding and interpreting soils at a grand scale.
- Suborder: properties that have a major influence or that reflect these influences on current soil formation processes. Many are also important for plant growth and interpreting soil behavior.
- Great group: properties that impose or reflect subordinate or additional controls on current soil-forming processes and soil behavior such as horizons that retard water movement and root extension.
- Subgroup: properties that reflect either (1) a transition from one taxon to another at a higher category, (2) a transition to properties not recognized at higher categories but are common among many classes (shallow rock, water, etc.), or (3) the central concept of the great group (Typic).
- Family: properties that reflect important conditions affecting soil behavior or potential for further change.
- Series: lowest level of *Soil Taxonomy*. Differentiating criteria are the same as those for higher categories, but ranges in properties are defined more narrowly to aid interpretations of soil behavior and response to management at a local level.

A robust classification system must be based on properties of the population of individuals being classified and not abstract concepts of the processes that have led to the different individuals. Thus, differentia used to separate classes in *Soil Taxonomy* are based on soil properties. However, because understanding a soil's genesis is important for understanding its properties and expected behavior, properties that reflect or influence processes of soil formation have great importance in this system. For this reason, *Soil Taxonomy* is considered a morphogenetic system, i.e., the system is based on observable and measurable soil properties, but many of these properties represent pathways and processes important to soil genesis.

A soil's placement in a particular taxon in *Soil Taxonomy* depends on the presence or absence of diagnostic horizons and features that are considered to be marks of the soil's genesis but that are rigidly defined by morphological, physical, chemical, and mineralogical properties of the soil. Thus, a soil's classification offers information on processes that have been important in its development, but more importantly, because taxa are defined by soil properties, they can be interpreted in terms of expected behavior and response to management. The interpretive detail that can be ascertained from a soil's classification depends on the categorical level at which the interpretations are made. At the order level, few specifics can be said about interpretation for a particular use. The number of specific interpretative statements increases at lower levels of classification to a maximum at the series level.

Most users of soil information that includes a classification are unlikely to have the depth of understanding of diagnostic horizons and features needed to properly classify a soil. However, with an understanding of the nomenclature is used to indicate specific horizons and features, a great deal of information about the properties of a soil can be determined from its classification. In *Soil Taxonomy*, most of the formative elements used to name classes are terms derived from Latin or Greek, and many have similar meaning to terms used in everyday speech. Thus, the nomenclature of a class can reveal many general properties of soil even if the exact definition of the diagnostic horizon or other differentiating characteristic is unknown. The formative elements and concept of the 12 orders is given in **Table 1**. A list and brief definition of formative elements for properties most important to forest management are given in **Table 2**.

Orders

Names of orders end in 'sol.' The formative element for orders begins with the vowel preceding the 'o' or 'i' before 'sol' and ends with the last consonant before the 'o' or 'i.'

Suborders

Names of suborders have two syllables. The first connotes something about the diagnostic properties of the soil, and the second is the formative element from the order. For example: Udalfs – Alfisols with udic moisture regimes, Psamments – sandy Entisols, Aquults – Ultisols with an aquic moisture regime.

Great groups

Names of great groups consist of the suborder and a prefix that is formed by one or two formative elements suggesting something of the diagnostic properties of the soil. For example: Paleudalfs – old (deeply weathered) Udalfs, Udipsamments – Psamments with a udic moisture regime, Epiaquults – Aquults with seasonal saturation from water perched above a water restrictive horizon.

Table 1 Formative elements and the central concept of the 12 orders in *Soil Taxonomy*

Order	Formative element	Central concept
Alfisols	alf	Soils with an argillic or kandic horizon and greater than 35% base saturation in the lower subsoil. Generally considered to have developed under forest vegetation.
Andisols	and	Soils developed from volcanic ejecta.
Aridisols	id	Soils occurring in a dry climate that have undergone sufficient soil development to have a diagnostic horizon.
Entisols	ent	Soils with no diagnostic horizon because of young age, resistant parent materials, or other factors that prevented soil development.
Gelisols	el	Soils in cold climates that have permafrost within 100 cm.
Histosols	ist	Soils composed of organic soil materials.
Inceptisols	ept	Weakly to moderately developed soils that do not have horizons or features that are diagnostic for other orders.
Mollisols	oll	Soils with mollic epipedons generally considered to have developed under grassland vegetation.
Oxisols	ox	Soils that have an oxic horizon or clayey surface horizon with a kandic horizon; commonly found on old stable tropical landscapes.
Spodosols	od	Soils with a spodic horizon; commonly sandy and developed under coniferous or other vegetation that produces acid leachates.
Ultisols	ult	Soils with an argillic or kandic horizon and less than 35% base saturation in the lower subsoil. Generally considered to have developed under forest vegetation.
Vertisols	ert	Soils with the amount and type of clay to generate high shrink – swell.

Table 2 Formative elements used in names of suborders, great groups, and subgroups that relate to forest composition and productivity

Formative element	Derivation[a]	Connotation
Abruptic	L. *abruptum,* torn off	Abrupt textural change
Aeric	Gr. *aerios,* air	Aeration (not as wet)
Al	Modified from Aluminum	High aluminum, low iron
Alb, Albic	L. *albus,* white	An albic horizon
Aqu	L. *aqua,* water	Aquic moisture regime
Ar	L. *arare,* to plow	Mixed horizons
Arenic	L. *arena,* sand	Sandy epipedon between 50 and 100 cm thick
Arg	L. *argilla,* white clay	Presence of argillic horizon
Cry	Gr. *kryos,* icy cold	Cold
Cumulic	L. *cumulus,* heap	Thickened epipedon
Dystr, Dys, Dystic	Gr. *dys,* ill	Low base saturation
Endo	Gr. *endo,* within	Saturated by a groundwater table
Epi	Gr. *epi,* on, above	Saturated by a perched water table
Eutro, Eu Eutric	Gr. *eu,* good	High base saturation
Fluv	L. *fluvius,* river	Floodplain
Frag	L. *fragilis,* brittle	Presence of a fragipan
Fragloss		Combination of frag and gloss
Grossarenic	L. *grossus,* thick + L. *arena,* sand	Sandy epipedon > 1 m thick
Hist	Gr. *histos,* tissue	Presence of organic materials
Hydr, Hydric	Gr. *hydor,* water	Presence of water
Lithic	Gr. *lithos,* stone	Presence of shallow lithic contact
Molli	L. *mollis,* soft	Presence of a mollic epipedon
Natr, Natric	L. *natrium,* sodium	Presence of natric horizon
Oxyaquic	Combination of oxy (oxygen) and aquic	Aerated
Pachic	Gr. *pachys,* thick	A thick epipedon
Pale	Gr. *palaeos,* old	Excessive development
Petroferric	Gr. *petra,* rock + L. *ferrum,* iron	Presence of a petroferric contact (continuous ironstone)
Psamm	Gr. *psammos,* sand	Sand texture
Quartz	Ger. *quarz,* quartz	High quartz content
Terric	L. *terra,* earth	A mineral layer under organic soil
Torr	L. *torridus,* hot and dry	Torric moisture regime
Ud	L. *udus,* humid	Udic moisture regime
Ultic	L. *ultimus,* last	Low base saturation
Umbr, Umbric	L. *umbra,* shade	Presence of umbric epipedon
Ust	L. *ustus,* burnt	Ustic moisture regime
Xer	Gr. *xeros,* dry	Xeric moisture regime

[a]Gr., Greek; L., Latin.

Subgroups

Names of subgroups consist of the great group modified by one or more adjectives. The adjective 'Typic' is used for the subgroup thought to typify the central concept of the great group. Other types of subgroups are (1) intergrades toward other great groups, e.g., Aquic Paleudalfs are intergrades to the Paleaqualfs, and (2) extragrades – subgroups not intergrading toward any known kind of soil, e.g., Lithic Udipsamments are intergrading to rock.

Families

Names of families are polynomial and consist of the subgroup and three or more descriptive terms that indicate the particle-size class, mineralogy, cation exchange activity, soil temperature, and other properties of the soils. For example, fine, smectitic, active, thermic Aquic Paludalfs are the Aquic Paleudalfs that

have a fine particle size class (35–60% clay), dominantly smectitic clays, an active cation exchange capacity class (0.4–0.6 cmol kg^{-1} clay), and a thermic temperature regime (18–22°C mean annual temperature at 50 cm). The particle-size, mineralogy, and cation exchange activity classes are based on the weighted average of upper part of the subsoil. More or fewer terms may be part of the family depending on the subgroup.

Series

Names of series are abstract place names. The name of a series has no meaning to people who have no other source of information about properties that define the series. Common use of classification systems specific to forest management raises the question of the utility of Soil Taxonomy or other natural classification systems to management of the forest resource. By definition, forest management classification systems only consider a subset of soil properties and are often developed for use in a specific region. Thus, properties considered and terminology used to describe these properties may vary among systems. Because of these variations, communication, soil-based technology transfer, and understanding of the soil system across wide regions can be enhanced through use of classification based on Soil Taxonomy or other natural classification systems.

Soils and Landscapes

Because topography is one of the five state factors (climate, topography, biotic influences, parent material, and time) that control soil formation, soils and landscapes are intimately linked. Likewise, the slope, aspect, and shape of the landscape have a strong influence on forest ecology and productivity. Major landscape influences on both soil and ecosystem properties are related to redistribution of water from precipitation, landscape redistribution of solutes, parent material, and, in steep landscapes, slope and slope aspect.

Slope shape is the three-dimensional geometry of a slope which is derived by combining the shape of the vertical slope profile with the shape of the profile along the slope contour. In each direction, the slope can be linear, concave, or convex, and any point in the landscape can be designated as concave – concave, concave – linear, etc. to better communicate the conformation of the landscape. The shape of hillslopes strongly influences lateral movement of water across the landscape as both overland flow and in the shallow subsurface as throughflow. Flow tends to be parallel on linear slopes, convergent in landscape segments with concave slope, and divergent in landscape segments with convex slope. The influence of slope shape on redistribution of water from precipitation creates microenvironments on the landscape in which areas of divergent flow are drier than the landscape as a whole and areas of convergent flow are wetter than the general landscape. These microclimates influence both soil development and vegetation composition and productivity.

Hillslopes can be divided into segments along a two-dimensional profile that is based on slope shape and inflections in the slope gradient. In humid climates, the most commonly used terms for these segments are summit, shoulder, backslope, footslope, and toeslope (**Figure 1**). The summit is the level or slightly convex uppermost part of a hillslope profile. Water movement on summits is mostly vertical although there may by an appreciable lateral

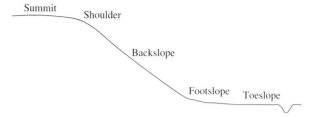

Figure 1 Terms used to describe various hillslope positions.

component on narrow convex summit positions. Soils on summits are often well drained, but the interior of broad level summits may have poorly drained soils if soil horizons or geologic strata slow the rate of vertical water movement. The shoulder is the convex portion of the hillslope below the summit. The shoulder position commonly has greater lateral flow of water and soils may be drier than the summit. Below the shoulder is the more linear backslope where surface runoff is greatest. Relative proportion of lateral and vertical water movement on backslopes depends on slope gradient and the stratigraphy of soil horizons and geologic strata. The backslope descends to the concave footslope which is an area of convergent flow and accumulation of sediments and solutes transported from upslope by overland flow and throughflow. Downslope from the footslope is the toeslope which has linear or slightly concave slope shapes and low slope gradient. Toeslopes tend to have alluvial parent materials from adjacent or upslope streams.

General types of soil parent material are commonly related to certain landscape positions and/or geomorphic surfaces. Although exceptions are common, especially in areas with extensive windblown materials, soils on summit, shoulder, and upper backslope positions tend to be developed from residual parent materials, and soil properties will be related to properties of the underlying rock or sediment. Gravity and water transported colluvial parent materials are usually found on lower backslope and footslope positions, and soil properties will be influenced by the properties of the colluvium which may or may not be similar to that of the subjacent residuum. Alluvial parent materials are found on floodplains and terraces, and properties of the soils in these settings will be influenced by the textural, chemical, and mineralogical characteristics of the sediment and by the position of the soil within the floodplain or terrace as it relates to stream transport capacity during deposition, i.e., coarse-textured sediments on levees and fine-textured sediments in backswamp positions.

Slope gradient and aspect can have implications for forest productivity and ecology. Slope gradient impacts are mostly related to its effects on rate and amount of overland flow, especially in managed forests. Both tree harvest and forest roads can lead to high amounts of soil erosion in strongly sloping areas if management and construction practices are not carefully planned and implemented. Slope aspect, especially on steep mountainous slopes, has impact on species composition, forest productivity, and soil development. These impacts arise from differences in the amount of solar radiation and corresponding temperature differences that are related to direction to which the slope faces. Because of the sun angle, aspects that face the equator and the afternoon sun (south and west in the northern hemisphere) receive more solar radiation and are warmer than those that face away from the equator. Higher temperature results in greater amounts of evapotranspiration and thus, these slopes have drier soils and less water available for plant growth than those facing away from the equator. This difference in water availability affects species composition and productivity and soil properties, especially thickness and organic carbon content of the surface horizon. In addition, reduced evapotranspiration on slopes facing away from the equator results in more water leaching through the soil, and soils on these slopes often are more developed than soils on similar warmer and drier slopes facing the equator.

In most cases, landscape differences will be reflected in soil map units and/or the classification of the named soil. There may be landscapes, however, in which differences are not reflected in the soil map units because of scale of mapping or intensity of the soil survey. In these cases, it may be useful to employ differences in landscape properties in conjunction with the classification and properties of the soil in evaluating forest ecology and productivity of a site.

Soil Survey

Although classification and mapping are closely related, they are not the same thing. Classification is best applied to individual pedons, and the classification of the pedon is a product of the classification system, which have arbitrary definitions. As a means to inventory the soil resource and/or provide a basis for land management, soil classification has limited applicability. Only when the classification is applied to land areas through a soil survey is the full utility of the classification systems realized for management.

A soil map unit is a natural segment of the landscape that is composed of one or more dominant soils. Environmental factors that influence soil formation (parent material, topography, and vegeta-

tion) are generally observable on the landscape, and when one or more of these factors changes, it reflects a change in the soil. Thus, landscape properties are used to infer occurrence of a particular soil on that landscape segment. This is the science that is the basis for soil survey. After relationships between type of soil and landscape properties have been identified through careful study, the landscape characteristics can be used to identify and map soils with only limited observations of the soil with depth.

Because soil map units are geographical bodies that are delineated on the ground, they almost always contain soils different from the named taxonomic unit. The soils other than the named taxa are referred to as inclusions. Inclusions are commonly categorized as similar to the named soil, i.e., different taxonomically but having similar interpretations of behavior, or dissimilar from the named soil, i.e., different both taxonomically and interpretively. Similar inclusions may be present by design in order to reduce map clutter and the number of potential management units. However, soil properties that result in similar interpretations for one land use may result in different interpretations for a different use. Thus, expected land use over the foreseeable future must be a consideration in map unit design.

Dissimilar inclusions occur because of (1) an incomplete understanding of the relationship between observable landscape characteristics and the type of soil or, more commonly, (2) because of map scale. If the smallest feature that can be drawn on the map is 2 ha in size, soils that occur as smaller bodies cannot be shown on the map even if the soil surveyor is aware they are present. Thus, the goal of soil mapping is to design and delineate map units that have a minimum amount of dissimilar inclusions.

Soil–Site Productivity Relationships

Soils and vegetation are intimately linked. A forest soil has been defined as one developed under and currently supporting forest vegetation. This implies that given sufficient time, properties of soils developed under a forest will have different properties from those developed under types of vegetation. These differences in genesis are reflected in soil classification systems. Differences in root distribution and relative amounts of above and below ground biomass between trees and grasses result in different surface soil properties which are reflected in differentia for Mollisols from other orders. Acid leachate from coniferous forest litter combined with sandy parent material results in podzolization being a dominate soil forming process leading to

Table 3 Recognition of soil properties that affect forest composition and productivity by taxa in *Soil Taxonomy*

Soil property	Relation to site quality	Indicative classes in Soil Taxonomy
pH (base saturation as covariable)	Affects nutrient availability	Soil orders (Mollisols, Alfisols, Ultisols), dystric and eutric great groups and subgroups, acid and nonacid families
Base saturation	Affects K, Mg, and Ca supply	Soil orders (Mollisols, Alfisols, Ultisols), dystric and eutric great groups and subgroups
Organic matter content	Source of N and P, promotes structure	Mollisols, umbric great groups and subgroups
Particle size distribution	Affects water and nutrient storage	Family particle-size class
Cation exchange capacity	Affects nutrient storage	Family cation exchange capacity classes, family particle-size and mineralogy classes, kandi and kanhapl great groups
A horizon structure	Promotes aeration and root proliferation	Mollisols and umbric great groups and subgroups
Depth of A horizon	Affects biological activity	Mollisols and umbric great groups and subgroups
Root restrictive horizons and strata	Limits rooting depth	Fragi great groups and subgroups, lithic subgroups, shallow families
Soil moisture regime	Soil moisture availability and aeration	Aquic, udic, ustic, xeric, and aridic suborders, great groups, and subgroups
Soil temperature regime	Affects root growth and microbial activity	Soil temperature regimes as family classes
Depth to redoximorphic features	Depth to seasonal saturation and related aeration	Aquic suborders, aquic and oxyaquic subgroups

development of spodic horizons and Spodosols (Podzols). Ancient conversion of forests to cropland has been shown to appreciably alter subsoil properties and resulting classification (Spodosols converted to Inceptisols). Numerous other examples of vegetation affects on soil development are available in the literature. Because vegetation affects soil genesis and properties, it is reasonable to expect the converse to be true. Soil conditions will have a major effect on forest composition and productivity.

The composition and productivity of a site depends on the inherit quality of the site and management inputs. Site quality is strongly influenced by soil, topography, and climate. Soil properties that affect site quality include soil temperature, nutrient supply and availability, soil organic matter content, texture, structure, consistence, depth to redoximorphic features (drainage), thickness of the A horizon, stone content, depth to horizons that restrict water movement and root elongation, and the thickness of the B horizon. Many of these properties are used to differentiate among taxa in *Soil Taxonomy* and other natural classification systems (**Table 3**).

Thus, classification and soil map units have often been interpreted as to their potential forest composition and productivity. These interpretations are based on observations, often unsystematic, of forest conditions over the area in which the soil occurs. Attempts to develop firm relationships between soil map units and forest productivity, however, have met with mixed success. Many studies have used soil map units to predict site productivity with considerable

success while others have reported little or no relationship between map units and productivity. A part of this discrepancy is related to the landforms and species being considered, but the major factor may lie in the fact that map units in most soil surveys, at least in the USA, were designed for agricultural purposes with forest management as a secondary consideration if considered at all. Better communication and cooperation between forest managers and soil scientists during the initial stages of a soil survey so that soil and landscape differences that are important for forest management can be considered in map unit design may well improve the utility of soil surveys for forest management.

See also: **Soil Biology and Tree Growth**: Soil and its Relationship to Forest Productivity and Health. **Soil Development and Properties**: Forests and Soil Development; Nutrient Cycling.

Further Reading

Ahrens RJ and Arnold RW (2000) Soil taxonomy. In: Sumner ME (ed.) *Handbook of Soil Science*, pp. E117–E135. Boca Raton, FL: CRC Press.

Arp PA and Krause HH (2002) Forest soil properties and site productivity. In: Lal R (ed.) *Encyclopedia of Soil Science*, pp. 590–593. New York: Marcel Dekker.

Buol SW, Hole FD, McCracken RJ, and Southard RJ (1997) *Soil Genesis and Classification*, 4th edn. Ames, IA: Iowa State University Press.

Carmean WH (1975) Forest site quality evaluation in the United States. *Advances in Agronomy* 27: 209–269.

FAO/ISRIC/ISSS (1998) *World Reference Base for Soil Resources*. World Soil Resources Report no. 84. Rome: Food and Agriculture Organization.

Fisher RF and Binkley D (2000) *Ecology and Management of Forest Soils*, 3rd edn. New York: John Wiley.

Krogh L (2002) Classification systems, major. In: Lal R (ed.) *Encyclopedia of Soil Science*, pp. 176–182. New York: Marcel Dekker.

Nortcliff S (2002) Classification, Need for. In: Lal R (ed.) *Encyclopedia of Soil Science*, pp. 166–168. New York: Marcel Dekker.

Spaargaren OC (2000) Other systems of soil classification. In: Sumner ME (ed.) *Handbook of Soil Science*, pp. E137–E174. Boca Raton, FL: CRC Press.

Soil Survey Staff (1999) *Soil Taxonomy: A Basic System of Soil Classification for Making and Interpreting Soil Surveys*, 2nd edn. Agricultural Handbook no. 436. Washington, DC: US Department of Agriculture Natural Resources Conservation Service.

Wysocki DA and Schoeneberger PA (2000) Geomorphology of soil landscapes. In: Sumner ME (ed.) *Handbook of Soil Science*, pp. E5–E39. Boca Raton, FL: CRC Press.

The Forest Floor

R D Briggs, State University of New York, Syracuse, NY, USA

Introduction

One of the most striking features of forests is the canopy, which consists of leaves and branches forming a noticeable layer that shades the ground and provides habitat for numerous birds, mammals, and insects. In addition to providing habitat, the canopy provides a substantial input of organic litter to the soil surface as the trees cyclically shed foliage, flowers, fruit, twigs, and bark. Over time as forests grow and develop, organic remains of plants and animals accumulate on the soil surface. The accumulation of foliage and branches is collectively referred to as the forest floor. The forest floor, along with tree roots, is an integral component of the forest soil system that distinguishes forest soils from agricultural soils.

The forest floor has a tremendous impact on the soil environment. One of the most important factors affecting tree growth is the capacity of the soil to transfer energy, water, and gases from the soil surface to organisms and roots living deeper in the soil. One of the fundamental soil physical properties influencing this transfer is soil structure, which refers to the aggregation of primary soil particles (sand, silt, clay)

into secondary units. Well-developed granular structure occurs in the surface mineral soil horizons creating pores that are large enough for water to flow freely through. Soil structure is described by shape (i.e., granular refers to small spheres, and blocky refers to larger aggregates). There is no quantitative expression currently available to describe soil structure.

Bulk density is a commonly used soil physical property that is influenced by soil structure. Bulk density is a measure of dry mass per unit volume of undisturbed soil. The undisturbed volume includes both the solid particles as well as pore space. For a given type of soil particle (organic vs. mineral), increased pore space results in lower values of bulk density. The particle density of organic matter is approximately half that of mineral soil, which averages $2.65 \, \text{Mg m}^{-3}$. The combination of low particle density and a relatively high volume of pores impart a low bulk density to the forest floor, which ranges from less than 0.1 to $0.30 \, \text{Mg m}^{-3}$. Contrast that figure with the range for typical surface mineral soil horizons of $1.0–1.3 \, \text{Mg m}^{-3}$. For purposes of comparison, the density of water is $1.0 \, \text{Mg m}^{-3}$.

The large pore space volume associated with the forest floor has several important consequences. Air filled pores of forest floors act as an insulator, buffering soil temperature by reducing daily high and increasing daily low temperatures. Water infiltration, the movement of water into the soil, and water storage capacity are high because of the large volume of pore space. Consequently, overland water flow in forest soils is rare. The forest floor provides a physically favorable environment for plant roots and soil fauna. Low bulk density does not restrict root growth or organism movement, while high pore space and water holding capacity ensure adequate moisture and aeration required by aerobic organisms. These favorable physical properties promote a high level of biological activity which decreases with depth below the soil surface.

Characterization of Organic Horizons

The forest floor is differentiated from mineral soil on the basis of organic matter expressed as carbon (C) concentration. The organic material comprising the forest floor exists in a decay continuum, ranging from relatively undecayed plant material on the surface to black, highly decomposed organic material referred to as humus. The US soil classification system divides the decay continuum into three discrete layers or horizons (**Figure 1**): (1) Oi, fibric material, relatively undecomposed; (2) Oe, hemic material, moderately decomposed; and (3) Oa, sapric

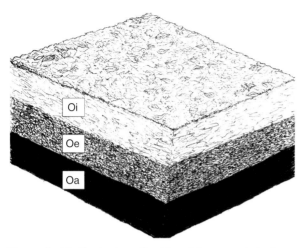

Figure 1 Idealized schematic of forest floor organic horizons. Proceeding downward from the fibrous Oi to the highly decomposed Oa horizon, litter identity is lost and the C : N ratio becomes smaller. *In situ* boundaries among organic horizons often are indistinct along the decay continuum and are not easily differentiated. Illustration by Rachael Briggs.

Table 1 Comparison of organic horizon designations for three soil classification systems

US	Canada	FAO[a]
Oi (L)	Of	O
Oe (F)	Om	O
Oa (H)	Oh	O

[a] The Food and Agriculture Organization (FAO) system does not differentiate on the basis of degree of decomposition among organic horizons. Organic horizons that are saturated are designated as H.

material, highly decomposed amorphous humus. Comparison with other classification systems is provided in **Table 1**. The letter O signifies the organic master horizon. The accompanying lower-case letters indicate the relative degree of decomposition. All three horizons may not always be present in the forest floor. The presence or absence and degree of development of each horizon depends on a variety of factors including amount and type of organic inputs, decomposition rate, and the activity of soil fauna.

Degree of decomposition is quantitatively defined on the basis of rubbed fiber content. Rubbed fiber content is the proportion of sample volume comprised of fibers that remain after rubbing between the fingers under a stream of water. Highly decomposed material is removed by this simple process, leaving only fibers. The Oi horizon, which consists of relatively undecomposed material that can be identified as to original plant component, has a rubbed fiber content exceeding 75%. At the other extreme, the highly decomposed Oa horizon has a rubbed fiber content less than 17%. The Oe horizon has a rubbed fiber content between 17% and 75%.

The use of quantitative criteria has improved field identification of the boundaries among organic horizons as well as the boundary between the Oa and the mineral soil. Mineral soil horizons contain less than 18% organic carbon on a weight basis. Laboratory analysis is often used to confirm field determinations. Prior to the use of rubbed fiber content to classify organic horizons, they were designated qualitatively as L (litter), F (fermenta-

tion), and H (humus) layers. Those classes approximately correspond to the current Oi, Oe, and Oa horizons, respectively. Differentiation among L, F, and H horizons in the absence of quantitative criteria often proved difficult; there was considerable inconsistency among forest soil scientists. Inconsistency was also noted for individual scientists over time.

Forest Humus Types

The concept of humus type, which is the classification of forest floors on the basis of morphology and arrangement of organic horizons, originated in Denmark in the late nineteenth century. The concept has evolved to generate detailed hierarchical classification systems with numerous subcategories. One of the most comprehensive was published in 1993 as a monograph. Three general categories associated with productivity and the rate of nutrient cycling described in this early work continue as the foundation for all of these systems: mor, duff mull (also referred to as moder), and mull.

The mor forest humus type is sometimes referred to as acid humus. It is associated with coniferous species that produce recalcitrant, nutrient poor litter. In this humus type, there is an abrupt boundary between the Oe or Oa and the mineral soil horizon. This abrupt boundary indicates that there is very little if any incorporation of organic matter with the underlying mineral soil, reflecting a relatively low level of biological activity. In addition, incomplete decomposition of the nutrient poor organic material generates large quantities of organic acids. As the organic acids are washed down the profile by percolating water, they strip organic matter and sesquioxides from mineral soil particle surfaces, carrying them downward and depositing them in an underlying horizon.

The mull forest humus type, associated with fertile systems and high rates of nutrient cycling, represents the other extreme of the spectrum. The mull is characterized by highly decomposed, amorphous organic matter intimately incorporated into the mineral soil (A horizon). Thick organic horizons do not accumulate; Oe and Oa horizons are absent due to the high rate of biological activity. Decomposition is relatively rapid, releasing nutrients and preventing immobilization in organic residues. The mull forest humus type is associated with fertile sites supporting nutrient demanding species such as sugar maple (*Acer saccharum*), basswood (*Tilia americana*), and white ash (*Fraxinus americana*).

The duff mull forest humus type is intermediate between the mor and mull types described above. There is greater incorporation of organic matter in the mineral soil than for the mor forest humus type but less than the complete incorporation associated with mulls. The rate of nutrient cycling and decomposition is intermediate.

Decomposition and Nutrient Cycling

The forest floor serves an important role in cycling of nutrients and organic matter. Organic matter chemical composition reflects that of the material from which it originated; approximately 90% of plant dry weight consists of carbon, hydrogen, and oxygen. Nitrogen comprises 1–2% and the remainder is comprised of plant nutrients such as phosphorus, potassium, calcium, magnesium, etc. The organic horizons provide habitat for a diverse biota. In addition, organic matter is a substrate, serving as a source of energy and nutrition for a multitude of organisms. Ultimately, aerobic organisms convert organic matter to carbon dioxide and water. In the process, essential plant nutrients are converted from organically bound to soluble plant available forms, a process known as mineralization. Biological activity is greatest for mull and least for mor forest humus types.

A host of organisms ranging in size from moles and gophers down to microscopic bacteria and fungi participate in mineralization. Macrofauna that tunnel and burrow generate large pores that facilitate removal of excess moisture and transfer of oxygen from the atmosphere to the soil atmosphere. These macrofauna indirectly affect decomposition by improving soil aeration. The role of earthworms in improving soil physical properties, as well as soil chemical properties, is well documented. A variety of organisms physically reduce particle size, a process known as comminution. Reduced surface area: volume ratio facilitates microbial attack, biochemical decomposition and synthesis of new compounds.

Organic matter decomposition rates can be estimated by successively measuring mass loss of confined organic residues (i.e., foliage, fine roots) in nylon mesh bags over time. The mesh is small enough to contain decaying material and large enough to permit mesofauna entry. Numerous such studies have found that the negative exponential function can be used to model the loss of mass over time:

$$y = e^{kt}$$

where y is the proportion of mass remaining at time t, k is the decomposition constant, and t is time (years). This model is convenient because the proportion of mass remaining over time can be described by a single variable, k. The model is a monotonically decreasing function bounded by 1 and 0 (**Figure 2**).

Environmental Variables Constraining Decomposition

Numerous studies in forest systems have demonstrated the degree to which organic matter decomposition rates are constrained by aeration, temperature, precipitation, and litter quality. Decomposition is promoted by a plentiful supply of oxygen for aerobic organisms. In the absence of oxygen, organic matter decomposition is very slow and organic matter builds up. Organic soils, which form in saturated conditions, illustrate what happens in the absence of oxygen. Saturated conditions prevent aerobic organism activity, effectively stopping the decomposition process. When organic soils are drained, they are very productive for both agriculture and forestry because of their desirable physical and chemical properties. One of the problems associated with drainage of organic soils is subsidence. Organic matter exposed to atmospheric oxygen decomposes and the organic soil depth decreases rapidly.

Given adequate oxygen, temperature and moisture constrain decomposition. In the absence of adequate

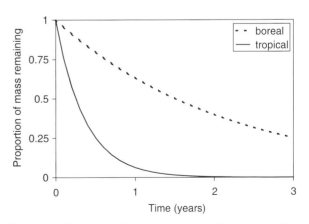

Figure 2 Mass of deciduous leaves over time modeled for deciduous leaves using the model $y = e^{kt}$, with $k = -0.46$ for *Betula papyrifera* in the boreal forest and $k = -2.77$ for *Pentaclethra macroloba* in the tropical forest. Values of k were obtained from published literature.

moisture, biologic activity is limited and decomposition proceeds slowly even at warm temperatures. Decomposition rates are notably reduced in arid environments. When moisture is not limiting, decomposition rates increase with increasing temperature and litter disappears more rapidly. The minimum temperature for appreciable biological activity ($5°C$) is often referred to as biological zero. Comparison of the rate of mass loss for deciduous leaves in boreal and tropical rainforests illustrates the influence of temperature on decomposition (**Figure 2**). Organic matter builds up in cold, wet conditions characteristic of the boreal forest and the tundra.

Within a given climatic regime, decomposition rate increases with increasing litter quality. Generally, high quality litters have narrow C:N ratios and relatively low proportions of recalcitrant constituents such as complex fats and waxes. Nitrogen is required by the bacteria and fungi that decompose plant tissue. When adequate quantities of nitrogen are available to those organisms, decomposition proceeds more rapidly. As decomposition proceeds, the C:N ratio decreases. Consequently, the C:N ratio is higher for the Oi than the Oa horizon.

Decomposition Influences Productivity

Rates of organic matter decomposition, which are reflected in the forest humus type classification, are related to forest productivity. During the process of decomposition, carbon bound in the forest floor is converted to carbon dioxide. Plant essential nutrients undergo mineralization, which is the conversion from organic to a readily soluble plant available form. Higher rates of decomposition result in a more rapid cycling of essential plant nutrients and higher productivity.

The thick forest floors of boreal forests accumulate and immobilize large quantities of nutrients. In some boreal forests, the average time litter resides in the forest floor before it is completely decomposed, or its mean residence time, is 350 years. Thus, in spite of the large amount of nitrogen contained in the forest floors, trees in the boreal forest may exhibit nitrogen deficiency because the nitrogen is bound in an organic form that is unavailable to plants. This situation also may occur in upland conifer forests where litter quality is low. Rates of nutrient cycling in the humid tropical forests, in contrast, are much more rapid. Mean residence time for organic matter in tropical rainforests is on the order of 4 years. Consequently, forest floors generally do not build up except where saturated conditions prevent aerobic organism activity.

Forest Floor Mass: Accumulation – Decomposition

Forest floor mass is the difference between litter accumulation and decomposition. Global patterns for litterfall reflect the effects of climate on production. Although there are wide ranges within latitudinal zones, annual litterfall generally increases with decreasing latitude from boreal (2–4 Mg ha^{-1}) to tropical (5–13 Mg ha^{-1}) forests. Rates of organic matter decomposition also vary with latitude, increase with increasing temperature from the boreal forests to the tropics when moisture is not limiting.

Published values for forest floor mass range from a few to more than 100 Mg ha^{-1}. Although accumulation and decomposition vary with latitude, it is not possible to make generalizations regarding forest floor mass because of additional factors that operate at a more local scale. Disturbances such as fire, tornadoes, hurricanes, and timber harvesting are common features of all forest ecosystems. The cyclical nature of disturbance in a variety of ecosystems has a profound effect on density and species composition. Large-scale disturbances that remove portions of the canopy reduce litter inputs for a given time period. In addition, the exposure of the forest floor to increased light and moisture levels due to reduction of the canopy and in plant transpiration, increases the rate of decomposition. At some point in stand development, accumulation rate may equal decomposition rate and the forest floor mass remains relatively constant. Steady state is the term used to describe this condition.

Forest Management and the Forest Floor

An important goal of forest management is to minimize disturbance to the forest floor, in order to preserve the integrity and function of this vital component of the forest ecosystem. The intact forest floor has a high infiltration capacity and absorbs the kinetic energy of falling raindrops. The combined effects of the highly absorbent forest floor and the presence of numerous large pores from roots and organism activity eliminates overland flow of water and prevents soil erosion. Soil loss from forested systems, the result of streams cutting through their banks, is the benchmark rate of natural erosion, against which rates of accelerated erosion are compared.

It is clear that the forest floor is a dynamic entity having a profound impact on the functioning of forest ecosystems. The forest floor modifies the forest soil environment, increasing the capacity for exchange of water, energy, and gases between the atmosphere and the soil system. Decomposition of the forest floor over time provides a continual source of nutrients for vegetation preventing excessive losses through leaching and insuring high levels of forest productivity. In addition, the forest floor provides favorable habitat and substrate for a diversity of organisms that contribute to cycling of nutrients through the forest ecosystem.

See also: **Ecology**: Forest Canopies; Natural Disturbance in Forest Environments. **Soil Biology and Tree Growth**: Soil and its Relationship to Forest Productivity and Health; Soil Biology. **Soil Development and Properties**: Forests and Soil Development; Water Storage and Movement. **Tree Physiology**: Physiology and Silviculture; Root System Physiology.

Further Reading

Federer CA (1982) Subjectivity in the separation of organic horizons of the forest floor. *Soil Science Society of America Journal* 46: 1090–1093.

Fisher RF and Binkley D (2000) Soil organic matter. In: *Ecology and Management of Forest Soils*, pp. 139–160. New York: John Wiley.

Green RN, Trowbridge RL, and Klinka K (1993) *Towards a Taxonomic Classification of Humus Forms*. Forest Science Monograph no. 29. Bethesda, MD: Society of American Foresters.

Hole FD (1981) Effects of animals on soil. *Geoderma* 25: 75–112.

Post WM, Emanuel WR, Zinke PJ, and Stangenberger AG (1982) Soil carbon pools and world life zones. *Nature* 298(8): 156–159.

Waring RH and Schlesinger WH (1985) Decomposition and soil development. In: *Forest Ecosystems: Concepts and Management*, pp. 181–210. New York: Academic Press.

Nutrient Cycling

L A Morris, University of Georgia, Athens, GA, USA

Introduction

Worldwide, healthy, productive forests grow on a variety of sites that are of low fertility such as mountains, coastal plain deposits, old highly weathered tropical soils, abandoned agricultural lands, and lands reclaimed after mining. The ability of forests to grow and prosper on such sites is due to the ability of forests to accumulate essential plant nutrients, to utilize these nutrients in production of foliage, and to return these nutrients to the soil or recapture them internally for reuse in subsequent year's growth. This is the process of nutrient cycling.

Geochemical, Biogeochemical, and Biochemical Nutrient Cycles

Nutrient cycling in forests can be divided into three individual but interconnected cycles (**Figure 1**).

The Geochemical Cycle

The geochemical cycle is associated with transfers of elements into or out of the ecosystem. Inputs to the forest from the geochemical cycle include nutrients added to the forest as solutes in precipitation, associated with fine particulates or as aerosols. Additionally, nitrogen (N) can be removed from the atmosphere and added to the forest ecosystem through symbiotic associations of nitrogen-fixing rhizobium or actinorrhiza or through free-living nitrogen fixing organisms. Weathering and release of nutrient elements from parent rock is also considered an addition in the geochemical cycle because of long time factors involved in this process and the conversion of nutrient elements from non plant available to plant available forms. Losses of nutrients from the forest occur as ions dissolved in runoff water and associated with soil particles eroded from the site and moved as suspended sediment or bed load in streams. Nutrients can also be leached below the rooting zone. Fires can play an important role in the geochemical cycle of forests. Large quantities of N and sulfur (S) can be volatilized by fire and returned to the atmosphere. Ash produced during forest fire can be transported long distances and be a significant loss of nutrients from the forest.

The Biogeochemical Cycle

The biogeochemical cycle involves external transfers of elements among different components of a forest system. Uptake of nutrients from the soil and return of these nutrients in leaf fall, branch shedding, root growth and death, or through tree mortality is a major component of the biogeochemical nutrient cycle. Nutrients returned to the soil in this way are not available for plant reuse until decomposition occurs and nutrients are converted from organic to mineral forms, a process termed mineralization. Mineralization of nutrients from organic matter of the forest floor plays an important role in the supply of nutrients available for forest growth. Also included with the biogeochemical cycle is the washing of nutrients from leaves and stem tissue and its return to the soil in precipitation falling through the canopy or flowing down the stem as stemflow.

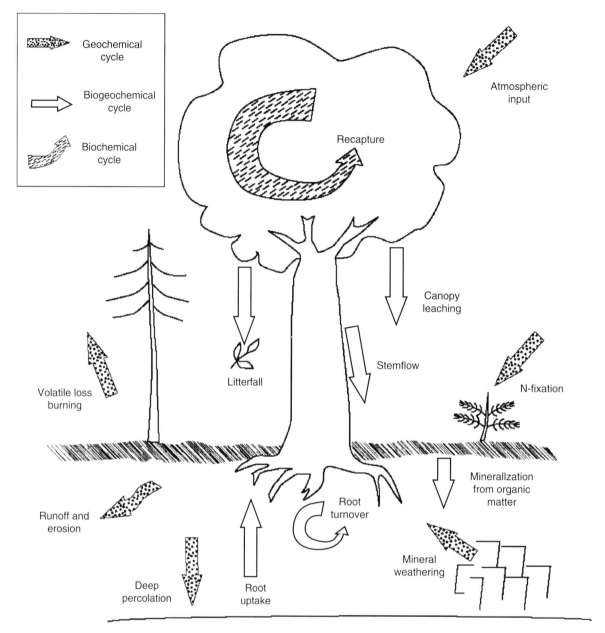

Figure 1 Potential pathways of nutrient flux within the geochemical, biogeochemical, and biochemical nutrient cycles.

The Biochemical Cycle

The biochemical cycle involves the process of transfer and retention of nutrients within an individual plant. In particular, trees can withdraw some nutrients from leaves prior to abscission and store these nutrients within woody tissue where they can be mobilized to supply a portion of the nutrient requirements for subsequent growing seasons.

Contribution of Nutrient Cycles to Nutrient Requirements for Growth

A major portion of the annual nutrient requirements of a forest for growth is supplied by recycling and reuse of nutrients. An example annual nutrient cycle is presented for a hypothetical *Pinus elliottii* forest in the southeastern USA in **Table 1**. On an annual basis, fluxes of nutrients through the geochemical cycle are small in comparison to fluxes through the biogeochemical and biochemical cycles. While the balance of nutrients in the geochemical cycle is important from a long-term forest productivity standpoint, the biogeochemical and biochemical cycles play a much more important role in supplying the annual nutrient requirements for foliage production and annual growth increment.

Major differences exist among individual nutrients in the predominant pathways of transfer within

Table 1 Annual fluxes (in kg ha^{-1} year^{-1}) of nutrients through three components of the nutrient cycle for a mature *Pinus elliottii* forest in the Coastal Plain of the southeastern USA

Cycle and pathway	Nitrogen	Phosphorus	Potassium	Calcium
Geochemical				
Inputs to ecosystem ($+$)				
Atmospheric	7.8	0.2	6.0	15.0
N-fixation	2.0			
Weathering	0	0	0	0
Export from ecosystem ($-$)				
Watershed runoff	6.0	0.13	2.3	5.8
Leaching	0.1	0.03	0.1	1.1
Forest ecosystem balance	$+3.7$	$+0.04$	$+3.6$	$+8.1$
Biogeochemical				
Mineralization of forest floor (0)	10.2	0.3	3.2	22.8
Inputs to trees ($+$)				
Root uptake	56.0	3.4	21.0	50.0
Losses from trees ($-$)				
Litterfall return to forest floor	23.2	0.8	2.7	19.1
Root mortality (turnover)	23.5	1.7	8.5	9.6
Canopy leaching	4.4	0.35	7.3	14.5
Stemflow	0.1	0.01	0.1	0.4
Net tree balance	$+4.8$	$+0.5$	$+2.4$	$+6.4$
Biochemical				
Retention by trees ($+$)	28.3	1.5	8.1	0

Based on data of Riekerk H, Jones SA, Morris LA, and Pratt DA (1979) Hydrology and water quality of three small Lower Coastal Plain forested Watersheds. *Soil Crop Science Society of Florida Proceedings* 38: 105–111. Burger JA (1979) *The Effects of Harvest and Site Preparation on the Nutrient Budgets of an Intensively Managed Southern Pine Forest.* PhD thesis, University of Florida, Gainesville. Shan J (2000) *Accumulation, Allocation and Dynamics of Carbon in Slash Pine along a Management Intensity Gradient.* PhD thesis, University of Georgia, Athens and others.

biogeochemical and biochemical pathways. Nitrogen is the nutrient most often limiting growth of forests. It is recycled through the pathway of leaf fall, root mortality, and biochemical retention in almost equal amounts. Canopy leaching and stemflow play a relatively small role in the cycling of nitrogen. This pattern can be contrasted with the patterns of cycling for calcium (Ca) and potassium (K). Calcium is structurally bound with the cell wall of foliage and woody tissue and there is little retention of Ca through the biochemical cycle or return of Ca to the soil in canopy leaching and stemflow. In contrast, K is not structurally bound within the cell and can be leached from plant tissue. The result is that stemflow, in particular, plays an important role in return of K to the soil where it can be recycled through root uptake. Biochemical cycling plays a particularly important role in phosphorus (P) nutrition. Soils of the southeastern USA where the *Pinus elliottii* forest is found contain low amounts of P and are also acidic. Because of high acidity in these soils, and fixation of P by oxides of aluminum and iron, concentrations of P in soil solution where it is available for plant uptake are low. Pine forests growing on these sites have adapted to ensure adequate quantities of P for future growth by translocating a major portion of the P contained in foliage (up to 60%) into permanent woody tissue prior to leaf abscision at the end of the growing season. This P is then available to be recycled back to the foliage at the start of the subsequent growing season.

Species differences, age and differences in inherent site fertility all influence nutrient cycling patterns. For example, differences in geochemical cycling occur for forests located within industrialized areas of the world such as in the northeastern USA and central Europe. These forests receive greater atmospheric inputs of nutrients, particularly N. In some places, high N inputs threaten long-term productivity of the forests. Forests containing N-fixing species as a significant component of the stand have much greater geochemical inputs and outputs of N. For instance, N inputs in red alder stands of the northwestern USA can exceed 100 kg ha^{-1} year^{-1}. Biogeochemical and biochemical fluxes also vary as a function of species and site characteristics. Forests located on young soils with high concentrations of easily weathered primary minerals often export quantities of K, Ca, and other nutrients in runoff that greatly exceed the amounts entering the forest in atmospheric inputs. Hardwood species generally have higher Ca demands and uptake than do pine species. Consequently, uptake and return of Ca is much greater in hardwood stands than in conifer stands grown on similar sites. Species differences in the capacity for biochemical withdrawal of P from senescing foliage occur and these differences produce differences in nutrient cycling for different species grown on the same site. Thus, while nutrient cycling plays a role in the growth of all forests, the role varies depending on specific conditions of the forest and nutrient of interest.

Nutrient Accumulation in Forests

The accumulation of specific nutrient elements varies widely among forest ecosystems. Large differences occur among climatic regions due to factors that control overall biologic activity such as temperature and moisture, but other differences are associated with species, age, and overall site fertility. **Table 2** provides examples of accumulation of macronutrients in some forest ecosystems. Observe that each nutrient element has a unique distribution pattern within the forest ecosystem and that this distribution pattern varies among forests. For example, forest ecosystems on young soils in fertile regions contain large amounts of nutrients such as P, K, and Ca found in minerals of parent rocks (e.g., mixed *Quercus*). In contrast, forests growing on quartz sands of marine origin contain low amounts of these nutrients in soil and relatively greater amounts of storage is associated with biomass of the vegetation and the forest floor (organic soil horizon) (e.g., *Pinus elliottii– P. palustris*). Accumulations of these nutrients in mineral soils also appear to be particularly low in tropical regions (*Celtis–Triplochiton*). It is important to note that the soil accumulations presented in **Table 2** represent different analytical techniques and different soil depths. Depth of rooting is great in many tropical soils and, thus, the content of nutrients available to trees is greater than is represented by the shallow depth of soil included in the contents presented in this table.

A number of other general differences in nutrient accumulation exist among forest ecosystems. Relatively greater accumulations of nutrients occur in the forest floor of boreal forest ecosystems than in either temperate ecosystems or in the tropics. This is due both to the low temperature and reduced biological activity in boreal ecosystems and the relatively low decomposability of foliage of coniferous tree species characteristic of boreal forests. These accumulations can be contrasted with the low accumulations of nutrients in forest floors of tropical systems. Although nutrient inputs in litter of tropical systems are much greater, rates of decomposition and

Table 2 Nutrient content (in kg ha^{-1}) and distribution in aboveground biomass, forest floor, and mineral soils of several forest ecosystems

Forest type, location	Vegetation				Forest floor and organic debris				Mineral soil[a]				Reference
	N	P	K	Ca	N	P	K	Ca	N	P	K	Ca	
Abies procera, subalpine, USA	347	54	843	1025	675	57	312	568	15855	3212	85780	180960	Turner and Singer (1976)
Picea – Abies, boreal, Canada	387	52	159	413	1465	100	1052	253	559	114	9383	766	Weetman and Webber (1972)
Pinus banksiana, boreal, USA	346	29	146	294	544	40	37	254	5554	495	500	1727	Green and Grigal (1980)
Pseudotsuga menziesii – Tsuga temperate, USA	566	86	189	687	445	62	80	619	4560	660	2040	34	Cole and Rapp (1981)
Mixed Quercus, temperate, USA	415	29	185	1250	150	12	20	160	3725	1041	23205	6270	Johnson and Todd (1987)
Fagus sylvatica, temperate, Europe	285	39	187	152	180	11	20	51	6640	42	254	365	Ovington (1962)
Pinus taeda, temperate, USA	320	48	225	ND	306	30	28	ND	1752	270	403	ND	Wells and Jorgensen (1975)
Pinus elliottii – P. palustris, subtropical, USA	140	12	43	150	271	10	9	96	2959	24	82	396	Morris and Pritchett (1982)
Celtis – Triplochiton, tropical, Nigeria	1530	103	702	2140	514	34	204	530	4592	13	650	2576	Greenland and Kowal (1960)

ND, not determined.
[a] To approximate rooting depth using a variety of extraction procedures. Refer to original citation for information on soil depth and method utilized.

mineralization of nutrients are also much greater; consequently, storage is low. Except in the tropics, accumulations of nutrients in the forest floor are relatively large and, in many systems, exceed accumulation in tree biomass.

Forest age also has a major influence on nutrient accumulation in biomass. A typical pattern of nutrient accumulation for a developing forest is illustrated in **Figure 2**. Accumulations of nutrients over time reflect both tree demands and the physiological use of the nutrient. Nitrogen and Ca are both used in large quantities and for the example illustrated are accumulated more than other nutrients. Nitrogen accumulation is much more rapid early in stand development as it is concentrated in foliage, which develops rapidly. In contrast, Ca is accumulated more slowly, but because it is an integral part of the cell wall of woody tissue, it tends to continue to accumulate as long as the forest is continuing to increase biomass.

Mineralization of Nutrients Accumulated in Biomass

Nutrients contained in organic matter returned to the forest floor or soil are not available for plant use until they are released from the structures in which they are

chemically bound. The processes of release of nutrients into inorganic plant available forms is termed mineralization. As organic matter is decomposed, CO_2 is released through respiration and bonds between elements and organic molecules are broken. Mineralization rates are, thus, closely associated with overall decomposition rates. Both characteristics of the substrate being decomposed and environmental conditions affect the rate of decomposition and mineralization. Organic materials that contain a relatively high concentration of compounds easily used by microorganisms involved in decomposition, such as sugar and cellulose, are more rapidly decomposed than compounds that have complex bonds that are not easily broken and used by this decomposer community. Examples of such compounds are polyphenols and lignin. Differences in the decomposition rate among substrates under the same environmental conditions are expressed in terms of a substrates decomposition rate constant. Decomposition rate constants are based on the observation that decomposition of most organic materials tends to follow the pattern of a negative exponential curve:

$$C_t = C_i e^{-kt}$$

where C_i is initial carbon (or organic matter) mass, C_t is carbon (or organic matter) remaining at time t, k is the decay rate constant, and t is time (usually expressed in days or years).

For comparison among species, decay rate constants are usually developed for leaves or ground materials and, thus, are not limited by physical characteristics of the material. Foliage of coniferous species tends to have lower decay rates than species of deciduous angiosperms. Wood and branches have lower decay rates than leaves due to chemical differences. In addition, few surfaces available for microbial colonization exist in branch and stemwood falling to the forest floor. Decomposition of these materials is greatly accelerated by the activity of soil fauna that bore into, create galleries in, or otherwise expose internal surfaces to microbial colonization.

Nutrient mineralization can also be modeled using an exponential decay model, but the actual process is more complicated. Before nutrients will be released into the soil where they are available for plant uptake, the nutrient requirements of decomposing organisms must be satisfied. When a large amount of C, the energy source of heterotrophic decomposers, is available, nutrients released from broken chemical bounds of organic molecules are immediately reincorporated into the bodies of the decomposing community, a process termed immobilization. This

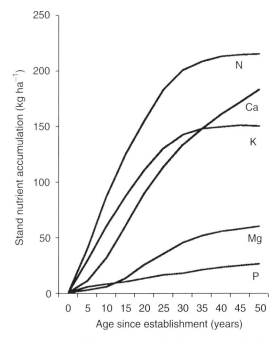

Figure 2 Accumulation of nutrients in biomass of a pine forest in the southern USA. Note the differences in total accumulation among nutrients as well as the difference in pattern. Based on Switzer GL and Nelson LE (1972) Nutrient accumulation and cycling in loblolly pine (*Pinus taeda* L.) plantation ecosystems: the first twenty years. *Proceedings of the Soil Science Society of America* 36: 143–147.

occurs because under this condition, nutrients are in low supply relative to C. Only after a balance is achieved between C availability and nutrient availability does net mineralization of nutrients occur.

The chief environmental variables affecting mineralization of nutrients are temperature, moisture, and oxygen availability. The rate of decomposition, expressed as the decay rate, approximately doubles for each $10°C$ increase in temperature between $5°C$ (biological zero) and $35°C$. Decomposition and mineralization rates in subpolar regions are so slow that despite large storage of nutrients in the forest floor, forest growth is constrained by low nutrient availability. In contrast, many tropical forests with relatively low nutrient storage have high growth due to rapid decomposition and mineralization of nutrients in organic debris falling to the forest floor. Moisture limits decomposition under either extremely wet or extremely dry conditions. Oxygen does not diffuse rapidly through water. When soils are saturated and all pores filled with water, oxygen will be, essentially, unavailable below the water surface and decomposition and mineralization will not proceed. Bog forests of subpolar regions and swamp forests throughout the world contain large amounts of nutrients but growth is slow because of nutrient limitations. Decomposition also ceases under very dry conditions because water remaining in soil is held so tightly by particle surfaces that microbes cannot incorporate it into their bodies to support their growth. Decomposition is most rapid under moist soil conditions when water is available and soils contain air-filled pores to facilitate oxygen transport.

Forest Management Impacts on Nutrient Cycles

Forest management affects nutrient cycling in a variety of ways. Selection of species for rapid growth increases the demand for, and accumulation of, nutrients in the forest. Harvesting of wood, branches, and/or foliage removes nutrients from the system. Losses of nutrients may be accelerated due to more rapid mineralization and leaching loss or through increased erosion following harvest. Slash reduction and preparation of the site for planting also accelerate leaching and erosion losses. Finally, efforts to reduce competing vegetation regrowth through herbicide application or mechanical removal can contribute to this accelerated leaching and erosion. On the other hand, fertilization or use of N-fixing species has the opposite effect and can greatly increase both the storage and rate of nutrient cycling within forest ecosystems. A summary of the effects that forest management can have on nutrient cycling is presented in **Table 3**.

In undisturbed forests, atmospheric inputs of most nutrients, or inputs from weathering, exceed losses and these systems accumulate nutrients. Over time, forests tend to become more productive as their storage of nutrients increases and the potential for nutrient cycling increases. Removal of wood, branches, and leaves for fuel, timber, or pulp can remove nutrients more rapidly than they are naturally replaced. Over the long term, this can lead to declines in forest growth.

The greatest concentrations of plant nutrients are found in needles and leaves. Wood and branches contain relatively low concentrations of nutrients. Since foliage contains a disproportionate amount of nutrients, harvesting foliage will increase nutrient removal and, in the absence of fertilization or other inputs, can lead to a reduction in nutrient storage and, eventually, loss of productivity. The significance of this tends to be greatest with genera that retain many years of needles (e.g., *Picea*, *Abies*) than in genera that retain only a few years' worth of leaves or needles. Also, because forests tend to accumulate nutrients most rapidly when they are young, shortening the period between harvests can also increase nutrient removal (**Table 4**). Generally, periodic removal of just the wood does not remove an unsustainable amount of nutrients from a forest site. However, frequent harvests especially when coupled with foliage removal will likely lead to unsustainable reductions of nutrient storage in forest ecosystems.

In intensively managed industrial forests, it is common practice to reduce slash from harvest prior to soil preparation and planting. Burning is one common method of slash reduction that can result in volatile losses of nitrogen. Volatile loss of N during burning tends to be very site-specific. Losses during site preparation can be large because large amounts of logging slash are often on the ground and fires are hot. Nitrogen volatilization during site preparation burns following harvest of forests in the northwestern USA may exceed $800 \, kg \, ha^{-1}$. In contrast, cooler fires associated with understory control beneath an established forest canopy may volatilize only $20–50 \, kg \, ha^{-1} \, N$. A second method of slash reduction involves pushing slash and soil into long rows or piles. Such operations have been shown to displace large quantities of nutrients from the majority of the soil surface, concentrating them in a small area where they cannot be efficiently used. In some cases, two or three times more nutrients can be displaced from the soil surface during these operations than are removed from the site in harvest.

Table 3 Potential effects of selected forest management activities on nutrient cycling

Activity	Geochemical cycling	Biogeochemical and Biochemical cycles
Conversion of natural mixed forests to conifer plantation	Differences are small except where N-fixing species are used	Reduced uptake of base cations, decreased forest floor mineralization, lower overall biogeochemical cycling rates
Shortening length of time between harvests	Increase nutrient removal and slight increase in runoff and leaching losses due to accelerated erosion and increased mineralization	Young forests are building crown and biomass so uptake from soil and accumulation of nutrients predominates; biochemical transfer is less important than in mature forests
Increased utilization of branches and foliage	Foliage and small branches contain a disproportionate quantity of nutrients; utilization of foliage and branches can double the average annual nutrient removal by harvest	Short-term effects will be minor; long-term effects may be to reduce mineralization of nutrients from forest floor
Burning for slash reduction	Increase N losses from forest; amount varies from a low of 25 kg ha^{-1} to more than 800 kg ha^{-1}	More rapid mineralization due to warmer soil temperatures and the absence of carbon-rich woody debris
Piling of slash for improved access	Displaces nutrients from planting surface; N displacement from 200 to 600 kg ha^{-1} observed; small increase in actual loss from system due to accelerated leaching and erosion	More rapid mineralization due to mixing of mineral soil, forest floor and organic debris during operation
Soil tillage (disking or mounding)	Can be associated with small increase in nutrient loss in runoff and erosion	More rapid mineralization due to mixing of mineral soil, forest floor, and organic debris
Herbicide use to control competition	Operational herbicide application has little impact on geochemical cycle; repeated control of regrowth will increase nutrient losses and erosion	Reduced uptake and accumulation in vegetation early in the rotation
Use of N-fixing species	Potential to increase N inputs to forest by 50–150 kg ha^{-1} year^{-1}	Annual uptake and cycling of N will be increased
Fertilization	Can increase ecosystem storage of applied nutrients and compensate for harvest removals; small increases in runoff losses of applied nutrients can occur	Uptake of applied nutrients is increased; quantities of nutrients transferred in the biogeochemical cycle are often increased; absolute quantities of nutrients retained by biochemical cycling may be increased

Accelerated erosion losses are another impact on nutrient cycles. Losses associated with erosion can be considered either displaced productivity or as site loss. Generally, a strong relationship exists between bare mineral soil and erosion loss. Losses are often greatest during first year following harvest and planting and decrease as vegetation regrowth occurs on the site. Increased soluble losses of nutrients can also occur following forest operations due to improved conditions for decomposition. These losses are generally ephemeral and low in comparison to geochemical inputs over a rotation for many forests.

Fertilization is an important silvicultural technique for adding nutrients to forest ecosystems and balancing losses of nutrients in the industrialized world where the value of wood production provides economic justification. Nitrogen-fixing species also provide a way to add nitrogen to managed forests. Planting or seeding of N-fixing species at the time of forest establishment can add from 50 to 150 kg ha^{-1} N to the forest in the years prior to crown closure, sufficient N to more than balance losses associated with harvest and site preparation.

Summary

Nutrient cycling plays an important role in the nutrition of forest stands. The balance between inputs and exports of nutrients from the forest ecosystem included within the geochemical cycle has implications for long-term sustainability. Fluxes of nutrients through the biogeochemical and biochemical cycles are larger than through the geochemical cycle and supply a major portion of the annual nutrient requirements of the forest. These cycles provide a framework within which forest management activities can be evaluated. Activities that result in nutrient exports in excess of nutrient

Table 4 Comparison of nutrient removals and annualized removal rate with different levels of biomass utilization and rotation length for two commercial forest species

Forest type	Harvest utilization	Rotation length (age)	Nitrogen		Phosphorus		Potassium		Calcium	
			$kg\,ha^{-1}$	$kg\,ha^{-1}\,year^{-1}$	$kg\,ha^{-1}$	$kg\,ha^{-1}\,year^{-1}$	$kg\,ha^{-1}$	$kg\,ha^{-1}\,year^{-1}$	$kg\,ha^{-1}$	$kg\,ha^{-1}\,year^{-1}$
Pinus taeda	Stem only	20	293	14.6	17	0.8	169	8.4	178	8.9
		40	464	11.6	28	0.7	293	7.3	304	7.6
	Whole tree	20	385	19.2	27	1.4	212	10.6	205	10.2
		40	570	14.2	40	1.0	346	8.6	348	8.7
Picea	Stem only	50	217	4.3	20	0.4	248	5.0	278	5.6
		85	328	3.1	23	0.3	161	1.9	390	4.6
	Whole tree	50	842	16.8	80	1.6	442	8.8	463	9.2
		85	722	8.5	78	0.9	330	3.9	521	6.2

After Switzer GL and Nelson LE (1973) Maintenance of productivity under short rotations. *Proceedings of the International Symposium on Forest Fertilization*, pp. 365–389. Paris: International Union of Forestry Research Organizations and Tamm CO (1969) Site damage by thinning due to removal of organic matter and plant nutrients. *Proceedings of the International Union of Forestry Research Organizations Meeting on Thinning and Mechanization*, pp. 175–184. Stockholm: IUFRO.

inputs are unlikely to be sustainable without nutrient amelioration through fertilization or use of N-fixing species.

See also: **Environment**: Carbon Cycle; Environmental Impacts. **Hydrology**: Impacts of Forest Management on Water Quality; Soil Erosion Control. **Soil Biology and Tree Growth**: Soil and its Relationship to Forest Productivity and Health; Soil Organic Matter Forms and Functions. **Soil Development and Properties**: Nutrient Limitations and Fertilization; The Forest Floor.

Further Reading

Burger JA (1979) *The Effects of Harvest and Site Preparation on the Nutrient Budgets of an Intensively Managed Southern Pine Forest*. PhD thesis, University of Florida, Gainesville.

Cole DW and Rapp M (1981) Elemental cycling in forest ecosystems. In: Reichle DE (ed.) *Dynamic Properties of Forest Ecosystem*, pp. 341–409. Cambridge UK: Cambridge University Press.

Green DC and Grigal DF (1980) Nutrient accumulation in jack pine on deep and shallow soils over bedrock. *Forest Science* 26: 325–333.

Greenland DJ and Kowal JML (1960) Nutrient content of the moist tropical forests of Ghana. *Plant Soil* 12: 154–173.

Johnson DW and Todd DE (1987) Nutrient export by leaching and whole tree harvesting in a loblolly pine and mixed oak forest. *Plant Soil* 102: 99–109.

Manhendrapa MK, Foster NW, Weetman GF, and Krause H (1986) Nutrient cycling and availability in forest soils. *Canadian Journal of Soil Science* 66: 547–572.

Morris LA and Pritchett WL (1982) Nutrient storage and availability in two managed pine flatwoods forests. In: Coleman C, Mace AC, and Swindel BF (eds) *Proceedings of the Intensive Forest Management Practices Symposium*, pp. 17–26. Gainesville, FL: University of Florida.

Ovington JD (1962) Quantitative ecology and the woodland ecosystem concept. *Advances in Ecology Research* 1: 103–192.

Riekerk H, Jones SA, Morris LA, and Pratt DA (1979) Hydrology and water quality of three small Lower Coastal Plain forested Watersheds. *Soil Crop Science Society of Florida Proceedings* 38: 105–111.

Shan J (2000) *Accumulation, Allocation and Dynamics of Carbon in Slash Pine along a Management Intensity Gradient*. PhD thesis, University of Georgia, Athens.

Switzer GL and Nelson LE (1972) Nutrient accumulation and cycling in loblolly pine (*Pinus taeda* L.) plantation ecosystems: the first twenty years. *Proceedings of the Soil Science Society of America* 36: 143–147.

Switzer GL and Nelson LE (1973) Maintenance of productivity under short rotations. *Proceedings of the International Symposium on Forest Fertilization*, pp. 365–389. Paris: International Union of Forestry Research Organizations.

Tamm CO (1969) Site damage by thinning due to removal of organic matter and plant nutrients. *Proceedings of the*

International Union of Forestry Research Organizations Meeting on Thinning and Mechanization, pp. 175–184. Stockholm: IUFRO.

Turner J and Singer MJ (1976) Nutrient distribution and cycling in a subalpine coniferous forest ecosystem. Journal of Applied Ecology 13: 295–301.

Weetman GF and Webber B (1972) The influence of wood harvesting on the nutrient status of two spruce stands. Canadian Journal of Forest Research 3: 351–369.

Wells CG and Jorgensen JR (1975) Nutrient cycling in loblolly pine plantations. In: Bernier B and Winget CH (eds) Forest Soils and Forest Land Mangement, pp. 137–158. Quebec: Laval University Press.

Nutrient Limitations and Fertilization

H G Miller, University of Aberdeen, Aberdeen, UK

Historical Background

While the benefits of applying manure to land has long been appreciated the idea of a plant nutrients probably only dates from 1727 when Stephen Hale noted that 'we find by chemical analysis of vegetables, that their substance is composed of sulphur, volatile salt, water and earth.' Despite observed growth responses of plants to compounds such as saltpetre (a nitrate salt), Epsom salts (magnesium sulfate), and phosphates, further advance in the understanding of plant nutrition was stymied by the widespread acceptance of the idea of Wallerins that humus itself was the fundamental source not only of nutrients but also of carbon. Progressively this came to be questioned and in 1845 Liebig, on the basis of calculations of the yield of carbon as wood and agricultural produce from nonmanured land, concluded that 'it is not denied that manure exercises an influence upon the development of plants; but it may be affirmed with positive certainty, that it neither serves for the production of carbon, nor has any influence on it.'

Building upon the work of Liebig, chemists such as Bossingault in France and Lawes and Gilbert in Britain weighed and analyzed manure and plants to construct early nutrient input–output balance sheets for a range of agricultural crops. Bossingault's data were used by Ebermayer in 1882 to compare nutrient accumulation in forest stands with that in agricultural crops. Earlier Ebermayer had been the first to diagnose nitrogen (N) deficiency in trees in Bavaria on sites that had been degraded by long histories of litter removal for animal bedding and other agricultural purposes. Despite this new understanding, foresters of a century ago seldom showed much interest in tree nutrition, being able to turn to the work of Dengler who had demonstrated that the nutrient requirements of a closed-canopy forest stand were on average only about one-twelfth of that of agricultural crops. Indeed, in his silvicultural textbook of 1904 Schlich enunciated the orthodoxy of his time when he stated that 'almost any soil can furnish a sufficient quantity of mineral substances for the production of a crop of trees, provided the leaf mould is not removed.' This sentiment was echoed by Baker in his book of 1934, for long one of the standard silvicultural texts.

Despite this complacency, at the start of the twentieth century foresters in Belgium, and later in Ireland and Scotland, were finding that trees newly planted on poor soils could show dramatic growth responses by application of the phosphate-containing basic slag (thomasphosphat) and some responses to wood ash application were reported from the Nordic countries (probably a response to potassium (K)). Similarly, in both Australia and New Zealand growth of the new forest plantation were found to be dependent on the application of phosphorus (P). In South Australia trees sometimes failed even where P had been applied until it was noted that those grown adjacent to galvanized wire fences were better than those distant from them, and so zinc deficiency was identified. In the decades that followed, forest scientists from many of the countries with large afforestation programs have identified deficiencies of one or more of nitrogen (N), phosphorus (P), potassium (K), magnesium (Mg), iron (Fe), zinc (Zn), copper (Cu), molybdenum (Mo), and boron (B) in young plantation trees. Calcium (Ca) deficiency has been confirmed in the nursery but the few reports of deficiencies of this element in the forest remain rather unconvincing. Additionally, by the middle of the twentieth century reports were also coming in of nitrogen deficiency in older coniferous forests in the boreal regions of Europe and North America.

Nutrient Cycles and Fertilizer Need

The study of nutrient cycling in forests of various ages has provided the explanations to a number of the conundrums posed by early work on fertilizer responses. The cycles within a well-established forest are characteristically very tight, that is there is efficient reuse of nutrients, largely through recovery (retranslocation) of nutrients from dying organs, notably leaves before they are shed, and through the efficient capture by roots and mycorrhizae of nutrients released through decomposition of litter. **Table 1** shows that retranslocation from foliage can contribute a quarter to half of the N, P, and K needed for new growth, and various studies suggest that the contribution from the decomposition of litter fallen from the same trees is not dissimilar (although with a lag phase for the time decomposition takes). The net consequence of this efficient recovery is that in a closed canopy forest, in which the amount of leaves produced annually is more or less equal to the amount dropped, the demand on fresh supplies of nutrients from the soil can be quite low. The position prior to canopy closure, however, when the both the green crown and the fine root biomass (both of which contain high concentrations of nutrients) are expanding the contribution internal cycling or litter decomposition can make to nutrient demands is limited and so a greater contribution has to come from the soil reserves (**Table 2**). Even though the total nutrient demands by the young trees are less than those of the older trees, the latter are asking much less of the soil reserves. Thus, the picture is one of high demands on soil reserves when a young crop is establishing its canopy, a demand that relaxes thereafter as the contribution from nutrient cycling increases. It is therefore, not surprising that nutrient deficiencies were seldom encountered until the twentieth century expansion of plantations onto poor ground.

As a forest ages further, if it is not harvested it starts to break up and growth declines while mortality increases. Uptake of nutrients may then become less than the release on decomposition and nutrients start to be lost from the site. However, prior to this stage in the coniferous forests of the boreal region the slow decomposition of litter can lead to such an accumulation of humus that an unacceptable proportion of the nitrogen capital of the site becomes locked up, the supply of available nitrogen progressively declines, and the trees start to show nitrogen deficiency. This seems to be the explanation for N fertilizer responses in areas such as Sweden, Finland, Canada, northwestern USA, and mountain forests in central Europe. The industrial importance of such forests has meant that considerable research effort has been devoted to them, contributing to the belief that N is the nutrient most commonly limiting in the forests of the world. However, this accolade should probably be given to P.

Because of the importance of nutrient retranslocation in nutrient cycles, anything that causes major loss of green foliage (i.e., before nutrients can be retranslocated back into the tree) can cause a short-term reappearance of any nutrient deficiency previously seen in youth. Such events include hail damage, insect damage, or even removal of trees in thinning. When a forest is thinned a significant proportion of the green foliage is deposited on the forest floor and the nutrients within it can no longer be accessed in the short-term through retranslocation. They will only become available in the medium term through mineralization on decomposition. Meanwhile, the remaining main crop trees have to fill the gaps that have been created in the canopy without recourse to the nutrients in the leaves that previously occupied these spaces. Their own internal supplies, coupled with whatever is available to the roots, may now be inadequate and deficiencies occur. Indeed, a positive interaction between thinnings and fertilizer application has often been recorded in situations where unthinned stands show no fertilizer response.

Table 1 Estimates of the contribution to nutrient demands by new growth that are met by retranslocation from old foliage prior to abscission

Species	Age (years)	Percentage of nutrient requirement		
		N	P	K
Pinus taeda	20	39	60	22
Pinus sylvestris	15	30	23	19
Pinus sylvestris	46	55	64	57
Pinus sylvestris	100	41	34	27
Pinus nigra	40	50	57	58
Abies amabilis	175	54	59	38
Mixed deciduous	Mature	54	25	15
Mixed deciduous	Mature	79	74	41
Eucalyptus obliqua	Overmature	34	46	28

Table 2 Sinks and sources ($kg\,ha^{-1}\,year^{-1}$) of nitrogen (N) and potassium (K) in young (2-m tall) and old (11-m tall) stands of *Pinus nigra*

	Nitrogen		Potassium	
	Young	Old	Young	Old
(1) Total required for new growth	66	138	29	66
(2) Supplied by retranslocation	11	69	7	38
(3) Taken by roots (i.e., 1 − 2)	55	69	22	28
(4) Available from litter decomposition[a]	7	39	1	16
(5) Uptake from soil reserves (i.e., 3 − 4)	48	30	21	12
(6) Net annual accumulation in trees	45	18	18	11

[a]Decomposition of litter fallen from current crop of trees only, release from pre-existing organic matter considered as being from soil reserves.

Predicting and Diagnosing Nutrient Deficiencies

The occurrence of nutrient deficiencies varies with the age of stand, soil type, and to some extent with species. Clearly, the forest manager needs to be able to diagnose a deficiency should this occur and, preferably, be able to predict what ameliorative treatment may be required. Four options are available; diagnosis on the basis of visual crop symptoms, diagnosis on the basis of soil analysis, diagnosis on the basis of tissue analysis, and prediction on the basis of some characteristic feature of the site.

Visual Symptoms

The various nutrients play specific physiological roles and if present in insufficient quantity disorders result which can lead to diagnostic visual symptoms. There is some variation between species, particularly between conifers and broadleaves, but general symptoms are as shown in **Table 3**. Because, these visual symptoms can be misleading, they are usually confirmed by foliar analysis.

Soil Analysis

Soil analysis has proved to be very useful in both agriculture and horticulture. In the forest, however, soil analysis has seldom proved to be of consistent value. In part this is because the perennial roots of trees, together with their mycorrhizae, seem able to access forms of nutrient elements not accessible to short-lived arable plants so the chemical soil extractants developed for agriculture may not be appropriate. Perhaps more significant, however, is that over time tree roots can exploit all the rooting volume available to them. This volume can be very variable between sites, often more variable than the quantities of available nutrients per unit volume (in agriculture and horticulture rooting is essentially consigned to the uniform depth of the plow layer). At all events, soil analysis in forestry has only proved most useful over limited areas where rooting volume is not a variable, such as glacial outwash plains, volcanic ash, or extensive areas of loess.

Foliar Analysis

Analysis of almost any living tissue will give an indication of the nutrient status of a plant; however, foliage has consistently proved to be the most useful for this purpose. Nutrient concentrations in foliage vary both with position in the tree and with age of the leaf. Generally, the physiologically active nutrients increase in concentration up the tree, as illumination increases, although Ca usually shows the reverse trend. Some authorities have advocated using lower crown foliage on the grounds that it is from these that any nutrient under stress would be removed first. However, the position of the lower crown varies with stocking density so it is difficult to standardize and ensure comparability. The effect of age on nutrient concentrations is shown in **Figure 1**, emphasizing the need to standardize the time of sampling. These considerations have led most forestry organizations to standardize sampling such that for conifers current fully formed needles (usually sampled around October in northern regions and April in southern regions) are taken from the top whorl in high latitudes or the top three whorls in lower latitudes, whereas samples from broadleaved trees are taken from the upper third of the crown (ensuring full illumination) in August in northern latitudes or February in Southern latitudes.

The theoretical dependence of growth on nutrient concentration is shown in **Figure 2**. The optimum on this curve can be a well-developed turning point, which is usually the case for N, P, and K, or it can take the form of a long plateau, which is typically the case for Cu and particularly Mn. Along this plateau the plant is taking up increasing amounts of a nutrient without showing any change in growth. Uptake over this range is often referred to as 'luxury

Table 3 Visual symptoms of nutrient deficiencies

Nutrient	Symptoms
Nitrogen (N)	Needles or leaves are small and pale green turning yellow throughout the crown but most severe on young foliage
Phosphorus (P)	Reduced needle or leaf size and an exaggerated if rather dull green color; in extreme cases a brownish tinge may develop and buds towards the top of the tree may die
Potassium (K)	A pale straw-yellow color that appears first on needles at the tips of current shoots or leaf margins; color may develop to a pinkish brown and is often more severe in winter
Magnesium (Mg)	Golden yellow discoloration of needle tips or of irregular blotches on broadleaves; this is more pronounced on upper parts of the tree and in autumn
Copper (Cu)	Little change in leaf size or color although there may be dark blotches on broadleaves; branches droop and leading shoot is very sinuous or even pendulous
Boron (B)	Death of buds and shoots, particularly after growth has commenced in summer; problem most pronounced on leading shoot and as tree dies back it becomes very misshapen; pith in shoots may show brown necrosis

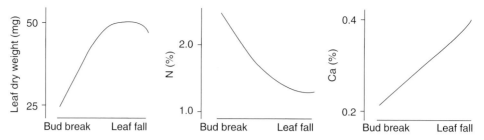

Figure 1 Changes in leaf dry weight and concentrations on nitrogen and calcium through the growing season from bud break to maximum leaf fall for a conifer such as pine.

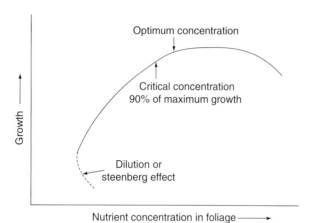

Figure 2 Generalized relationship between growth and foliar nutrient concentration.

Table 4 The foliage concentrations of nutrients below which tree growth starts to decline. These are values for young trees in the forest (c. 0.5–4.0 m tall) at the time when nutrient problems are most likely; for younger and perhaps older trees somewhat higher concentrations are necessary

Nutrient	Evergreen conifers	Broadleaves and deciduous conifers
Nitrogen (N)	1.50%	2.20%
Phosphorus (P)	0.14%	0.20%
Potassium (K)	0.50%	0.90%
Magnesium (Mg)	0.10%	0.10%
Boron (B)	8 ppm	ND
Copper (Cu)	2 ppm	ND

ND, no adequate data.

uptake,' although (as will be discussed later) this is a rather misleading concept in the case of perennial plants such as trees.

One factor that has to be kept in mind when using foliar analysis is that at least for N, and probably for the other major nutrients, the optimum concentration does shift with age of the tree. It is usually high in young seedlings but the declines as the tree becomes established, thus optimum N for seedling pine is about 3% but by the time the tree has reached a height of 2 m may be only 1.5%, rising to around 2% in a closed canopy crop. Suggested optimum concentrations are shown in **Table 4**.

Because the growth response to a fertilizer applied nutrient at the upper part of the curve, just below the optimum point, is small the concept of a critical nutrient level, usually 90% of the optimum, has been introduced. Below this critical level fertilizer responses may be worthwhile but above it not so.

When diagnosing on the basis of foliar analysis, results are presented as a concentration, that is the ratio of the weight of an element present to the weight of the leaf. Changes above or below the line will result in a change of concentration. For example, if a pollutant gas is reducing carbohydrate production this will be accompanied by an increase in

concentration of nutrient elements without there having been any increase in nutrient uptake. Similarly, if growth is being reduced by a severe deficiency of one element, say P, other elements may appear to be present in adequate amounts. If the deficiency is alleviated by the application of the appropriate fertilizer a secondary deficiency of another element may be revealed the supply of which was sufficient when growth was restricted but not so after the restriction is removed.

Caution has to be exercised when interpreting foliar analysis and if time is available a small trial to confirm the diagnosis is often advisable. In Canada, a short cut has been devised, 'trajectory analysis,' whereby fertilizers are first applied and then the response measured in terms of needle weight and nutrient concentrations to determine which element, if any is deficient. This has some advantages in reducing the time to gain a diagnosis but is unlikely to be as accurate as more conventional approaches. If carefully used the straightforward use of concentrations of individual nutrient, coupled with sensible assessment of the site and, if need be, a confirmatory trial, remains the best approach.

Site Characteristics

Site as classified by one or more of soil type, geology, and ground vegetation can give a very good indication of whether any particular nutrient deficiencies might be anticipated. This is particularly valuable when creating a plantation on bare land. Of course such classifications will differ between bioclimatic regions but many forest services have developed classifications, or lists of indicator plants, based largely on experience, to predict future fertilizer needs if any. Such an approach has the great advantage of enabling advance assessment of the costs that might be incurred in plantation creation.

Effect of Species

As previously discussed, once a forest crop has closed canopy nutrient demands decline. The only continuing net accumulation is in the biomass of wood. Concentrations of nutrients in wood are low and usually do not differ much between species. Differences in nutrient demands reflect differences in growth rate of wood such that a linear relation can be demonstrated for this stage between uptake of N and P and mean annual increment. Prior to canopy closure, however, the situation is different for different species will develop very differing amounts of foliage in these early years. Generally, deciduous tree carry 3–6 tonnes ha^{-1} of foliage, pines some 6–12 tonnes ha^{-1}, and the white wooded conifers (spruces, firs, Douglas-fir, hemlock, etc.) 10–20 tonnes ha^{-1} of foliage. Differing amounts of nutrients, therefore, will need to be found in the early years of the rotation to develop the canopies of these trees to the stage when nutrient cycling will cover much the nutritional needs of the new leaves produced each year. This early difference is illustrated in **Table 5**.

Such a model produces the intuitively sensible prediction that spruces are more nutrient-demanding than pines. It also predicts that oak is less nutrient-demanding than either of them which does not concur with their known site requirements, oak usually requiring much more fertile soils. This introduces an important distinction between 'nutrient demands' and 'site demands.' Nutrient demands differ among species because of the amount of foliage they initially need to accumulate and, thereafter, because of differences in volume growth. Site demands, by contrast, reflect not only differences in nutrient demand but also the ability of the roots and associated mycorrhizae to obtain nutrients from intractable soil sources. Pine is good at this, oak is poor.

Use of Fertilizers

As a result of a desire to minimize the use of chemicals in forests, application of fertilizers is considered a remedy of last resort. Whereever possible, other approaches should be considered, notably selecting a species better suited to the site. Sometimes, however, this option may not be possible, either because the trees are already established or the soil is extremely nutrient deficient, as may be the case in nonnatural soils such as mine waste. In such cases fertilization is necessary.

Forms of Fertilizers

A wide choice in chemical forms of fertilizers is available. The decision of what to use is in part a function of ease of application and application cost, so urea which is 46% N has attractions over ammonium sulfate at 21% or ammonium nitrate at 35% because the cost of application is lower per unit weight of N. Availability is also important and so choice is often dictated by what is being used in agriculture.

In Finland and Scandinavia concern that rainwater acidity might accelerate soil leaching, or that N inputs in polluted rain might lead to 'unbalanced' nutritional conditions, has led to the development of complex mixed fertilizers ('reconditioning fertilizers') containing up to eight nutrient elements. In the medium to long term these may serve such a purpose but in the shorter term they appear to have no advantage over the application of the one or two elements known to be deficient. Acid rain has also led to a renewed interest in the application of lime to forests. Many thousands of hectares have been so treated but the advantages remain unproven. A vast number of liming trials have been carried out since the nineteenth century and these usually show no growth response, or even a short-lived depression. In a few cases, an eventual improvement in humus form has lead to better tree health but the response is long delayed and hard to predict.

Response to Fertilizers

If a nutrient deficiency is correctly diagnosed, application of an appropriate fertilizer will lead first

Table 5 Rate of change in weight of foliage carried with age for even-aged stands of pine and spruce at comparable locations

Age period (years)	Increase in weight of foliage (tonnes ha^{-1}year^{-1})	
	Pine	Spruce
0–10	+ 0.2	+ 0.5
10–15	+ 0.4	+ 1.0
15–20	+ 0.8	+ 1.4
20–25	+ 0.2	+ 0.2
25–30	− 0.1	− 0.3

to both a reduction in number of leaves shed and to an increase in photosynthetic efficiency of the leaves retained, and then to an increase in the number of leaves formed (this being the most important factor). Thus, by the second growing season the photosynthetic area will have been considerably increased leading to an increase in net primary production and so greater stem wood growth. Thereafter, the duration of the response is a function of the amount of the fertilizer nutrient the trees have been able to accumulate in their tissues. As shown in **Figure 3**, increasing the rate of fertilizer application may not lead to continuing growth rates in the years immediately after application but because more nutrient element might have been stored the response period will continue longer.

Only a portion of the added fertilizer nutrient is used by trees. A major portion goes into the ground vegetation, the soil microbial population, and, particularly in the case of P, becomes chemically fixed within the soil. The rate at which the nutrient will be then released from such pools is so slow as to be of negligible importance for subsequent tree growth. The only fraction that is important for tree growth, therefore, is that taken up by the trees soon after application and as this is used up growth declines until no further response is detected. This leads to the simple concept that fertilizers are applied to the trees, not the site. However, where the amount of nutrient applied is high relative to the active reserves within the soil, as can be the case with P or some trace elements, a long-term response may be recorded. Indeed in many areas around the world it is observed that

although P had to be applied to the first rotation no further application may be needed in the second rotation.

When and How Much Fertilizer to Apply

In old coniferous forests of northern regions the immobilization of large amounts of N in the humus can lead to N deficiency and growth will respond to the application of fertilizer. For reasons of discounted cash flow such an application is usually made only 5–10 years before felling. More generally, however, fertilizer use is only necessary prior to canopy closure so a schedule such as that in **Table 6** might be appropriate.

The recommended rates of application vary remarkably little around the world and are generally, in terms of fertilizer element, are $150–200 \, kg \, N \, ha^{-1}$, $60–80 \, kg \, P \, ha^{-1}$, around $100 \, kg \, K \, ha^{-1}$, and $7–10 \, kg \, ha^{-1}$ for both B and Cu.

Methods of Application

Often the most reliable method of application is still by hand to individual trees. An alternative while trees are still small is use of ground-based broadcast spreading equipment. However, as canopy starts to close both of these become impossible. Following crown closure aerial application, usually by helicopter, is the only option.

Environmental Considerations

Forest fertilization must be conducted so as to minimize negative environmental effects. The main concern is loss of nutrient into waterways where this might lead eutrophication, algal blooms and consequent damage to aquatic life, fisheries, and quality of drinking water. Applied fertilizer, therefore, must not fall into drains, streams, rivers, lakes, or reservoirs. This can seriously constrain the method of application chosen. The method often preferred is to apply by hand to individual trees. If other approaches are used, particularly involving aircraft,

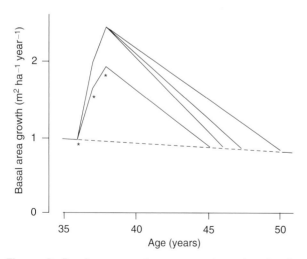

Figure 3 Basal area growth response shown by pine to nitrogen fertilizer applied at four rates in the 3 years marked with asterisks. Fertilizer treatments shown by solid lines and the untreated control by the dashed line.

Table 6 Suggested schedule for fertilizer application to spruce on different soil types (brackets indicate possible benefit)

Soil type	At planting	Years after planting			
		6	9	12	15
Brown earth	(P)	—	—	—	—
Iron podzol	P	—	P	—	—
Peaty podzol	P	—	P K	—	—
Heathland podzol	P	(N) P	N	N P	N

there has to be very careful planning and precise guidance (ideally using geographical positioning system (GPS)), accompanied by suitable supervision and monitoring, even although this may necessitate leaving significant areas untreated. Care must also be taken to ensure that that no leakage occurs from any storage stack in the woods and that all fertilizer bags are properly disposed of.

See also: **Health and Protection**: Biochemical and Physiological Aspects. **Soil Biology and Tree Growth**: Soil and its Relationship to Forest Productivity and Health. **Soil Development and Properties**: Nutrient Cycling. **Tree Physiology**: A Whole Tree Perspective; Mycorrhizae; Nutritional Physiology of Trees.

Further Reading

Attiwill PM (1987) *Forest Soils and Nutrient Cycles*. Melbourne, Victoria: Melbourne University Press.

Baule H and Fricker C (1970) *The Fertilizer Treatment of Forest Trees*, transl. CL Whittles. Munich, Germany: BLV.

Binns WO, Mayhead GJ, and MacKenzie JM (1980) *Nutrient Deficiencies of Conifers in British Forests*: An Illustrated Guide, Forestry Commission Leaflet no. 76. London: HMSO.

Bowen GD and Nambiar EKS (1984) *Nutrition of Plantation Forests*. London: Academic Press.

Cole DW and Gessel SP (eds) (1988) *Forest Site Evaluation and Long-term Productivity*. Seattle, WA: University of Washington Press.

Luxmore RJ, Landsberg JJ, and Kaufmann MR (eds) (1986) *Coupling of Carbon, Water and Nutrient Interactions in Woody Plant Soil Systems*. Victoria, Canada: Heron.

Mälkönen E (ed.) (2000) *Forest Condition in a Changing Environment: The Finnish Case*, Forest Sciences no. 65. Dordrecht, The Netherlands: Kluwer Academic Press.

Miller HG (1981) Forest fertilization: some guiding concepts. *Forestry* 54: 157–167.

Miller HG (1995) The influence of stand development on nutrient demand, growth and allocation. *Plant and Soil* 168/169: 225–232.

Nambiar EKS and Fife DN (1991) Nutrient retranslocation in temperate conifers. *Tree Physiology* 9: 185–207.

Nambiar EKS, Squire R, Cromer R, Turner J, and Boardman R (eds) (1990) *Management of Water and Nutrient Relations to Increase Growth*. Special issue of *Forest Ecology and Management* 30 (1–4).

Taylor CMA (1991) *Forest Fertilization in Britain*, Forestry Commission Bulletin no. 95. London: HMSO.

Will G (1985) *Nutrient Deficiencies and Fertilizer Use in New Zealand Exotic Forests*, FRI Bulletin no. 97. Rotorua, New Zealand: Forest Research Institute, New Zealand Forest Service.

Soil Contamination and Amelioration

H Goldemund, GeoSyntec Consultants, Atlanta, GA, USA

Introduction

Human activities have shaped and altered essentially all ecosystems on earth. Forest ecosystems are no exception to this and the effects of these activities can be observed throughout the forests of the world. While many of the activities leading to soil contamination have been necessary and positive (e.g., development of a sustainable agricultural system capable of feeding a growing world population), negative side effects are also widespread. Impacts range from clearly visible effects like unsustainable and large-scale logging and surface mining with all their associated problems of erosion, loss in soil fertility and productivity, and acid mine drainage, to less obvious effects including diffuse deposition of atmospheric pollutants or acid rain due to burning of fossil fuels. Many of these negative effects are reversible, and in particular, forested areas have the ability to buffer environmental impacts. Many physiological processes in forest systems such as evapotranspiration, photosynthesis, solute uptake, and effects of plant root exudates on contaminant degradation can be used to mitigate negative impacts and/or remediate existing contamination. This article focuses on forest soil contamination with regard to inorganic and organic contaminants and potential remedial strategies.

Soil Contamination

Contamination is generally grouped by origin as resulting from point (direct) or nonpoint (diffuse) sources. Point sources of soil contamination include spills and leaks, local emissions, and land applications, while atmospheric deposition and agricultural runoff are the main nonpoint sources of contamination. Point sources such as industrial outfall pipes or chemical spills are discrete, localized, and can be readily assessed and delineated, while nonpoint sources are more difficult to assess due to the large areas that can be affected and multiple sources that may contribute to the problem. Inorganic contaminants like trace metals and in some cases radionuclides (e.g., Chernobyl accident in 1986) can originate as both point sources and nonpoint sources. Organic contamination generally results from point sources, although elevated levels of some recalcitrant semivolatile organic compounds (SVOCs) including polychlorinated biphenyls (PCBs) and polycyclic aromatic hydrocarbons (PAHs) are becoming more ubiquitous and are the result of atmospheric pollution and subsequent deposition.

Once contaminants enter the soil environment, they undergo a multitude of processes that affect their fate and subsurface mobility, which in turn alters their bioavailability and risk to potential human and ecological receptors. These processes include sorption and desorption (organic and inorganic contaminants), precipitation (inorganic contaminants) and dissolution (organic and inorganic contaminants), complexation (organic and inorganic contaminants), leaching (organic and inorganic contaminants), volatilization (mainly organic, but some inorganic contaminants), and degradation (organic contaminants). Biogeochemical and physical soil properties affecting the fate and transport of contaminants include pH, oxidation–reduction potential (redox conditions), organic matter (OM) content, and the amount of clay and sesquioxides present in soils. The amounts of OM and clays affect the cation-exchange capacity (CEC) of a soil, a variable that indicates the soil's ability to retain positively charged ions, some of which are contaminants such as many trace metals. Trace metals also form strong complexes with organic matter, which may lead to both immobilization due to complexation with insoluble organic matter in surface soils, as well as mobilization due to complexation with dissolved organic carbon (DOC).

Furthermore, nonionic organic contaminants have a strong affinity for soil organic matter, which in general renders them fairly immobile. Redox conditions affect the speciation, and therefore the mobility, of inorganic contaminants, as well as the geochemical environment for the potential degradation of organic contaminants. For example, many chlorinated organic compounds are completely degraded under reducing conditions, while most volatile organic compounds and explosives degrade more readily under aerobic conditions. For trace metals, pH is the master variable. With the exceptions of arsenic (As), molybdenum (Mo), selenium (Se), vanadium (V), and chromium (Cr), metals are more mobile under acidic soil conditions.

While this article focuses on soil contamination, it should be noted that soil contamination frequently leads to groundwater contamination. About 75% of all contaminated sites regulated under Federal programs in the USA involve groundwater contamination. Once in groundwater, contaminants that may have originated from a small localized area, such as a spill, may spread over a much larger area due to plume migration along a groundwater flow path or as separate-phase migration of a dense nonaqueous phase liquid (DNAPL) such as trichloroethylene (TCE). **Figure 1** conceptualizes soil contamination and remediation.

Table 1 summarizes the main classes of contaminants commonly found in soils and some of their important characteristics.

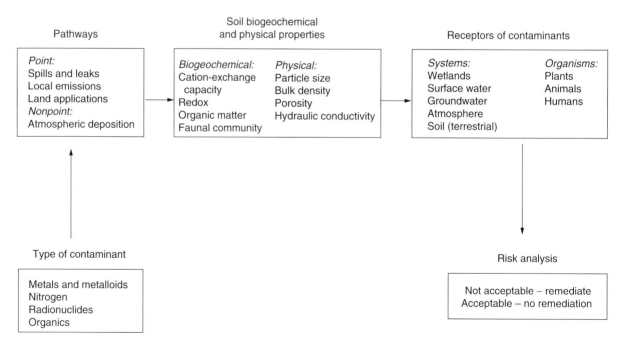

Figure 1 Conceptual model of soil contamination and remediation. Reproduced with permission from Adriano DC, Bollag JM, Frankenberger WT Jr., and Sims RC (1999) *Bioremediation of Contaminated Soils*. Madison, WI: American Society of Agronomy.

Table 1 Contaminant classes and compounds commonly found in soils

Contaminant class	Compound class	Example compounds	Environmental characteristics	Potential sources	Remedial options
Inorganic contaminants	Salts	NaCl, MgCl$_2$	High solubility/mobility; some plant toxicity; minimal human health risks	Ocean spray, roadside salts	Leaching; application of CaSO$_4 \cdot$ 2H$_2$O
	Trace metal(loid)s	Hg, As, Pb, Cr, Cd	Mobility depending on pH and redox conditions; plant toxicity; significant human health risks	Metallurgy, paints, parent rock	Excavation; soil washing; liming; stabilization; phytoremediation
	Radionuclides	^{137}Cs, ^{238}U, ^{90}Sr	Geochemical behavior similar to certain plant nutrients (K, Ca); human exposure to radioactivity	Nuclear reactors and weapons	Similar to trace metals; mainly stabilization and excavation
Organic contaminants	Polycyclic aromatic hydrocarbons (PAH)	Naphthalene, phenanthrene, benzo(a)pyrene	Varying solubilities and mobility; significant human health risks	Coal tars, asphalt, fossil fuels	Solidification; composting; chemical extraction
	Nitroaromatics	TNT, RDX, HMX; pesticides	Human health risks; risk of initiation	Military explosives; pesticides	Biodegradation; soil washing; composting; phytoremediation
	Phenols	Pentachlorophenol, phenol, nitrophenol	Bioavailability depending on soil pH and OM content; human health risk	Wood preservatives, solvents; refineries	Biodegradation; solidification; soil flushing; land farming
	Halogenated aromatics	PCBs, pesticides, dioxins	Low solubility; limited mobility; toxic to humans	Pesticides, waste incineration	Solidification; excavation; dehalogenation
	Halogenated aliphatics	TCE, PCE, CCl$_4$	Present as NAPL and dissolved phase; high toxicity	Solvents, plastics	Bioremediation; chemical oxidation
	Petroleum hydrocarbons	Petroleum products (crude and refined oil)	Complex mixture of compounds; significant solubility/ toxicity	Cars, refineries, industry	Land farming; thermal desorption, biodegradation

HMX, cyclotetramethylenetetranitramine; NAPL, nonaqueous phase liquid; PCBs, polychlorinated biphenyls; PCE, tetrachloro ethylene; RDX, cyclotetramethylenetetranitramine; TCE, trichloroethylene; TNT, trinitrotoluene.

Salt-Affected Soils

In general, two types of salt-affected soils are distinguished: saline soils that have high electrical conductivity ($>4\,dS\,m^{-1}$) but low sodium content, and sodic soils that have high electrical conductivity ($>4\,dS\,m^{-1}$) and high sodium content. Salinity affects soils in three ways:

1. Excess sodium (Na) can lead to the destruction of soil structure through its ability to disperse clays. This leads to decreased aeration and consequently, restricts root growth.
2. Excess salts in soil solution affect the osmotic potential of soil water. The increase in soil water potential (i.e., more negative) makes water harder to extract and less available to plant roots, which can lead to water stress in plants.
3. The uptake of excess chloride can lead to direct damage to plant leaves. Roots of non salt tolerant plants have no mechanism to exclude the very mobile and soluble chloride ion. Once absorbed, chloride is quickly transported with the transpirational stream through the stem to the leaves, where it accumulates at the outer fringes of the leaves. This excess chloride leads to chlorosis of the leaves decreasing their capacity to conduct photosynthesis.

Four main sources of salinity exist. Three of these are anthropogenic sources with the fourth one being a natural source. A natural source of salts that may affect the species composition of forests originates from ocean sprays. Due to strong winds in the vicinity of large bodies of water, small droplets of salt water can be carried inland from oceans and seas and deposited onto forests along coastlines. While this may not be considered 'contamination,' it can clearly affect soils and tree species composition within these forests.

The three main anthropogenic sources of salinity to forests originate from the use of roadside deicing salts in cold climates, the land application of wastewater and biosolids and accidental spills of brines from the production of oil. Deicing salts can be carried into forests along roadsides through splashes and runoff of melted snow. In general, these transport processes are limited to within a few meters of a road, although salt effects have been measured as far away as 200 m into a forest stand. While small areas of forested lands can be affected by deicing salts, the soil chemical and plant physiological effects are more visible in urban areas where other factors contribute to tree stress and mortality such as air pollution, confined rooting space, and physical tree damage from parked cars.

During the last two decades the practice of land application of wastewater and biosolids has become more common as a means to manage the large quantities of treated wastewater and sludges generated in the industrialized world. While this practice has great potential for the beneficial reuse of 'waste' by providing a cost-effective source of nutrients, organic matter, and irrigation water, it may also lead to increased soil salinity.

The production of oil produces large quantities of brine (mainly connate brines) that pose a serious problem for treatment and disposal. Occasionally, brine spills and slow seepage through unlined impoundments can contaminate forests. Unlike damage from deicing salts, concentrated brines can kill entire forest stands.

Amelioration of saline and sodic soils is generally accomplished by leaching soils with low-electrolyte water and by applying gypsum ($CaSO_4 \cdot 2H_2O$) or $CaCl_2$ to the soil. In humid climates where infiltration exceeds evapotranspiration, it may be sufficient to stop the salt addition and allow for natural leaching of excess salts.

Trace Metals and Metalloids

Contamination of agricultural and forest soils with trace metals and metalloids has been a major concern for many decades. While metals in contaminated agricultural soils can enter the food chain and increase human exposure and risk (both carcinogenic and noncarcinogenic risks), metals in forests are mainly a potential problem for groundwater resources, ecological risk, and forest health.

There are both natural and anthropogenic sources contributing to elevated soil concentrations of trace metals. Natural sources are generally limited to weathering of parent rocks that contain appreciable concentrations of metals, and volcanic inputs. Anthropogenic sources are widespread and include fertilizers, pesticides, wastewater and biosolids, coal combustion residues, and atmospheric deposition. The main source of trace metals in natural forest ecosystems is atmospheric deposition. In intensively managed forest plantations, application of biosolids and the use of pesticides and fertilizers can also contribute trace metals to the system. Wood treatment facilities that used chromated copper arsenate (CCA) as a wood treatment product resulted in sites contaminated with arsenic and chromium as well as a variety of other (organic) constituents. Between 50% and 70% of contaminated sites regulated under Federal cleanup programs in the USA contain metals as major contaminants. Many of these sites, especially sites managed by the US Department of Defense and the US Department of Energy, contain large tracts of forested lands.

In general, forest soils are more acidic than agricultural soils, which are regularly limed and therefore, forest soils tend to have greater availability of trace metals. Among forest types, coniferous forests exhibit a lower soil pH than deciduous hardwood forests due to slower forest floor decomposition, greater concentrations of organic acids from decomposing litter, and lower contents of base cations. Furthermore, forest soils contain numerous old root channels that provide pathways for preferential water flow. Preferential flow bypasses the soil matrix, which may lead to increased mobility of contaminants to deeper depths. In addition, decomposing organic matter may yield appreciable concentrations of DOC to the soil solution, which can increase metal mobility due to metal–DOC complexes that move readily with percolation water. Therefore, potential subsurface metal mobility is higher in forested settings in comparison to agricultural systems. However, phytostabilization of metals in the root zone through root sorption (absorption and adsorption) may provide a mechanism for immobilization of otherwise mobile metal contaminants. **Figure 2** illustrates a generalized biogeochemical cycle for trace elements in forest ecosystems.

The most commonly found trace metals at contaminated sites include lead (Pb), cadmium (Cd), zinc (Zn), nickel (Ni), mercury (Hg), chromium (Cr), and arsenic (As). Forests (especially at higher elevations) sometimes act as 'filters' for airborne

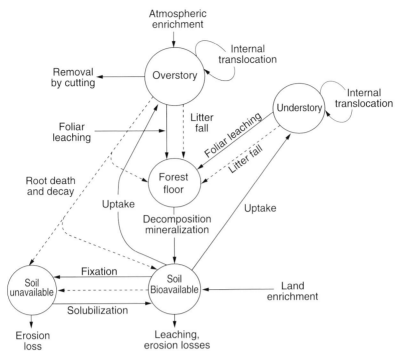

Figure 2 Generalized biogeochemical cycle for trace elements in forest ecosystems. Reproduced with permission from Adriano DC (2001) *Trace Elements in Terrestrial Environments*, 2nd edn. New York: Springer-Verlag.

metal contamination, rendering even remote forest stands into metal sinks. Lead is a widespread metal contaminant in forests due to airborne deposition and the use of forested areas as shooting ranges. In some alpine areas, for example, Pb concentrations of up to $700 \, mg \, kg^{-1}$ have been measured in forest soils far away from potential industrial point sources. Excess metal deposition in conjunction with acidic atmospheric deposition (i.e., 'acid rain') may lead to a decrease in forest health due to phytotoxic effects of metals, as well as create a potential groundwater problem. In Europe, the concept of calculating critical loads for deposition of metals to forest systems is commonly applied. Metal depositions below a critical load are considered harmless to the environment.

Unlike organic contaminants, metals do not degrade and have to be either immobilized or extracted. Potential technologies for remediating metals-contaminated soils are fairly limited and include *ex situ* technologies (e.g., excavation and disposal, incineration, soil washing, and thermal desorption) and *in situ* technologies (e.g., liming, solidification/stabilization, capping in place, electrokinetics, natural attenuation, and phytoremediation). Due to limited access in established forest stands, relatively low concentrations of metal contaminants, and the desire to apply less invasive approaches over larger areas, *in situ* approaches such as liming and

phytoremediation are the preferred options for metal-contaminated forest soils.

Acid Deposition

Acid deposition, commonly referred to as 'acid rain,' has long been suspected as a contributing factor to the decline in forest vigor and the observed dieback of forests in central Europe, Scandinavia, and North America (USA and Canada). While agricultural soils and most soils under deciduous forests have sufficient capacity to buffer acidic atmospheric inputs, some coniferous forests, especially on shallow, nutrient-poor soils derived from 'acidic' parent rocks like granite, are susceptible to acid rain. Acid rain is a consequence of the combustion of fossil fuels, which leads to the emission of sulfur and nitrogen compounds (i.e., SO_x and NO_x) that form strong acids in contact with water (i.e., H_2SO_4 and HNO_3). While the emission of sulfur compounds has decreased dramatically over the past 30 years, the emission of nitrogen compounds has continued at a very high level. These acids accelerate the natural process of soil acidification under forest stands and may contribute as much as 40% to soil acidification. This process leads to excessive leaching of base cations (especially Ca and Mg), decreases a soil's acid neutralizing capacity, increases the mobility of potentially toxic trace metals, and releases excess aluminum into soil solution. Elevated concentrations of aluminum are toxic to tree roots and cause an antagonistic effect on ion uptake (especially with Mg). In combination with an increasing ratio of aboveground to belowground biomass, such as observed in nitrogen-saturated forest systems of central Europe, this increases drought stress and the susceptibility to windfall and disease. The combined effects of these and other stresses such as shallow, naturally poor or acidic soils, drought conditions, management practices like removal of forest litter that lead to decreased fertility, other air pollutants, and animal damage are believed to be responsible for forest diebacks and the decline in tree vigor.

Strategies for mitigating these effects include continued efforts to limit the emissions of N- and S-containing compounds, improvements in forest management practices, and liming and fertilization of susceptible sites.

Organic Contaminants

With the exception of some pesticides originating from agricultural runoff and carbonaceous particles originating from industrial coal processing, most organic contaminants are generated from point sources. However, recently there has been mounting evidence that many PAHs and PCBs can be found in areas far away from local point sources, indicating long-range transport as a significant source of forest soil contamination by organic compounds. Due to much higher concentrations of organic carbon in forest soils as compared to agricultural soils, organic contaminants originating from diffuse sources are usually found at much higher concentrations in forest soils. As previously mentioned, organic contaminants have a strong affinity for soil organic carbon.

Typical sources of organic contaminants include the combustion of organic materials such as coal, oil, or wood (PAHs), smelting processes (PCBs), pesticide production and application for agricultural, industrial, and residential pest control (dioxins, dichlorodiphenyltrichloroethane (DDT), chlorinated pesticides), accidental releases from oil producing facilities and during transportation of oil in tankers and (leaky) pipelines (petroleum hydrocarbons), wood treatment facilities (creosotes, pentachlorophenol (PCP)), production and use of explosives (cyclotetramethylenetrinitramine (RDX), trinitrotoluene (TNT), cyclotetramethylenetetranitramine (HMX)), and production and use of industrial solvents for dry-cleaning, degreasing, and plastics manufacturing (trichloroethylene (TCE), tetrachloroethylene (PCE), vinyl chloride).

Volatile organic compounds (VOCs), primarily in the form of BTEX (benzene, toluene, ethylbenzene, and xylene) compounds, are generally found in localized areas. Over two-thirds of sites regulated under Federal programs in the USA contain VOCs, which are also primary contaminants in many underground storage tank sites. Unless spills occur in or near forested sites, forest stands are rarely affected by VOCs. Nonhalogenated VOCs readily degrade under a variety of conditions, and are therefore prime candidates for bioremediation and/or natural attenuation. Halogenated VOCs (such as TCE, PCE, CCl_4) are also completely biodegradable, but require anaerobic conditions for the reductive dechlorination process to proceed.

Semivolatile organic carbons (SVOCs) include a large number of organic contaminants ranging from PAHs (such as naphthalene and pyrene), to PCBs (such as aroclors) to chlorobenzenes and chlorophenols, to pesticides and dioxins. There is a wide array of technologies available for the remediation of SVOCs, and with regard to contaminated forest soils, *in situ* biological approaches like bioremediation and phytoremediation appear to be the most applicable technologies.

Since the military uses large areas of land (quite often heavily forested as well) as military bases and for training purposes, these sites are greatly impacted by a wide variety of contaminants ranging from metals to solvents and explosives (including unexploded ordinance). More recently, perchlorate (ClO_4^-) has been identified as a major contaminant on virtually every military site where it has been included as a target analyte. Consequently, inorganic and organic contaminants in soils (and groundwater) are frequently commingled at these sites. This poses a significant challenge for remediation efforts since many cleanup technologies are specific to contaminants or groups of contaminants. For soil (and groundwater) remediation, the application of bioremediation (especially by creating reducing conditions) may be a feasible and cost-effective approach to simultaneously treat a variety of contaminants. However, highly contaminated (and toxic) areas containing nitroaromatics (i.e., explosives) and/or other organic contaminants may continue to require excavation and incineration.

Phytoremediation

A variety of *in situ* and *ex situ* remedial technologies are available to treat soils affected by the many contaminants described above. Environmental managers quite often prefer less invasive and more cost-effective approaches than excavation and disposal or incineration. Over the last two decades, phytoremediation has emerged as a feasible alternative to more active and costly technologies, especially for large areas with relatively low levels of contamination.

Phytoremediation – more recently, the term 'phytotechnologies' has been introduced since this remedial approach covers a number of technologies and applications – is the use of plants to remediate or contain contaminants in soil, groundwater, surface water, and sediments. The technology is rapidly gaining acceptance within regulatory agencies as well as the public. In general, six main mechanisms are involved in the application of phytotechnologies:

1. Phytostabilization (inorganic and organic contaminants) is the use of plants to immobilize contaminants in soil, sediments, and groundwater through the absorption and accumulation into the roots, the adsorption onto the roots, or the precipitation or immobilization within the root zone.
2. Rhizodegradation (organic contaminants) refers to the breakdown of contaminants in soil through the bioactivity that exists in the rhizosphere (an area about 1 mm away from a root surface).
3. Phytoaccumulation (inorganic contaminants) is the process of metal- or salt-accumulating plants to translocate and concentrate inorganic contaminants into the roots and aboveground biomass.
4. Phytodegradation (organic contaminants) refers to the uptake of organic contaminants from soil, sediments, and water with subsequent transformation by the plants.
5. Phytovolatilization (inorganic and organic contaminants) is the mechanism of uptake and translocation of the contaminant into the leaves with subsequent release to the atmosphere through transpiration.
6. Evapotranspiration of plants can be used to significantly affect the local hydrology through interception of rain on leaf surfaces and transpirational uptake by the plant root system.

The first five mechanisms have been successfully used to remediate or contain contaminated soils, while the use of evapotranspiration applies more to groundwater contamination. Contaminated forested areas are good candidates for the application of these technologies since they are generally impacted over large areas, but at relatively low concentrations. Phytoremediation is limited by the effective rooting depth of plants, as well as the phytotoxicity and/or plant-availability of contaminants. Quite often, only a fraction of the total concentration of a specific contaminant is in a potentially bioavailable form that is accessible for plant uptake. However, given that many regulated environmental sites are actually managed using a risk-based approach, it may be sufficient to remediate the bioavailable contaminant fraction rather than achieving a low total concentration of a specific contaminant.

See also: **Environment**: Impacts of Air Pollution on Forest Ecosystems; Impacts of Elevated CO_2 and Climate Change. **Health and Protection**: Biochemical and Physiological Aspects. **Silviculture**: Forest Rehabilitation. **Site-Specific Silviculture**: Reclamation of Mining Lands; Silviculture in Polluted Areas. **Soil Development and Properties**: Waste Treatment and Recycling.

Further Reading

Aamot E, Steinnes E, and Schmid R (1996) Polycyclic aromatic hydrocarbons in Norwegian forest soils: impact of long range atmospheric impact. *Environmental Pollution* 92(3): 275–280.

Adriano DC (2001) *Trace Elements in Terrestrial Environments: Biogeochemistry, Bioavailability, and Risks of Metals*, 2nd edn. New York: Springer-Verlag.

Adriano DC, Bollag JM, Frankenberger WT Jr., and Sims RC (1999) *Bioremediation of Contaminated Soils*. Agronomy Monograph no. 37. Madison, WI: American Society of Agronomy, Crop Science Society of America, and Soil Science Society of America.

Bindler R, Brännvall ML, and Renberg I (1999) Natural lead concentrations in pristine boreal forest soils and past pollution trends: a reference for critical load models. *Environmental Science and Technology* 33: 3362–3367.

Federal Remediation Technology Roundtable (2003) *Remediation Technologies Screening Matrix and Reference Guide*, Version 4.0. Available online at http://www.frtr.gov/matrix2/top_page.html.

Horstmann M and McLachlan MS (1996) Evidence of a novel mechanism of semivolatile organic compound deposition in coniferous forests. *Environmental Science and Technology* 30(5): 1794–1796.

ITRC (2001) *Phytotechnology Technical and Regulatory Guidance Document*. Interstate Technology and Regulatory Cooperation Work Group. Available at: http://www.itreweb.org/PHYTO2.pdf/.

Markewitz D, Richter DD, Allen LH, and Urrego JB (1998) Three decades of observed soil acidification in the Calhoun Experimental Forest: has acid rain made a difference? *Soil Science Society of America Journal* 62: 1428–1439.

Matzner E and Murach D (1995) Soil changes induced by pollutant deposition and their implication for forests in Central Europe. *Water, Air and Soil Pollution* 85: 63–76.

US Environmental Protection Agency (1997) *Cleaning Up the Nation's Waste Sites: Markets and Technology Trends*, 1996 edn. EPA 542-R-96-005. Washington, DC: US Government Printing Office.

Van der Lelie D, Schwitzguébel JP, Glass DJ, Vangronsveld J, and Baker A (2001) Assessing phytoremediation's progress in the United States and Europe. *Environmental Science and Technology* 35(21): 447A–452A.

Waste Treatment and Recycling

W L Nutter, Nutter & Associates, Inc., Athens, GA, USA

L A Morris, University of Georgia, Athens, GA, USA

Introduction

Land treatment is the practice of applying waste to a vegetation–soil complex with the intention of further treatment or renovation. Land treatment is based on well-documented scientific concepts which have been used successfully for wastewater (i.e. liquid sewage effluent) treatment at thousands of sites throughout the world. Properly designed and managed, land treatment systems can enhance productivity of forest ecosystems and, at the same time, protect the quality of surface and groundwaters. Of the various methods of wastewater land treatment, spray irrigation (also referred to as slow rate), achieves the highest degree of renovation and beneficial reuse of nutrients and water. The US *EPA Process Design Manual – Land Treatment of Municipal Wastewater*, published in 1981, describes land treatment by spray irrigation as: the application of wastewater to a vegetated land surface with the applied wastewater being treated as it flows through the plant–soil matrix. A portion of the flow percolates to the ground water and some is used by the vegetation. Treated wastewater produced by municipalities must be disposed of and one way of providing further treatment and reaping some benefits is to apply the wastewater to land, of which forest land is often the most suitable from an environmental and public acceptance viewpoint.

Assimilative Capacity of Forests for Wastewater Renovation

Wastewater is applied to a land treatment system at a rate designed to optimize the renovative capacity of the soil–plant complex and to maximize the utilization of the available nutrients in the wastewater. Renovation of the wastewater is accomplished through degradation by microorganisms, chemical precipitation, ion exchange, biological transformation, and biological absorption through the soil and vegetative cover complex. Utilization of a vegetative cover is an integral part of the land treatment system and complements the soil microbiological and physicochemical systems. Vegetation is one of the most essential elements of the land treatment concept and provides for the maximum renovation capacity and durability of the system.

Wastewater irrigation in a properly designed and operated land treatment system is such that all the applied wastewater will enter the soil and no overland flow will occur. In this respect, forested sites are often better suited for land treatment than agricultural sites because undisturbed forest soils often have infiltration and percolation rates far in excess of normal hydraulic loading rates. Once in the soil, wastewater is renovated relatively quickly by the various chemical, physical, and biological processes. Chemical constituents of the wastewater such as dissolved salts, metals, phosphorus (P), and nitrogen (N) are considerably reduced in concentration. Organic compounds are usually not found in domestic wastewaters or are only present in small amounts and have not been found to be a limiting factor in the functioning of a land treatment system. Organic compounds are readily absorbed to the organic surfaces of the soil system and thus have limited mobility through the soil profile. Pathogens and viruses in wastewater are filtered out in the upper soil profile. Survival time for most microorganisms following land treatment is typically very short. Viability depends upon a variety of soil and climatic conditions including temperature, soil moisture, and pH. Most bacterial and viral pathogens will die off to negligible numbers within 2–3 months following application. Research has shown that in a properly designed and managed system these organisms remain in the surface soils for the duration of their survival period and do not leach through the soil profile.

The assimilative capacity of a land treatment site is the amount of wastewater, on a constituent by constituent basis, that can be optimally applied to the land. The basic environmental constraint of nondegradation is used to develop the assimilative capacity for each constituent. The nondegradation constraint is stated: each constituent is applied at a rate over a time period (mass of chemical species per unit area per unit time, i.e., $kg\,ha^{-1}\,year^{-1}$) that the land and water resources are not irreversibly converted to an unproductive condition or environmentally degraded. Use of such a strong constraint parallels environmental regulatory intent and provides for long-term and successful wastewater irrigation.

Wastewater Constituents and System Design

Land-applied wastewater constituents can be divided into three primary groups:

1. Those compounds that degrade or require plant uptake for assimilation in the plant–soil system (e.g., N, oil, organics).
2. Those mobile and nondegradative compounds that must be assimilated over land areas such that groundwater is not altered to a degree that would require further treatment to meet drinking water or other applicable standards (e.g., anionic species such as sulfate, chloride, boron, and fluoride).
3. Those compounds that are relatively immobile and nondegradative, and thus are permitted to accumulate in the soil to predetermined acceptable levels (e.g., trace metals). For calculation purposes, an operations period must be specified over which the total mass loading of constituents will be distributed.

Development of design criteria for a land irrigation system involves identification of the significant constituents of the waste stream, classification of each constituent into one of the above categories, and evaluation of the assimilative pathway(s) utilized for that constituent. The three principal components of assimilative pathways are the soil, vegetation, and groundwater. The land-limiting constituent (LLC), the waste constituent requiring the greatest land area, is determined from the assimilative capacities and wastewater characteristics. The LLC is determined by dividing the total mass of each constituent to be applied on an annual basis (kg year^{-1}) by the site assimilative capacity (kg ha^{-1} year^{-1}). Typically for municipal wastewater the LLC is either hydraulic loading or nitrogen.

The amount of wastewater irrigated is referred to as the hydraulic loading. Hydraulic loading must be balanced with vertical and lateral water movement in the soil, ground water movement, vegetation tolerances for soil wetness, and losses by evapotranspiration. Determination of hydraulic loading requires characterization of soil water movement to estimate the percolation rate, or rate of water movement through the hydraulically restrictive soil horizon (i.e., the first horizon encountered in the soil profile with a reduced permeability). This is accomplished by direct field testing of soil hydraulic conductivity. The irrigation system design and management is specified such that no overland flow of applied wastewater will occur, that is, all applied wastewater must infiltrate, or enter, the soil surface. Thus, the only pathways by which applied water may leave the site are evapotranspiration and percolation through the soil profile. Application of these principles in design and operation meets regulatory compliance for water quality and best management practices. Infiltrated wastewater that percolates through the soil profile (sometimes referred to as interflow) may emerge downslope in stream channels or seepage areas at the base of slopes as return flow, or percolate directly to groundwater and eventually to a stream channel or a regional groundwater aquifer. Residence time of water in the soil must be sufficient for all the physical, chemical, and biological renovation processes to occur and is controlled through timing of wastewater application and application rates. Typically, application rates are low (less than 6 mm h^{-1}) to achieve long residence times and slow rates of subsurface flow and, consequently slow return flow and/or percolation to groundwater. It is this long residence time and the high renovation capacity of the soil and vegetation complex which yields highly renovated subsurface flow (interflow) that emerges as return flow or percolates to groundwater. For most wastewater constituents, travel through only a few inches of soil and forest floor achieves 90–100% of the potential renovation. In humid regions, where rainfall exceeds evapotranspiration by 25–30%, strong development of subsurface flow and return flow in forested landscapes is a common occurrence, particularly during the wetter seasons of the year. Wastewater irrigation accentuates these processes such that they occur throughout the year.

The N cycle in a forest ecosystem is complex, dynamic, and varies with species, growth rates, soil morphology and fertility, climate, and other environmental factors. To determine the N assimilative capacity, a N budget is constructed to balance inputs with losses. All the N in municipal wastewater is typically plant available because the organic N will be readily mineralized to ammonia. Ammonia-nitrogen is not highly mobile, is retained within the soil complex, and is taken up by plants. Nitrate-nitrogen, on the other hand, is easily leached from the root zone and its assimilation is controlled through plant uptake and denitrification. Control of nitrate leaching is critical to maintain nitrate in groundwater at the drinking water standard (typically 10 mg l^{-1} nitrate-nitrogen). Nitrogen may be stored on the site as organic-nitrogen in bacterial cells as well as in living and dead plant material. It may also be stored as ammonia-nitrogen adsorbed on soil cation exchange surfaces. Ammonia-nitrogen may be volatilized to the atmosphere, transformed to nitrate-nitrogen by nitrifying bacteria, and/or taken up by vegetation. Nitrate-nitrogen may be taken up by vegetation, transformed to nitrogen gas by denitrifying bacteria, or leached to the groundwater. All of the N assimilative pathways occur simultaneously in natural systems. Nitrogen is removed primarily by crop uptake, which varies with the type of crop grown and the crop yield.

To remove the N effectively, the forest crop must be harvested periodically. Denitrification can also be significant, even if the soil is in an aerobic condition most of the time. Other N removal mechanisms include ammonia volatilization and storage in the soil.

Thus, N management in a land treatment system is achieved through management of vegetation and denitrification. Vegetation must be harvested and N removed in the biomass. Denitrification occurs naturally but can be enhanced by creating periodic soil saturation and providing available carbon. Irrigated wastewater and forest ecosystems have adequate supplies of organic carbon and management of hydraulic loading can create the requisite soil wetness. Management of denitrification is further enhanced in sloping sites because the infiltrated wastewater can move laterally through the soil profile maintaining the wet soils for the short periods required to drive the denitrification process.

Phosphorus added to the soil from wastewater undergoes a variety of biological and chemical reactions. The predominant phosphorus pool in the soil is in the inorganic form. That is, the P is physically part of the soil matrix. A much smaller pool of P is in the organic matter (organic phosphorus) and in a soluble form as part of the soil pore water. Soluble P is the only form that is available to the plant. Chemical fixation of P in the soil occurs under all soil pH ranges with the least occurring in the range of 5.8 to 6.8. The adsorption and precipitation processes at low soil pH are dependent on the amount of aluminum (Al), iron (Fe), and manganese (Mn) present. These elements are abundant in the highly weathered soils. Natural occurring P in geologic materials is also relatively low. Thus, acidic soil pH, abundant Al, Fe, and Mn, and low residual P levels in forest soils provide a high capacity for sequestration of P added from wastewater irrigation. A study of a forest wastewater irrigation site in north Georgia (southeastern USA) showed there was a residual P fixation capacity of over 100 years in the surface soils. The residual capacity of soils to chemically fix P is determined by laboratory determination on soil samples of adsorption and precipitation isotherms. Vegetation uptake and incorporation of organic P is minor compared to the capacity of the soil to fix and retain P. The residual forest floor (leaf litter and partially decomposed material) retains P also in a form that is largely unavailable to plant uptake or leaching. Phosphorus removal efficiencies are generally very high for spray irrigation systems and are more dependent on the soil properties than on the concentration of the P applied. Although P is held within the soil at different energy levels, little or no leaching occurs. This is demonstrated by groundwater concentrations beneath both natural and wastewater irrigation forested sites on the order of 0.01 to 0.1 mg l^{-1}. The principal nonpoint source of P to streams is runoff of soil and organic particles with 'attached' P.

Organics applied in the wastewater are reduced substantially within the top 1.5–2.5 cm of soil. Filtration and adsorption are the initial steps in biological oxygen demand (BOD) removal, but biological oxidation is the ultimate treatment mechanism. Filtration is the major removal mechanism for suspended solids. Residues remaining after oxidation and the inert solids become part of the soil matrix.

Metals, much like P, are retained in the soil complex and are immobile. Metals in municipal wastewater are rarely found in concentrations that result in any one becoming a land-limiting constituent.

Impacts of Wastewater Treatment: Case Study of Clayton County, Georgia, USA

Irrigation of secondary treated wastewater to a 1000 ha and mixed pine (*Pinus taeda*) and hardwood (*Quercus, Carya, Liquidambar*) forest site began in 1983 and continues to the present with an average flow of 0.85 m^3 s^{-1}. Clayton County is located in the metropolitan Atlanta, Georgia area and has few heavy industry waste dischargers. Wastewater treatment by activated sludge occurs at two plants and the wastewater is combined and pumped 11 km to the land treatment site.

The site is within the headwaters of Pates Creek. The site is entirely forested and about 50 ha are harvested annually. Geologic structure is dominated by granitic gneiss with some fracturing and jointing. Groundwater occurs under water table conditions and most of the recoverable water is above the bedrock at depths of 3–25 m. Hydraulic conductivities of the saprolite overlying the bedrock are low, averaging 5 × 10^{-4} cm s^{-1}. Dominant soils are typic hapludults with A horizon textures ranging from fine sandy loam to sandy clay loam. The B horizon is argillic with sandy clay to clay textures. Depth of the A is shallow due to past erosion history and rarely exceeds 15 cm. B horizon hydraulic conductivities average 9 × 10^{-4} cm s^{-1}. Soils are classified as well drained except in alluvium along streams.

Wastewater loading is limited by nitrogen and water assimilative capacities of the site. Wastewater irrigation is limited to 6.3 cm water week^{-1} which has resulted in maximum N applications of about 395 kg ha^{-1} year^{-1}. The irrigation system is solid-set buried PVC and ductile iron with galvanized steel risers and brass and plastic sprinklers. There are over 18 000 sprinklers and the pressure at the nozzles is about 345 kPa for an application rate of 5 mm h^{-1}. Storage equivalent to 12 days' flow is provided for flow equalization and inclement weather.

An intensive environmental monitoring program has been implemented at the Clayton County land treatment site that includes groundwater, surface water, soil, and vegetation. In addition numerous research projects have been undertaken that include changes in streamflow from the first order basins, changes in streamflow and water budget for the entire irrigated watershed, nitrogen gas evolution from the soil, earthworm populations, and soil hydraulic properties. Twenty-two groundwater wells as well as several private water supply wells in and around the site have been monitored. In the early years of operation, the wells were monitored monthly and as the project progressed and no significant impacts to water quality were demonstrated, the regulatory permit was modified to a mix of quarterly, semi-annual, and annual monitoring for different wells. The most frequent monitoring is conducted at wells located down gradient from the irrigation site. Surface water as it discharges from the site is monitored at Clayton County's water supply intake about 10 km downstream.

Groundwater quality has been monitored since 1979, over 4 years prior to commencement of wastewater irrigation. Initially, many inorganic parameters were monitored, including nitrate-nitrogen, phosphate, chloride, specific conductivity, a number of metals, and coliforms. Later, analysis of metal and coliforms was discontinued except for a few interior and down gradient wells on an annual basis.

Wells have been grouped by permit conditions as up gradient, interior, and down gradient. Considering the most mobile constituents monitored (chloride and nitrate-nitrogen) and specific conductivity, there have been increasing trends to what appears to be a plateau concentration for chloride and specific conductivity and an initial slight increase in nitrate-nitrogen with no long-term increasing trend since irrigation began in 1983. Chloride and nitrite-nitrogen concentrations and specific conductivity in the background (up gradient) wells average about 10 mg l^{-1}, 0.1 mg l^{-1}, and 80 uSc m^{-1}, respectively, and have remained somewhat constant since monitoring began in 1979. In contrast, chloride concentrations and specific conductivity in the down gradient wells (immediately outside the irrigation area) have steadily increased from 10 to 20 mg l^{-1} and from 80 to 150 uSc m^{-1}, respectively. This represents a doubling in 12 years of irrigation. Both parameters, however, are well below the maximum contaminant level (MCL) for drinking water. Nitrate-nitrogen concentrations, on the other hand, in the down gradient well have increased to an average of 0.5 mg l^{-1}. Most of the increase in nitrate-nitrogen concentration came within 10 years of commencement of irrigation and has remained at the increased level since (**Figure 1**). Nitrate-nitrogen increases in the down gradient wells are not significantly different from preirrigation levels.

Monitoring also indicates that irrigated wastewater is percolating to the groundwater as evidenced by increases in chloride and specific conductivity. The interpretation drawn from the steadily increasing chloride and specific conductivity and no increasing trend in nitrate-nitrogen is that plant uptake and denitrification, which occurs at higher rates in irrigated areas than in nonirrigated forests (**Figure 2**), are occurring to the extent that little nitrate is reaching the groundwater.

About 8% of Pates Creek watershed above the drinking water supply reservoir is irrigated with wastewater. Water quality monitoring has been

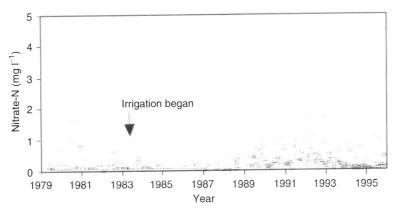

Figure 1 Trend of nitrate-nitrogen in the down gradient monitoring wells. The line is a moving mean and the symbols represent readings from five wells.

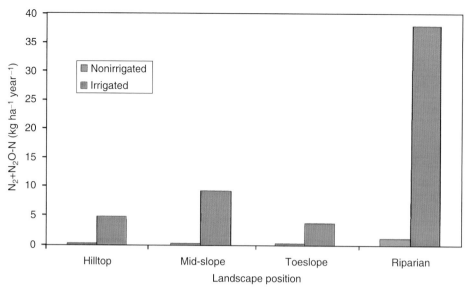

Figure 2   Annual denitrification in wastewater irrigated forests and adjacent nonirrigated forests in the Piedmont of the southeastern USA.

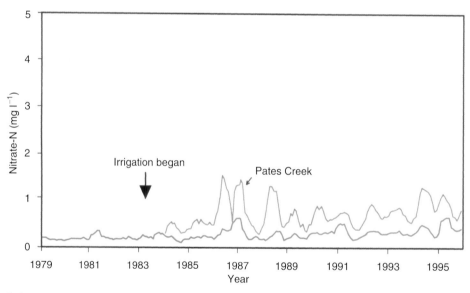

Figure 3   Trend of nitrate-nitrogen in Pates Creek draining the land treatment system compared to two nearby streams. Pates Creek flows directly to the drinking water reservoir.

conducted at the head of the reservoir and at two tributary streams that do not receive wastewater irrigation but are experiencing expanding urbanization. Pates Creek exhibits similar water quality changes that have occurred in the groundwater. Although there is greater variation in streamwater quality than groundwater quality, specific conductivity in Pates Creek has remained steady at an average of about $100 \, \mu S \, cm^{-1}$. Nitrate-nitrogen has also remained steady at about $1.0–1.5 \, mg \, l^{-1}$ (**Figure 3**) but chloride has steadily increased from an average of about $10–20 \, mg \, l^{-1}$. These later results are in direct correspondence with groundwater quality.

Reeves Creek and Rum Creek, the two nonirrigated background monitored streams, have similar specific conductivity and nitrate-nitrogen concentrations as Pates Creek and chloride concentrations are similar to and unchanged from the initial preirrigation concentrations in Pates Creek.

Infiltration rates have remained high on the site due, in part, to the activity of earthworms, which occur in much higher numbers within irrigated forests than in nonirrigated forests. Tree growth and nutrient accumulation has been periodically assessed at Clayton County. In general, trees irrigated with wastewater have higher foliage nutrient concentrations and exhibit more rapid growth than trees grown on adjacent sites without irrigation.

Summary

1. The concept of land treatment of wastewater has a sound scientific and experience foundation which has proven that land can be used to renovate wastewater in a environmentally acceptable manner and that such land is not irreversibly withdrawn from any present or future societal use.

2. No human or animal health problems have been reported and studies have concluded that properly designed and operated wastewater irrigation systems are likely to pose less environmental health problems than most other wastewater treatment technologies.

3. Forests can be successfully used as the principal vegetative cover in a land treatment system. It has in fact a number of advantages over agronomic crops including greater flexibility to operate around climatic conditions, fewer interruptions to the irrigation schedule, and can be operated year-round.

4. The design of a forest system must be based on potential performance of the site to meet water quality performance criteria objectives including hydraulic capacity as well as nitrogen assimilative capacity. Both of these factors normally influence the total performance of the land treatment system.

5. Successful operation of the land treatment system is evaluated on the basis of performance standards established by water quality objectives.

See also: **Hydrology**: Impacts of Forest Conversion on Streamflow. **Silviculture**: Forest Rehabilitation. **Site-Specific Silviculture**: Silviculture in Polluted Areas. **Soil Development and Properties**: Water Storage and Movement. **Tree Breeding, Practices**: Nitrogen-fixing Tree Improvement and Culture.

Further Reading

Cole DW, Henry CL, and Nutter WL (eds) (1986) *The Forest Alternative for Treatment and Utilization of Municipal and Industrial Wastes*. Seattle, WA: University of Washington Press.

Hamsley WD (1979) *Estimation of Soil Phosphorus Fixation Capacity on a Forested Wastewater Land Treatment Site*. M.Sc. thesis, University of Georgia School of Forest Resources.

Henry CL, Harrison RB, and Bastian RK (eds) (2000) *The Forest Alternative: Principles and Practice of Residuals Use*, Proceedings of a Conference held at University of Washington, Seattle, July 14–16, 1997.

Iskander IK (1981) *Modeling Wastewater Renovation Land Treatment*. New York: John Wiley.

McKim HL, Sopper WE, Cole D, *et al.* (1982) *Wastewater Application in Forest Ecosystems*. CRREL Report no. 80-19. Hanover, NH: US Army Cold Regions Research and Engineering Laboratory.

Moffat AJ, Armstrong AT, and Ockleston J (2001) The optimization of sewage sludge and effluent disposal on energy crops of short rotation hybrid poplar. *Biomass and Bioenergy* 20(3): 161–169.

Nutter WL (1986) Forest land treatment of wastewater in Clayton County, Georgia: a case study. In: *The Forest Alternative for Treatment and Utilization of Municipal and Industrial Wastes*, pp. 393–405. Seattle, WA: University of Washington Press.

Nutter WL (2000) Implementation and operation of wastewater irrigation systems in forests. In: *The Forest Alternative: Principles and Practice of Residuals Use*, pp. 135–138. Proceedings of a Conference held at University of Washington, Seattle, July 14–16, 1997.

Nutter WL, Schultz RC, and Brister GH (1979) Renovation of municipal wastewater by spray irrigation on steep forest slopes in the Southern Appalachians. In: *Utilization of Municipal Sewage Effluent and Sludge on Forest and Disturbed Land*, pp. 77–85. Philadelphia, PA: Pennsylvania State University Press.

Overcash MR and Pal D (1979) *Design of Land Treatment Systems for Industrial Wastes: Theory and Practice*. Ann Arbor, MI: Ann Arbor Science.

Reed SC, Middlebrooks EJ, and Crites RW (1988) *Natural Systems for Waste Management and Treatment*. New York: McGraw-Hill.

US Environmental Protection Agency (1981) *Process Design Manual for Land Treatment of Municipal Wastewater*. EPA 625/1-81-013 (COE EM1110-1-501). Washington, DC: US Government Printing Office.

Water Storage and Movement

M Weiler, University of British Columbia, Vancouver, BC, Canada
J J McDonnell, Oregon State University, Corvallis, OR, USA

Introduction

Water storage and movement in forest soils is a key regulator for a variety of hydrological, physiological, and biogeochemical processes in a forest. The climate and geology controls on soils vary around the world; these can range from conditions of colluvial infilling of steep unstable hollows in and around the Pacific Rim, to till soils that develop on recently glaciated sites in Scandinavia, eastern Canada, and Russia, and deeper clay-rich soils in lower-latitude regions. While the physics of flow in porous media is the same regardless of land-use type, forest soils often have rather different depth-integrated and spatially variable properties relative to soils in agricultural or suburban areas. This entry considers a number of properties of forest soils as it relates to some of the basic definitions and physical processes governing water storage and movement. It then considers in detail the main processes of how water moves vertically and laterally through forest soils – from the plot scale, to hillslope scale, and catchment scale. Finally, influences of forest management and forest fires on water storage and movement are discussed. This entry focuses on some of the first-order controls common to most landscapes. The reader should consult material provided in the Further Reading section for a comprehensive review of water storage and movement in all climatic and physiographic regions of the world.

Soil Physics Terminology and Measurement

Soils, especially forest soils, are a complex mixture of organic and inorganic, living and dead, or solid, liquid, and gaseous materials. This complexity appears at first glance difficult to characterize; however, classifying soils into three phases – air, water, and solids – provides a convenient means to define the basic physical soil properties (**Figure 1**).

The particle density is equal to the ratio of mass to volume of solids. In contrast, the bulk density is the ratio of mass of solids to the total volume. The porosity is the proportion of pore space (air and water) in a given volume of soil. The water content of the soil is described in two ways, as the ratio of water to soil volume, if it is volumetrically defined, or mass, if it is gravitationally defined. Given the water content, the degree of saturation can be calculated as the ratio between volumetric water content and porosity. The water content is an

important hydrological property of soils. It can be determined in the laboratory or using field methods. In the laboratory, one weighs a field-extracted intact core of known volume, dries it at $105°C$ for $24 h$, and then weighs it again. The difference is used to compute the volumetric water content. In the field, water content is most often measured by time–domain reflectometry (TDR), although many investigators still use neutron probes, gypsum blocks, and capacitance techniques. TDR instruments operate by measuring the propagation velocity in the soil of an electric pulse that is related to the dielectric permittivity or dielectric constant, which is closely related to water content.

Energy State of Water in Soil

Knowing the temporal and spatial variation of water content in the soil is sufficient for determining the total soil water storage (usually expressed as a depth or volume per unit area). For measuring and defining the direction of water movement in soils, the energy state of soil water must be defined since differences in the energy state (potential) drive the direction of water movement. The total soil water potential is the sum of various forces acting on the soil water: gravitational potential, pressure potential, matric potential, and osmotic potential. The gravitational potential depends on the position in the gravitational force field relative to some reference level. Pressure potential is the hydrostatic pressure of the water column under saturation. The matric potential (also referred to as matric suction or capillary potential) is defined under unsaturated conditions, where capillary and adsorptive forces act to create a negative pressure (often called tension or suction). This is measured in soils relative to the external gas pressure. The osmotic potential is attributed to the presence of solutes in the soil water and only in arid environments significantly affects the water movement compared to pressure and matric potential. The primary effect of osmotic potential relates to the uptake of water by vegetation. In this case, the roots act as a membrane which regulates the movement of water as a function of osmotic potential, since water vapor pressure is lowered by the presence of solutes. The pressure potential of soil water is often measured with piezometers. Piezometers are tubes augered into the soil below the water table and only open at the bottom of the tube. Thus, the pressure potential at the bottom of the tube is reflected by the height of water rise in the standing water column within the tube. The soil matric potential is measured with porous cup devices called tensiometers that have a practical range from 0 to $800 cm$ ($0–78 kPa$). This

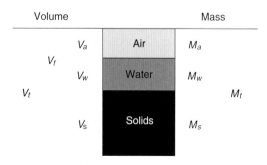

Figure 1 Soil and its three phases: air, water, and solids. V_t and M_t are totals.

range covers most of the naturally observed tensions in forest soils. For higher tensions, thermocouples, psychrometers, or gypsum electrical-resistance blocks are available.

Soil Moisture Characteristic Curve

The relationship between soil moisture and tension is called soil moisture characteristic curve (also soil moisture release curve, retention curve) and is an important property of unsaturated soil. This relationship strongly depends on the soil texture, but also on other soil properties like soil structure, organic matter, and bulk density. No universal theory yet exists to describe or predict the soil moisture characteristic curve (SMCC) from soil properties. In addition, the value of tension at a given water content is not unique, but depends on the soil history of wetting and drying. This hysteresis can have a significant influence on water movement, but is often not considered in describing water movement in hydrological models, since no unique functional relationship can be easily assumed.

The SMCC of forest soils is often highly nonlinear. **Figure 2** shows drying curves for forest soils in old-growth Douglas–fir at three soil depths. The water content decreases by 10–30% between saturation and 20–40 cm of tension. This typical 'drop' for many forest soils is related to soil structure and the macroporosity (large pore space) related to the effect of roots, especially in the topsoil. These macropores in the upper soil horizons drain water at a very low tension (low capillary). This nonlinearity often declines with soil depth (**Figure 2**) since the pore space often declines rapidly into the profile, with concomitant increases in bulk density.

Field Capacity and Permanent Wilting Point

Two points of the SMCC are particularly important: the field capacity and the permanent wilting point. Field capacity is the water content of a soil after gravitational drainage over approximately a day. The suction that defines this value varies from soil to soil, but is generally in the range of 10–33 kPa. Drainable porosity of a soil is defined as the water content between field capacity and saturation. The drainable porosity controls the transient water-table dynamic that often develops at the soil–bedrock interface or some zone of low permeability at depth (hardpan, duricrust, or other layer). The permanent wilting point is the water content at which plants start to wilt during daytime – indicating that they are no longer able to extract water from the soil. The suction at this point is very high, about 1470 kPa. The difference of water content between field capacity and permanent wilting point is often called the available water content.

Water Storage

Water storage in soils depends on the water balance of a soil pedon. The water balance represents one of the most basic equations in hydrology. The change in water storage is equal to the changes in input and output (**Figure 3**). The principal input flux in forest

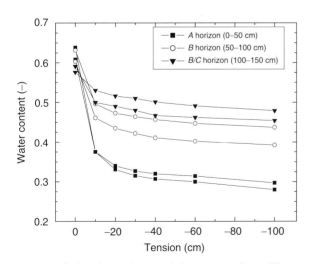

Figure 2 Soil moisture characteristic curves at three different depths of a forest soil (data from HJ Andrews Experimental Forest, Oregon, USA). Note the flattening of the curves deeper in the profile. These curves represent the trajectory of water content and water suction upon drying. Often, soils show differences in these curves during wetting. This difference, called hysteresis, can be significant for some forest soils.

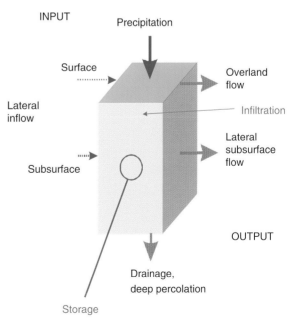

Figure 3 Water storage, input, and output fluxes for a soil column.

soils is precipitation. Only a proportion of total precipitation, termed throughfall, reaches the forest floor. The difference between total amount of precipitation and throughfall results from interception and storage by the forest canopy. Throughfall or snowmelt from snow accumulated above the forest floor infiltrates into the soil, flows over the soil surface, or is stored within surface depressions. While forest soil infiltration rates almost always exceed the precipitation input to the soil surface, 'excess water' may flow on the soil or decayed-leaf surfaces and become stored in small microtopographic depressions in the forest soil surface. Vertical inflow to the soil pedon may therefore originate as ponded overland flow or by lateral subsurface flow.

Three mechanisms act to deplete water in the soil pedon. The first includes direct evaporation from the soil surface and plant uptake in the rooting zone and then transpiration by plants. This loss is collectively termed evapotranspiration. The second is the vertical drainage into the underlying bedrock and possible recharge into underlying groundwater. The third mechanism is lateral subsurface flow within the soil. The dynamics of these fluxes in forest soils are unique as compared to soils under other land use. The modulation of the incoming precipitation by the canopy results in a reduction of both the rainfall intensity and the total amount of precipitation. In addition to trees, smaller plants (e.g., shrubs and bushes) as well as moss and the litter layer affect the disposition of incoming precipitation. Direct evaporation rates from the soil surface are generally lower than the transpiration rates by plants in forested settings. Since trees extract water from soil and have a deep root zone, the reduction of the water content with depth during dry periods is much more sustained in forest soils compared to soils under other land use. Alternatively, direct evaporation of water at the soil surface is reduced under the forest canopy. Water redistribution in forest soils by tree roots, especially by water uptake from the saturated zone (groundwater), and redistribution into the unsaturated zone is an important process, particularly in semi-arid climates.

Spatial Variability

The heterogeneous structure of forests, in combination with complex topography and soil heterogeneity, results in significant spatial variability of water storage within forest soils. The plant canopy modifies precipitation input and also produces a persistent spatial pattern of throughfall to the soil surface. Studies under coniferous canopies have shown up to 100% differences in throughfall application to the

soil surface over distances of less than 1 m. In addition, flow down the tree stem (stem flow) further increases this variability of precipitation input to the soil. Snowmelt may produce a similar spatial variability through factors affecting the energy budget of the snow (e.g., slope aspect, inclination, and cover type). Lateral flow of water within the soil or upwards movement of groundwater into the soil profile is often described by topography. Thus, topographic position, local slope angle, and upslope contributing area are key variables to explain larger-scale spatial variability of soil water storage. These influences are most pronounced in areas with significant topographic relief, shallow lateral flow pathways, and under humid conditions. Finally, the variability of transpiration by trees and other plants may also affect a spatial variability of soil water storage within forests.

Water Movement

Hydrological Concepts – Runoff Generation Processes

Runoff generation processes during rainfall or snowmelt events are often separated into two classes: those processes which were relevant for generating overland and those processes that are relevant for generating lateral subsurface flow. Overland flow can be generated by infiltration excess (rainfall intensity is larger than the soil's infiltration capacity) or by saturation excess (where soils become saturated by a rising water table). In forest soils, overland flow is usually generated by the saturation excess mechanism. One exception is where infiltration excess overland flow may be produced on logging roads and other low-permeability areas (e.g., compacted soils) or on soils with seasonal water repellency due to fire (see **Health and Protection**: Forest Fires (Prediction, Prevention, Preparedness and Suppression)). Saturation overland flow is most common in areas where soils are often waterlogged (topographic confluence zones, near springs, and in riparian zones).

On steeper hillslopes, water infiltrating into the soil will either be stored in the soil or will continue moving vertically to recharge local groundwater or flow as lateral subsurface flow. This lateral subsurface flow (also called subsurface stormflow, interflow, and throughflow) are very common in forest soils since the lateral hydraulic conductivity and the gravitational gradients (in areas with a steep relief) are often high, and additional preferential flow pathways are present to enhance the downslope flow. Knowing the dominant runoff generation processes at a site is an important first step to understand runoff generation in a catchment, as well as flood generation, nutrient transport, and prediction of forest management practices on water quantity and quality.

Vertical Movement

Water movement in porous media like soils is often described based on the Darcy equation that flow is proportional to the hydraulic potential times the hydraulic conductivity:

$$q = -K \frac{\Delta H}{\Delta z}$$

where q is the water flow (length per time), K is the saturated hydraulic conductivity (length per time), ΔH is the hydraulic head difference, and Δz the distance. The saturated hydraulic conductivity (or permeability) is a spatially variable property of soils (over several orders of magnitude over short distances). Hence, it varies with the scale of measurement. It depends on the soil texture, but also on the soil structural features. Due to these structures, the saturated hydraulic conductivity of forest soils is usually much smaller in the vertical direction than in the horizontal direction (known as anisotropy). In addition, the hydraulic conductivity depends strongly on the degree of saturation and thus on the soil water tension. Based on this functional relationship, the Richards equation was developed by combining the Darcy equation with the continuity equation to describe flow in unsaturated porous media:

$$\frac{\partial \theta}{\partial t} = \frac{\partial}{\partial z} \left[K(h) \left(\frac{\partial h}{\partial z} + 1 \right) \right]$$

where $K(h)$ is the unsaturated hydraulic conductivity and θ the water content. Both equations are based on the capillary concept and work well in relatively homogeneous soils. However, in forest soils, the influence of plant roots, soil structure, burrowing animals, and worm casts creates a variety of larger pores (macropores) that water may follow preferentially (**Figure 4**). Due to these macropores, the unsaturated hydraulic conductivity relationship often shows a significant reduction (one to some orders of magnitude) at values near saturation. Thus, while macropores may comprise only a small part of the total soil porosity, they may control almost all the water flow at or near saturation within the profile. The water flow in these macropores is often turbulent and mostly driven by gravity. The resulting water movement in the soils is very heterogeneous and dry areas within the soil may be bypassed. These processes run counter to the Darcy and Richards formulations that rely exclusively on capillary-driven laws of fluid flow.

Water movement that may be influenced by preferential flow can be visualized by adding a dye tracer to the infiltrating water. **Figure 5** shows some experimental results where a food dye (Brilliant Blue FCF) was added to a simulated rainfall event. Soil profiles were excavated and pictures were taken from these vertical soil sections. **Figure 5** shows two examples of these dye patterns for forest soils in Oregon, USA. The patterns show that the soil surface itself may affect the disposition of infiltrating rainfall. The litter layer may be a significant generator of flowpath heterogeneity near the soil surface. Deeper in the soil profile, water flow may occur only in macropores, bypassing large dry areas of matrix in the soil profile. In contrast to homogeneous infiltration, the process of water flow into the macropores (initiation) and water flow from macropores into the surrounding soil matrix (interaction) mainly controls the vertical water movement of water in forest soils. In general, macropore flow results in a much faster flow and increased transport of solutes and nutrients.

Lateral Movement

Lateral water movement in the soil is an important process for redistribution of water, nutrients, and solutes in the environment. This process also controls the generation of storm runoff in many upland forested environments. Detailed process studies in forest soils in the last half-century have revealed a variety of flow pathways in forest watersheds. **Figure 4** illustrates the most important of these pathways. If the bedrock is relatively impermeable compared to the soil, infiltrating water perches on the soil–bedrock interface and flows laterally downslope along this interface. Since this interface is generally topographically 'rough' due to weathering and mass movement, water concentrates in hollows and depressions. The resulting channalized flow acts similarly to macropore flow whereas the average flow velocity increases and areas with a relatively higher soil–bedrock relief interface are bypassed. The lateral flow is less preferential if the soil–bedrock interface is more gradual in texture and where the hydraulic conductivity decrease with depth is more gradual. This gradual decline can be observed in soils developed from glaciated deposits (e.g. till).

Macropore flow is also a major control on lateral flow on forest hillslopes. Similar to the processes governing vertical flow in macropores, laterally oriented macropore flow may dominate in many forest environments where macropores are generated by plant roots and burrowing animals. These

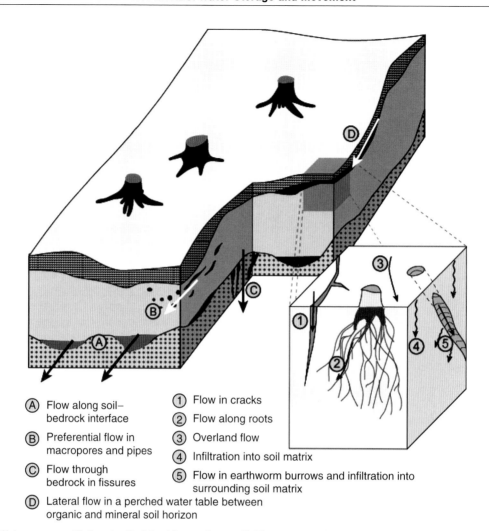

(A) Flow along soil–bedrock interface

(B) Preferential flow in macropores and pipes

(C) Flow through bedrock in fissures

(D) Lateral flow in a perched water table between organic and mineral soil horizon

(1) Flow in cracks

(2) Flow along roots

(3) Overland flow

(4) Infiltration into soil matrix

(5) Flow in earthworm burrows and infiltration into surrounding soil matrix

Figure 4 Water movement in forest soils: lateral flow pathways (A–D) and vertical flow pathways (1–5). Note the complexity of water flow pathways due to physical and biological agents acting on soil.

50 cm

Stained area

Area above soil surface

Figure 5 Dye patterns from two different forested sites: (a) HJ Andrews Experimental Forest, Oregon, USA; (b) Low Pass Area, Coastal Range, Oregon, USA. Note the spatial heterogeneity of dyed water and preferred nature of water flow vertically within the forest soil profile.

macropores are often termed soil pipes. If a connected network is developed due to internal erosion and connection of the macropores, piping can provide effective drainage augmentation to hillslopes. If the underlying bedrock is more permeable, water can infiltrate into the bedrock and then percolate vertically in fissures and cracks. The top soil layer (litter or organic layer) in forest soils includes a high proportion of organic material and roots that enhance the hydraulic conductivity. If the underlying mineral soil has a low hydraulic conductivity, a perched water table can sometimes develop during rainfall and snowmelt events within the organic horizon. Under these conditions, water may flow laterally within this layer.

Important Issues

Harvesting and Forest Management

Harvesting and forest management operations can strongly influence water storage and movement in soil. An important issue is soil compaction by using heavy machinery for timber harvesting. Depending on the soil texture, soil structure, and the soil moisture content during the operations, soil compaction can occur. Soil compaction is defined as an increase in bulk density and a decrease in soil porosity resulting from applied loads, vibration, or pressure. Compaction can reduce infiltration, leading to the development of areas that can produce infiltration excess and overland flow. Water storage capacity of the soil can also be reduced since the proportion of larger pore space may be reduced through compression. A specific feature of forest soils is the organic layer on top of the mineral soil. This organic layer modulates infiltration, reduces evaporation, and increases water storage. Removing this organic layer by forest management (mechanical removing and burning) often negatively changes the hydrological behavior of a site. While much progress has been made in forest operations in the developed world in reducing site disturbance associated with logging, poor logging practices can have deleterious effects on soil water storage and movement.

Fire

Forest fires may consume a large part of the forest floor, eliminating beneficial effects of the organic layer on soil properties. However, the effects of low-temperature fires (e.g., from controlled burning) are generally less than the effects from hot wildfires. The most pronounced impact of forest fires on soil properties is the reduction of infiltration rates due to water repellency. This reduced infiltration not only increases the amount of overland flow and thus soil erosion, but may further reduce the availability of soil water for plants, especially in semiarid regions. Water-repellent soils can develop from hydrophobic substances vaporized during burning of the surface litter layers. The degree and persistence of these hydrophobic substances depend not only on the temperatures during the fire but also on the timing, number, and magnitude of subsequent rainfall events on the burned site (as water repellency can decrease with time). In addition, drier soils show higher water repellency than wetter soils, which should be kept in mind considering these effects in different climate zones.

Measuring the effects of fire on water movement and storage in soils is difficult, and results from experimental studies concerning the effects of fire on changes in infiltration rate are equivocal. The major problem is to determine if small-scale effects due to hydrophobic substances translate into larger-scale (hillslope and watershed) behavioral changes. One possibility to explore the effects of forest fire on infiltration is to perform infiltration experiments in combination with dye patterns. **Figure 6** shows the impact of the water-repellent surface layer. Water was only able to infiltrate at few locations within the profile, coincident with local depressions or plant roots. Thus, the resulting dye pattern shows only a thin staining near the soil surface and some isolated 'spots' within the soil. Nevertheless, comprehensive analysis of the effects of fire on water storage and movement in forest soils on larger scales remain the topic of future research.

50 cm

■ Stained area

□ Area above soil surface

Figure 6 Dye pattern from a recently burned forest soil in the Western Cascades, Oregon, USA.

Summary

Water movement and storage in soils are regulated by a variety of temporally and spatially variable processes. This article presents an overview of the most important properties and processes influencing water movement and storage in forest soils. Soil water storage and movement are controlled by the size and spatial distribution of macropores, through which water can move rapidly but which drain under gravity, and micropores, through which water moves more slowly but can retain water against gravity. The relationship between water content and soil water tension is described by the soil moisture characteristic curve. Two points on this curve, field capacity and permanent wilting point, are particularly important as they describe storage of plant available water. Runoff from forests can be generated by overland flow and lateral subsurface flow. Overland flow usually only occurs on sites compacted by harvesting or which have water-repellent surfaces resulting from fire. Lateral subsurface flow is very common in forests since the lateral hydraulic conductivity and the gravitational gradients (in areas with a steep relief) are often high, and additional preferential flow pathways are present to enhance the downslope flow. The described processes of water storage and movement are applicable in various climates and geographical locations. However, certain processes dominate in certain locations – predicting and understanding water storage and movement in soils require one to use critical thinking to define the first-order controls at a particular site.

See also: **Ecology**: Forest Canopies; Natural Disturbance in Forest Environments. **Health and Protection**: Forest Fires (Prediction, Prevention, Preparedness and Suppression). **Hydrology**: Hydrological Cycle; Impacts of Forest Conversion on Streamflow; Impacts of Forest Management on Streamflow; Impacts of Forest Management on Water Quality. **Soil Biology and Tree Growth**: Soil Organic Matter Forms and Functions; Tree Roots and their Interaction with Soil. **Soil Development and Properties**: Forests and Soil Development; Landscape and Soil Classification for Forest Management; Nutrient Cycling; The Forest Floor.

Further Reading

Beven K (1989) Interflow. In: Morel-Seytoux HJ (ed.) *Unsaturated Flow in Hydrologic Modeling Theory and Practice*, pp. 191–219. Dordrecht, Germany: Kluwer Academic Publishers.

Beven K and Germann P (1982) Macropores and water flow in soils. *Water Resources Research* 18(5): 1311–1325.

Bonell M (1993) Progress in the understanding of runoff generation dynamics in forests. *Journal of Hydrology* 150: 217–275.

DeBano LF (2000) The role of fire and soil heating on water repellency in wildland environments: a review. *Journal of Hydrology* 231: 1–4.

Feddes RA, Kabat P, van Bakel PJT, Bronswijk JJB, and Halbertsma J (1988) Modelling soil water dynamics in the unsaturated zone – state of the art. *Journal of Hydrology* 100: 69–111.

Grayson R and Blöschl G (eds) (2000) *Spatial Patterns in Catchment Hydrology: observations and modeling*. Cambridge, UK: Cambridge University Press.

Hillel D (1998) *Environmental Soil Physics*. San Diego, CA: Academic Press.

Jury WA, Gardner R, and Gardner WH (1991) *Soil Physics*. New York: John Wiley.

Klute A (ed.) (1986) *Methods of Soil Analysis*, Part I, *Physical and Mineralogical Methods*. Madison, WI: American Society of Agronomy.

Kutílek M and Nielsen DR (1994) *Soil Hydrology*. Cremlingen-Destedt, Germany: Catena-Verlag.

McDonnell JJ (1990) A rationale for old water discharge through macropores in a steep, humid catchment. *Water Resources Research* 26(11): 2821–2832.

Pritchett WL and Fisher RF (1987) *Properties and Management of Forest Soils*. New York: John Wiley.

Weiler M and Naef F (2003) An experimental tracer study of the role of macropores in infiltration in grassland soils. *Hydrological Processes* 17(2): 477–493.

Weyman DR (1973) Measurements of the downslope flow of water in a soil. *Journal of Hydrology* 20: 267–288.

Youngs EG (1995) Developments in the physics of infiltration. *Soil Science Society of America Journal* 59: 307–313.

SOLID WOOD PROCESSING

Contents

Adhesion and Adhesives

C E Frazier, Virginia Technical Institute, Blacksburg, VA, USA

Introduction

Adhesion science and technology has developed since our earliest ancestors struggled to enhance their conditions. The struggle continues, and as with all modern technologies it is apparent that adhesion has evolved into a highly multi- and interdisciplinary activity. Three disciplines define the foundation of adhesion science and technology: chemistry, materials science, and mechanics of materials. It so happens that wood is a peculiar material with respect to each of these disciplines. The following discussion of wood adhesion touches upon the chemical and material sciences and is intended to direct the reader to the more complete treatments found in the recommendations for further reading. Afterwards, some of the more common wood adhesives are reviewed briefly.

Requirements for Adhesion

Adhesion is the process of 'making things stick.' By this definition, one appreciates that adhesive phenomena are widespread because sticky things and processes are all around us. However, this article focuses on applications in the forest products industry, a more narrow view because typical wood applications not only require 'stickiness,' but also structural integrity and long-term durability. There are three essential requirements for a durable, structurally sound adhesive bond:

1. Surface preparation.
2. Adhesive wetting.
3. Adhesive solidification.

While this seems like a simple plan, and it can be, each step is based upon numerous interacting variables. The highlights of each requirement follow.

Surface Preparation

The preparation of bonding surfaces involves chemical and physical parameters. Physically, a clean bonding surface is required, devoid of loose particles and other weak boundary layers. For wood bonding, most desirable is a well-machined smooth surface with minimal cellular damage and compression. Machining processes such as knife planing and veneer slicing produce smooth surfaces with little damage, when the blades are sharp. In contrast, processes such as abrasive planing and sawing produce more cell damage and a weakened surface layer. Under loading, such defects may concentrate stress and promote bond failure. Understand that all machining processes cause some level of wood surface damage. But again, planing and slicing with sharp blades provides the smoothest and most structurally sound surface; this is generally best. However, contradictory findings exist. For example, there are times when wood surface roughening improves bond test-strengths. However, any benefits from wood surface roughening are difficult to reproduce due to changes in other influential parameters, such as adhesive layer thickness, physical interlocking of wood surfaces, and stress concentrations. Predicting when wood surface roughening may improve bond test-strength is difficult at best. Consequently, a safer approach is to machine a smooth, sound surface with minimal cellular damage.

The chemical aspects of wood surface preparation are also important, and this addresses the concept of surface energy. Surface energy is a chemical manifestation of solids and liquids. It reflects the nature of electrical charges present on the surfaces of all molecules. A higher surface energy reflects a higher degree of surface charge, lower surface energy, less charge. All molecules have surface charge, positive and negative, and all molecules tend to orient themselves in an attempt to neutralize this charge. This is the essence of adhesion; but these attractive adhesive forces act only over very small distances, under 10 nanometers, or on the order of molecular dimensions. This fact explains why all adhesives must be liquid at some stage, because only liquids can readily achieve intimate molecular contact over large bond areas. When liquid adhesives contact solid surfaces, the force of attraction depends upon the molecular surface charges, the surface energies of the liquid adhesive and the solid wood surface. Wood machining exposes 'fresh wood,' providing the highest possible surface energy which is very desirable for bonding. Unfortunately, there are many factors that tend to reduce the surface energy of wood, producing what is termed a deactivated or aged surface. These include: the simple deposition of airborne organic materials, ultraviolet radiation from the sun, excessive heat over time, and of course, dirt, grime and even oily human hands.

Adhesive Wetting

Wetting is the term used to describe how liquids adhere to solid surfaces. The quality of wetting, be it favorable or unfavorable, is a function of surface energy. This is why we are first concerned with surface preparation, and maximizing the wood surface energy. But we are also interested in the surface energy of the liquid adhesive. A relative measure of solid and liquid surface energy is observed through the 'contact angle,' as depicted in **Figure 1**. Also shown in **Figure 1** is the Young equation, which explains that the contact angle reflects the balance of surface energies (γ), that of the solid, the liquid, and the solid–liquid interface.

Arbitrarily, 'favorable wetting' is defined by a contact angle less than 90°. When the contact angle exceeds 90°, wetting is 'unfavorable.' When a liquid adhesive favorably wets the bonding surface, the attractive forces at the solid–liquid interface are greater than the cohesive forces acting within the liquid adhesive. Generally, favorable adhesive wetting provides good bonding, but there is no guarantee because good wetting is but one aspect of good bonding. On the other hand and invariably, unfavorable wetting will result in a poor adhesive bond. Consequently, the concepts of surface energy and wetting are critical aspects of adhesion.

Figure 2 depicts two strategies for controlling adhesive wetting. First, let us consider some unchanging solid surface, which is wetted by three different liquids. As the surface energy of the liquid is reduced, wetting becomes more favorable and the contact angle is reduced. For example, consider the wetting properties of two liquids, water and isopropanol (rubbing alcohol). Water is polar and has a high surface energy, whereas, isopropanol is less polar with a lower surface energy. (The term 'polar' also refers to molecular surface charge; polar

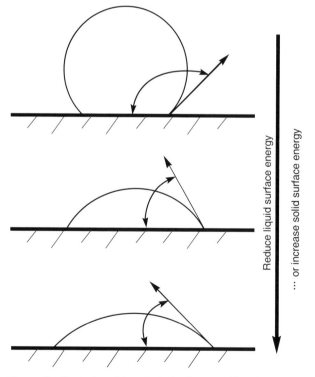

Figure 2 Illustration of two strategies for controlling the contact angle, or the wetting, of liquid adhesives on solid surfaces. Strategy 1: Three identical solid surfaces are contacted by three different liquids; wetting improves as the liquid surface energy is reduced. Strategy 2: Three different solid surfaces contacted by water in each case; water wetting improves as the solid surface energy is increased.

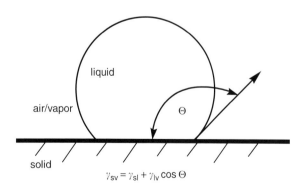

$$\gamma_{sv} = \gamma_{sl} + \gamma_{lv} \cos \Theta$$

Figure 1 Depiction of the contact angle of a liquid on a solid surface. Also shown is the Young equation which describes the balance of surface energy (γ) between the solid, liquid and vapor phases.

molecules have higher surface charge. Polarity and surface energy are generally related, but the terms should not be interchanged freely.) Isopropanol will wet any particular surface more favorably than will water. In other words, on a given surface the contact angle of isopropanol will be lower than that of water. Furthermore, one can improve the wetting of a liquid adhesive by simply reducing the surface energy of the adhesive. This is commonly achieved by adding wetting agents, chemicals that reduce the surface energy of aqueous solutions. Wetting agents are also referred to as surface active agents, or surfactants. Very small quantities of wetting agents dramatically reduce the surface energy of aqueous adhesives; wetting improves. Now look back at **Figure 2** as we discuss the second strategy to improve wetting.

If we consider a single unchanging liquid, we can improve the wetting of that liquid by increasing the wood surface energy. Imagine that **Figure 2** shows three different wood surfaces, each wetted by a drop of water. The topmost wood surface exhibits a low surface energy because the water contact angle is well over 90°. Likewise, the bottom surface has the highest surface energy, indicated by the lowest contact angle. The best bonds result from favorable wetting that is driven by a high wood surface energy. Unfortunately, we may not always control the wood surface energy. For example, remachining a deactivated wood surface immediately prior to bonding might not be feasible. One may then be forced to improve adhesive wetting by adding wetting agents. If given the choice, one should always achieve and maintain a high wood surface energy.

A simple test reveals differences in wood surface energy. One could measure the water contact angle on wood surfaces, but this is often impractical. However, it is easy to measure the time it takes a water drop to absorb into wood. If a water drop wets favorably, capillary forces rapidly draw the water into the wood. **Figure 3** shows data collected by a group of college students in the author's adhesion class. Water drops (10 μl in volume) were applied to red oak (*Quercus rubra*) samples having different surface treatments. The water absorption time is fastest on the freshly sanded surface; the sanded surface has the highest surface energy. Samples with the 'old surface' were stored in a plastic bag for 1 year, and they apparently lost surface energy because the absorption time is nearly doubled. The remaining samples were sanded and then heated at 185°C for 5 min, which caused a severe deactivation. Data on the far right of **Figure 3** demonstrate the power of wetting agents. In this case, the water drops contained 10% isopropanol, which causes a remarkable reduction in absorption time; wetting was

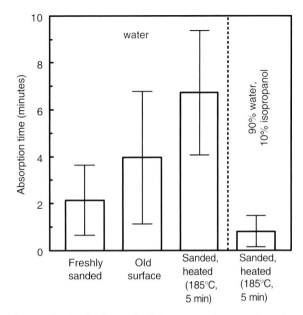

Figure 3 A simple method for comparing wood surface energies involves measuring the time it takes a 10 μl drop of water to absorb into the wood surface. The data shown are for red oak samples exposed to different surface treatments as described in the text.

improved. The broad variation in the absorption times is caused by the natural variability of wood.

Adhesive Solidification

Favorable wetting is required because it ensures strong and intimate molecular contact between wood and adhesive. However, favorable wetting is not enough. After wetting, the adhesive must solidify in order to transmit load. Through wetting we achieve intimate contact and adhesion, but through solidification the adhesive forces are essentially locked into a solid state having mechanical integrity. Small molecules like water do not solidify under convenient conditions. In contrast, the very large polymer molecules solidify into strong solids under desirable circumstances. This is why nearly all adhesives are polymeric. Polymeric molecules, polymers or macromolecules, are extremely large chainlike molecules that may be linear, branched, or crosslinked into network structures. There are three general mechanisms for adhesive solidification: (1) solvent loss, (2) chemical reaction or polymerization, and (3) cooling of a molten adhesive. In all three cases, we are manipulating an important physical parameter of the adhesive, and this is the temperature at which the adhesive changes from a liquid into a solid. For many adhesives, this temperature is referred to as the glass transition temperature, T_g. For other adhesives, hot melt adhesives in particular, this may be the melting temperature, T_m.

Certain adhesives are actually solutions of polymers in organic solvents. While dissolved in the solvent, the polymers are fluid, capable of flow and wetting. Afterwards, the solvent evaporates and/or absorbs into the wood. As the solvent evaporates, the adhesive polymers become less mobile, eventually transforming into a tough, solid adhesive layer (**Figure 4a**). Solvent loss also occurs for another common class of wood adhesive; these are latex adhesives, the water-based 'white glues.' Latex adhesives are actually water dispersions of soft microscopic polymer particles. The fluid latex wets and flows. As water is absorbed into the wood, the particles pack together and deform as they begin to coalesce. When completely dry, the particles have fused into a solid, tough and continuous adhesive film (**Figure 4b**). Adhesives that solidify through solvent loss are typically thermoplastic, meaning they will deform and flow under elevated temperatures. Such thermoplastic adhesives are not designated as structural adhesives because they may deform, or creep, under loading. Creep is avoided in adhesives that solidify through chemical reaction (polymerization) into rigid network structures. These adhesives are called thermosetting adhesives or resins. During application, thermosetting resins are chemically reactive fluid mixtures. While heated, they react into highly crosslinked, rigid network structures (**Figure 4c**). All wood adhesives that satisfy structural applications are thermosetting. Finally, hotmelt adhesives solidify by simply cooling from the molten state into a tough solid. The polymers in hotmelt adhesives are often semicrystalline. Semicrystalline polymers are typically linear and actually pack into three-dimensional crystal structures, or crystallites. Separate polymer chains pack into the crystallites and become 'physically crosslinked.' The hotmelt adhesive must be heated above the T_m of the crystallites, breaking the physical crosslinks and allowing the polymers to flow and wet. Upon

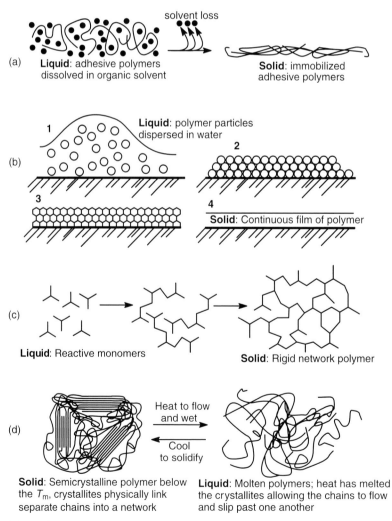

(a) **Liquid:** adhesive polymers dissolved in organic solvent

solvent loss

Solid: immobilized adhesive polymers

(b) 1 **Liquid:** polymer particles dispersed in water

2

3

4 **Solid:** Continuous film of polymer

(c) **Liquid:** Reactive monomers

Solid: Rigid network polymer

(d) Heat to flow and wet

Cool to solidify

Solid: Semicrystalline polymer below the T_m, crystallites physically link separate chains into a network

Liquid: Molten polymers; heat has melted the crystallites allowing the chains to flow and slip past one another

Figure 4 Illustration of four different ways that adhesives solidify to achieve structural integrity.

cooling, the crystallites reform and the adhesive is again a tough solid (**Figure 4d**).

Theories of Adhesion

There are generally five recognized mechanisms or theories of adhesion: (1) the theory of mechanical interlock, (2) the adsorption theory, (3) the covalent bonding theory, (4) the interdiffusion theory, and (5) the electronic theory. Not all of these theoretical mechanisms are important for wood bonding; we shall limit our attention to those that are. The reader interested in all theories should consult the recommendations for further reading.

Mechanical Interlock

The mechanical interlock theory states that adhesives must flow onto the bonding surfaces and into macro- and microscopic voids. After solidification, the adhesive and bonding surfaces are interlocked, or keyed, and capable of withstanding great shear forces. Of course, wood is porous and experience has shown that ideal performance results from adhesive penetration into the cell layers beneath the bonding surfaces. Consequently, it is clear that mechanical interlock contributes to wood adhesion. In the past some have argued that the interlocking mechanism is most important for wood adhesion. While mechanical interlocking is important, it cannot be described as the primary wood adhesive mechanism, for reasons that we shall discuss. Aside from the interlocking mechanism, one should appreciate that adhesive penetration reinforces the damaged surface cells, preventing crack initiation in the bondline.

Adsorption

We have already touched upon issues related to the adsorption theory; these are the concepts of surface energy and wetting. The adsorption theory states that adhesion results from intermolecular forces, also called secondary forces or secondary bonds, between the adhesive and substrate. The secondary forces are merely electrostatic attractions between complementary charges on molecular surfaces. All molecules possess positive and negative surface charge because atoms and molecules contain charged particles, the negative electrons and the positive protons. Depending upon the atomic elements and their molecular configuration, molecules may have permanent and relatively high-magnitude surface charge (polar molecules), or they may have temporary and lower-magnitude surface charge (nonpolar molecules). The secondary forces described in the adsorption theory

are the simple electrostatic attractions between opposite charges on molecular surfaces. Collectively, these forces are referred to as the Van der Waals forces which includes the weak London, or dispersion, forces and the very strong hydrogen bond. Wood forms strong hydrogen bonds with water, and also with many types of adhesives. The adsorption theory is the most important adhesive mechanism for bonding all materials. So while mechanical interlock is important for wood bonding, adsorption and intermolecular forces are always dominant. Without favorable wetting and secondary forces, adhesive penetration is impaired and mechanical interlock becomes much less effective (**Figure 5**).

Covalent Bonding

The covalent bonding theory states that adhesion results from covalent, or primary, bonds between adhesive and substrate. Primary bonds are the very strong bonds that hold atoms together as molecules, and are an order of magnitude stronger than secondary bonds. Consequently, adhesion through covalent bonding is highly desirable because such bonds are not easily broken. In contrast, secondary bonds may be disrupted by water and/or elevated temperatures. Covalent bonding could be very important for wood adhesion because wood contains many chemically reactive sites that could provide strong covalent bonds to the adhesive. Not all adhesives possess the chemical properties that promote covalent bonding. Consequently, this adhesive mechanism is relatively specialized, but occasionally important for wood.

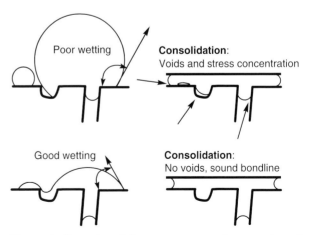

Figure 5 Illustration of the consequences of poor and good adhesive wetting on wood surfaces. Poor wetting promotes void formation by the inefficient coalescence of adjacent adhesive drops, and also by the inability to force air out of small crevices. Also, poor wetting inhibits adhesive penetration and promotes stress concentration. On the other hand, good wetting prevents these problems.

In summary, adsorption and mechanical interlock both contribute to wood bonding, and under special circumstances covalent bonding may also be important. While covalent bonding deserves special consideration, this adhesive mechanism does not improve the tested strength of wood bonds. Adhesion through adsorption and mechanical interlock produces very strong bonds that prove to be stronger than wood (depending upon the test method). However the special case of adhesion through covalent bonding would dramatically improve bond durability.

Wood-Related Factors that Impact Bond Performance

Wood Moisture Content

Wood is a hygroscopic material. Consequently, wood moisture content is determined by the prevailing environmental conditions (*see* **Wood Formation and Properties**: Formation and Structure of Wood; Physical Properties of Wood). Generally speaking, dry wood is easiest to bond, whereas very wet or green wood is difficult to bond for at least two reasons. The first is that wet wood is essentially encased in a layer of water; this prevents molecular contact. Secondly, as moisture is lost the wood shrinks, creating large bond stresses that may promote delamination. This is particularly troublesome when bonding cross-grain assemblies (**Figure 6**). The moisture-related dimensional change of wood in the longitudinal direction is quite small, whereas the same change in the radial and tangential directions is large. These dimensional changes oppose each other in cross-grain assemblies, creating potentially damaging bond stresses. The solution is to avoid cross-grain joints, use lower-density woods that exhibit less moisture-related

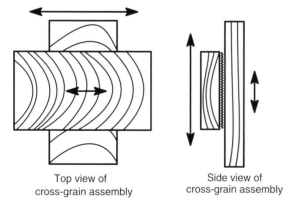

Top view of
cross-grain assembly

Side view of
cross-grain assembly

Figure 6 Illustration depicting the stresses that form in cross-grain assemblies, when solid wood is bonded such that the moisture-related dimensional changes in one piece oppose those in the other piece. The size of the double arrows indicates the relative degree of moisture-related dimensional change.

dimensional change, and use compliant adhesives not brittle ones. Of course, each of these solutions entails a peculiar set of trade-offs.

Another important aspect of wood moisture content impacts bond assembly with waterborne adhesives. Optimum bonding requires attention to consolidation pressure, adhesive viscosity and wood porosity; all of this controls penetration and bond thickness. Wood absorbs adhesive moisture, which rapidly changes the viscosity. If the bonded wood is excessively dry or wet, the adhesive will respectively dry out rapidly, or not at all. In either case, this influences how adhesive viscosity interacts with consolidation pressure and wood porosity to achieve the proper penetration and bond thickness.

Wood Density and Porosity

Dense woods have low porosity, and this often impairs adhesive penetration. Similarly, woods with uneven grain (nonuniform density from abrupt earlywood–latewood transitions), typically exhibit nonuniform penetration which can lead to undesirable stress concentrations. Likewise very-high-porosity, low-density woods may promote over penetration if the adhesive and consolidation parameters are not adjusted.

Very-high-density woods may also promote durability problems arising from moisture-related dimensional change, as mentioned previously. Higher-density woods shrink and swell to a greater degree, thus generating larger stresses on the bond. Regarding this point, also note that larger more massive wood components generate greater forces during moisture-related dimensional change, regardless of the wood density.

Extractives

Extractives are nonstructural organic molecules that result from primary and secondary metabolic functions in the living tree (*see* **Non-wood Products**: Chemicals from Wood. **Papermaking**: Paper Raw Materials and Technology. **Wood Formation and Properties**: Chemical Properties of Wood). This general term, extractives, represents a tremendous variety of chemical compounds. Collectively, the extractives are often cited as a major source of bonding problems. The resinous and fatty compounds are particularly troublesome because they may impair wetting by forming a nonpolar film on the wood surface. This process is often referred to as extractives migration, and is accelerated by heat. The loss of wood surface energy, or deactivation, caused by excessive thermal treatment is thought to arise from extractives migration to the wood surface.

Besides the lipid-like extractives, other extractive compounds may interfere with adhesives that cure under acidic or basic conditions. Certain acid and phenolic extractives influence the buffering capacity of wood, as discussed in the following section.

Wood Buffering Capacity

A buffer, or buffer solution, is an aqueous mixture that resists changes in pH. Different woods often behave as buffers and so may influence the cure of aqueous adhesives that polymerize under acidic or basic conditions. As with most properties, the buffering capacity is highly variable between woods. Within woods, there is often a marked difference between heart- and sapwood. Unfortunately, no commonality exists; in certain woods the heartwood is more buffering, while the sapwood is more so in other trees. When wood buffering is a problem, it either retards or accelerates cure. In the latter case, premature reaction is undesirable if it occurs prior to complete bond consolidation because adhesive flow and penetration may be impaired.

Drying and Surface Aging

This wood-related variable has been touched on previously. The vast majority of wood is dried prior to use, and so there is always an opportunity for surface deactivation. Recall that excessive heating may reduce the wood surface energy to the point that adhesive wetting is harmed. Drying will always reduce wood surface energy below its maximum, which is achieved after machining. However, only severe thermal treatments result in bonding problems. The sensitivity to thermal deactivation is highly variable among different woods.

Common Wood Adhesives

Phenol-Formaldehyde (PF) Resins

Thermosets made from phenol and formaldehyde (PF) are the first synthetic polymers to have been commercialized, which occurred early in the twentieth century. Two classes of PF resins exist: novolaks and resols. Novolaks function under acid conditions, and also require addition of formaldehyde 'hardeners' to cure. Resols operate under alkaline (basic) conditions, and only heat is required for cure. Of resols and novolaks, it is the resols that are preferred in the forest products industry, most commonly in liquid form. They are also prepared as powders and supported films.

PF resols are commonly used for the manufacture of structural composites such as oriented strandboard (OSB), plywood, parallel strand lumber, and laminated veneer lumber, and for nonstructural composites like hardboard. PF resins are highly durable and are exterior grade, weather-resistant structural thermosets. PF formulations vary widely according to application, i.e., hardboard resins versus plywood resins. PF resols are moderately priced compared to other wood adhesives, but they are probably the least expensive exterior grade wood adhesive.

Since PF resols contain formaldehyde, there is minor concern about the potential health risks of formaldehyde emissions. However, this concern exists only during wood composite manufacture where some free formaldehyde may emit during hotpressing. Any formaldehyde within composite products dissipates rapidly, so long-term formaldehyde emission is absent in PF-bonded wood products.

Urea-Formaldehyde (UF) Resins

Wood-bonding thermosets made from urea and formaldehyde (UF) are the largest production-volume wood adhesives in the world. UF resins are used for interior applications as in the case of particleboard, medium density fiberboard or decorative plywood. In other words, UF resins are not hydrolytically stable; moisture exposure causes adhesive degradation. UF resins are highly versatile and may be synthesized and formulated in many ways for a vast array of applications. Most UF resins are used in water-based liquid form, but they may also be produced as powders and films. In addition to their excellent performance, UF resins are very inexpensive.

While liquid PF resols are stored under alkaline conditions, liquid UF resins are stored very near neutral conditions (pH ~ 7). Liquid UF resins require an acid catalyst which is added immediately prior to cure. UF resin formaldehyde emission has received great research attention and regulation. Atmospheric moisture causes a very slow decomposition of the cured resin that causes long-term formaldehyde emissions in products like particleboard. To its credit, the UF resin industry has drastically reduced formaldehyde emissions while maintaining excellent performance. Formaldehyde emissions are controlled by manipulating the formaldehyde : urea mole ratio. This is accomplished by blending resins made with different mole ratios, or by adding formaldehyde scavengers such as urea.

Melamine-Formaldehyde (MF) Resins

Resins made from melamine and formaldehyde (MF) are similar to UF resins; however, they are superior to UF resins in many respects. MF thermosets are more durable and emit less formaldehyde than UF resins.

MF resins are used to produce plywood and particleboard for exterior or semiexterior applications. Melamine is a very expensive chemical, and so MF resins are commonly prepared with urea (MUF resins) to reduce costs.

A distinguishing characteristic of MF resins is chemical inertness, as well as hardness, lack of porosity and nonabsorbency in the cured state. These traits have provided endless lamination applications for MF resins. For example, paper sheets are impregnated with liquid MF and subsequently dried to produce supported, nontacky films that may be stacked and thermoformed onto various substrates including wood-based panels. Consequently, MF resins are commonly used for low- and high-pressure paper laminates and overlays, producing durable tabletops, industrial bench tops, etc.

Polymeric Methylenediphenyldiisocyanate (pMDI) Resins

Polymeric methylene bis(phenylisocyanate) is commonly referred to as pMDI or MDI, or even just as 'isocyanate.' Its use as a wood binder is relatively recent, growing in importance over the past 30 years. pMDI is commonly used for particulate wood-based composites such as OSB and laminated strand lumber. It is a highly durable, exterior grade structural thermoset. While formaldehyde is used in its preparation, pMDI resin does not emit formaldehyde, not at all. pMDI is more acutely toxic than the adhesives mentioned above. However, very standard precautions allow the safe and routine use of this material.

In a sense, pMDI is a two-part adhesive where the second component is wood moisture. This resin polymerizes by reacting with wood moisture. pMDI is hydrophobic (water insoluble), and therefore moisture tolerant, or insensitive to the steam that forms during hotpressing. This important property explains why pMDI resins are the only wood binders used for steam injection hotpressing. This is the purposeful injection of steam during panel hot compression, accelerating heat transfer in very thick panels, and also providing other product benefits.

Another significant characteristic of pMDI resins is their tendency to adhere to metal surfaces. This causes unacceptable problems during wood-based composite manufacture because the platens will adhere to the panel surface. Release agents (low surface-energy surface active molecules) applied to the platens will prevent this problem. Alternatively, a common practice is to use PF resins in the 'surface layers' and pMDI in the 'core layer,' as in OSB manufacture.

Resorcinol-Formaldehyde (RF) and Phenol-Resorcinol-Formaldehyde (PRF) Resins

Resorcinol-formaldehyde (RF) resins are generally considered to be the most durable and best-performing structural thermosetting wood adhesives. They are not commonly used for the production of wood-based composites such as plywood and OSB because the resin is very expensive. Resorcinol is very costly, and this fact led to the related adhesive in which some of the resorcinol is replaced by the much cheaper phenol molecule, producing the PRF adhesive. Resorcinol is highly reactive and so RF and PRF adhesives are two-part cold-setting resins. Typically, the resorcinolic liquid resin is mixed with a formaldehyde hardener and polymerization begins immediately, followed by solidification in 30–180 min after mixing. These adhesives are particularly well suited for structural wood-bonding applications in which the bonded assembly is not conveniently hotpressed, as in finger-jointed lumber, large laminated timbers, and wood-based I-beams.

Two-Part Isocyanate Curing Latex Adhesives (Emulsion Polymer Isocyanate, EPI)

Emulsion polymer isocyanate (EPI) adhesives are commonly used for the secondary assembly of a vast array of forest products, examples including finger-jointed lumber, furniture and wood lamination. This adhesive has two parts: a water-based latex that visually resembles the common 'white glue,' and pMDI, as in the wood binder mentioned above. As with RF and PRF adhesives, EPI is a cold-setting system that must be applied soon after mixing the latex and pMDI components. EPIs are durable exterior-grade structural thermosets that provide excellent performance.

Poly(vinyl Acetate) Latex (PVA)

Poly(vinyl acetate) latex (PVA) is a nonstructural thermoplastic latex adhesive which is familiar to many as the ubiquitous 'white glue.' PVA technology is extremely versatile because it is prepared in many ways and with a wide variety of monomers besides its namesake, vinyl acetate. PVA adhesives are commonly used for the assembly of many wood products such as furniture, window and door frames, and decorative panels. These waterborne adhesives are not weather durable; however, a common formulation includes comonomers and other additives that provide crosslinking. These more durable systems are referred to as crosslinking-PVAs. The crosslinking-PVAs also serve more demanding industrial applications where additional crosslinking is achieved by adding catalysts.

See also: **Non-wood Products**: Chemicals from Wood. **Papermaking**: Paper Raw Materials and Technology. **Solid Wood Products**: Glued Structural Members; Wood-based Composites and Panel Products. **Wood Formation and Properties**: Chemical Properties of Wood; Formation and Structure of Wood; Physical Properties of Wood. **Wood Use and Trade**: History and Overview of Wood Use.

Further Reading

Kendall K (2001) *Molecular Adhesion and Its Applications: The Sticky Universe*. New York: Plenum Press.

Kinloch AJ (1987) *Adhesion and Adhesives, Science and Technology*. London: Chapman & Hall.

Marra AA (1992) *Technology of Wood Bonding: Principles in Practice*. New York: Van Nostrand Reinhold.

Pizzi A (1994) *Advanced Wood Adhesives Technology*. New York: Marcel Dekker.

Pizzi A and Mittal KL (2003) *Handbook of Adhesive Technology*, 2nd edn. New York: Marcel Dekker.

Vick CB (1999) Adhesive bonding of wood materials. In: United States Department of Agriculture Forest Service, Forest Products Laboratory (eds) *Wood Handbook: Wood as an Engineering Material*, pp. 1–24. Madison, WI: US Department of Agriculture Forest Service.

Chemical Modification

R M Rowell, University of Wisconsin–Madison, Madison, WI, USA

Introduction

Wood is a hygroscopic resource that was designed to perform, in nature, in a wet environment. Nature is programmed to recycle wood in a timely way through biological, thermal, aqueous, photochemical, chemical, and mechanical degradations. In simple terms, nature builds wood from carbon dioxide and water and has all the tools to recycle it back to the starting chemicals. We harvest a green tree and convert it into dry products, and nature, with its arsenal of degrading reactions, starts to reclaim it at its first opportunity.

The properties of any resource are, in general, a result of the chemistry of the components of that resource. In the case of wood, the cell wall polymers (cellulose, hemicelluloses, and lignin) are the components that, if modified, would change the properties of the resource. If the properties of wood are modified, the performance of wood will be changed. This is the basis of chemical modification of wood to change properties and improve performance.

Wood changes dimensions with changing moisture content because the cell wall polymers contain hydroxyl and other oxygen-containing groups that attract moisture through hydrogen bonding. The hemicelluloses are mainly responsible for moisture sorption, but the accessible cellulose, noncrystalline cellulose, lignin, and the surface of crystalline cellulose also play major roles. Moisture swells the cell wall, and the fiber expands until the cell wall is saturated with water (fiber saturation point, FSP). Beyond this saturation point, moisture exists as free water in the void structure and does not contribute to further expansion. This process is reversible, and the fiber shrinks as it loses moisture below the FSP. The swelling pressures exerted when wood swells due to the uptake of water are very large. Stamm estimated these forces to be approximately 24 000 psi (165 MPa) but could only measure a swelling force of 12 000 psi (82.7 MPa). The ancient Egyptians split their large granite stones using the swelling forces of wood. They would chip rectangular holes (approximately 7×15 cm and 10 cm deep) into the rock the desired distance from the face of the mountain. They would then drive dry wooden stakes into the holes and wet them with water. The swelling forces would then split the granite stone from the face of the mountain.

Wood is degraded biologically because organisms recognize the carbohydrate polymers (mainly the hemicelluloses) in the cell wall and have very specific enzyme systems capable of hydrolyzing these polymers into digestible units. Biodegradation of the cell wall matrix and the high molecular weight cellulose weakens the fiber cell. Strength is lost as the cell wall polymers and matrix undergo degradation through oxidation, hydrolysis, and dehydration reactions.

Wood exposed outdoors undergoes photochemical degradation caused by ultraviolet radiation. This degradation takes place primarily in the lignin component, which is responsible for the characteristic color changes. The lignin acts as an adhesive in the cell walls, holding the cellulose fibers together. The surface becomes richer in cellulose content as the lignin degrades. In comparison to lignin, cellulose is much less susceptible to ultraviolet light degradation. After the lignin has been degraded, the poorly bonded carbohydrate-rich fibers erode easily from the surface, which exposes new lignin to further degradative reactions. In time, this 'weathering' process causes the surface of the composite to become rough and can account for a significant loss in surface fibers.

Wood burns because the cell wall polymers undergo reactions with increasing temperature to give off volatile, flammable gases. The hemicellulose and cellulose polymers are degraded by heat much before the lignin. The lignin component contributes to char formation, and the charred layer helps insulate the material from further thermal degradation.

This article discusses the concept of chemically modifying wood and then briefly reviews three types of treatments, monomer–polymer treatments, surface impregnation, and heat treatment for accomplishing chemical modification. The subject of cell wall bonded chemical modification is covered in more detail because of the large amount of interest in this subject. Typical uses for each of these modification technologies are also covered.

Chemical Modification

The term 'chemical modification' has been used to mean different things by different authors over the years. Here chemical modification will be defined as a chemical reaction between some reactive part of a lignocellulosic cell wall polymer and a simple single chemical reagent, with or without catalyst, to form a covalent bond between the two. This excludes chemical impregnation treatments (such as simple dip or pressure treatments with wood preservatives or fire retardants, or stains or penetrating oils), which do not form covalent bonds, monomer impregnation that polymerize *in situ* but do not bond with the cell wall, polymer inclusions, coatings (such as paints, varnishes, urethanes), or heat treatments. Wood finishes, preservatives, and adhesives are covered elsewhere (*see* **Solid Wood Processing**: Adhesion and Adhesives; Finishing; Protection of Wood against Biodeterioration). Other treatments that modify wood properties without bonding in the cell wall are described briefly. Many wood-based composites can be easily chemically modified (*see* **Solid Wood Products**: Wood-based Composites and Panel Products).

Monomer–Polymer Treatments

The objective of the monomer–polymer treatments is to produce a product with greatly enhanced physical properties. A monomer, such as an acrylic derivative dissolved in a suitable solvent, is impregnated into wood using a vacuum-pressure cycle. In most systems used today, the treating solution contains both a crosslinking agent and a catalyst. After treating with this solution, the treated wood is heated to a temperature where the catalyst becomes active and polymerization, *in situ*, takes place. In most cases, the polymer is located in the cell lumen but in cases (such as phenol-formaldehyde systems) where cell wall penetration takes place by the monomer, some of

the polymer may reside in the cell wall. The final wood polymer composite (WPC) is much harder than the untreated wood and is mainly used as flooring where heavy wear is anticipated. A fire retardant can also be incorporated into the treating solution mixture to add fire retardance to the product as long as the fire retardant chemicals do not interfere with the polymerization.

Surface Impregnation

In the case of surface impregnation technology, this involves the treatment of wood with polymers that are too large to penetrate very far into the wood structure. This type of treatment is mainly done with epoxy resins that increase surface hardness and can also act as an adhesive. This technology is being used to make cold-molded boat hulls and in the preservation of degraded historical wooden objects. The object is treated with a diluted solution of the polymer (or in some cases, with an undiluted liquid polymer directly) where some surface penetration occurs.

Heat Treatment

In the heat treatments, the objective is to heat the wood to increase dimensional stability and moisture resistance. The mechanisms of the increased dimensional stability and reduced hygroscopicity achieved from high temperature treatment of wood may be a combination of one or more factors. These include:

1. Degradation of the hygroscopic hemicelluloses to form soluble sugars which may undergo reversion reactions to form less hygroscopic, highly branched polysaccharides.
2. Degradation of the hemicelluloses to form free sugars which, in turn, form furan intermediates that can undergo polymerization during hot-pressing resulting in the formation of an adhesive.
3. Thermal softening of the cell wall matrix, mainly lignin, to allow reformation of a new less stressed matrix after pressing.
4. Degradation of the hygroscopic hemicelluloses to form volatile break down products that are lost during hot-pressing.
5. Crosslinking between carbohydrate polymers and/or between lignin and carbohydrate polymers.
6. Densification of the wood resulting in a reduction of pore size and void volume which restricts the flow of moisture back into the pressed wood.
7. High temperature compression to increase cellulose crystallinity.

The temperature of treatment and the presence of oxygen are critical as heating at too high a temperature can cause great strength losses especially in the presence of oxygen. This technology is now being applied for both solid wood and wood composites. Heating wood fiber in a closed heated press, for example, at 200°C for 8 min, results in a fiberboard with an 80% reduction in dimensional instability.

Cell Wall Bonded Chemical Modification

For cell wall bonded chemical modification the chemicals to be used must be capable of reacting with wood cell wall hydroxyls under neutral, mildly alkaline or acid conditions at temperatures below 170°C. The chemical system should be simple and capable of swelling the structure to facilitate penetration. The complete molecule should react quickly with wood components yielding stable chemical bonds, and the treated wood must still possess the desirable properties of untreated wood. Many chemical reaction systems have been published for the modification of various agrofibers and these systems have been reviewed in the literature several times in the past. These chemicals include anhydrides such as phthalic, succinic, malaic, propionic and butyric anhydride, acid chlorides, ketene carboxylic acids, many different types of isocyanates, formaldehyde, acetaldehyde, difunctional aldehydes, chloral, phthaldehydic acid, dimethyl sulfate, alkyl chlorides, β-propiolactone, acrylonitrile, epoxides, such as, ethylene, propylene, and butylene oxide, and difunctional epoxides (see **Table 1**).

Acetylation Chemistry

While there has been much research on many different chemical reaction systems, the most research and interest, both in the past and the present,

has been in the reaction of acetic anhydride with cell wall polymer hydroxyl groups to give an acetylated wood. The acetylation process has been applied to solid wood, veneers, and many different types of wood composites. For this reason, the acetylation of wood using new acetylation technology is reviewed in detail here. Application of this technology has mainly been considered for improving both dimensional stability and decay resistance.

The reaction of acetic anhydride with cell wall polymer hydroxyl groups is shown below. The anhydride reacts to form an ester with the wood hydroxyl group and the reminder of the molecule results in byproduct acetic acid.

$$\text{Cell Wall-OH} + CH_3C(=O) - O - C(=O) - CH_3$$
$$\rightarrow \text{Cell Wall} - O - C(=O) - CH_3$$
$$+ CH_3C(=O) - OH$$

Properties of Acetylated Solid Wood

As the level of acetyl weight gain increases, the equilibrium moisture content (EMC) and FSP of control and acetylated pine and aspen goes down and the dimensional stability, as measured by antishrink efficiency (ASE), as calculated below, goes up.

$$S = \frac{V_2 - V_1}{V_1}$$

where S is volumetric swelling coefficient, V_1 is wood volume after wetting with liquid water, and V_2 is wood volume of ovendried wood before wetting.

Then:

$$\text{ASE} = \frac{S_2 - S_1}{S_1} \times 100$$

where ASE is antishrink efficiency resulting from a chemical modification, S_2 is reacted wood volumetric

Table 1 Dimensional stability and resistance to decay with a brown-rot and white-rot fungi achieved by various chemical reaction systems on pine wood

Chemical	Weight percent gain (WPG) (%)	Antishrink efficiency (ASE) (%)	Weight loss after 12 weeks fungal test	
			Brown-rot[a]	White-rot[b]
None	0	—	57.8	39.6
Methyl isocyanate	25	65	1.7	1.0
Butyl isocyanate	25	70	>3	>1
Acetic anhydride	20	75	>2	>1
Propylene oxide	28	65	32.8	4.8
Butylene oxide	25	70	2.0	1.8
Acrylonitrile	25	50	—	—
β-Propiolactone	30	60	—	—
Formaldehyde	10	85	>3	>2

[a] Brown-rot fungus: *Gloephyllum trabeum.*
[b] White-rot fungus: *Trametes versicolor.*

swelling coefficient, and S_1 is unreacted wood volumetric swelling coefficient.

Solid acetylated wood has been tested for resistance to several different types of organisms. In a 2-week termite test using subterranean termites (*Reticulitermes flavipes*), boards acetylated at 16 to 17 weight percent gain (WPG) were very resistant to attack, but not completely so. Control and acetylated pine were exposed to a 12-week soil block test using the brown-rot fungus *Gloeophyllum trabeum* and the white-rot fungus *Trametes versicolor*. All of the acetylated boards at a WPG over about 17 show good resistance to brown- and white-rot fungi.

Acetylated Composites

Wood veneers, chips, particles, and fibers can also be acetylated using the same chemistry. These acetylated materials can be formed into plywood, chipboard, particleboard, or fiberboard. Fibers, for example, can be formed into flexible fiber mats, which can be made by physical entanglement (carding), nonwoven needling, or thermoplastic fiber melt matrix technologies. In carding, the fibers are combed, mixed, and physically entangled into a felted mat. These are usually of high density but can be made at almost any density. A needle-punched mat is produced in a machine, which passes a randomly formed machine-made web through a needle board that produces a mat in which the fibers are mechanically entangled. The density of this type of mat can be controlled by the amount of fiber going through the needle board or by overlapping needled mats to give the desired density. In the thermoplastic fiber matrix, agricultural fibers can be held in the mat using a thermally softened thermoplastic fiber such as polypropylene or polyethylene.

These acetylated mats can then be used as geotextiles, oil sorbents, or filters, or can have an adhesive added and be formed into molded products. If a thermosetting resin is used, the composites can be used for structural applications. If the acetylated fiber is mixed with a thermoplastic, then the composites can be thermomolded into a large variety of shapes for nonstructural applications. Composites made from acetylated fiber have many of the same properties of solid wood, i.e., increased dimensional stability and improved biological resistance.

Thickness swelling and linear expansion at various levels of relative humidity are greatly reduced as a result of acetylation. Increasing the adhesive content can reduce the thickness swelling but not to the extent that acetylation does.

Biological resistance has also been demonstrated with acetylated composites using brown-, white-, and soft-rot fungi and tunneling bacteria in a fungal cellar. Nonacetylated (i.e., control) flakeboards were

Table 2 Modulus of rupture (MOR), modulus of elasticity (MOE), and internal bond strength (IBS) of fiberboards made from control and acetylated pine fiber (10% phenolic resin)

Weight percent gain	MOR (MPa)	MOE (GPa)	IBS (MPa)
0	53	3.7	2.3
19.6	61	4.1	2.3
ANSI standard	31	—	—

Data from Simonson R and Rowell RM (2000) A new process for the continuous acetylation of lignocellulosic fiber. In: Evans PD (ed.) *Proceedings of the Fifth Pacific Rim Bio-Based Composite Symposium*, pp. 190–196. Canberra, Australia.

destroyed in less than 6 months while flakeboards made from acetylated flakes above 16 WPG showed no attack after 1 year. These data show that no attack occurs until swelling of the wood occurs. This is evidence that moisture content of the cell wall is critical before attack can take place. This fungal cellar test was continued for an additional 5 years with no attack at 17.9 WPG.

Table 2 shows data on strength properties of fiberboards made from both control and acetylated fiber. The board made from acetylated fiber has a higher modulus of rupture (MOR), modulus of elasticity (MOE), and equal internal bond strength (IBS) as compared to control boards.

Commercialization of Acetylated Wood Materials

In spite of the vast amount of research on the acetylation of both solid wood and wood composites, commercialization has been slow in coming. Two attempts, one in the USA and one in Russia, came close to commercialization but were discontinued presumably because they were not cost-effective. There are reports of a commercial acetylation plant for solid wood in Japan and a pilot plant for solid wood in the Netherlands but few details are available.

Two new processes are presently under way in Sweden to commercialize the acetylation of wood. One is a fiber process and the second a process to acetylate wood of large dimensions using microwave technology.

The Fiber Process

There is a pilot plant in Sweden with a capacity of approximately 4000 tonnes year^{-1} of acetylated fiber. **Figure 1** shows the schematic of the new continuous fiber acetylation process. The fiber is first dried in an optional dryer section to reduce the moisture content to as low a moisture content as is economically feasible realizing that the anhydride will react with water to form acetic acid and that a certain amount of acetic acid is needed to swell the fiber wall for chemical access.

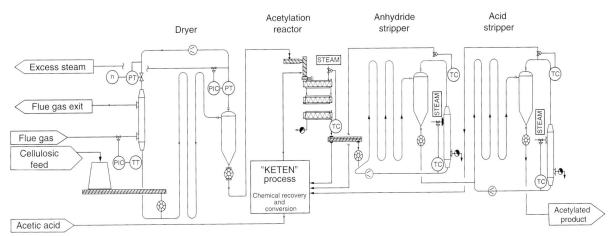

Figure 1 Schematic of the new fiber acetylation process. Reproduced with permission from Simonson R and Rowell RM (2000) A new process for the continuous acetylation of lignocellulosic fiber. In: Evans PD (ed.) *Proceedings of the Fifth Pacific Rim Bio-Based Composite Symposium*, pp. 190–196. Canberra, Australia.

The dried fiber is then introduced, by a screw feeder, into the reactor section and the acetylating agent is added. The temperature in this section is within the range of 110–140°C so the acetylating agent is in the form of a vapor/liquid mixture. Back flow of the acetylating agent is prevented by a fiber plug formed in the screw feeder. A screw-conveyor or similar device is used to move the material through the reactor and to mix the fiber–reagent mixture. During the acetylation reaction, which is exothermic, the reaction temperature can be maintained substantially constant by several conventional methods. The contact time in the reactor section is 6–30 min. The bulk of the acetylation reaction takes place in this first reactor.

The resultant acetylated fiber from the first reactor contains excess acetylating agent and forms acetic acid as it is fed by a star feeder into the second reactor, designed as a long tube and working as an anhydride stripper. The fiber is transported through the stripper by a stream of superheated vapor of anhydride and acetic acid. The temperature in the stripper is preferably in the range of 185–195°C. The primary function of this second step is to reduce the content of the unreacted acetylating medium remaining in the fiber emerging from the first reactor. An additional acetylation of the fiber is, however, also achieved in this step. The residence in this step is relatively short and normally less than 1 min. After the second reactor (stripper), superheated vapor and fiber are separated in a cyclone and part of the superheated vapor is recirculated after heating to the stripper fiber inlet and part is transferred to the system for chemical recovery.

The acetylated fiber from the second reactor may still contain some anhydride and acetic acid that is sorbed or occluded in the fiber. In order to remove remaining chemicals and the odor from them, the acetylated fiber is introduced into a second stripper step also acting as a hydrolysis step. The transporting medium in this step is superheated steam, and any remaining anhydride is rapidly hydrolyzed to acetic acid, which is evaporated. The acetylated fiber emerging from the second stripper is essentially odor-free and is completely dry. The acetylated fiber can as a final treatment be resinated for fiberboard production or conditioned and baled for other uses as desired. The steam and acetic acid removed overhead from this step is processed in the chemical recovery step.

The preferred recovery of chemicals includes separation of acetic anhydride from acetic acid by distillation, and conversion of acetic acid, recovered as well as purchased, by the ketene process into anhydride. The raw materials entering the production site is thus fiber and acetic acid to cover the acetyl groups introduced in the fiber. This minimizes the transportation costs and the chemical costs and makes the process much more cost effective.

The plant was built during the spring of 2000, taken apart, and reassembled in Kvarntorp, Sweden in the summer. The designated production rate is 500 kg h^{-1} or 12 tonnes day^{-1} or about 4000 tonnes-year^{-1} of acetylated wood fiber. The process can be applied to any lignocellulosic fiber and fibers other than wood will be used.

Solid Wood Microwave Process

Microwave energy has been shown to heat acetic anhydride and acetic anhydride impregnated wood. The absorption of microwave energy in acetic anhydride impregnated wood is preferred over other methods of heating since it heats less of the wood, provides some self-regulation of the overall temperature rise, and promotes a more uniform heating pattern. Acetic anhydride is supplied to the reactor, under vacuum, then a pressure is applied for a short time, and then another vacuum step to remove excess anhydride is used. Microwave energy is then applied to heat the anhydride soaked wood.

The penetration depth of the microwaves at 2450 MHz is approximately 10 cm, which means this technology can be used to acetylate large wood members. The variation in acetyl content, both within and between samples, is less than 2%. Microwave energy can also be used to remove the excess acetic anhydride and by-product acetic acid after acetylation.

One of the concerns about the acetylation of lignocellulosics, using acetic anhydride as the reagent, has been the by-product acetic acid. Many attempts have been made for the 'complete removal' of the acid to eliminate the smell, make the process more cost effective, and to remove a chemical potentially causing ester hydrolysis. Complete removal of by-product acetic acid has now been achieved in both the fiber process and the solid wood microwave process.

See also: **Solid Wood Processing**: Adhesion and Adhesives; Finishing; Protection of Wood against Biodeterioration; Wood-based Composites and Panel Products. **Wood Formation and Properties**: Chemical Properties of Wood; Formation and Structure of Wood.

Further Reading

Larsson Brelid P, Simonson R, and Risman PO (1999) Acetylation of solid wood using microwave heating. *Holz als Roh- und Werkstoff* 57: 259–263.

Rowell RM (1983) Chemical modification of wood: a review. *Commonwealth Forestry Bureau, Oxford, England* 6(12): 363–382.

Rowell RM (1984) *The Chemistry of Solid Wood.* Advances in Chemistry Series no. 207. Washington, DC: American Chemical Society.

Rowell RM, Young RA, and Rowell JK (1996) *Paper and Composites from Agro-Based Resources.* Boca Raton, FL: CRC Press.

Stamm AJ (1964) *Wood and Cellulose Science.* New York: Ronald Press.

Protection of Wood against Biodeterioration

T P Schultz and D D Nicholas, Mississippi State University, MS, USA

Introduction

Wood and wood composites are degraded by many organisms, including brown, white and soft rot fungi, termites and other insects, bacteria, and marine borers. Traditionally, the wood protection industry has relied on a few preservatives which have a broad range of activity, with cost and efficacy being the major considerations. However, governmental regulations, public perceptions, and environmental and disposal issues have resulted in rapid and profound changes. Further compounding the difficulty for industry is the relatively low market value for wood-preserving biocides, about US$200 million in direct sales annually worldwide in 2000, two-thirds of that in North America. Other problems are that the cost of the biocide is only a small fraction of the total value of the treated wood product, but biocide failure will entail replacement of the entire product (i.e., the biocide has a relatively low value but carries a high liability potential), and the long service life expected of treated wood products.

Biocides

Wood can be colonized and degraded by a variety of organisms. In addition, a preservative must be effective for many years during which the biocide level can be reduced by leaching, evaporation, and/or degradation. Thus, biocides for preservatives must be thoroughly tested by lengthy outdoor exposure. Even after years of testing and commercial use, unforeseen problems may arise. Also important is the biocide level required to protect wood adequately for a particular application and location. Warm and moist climates generally have greater decay and/or insect hazard than cool and/or dry locations and, thus, require higher biocide levels. Generally, biocide levels vary for different applications such as above-ground, ground-contact/residential, ground-contact/industrial, and marine exposure. For example, retentions for chromated copper arsenate (CCA) treated southern pine wood in the United States are 4.0, 6.4, 9.6 or 12.8, and 24 or $40 \, \mathrm{kg \, m^{-3}}$ for the above applications, respectively.

All biocides must be registered with the appropriate governmental agency which ensures that all products are safe; in the United States the agency is the Environmental Protection Agency (EPA) under the Federal Insecticide, Fungicide and Rodenticide Act, with other possible additional requirements by individual state agencies. Other countries have similar agencies and requirements. Use of a registered bioactive compound still carries some inherent health risk, however. To register a compound, a company must conduct extensive testing on the toxicological and other health effects, environmental fate, etc. Once registered the company then develops a 'label' which, after acceptance by the appropriate regulatory agency, clearly lists the specific applications and quantifies the amounts for which the formulated biocide product can be legally used; use of a registered biocide for any nonlabeled application is not permitted. Additional nonlabeled applications for a registered compound can be proposed following further testing, termed supplemental labeling or label expansion.

The 'traditional' wood preservatives are creosote oil, oilborne pentachlorophenol (penta), and waterborne arsenicals. These three systems effectively and economically control many of the fungi, insects, and marine borers that attack wood. Arsenicals, principally CCA, currently are, or were, the major preservatives in many countries. For example, in 1997 CCA was used for about 80% of all wood treated in the United States. However, recent public concerns about arsenic have led to restrictions that will reduce CCA usage by about 70% in the United States as CCA is delabeled (no longer approved) for residential applications by 2004. Most European countries have already limited or totally banned CCA with further restrictions likely, and Japan has almost entirely converted to preservatives without arsenic or chromium. Use of alternative copper : organic systems is expanding, but these copper-rich second-generation systems may also be restricted in the future with totally organic preservatives mandated; this trend is already apparent in some European countries.

Commercial Wood Preservatives

Biocides that are commercially used at this time to protect wood are discussed below and shown in Table 1, starting with the three traditional systems and then listing the 'newer' systems alphabetically, with potential biocides then discussed and shown in Table 2.

Chromated copper arsenate/arsenicals Of the arsenicals, CCA is unquestionably the principal wood preservative in many countries. CCA is very effective, economical, dependable, waterborne and leaves lumber with a clean and nonoily surface. Thus, CCA usage has greatly increased in the past 30 years, especially for residential applications. About 75 000 tonnes (oxide basis) was consumed in 2000 in North America and about 15 000 tonnes in Europe, but

Table 2 Biocides with the potential to protect wood, pending further development

Common name	Chemical name
Chlorothalonil	2,4,5,6-Tetrachloroisophthalonitrile
CDDC	Copper(II) mono(dimethyldithiocarbamate)
Dichlofluanid, DCFN	1,1-Dichloro-N-[(dimethylamino) sulfonyl]-1-fluoro-N-phenylmethanesulfenamide
Imidacloprid	1-[(6-chloro-3-pyridinyl) methyl]-N-nitro-2-imidazolidinimine
Fipronil	5-Amino-1-[2,6-dichloro-4-(trifluoromethyl)phenyl]-4-[(trifluoromethyl)sulfinyl]-1H-pyrazole-3-carbonitrile
Kathon 930[TM]	4,5-Dichloro-2-n-octyl-4-isothiazolin-3-one
PXTS	Polymeric xylenol tetrasulfide
TCMTB, Busan 30[TM]	2-(Thiocyanomethylthio) benzothiazole

Table 1 Biocides and biocide combinations used commercially as wood preservatives

Common name(s)	Chemical name
Arsenicals (CCA)[a]	Chromated copper arsenate, CuO, CrO$_3$, As$_2$O$_5$
Creosote	Creosote, Coal tar distillate
Penta, PCP	Pentachlorophenol
Azoles (Tebuconazole)[a]	(3RS)-5-(4-chlorophenyl)-2, 2-dimethylethyl-3-1H-[1,2,4-triazole)methyl]-3-pentanol
Borates, Timbor[TM], DOT	Disodium octaborate tetrahydrate
Copper/chromium systems (CCB)[a]	Chromated copper borate, CrO$_3$, CuO, B(OH)$_3$
Copper azole, CA, CBA	Copper(II) + tebuconazole + [boron]
Cu-HDO	Copper(II) bis-N-cyclohexyldiazeniumdioxy + CuO + boric acid
Copper citrate, CC	Ammoniacal copper(II) citrate
Copper quats, ACQ	Alkaline copper(II) quats, CuO + quats
Oxine copper, copper-8	(bis)Copper-8-quinolinolate
Copper naphthenate	Copper(II) naphthenate
IPBC, Polyphase[TM]	3-Iodo-2-propynlbutyl carbamate
Quats (DDAC)[a]	Quaternary ammonium compounds (didecyldimethylammonium chloride)
Synthetic pyrethroids (Permethrin)[a]	Cyclopropanecarboxylic acid, 3-(2,2- dichloroethenyl)-2, 2-dimethyl-(3-phenoxyphenyl) methyl ester
TBTO	Tributyltin oxide
Zinc borate	Boric acid + zinc salt, 2 : 3

[a] A class of compounds, of which several individual compounds are used to protect wood. An example of one compound is shown.

usage will shortly be dramatically lower. Formulations with different ratios of chromium, copper, and arsenic are available; in the United States CCA-type C is used which contains 18.5% copper (as CuO), 47.5% chromium (as CrO_3), and 34.0% arsenic (as As_2O_5). CCA is effective against a wide variety of wood-consuming fungi, insects, and marine borers, but ineffective against the small fraction of insects, marine borers, and stain/mold fungi that inhabit but do not consume wood as a food source. Waterborne, CCA becomes fixed by a complex series of redox, complexing and precipitation reactions with wood and, once fixed, resists leaching. CCA-treated softwoods perform extremely well, but CCA-treated hardwoods can sometimes fail due to poor microdistribution. Another arsenical preservative is ammoniacal copper zinc arsenate (ACZA). ACZA is limited to treating refractory (difficult to treat) species, such as those present in western North America where the alkaline solution provides better penetration, but it is not as highly fixed as CCA.

Creosote Creosote is a preservative oil that has been used for more than 150 years. It is a coal tar distillation product, and is mainly composed of a complex mixture of polyaromatic hydrocarbons. It is sometimes combined with coal tar, especially for marine systems. Creosote is a thick black tar which is generally heated prior to impregnation into the wood. It is effective against a variety of wood-colonizing organisms and used to treat railroad ties, utility poles, and pilings, accounting for about 10% of the treated wood volume in North America. Recent concerns over possible mutagenic properties have reduced usage in some countries. A pigmented and emulsified formulation (PEC) is available in Australia, but treatment problems have arisen and interest has waned. An emulsion system is being examined in Europe.

Pentachlorophenol Pentachlorophenol (penta, PCP) is effective against a variety of wood-destroying organisms and stain and mold fungi, is inexpensive and readily soluble in hydrocarbons. Thus, penta has replaced creosote in many industrial applications. However, due to environmental concerns many countries have reduced or banned penta. It is currently used in about 10% of all treated wood in North America, primarily for utility poles. It can be formulated with a variety of heavy or light organic solvents, and salt and emulsion water-based systems are also possible. Poor performance can occur with some light solvent, emulsion, and salt-based systems because of inadequate distribution and/or leaching.

Azoles The azoles, or more properly triazoles, include cyproconazole (1H-1,2,4-triazole-1-ethanol, α-(4-chlorophenyl)-α-(1-cyclopropylethyl)), propiconazole ((2RS, 4RS)-2-(2,4-dichlorophenyl)-2-[1-1H-(1,2,4-triazole)methyl]-4-propyl-1,3-diaxolane), and tebuconazole ((3RS)-5-(4-chlorophenyl)-2,2-dimethylethyl-3-(1H-[1,2,4-triazole]methyl)-3-pentanol). They are highly active against wood-decaying fungi, readily soluble in hydrocarbon solvents, and exhibit good stability and leach resistance in wood. Although azoles are expensive, their high activity makes them relatively cost effective. Disadvantages include minimal or no activity against sapstains, molds, and insects/termites. Thus, azoles are usually combined with other fungicides and/or termiticides. Copper azoles (CA), and other commercial preservatives in Europe based on an azole combined with another biocide, are discussed below.

Borates Borates (borax, boric acid, disodium octaborate tetrahydrate (DOT), sodium borate) are inorganic boron-based biocides, generally formulated as a mixture of borax and boric acid. Borates have extremely low toxicity to mammals and a broad range of activity against decay fungi and insects, and are inexpensive and readily soluble in water. However, water solubility limits applications to those with minimal or no leaching exposure. Borates are used as a sole biocide in many countries. Borates are also a component in some newer nonarsenical copper:organic systems, but the boron is highly susceptible to leaching. Borates are also used as a diffusible biocide for the remedial treatment of millwork and related applications in many countries. Studies examined treating wood by a vapor process with trimethyl borate, which then reacts with the residual water in lumber to form boric acid. Several groups have examined compounds which form complexes with borates, or the use of water repellents, to reduce leaching.

Copper/chromium systems Chromated copper borate (CCB) and related copper/chromium systems are used in Europe, but environmental concerns may limit future applications of these systems. In the United States acid copper chromate (ACC) is listed in the American Wood-Preservers' Association (AWPA) Standards and, while not commercially used for some time, is being reconsidered. However, ACC is weak against copper-tolerant fungi and future disposal might be regulated.

Copper azole Copper azole, either with (CBA) or without added boron (CA), consists of the biocides copper(II), boron, and tebuconazole (or propiconazole). CBA is one of the newer nonarsenical water-based preservatives for aboveground and ground-contact applications in Europe, the United States, and Asia. CBA is listed in the AWPA Standards as CBA-type A, with a copper:boric acid:tebuconazole composition of 49:49:2. A modified formulation without boron (CA-type B) has just been introduced in the United States. CAs are formulated with relatively expensive ethanolamine to minimize metal corrosion at treating facilities and improve penetration and distribution of the biocide within wood.

Cu-HDO The copper bis-(N-cyclohexyldiazenium-dioxy) system (Cu-HDO, CX) consists of the biocides Cu-HDO, additional uncomplexed copper (II), and boron. The Cu-HDO portion exhibits good stability, but the borate component can quickly leach and the uncomplexed copper is also subject to some leaching. A water-based Cu-HDO standard has just been developed by the AWPA for aboveground applications, CX-type A, and which may be available once Cu-HDO is registered by the EPA. It is formulated with an organic amine having 93.6% of the copper as copper(II) carbonate and the remaining 6.4% copper as Cu-HDO, with a CuO:boric acid:HDO ratio of 4.38:1.75:1. A similar product is one of the major preservatives in Europe for aboveground and ground-contact applications.

Copper citrate Copper citrate (ammoniacal copper citrate (CC)) is formed by the combination of copper and citric acid. It is effective against most wood-destroying fungi and insects but weak against copper-tolerant fungi and susceptible to copper leaching. Thus, CC may be best suited for aboveground applications. Only small amounts are available in North America.

Copper quaternary ammonium compounds Copper quats (alkaline copper quat (ACQ), amine copper quat, ammoniacal copper quat) combine the biocides copper(II) and one of the quaternary ammonium compounds (quats) discussed below, usually with a CuO:quat ratio of 2:1. These are formulated in aqueous solutions using ammonia or a relatively expensive organic amine. Three types of ACQ are available in North America, with various formulations and types of quat. ACQ has been available in the United States and Australia for about 10 years and even longer in Europe and Japan. ACQ may soon be one of the major preservatives in North America.

Oxine copper (Bis)-copper-8-quinolinolate (oxine copper, copper-8, Cu-8) is an organometallic with very low acute toxicity to mammals, excellent stability and leach resistance, broad activity against decay fungi and insects, and has been used for minor applications for over 30 years. It is insoluble in water and most organic solvents and thus difficult to formulate. An oil-soluble formulation uses relatively expensive nickel-2-ethylhexoate as a cosolvent. A water-soluble form is made with dodecylbenzene sulfonic acid, but the solution is highly corrosive to metals. Cu-8 is currently the only biocide listed in the AWPA Standards for treating wood that comes in contact with foodstuffs. A small volume of Cu-8 is used in the United States for aboveground applications and for sapstain and mold control, and minor amounts are sold as a brush-on preservative. The mono form of Cu-8 is being studied.

Copper naphthenate Copper naphthenate is an organometallic biocide made by combining copper (II) with naphthenatic acid mixtures. Copper naphthenate is relatively low cost and has been used for over 50 years for various applications in North America, including treating wood during World War II. It has low toxicity to mammals, broad activity against decay fungi and insects, is readily soluble in hydrocarbons, and has good stability and leach resistance. Since the 1990s some utility poles have been treated with copper naphthenate in North America. Another commercial product used in several countries is the combination of copper naphthenate, borate, water, and a thickening agent, with the mixture applied as a remedial ground treatment to utility poles followed by a tarpaper or plastic wrap. Small amounts of copper naphthenate are also sold over the counter to homeowners. Copper naphthenate imparts a green color to wood; for applications where color is objectionable the slightly less effective zinc naphthenate can be used. A water-based system is available in North America for brush-on (nonpressure) applications, and may be available soon for pressure treating.

Polyphase[TM] 3-Iodo-2-propynylbutyl carbamate (IPBC, Polyphase[TM]) is an organic biocide with low toxicity to mammals, is readily soluble in hydrocarbon solvents, has a broad range of activity against decay and mold fungi, but has no activity against insects and may be slowly degraded. In the United States, as a sole biocide IPBC is currently used for millwork-type applications, and IPBC was combined with the insecticide chlorpyrifos as an oilborne treatment for aboveground beams, etc. A formulation containing IPBC, propiconazole, and tebuconazole has recently been introduced as a millwork preservative in the US. In Europe many combinations of IPBC and propiconazole, or IPBC, propiconazole and tebuconazole, solvent- or waterborne, are used in aboveground applications. IPBC is the active ingredient in many brush-on systems sold in North America, and the combination of IPBC and DDAC is used for sapstain and mold control.

Quaternary ammonium compounds   Several quaternary ammonium compounds (quats) are available, including didecyldimethylammonium chloride (DDAC, Bardac 22^{TM}) and other similar dialkydimethylammonium chlorides with C$_8$–C$_{14}$ alkyls, and the alkyldimethylbenzyl ammonium chlorides (alkyl benzyldimethylammonium chlorides, benzalkonium chlorides, ABACs, ADBACs), usually sold as a mixture with C$_{12}$–C$_{18}$ alkyl groups. The quats have very low toxicity to mammals, are relatively inexpensive, have broad activity against decay fungi and insects, are soluble in both water and hydrocarbon solvents, and exhibit excellent stability and leach resistance due to ion exchange fixation reactions with wood. However, their efficacy is only moderate and when used alone may not be adequate. Another disadvantage is that quats, as surfactants, make exposed wood wet more easily. Due to their surfactant properties and low cost quats are often combined with other biocides. For example, copper and quats are the active ingredients in ACQ, discussed above, and DDAC plus IPBC is a commercial sapstain and mold agent. Quats will undoubtably continue to be considered in the development of new preservative systems.

A relatively new quat analog is an oligomer of alternating quat and borate ether units, commonly called polymeric betaine (didecyl-bis(2-hydroxyethyl) ammonium borate or didecylpolyoxethylammonium borate). Both the quats and borate ethers can bind to wood and, thus, the structure of the active ingredient changes when exposed to wood. The oligomeric structure makes the borate relatively less susceptible to leaching. Being composed of both quats and borates, polymeric betaine is active against both decay fungi and insects. Several water-based polymeric betaine systems are commercially available in Europe, including systems with polymeric betaine alone or combined with an insecticide for above-ground use, or with co-added copper for ground-contact applications.

Synthetic pyrethroids   The synthetic pyrethroids (Permethrin, Bifenthrin, Cypermethrin, Cyfluthrin, and Deltamethrin), analogs of chrysanthemum-derived terpenoid pyrethrins, have low toxicity to mammals, exhibit good efficacy against insects (but are not fungicidal), and are soluble in many hydrocarbon solvents. (Only the structure of Permethrin is shown in **Table 1**.) In the United States research on the combination of a synthetic pyrethroid and fungicide has been conducted but no commercial applications currently exist. In Europe several combinations of a synthetic pyrethroid and other biocide(s) are available, including the quat benzalkonium chloride combined with permethrin and tebuconazole, or a cypermethrin and tebuconazole mixture.

Tributyltin oxide   Tributyltin oxide (TBTO) is an organometallic biocide which exhibits good activity against fungi and insects, is soluble in most hydrocarbons, and has good leach resistance. It is used as an aboveground treatment for millwork and related applications in many countries. However, it undergoes slow dealkylation which reduces its fungicidal properties. Consequently, TBTO has been used for reduced decay applications such as millwork in Europe and the US.

Biocides with the Potential to Preserve Wood

Some biocides are being evaluated for wood preservation. Most of these are already registered and labeled for non-wood agricultural applications. Examining the potential of registered agrochemicals to protect wood has the advantage that the cost of label expansion is less than the expenditure required to develop, test, then register and label an entirely new biocide developed for only the relatively small wood preservation market. Potential biocides shown in **Table 2** are briefly discussed below.

Chlorothalonil   Chlorothalonil (2,4,5,6-tetrachloro-isophthalonitrile) is an organic biocide with very low toxicity to mammals, broad activity against decay fungi and insects, relatively low cost, and good stability and leach resistance in wood. A major research effort in the 1990s examined chlorothalonil as an alternative for penta. However, the poor solubility of chlorothalonil in most organic solvents made formulation difficult and interest has waned.

Copper bis(dimethyldithiocarbamate)   Copper bis (dimethyldithiocarbamate) (CDDC), with the mono form preferred, is formulated with copper(II), ethanolamine, and sodium dimethyldithiocarbamate (SDDC). Since copper reacts rapidly with SDDC to form an insoluble complex, a two-step treating process is required. This results in a stable preservative with good activity against most wood-destroying organisms, but the dual treatment increases the cost.

Dichlofluanid   Dichlofluanid (1,1-dichloro-N-[(dimethylamino)sulfonyl]–1-fluoro -N-phenyl-methanesulfenamide (DCFN)) is a fungicide used in paints and stains in Europe, and which may have potential as a fungicide in wood preservative systems.

Kathon 930™   The isothiazolone 4,5-dichloro-2-n-octyl-4-isothiazolin-3-one (Kathon 930™) is a biocide with moderately low toxicity to mammals and broad activity against decay fungi and termites. It is readily soluble in hydrocarbons, and exhibits excellent stability and leach resistance in wood. Research has shown that Kathon 930 effectively protects wood in both aboveground and ground-contact applications, but no commercial formulations are currently available. Other isothiazolone analogs are used for short-term control of mold and sapstain fungi on wet, freshly treated lumber.

Fipronil   Fipronil   (5-amino-1-[2,6-dichloro-4-(trifluoromethyl)phenyl]-4-[(trifluoromethyl)sulfinyl]-1H-pyrazole-3-carbonitrile) is an α-phenyl pyrazole-type insecticide. When combined with a fungicide it has been examined as a wood preservative.

Imidacloprid   Imidacloprid   (1-[[(6-chloro-3-pyridinyl)methyl]-N-nitro-2-imidazolidinimine) is a neonicotinoid insecticide. Field tests in the United States showed that imidacloprid had much greater efficacy than chlorpyrifos in protecting wood against termite attack, but it may be degraded relatively rapidly.

Polymeric xylenol tetrasulfide   Polymeric xylenol tetrasulfide (PXTS) is an oligomer consisting of a mixture of alkylphenols linked by 2-10 sulfurs, with a low degree of polymerization. This biocide has many of the same characteristics and efficacy as creosote so far in marine and ground-contact tests currently under way. Being an oligomer PXTS should have minimal leaching, which would reduce the retention necessary for long-term protection and be suitable for environmentally sensitive applications. PXTS has exhibited low toxicity to mammals in tests to date.

2-(Thiocyanomethylthio) benzothiazole   2-(Thiocyanomethylthio) benzothiazole (TCMTB, Busan 30™) is an organic biocide with a broad range of activity against both fungi and insects. It is readily soluble in hydrocarbons and exhibits good leach resistance in wood, but it is susceptible to biodegradation.

Trends in Biocides Used to Preserve Wood

Wood preservation is rapidly changing. In North America CCA is currently the most important preservative–by far–for residential applications, and penta, creosote, and CCA are used for industrial applications. However, CCA will be restricted to industrial applications starting in 2004 in North America, and residential lumber will be treated with alternative second-generation waterborne copper: organic systems which are copper-rich and possibly the older ACC system. ACQ, CA, Cu-HDO, copper and polymeric betaine, and possibly CCB and related copper/chromium systems, will probably be the main systems in Europe, Japan, and/or North America for the next several years. The newer preservatives are relatively expensive, more corrosive to metal fasteners, and apparently leach more copper than CCA-treated lumber. While these problems are avoided by the copper/chromium systems such as CCB and ACC, disposal concerns may soon lead to restrictions on chromium-containing systems. Another problem is that all lumber which has been treated with a waterborne preservative system and not yet redried (including wood treated with CCA) is susceptible to growth of molds and sapstains on the lumber surface, but the organic amine in many of the new copper-based preservatives may exacerbate mold growth. (Many preservative formulations also contain a biocide for short-term control of molds and sapstains on wet, freshly treated lumber.) New preservatives may also require more attention in the treating plant than CCA; indeed, many new systems have initial problems. Copper has some environmental and disposal concerns, and systems with relatively low copper levels plus one or more organic cobiocides might be eventually required. Alternatively, totally organic biocides might be mandated, a trend already happening in some European countries. Borates are being used to a greater extent for nonleaching residential applications.

Disposal of treated wood is, or will shortly be, a major issue in many countries and could be a principal factor determining which biocides are permitted. An intriguing possibility being studied in Europe is to utilize organic biocides which slowly degrade, and would protect wood for a specified time but then allow the product to be safely disposed of. The recycling of treated wood, such as grinding CCA-treated lumber into particles for particleboard furnish, may prove difficult due to liability concerns.

Many new organic biocides are extremely effective against some, but not all, wood-destroying organisms. Thus, future totally organic preservatives will likely consist of a combination of biocides, possibly including other nonbiocidal additives such as water repellents, to enhance the biocide's efficacy. Any synergism observed by combining multiple biocides would be a bonus. A preservative system used to treat lumber for residential construction will likely be water-based, but most organic biocides are not water soluble. Consequently, stable emulsions must be developed. Another problem is that organic biocides can be degraded by various chemical, biological, thermal, and/or photolytic mechanisms and thus rendered inactive; in contrast, the inorganic metals, such as the components in CCA, are 'permanent' and will only undergo a change in oxidation state. Thus, developing economical and effective totally organic systems, especially for locations with severe decay and/or termite conditions, will be a difficult, long-term, and costly process. At the present time no totally organic, aqueous-based system capable of protecting ground-contact wood for residential applications in the United States has even been proposed to a regulatory agency.

The high cost of new biocides, along with environmental concerns, will undoubtedly result in efforts to reduce the biocide level in totally organic systems to about 0.4% to 0.01% mass per mass of wood. By contrast, the traditional CCA and penta systems use about 1% mass per mass. Since wood is inherently variable this results in lumber from one commercial treating charge having a wide range of within- and among-board biocide retentions. With the highly effective traditional systems biocide retention variability is not serious, but it may become an important factor with the newer systems which have lower retention levels, and possibly less efficacy, than CCA or penta.

The total yearly cost to US homeowners due to fungal and termite attack is estimated at about US$5 billion. Some of these costs could be avoided by better design and construction techniques, but wood preservatives will still be needed for many applications.

Formulations

Once a particular biocide(s) has been selected it must be formulated into a preservative system suitable for commercial applications, in which the active ingredient (the biocide) is combined with various inactive compounds. For treating solid wood and many composites, the biocide must be dissolved in a solvent (the carrier) or an emulsion developed. For industrial applications a heavy or light organic solvent, or water, can be used. Better efficacy with organic biocides is usually obtained with heavy oils, which by themselves often exhibit some biocidal activity and impart water repellency. For residential applications most systems are water-based; a light hydrocarbon is feasible but not likely due to cost and solvent emission issues. Since most organic biocides are not soluble in water an economical and stable oil-in-water emulsion must be developed.

Other characteristics of a viable preservative formulation, especially for residential applications, include:

- low cost
- good efficacy
- broad activity
- good permanence under long-term use
- no significant effect on wood strength
- low or no odor
- not corrosive to metal fasteners
- good penetration
- safe to handle and use
- leaves wood paintable and with an attractive appearance
- allows the wood to be disposed of or recycled at the end of the product's life
- capable of being concentrated (for shipment)
- formulated using only registered biocides.

Standards and Organizations that Set Specifications

Once a preservative system formulation has been developed it is subjected to various tests with the results submitted to the appropriate standard-producing organization. Many organizations worldwide help set standards. In the United States over 10 organizations are involved to some degree in wood preservation; the major US organizations which develop standards are the AWPA and the American Society for Testing Materials (ASTM). The AWPA and/or ASTM Standards specify the formulations and retentions of various preservative systems for a wide variety of applications, as well as penetration requirements, treating processes, analysis procedures, laboratory and outdoor efficacy evaluation tests, etc.

A proposal of a new wood preservative system submitted to the AWPA for standardization typically includes the exact formulation, safety and health aspects, and results from various laboratory and field tests on corrosion, leaching, efficacy, etc., with the proposal listing the desired application(s) and retentions. The proposal is subjected to a peer review process by various industrial, governmental, and academic professionals, with an initial period of back-and-forth written questions followed by oral discussion at an AWPA meeting and then further time for additional written comments. If the proposal is accepted AWPA Technical Committees develop specifications that list the minimum requirements covering specific wood products recommended for a given preservative. Sponsors of the preservative system are required to submit periodic updates of long-term efficacy data generated in outdoor exposure trials. Standard development by organizations in other countries may follow a different format, but all are designed to ensure that the consumer obtains a reliable and safe product.

Treatment Processes

Over-the-counter wood preservatives are generally brushed on by homeowners and only provide short-term protection. Control of sapstain and mold in green (never dried) lumber is accomplished by dip- or spray-treating with aqueous formulations. Millwork is generally treated by dipping or spraying dried wood. Most wood products are treated by a vacuum/pressure process, which gives the high loading and uniform penetration necessary for good quality control and long-term performance. In this process the wood product is usually first dried so that some or all of the free water in the cell lumen is replaced with air. The dried wood is placed in a pressure-treating cylinder, a vacuum drawn, then the preservative solution added to the cylinder so that the wood is fully immersed. Pressure is then applied to force the solution into the porous wood, with the preservative solution filling some or all of the lumen air-void volume; a vacuum may be drawn as a final step. The pressure treatment processes have basically remained the same for many years.

Preservation of Wood Composites

Most preservatives are used to treat solid wood products such as lumber, ties, poles, etc., but the protection of wood composites is increasingly important. The treatment of composites involves special considerations. Generally, the furnish used to make wood composites is either treated with a biocide prior to manufacturing (preprocess) or a biocide is added during manufacture (in-process), or the composite is treated after manufacture (postprocess). The particular method and biocide system depends on the composite.

An example of a preprocess method is gluing lumber, which had been previously treated with CCA, into glulam beams. This process is only used with a few wood composites, using preservatives that do not negatively affect the adhesive. Postprocess treatment of an already manufactured composite is used where treatment will not adversely affect the product, and usually involves composites manufactured from lumber or veneer. In-process, where the biocide is added to the furnish just before mat formation and/or pressing occurs, is used where a postprocess treatment will cause undesired swelling and/or delamination of the composite and is usually practiced with composites manufactured from flakes, particles, or fibers. Postprocess treatments use standard preservative systems, are relatively easy and require no modification of the manufacturing process, but can result in only the outer shell being treated and some dimensional changes and strength loss. The in-process method gives protection throughout the composite, but the preservative can interfere with the adhesive and thermal degradation of organic biocides might occur during hot-pressing.

Because of its low cost, relatively good leaching properties, broad activity against a wide range of wood-destroying organisms, low toxicity to mammals, and good thermal stability, zinc borate has become one of the principal biocides used to treat in-process composites. Wax-based water repellents, either alone or in combination with a biocide, are also used.

Naturally Durable Woods

The heartwood of some woods is naturally resistant to biodegradation. Commercially available durable woods include western red cedar, redwood, and cypress in North America, larch and pine heartwood in Europe, some woods from tropical forests, some eucalypts in Australia, etc. A major drawback is that most of these woods are not highly durable and may have a relatively short service life in certain applications or locations. Also, the availability of durable woods is not equal to the volume of pressure-treated wood produced in North America. Finally, some lumber with nondurable sapwood can be mixed in, durability varies greatly among and within trees, and the heartwood extractives which impart durability are often toxic or irritants.

Nonbiocidal Additives to Enhance Biocide Efficacy

In addition to protecting wood, an ideal wood preservative system should improve the weathering characteristics by reducing water sorption. Consequently, the addition of water repellents to wood preservative systems is desirable. Besides improved weathering, durable water repellents enhance the biocide's efficacy by reducing leaching and lowering the moisture content of exposed wood. Water repellents are usually benign and can be extremely cost-effective. For example, most water repellents are wax- or oil-based and, on a weight basis, are about 100-fold cheaper than most organic biocides.

Lumber treated with several water repellent and preservative combinations is available in North America, and linseed oil-treated wood is being studied in Europe.

It is well known that decay fungi utilize free radicals generated by metals and/or organometallics to degrade wood. This, and the knowledge that extractives in durable woods have excellent antioxidant and metal chelating properties, suggested that antioxidants and/or metal chelators might help protect wood against fungal attack. Laboratory experiments have shown that antioxidants or metal chelators alone provide little protection to wood, but when combined with organic biocides enhance the efficacy of all biocides studied. Ground-contact and aboveground outdoor exposure trials are now under way and results so far are promising. This approach will likely be suitable only with totally organic systems.

Other possible additives include the in situ polymerization of nonbiocidal monomers. A portion of the monomers may covalently bond to the wood structural components to make the wood both more hydrophobic and impervious to enzymatic degradation. A similar concept involves reagents which form ester or ether linkages with the polysaccharide hydroxyls. Alternately, a resin could be impregnated into wood followed by polymerization. However, these treatments are expensive and require careful control and monitoring and so far have limited applications.

Thermal Modification of Wood

In the past decade European researchers have re-examined the thermal modification of wood. As a result several processes have been developed and commercial production of heat-treated wood is growing rapidly. Generally, lumber is heated to at least 180°C in a nonoxidizing atmosphere. This causes some chemical degradation of the wood and, consequently, the wood has some decay resistance but mechanical properties are reduced. Also, greatly reduced hygroscopicity gives the lumber improved weathering characteristics. Although the durability of heat-treated wood is not equivalent to pressure-treated wood, it is suitable for low-hazard, non-structural, above-ground applications.

Biocontrol

Another biocide-free approach is to use microorganisms that are antagonistic to wood-degrading fungi and insects. This bioprotectant approach has been marketed in Europe to a limited degree, but there are some concerns about long-term effectiveness. Based on research to date, it appears that the most promising use for this concept is to control sapstain and mold fungi where only short-term protection is required.

See also: **Pathology**: Heart Rot and Wood Decay; Insect Associated Tree Diseases. **Wood Formation and Properties**: Biological Deterioration of Wood.

Further Reading

Anonymous (2002) *American Wood-Preservers' Association Standards 2002*. Granbury, TX: American Wood-Preservers' Association.

Barnes HM (2001) Wood: preservative treated. In: *Encyclopedia of Materials: Science and Technology*, pp. 9683–9688. London: Elsevier Science.

Barnes HM and Murphy RJ (1995) Wood preservation: the classics and the new age. *Forest Products Journal* 45(9): 16–26.

Eaton RA and Hale MDC (1993) *Wood: Decay, Pests and Protection*. London: Chapman & Hall.

Edlund M-E and Jermer J (2002) *Evaluation of Wood Preservatives for Nordic Wood Preservation Class AB*, Paper IRG/WP no. 02-30297. Stockholm, Sweden: International Research Group on Wood Preservation.

Goodell B, Nicholas DD, and Schultz TP (2003) *Wood Deterioration and Preservation: Advances in our Changing World*, ACS Symposium Series no. 845. Washington, DC: American Chemical Society.

Morrell JJ and Morris PI (2002) *Methods for Improving Preservative Penetration into Wood: A Review*, Paper IRG/WP no. 02-40227. Stockholm, Sweden: International Research Group on Wood Preservation.

Nicholas DD (ed.) (1973) *Wood Deterioration and Its Prevention by Preservative Treatments*, vols. 1 and 2. Syracuse, NY: Syracuse University Press.

Nicholas DD (2001) The preservation of wood. In: Hon DN-S and Shiraishi N (eds) *Wood and Cellulosic Chemistry*, 2nd edn, pp. 795–806. New York: Marcel Dekker.

Preston AF (2000) Wood preservation: trends of today that will influence the industry tomorrow. *Forest Products Journal* 50(9): 12–19.

Rapp AO (ed.) (2001) *Review of Heat Treatments of Wood*, COST Action E22, Report EUR 19885. Brussels: European Commission.

Suttie ED, Bravery AF, and Dearling TB (2002) *Alternatives to CCA for Ground-Contact Protection of Timber: A Perspective from UK on Performance and Service Life Expectations*, Paper IRG/WP no. 02-30289. Stockholm, Sweden: International Research Group on Wood Preservation.

Wilkinson JG (1979) *Industrial Timber Preservation*. London: Associated Business Press.

Zabel RA and Morrell JJ (1992) *Wood Microbiology: Decay and Its Prevention*. New York: Academic Press.

Protection from Fire

C R McIntyre, McIntyre Associates, Walls, MS, USA

Introduction

Wood has been an excellent building material for many centuries; however, its ability to ignite and burn has limited its use in many applications. Applications of various fire retardant chemicals has expanded the use of wood and provided significant safety to occupants of wooden buildings. The fire-retardant systems used for wood generally contain nitrogen, boron, and phosphorus chemicals. The properties of specific formulations and their advantages and disadvantages are discussed in this article, and the modes of action and testing procedures for fire retardants are also given.

History of Fire Retardants

Although various chemicals were utilized through history, the modern use of fire retardants for wood stems from 1820 when Gay-Lussac developed treatments with ammonium phosphates and borax. The full impact of this invention can be gauged by the realization that systems similar to this are still in use today. But there have been many other inorganic chemicals investigated as fire retardants in the intervening years. Around 1900, formulations based on silicates, sulfates, borates, phosphates, zinc, tin, and calcium were in vogue and by 1915, ammonium chlorides, phosphates, and sulfates were known to be effective for wood.

From 1930 to 1935, researchers at the US Department of Agriculture Forest Products Laboratory (FPL) reported on investigations of about 130 different inorganic fire retardant formulations. It was found that diammonium phosphate was the most effective for reducing flame spread while mono-ammonium phosphate, ammonium chloride, ammonium sulfate, borax, and zinc chloride were also active. However, many of the chemicals in this test program had associated problems of high cost, corrosion, hygroscopicity, strength reduction, or glow promotion. Therefore, other approaches such as *in situ* polymerizations or reactions of retardants with wood components were investigated.

By the 1950s, there were several formulations in commercial use for pressure treating wood. (Fire retardant coatings were also being investigated but, as discussed later, their acceptance and regulation lagged that of pressure treated products.) The

American Wood-Preservers' Association (AWPA) listed four formulations and the US Navy allowed several others for shipboard use (**Table 1**). All of these formulations were inorganic combinations blended to achieve a reasonable compromise of cost and acceptable performance. However, in the 1960s, three formulations similar to the four AWPA formulations had supplanted the previous ones and were by far the dominant retardants (**Table 2**).

In the late 1960s, formulations were introduced in the USA and Canada that protected exterior products such as shingles, shakes, and siding or scaffold planking that are exposed to the elements. These systems typically injected the precursors to a nitrogenous polymer system such as urea-formaldehyde or melamine-formaldehyde along with phosphoric acid into the wood. Then a special kiln cycle was used to effect an *in situ* polymerization that encapsulated the phosphoric acid and rendered it

Table 1 1950s formulations for five retardants

AWPA formulation ingredients	Percent
1. Chromated zinc chloride (CZC)	
$ZnCl_2$	>77.5
$Na_2Cr_2O_7.2H_2O$	>17.5
2. Chromated zinc chloride FR	
CZC (above)	80
H_3BO_3	10
$(NH_4)_2SO_4$	10
3. Minalith	
$(NH_4)_2SO_4$	60
H_3BO_3	20
$(NH_4)_2HPO_4$	10
$Na_2B_4O_7$	10
4. Pyresote	
$ZnCl_2$	35
$(NH_4)_2SO_4$	35
H_3BO_3	25
$Na_2Cr_2O_7.2H_2O$	5
Other formulation ingredients	
5.	
$(NH_4)_2SO_4$	>78
$NH_4H_2PO_4$ or $(NH_4)_2HPO_4$	>19
6.	
$Na_2B_4O_7$	60
H_3BO_3	40
7.	
$Na_2B_4O_7$	67–70
$NH_4H_2PO_4$	33–30
8.	
$ZnCl_2$	54
$NH_4H_2PO_4$	46

Source: Prepared from AWPA and other documents cited.

Table 2 Interior formulations from the 1960s and 1970s

Formulation ingredients	Percent
1.	
$(NH_4)_2SO_4$	50
$NH_4H_2PO_4$	41
$Na_2B_4O_7$	7
Moldicide	2
2.	
$(NH_4)_2SO_4$	45
$NH_4H_2PO_4$	45
$Na_2B_4O_7$	6
H_3BO_3	4
3.	
$NH_4H_2PO_4$	65
H_3BO_3	35

Source: Prepared from AWPA and other documents cited.

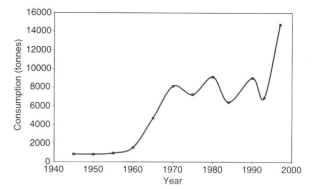

Figure 1 US consumption of fire retardants for wood. Prepared from AWPA publications.

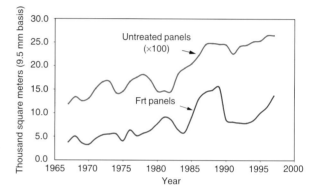

Figure 2 Annual production in the USA of fire retardant treated and untreated panels. Prepared from AWPA and FPL publications.

leach resistant. The kiln cycle called for moderate temperatures (70°C) for 2–3 days or until the wood was below 25% moisture content and then elevation of the kiln temperature to 100°C for up to 24 h to complete the reaction.

The use of fire retardants climbed very slowly in the USA until the 1960s (**Figure 1**). Then from 1960 to 1970, the use quadrupled as new formulations became available that expanded the useful applications for fire retardants. There was also an increased awareness of the considerable safety benefits of fire retardants. However, the emergence of corrosion, hygroscopicity, and strength problems began to plague the industry and the market grew only slightly until 1980. Building code changes were implemented in the late 1970s that opened up a major new end use for roof framing and sheathing (predominately plywood) in buildings that otherwise were required to be constructed from noncombustible materials. At about that time, replacements for the above first-generation retardant systems were also being developed.

In the early 1980s, second-generation fire retardants were introduced to address the corrosion and hygroscopicity problems of the first-generation inorganic formulations. One new product was an 'organic' that was a blend of guanylureaphosphate (GUP, formed by the reaction of dicyandiamide with phosphoric acid) with boric acid. There were several other second-generation formulations that were based on ammonium polyphosphates with or without various additives in small quantities. The additives included boric acid, borax, moldicides, and the like.

However, in the late 1980s, reports began to surface that some of the second-generation formulations were experiencing strength loss in high temperature applications such as roof sheathing. After

the initial concern that all second-generation products were involved, it was found that problems were occurring with only some formulations. Multiple lawsuits occurred and further investigations revealed that high humidity conditions frequently existed in problem installations. Numerous causes were alleged for the strength problems and the end result was that the overall market for fire retardants was severely impacted.

Prior to these problems, the market had accepted the second-generation products and growth in treated panels had matched that of untreated panels (**Figure 2**), but the threat of litigation soon caused a steep decline in volume in the early 1990s. Most of the ammonium polyphosphate containing products were removed from the market as well.

At the onset of the heat degradation problem, researchers at the FPL and elsewhere began investigating the issue. During the next several years a series of publications delineated that certain combinations of fire retardant ingredients with elevated temperatures and humidities would cause liberation of acidic moieties that in turn attacked certain components of the wood. Without these components, the wood quickly lost its strength. Throughout this work, various laboratory tests were performed for exposure periods of up to 5 years at elevated temperatures and strength testing was done on the aged wood. These results led to development of test protocols for evaluating strength properties of fire retardant wood.

In particular, two organizations, ASTM International (American Society for Testing and Materials, ASTM) and AWPA, were very active in developing new test procedures and standards to address strength issues. In the late 1980s when the apparent strength problem was first becoming known, ASTM issued an emergency standard that addressed strength losses for plywood exposed at elevated temperatures and humidities. In this emergency standard, which later became ASTM D5516, plywood is exposed for at least 60 days at temperatures of 77°C and 50% relative humidity. The strength reductions from exposure can then used to develop design adjustment factors for the fire retardant formulation using a computer based modeling approach detailed in ASTM D6305 that considers climatic data. Similar testing procedures and design adjustment methodology for fire retardant lumber are detailed in D5664 and D6841. The AWPA have revised their standards related to fire retardants to require strength testing by the above ASTM procedures and incorporated recommended minimum acceptable levels of strength loss.

These actions have given specifiers the needed confidence to again use fire retardant treated wood without fear of premature strength loss. These tests were quickly adopted by building codes and other regulators with the result that several products are currently available that give excellent strength performance. Corrosion and hygroscopicity concerns that had plagued the first-generation products have also been addressed. Today's products are no more corrosive than untreated wood and do not display any significantly different moisture content up to 92% relative humidity.

The significant commercial formulations now accepted in the US and Canada are the GUP/BA combination, a similar urea-boric acid combination, a nonphosphate containing mixture of nitrogen and borate compounds, and a combination of diammonium phosphate and boric acid where sufficient boric acid is available to buffer any free phosphate acids produced. The market has readily accepted the current formulations and substantial growth has occurred in the last decade (**Figure 1**).

Testing of Fire Retardants

Commercial Testing

For commercial purposes, the dominant test for fire retardant treated wood is the measurement of surface flame spread by use of ASTM E84. In this test, the treated material forms the roof of a 24-ft long (7.3 m) tunnel and the wind-aided spread of flame is tracked for 10 min. For all structural applications of fire retardant treated wood, building codes require that the test duration be extended an additional 20 min without significant progressive combustion. A standard ignition flame is used and the tunnel is calibrated to have a flame spread rating of 0 using an inert cement board and a rating of 100 using red oak flooring. The flame spread of the test product is determined under these standard conditions and flame spread ratings for fire retardant treated and untreated wood are discussed later. A smoke rating is also obtained during the tunnel test and most uses allowed in the building codes require a smoke level of less than 450.

Typically, a supplier of a fire retardant formulation will contract with a testing laboratory such as Underwriters Laboratory (ULI) to conduct the testing on a number of species of lumber. Various plywood species and grades may also be tested. The testing laboratory monitors all phases of the preparation of the test material. Upon completion of successful testing, the laboratory then lists the materials as acceptable in their publications and issues identification stamps or labels that are used to indicate to others that the material passes recognized testing protocols.

The building codes classify materials in broad ranges of flame spread based on the first 10 min of test: Class I or A has a flame spread of 0–25, Class II or B is 26–75, and Class III or C is 76–200. Class I material can be used in more critical applications such as on the walls of exit corridors while the others are used in less critical applications where there is less risk to human life if a fire occurs. For structural uses of fire retardant treated wood where the E-84 test is extended for an additional 20 min of flame there cannot be any sign of significant progressive combustion as defined in the standard.

When treated with fire retardants, structurally qualified species have a 10-min rating of less than 25 and there is no significant progressive combustion when the test is extended to a 30-min total burning time. All of the commonly available lumber species and plywood sizes are available with this classification. Understandably, the flame spread ratings of untreated wooden commodities lie near 100 since the tunnel is calibrated at that value for red oak. A number of important species and materials have been tested and the flame-spread values for the untreated wood are given in **Table 3**. Note though that some species such as southern pine (*Pinus*) can have a much higher flame spread than the others when untreated due to their higher resin content.

Table 3 Flame spread indices for untreated wood

	Flame spread index
Lumber	
Western redcedar	70
Douglas-fir	70–100
Maple (flooring)	105
Oak, red	100
Pine, white	75–85
Pine, southern yellow	130–195
Redwood	70
Spruce, Sitka	75
Plywood	
Softwood	
Douglas-fir (10 mm)	110–150
Southern pine (10 mm)	100–105
Hardwood	
Birch (6 mm)	115–185
Lauan (6 mm)	100–140
Oak (6 mm)	125–185

Source: Prepared from American Wood Council *Flame Spread Performance of Wood Products*. Available online at http://www.awc.org.

Spray or brush applied fire retardant coatings for wood differ significantly from pressure treated formulations in that they are only tested for 10 min total and then assigned a flame spread rating. Thus, they do not have the additional structural designation. Also, coatings are limited to only one species, Douglas-fir (*Pseudotsuga menziesii*), and are not available for a wide variety of products.

Other important tests for commercial fire retardants include measuring:

- heat release rate
- smoke density
- lateral spread of flame
- smoke toxicity
- ancillary properties: corrosion, hygroscopicity, strength.

There are a number of test procedures used to document the above properties and specific protocols can be found in ASTM, AWPA, Factory Mutual (FM), International Standards Organization (ISO), and ULI documents. It should be noted that in recent years, the fire research community has expended great effort to harmonize the North American and ISO standards on fire testing. However, many differences still exist in the standards and one should not assume interchangeability of the standards from different organizations.

There are also applications where the fire resistance properties of fire retardant wood are more important than the surface spread of flame. For these

tests, the ability of wood to resist burn through is challenged and typically these tests are done on large assemblies such as walls or doors. In these cases, the fire retardant wood contributes a portion of the total assembly properties.

Historically, in Europe, fire resistance properties have been more important than flame spread and the test procedures produce ratings based on measuring resistance. Imparting resistance requires significantly higher retentions of fire retardants wood and this leads to higher costs. Therefore the use of fire retardants in Europe has lagged behind that of North America.

In recent years, there has been an increasing use of fire retardants in Europe for nonstructural products such as wall linings and siding (cladding). There is still only limited use in structural applications. However, there are a number of modified protocols being proposed and/or accepted as part of the European Union process so current affairs in Europe regarding fire retardants for wood are in a state of flux. Presumably these changes will lead to further increases in use.

Laboratory Testing

A number of testing techniques are used for the development of fire retardant formulations. In the past, the fire tube test (ASTM E69), 2-ft (60 cm) tunnel, and other small-scale fire tests were used. However these tests were frequently misleading in that their reproducibility is relatively poor. Consequently, in recent years most researchers have migrated to thermal analysis and other more sophisticated test equipment such as the cone calorimeter.

For fire retardants, the two most important thermal tests are thermogravimetric analysis (TGA) and differential thermal analysis (DTA). TGA measures weight loss as the sample is heated while DTA measures exothermic or endothermic reactions that occur as the sample is heated. Most modern thermal analysis equipment can provide TGA and DTA data simultaneously and the combination can help guide the researcher. The testing can be done in an inert gas atmosphere so that pyrolysis occurs or in oxygen so that combustion occurs. Although the chemical processes for pyrolysis and combustion are similar, the relative degree of formation of various products can greatly differ.

Typical TGA curves are shown in **Figure 3** for untreated and wood treated with two different commercial fire retardant formulations. Note that the dominant effect of the fire retardants is to reduce the onset of decomposition to around 200°C and to increase the amount of residue (char) from 1–2% to about 20% when the TGA furnace reached 500°C.

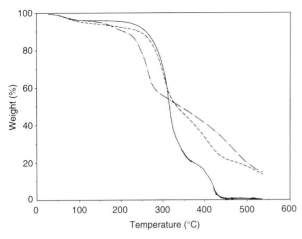

Figure 3 Typical thermogravimetric analyses of fire retardant treated and untreated wood. Solid line, untreated wood; dashed line, commercial formula A; dash–dot line, commercial formula B.

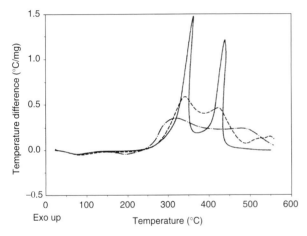

Figure 4 Typical differential thermal analyses of fire retardant treated and untreated wood. Solid line, untreated wood; dashed line, commercial formula A; dash–dot line, commercial formula B.

The DTA curves that correspond to these samples are shown in **Figure 4**. In these cases, most of the samples absorb small amounts of energy (i.e., are slightly endothermic) up to about 250°C and then liberate that energy (i.e., become exothermic) during the later stages of heating. The extent and location of the various thermal events guide the development researcher in the search for fire retardant formulations. Successful laboratory candidates are further tested with the commercial procedures discussed above.

Pricing of Fire Retardant Wood

For most species, the pressure treatment process must leave 32–48 kg m^{-3} retention of the fire retardant formulation in the wood to achieve a Class I flame spread rating of 25 or less. This degree of protection costs about US\$50–60 m^{-3} for the chemicals alone and there is additional cost of about US\$30 m^{-3} for the processing. In addition, building codes require redrying after treatment which generally costs at least US\$40 m^{-3}. Thus, most commercial fire retardants add nearly US\$140 m^{-3} to the untreated price of the wood.

Mechanism of Fire Retardant Action

A number of mechanisms through which fire retardants exert their influence on the combustion of wood have been proposed over the years. For combustion to occur, the larger polymeric molecules in wood must be broken down into small, volatile fragments. This breakdown can occur in a variety of ways and it is recognized that combinations of the various mechanisms actually occur during combustion. For convenience though, the various mechanisms can be grouped into six different theories.

Increased Char Formation Theories

In this theory, the fire retardant chemicals dominant influence is on the various chemical mechanisms that promote char formation while liberating small, highly oxidized fragments of the polymers in wood. Typically, these mechanisms are of the decarboxylation, decarbonlylation, and dehydration types where, say, cellulose is transformed into levoglucosan which further degrades to char and small volatiles. (A somewhat simplistic way of thinking of this is to say that the carbon framework of wood is largely charred in place while small fragments such as water, carbon dioxide, and carbon monoxide are liberated.)

Reduced Volatiles Formation Theories

An adjunct to the increased char theory is the reduced volatile theory that in fact means that the heat content of the volatile products is reduced. Since there is less heat generated by the combustion of the volatiles, the propensity for self-sustaining burning is reduced.

Coating or Barrier Theories

It is thought that some fire retardants create physical barriers such as glasses or rigid foams that inhibit oxygen transport necessary to support combustion. The barriers can also provide thermal insulation to prevent heat transfer. Many fire retardant formulations for wood intumesce or swell when heated and this mechanism may be important for these types.

Gas Theories

The gas theories state that fire retardants cause dilution of the combustible gases with noncombustible gases during the early stages of pyrolysis and this inhibits subsequent combustion. In effect, there is a gaseous barrier to combustion.

Free Radical Inhibition Theories

This theory proposes that fire retardants act as traps to inhibit free radical propagations. Thus the various radicals formed by scission mechanisms are not available and subsequent combustion is retarded.

Thermal Theories

The thermal theories predict that fire retardants reduce the capacity of the wood to absorb heat. Consequently, they limit the amount of heat available for pyrolysis reactions.

The first two theories above seem especially important for fire retardants for wood since effective agents demonstrate the two properties of increased char and decreased combustible volatiles over and over again. Many authors have proposed specific chemical mechanisms for the pyrolysis and burning of wood and the interaction of fire retardants with these mechanisms. However these detailed discussions are beyond the scope of this article and the interested reader is directed to the Further Reading section below.

See also: **Solid Wood Processing**: Protection of Wood against Biodeterioration. **Solid Wood Products**: Structural Use of Wood; Wood-based Composites and Panel Products. **Wood Formation and Properties**: Chemical Properties of Wood; Physical Properties of Wood.

Further Reading

Browne FL (1963) *Theories of the Combustion of Wood and Its Control*. US Department of Agriculture Forest Products Laboratory Report no. 2136. Madison, WI: US Department of Agriculture Forestry Service.

Goldstein IS (1973) Degradation and protection from thermal attack. In: Nicholas DD (ed.) *Wood Deterioration and Its Prevention by Preservative Treatments*, vol. I, pp. 307–339. Syracuse, NY: Syracuse University Press.

Holmes CA (1977) Effect of fire-retardant treatments on performance properties of wood. In: Goldstein IS (ed.) *Wood Technology: Chemical Aspects*. Washington, DC: American Chemical Society. Available online at http://www.fs.fpl.fed.us/publications

Levan SL (1984) Chemistry of fire retardancy. In: Rowell RM (ed.) *The Chemistry of Solid Wood*, pp. 531–574. Washington, DC: American Chemical Society. Available on line at http://www.fs.fpl.fed.us/publications.

Lyons JW (1987) *The Chemistry and Uses of Fire Retardants*. Malabar, FL: Robert E. Krieger.

Shafizadeh F (1984) The chemistry of pyrolysis and combustion. In: Rowell RM (ed.) *The Chemistry of Solid Wood*, pp. 489–529. Washington, DC: American Chemical Society. Available online at http://www.fs.fpl.fed.us/publications.

Shafizadeh F, Sarkanen KV, and Tillman DA (eds) (1976) *Thermal Uses and Properties of Carbohydrates and Lignins*. New York: Academic Press.

Winandy JE (2001) Thermal degradation of fire-retardant-treated wood: predicting residual service life. *Forest Products Journal* 51(2): 47–54.

Recycling

J I Zerbe, Madison, WI, USA

Introduction

Paper has been the mainstay of recycling efforts for many years, but other forest products are making increasingly larger impacts on recycling. This means a growing contribution to environmental benefits from conserving resources and energy as well as reducing the need for landfill space.

Other forest products for recycling include wood in many forms from construction sites to 55-m depths in Lake Superior, from logs with fine-textured growth that are much sought after to much more common products that clutter and are sometimes hazardous, and from spruce milled from the millennium Christmas tree on the White House lawn to live oak from the U.S.S. *Constitution* that was launched in 1797.

Recycled wood is converted into products from fuel to fine furniture, and from carvings and sculpture to composites with plastics and concrete.

Recycling

Problems in Recycling Wood

Major sources of wood for recycling are used pallets from commodity distribution channels and all types of wood from municipal solid waste collection sites. Pallets during their lifetimes could have carried hazardous materials, and there could have been spills of undesirable substances onto pallet frames. However the likelihood of such occurrences is remote.

Similarly municipal solid waste may have unknown constituents that could impact adversely on derived products that find their way into processing and use streams. Panel products containing adhesives that were formulated with formaldehyde, wood containing preservatives to protect against insects and decay, painted wood from older structures that were painted with paint containing lead, and wood that emits volatile organic compounds to the air or produces ash with undesirable components on burning must all be handled and used judiciously.

On 12 February 2002 manufacturers of chromated copper arsenate (CCA)-treated wood products reached a voluntary agreement with the US Environmental Protection Agency to stop the use of these products in residential applications by the end of 2003. This could lead to a massive disposal problem when existing CCA-treated products reach the end of their service lives, or if they are replaced sooner with products such as copper-based preservatives with organic biocides that do not contain arsenic. But consumers can benefit from safe recycling of these and other contaminated products through such approaches as safe combustion of hazardous waste for fuel or reconstituting the wood products for other nonresidential applications such as marine pier pilings and highway sound barriers.

Despite some recognized problems in recycling wood products, with proper attention to circumventing the potential dangers, recycled wood is gaining momentum and increasingly contributing to the overall conservation of material and energy.

Recovery of Wood from New Building Sites

In the USA wood is a favorite material for residences. Single family detached homes usually have some wood building components. Wood framing is common for walls, and almost universal for roofs. Ideally wood components would be furnished to these construction sites so that they could be fastened together without waste. But this is rarely the case except for manufactured homes. Most housing construction sites are a treasure trove of sawn ends and other trimmings of clean wood in various forms that are well suited for recycling.

Recovery of Wood from Building Demolition and Restoration

Other building sites also have wood suitable for recycling, but the residues from these sites are less advantageous. Where buildings are being demolished to free land for other purposes, or, to some degree, where buildings are being renovated, wood is generally available. However often it is in admixtures with other contaminating materials such as gypsum wallboard, plaster, carpeting, plastics, steel, and concrete.

Deconstruction of Buildings

Deconstruction of wood construction components in buildings that are being renovated or razed is often a good source of high-quality forest products for reuse. Planned disassembly to yield wood without attachment to other materials is a means of avoiding problems in recycling such are normally encountered with wood from demolished buildings.

But there are other problems. While larger timbers command a high price and are regularly recycled wood members of smaller cross-section are seldom reused. One reason is because such lumber often sustains some consequential damage in both the construction and deconstruction processes that makes it less competitive with new products such as low-cost studs for house wall construction.

In a study to determine strength properties and market value of timbers deconstructed from buildings at military bases, researchers at the US Forest Products Laboratory found some reduction in comparison with new timbers. As a result of damage, the quality of lumber from nonindustrial military buildings was found to average one grade lower than that of freshly sawn lumber. Types of damage included holes resulting from nails or bolts, splits resulting from factors other than drying, saw cuts, notches, decay, and mechanical damage (such as gouges and broken ends).

Recovery of Wood from Municipal Solid Waste

In 1998, 16.9% of municipal solid waste generated in the USA was solid wood. This amounted to 37 009 000 short tons (33 575 000 metric tonnes). Of this amount 11 700 000 tons (10 611 000 metric tonnes) were recovered, 7 025 000 tons (6 373 000 metric tonnes) were combusted, 6 096 000 tons (5 530 000 metric tonnes) were not usable, and 12 191 000 tons (11 060 000 metric tonnes) were available for recovery (**Figure 1**). Wood that is recovered from the waste stream for recycling is economically sound, conserves natural resources, and benefits the environment by reducing requirements for landfill space and by reducing the accumulation of greenhouse gases in the atmosphere.

Recovery of Wood from Industrial Sites

Industrial sites are other sources of wood for recycling. Large components of industrial waste are railroad ties, used pallets, reels, and containers.

Nationally there are 750 million railroad ties in the USA and Canada, and approximately 12 million of these ties, or 1.6%, are replaced annually. Throughout North America, 62% of used ties are sold to contractors who sell them to commercial landscapers

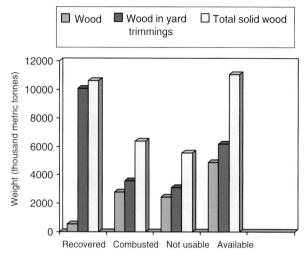

Figure 1   Wood in municipal solid waste (MSW) in 1998 in the USA.

or lumberyards. One-fifth of old ties are landfilled, 15% are sold to cogeneration facilities, and 3% are stored.

Some used pallets, reels, and containers are constituents of municipal waste streams, but often they are disposed through other means. Industry data in the USA indicate that the wood pallet, reel, and container manufacturing industry produces nearly 500 million new units per year and uses over 9 million tons of wood (based on dry moisture content). About half of these units are returnable and are reused as is or they are reused after undergoing repair, but they must all be disposed after a few to several service cycles. Wood pallet suppliers are often asked to provide pick-up and disposal service for broken pallets.

Millions of wood electric and telephone utility cable reels weighing from 22.7 to 227 kg (50 to 500 pounds) each, and a much larger number of smaller plywood reels are discarded each year.

Wood shipping crates used for crating machinery, machinery spare parts and other items are handled and disposed of daily by tens of thousands of manufacturing plants across the USA.

Recycling of Wood from Brush and Tree Trimmings and Tree Removals

The waste stream from brush and tree trimmings and tree and stump removals results from residential tree pruning, street clean-up after storm damage, diseased tree removal, clearings for new construction, and tree pruning along utility rights of way. This wood is often available chipped and used for fuel. Some can be used in papermaking. Some is used as a bulking agent in yard waste composting, and some is screened for landscaping and architectural mulch.

For these purposes it may be blended with other wood or manufacturing wood waste such as cedar, and be dyed in various colors. Clean wood fines can be used in animal bedding, or wood flour, and animal feed.

Recycled Products

Products from Used Pallets

Once pallets are recovered from the waste stream, they are most likely to be repaired and reused for their original purpose. Of the wood contained in pallets recovered by the industry in the USA in 1995, 87% was used again in other pallets.

It was estimated that one in four wood pallets sold by firms in the industry consisted of recovered material. About 10% of the wood (by volume) from used pallets was ground or chipped. Tub grinders facilitated separation and removal of nails in recycling pallets. Chipped and ground material was used for products such as animal bedding, mulch, and composite products. Some of the better wood from pallets could also be used for higher-value products such as flooring, paneling, or furniture.

Shop-Fabricated Specialized Retail Sale Items

Sometimes pallet lumber and other reclaimed wood material is made for market sale items. An example is box shapes for purposes that include flower boxes, planters, bird houses and feeders, and storage chests. One manufacturer made fine-quality jewelry boxes from high-quality recycled lumber. Other popular fabricated products from recycled wood are folding chairs.

Unique Products that Use High-Quality Characteristics of Certain Woods Advantageously

Sometimes recycled wood is imbued with desirable characteristics inherent in wood harvested from virgin forests that are difficult to find in second-growth material which is typical of new lumber on the market today. Or lumber takes on desirable properties as a result of its service life in buildings or other applications.

After years of aging, wood takes on a patina that can be pleasing and desirable for specialty products such as flooring. Floors made from recycled pine often have a natural beauty of distinctive coloring together with other special features such as knots and worm and nail holes, and occasional plugged bolt holes. Sometimes the source of older material is not from previous construction, but from logs salvaged from river bottoms. In Kentucky desirable white oak wood from used whiskey barrels is available. In

California deconstruction of sawmills yields old fine grain timbers of Douglas fir, sugar pine, and incense cedar that may be used for fine millwork and other purposes.

In Pennsylvania old barns are disassembled piece by piece to save the flooring, siding, windows, doors, roofing, beams, joists, and even contents such as hog troughs. Deconstruction can take considerably longer than standard demolition by heavy equipment, but deconstruction costs much less than demolition. People who own old barns often want to keep them looking like they did 150 or 200 years ago. If a barn is not structurally suited for reconstruction, its materials are used for repair parts, new construction, siding, flooring, or structural or decorative beams.

Sunken Logs from Lake Superior as a Source for Recycled Wood Products

In Chequamegon Bay on the Wisconsin shore of Lake Superior a company recovers sunken logs from a depth of 18.3 m (60 feet). Because the logs have been in cold water from as long ago as the 1880s to as recently as the 1930s they are well preserved. Logs are sold at premium prices to furniture makers, architects, contractors, and instrument makers in the USA and Japan. The wood includes 12.2-m (40-foot) lengths of red oak and other logs of white pine, richly figured maple, hemlock, yellow birch, and red elm. Because this maple wood is so fine grained, compared to wood from the remaining forest, it is highly valued for specialty purposes such as violin making. All of the woods are highly prized by artisans, custom furniture makers, and makers of other musical instruments.

The recycled red oak was used for paneling in the dome where the Calgary Flames ice hockey team plays. Other orders have come from the Getty Museum in Los Angeles, the Boeing Company in Seattle, and the William Gates residence in Seattle.

Composite Products from Recycled Wood

In addition to about 19.7% wood in municipal solid waste from wood and yard trimmings categories in the USA there is about 38% paper and paperboard and close to 10% plastics (**Figure 2**). These three sources of material offer opportunities for recycling into wood fiber–plastic composites.

Laboratory research has demonstrated that with air-laid composite technology composites very similar to commercial composites could be made from demolition wood waste and waste plastic from milk bottles (polyethylene) and beverage bottles (polyethylene terephthalate). Waste materials consisting of waste paper, polyethylene from milk bottles, and polypropylene from automobile battery cases or ketchup bottles could be melt-blended into promising products. Generally the properties of the recycled composite products are comparable to those of the original plastics.

A composite wood–concrete wall forming system has performed successfully on the international market. The original insulated concrete form has been manufactured in Canada since 1953. The low-density cement-bonded wood fiber composite is made from postindustrial recycled waste lumber and Portland cement. The product is resistant to fire, mold, and decay.

At an international builders' show in Atlanta, Georgia in February 2002, a large US forest products company demonstrated new composite decking

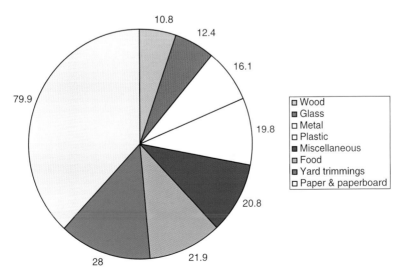

Figure 2 Categories of municipal solid waste (MSW) generated in the USA in 1996.

manufactured from polyethylene plastic and wood fiber residues. It has been marketed throughout the US through a major home-building products chain since March 2002.

The termite-proof material is marketed as not susceptible to decay, splintering, swelling, twisting, or warping. It is specially designed to acquire the weathered look of natural wood, and it is slip-resistant when wet. It is marketed as a system with other composite accessories. Consumers may choose spindles or square balusters and choices of rails, post caps, and post collars. The decking may be installed with nails or screws, and painting of the surface is not required.

Recycling into Mulch, Compost, Wood Flour, Chips, and Shavings

Mulch Mulch is commonly composed of recycled wood particles that are used in landscaping around plants, shrubs, and trees to retain moisture and suppress weeds. Some companies manufacture a blend of recycled wood and paper fibers as a mulch to enhance seed germination and minimize erosion on revegetation projects. These products soak up water, allowing seed and fertilizer to form a homogeneous slurry that enables a uniformly distributed stand of grass, suitable for turf lawns and all general-purpose planting.

Wood chips make excellent mulch that resists compaction, remains in place, and weathers to an attractive silvery-gray color. Sawdust is often readily available and may be helpful in acidifying the soil around rhododendrons and other acid-loving plants. Sawdust, however, tends to cake, making it harder for water to soak into the ground. Sawdust is low in nitrogen, so it robs nitrogen from the soil as it decomposes. Therefore, more nitrogen fertilizer may be needed. A 7–15-cm (3- to 6-inch) layer of sawdust does work well, however, for mulching pathways.

Mulches colored with natural colorants are popular for landscaping and special uses such as ground covering under playground equipment.

Compost Compost from recycled wood is a blend of chips mixed with other organic materials such as horse, chicken, and turkey manures. Compost keeps the soil loose and allows more retained moisture. Compost materials are decomposed and composted to create a dark product that is commonly used for potting plants and adding nutrients to the soil. During composting, microorganisms (bacteria, fungi, actinomycetes) from the soil eat the organic (carbon-containing) waste and break it down into its simplest parts. This produces a fiber-rich, carbon-containing

humus with inorganic nutrients like nitrogen, phosphorus, and potassium.

Wood chips, sawdust, and bark are used as bulking materials in composting sewage sludge, although some governmental jurisdictions may have regulations against this practice.

Wood flour Wood flour is a by-product of wood processing. It consists of fine screened wood particles that are dried to an unusually low 6–8% moisture content.

Wood flour is commonly used as a filler material. One major outlet has been for mixing with glues and adhesives. More recently wood flour is used as a filler with plastics. A manufacturer in Wisconsin makes automotive interior panels such as side door panels with polypropylene and 40–55% wood flour. A large millwork manufacturer in Minnesota makes door sills and windows with waste polyvinyl chloride and wood flour. Plastic lumber is another product that may use wood flour. A company in Billingfors, Sweden makes a recycled wood flour–polyethylene plastic compound for use in further processing to plastic products.

Chips By far, the primary use of wood residue is burning for energy, and chips are a convenient form for use in combustors of advanced design. Wood chips from slabs, edgings, and trim ends are also often used for pulp to make paper. Some wood chips are pyrolyzed to make extenders that can substitute for up to 50% of the phenol in phenolic resin adhesives.

Shavings Shavings often result from turning poles on a lathe as in the manufacture of logs for rustic building construction. These residues often are used to advantage for higher moisture content fuel. Planer shavings from millwork, molding, and other product manufacture make good dry fuel.

Compressed Logs, Charcoal, Wood Briquettes, and Wood Pellets

Compressed logs Fireplace logs made from wood residues are popular retail items in areas where fireplaces are common. They may be made entirely of wood, or use wood in combination with 50% or more wax. The use of wax detracts from the environmental advantages gained as a result of displacing nonrenewable fossil fuels, but wax logs do burn with fewer emissions to the air.

Wood briquettes Wood briquettes are usually made in the same machines that are used to make all-wood fireplace logs. They are used primarily as stoker-fed fuel for industrial boilers.

Wood charcoal Charcoal briquettes have limited markets in the USA, but they can be readily manufactured from waste wood. A disadvantage is the difficulty in preventing high rates of air pollution in charcoal manufacture.

Wood pellets Wood pellets are made from dry wood residues, and, optimally, they are made from wood with a minimum of bark. Pellets are a desirable form of wood fuel, and modern stoves and furnaces for burning pellets have automatic feed and control modules. Pellets may therefore be burned without undue exertion. Moreover they are usually cost-effective, and the combustion units are reliable. Usually there is little ash, especially if excessive amounts of bark in pellet manufacture are avoided.

Animal Bedding

When wood is placed in contact with soil, the action of bacteria in the decomposition of the soil traps much of the soil nitrogen. This can cause a condition known as 'nitrogen starvation' for plants growing in the soil. An attractive solution for this problem is to use the wood as animal bedding prior to spreading it on the soil. Wood bedding reduces manure runoff and helps to control odors.

Dry wood, especially that from planer shavings, tends to get dusty and is good for poultry bedding and some other domestic animal bedding.

Although the smell of cedar makes it a preferred species for use in home pet care, other species may be used. The freedom from splinters and the clean smell of aspen and cottonwood make them desirable for some animals, including mink that are raised for fur production.

See also: **Non-wood Products**: Energy from Wood. **Packaging, Recycling and Printing**: Paper Recycling Science and Technology. **Wood Use and Trade**: Environmental Benefits of Wood as a Building Material.

Further Reading

Bratkovich SM (2001) *Utilizing Municipal Trees: Ideas from Across the Country*, Report no. NA-TP-06-01. St Paul, MN: Northeastern Area State and Private Forestry.

Bush RJ, Araman PA, and Reddy VS (1997) Pallet recycling and material substitution: how will hardwood markets be affected? In: Wiedenbeck J (ed.) *Eastern Hardwoods: Resources, Technologies, and Markets*, pp. 67–73. Madison, WI: Forest Products Society.

Denison RA and Ruston J (1990) *Recycling and Incineration: Evaluating the Choices*. Washington, DC: Island Press.

Falk RH (1999) The properties of lumber and timber recycled from deconstructed buildings, Research Bulletin

no. 212. In: Walford GB and Gaunt DJ (eds) *Proceedings of the Pacific Timber Engineering Conference*, pp. 255–257. Rotorua, New Zealand: New Zealand Forest Research Institute.

Ince PJ (1994) *Recycling and Long-Range Timber Outlook*, Background Research Report 1993 RPA Assessment Update, US Department of Agriculture Forest Service, Technical Report no. FPL-RP-534. Madison, WI: US Forest Products Laboratory.

Jones CH (ed.) (1996) *National Wood Recycling Directory*. Washington, DC: American Forest and Paper Association.

Rosenberg N (1976) *Perspectives on Technology*. Cambridge, UK: Cambridge University Press.

Sherwood GE (1984) *Renovate an Old House*? US Department of Agriculture, Forest Service Home and Garden Bulletin no. 212. Washington, DC: US Government Printing Office.

US Department of Agriculture (1991) *Agriculture and the Environment: The 1991 Yearbook of Agriculture*. Washington, DC: US Government Printing Office.

US Department of Agriculture (1992) *New Crops, New Uses, New Markets – Industrial and Commercial Products from US Agriculture: The 1992 Yearbook of Agriculture*. Washington, DC: US Government Printing Office.

US Environmental Protection Agency (1995) *Manufacturing from Recyclables: 24 Case Studies of Successful Recycling Enterprises*, EPA-R-95-001. Washington, DC: US Government Printing Office.

Youngquist JA, Myers GE, Muehl J, Krzysik A, and Clemons CC (1993) *Composites from Recycled Wood and Plastics*, Report no. IAG DW12934608-2. Cincinnati, OH: Environmental Protection Agency.

Drying

M R Milota, Oregon State University, Corvallis, OR, USA

History of Wood Drying

Evidence exists in furniture, carvings, and artwork that survive from millennia ago that the importance of drying and how wood responds to changing ambient conditions has long been recognized. Until the turn of the twentieth century, however, only limited quantities of wood were artificially (kiln) dried. Natural (air) drying was generally sufficient because the practice of heating all rooms in a house was not common. The smoke kiln was developed in Europe 200 to 250 years ago. As the name implies, a fire burned under a perforated floor and the wood was stacked above the floor. In the late nineteenth century, humidity was added to help control the drying rate. A few smoke kilns were still in use in the United States in 1926, but they had disappeared in Europe.

The lumber dry kiln as we know it today has its origins in the late nineteenth and early twentieth century. By the time of World War I, drying methods had been established and texts from the 1920s have much the same basic information as those written today. Since that time our understanding of what happens at the cellular level has advanced, improvements have been made in the equipment, and techniques have been developed for many species. The advancement of other types of dryers, for example veneer and particle dryers, was in parallel with the development of these industries during the twentieth century.

Why Wood is Dried

It is generally desirable for the shrinkage associated with moisture loss to occur before products are produced. For example, furniture parts will not fit together if they change moisture content after manufacturing. It is most desirable to dry the wood to the moisture content it will eventually achieve in service. This depends on relative humidity at the location of installation and varies from summer to winter, but ranges from 5% to 15% for indoor applications. In temperate climates, 7% to 9% is a common indoor equilibrium moisture content.

As wood dries, some defects such as splitting and warping are likely to happen in some pieces. It is desirable for these to occur prior to using the wood in an appearance application.

In some cases wood is dried to improve its ability to accept adhesives, paints, preservative treatments, or finishes. Moisture content is critical for adhesive penetration and most surface coatings need to be applied over dry wood. The quality of a machined surface will not be good if the moisture content is not correct for the machine tools. The strength of wood increases as it is dried. This allows dry wood to be assigned higher strength properties than green wood in some applications. If green wood is used at the dry wood design values, excessive deflection or even failure might result before it has a chance to dry in service.

When sufficiently high temperatures are used, insects and their eggs are killed as are some fungi. The temperatures normally used in kiln drying are sufficient to accomplish this as well as set the pitch. When the wood is at 20% or less in moisture content, fungal attack is prevented and most insects lose interest in the wood. Setting the pitch means that

the wood resins no longer flow at in-service temperatures. For some species the drying process gives a desirable color to the wood, for example in walnut (*Juglans* spp.), maple (*Acer* spp.), and red alder (*Alnus rubra*). Drying also reduces the shipping weight.

How Water Moves in Wood

For wood with a wet surface, a boundary layer of air near the surface of the wood limits the drying rate. Increased airflow reduces the thickness of the boundary layer and lower relative humidity increases the driving force for mass transfer across it. This boundary layer is most important for small pieces of wood, such as particles or veneer, for which the internal resistance to drying is minimal and when the moisture content is high.

Moisture moves from wetter areas to dryer areas. Within the wood, free (liquid) water can move through the capillary structure if the wood is permeable enough. This can keep the surface wet and the drying rate high. This mode of mass transfer is important in fast-drying woods such as the pines (*Pinus* spp.). Capillary forces, and to a certain extent heating of the wood, cause pressure gradients which result in free water movement. Smaller capillaries tend to pull water from large capillaries so that evaporation from pits near the surface can pull water from the interior of the wood. Once some cells lose most of the free water, a continuous pathway of water is no longer present and moisture cannot move as a liquid.

Water can also diffuse through the wood as a vapor or in the bound state. Vapor diffusion requires a continuous gaseous pathway such as open vessels or cell lumens connected by unaspirated pits. Bound water diffusion occurs through the cell wall material. While vapor diffusion coefficients are much greater than bound water diffusion coefficients, the pathways for vapor diffusion are small compared with those for bound water. Therefore, bound water diffusion dominates moisture movement at low moisture contents. The difference between the equilibrium moisture content and the wood moisture content is often used as the driving force for diffusion at moisture contents below fiber saturation. Diffusion rates increase with increasing temperature, moisture content, and wood permeability. High temperatures (70°C and higher) are used as the wood gets low in moisture content to prevent prolonged drying times.

All modes of moisture movement may be occurring simultaneously at different locations within a piece of wood. Near the center of a piece the moisture content might be high enough for free water movement to occur. At some plane the moisture content is too low to support free water movement and the liquid water evaporates. From there it can move to the surface in the vapor or bound phase.

Lumber

Lumber refers to wood that is typically greater than 5 mm in thickness and sawn. It is either air dried, kiln dried, or dried by a sequence of these. In either type of drying the wood is stacked so that there is airflow around each piece. In developing regions, lumber may be air dried by leaning the pieces almost vertically against a support. In industrial facilities, it is common to lay the pieces horizontally and use narrow strips of dry wood as spacers (**Figure 1**). These are called stickers or fillets. Almost all kiln drying is done on stickers which range from 12 to 24 mm in thickness and 36 to 100 mm in width. Wider stickers are used on heavy woods with low basic density to reduce crushing. The wood is stacked in cuboid packages so the air can move horizontally, perpendicular to the long axis of the wood.

Quality Considerations

Maintaining product quality is a major concern in lumber drying. Stains (chemical or biological) need to be prevented by rapid drying; however, slow drying is often needed to prevent structural damage. Water evaporating from the surface can create enough capillary force to cause the cells to collapse early in the drying process (**Figure 2**). As the surface dries below the fiber saturation point and shrinks, surface checks may appear on the face of the board. These are splits which may be from one to several centimeters in length and from very narrow to a millimeter or two in width (**Figure 3**). The likelihood of surface checking decreases as the wood gets drier. They are most likely to appear in the rays on the bark side of wide, flat sawn pieces.

Early in drying while the shell of the wood has tensile stress, the core of the piece has compressive stress. The tension in the shell prevents it from shrinking as much as a stress-free section. The compression in the core causes it to decrease slightly

Figure 1 Lumber is stacked in cuboid packages with the layers separated by stickers so air can move between the layers.

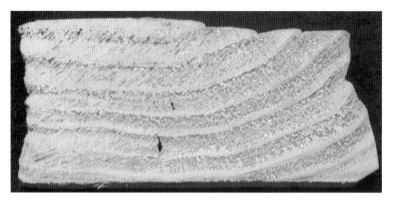

Figure 2 Capillary forces, especially in low density species with high moisture content, can result in collapse. Wood can be steamed to recover minor collapse if no cracks have occurred.

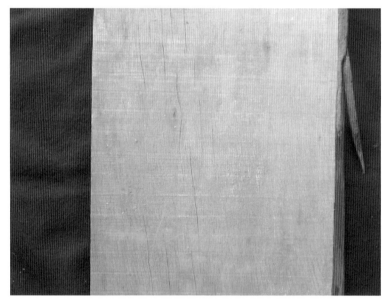

Figure 3 Surface checks can occur if the surface of the board shrinks too much or too quickly compared to the center. This can happen early in lumber drying and the checks close part way through the drying cycle. They are still considered a defect after they close.

in size due to creep and mechanosorptive effects. Later in drying, the core begins to dry below the fiber saturation point and shrink. However, it has already changed size somewhat and the additional size change due to shrinkage causes the stress state in the wood to reverse. After the core begins to shrink there is tensile stress in the core and a compressive stress in the shell. Surface checks close and internal checks, called honeycomb, can form on the inside of the piece (**Figure 4**).

At the end of drying, even if there is no moisture content difference between the shell and the core, there is still tensile stress in the core and compressive stress in the shell. The term 'casehardening' has been applied to this even though the shell is no harder than the core. If the lumber is not resawn or machined extensively, this is not a defect. In many products,

however, internal stress will cause warp in pieces that are resawn or machined. Casehardening is relieved at the end of drying with a conditioning step, a process in which the moisture content of the wood is raised by exposing it to using a high relative humidity at a high enough temperature ($>70\,^{\circ}$C). The degree of casehardening in wood is determined by the prong test or a similar method (**Figure 5**). The prong test should be evaluated 24 h after cutting to allow for moisture and mechanical equilibrium.

Pieces of lumber can change shape during drying (**Figure 6**). The difference in tangential and radial shrinkage results in diamonding and cup. Differences in longitudinal shrinkage from one side or face of the board to the other results in crook or bow. Spiral grain in the tree leads to twist in lumber. These defects are worsened by drying to low moisture

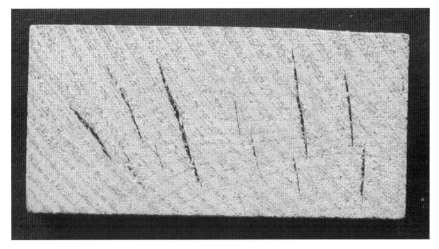

Figure 4 Honeycomb can occur if the internal tensile stress is high enough. This occurs when the core of the piece is near or below the fiber saturation point. These cracks would not be visible on the end of the piece.

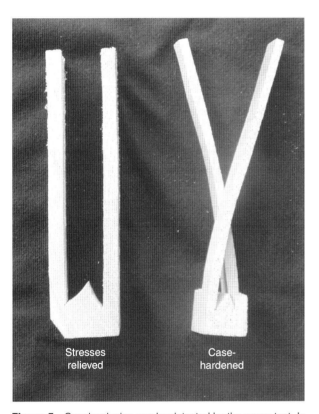

Figure 5 Casehardening can be detected by the prong test. In some regions it is more common to saw the board into two pieces rather than cutting prongs.

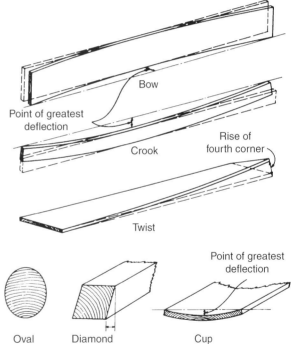

Figure 6 Lumber can distort due to differences in the amount of shrinkage in different locations of directions. From Simpson WT (ed.) (1991) *Dry Kiln Operator's Manual*. US Department of Agriculture.

contents. Stacking boards so they are restrained by the boards above them helps to minimize warp. In some regions it is common to put concrete or steel weights on top of the stacks to reduce warp.

Air Drying

Air drying is used on woods that need to be dried slowly to avoid defects such as collapse and surface checks. To dry slowly in a kiln is very expensive from a capital investment and energy standpoint. During air drying the wood is exposed to uncontrolled conditions and large losses in wood value can occur. For example, one day of hot, windy, dry, weather can cause oak (*Quercus* spp.) to check so badly that it cannot be used for a high-quality product. Conversely, extended humid weather with little wind can result in lumber that is stained.

Air drying is done in open areas with good airflow. The package arrangement is a trade-off to achieve good airflow, forklift access, and to maximize solar gain to promote faster drying. When slower drying is desired, the piles might be covered with a porous cloth to reduce airflow. In rare cases, water mists are used to raise the relative humidity so freshly sawn lumber does not dry too fast. Drier lumber is sometimes placed on the windward side of the yard and the fresh, wetter lumber on the cooler, more humid leeward side to reduce the drying rate and avoid degrade. The inventory in an air yard must be controlled so wood is removed when it reaches the appropriate moisture content.

For some outdoor applications, air drying alone is sufficient. However, the lowest moisture content that can be achieved is about 12% in most regions. This is too high for applications such as furniture and flooring. Also, as the wood approaches the ambient equilibrium moisture content it dries very slowly which would result in large inventories and much land area for drying. Therefore air drying is often followed by kiln drying.

Kiln Drying

Kiln drying occurs in a building with a way to control the temperature, humidity, and airflow (**Figure 7**). The temperature most often is controlled by steam in pipes or coils. The humidity is controlled by limiting how much water leaves the building through vents. If the wood is not losing moisture fast enough, live steam or a water mist might be used to raise the humidity. The air is circulated with fans. Modern kilns use electronic instrumentation and controls; however, pneumatic instrumentation is the norm in many parts of the world.

The packages of wood are loaded into the kiln by forklift (package kilns) or rolled in on tracks (track kilns). Package kilns are more common for species with longer drying times, making the turn around time between charges less important. Package kilns occupy less land area. Track kilns are more common for softwoods. There are some semicontinous track kilns; however, almost all kiln drying is done as a batch process. That is, the kiln is loaded with a charge of wet lumber, it is dried, then removed.

Lumber is kiln dried using a set of environmental conditions called a schedule (**Figure 8**). The schedule is highly dependent on the species and thickness and somewhat dependent on the width and the eventual product. The purpose of the schedule is to minimize defects in the product while also minimizing drying time and cost. Published schedules are available for most species and thicknesses of wood; however, in practice most mills have their own schedules.

While the wood is at high moisture content, the temperature in the kiln is kept low and the relative

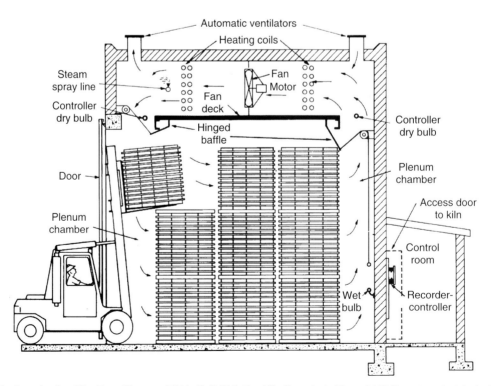

Figure 7 Package lumber kiln. From Simpson WT (ed.) (1991) *Dry Kiln Operator's Manual.* US Department of Agriculture.

Moisture content-based drying schedule					
Step	MC, %	T_{db}, °C	T_{wb}, °C	EMC, %	RH, %
1	above 35	43.3	41.1	17.6	87
2	35 – 30	43.3	40.6	16.3	84
3	30 – 25	48.8	44.4	13.5	77
4	25 – 20	54.4	46.6	10.1	65
5	20 – 15	60.0	43.3	5.8	38
6	15 – dry	82.2	60.0	3.5	26
Equalize and condition as necessary					

Time-based drying schedule					
Step	Time, hrs	T_{db}, °C	T_{wb}, °C	EMC, %	RH, %
1	0 – 12	76.7	73.3	14.1	86
2	12 – 24	76.7	71.1	11.4	78
3	24 – 48	79.4	71.1	9.1	69
4	48 – 72	82.2	71.1	7.7	62
5	72 – dry	82.2	60.0	4.5	36
Equalize and condition as necessary					

Figure 8 Drying schedules. The upper schedule is based on the moisture content of the wood in the kiln. The lower schedule is based on time. Moisture-based schedules are used for species that are difficult to dry. Time-based schedules are used for species that are easy to dry. EMC, equilibrium moisture content.

humidity high to restrict the drying rate. After the surface has dried and the wood has lost about one-third of its moisture, the relative humidity is gradually lowered. When the free water has evaporated from the center of the piece, the temperature is raised and the relative humidity reduced further. After some of the pieces reach the desired moisture content, the humidity is raised to prevent the driest pieces from getting even drier while the wetter pieces continue to lose moisture. This is known as an equalization step. Finally, after the moisture content distribution among the pieces is acceptable, a conditioning step may be employed to eliminate internal stress. The acceptable moisture content distribution depends on final moisture content and end use. For furniture, 7% plus or minus 0.5% to 1% might be necessary whereas for structural lumber 15% plus or minus 2% to 4% or more may be acceptable.

The above schedule description is for species that are prone to defects which result from fast drying, such as oak and eucalyptus (*Eucalyptus* spp.). Many species dry quite easily and the drying schedules are very simple. For example, *Pinus taeda* and *P. radiata* can be dried rapidly with little defect. In easy-to-dry species the kiln is often brought up to the final temperature as rapidly as practical, then the relative humidity is lowered to achieve a high drying rate.

Initial kiln conditions for difficult-to-dry woods may be as low at 35°C with a relative humidity of 85% while easy-to-dry species may be dried with initial

temperatures of 120°C or occasionally higher. At the end of drying and before equalization, most dry kiln schedules for difficult-to-dry species call for a temperature greater than 70°C but generally not higher than 85°C. Air velocity varies from 2 to 8 m s^{-1} through the sticker spaces with the greater values used for rapid drying. Kiln drying takes from 16 h to 60 days, depending on the species and thickness.

Sorting the lumber into groups with similar drying properties is desirable prior to drying. Wood is almost always sorted by species and thickness. Some other possible sorting criteria include: initial moisture content, length, width, heartwood content, sawing pattern, or grade. The equipment at the mill and the number of kilns limit how much sorting can practically be accomplished. It is also possible to sort wet pieces after drying and before planing and redry them. This reduces the overall kiln time required to produce a given quantity of dry lumber, reduces the number of overdried pieces, and eliminates the problem of wet pieces in the final product.

Veneer

Veneer is cut with a knife and ranges from 1 to 5 mm in thickness. Some veneer, most likely from a slicing process, is dried in the same manner as lumber, i.e., placed on stickers and loaded into a kiln. Several veneer layers are left together when dried in this way.

More commonly, however, veneer is dried in a conveyor dryer. The veneer is placed on rollers or wire mesh at one end of the dryer and moves through. There may be multiple decks of veneer vertically and three to five zones of different temperature along the dryer length. Rolls or mesh hold the veneer flat and play a significant role in heat transfer to the wood. A moisture meter at the end of the dryer automatically identifies wet pieces which are then redried. The moisture meter is also used to control the speed of the veneer through the dryer and hence its moisture content.

The airflow in older veneer dryers, called longitudinal dryers, is parallel to the surface veneer. Because veneer is thin, the external boundary layer is more significant than internal resistance to moisture movement and newer dryers (called jet or impingement dryers) have manifolds above and below the veneer that direct the airflow perpendicular to it. The temperatures in veneer dryers are limited to approximately 200–260°C because visible hydrocarbon emissions would be generated at higher temperatures. The highest temperatures are found in the early zones where evaporation keeps the wood cool. High wood temperature can inactivate the veneer's surface and prevent the adhesive from wetting the wood and penetrating. Overdried pieces may reach too high a temperature and show surface inactivation. The relative humidity is necessarily low because the dryers are operated at ambient pressure and well above the boiling point of water. Because of this, an attempt is made to minimize the amount of intake air and operate with a high absolute humidity.

Particles

Rotary dryers are often used for particulate material. Particles and hot air are continually fed to the drum. These large rotating drums have lifting flights which carry the particles upward as the drum rotates. The particles leave the lifting flight near the top of the drum and fall through the air stream. Heat is transferred to the particles both from the air and from contact with the dryer. The drums may have concentric sections so that the particles and air traverse the length of the drum up to three times. Residence time is on the order of minutes. Friable material, such as wafers or flakes, may be dried on trays or belts instead of in drums. Very fine material, such as fiber board furnish, might be dried in a tube dryer in which the air carries the fiber through the tube in seconds.

Moisture Content Measurement

Measuring moisture content is an important part of the drying process. Green lumber is sometimes sorted based on moisture content by simply weighing the pieces, measuring their size, and calculating a green density. In this case, accuracy is not critical and it is simply assumed that basic density does not vary among the pieces. At this point, no other good automated way exists to estimate the moisture content of green wood.

Hand-held meters (**Figure 9**) are used to measure the moisture content of dry wood. Conductance-type moisture meters have needles that are pressed or pounded into the wood and the electrical conductivity of a circuit including the pins and the wood is measured. The pins are about 3 cm apart and put into the wood to the depth at which the reading is desired. Pins up to 100 cm long are available for thick lumber while 0.5-cm needles might be used for veneer. Hand-held capacitance-type moisture meters are used by placing the meter on the surface of the wood. The meter generates an electric field into the wood to a depth of 2–3 cm. Based on the energy lost to the wood, moisture content is estimated. Several frequencies might be used simultaneously to reduce the effects of temperature and basic density. Pin-type moisture meter readings are corrected for species and temperature. Capacitance-type moisture meter readings are corrected for basic density and temperature. In modern meters these corrections are internal to the meter with user input for species, temperature, and/or density. Hand-held meters work well up to about 25–30% moisture content.

A capacitance-type moisture meter is often used in production to check the moisture content of each piece of dry lumber. If done before planing, the meter can be used to sort wet pieces for redrying. For veneer, the production line meter is often of conductance type with metal brushes instead of pins. It is located at the outfeed of the dryer. In particle

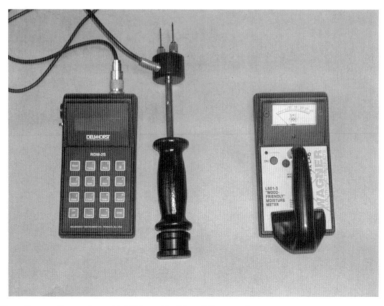

Figure 9 Pin-type (left) and capacitance-type (right) hand-held moisture meters.

operations, an infrared sensor is used to measure the moisture content of furnish as it moves along a belt.

Inside veneer and particle dryers, there is no moisture content measurement. The traditional method in lumber kilns is to weigh 0.5–1-m-long samples of the wood being dried (**Figure 10**). Approximately six to 12 samples are used to monitor a kiln charge. These samples are intended to represent the wettest (or slowest to dry) lumber and driest (or fastest to dry) lumber in the charge. The wettest pieces will control the schedule because these are most likely to surface check, collapse, and honeycomb. The driest pieces tell the operator when to start the equalization step. This technique is well developed and described in many texts. Variations on this technique include putting pins in the samples to measure conductance or having load cells inside the kiln to weigh the samples without the operator entering the kiln.

Some in-kiln systems utilize metal capacitance plates inserted into the lumber stack. Recently developed in-kiln meters can give a moisture content from about 60% to 80% to dryness and are accurate enough that operators typically do not enter the kiln with a hand-held meter. In-kiln will probably become standard for easy-to-dry species; however, for difficult-to-dry species operators want to know the variability and especially the moisture content of the wetter pieces. Therefore, acceptance into the hard- wood industry is uncertain. Any of the in-kiln systems can be integrated with the kiln controller so that the schedule can be advanced based on the moisture content or the rate of moisture content change.

Energy and Environmental Considerations

Drying is a very energy-intensive process and uses up to 85% of the manufacturing energy. Energy use varies greatly, depending on dryer conditions. Difficult-to-dry products require more energy, 7–9 MJ per kilogram of water removed, because more make-up air is required due to the low temperature and humidity. Easy-to-dry products might require 3–6 MJ per kilogram of water removed with particles being on the low end of this range. Of this, approximately 2.3 MJ is used to evaporate each kilogram of water and the remainder consumed by heating make-up air, the kiln structure, the wood and water, by heat transfer through the structure, and electrical inefficiencies. Some dryers are equipped with heat exchangers to recover some of the energy in the vent gas. They have the greatest potential on low temperature dryers with large make-up air requirements. Fan speeds are reduced later in drying in lumber kilns to reduce consumption of electricity when high air velocities are not needed.

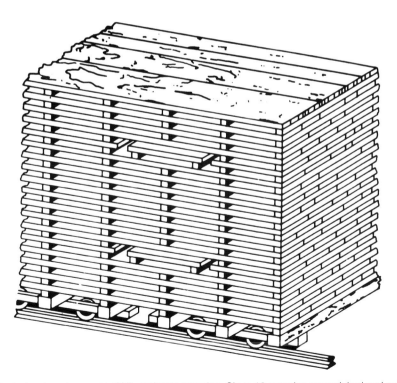

Figure 10 Lumber stack showing placement of kiln moisture samples. Six to 12 samples are weighed and selected to represent the moisture content range in the kiln and are used for determining the step in moisture content-based drying schedules. From Simpson WT (ed.) (1991) *Dry Kiln Operator's Manual*. US Department of Agriculture.

Perhaps the greatest environmental impact of drying is generating energy, either at the on-site boiler or off-site electrical power supplier. Additionally, the exhaust from wood dryers contains a small amount of organic material. Most of this is from volatile material in the wood, such as terpenes, and ranges from 0.1 to $3 \, g \, kg^{-1}$ (grams emitted per kilogram of oven-dry wood processed). Release of some organic compounds may be the result of breakdown of the wood, especially at high temperatures. The main breakdown product with toxicity is methanol which is emitted in quantities from less than 0.01 to $0.3 \, g \, kg^{-1}$. Methanol generation is very dependent on temperature and the moisture removed. A small amount of liquid effluent may come from some kilns, particularly if they are poorly insulated.

Other Technologies

Dehumidification kilns utilize heat pumps to remove water and recover energy. They are very energy efficient, consuming 1.4–2.3 MJ of electrical energy per kilogram of water removed. The operating cost is higher due to electrical energy costs; however, they offer an attractive alternative for low-volume producers because there is no boiler and the initial capital cost is low. An atmospheric pressure steam generator is sometimes added to these kilns to relieve stress. The effluent is water and must be treated prior to being released into the environment.

Solar kilns are used in tropical and even temperate regions. The slow drying and diurnal changes in temperature and humidity can produce lumber with minimal internal stress. Enough solar energy can be collected to evaporate about 5 kg of water per square meter of collector area per day.

Vacuum kilns operate at a pressure below atmospheric. This lowers the boiling point of water so that wood can be dried quickly at lower temperature. The wood remains stronger at lower temperature and fewer defects develop. Besides the cost of the vessel, a disadvantage of this method is that heat does not transfer in a vacuum and conductive metal blankets or electromagnetic energy is used to heat the wood. Rapid drying rates can be achieved when radio-frequency energy is combined with a vacuum. A variation on the vacuum kiln that has gained popularity is the superheated steam kiln. A partial vacuum is drawn and the remaining gas is circulated with fans. As water vapor is removed, the remaining gas becomes almost all water vapor and total pressure and temperature are used to control the drying rate. High air velocity, $10–20 \, m \, s^{-1}$, is needed for adequate heat transfer because of the low air density.

See also: **Solid Wood Processing**: Machining. **Solid Wood Products**: Lumber Production, Properties and Uses; Wood-based Composites and Panel Products. **Wood Formation and Properties**: Physical Properties of Wood. **Wood Use and Trade**: Environmental Benefits of Wood as a Building Material.

Further Reading

Boone RS, Kozlik CJ, Bois PJ, and Wengert EM (1988) *Dry Kiln Schedules for Commercial Woods: Temperate and Tropical*, General Technical Report no. FPL-GTR-57. Madison, WI: US Department of Agriculture, Forest Service, Forest Products Laboratory. (Available through Forest Products Society: www.forestprod.org)

Denig J, Wengert EM, and Simpson WT (2000) *Drying Hardwood Lumber*, General Technical Report no. FPL-GTR-118. Madison, WI: US Department of Agriculture, Forest Service, Forest Products Laboratory.

Forest Products Laboratory (1999) *Air Drying of Lumber*, General Technical Report no. FPL-GTR-117. Madison, WI: US Department of Agriculture, Forest Service, Forest Products Laboratory.

Mujumdar AS (1987) *Handbook of Industrial Drying*. New York: Marcel Dekker.

Siau JF (1984) *Transport Processes in Wood*. New York: Springer-Verlag.

Simpson WT (ed.) (1991) *Dry Kiln Operator's Manual*. Agriculture Handbook no. AH-188. Madison, WI: US Department of Agriculture, Forest Service, Forest Products Laboratory. (Available through Forest Products Society: www.forestprod.org)

Skaar C (1988) *Wood–Water Relations*. New York: Springer-Verlag.

Wengert EM and Toennisson RT (1998) *Lumber Drying Sourcebook: 40 Years of Experience*. Madison, WI: Forest Products Society.

Finishing

W C Feist, Middleton, WI, USA

Introduction

Like other biological materials, wood is susceptible to environmental degradation. When exposed outdoors above ground, a complex combination of chemical, mechanical, and light energy factors contribute to what is described as weathering. Weathering is detrimental to the surfaces and appearance of wood. Thus, weathering must be taken into account when considering the protection of outdoor wood but not indoor wood. Weathering of wood is not to be confused with wood decay (rot), which results from fungal organisms acting in the presence of excess moisture and air for an extended period. Under conditions suitable for decay, wood can deteriorate rapidly, and the result is far different from that observed for natural outdoor weathering.

The wide range of wood and wood-based materials and the variety of paints, stains, varnishes, and other finishes available provide a great latitude and flexibility for protecting and beautifying wood and wood structures both indoors and outdoors (interior and exterior). Indoors, many finishes can be used to provide a range of appearance to any wood product. Outdoors, there are stricter requirements for the finish since exposure to the weather (water and sunlight) can severely damage any sensitive finish. Thus, many finishes suitable for indoor use are not at all suitable outdoors. The choice of finishes outdoors must be made in concert with the design, good understanding of the wood materials being used, and knowledge about the weather conditions that will affect the structure.

Exterior Wood Finishes

The main function of any outdoor wood finish is to protect the wood surface, and secondarily, help maintain a certain appearance, and provide a cleanable surface. Although wood can be used both outdoors and indoors without finishing, unfinished wood surfaces exposed outdoors to the weather change color, are roughened by photodegradation and surface checking, and erode slowly. Unfinished wood surfaces exposed indoors may also change color; moreover, unfinished wood is more difficult to clean than is finished wood.

Wood and wood-based products in a variety of species, grain patterns, textures, and colors can be finished effectively by many different methods. Selection of a finish will depend on the appearance and degree of protection desired and on the substrates used. Because different finishes give varying degrees of protection, the type of finish, its quality and quantity, and the method used to apply the finish must be considered when finishing or refinishing wood and wood products.

Protective finishes and coatings for wood used indoors can perform for many years without refinishing or severe deterioration. The durability of finishes on wood exposed outdoors to natural weathering processes, however, depends first of all on the wood itself. Other factors that contribute are the nature and the quality of the finish used, application techniques, the time between refinishings, the extent to which the surfaces are sheltered from the weather, and climatic and local weather conditions.

The primary function of any outdoor wood finish is to protect the wood surface from natural weathering processes (sunlight and water), and help maintain appearance. Weathering erodes and roughens unfinished wood. Despite this, wood can be left unfinished to weather naturally, and such wood can often provide for extended protection of the structure.

The protection that surface treatment provides against light and water will be affected by the weather resistance of the bonding agents used in the finish (e.g., drying oils, synthetic resins, and latexes), as these agents are subject to some degree of photolytic degradation. The mechanism of failure of paints and other finishes has been described in great detail and will not be discussed further here. Protection of wood exposed outdoors by various finishes, by construction practices, and by design factors to compensate for effects of weather has also been addressed in great detail by others.

A variety of finishes can be applied to outdoor wood. These include clear finishes, which reveal and accentuate the natural beauty of wood; stains, which impart a rustic appearance; and paint or solid-color stains, which can be obtained in a multitude of colors. Finishes or coatings are applied to exterior wood surfaces for a variety of reasons. The particular reason will determine the type of finish selected and subsequently the amount of protection provided to the wood surface as well as the life expectancy for the finish. Finishes can be divided into two general categories: (1) film-forming opaque coatings, such as paints and solid-color stains, and (2) natural finishes, such as film-forming varnishes, and penetrating (nonfilm-forming) water repellents, water-repellent preservatives, oils, and penetrating semitransparent stains.

Film-Forming Opaque Finishes

Paints Paints are common film-forming coatings used on wood that provide the most protection against surface erosion by weathering and against wetting by water. They are also used for esthetic purposes and to conceal certain defects. Paints contain substantial quantities of pigments, which account for the wide range of colors available. Some pigments will essentially eliminate ultraviolet light degradation of the wood surface. Oil-based or alkyd-based paints are a suspension of inorganic pigments in a resin vehicle and a petroleum or turpentine solvent that helps carry the pigment particles and the bonding agent (resin) to the wood surface. Latex paints are likewise a suspension of inorganic pigments and various latex resins, but the solvent or dispersant in this case is water. Paint lifetimes up to 10 years are possible with good-quality paints applied as two coats over a coat of primer paint.

Oil-based paint films usually provide the best shield from liquid water and water vapor. However, they are not necessarily the most durable because they become brittle over time. No matter how well sealed, wood still moves with seasonal humidity, thus stressing and eventually cracking the brittle paint. On the other hand, latex paint films, particularly the acrylic paints, remain more flexible with age. Even though latex paints allow some water vapor to pass through (thus they are sometimes erroneously described as 'breathable'), they hold up better than oil-based paints by swelling and shrinking with the wood. They are also less prone to mildew growth and discoloration from dirt collection.

Paints perform best on edge-grained lumber of low-density wood species such as redwood and cedar. Paints are applied primarily to the wood surface and do not penetrate the wood deeply. Rather, the wood grain is completely obscured and a surface film is formed. This film can blister or peel if the wood is wetted or if inside water vapor moves through the house wall and wood siding because of the absence of a vapor barrier. Original and maintenance costs are often higher for a paint finish than for a nonfilm-forming water-repellent preservative or penetrating stain finish.

Solid-color stains Solid-color stains (sometimes called hiding, heavy-bodied, or opaque stains) are opaque, film-forming finishes that come in a wide range of colors and are essentially thin paints. Solid-color stains are made with a higher concentration of pigment than are the semitransparent penetrating stains discussed below, but a somewhat lower concentration of pigment than that of standard paints. As a result, solid-color stains obscure the natural wood color and grain, and they can also be applied over old paints or solid-color stains. However, surface texture is retained and a flat-finish appearance normally results. Like paints, solid-color stains protect wood against ultraviolet light degradation. Lifetimes of 3 to 7 years can be expected for two-coat applications. Solid-color stains can be both alkyd and latex based; they form a thin film much like paint and consequently can also peel loose from the substrate. They are often used on textured surfaces and panel products such as hardboard and plywood.

Transparent Natural Finishes

Varnishes and varnish stains Varnishes are composed primarily of resins or drying oils dissolved in a suitable solvent. The clear coatings of conventional spar, urethane, or marine varnish, which are film-forming finishes, are not generally recommended for exterior use on wood unless the finished wood is protected by a suitable roof or overhang. Ultraviolet light from the sun penetrates the transparent film and degrades the wood under it. Regardless of the number of coats applied, the finish will eventually become brittle as a result of exposure to sunlight, develop severe cracks, and peel, often in less than 2 years.

A finish that forms a thin, erodable film is popular in Europe and has had some limited success in the United States. This finish is sometimes called a varnish stain or a nearly film-forming stain. The film of varnish stain is thicker than that provided by a semitransparent stain, but thinner than that provided by a conventional film-forming varnish. Varnish stains contain a water repellent, special transparent iron oxide pigments, and mildewcides. The surface coating is designed to slowly erode and can be refinished more easily than a coating provided by a conventional varnish. Varnish stains are usually applied initially as two- or three-coat systems and may last 2 to 4 years.

Water-repellent preservatives Water-repellent preservatives contain a fungicide, a small amount of wax as a water repellent, a resin or drying oil, and a suitable solvent. Some contain ultraviolet light stabilizers. The wax reduces the absorption of liquid water by the wood, and the preservative prevents wood from darkening (graying) by inhibiting the growth of mildew and other staining organisms. Some waterborne or water-dispersed formulations are also available.

A penetrating water-repellent preservative may be used as a natural wood finish. These finishes have minimal protection for wood and may last only 1 to 2 years depending on exposure. The treatment reduces warping and checking, prevents water staining at the edges and ends of wood siding, and helps control mildew growth. Paintable water-repellent preservatives are available and may be used as a treatment for bare wood before priming and painting or in areas where old paint has peeled, exposing bare wood, particularly around butt joints or in corners. This treatment keeps rain or dew from penetrating the wood, especially at joints and on end grain, thus decreasing the shrinking and swelling of the wood. As a result, less stress is placed on the paint film, and its service life is extended. These treatments are nonfilm-forming and do not protect wood from water vapor.

Oils Many penetrating oil or oil-based natural wood finish formulations are available for finishing exterior wood. The most common drying oils used are based on linseed and tung. However, these oils may serve as a food source for mildew if applied to wood in the absence of a mildewcide. The oils will also perform better if a water repellent is included in the formulation. All these oil systems will protect wood, but their average lifetime may be only as long as that described for the water-repellent preservatives. Some oil finishes also contain alkyd resins.

Semitransparent penetrating stains Semitransparent penetrating stains are moderately pigmented water repellents or water-repellent preservatives, often containing higher amounts of drying oil or other resin. These penetrating stains are oil based (or alkyd based), and some may contain a fungicide (preservative or mildewcide), ultraviolet light stabilizer, or water repellent. Finish lifetimes may vary from 2 to 6 years depending on wood surface texture and quantity of stain applied.

The solvent-borne stains (alkyd or oil based) penetrate the wood surface to a degree, are porous, and do not form a surface film like paint. Thus, they do not totally hide the wood grain and will not trap moisture that may encourage decay. As a result, the stains will not blister or peel even if moisture penetrates the wood. Latex-based (waterborne) stains are also available, but they do not penetrate the wood surface as do their alkyd- or oil-based counterparts. Newer latex formulations are being developed that may provide some penetrating characteristics.

Lacquers and shellac Lacquers and shellac are often used as indoor finishes. However, they are not suitable for exterior application, even as sealers, because these resins in these coatings have little resistance to moisture. These finishes are also normally brittle and thus crack and check easily. However, specialty pigmented knot-sealer primers based on shellac are available for specific exterior applications.

Preservatives Although not generally classified as wood finishes, preservatives do protect wood against weathering and decay, a great quantity of preservative-treated wood being exposed without any additional finish. There are three main types of wood preservative: (1) preservative oils (e.g., coal-tar creosote), (2) organic solvent solutions (e.g., pentachlorophenol), and (3) waterborne salts (e.g., chromated copper arsenate). These preservatives can be applied in several ways, but pressure treatment generally gives the greatest protection against decay. Greater preservative content of pressure-treated wood generally results in greater resistance to weathering and improved surface durability. The chromium-containing preservatives also protect against degradation by ultraviolet light.

Wood treated with waterborne preservatives, such as chromated copper arsenate, can be painted or stained if the wood is clean and dry. Wood treated with a water-repellent preservative, by vacuum-pressure or dipping, is paintable. Wood treated with coal-tar creosote or other dark oily preservatives is generally not paintable.

Special Applications

Although general wood-finishing procedures are applicable to typical situations, some applications deserve special mention. These include the application of finish to decks and porches, fences, wood roofs, log structures, and structures in marine environments. Wood used in all of these applications is usually exposed to particularly harsh weathering conditions. Special consideration must be given to finish selection and application. Log structures need special consideration because of the large amounts of end grain exposed and the deep checking associated with large timbers as well as small, round logs.

Compliance of VOC Finishes with Pollution Regulations

Volatile organic compounds (VOCs) are those organic materials in finishes that evaporate as the finish dries and/or cures. These compounds are regarded as potential air pollutants, and the amount that can be released for a given amount of solids (for example, binder, pigments) in the paints is now regulated in many areas. Regulations that restrict the amount of VOCs in paints have been enacted in many states, including California, New York, Texas, Massachusetts, New Jersey, and Arizona, and legislation is pending in many others.

The existing and pending regulations are a serious concern throughout the United States because many traditional wood finishes may no longer be acceptable, including oil- and alkyd-based semitransparent stains, oil- and alkyd-based primers and top coats, solvent-borne water repellents, and solvent-borne water-repellent preservatives. Many current wood finishes, including some latex-based materials, may need to be reformulated. These changes could affect the properties of the finish, application, interaction with the wood (for example, adhesion, penetration, moisture-excluding effectiveness), and possibly durability.

Many penetrating finishes, such as semitransparent stains, have low solids content (pigment, oils, polymers) levels and are being reformulated to meet low-VOC regulations. To meet the VOC requirements, these reformulated finishes may contain higher solids content, reactive diluents, new types of solvents and/or cosolvents, or other nontraditional substituents. There is little information about the way these new penetrating finishes interact with the substrate to protect the wood or about the degradation mechanisms of these finishes when exposed to various outdoor conditions.

Interior Wood Finishes

Interior finishing differs from exterior finishing chiefly in that interior woodwork usually requires much less protection against moisture and ultraviolet light, but more exacting standards of appearance and cleanability. A much wider range of finishes and finish methods are possible indoors because weathering does not occur. Good finishes used indoors should last much longer than paint or other coatings on exterior surfaces.

Much of the variation in finishing methods for wood used indoors is caused by the wide latitude in the uses of wood – from wood floors to cutting boards. There is a wide range of finishing methods for just furniture. Factory finishing of furniture is often proprietary and may involve more than a dozen steps.

Color changes on wood surfaces can sometimes cause problems when wood is used indoors, particularly if the wood is finished to enhance its natural appearance with transparent finishes. This color change is a natural aging of the newly cut wood, and little can be done to prevent it, except, of course, to keep the wood in the dark. The color change is caused by visible light, not the ultraviolet light radiation associated with outdoor weathering, and by oxygen in the air. Most of this color change occurs within 2 to 3 months, depending on the light intensity, although some slight color changes due to visible light and air can slowly occur over 1 or 2 years.

Film-Forming Opaque Finishes

Interior surfaces may be easily painted by procedures similar to those for exterior surfaces. As a rule, however, smoother surfaces, better color, and a more lasting sheen are demanded for interior woodwork, especially wood trim; therefore, enamels or semigloss enamels are often used rather than flat paints.

Imperfections such as planer marks, hammer marks, and raised grain, are accentuated by enamel finish. Raised grain is especially troublesome on flat-grained surfaces of the denser softwoods because the

hard bands of latewood are sometimes crushed into the soft earlywood in planing, and later expand when the wood changes moisture content.

To effectively finish hardwoods with large pores, such as oak and ash, the pores must be filled with wood filler. After filling and sanding, successive applications of interior primer and sealer, undercoat, and enamel are used. Knots in the white pines, ponderosa pine, or southern pine should be sealed with shellac or a special knot-sealer before priming. A coat of pigmented shellac or special knot-sealer is also sometimes necessary over white pines and ponderosa pine to retard discoloration of light-colored enamels by colored matter present in the resin of the heartwood of these species.

Transparent Natural Finishes

Transparent finishes are often used on most hardwood and some softwood trim and paneling. Most finishing consists of some combination of the fundamental operations of sanding, staining, filling, sealing, surface coating, or waxing. Before finishing, planer marks and other blemishes on the wood surface that would be accentuated by the finish need to be removed.

Stains Both softwoods and hardwoods are often finished without staining, especially if the wood has a pleasing and characteristic color. When stain is used, however, it often accentuates color differences in the wood surface because of unequal absorption into different parts of the grain pattern. With hardwoods, such emphasis of the grain is usually desirable; the best stains for the purpose are dyes dissolved either in water or solvent. The water stains give the most pleasing results, but raise the grain of the wood and require an extra sanding operation after the stain is dry.

The most commonly used stains are the 'nongrain-raising' ones in solvents which dry quickly, and often approach the water stains in clearness and uniformity of color. Stains on softwoods color the earlywood more strongly than the latewood, reversing the natural gradation in color unless the wood has been sealed first with a wash coat. Pigment-oil stains, which are essentially very thin paints, are less subject to this problem and are therefore more suitable for softwoods. Alternatively, the softwood may be coated with penetrating clear sealer before applying any type of stain to give more nearly uniform coloring.

Fillers In hardwoods with large pores (e.g., oak and ash), the pores must be filled, usually after staining and before varnish or lacquer is applied, if a smooth coating is desired. The filler may be transparent and without effect on the color of the finish, or it may be colored to contrast with the surrounding wood. A filler may be a paste or liquid, natural or colored.

Birch has pores large enough to take wood filler effectively when desired, but small enough as a rule to be finished satisfactorily without filling. Hardwoods with small pores may be finished with paints, enamels, and varnishes in exactly the same manner as softwoods.

Sealers Sealers are thinned varnish, shellac or lacquer and are used to prevent absorption of surface coatings and also to prevent the bleeding of some stains and fillers into surface coatings, especially lacquer coatings. Lacquer and shellac sealers have the advantage of being very fast drying. Sealers are sometimes used as final finishes, often when applied in two or more coats.

Film-forming surface coatings Transparent surface coatings may be gloss varnish, semigloss varnish, shellac, nitrocellulose lacquer, conversion varnishes, wax, or similar finishes. Wax provides protection without forming a thick coating and without greatly enhancing the natural luster of the wood. Coatings of a more resinous nature, especially lacquer and varnish, accentuate the natural luster of some hardwoods and seem to permit the observer to look down into the wood. Shellac applied by the laborious process of French polishing probably achieves this impression of depth most fully, but the coating is expensive and easily marred by water. Rubbing varnishes made with resins of high refractive index for light (ability to bend light rays) are nearly as effective as shellac. Lacquers have the advantages of drying rapidly and forming a hard surface, but require more applications than varnish to build up a lustrous coating.

Varnish and lacquer usually dry with a highly glossy surface. To reduce the gloss, the surfaces may be rubbed with pumice stone and water or polishing oil. Waterproof sandpaper and water may be used instead of pumice stone. The final sheen varies with the fineness of the powdered pumice stone; coarse powders make a dull surface and fine powders produce a bright sheen. For very smooth surfaces with high polish, the final rubbing is done with rottenstone and oil. Varnish and lacquer made to dry to semigloss or satin finish are also available.

Flat oil finishes commonly called 'Danish oils' are also very popular interior wood finishes. This type of finish penetrates the wood and forms no noticeable film on the surface. Two or more coats of oil are usually applied, which may be followed with a paste wax. Such finishes are easily applied and maintained but are more subject to soiling than a film-forming type of finish. Simple boiled linseed oil or tung oil dissolved in a solvent are also used extensively as wood finishes. They are applied in excess and then wiped for a soft sheen surface appearance.

See also: **Solid Wood Processing**: Machining. **Wood Formation and Properties**: Chemical Properties of Wood; Formation and Structure of Wood; Mechanical Properties of Wood; Physical Properties of Wood.

Further Reading

Allen S (1995) *Classic Finishing Techniques*. New York: Sterling Publishing.

Carter D (1996) *The Complete Paint Book*. London: Conran Octopus.

Cassens DL and Feist WC (1991) *Exterior Wood in the South: Selection, Applications and Finishes*, General Technical Report no. FPL-GTR-69. Madison, WI: US Department of Agriculture, Forest Service, Forest Products Laboratory.

Feist WC (1990) Outdoor wood weathering and protection. In: Rowell RM (ed.) *Archaeological Wood: Properties, Chemistry, and Preservation*, pp. 263–298. Washington, DC: American Chemical Society.

Feist WC (1996) *Finishing Exterior Wood*. Blue Bell, PA: Federation of Societies for Coatings Technology.

Feist WC (2000) Wood: finishes and coatings. In: Beall F (ed.) *Encyclopedia of Materials: Science and Technology*, vol. 3, *Wood*, pp. 1–5. London: Elsevier Science.

Flexner B (1994) *Understanding Wood Finishing*. Emmaus, PA: Rodale Press.

Gorman TM and Feist WC (1989) *Chronicle of 65 Years of Wood Finishing Research of the Forest Products Laboratory*, General Technical Report no. FPL-GTR-60. Madison, WI: US Department of Agriculture, Forest Service, Forest Products Laboratory.

McDonald KA, Falk RH, Williams RS, and Winandy JE (1996) *Wood Decks: Materials, Construction, and Finishing*, Publication no. 7298. Madison, WI: Forest Products Society.

Satas D and Tracton AA (eds) (2001) *Coatings Technology Handbook*. New York: Marcel Dekker.

Tichy RJ (1997) *Interior Wood Finishing: Industrial Use Guide*, Publication no. 7288. Madison, WI: Forest Products Society.

Williams RS (1991) Effects of acidic deposition on painted wood: a review. *Journal of Coatings Technology* 63(800): 53–73.

Williams RS (1999) Finishing of Wood. In: *Wood Handbook: Wood as an Engineering Material*, Publication no. 7269, pp. 15-1–15-37. Madison, WI: Forest Products Society.

Williams RS, Knaebe MT, and Feist WC (1996) *Finishes For Exterior Wood: Selection, Application, and Maintenance*, Publication no. 7291. Madison, WI: Forest Products Society.

Machining

R Szymani, Wood Machining Institute, Berkeley, CA, USA

Introduction

Wood machining can be defined as the application of energy to sever the workpiece at a chosen internal surface. The purpose of wood machining is to produce a desired shape and dimension with requisite accuracy and surface quality in the most economical way. Major developmental trends in wood machining involve: attempts to reduce material losses in both the machined material and the cutting tools; improvement of the quality of machined products by attaining necessary accuracy of shape and dimensions as well as surface quality of the workpiece; increasing production output and minimizing cost; improvement of worker safety by machine guarding; and controlling generation of noise and dust.

Machining processes in the manufacture of wood products may be classified as follows: sawing; peeling and slicing; planing, molding, shaping, and routing; turning and boring; sanding; and nontraditional machining processes such as cutting with laser beam and high-energy liquid jet.

Wood as a Material to be Cut

Wood is anisotropic and a heterogeneous material. The structural nature of wood, in terms of its three-dimensional properties, is very important in wood machining, particularly the relationship between the strength of wood parallel and perpendicular to the grain. As indicated in **Figure 1**, the cutting force of birch wood is about two to four times as high across grain as along it.

Wood strength and cutting resistance are dependent on specific gravity, moisture content, and temperature during processing as well as growth-related characteristics of wood such as spiral or interlocked grain, presence of knots, growth stresses, reaction wood, and drying stresses.

Sawing Technology

Sawing is the most important frequent cutting process. Sawing machines are classified according to the basic machine design; that is, sash gang saws (reciprocating, multiple blade frame saws), circular saws, band saws, and chain saws. Circular saws are designated ripsaws if they are designed to cut solid wood along the grain,

as bucking or trim saws if they are designed to cut across the grain, or as combination saws if designed to cut along and across the grain, as well as at a certain angle to the grain (e.g., miter saws). Sawing machines are further classified according to their use. For example, a bucking saw is used for cutting logs to length, a headrig for primary log breakdown, a resaw for resawing cants into boards, an edger for edging boards, a trimmer for cutting boards to length, table saws for ripsawing and crosscutting of solid wood, panel saws for cutting plywood, fiberboards and particleboards, and a scroll saw for general-purpose cutting of intricate patterns.

In general, saw blades are made from cold-rolled, hardened, and tempered steel. For band saws a high carbon content, nickel-alloyed saw steel has been used in most cases (e.g., Uddelhom Steel UHB $15 N_2O$:0.75% C and 2.0% Ni). Other saw steel alloys may contain manganese, chromium, and vanadium. With the gradual transition from swaged saw teeth to Stellite-tipped saws, saw blade manufactures such as Uddeholm and Sandwik have developed special band saw steels. The Uddeholm ANKAR-R steel, formulated for Stellite tipping, has improved stability of tensioning stresses, welding properties, and mechanical strength. The Sandvik Multishift steel increased fatigue resistance and the capacity to operate at higher strain rates.

Circular saw blades made from stainless steel were recently introduced by California Saw and Knife Works to bring under control the problems associated with corrosion-initiated material loss in guided saws. Other benefits are attributed to thermal and mechanical properties which make stainless-steel saws stiffer when cutting, and which allow them better to retain their original flatness compared to saws made from alloy saw steels.

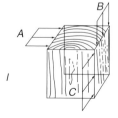

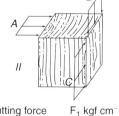

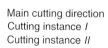

Main cutting direction	Main cutting force		F_1 kgf cm^{-1}
	A	B	C
Cutting instance *I*	7.75	2.90	1.65
Cutting instance *II*	8.35	3.15	1.85

Figure 1 Schematic illustration of main cutting directions in respect to the annual rings and values of the main cutting force obtained with a work-sharp normal knife and 0.1 mm chip thickness. The specific gravity of the birch used for the tests is 0.64 and moisture content 12%.

Circular saws typically range from 1.0 to 5.0 mm in thickness and from 150 to 1800 mm in diameter. The thickness of a bandsaw may range from 0.4 to 2.1 mm. Bandsaw width ranges from 60 to 360 mm for saws used in lumber manufacturing, and 6 to 50 mm for the narrow bandsaws used in furniture manufacturing and for portable sawing machines. As a rule, the saw blade thickness should not exceed 0.1% of the wheel diameter, and the bandsaw width should not be greater than wheel width plus gullet depth and an additional 5 mm. The typical sash gang saws used for primary wood processing are 2.0 mm in thickness and approximately 175 mm in width.

Saws vary considerably with regard to tooth and gullet design. The primary design considerations include tooth strength and gullet loading capacity, the function of the gullet being sawdust removal. Other important factors are tooth wear and noise generation. The typical bandsaw tooth geometry is described by specifying rake and clearance angle as depicted in **Figure 2**. If the saw tooth has a face and/ or top bevel, those angles should also be specified. The optimum tooth geometry, as determined from the measurement of cutting forces and power requirements, mainly depends upon cutting direction, wood species, density, and moisture content. Tooth geometry may vary considerably: for example, the rake angle for crosscut circular saws ranges from $+10°$ to $-30°$. In the case of circular ripsaws and band saws, the rake angle will vary from $10°$ for high-density hardwoods to $30°$ for softwood species. The top clearance angle may range from $8°$ for dense hardwoods to approximately $10°$ for softwoods. Many sawmills in the USA and Canada are currently using variable sawtooth spacing in order to reduce the problem of 'washboarding' during sawing.

The side clearance for wide bandsaws, which is required to reduce friction between the saw blade and generated surface, may range from 0.30 to 0.35 mm for hardwoods and from 0.50 to 0.60 mm for softwoods. Certain specialty circular saws such as miter saws can be tapered (hollow ground) to provide side clearance.

The purpose of tipping saw teeth with hard alloys is to increase their wear resistance, which prolongs the useful life of the blade. Most bandsaws are Stellite-tipped, while circular saws in addition to Stellite are tipped with tungsten carbide and poly-crystalline diamond (PCD) tips. Optimizing the relationship between the saw-tipping material properties and the cutting edge geometry is a precondition for high performance of circular and bandsaws.

Each single tooth will remove a certain volume of wood given by the feed per tooth and the cutting height. This volume should correspond to the chosen gullet capacity $V = 0.5 A$ up to $0.75 A$. The feed per tooth t is given by $t = p \ (F/C)$ where p is the pitch (mm), F is the feed rate (m min^{-1}), and C is the cutting speed (m min^{-1}). The average blade velocity C is about 3000 m min^{-1}.

The use of thin-kerf circular saws (thickness of cut 3 mm or less) has proved to be very beneficial to industry in the reduction of kerf losses, as long as saw stability is maintained. One of the principal manifestations of circular-saw instability is standing-wave resonance. The rotation speed, at which a standing wave is formed, is called the critical speed. All in-plane or membrane stresses (i.e., stresses due to temperature gradients, rotation, cutting forces, and tensioning or prestressing) shift the saw natural frequencies and alter its critical speed accordingly. Computer programs such as CSAW are available for estimating the critical speed of circular saws based on design and operation variables. The operating speed, for saws clamped in the center, should be at least 15% below their critical speed. The sawing accuracy improves with the increase of the critical speed margin. In the case of bandsaws, currently available computer programs can be used to evaluate bandsaw design relative to band vibration and stability. The effective stiffness and stability of circular saws can be increased by introducing radial slots, by prestressing or tensioning, by using guiding systems, by online cooling near the cutting edge, and by heating near the center (i.e., thermal tensioning). Radial slots in circular saws reduce compression hoop stresses at the saw periphery due to temperature gradients, introduce asymmetry into the saw-blade design and consequently reduce transverse vibration and reduce noise. The application of various guiding systems in conjunction with the use of splined-arbor saws, which can float on the arbor, is a common and particularly effective method used for stability control of thin-kerf circular saws. Most sawmills in North America resaw cants with spline arbor saw blades with fluid-lubricated guides which generally work

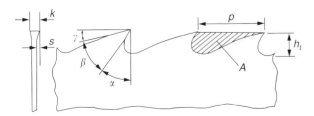

Figure 2 Bandsaw tooth geometry. α, rake or hook angle; p, pitch or tooth spacing; β, sharpness angle; h_t, depth of gullet or tooth height; γ, clearance angle; A, gullet area; k, kerf width (theoretical); s, side-clearance. Reproduced with permission from *The Wood Bandsaw Blade Manual* (1993), Uddeholm Strip Steel AB, Munkfors, Sweden.

better than clamped saws. Circular saw guides serve to position the saw blade relative to the workpiece, to lubricate and cool the saw blade, to stiffen the saw blade against the transverse forces generated during sawing, and to dampen saw vibrations. This sawing system allows the use of thin saw blades having a kerf width as small as 1.8 mm at a cutting depth of 140 mm and feed rate of 30 m min^{-1}.

In the case of bandsaws, in addition to prestressing and the use of saw-guiding systems, the type of straining mechanism for providing axial tension and its response will significantly affect saw stability and consequently sawing accuracy. The saw blade must operate under maximum applied tension force, consistent with the endurance strength of the saw blade material, in order to maximize stiffness and critical edge-buckling load.

The general practice in the industry has been to select saws on the basis of past experience or by an expensive trial-and-error process. Due to extensive research on saw dynamics, however, it is now possible to design both circular and bandsaws on the basis of sound engineering principles.

Regardless of the operating conditions, the stress level in saw blades must be kept constant. The online control of circular and bandsaw stability basically consists of either modifying the forces exciting the blade or altering the effective saw-blade stiffness and damping to reduce vibration. This can be achieved, for example, by online thermal tensioning of circular saws, i.e., introduction of thermal stresses beneficial to saw stability. At present, the trend is to use online monitoring of bandsaw displacements and measurement of sawing accuracy, and online control of feed speed.

Veneer Peeling and Slicing

Rotary cutting (peeling) and slicing of wood are used in the manufacture of veneer. At least 95% of veneer is produced by peeling, for which a veneer lathe is used, and about 5% by slicing, for which a horizontal or vertical slicer is used. The primary components of any lathe or slicer are the knife and pressure flat nose bar or powered roller nose bar. They are similar in both machines and perform the same function. The cross-section of a typical lathe presented in **Figure 3** illustrates the position of the knife and the pressure nose bar. The most common knife thickness for a lathe is 16 mm, and, for the face veneer slicer, 15–19 mm. The knife's Rockwell hardness on the C scale may vary from 56 to 60.

While the knife severs the veneer from the bolt or flitch, the pressure nose bar compresses the wood and thus reduces splitting of wood ahead of the knife.

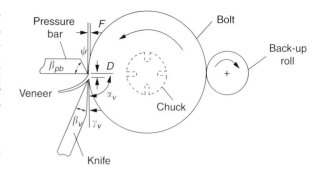

Figure 3 Cross-section of a veneer lathe with fixed pressure bar. α_v, knife angle; β_v, knife bevel angle; γ_v, clearance angle; D, lead or vertical gap; β_{pb}, pressure-bar bevel angle; ψ, pressure-bar compression angle; F, gap (horizontal gap).

The amount of compression depends on wood density and will vary from species to species. For Douglas-fir, it is about 15% of the veneer thickness; for western white spruce about 8%. In both lathe and slicer, the wood compression is important in controlling roughness, depth of checks, and thickness of the veneer. The slicer has a fixed nose bar while the lathe may have either a fixed nose bar or a rotating roller bar. The flitch on a slicer is backed by the flitch table while support for a veneer bolt may be provided by a powered back-up roll on a veneer lathe. Full-length powered back-up rolls reduce spin-outs, and prevent the bolt from flexing during peeling. For maximum yield of rotary peeled veneer it is essential that bolts are chucked in the geometric center. Laser scanning and computerized centering systems are currently used with modern *X-Y* lathe chargers, which allow determination of chucking centers for best yield of each individual block. Other developments in veneer manufacturing equipment include high-speed veneer lathes having spindle speeds of 500 rpm and over, digital carriage drive which eliminates the mechanical clutch assembly, hydraulic powered back-up rolls, and dual hydraulic spindles.

The production of high-quality veneer requires proper pretreatment of the wood prior to cutting. This is done by heating green wood in water or steam. Heating wood above 50°C makes it more plastic and reduces veneer checking during peeling or slicing. The recommended peeling temperature ranges from 50° to 90°C and will vary with the average specific gravity of the species.

Planing, Molding, Shaping, and Routing

Planing refers to the peripheral milling of wood. Its purpose is to smooth one or more surfaces of the workpiece and at the same time bring the workpiece to some predetermined dimension. The machinery used for planing operations includes: (1) surfacers designed to smooth one or two sides of the workpiece and reduce it to a predetermined thickness; and (2) planers and matchers defined as double surfacers which are further equipped with two opposed profile side heads that can simultaneously machine the two edges to the desired pattern or profile.

The molding operation aims to machine lumber into forms of various cross-sectional shapes, such as picture-frame moldings. Both planing and molding machines employ rotating cutterheads. By definition, a molder differs from a planer in that the molder side heads are staggered instead of directly opposed. The typical operating speed for multiknife cutter heads ranges from 3600 to 6000 rpm. The number of spindles may range from one to 10. Molding machines can be equipped with variable feed rate typically ranging from 6 to 60 m min^{-1}.

Shaping involves machining an edge profile or edge pattern on the side and/or periphery of a workpiece. The basic types of shapers include single and double spindle shapers, double head automatic shaper, and center profiler. The shaper spindle speeds range from 7200 to 10 000 rpm.

Routing is similar to the shaping operation. While a shaper always shapes the periphery, a router is used to make a variety of cuts such as mortises, irregularly shaped holes, and three-dimensional plunge cuts using computer numerical control (CNC). Most router spindle speeds are from 10 000 to 30 000 rpm, depending on the diameter of the cutter. When machining abrasive composite wood products, there is a trend to use PCD cutting tools in routing and shaping operations.

In all three operations, it is of prime importance to adjust the operating conditions and knife geometry so that machining defects are minimized. The most commonly encountered defects are torn or fuzzy grain, raised and loosened grain, and chip marks. These defects are caused by improper cutting angles, chip thickness which is too large, dull knives, low-density species, and often the presence of reaction wood. In the case where the torn-grain defect is highly probable, the most important variable is the number of marks per centimeter or inch (reciprocal of the feed per cutter). The marks per centimeter should be between three and five for rough planing operations and between five and six for finishing cuts. The clearance angle should in all cases exceed a value of 10°. The optimum cutting angle (angle between the knife face or knife bevel and a radius of the cutter head) lies between 20° and 30° for most planing situations; however, in the cases of interlocked or wavy grain, it may be necessary to reduce the cutting angle to 15° or even 10°.

Turning and Boring

Turning of wood is a machining process for generating cylindrical forms by removing wood, usually with a single-point cutting tool. The turning machines include single- and multiple-spindle lathes. The tools used for turning on the lathe perform operations primarily directed to machining the outer surfaces of the workpiece. From practical experience and experimental investigations, lathe clearance angles between 12° and 18° offer optimum cutting conditions. In practice, a lip or wedge angle between 20° and 30° is recommended for softwoods, the wedge angle corresponding to the sharpness angle in the case of saw teeth and to the knife bevel angle in the case of a veneer knife. For hardwoods, wedge angles between 50° and 60° are recommended. The quality of surfaces of most turned-wood articles is of the utmost importance, for example, for tool handles. The roughness perpendicular to the grain increases with the feed speed. The specific pressure of the tool on the turned surface also has a remarkable influence on the roughness.

Most machines which will perform turning operations can also perform boring operations, although machines are available which will perform boring, drilling, and other related operations. Boring machines can have many configurations, ranging from the simple vertical single-spindle boring machine to complex transfer machines involving multiple vertical, horizontal, and angular spindles. There are many specialized boring-bit designs in use. The common bit types include: (1) double-spur, double-lip solid-center bit on which the spurs cut ahead of the lips; (2) double-spur, double-twist bit on which the spurs cut after the lips; and (3) twist drill. The first is a fast-boring general-purpose bit; the second bit is particularly suited for boring to extreme depth. The twist drill is frequently used on machine boring equipment for drilling in end grain and for boring dowel holes. The quality of finish produced by a twist drill may be inferior to that produced by a bit equipped with spurs.

Sanding Technology

Sanding is the abrasive machining of wood surfaces to obtain a smooth surface quality. The abrasive tool consists of a backing material to which abrasive grains are bonded by an adhesive coat. The abrasive or sanding tool is specified by the sanding and backing materials. Sanding materials vary according to type, size, and form of grain. Typical abrasive materials for wood-working applications are garnet, aluminum oxide, and silicon carbide. Garnet is the most commonly used because of its low cost and acceptable working qualities. It is used with all types of machines for sanding softwoods. Aluminum oxide abrasives are used extensively for sanding hardwood, particleboard, and hardboard. Silicon carbide abrasive is used for sanding and polishing between coating operations and for sanding softwoods where the removal of raised fibers is a problem. The size of the abrasive particles is specified by the mesh number (i.e., the approximate number of openings per linear inch in the screen through which particles will pass); mesh numbers range from about 600 to 12.

Backing materials vary according to the strength, flexibility, and required spacing of the sanding tool and are made of paper, cotton, or polyester cloth, or cloth–paper combinations. Bonding materials are generally animal glues, urea resins, or phenolic resins. The choice of these materials depends upon the required flexibility of the tool and the work rate required of the tool. Animal-glue bonds are the most flexible, whereas resin bonds are harder, more moisture- and heat-resistant, and have superior grain retention.

Sanding machines include multiple-drum sanders, wide-belt sanders, automatic-stroke sanders, and contact wheel disk sanders. The drum sander is probably the oldest of all the wood-working machines using coated abrasive, and it is used in solid-wood furniture manufacturing.

The drum sanding machine is used following the planer or veneer press. Multiple-drum sanders are of the endless-bed or roll-feed type and have from two to six drums. The abrasive is usually a heavy paper-backed aluminum oxide product. In very heavy sanding operations, a fiber-backed abrasive is recommended. A sequence of 60, 80, and 100 mesh abrasive is frequently used on a three-drum endless-bed sander.

Wide-belt sanders use an abrasive belt at least 30 cm wide and are commonly used on panels (plywood, particleboard, hardboard). Silicon carbide is normally used as the abrasive. They have higher production rates and greater accuracy than multiple-drum sanders.

Heavy-duty high-speed (up to $600 \, \text{m min}^{-1}$ feed rate) wide-belt sanders are called abrasive planers when used for dimensioning and surfacing. Abrasive planers are used for dimensioning of accurately sawn, kiln-dried lumber, plywood and particleboard, and for furniture production. In comparison with the knife planer, the abrasive planer has in general higher production rates, a lower noise level, and virtually no machining defects. New developments in wide-belt sanding include the use of antistatic belts and sanding with aerostatic (air cushion) supported belts. It is critical when using sanders and abrasive planes to have an adequate dust removal system.

Surface finish during the sanding process is for the most part independent of pressure and cutting speed. The optimum belt speed as determined by the specific quantities of abrasion is about $30 \, \text{m s}^{-1}$ for particle size 60 and slightly less than $30 \, \text{m s}^{-1}$ for particle size 120.

Automatic-stroke sanders use a narrow abrasive belt and a reciprocating shoe which creates contact between the abrasive and the workpiece. This sanding machine is commonly used in furniture plants for final sanding operations and touch-up sanding.

The contact-wheel sander also uses a narrow abrasive belt. Contact wheels normally range from 150 to 350 mm in diameter. A typical application is the sanding head on an edge banding machine where the edging tape is given a finish after application to the board. Cloth belts are usually preferred because of their durability.

The disk sander consists of a revolving back plate to which a coated abrasive disk of paper or cloth is attached by an adhesive. It usually incorporates a tilting action for angle or miter sanding. The major disadvantage of this method is a pattern of circular scratches which have to be removed by other means before finishing.

Nontraditional Machining Processes

Various new cutting techniques have been investigated during the last 40 years for possible use in the wood industry in an effort to reduce or eliminate kerf losses. These include the laser beam and the high-energy water jet. Major advantages of a laser beam and water jet include the ability to cut intricate patterns, high cutting accuracy, and the possibility of numerical control.

A wide variety of materials can be cut using a continuous carbon dioxide laser. The laser beam produces a very narrow kerf, in most cases approximately 1 mm. The major disadvantages of cutting wood and wood-based panels with the laser are low feed rate, resulting in high cost per unit of lineal cut, and the charring of the generated surface. Therefore, the application of laser machining, most economically justified, includes laser engraving, automatic preparation of wooden die blocks for the folding-carton industry, cutting chair backs, and veneer inlays in furniture industry.

Cutting with abrasive liquid jet has been useful for a wide variety of materials but has rather limited application in the wood industry. The application of the liquid jet as a cutting tool depends on the availability of high-pressure pumping equipment capable of generating a high-velocity continuous jet. For the generation of a high-energy continuous flow, a pressure level of about $4100 \, \text{kp cm}^{-2}$ (60 000 psi) is required. The nozzles range from 0.1 to 0.4 mm in diameter and are made from ruby or sapphire. The liquid jet, like the laser, approaches the ideal single-point cutting tool, which can follow highly complicated patterns. It eliminates crushing or deformation of the material such as corrugated paper board and generation of dust. Water jet technology reduces cutting noise significantly and offers the ability to cut without high temperatures. The greatest use of liquid-jet cutting is in the paper and paperboard industry where it has been quite successful in cutting laminated paperboard into upholstery frames. In the paper industry liquid-jet slitting systems are used to cut paper at higher speeds than with a mechanical knife – as high as 3200 m min^{-1}.

See also: **Solid Wood Processing**: Finishing. **Solid Wood Products**: Construction; Logs, Poles, Piles, Sleepers (Crossties); Lumber Production, Properties and Uses; Structural Use of Wood. **Wood Formation and Properties**: Formation and Structure of Wood; Mechanical Properties of Wood; Physical Properties of Wood. **Wood Use and Trade**: History and Overview of Wood Use.

Further Reading

Baldwin RF (1975) *Plywood Manufacturing Practices*. San Francisco, CA: Miller Freeman.

Effner J (1992) *Chisel on the Wheel: A Comprehensive Reference to Modern Woodworking Tools and Materials*. Ann Arbor, MI: Prakken.

Ettelt B (1987) *Sawing, Milling, Planing, Boring: Wood Machining and Cutting Tools* (in German). Stuttgart, Germany: DRW-Verlag.

Handbook for Woodworking Machine Tools (2001) *The Leitz Lexicon*, 3rd edn. Oberkochen, Germany: Leitz.

Koch P (1985) Machining. In: *Utilization of Hardwoods Growing on Southern Pine Sites*, pp. 1687–2281. Washington, DC: Government Printing Office.

Lutz JF (1978) *Wood Veneer: Log Selection, Cutting and Drying, Technical bulletin* no. 1577. Madison, WI: US Department of Agriculture Forest Products Laboratory.

Maier G (1987) *Woodworking Machines: Requirements, Concepts, Machine Elements, Construction* (in German). Stuttgart, Germany: DRW-Verlag.

Mote CD Jr, Schajer GS, and Wu WZ (1982) Band saw and circular saw vibration and stability. *Shock Vibration. Digest* 14(2): 19–25.

Stephenson E (2001) *Circular Saws*. Hertford, UK: Stobart Davies.

Szymani R (1986) Status report on the technology of saws. *Forest Products Journal* 36(4): 15–19.

Szymani R (ed.) (2001) *Proceedings of SawTech 2001: The 7th International Conference on Sawing Technology*, November 8–9, 2001. Seattle, Washington.

Szymani R (ed.) (2001) *Proceedings of the 15th International Wood Machining Seminar*, July 31–August 2, 2001, Los Angeles, CA.

Wijesinghe R (1998) *The Bandmill Book: The Complete Guide to your Industrial Bandmill and Bandsaw*. North Vancouver, Canada: Tech Pubs, Western Technigraphics.

Willard R (1980) *Production Woodworking Equipment*, 4th edn. Raleigh, NC: North Carolina State University.

Williston EM (1989) *Saws: Design, Selection, Operation, Maintenance*, 2nd edn. San Francisco, CA: Miller Freeman.

SOLID WOOD PRODUCTS

Contents

Glued Structural Members

J A Youngquist, Forest Products Consultant, Verona, WI, USA
R Youngs, Virginia Polytechnic Institute and State University, Blacksburg, VA, USA

Published by Elsevier Ltd., 2004

Introduction

The material in this article is adapted from the Forest Products Laboratory *Wood Handbook*, which is especially concerned with use of wood as an engineering material in the USA. However, the use of wood in laminated form is common worldwide and the same principles apply. Glued structural members are manufactured in a variety of configurations. Structural composite lumber (SCL) products consist of small pieces of wood glued together into sizes common for solid-sawn lumber. Glued-laminated timber (glulam) is an engineered stress-rated product that consists of two or more layers of lumber in which the grain of all layers is oriented parallel to the length of the lumber.

Glued structural members also include lumber that is glued to panel products, such as box beams and I-beams, and structural sandwich construction.

Structural Composite Lumber

Structural composite lumber (SCL) was developed in response to the increasing demand for high-quality lumber at a time when it was becoming difficult to obtain this type of lumber from the forest resource. SCL products are characterized by smaller pieces of wood glued together into sizes common for solid-sawn lumber. SCL is a growing segment of the engineered wood products industry. It is used as a replacement for lumber in various applications and in the manufacture of other engineered wood products, such as prefabricated wood I-joists, which take advantage of engineering design values that can be greater than those commonly assigned to sawn lumber.

Types

One type of SCL product is manufactured by laminating veneer with all plies parallel to the length. This product is called laminated veneer lumber (LVL) and consists of specially graded veneer. Another type of SCL product consists of strands of wood or strips of veneer glued together under high pressures and temperatures. Depending upon the component material, this product is called laminated strand lumber (LSL), parallel strand lumber (PSL), or oriented strand lumber (OSL) (**Figure 1**). These types of SCL products can be manufactured from raw materials, such as aspen (*Populus* spp.) or other underutilized species, that are not commonly used for structural applications. Different widths of lumber can be ripped from SCL for various uses. Production of

Figure 1 Examples of three types of SCL (top to bottom): laminated veneer lumber (LVL), parallel strand lumber (PSL), and oriented strand lumber (OSL).

LVL uses veneers 3.2–2.5 mm thick, which are hot pressed with phenol-formaldehyde adhesive into lengths from 2.4 to 18.3 m or more. The veneer for the manufacture of LVL must be carefully selected for the product to achieve the desired engineering properties and is often sorted using ultrasonic testing. End joints between individual veneers may be staggered along the product to minimize their effect on strength. These end joints may be butt joints, or the veneer ends may overlap for some distance to provide load transfer. Some producers provide structural end joints in the veneers using either scarf or fingerjoints. LVL may also be made in 2.4-m lengths, having no end joints in the veneer; longer pieces are then formed by end-jointing these pieces to create the desired length. Sheets of LVL are commonly produced in 0.6–1.2-m widths in a thickness of 38 mm. Continuous presses can be used to form a potentially endless sheet, which is cut to the desired length. Various widths of lumber can be manufactured at the plant or the retail facility.

Parallel strand lumber (PSL) is defined as a composite of wood strand elements with wood fibers primarily oriented along the length of the member. The least dimension of the strands must not exceed 6.4 mm, and the average length of the strands must be a minimum of 150 times the least dimension. PSL is manufactured using veneer about 3 mm thick, which is then clipped into strands about 19 mm wide. These strands are commonly at least 0.6 m long. The manufacturing process was designed to use the material from roundup of the log in the veneer cutting operation as well as other less than full-width veneer. Thus, the process can utilize waste material from a plywood or LVL operation. Species commonly used for PSL include Douglas-fir (*Pseudotsuga menziesii*), southern pines (*Pinus palustris*, *P. echinata*, *P. taeda*, and *P. elliottii*), western hemlock (*Tsuga heterophylla*), and yellow-poplar (*Liriodendron tulipifera*), but there are no restrictions on using other species. The strands are coated with a waterproof structural adhesive, commonly phenol-resorcinol formaldehyde, and oriented in a press using special equipment to ensure proper orientation and distribution. The pressing operation results in densification of the material, and the adhesive is cured using microwave technology. Billets larger than those of LVL are commonly produced; a typical size is 0.28 by 0.48 m. This product can then be sawn into smaller pieces, if desired. As with LVL, a continuous press is used so that the length of the product is limited by handling restrictions.

Laminated strand lumber (LSL) and oriented strand lumber (OSL) products are an extension of the technology used to produce oriented strandboard

(OSB) structural panels. One type of LSL uses strands that are about 0.3 m long, which is somewhat longer than the strands commonly used for OSB. Waterproof adhesives are used in the manufacture of LSL. One type of product uses an isocyanate type of adhesive that is sprayed on the strands and cured by steam injection. This product needs a greater degree of alignment of the strands than does OSB and higher pressures, which result in increased densification.

Advantages and Uses

In contrast with sawn lumber, the strength-reducing characteristics of SCL are dispersed within the veneer or strands and have much less of an effect on strength properties. Thus, relatively high design values can be assigned to strength properties for both LVL and PSL. Whereas both LSL and OSL have somewhat lower design values, they have the advantage of being produced from a raw material that need not be in a log size large enough for peeling into veneer. All SCL products are made with structural adhesives and are dependent upon a minimum level of strength in these bonds, and are made from veneers or strands that are dried to a moisture content that is slightly less than that for most service conditions. Thus, little change in moisture content will occur in many protected service conditions. When used indoors, this results in a product that is less likely to warp or shrink in service. However, the porous nature of both LVL and PSL means that these products can quickly absorb water unless they are provided with some protection.

All types of SCL products can be substituted for sawn lumber products in many applications. Laminated veneer lumber is used extensively for scaffold planks and in the flanges of prefabricated I-joists, which take advantage of the relatively high design properties. Both LVL and PSL beams are used as headers and major load-carrying elements in construction. The LSL and OSL products are used for band joists in floor construction and as substitutes for studs and rafters in wall and roof construction. Various types of SCL are also used in a number of nonstructural applications, such as the manufacture of windows and doors.

Glulam

Structural glued-laminated timber (glulam) is one of the oldest glued engineered wood products. Glulam is an engineered, stress-rated product that consists of two or more layers of lumber that are glued together with the grain of all layers, which are referred to as laminations, parallel to the length. Glulam is defined as a material that is made from suitably selected and prepared pieces of wood either in a straight or curved form, with the grain of all pieces essentially parallel to the longitudinal axis of the member. The maximum lamination thickness permitted is 5 mm and the laminations are typically made of standard 25- or 50-mm thick lumber. Because the lumber is joined end to end, edge to edge, and face to face, the size of glulam is limited only by the capabilities of the manufacturing plant and the transportation system.

Douglas-fir, larch (*Larix occidentalis*), southern pine, western hemlock, firs (*Abies lasiocarpa*, *A. magnifica*, *A. grandis*, *A. procera*, *A. amabilis*, and *A. concolor*), spruce (*Picea rubens*, *P. glauca*, and *P. mariana*), and pine (*Pinus monticola*) are commonly used for glulam in the USA. Nearly any species can be used for glulam timber, provided its mechanical and physical properties are suitable and it can be properly glued. Industry standards cover many softwoods and hardwoods, and procedures are in place for including other species.

Advantages

Compared with sawn timbers as well as other structural materials, glulam has several distinct advantages in size capability, architectural effects, seasoning, variation of cross-sections, grades, and effect on the environment.

Glulam offers the advantage of the manufacture of structural timbers that are much larger than the trees from which the component lumber was sawn. By combining the lumber in glulam, the production of large structural elements is possible. Straight members up to 30 m long are not uncommon and some spans up to 43 m with sections deeper than 2 m have been used. Thus, glulam offers the potential to produce large timbers from small trees.

By curving the lumber during the manufacturing process, a variety of architectural effects can be obtained that are impossible or very difficult with other materials. The degree of curvature is controlled by the thickness of the laminations. Thus, glulam with moderate curvature is generally manufactured with standard 19-mm thick lumber. Low curvatures are possible with standard 38-mm lumber, whereas 13 mm or thinner material may be required for very sharp curves. As noted below, the radius of curvature is limited to between 100 and 125 times the lamination thickness.

The lumber used in the manufacture of glulam must be seasoned or dried prior to use, so that the effects of checking and other drying defects are minimized. In addition, design can be on the basis of seasoned wood, which permits greater design values than can be assigned to unseasoned timber.

Structural elements can be designed with varying cross sections along their length as determined by strength and stiffness requirements. The beams in **Figure 2** show how the central section of the beam can be made deeper to account for increased structural requirements in this region of the beam. Similarly, arches often have varying cross-sections as determined by design requirements.

One major advantage of glulam is that a large quantity of lower-grade lumber can be used within the less highly stressed laminations of the beams. Grades are often varied within the beams so that the highest grades are used in the highly stressed laminations near the top and bottom and the lower grade for the inner half or more of the beams. Species can also be varied to match the structural requirements of the laminations.

Much is being written and discussed regarding the relative environmental effects of various materials. Several analyses have shown that the renewability of wood, its relatively low requirement for energy during manufacture, its carbon storage capabilities, and its recyclability offer potential long-term environmental advantages over other materials (*see* **Wood Use and Trade**: Environmental Benefits of Wood as a Building Material). Although aesthetic and economic considerations usually are the major factors influencing material selection, these environmental advantages may increasingly influence material selection.

The advantages of glulam are tempered by certain factors that are not encountered in the production of sawn timber. In instances where solid timbers are available in the required size, the extra processing in making glulam timber usually increases its cost above that of sawn timbers. The manufacture of glulam requires special equipment, adhesives, plant facilities, and manufacturing skills, which are not needed to produce sawn timbers. All steps in the manufacturing process require care to ensure the high quality of the finished product. One factor that must be considered early in the design of large straight or curved timbers is handling and shipping.

Types of Glulam Combinations

The configuring of various grades of lumber to form a glulam cross-section is commonly referred to as a glulam combination. Glulam combinations subjected to flexural loads, called bending combinations, were developed to provide the most efficient and economical section for resisting bending stress caused by loads applied perpendicular to the wide faces of the laminations. This type of glulam is commonly referred to as a horizontally laminated member. Lower grades of laminating lumber are commonly used for the center portion of the combination, or core, where bending stress is low, while a higher grade of material is placed on the outside faces where bending stress is relatively high. To optimize the bending stiffness of this type of glulam member, equal amounts of high quality laminations on the outside faces should be included to produce a 'balanced' combination.

Glulam axial combinations were developed to provide the most efficient and economical section for resisting axial forces and flexural loads applied parallel to the wide faces of the laminations. Members having loads applied parallel to the wide faces of the laminations are commonly referred to as vertically laminated members. Unlike the practice for bending combinations, the same grade of lamination is used throughout the axial combination. Axial combinations may also be loaded perpendicular to the wide face of the laminations, but the nonselective placement of material often results in a less efficient and less economical member than does the bending combination. As with bending combinations, knot and slope-of-grain requirements apply based on the intended use of the axial member as a tension or compression member.

Efficient use of lumber in cross-sections of curved glulam combinations is similar to that in cross-sections of straight, horizontally laminated combinations. Tension and compression stresses are analyzed as tangential stresses in the curved portion of the member. A unique behavior in these curved members

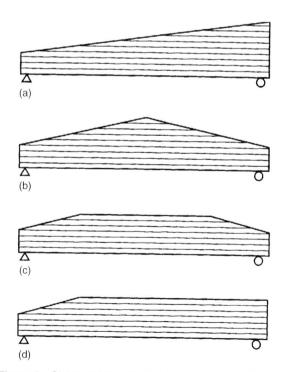

Figure 2 Glulam timbers may be (a) single tapered, (b) double tapered, (c) tapered at both ends, or (d) tapered at one end.

is the formation of radial stresses perpendicular to the wide faces of the laminations. As the radius of curvature of the glulam member decreases, the radial stresses formed in the curved portion of the beam increase. Because of the relatively low strength of lumber in tension perpendicular-to-the-grain compared with tension parallel-to-the-grain, these radial stresses become a critical factor in designing curved glulam combinations.

Glulam beams are often tapered to meet architectural requirements, provide pitched roofs, facilitate drainage, and lower wall height requirements at the end supports. The taper is achieved by sawing the member across one or more laminations at the desired slope. It is recommended that the taper cut be made only on the compression side of the glulam member, because violating the continuity of the tension-side laminations would decrease the overall strength of the member. Common forms of straight, tapered glulam combinations include: (1) single tapered, a member having a continuous slope from end to end on the compression side; (2) double tapered, a member having two separate slopes sawn on the compression side; (3) tapered at both ends, a member with slopes sawn on the ends, but the middle portion remaining straight; and (4) tapered at one end, similar to (3) with only one end having a slope. These four examples are illustrated in **Figure 2**.

Glued Members With Lumber and Panels

Highly efficient structural components can be produced by combining lumber with panel products through gluing. These components include box beams, I-beams, 'stressed-skin' panels, and folded plate roofs.

These highly efficient designs, although adequate structurally, can suffer from lack of resistance to fire and decay unless treatment or protection is provided. The rather thin portions of the cross-section (the panel materials) are more vulnerable to fire damage than are the larger, solid cross-sections.

Box beams and I-beams with lumber or laminated flanges and structural panel webs can be designed to provide the desired stiffness, bending, moment resistance, and shear resistance. The flanges resist bending moment, and the webs provide primary shear resistance. Proper design requires that the webs must not buckle under design loads. If lateral stability is a problem, the box beam design should be chosen because it is stiffer in lateral bending and torsion than is the I-beam. In contrast, the I-beam should be chosen if buckling of the web is of concern because its single web, double the

thickness of that of a box beam, will offer greater buckling resistance.

In recent years, the development of improved adhesives and manufacturing techniques has led to the development of the prefabricated I-beam industry. This product is a unique type of I-beam that is replacing wider lumber sizes in floor and roof applications for both residential and commercial buildings (**Figure 3**). Significant savings in materials are possible with prefabricated I-beams that use either plywood or oriented strandboard (OSB) for the web material and small-dimension lumber or SCL for the flanges. The high-quality lumber needed for these flanges has been difficult to obtain using visual grading methods, and both mechanically graded lumber and SCL are being used by several manufacturers. The details of fastening the flanges to the webs vary between manufacturers; all must be glued with a waterproof adhesive. Prefabricated I-beams are becoming popular with builders because of their light weight, dimensional stability and ease of construction. Their accurate and consistent dimensions, as well as uniform depth, allow the rapid creation of a level floor. Utility lines pass easily through openings in the webs.

Constructions consisting of structural panel 'skins' glued to wood stringers are often called stressed-skin panels. These panels offer efficient structural constructions for floor, wall, and roof components. They can be designed to provide desired stiffness, bending moment resistance, and shear resistance. The skins resist bending moment, and the wood stringers provide shear resistance.

Figure 3 Prefabricated I-beams with laminated veneer lumber flanges and structural panel webs. (a) one experimental product has a hardboard web. The other two commercial products have (b) oriented standboard and (c) plywood webs.

Structural Sandwich Construction

Structural sandwich construction is a layered construction formed by bonding two thin facings to a thick core (**Figure 4**). The thin facings are usually made of a strong and dense material because they resist nearly all the applied edgewise loads and flatwise bending moments. The core, which is made of a weak and low-density material, separates and stabilizes the thin facings and provides most of the shear rigidity of the sandwich construction. By proper choice of materials for facings and core, constructions with high ratios of stiffness to weight can be achieved. As a crude guide to the material proportions, an efficient sandwich is obtained when the weight of the core is roughly equal to the total weight of the facings. Sandwich construction is also economical because the relatively expensive facing materials are used in much smaller quantities than are the usually inexpensive core materials. The materials are positioned so that each is used to its best advantage.

Specific nonstructural advantages can be incorporated in a sandwich construction by proper selection of facing and core materials. An impermeable facing can act as a moisture barrier for a wall or roof panel in a house; an abrasion-resistant facing can be used for the top facing of a floor panel; and decorative effects can be obtained by using panels with plastic facings for walls, doors, tables, and other furnishings. Core material can be chosen to provide thermal insulation, fire resistance, and decay resistance. Because of the light weight of structural sandwich construction, sound transmission problems must also be considered in choosing sandwich component parts.

Methods of joining sandwich panels to each other and other structures must be planned so that the joints function properly and allow for possible dimensional change as a result of temperature and moisture variations. Both structural and nonstructural advantages need to be analyzed in light of the strength and service requirements for the sandwich construction. Moisture-resistant facings, cores, and adhesives should be used if the construction is to be exposed to adverse moisture conditions. Similarly, heat-resistant or decay-resistant facings, cores, and adhesives should be used if exposure to elevated temperatures or decay organisms is expected.

See also: **Solid Wood Processing**: Adhesion and Adhesives; Machining; Protection from Fire. **Solid Wood Products**: Lumber Production, Properties and Uses; Wood-based Composites and Panel Products. **Wood Formation and Properties**: Physical Properties of Wood. **Wood Use and Trade**: Environmental Benefits of Wood as a Building Material.

Further Reading

Forest Products Laboratory (1999) *Wood Handbook – Wood as an Engineering Material*. General Technical Report FPL-GTR-113. Madison, WI: US Department of Agriculture, Forest Service, Forest Products Laboratory.

Smulski S (ed.) (1997) *Engineered Wood Products: A Guide to Specifiers, Designers and Users*. Madison, WI: Product Fabrication Services Research Foundation.

US Department of Agriculture (1999) *Wood Handbook: Wood as an Engineering Material*. General Technical Report no. FPL-GTR-113. Madison, WI: US Department of Agriculture, Forest Service, Forest Products Laboratory.

Structural Use of Wood

S Smulski, Wood Science Specialists Inc., Shutesbury, MA, USA

Introduction

Wood is an indispensable structural material worldwide and has been so since antiquity. The global prominence of wood as a construction staple is owed not only to its desirable attributes, but also to the fact that the forest resources from which it is derived are universally distributed, abundant, and renewable. Whether in the form of traditional solid-sawn lumber or a modern engineered wood I-joist, wood is unique among load-bearing building products. The only structural material of biological origin, wood has a high strength-to-weight ratio, is easily cut to size and shape with simple tools, is readily joined with

Figure 4 Cutaway section of sandwich construction with plywood facings and a paper honeycomb core.

fasteners or adhesives to produce strong joints, and is prized for its natural beauty. The perceived limitations of wood as a structural material – combustibility and degradation by decay fungi and insects – were overcome long ago with advances in building design, construction practice, and the advent of preservative and fire-retardant treatments.

North America is both the world's largest producer and consumer of structural wood products. The majority of the structural wood products manufactured in the USA and Canada is used domestically to build more than 1 million single-family houses annually as well as thousands of other wood-frame structures of all kinds. The balance of North America's output of structural wood products is exported to Asia, Europe, and Australia and, more recently, to South America, where it is utilized for much the same purposes, but to a much lesser extent. While nearly all residential structures in North America are framed with wood, concrete and masonry dominate house building in Asia, Europe, and South America. Traditional on-site stick-building of houses is the norm in North America, but off-site factory-assembly predominates in Japan and Europe. Virtually all North American dimension lumber is made from softwoods, while much of Australia's native structural framing is manufactured from hardwoods. Wood-frame buildings in North America seldom exceed four stories in height, but those in Europe increasingly rise to six stories. Despite these and other regional differences, similar structural wood products are used for similar applications worldwide. It is for these reasons that the focus here is on the structural use of wood in North America, and by extension, around the globe.

Today, structural wood products are available in a wide array of forms useful in a broad spectrum of applications. The decision to use traditional solid-sawn products or modern engineered products is made based on the kind of structure under consideration, the distances to be spanned, the magnitude of the loads to be supported, and the desired aesthetics. Solid-sawn options are boards, dimension lumber, timbers, poles, piles, and construction logs. The choice of engineered wood products presently includes glue-laminated timber, laminated veneer lumber, wood I-joists, parallel strand lumber, laminated strand lumber, metal plate connected trusses, and panel products plywood and oriented strand board.

Structural Wood Product Allowable Design Values

Historically, the size of the solid-sawn lumber and timber needed to frame a structure was chosen based on rules of thumb borne from past success. This educated-guess approach of choosing structural wood products that are 'big enough' and thus 'strong enough' for the task at hand is still used locally in some parts of the world. In almost all industrialized nations, however, solid-sawn and engineered wood products intended for use in structural applications are stress-rated to ensure that they will safely support the loads imposed on them in service. This means that they have been assigned allowable design values for various mechanical properties such as modulus of elasticity in bending, extreme fiber stress in bending, tension, compression, and shear, based on the results of destructive tests conducted on full-size members. As a consequence of the built-in safety factor, the actual breaking strength of a structural wood product is four to five times greater than its allowable design value. All wooden structures are designed such that the stresses induced in the structural members by in-service loads are less than the allowable design values.

Allowable design values must sometimes be adjusted as part of the design process to account for the effect on member stiffness and strength of duration of loading, in-service conditions of use, and postgrading treatment. This is true for both solid-sawn and engineered wood products, although the adjustment factors for each type of member may differ. Published allowable design values apply to so-called normal load duration, which is the load that fully stresses a member to its allowable design value, intermittently or continuously, for a cumulative period of 10 years. Because wood can carry much higher loads for shorter periods of time than it can for longer periods, allowable design values for members subject to short-term, high-magnitude loads such as those imposed by snow, wind, and earthquakes must be adjusted for duration of loading. Modification of allowable design values is required whenever wood will experience sustained exposure to temperatures of 38–66°C (100–150°F) and whenever its in-service moisture content will exceed 19% for prolonged periods. Interaction between the chemicals in certain preservatives and fire retardants and heat during the treating process and posttreatment kiln-drying reduces wood's stiffness and strength. Because such formulations are proprietary, allowable design values for treated members must be altered as per the recommendation of the formulator or treater. Depending on the type of member and how it will be used, additional refinements to allowable design values for size, flat use, repetitive use, and curvature may also be warranted.

Solid-Sawn Wood Products

Boards, Dimension Lumber, and Timbers

Sawed directly from logs in an essentially finished form, boards, dimension lumber, and timbers are the oldest and still most widely used structural wood products. The three are differentiated on the basis of their nominal thickness (i.e., their smallest rough dimension as sawed from the log), not their actual thickness (i.e., their smallest finish dimension after surfacing). Boards are less than 38 mm (2 in.) thick; dimension lumber is 38 mm (2 in.) to, but not including, 127 mm (5 in.) thick; and timbers are 127 mm (5 in.) or more in thickness. Within each of the three nominal thickness classifications there are width categories, use categories, and grades. The names of the width and use categories indicate the intended application. Those for dimension lumber, for example, are light framing, stud, structural light framing, and structural joists and planks. Within width and use categories there are grades. Boards, dimension lumber, timbers, poles, piles, and construction logs are predominantly visually graded according to a set of rules that specify the natural and processing characteristics permitted in each grade. The higher the grade, the fewer and smaller the characteristics that are permitted and the higher the allowable design values. The grade names for dimension lumber structural joists and planks, for instance, are select structural (highest grade), no. 1, no. 2, and no. 3 (lowest grade). Dimension lumber used for fabricating trusses and glue-laminated timber, however, is graded mechanically and identified in the grade stamp as machine stress-rated or MSR.

The grade stamp printed on boards, dimension lumber, and timbers identifies the species, grade, and moisture condition of the member when it was machined to finish size. Knowledge of the moisture condition is especially useful in minimizing shrinkage, warpage, splitting, and other moisture-related problems that can arise after a member is placed in service. Solid-sawn products are either green (i.e., water-saturated) or dry (i.e., maximum 19% moisture content) when surfaced to finish dimensions. Most boards and dimension lumber are air- or kiln-dried to 19% moisture content or less prior to surfacing and thus shrink minimally after installation. Timbers are almost always green when surfaced because it is physically and economically impractical to kiln-dry members larger than 102×102 mm (4×4 in.). Consequently, the sometimes considerable postinstallation initial shrinkage of timbers must be accounted for during the design process. Attention must also be given to the initial shrinkage of boards and dimension lumber pressure-treated with water-borne preservatives. These products are saturated with water during treatment and seldom redried afterwards.

Boards   Compared with dimension lumber and timbers, stress-rated boards are of minor importance and see limited use. Employed occasionally for wall and roof sheathing, subflooring, collar ties, diagonal bracing, and decking, most are made from the pines, spruces, true firs, and other softwoods. Boards are manufactured in 25-mm (1-in.) increments from 51 to 305 mm (2 to 12 in.) wide; wider boards are made but difficult to find. Most boards are 1.8–6.1 m (6–20 ft) in length, in multiples of 0.3 m (1 ft).

Dimension lumber   By far the most widely used solid-sawn structural product, dimension lumber is routinely used for sill plates, wall studs, floor and ceiling joists, roof rafters, ridge boards, purlins, door and window headers, decking, and site-built nail-laminated girders. Manufactured in increments of 51 mm (2 in.) in width and thickness and in 0.6-m (2-ft) multiples in length beginning at 2.4 m (8 ft), virtually all dimension lumber is made from softwoods such as the pines, spruces, true firs, hemlocks, larches and Douglas-fir. Dimension lumber up to 305 mm (12 in.) wide and 4.9 m (16 ft) long is still readily available. Larger members are increasingly scarce because the inventory of large-diameter trees has essentially been depleted. Where wider or longer members are required, engineered wood products are used instead. Two engineered wood substitutes are themselves made from dimension lumber: metal plate connected trusses and glue-laminated timber.

Timbers   Made primarily from high-density softwoods and hardwoods such as the hard pines, Douglas-fir and the oaks, timbers are subdivided into two use and width categories: beams and stringers, which are plainly rectangular, and posts and timbers, which are essentially square. The nominal width of beams and stringers is more than 51 mm (2 in.) greater than their nominal thickness, while that of posts and timbers is 51 mm (2 in.) or less. Timbers are sawed in multiples of 51 mm (2 in.) in width and thickness and 0.3 m (1 ft) in length, starting at 1.8 m (6 ft) and ranging to 12.2 m (40 ft) and longer. As the name implies, beams and stringers are used as beams, stringers, girders, sills, purlins and other horizontally oriented primary and secondary supporting members. Posts and timbers are mainly employed as primary vertical supports such as posts and columns. Timbers of both width categories are widely used in pedestrian and vehicular bridges; piers, seawalls and other freshwater and marine structures; and as chords and webs in heavy timber trusses. Rough-sawn timbers are often employed in the construction and renovation of concrete and steel structures as temporary shoring and bracing.

Round Timbers

Poles Essentially tree-length logs shaved of their bark, poles are 127–762 mm (5–30 in.) in diameter at the butt and 6.1–36.6 m (20–120 ft) in length. Because straightness is important, virtually all poles are made from softwood trees whose excurrent form (i.e., a single, tapering main stem) is well suited for this purpose. Utility poles and utility pole structures carry electric power distribution wires and communications cables. Construction poles serve as both the foundation and main vertical supports in pole buildings and highway sound barriers. Often, a narrow flat plane extending from groundline to tip is machined on one face of construction poles to remove taper and facilitate attachment of framing, sheathing, and siding. Because the butt is embedded in the ground, both utility and construction poles function as cantilever beams. As such, they are stress-rated according to their allowable extreme fiber stress in bending. Utility and construction poles are routinely pressure-impregnated with a preservative such as creosote, pentachlorophenol, or chromated copper arsenate because of the decay hazard imposed by soil contact.

Piles Manufactured in the same manner and in essentially the same sizes as poles, piles are used in foundations under buildings and bridges. Most are made from softwoods such as the hard pines and Douglas-fir, although some are oak. End-bearing piles are driven down to bedrock so that the weight of the structure is transferred along the pile to this immovable base. Friction piles are used where soil is so deep that bedrock is inaccessible. So-called skin friction that develops between the wood and the surrounding soil prevents the pile from slipping downward under the load exerted by the structure. Because piles are loaded axially both when hammered into the ground and in service, they are stress-rated according to their allowable compression strength parallel to grain. Straightness is of utmost importance in minimizing pile breakage during driving. Often, the butt end of a pile embedded in soil is above the water table or even partially exposed above ground and thus vulnerable to decay fungi and insects. The submerged portion of piles supporting piers and other marine structures is susceptible to marine borers, while the above-water segment is threatened by decay fungi and insects. For these reasons, piles are routinely pressure-treated with the same preservatives as poles.

Construction logs Stacked vertically to form the walls of log buildings, construction logs are typically 203–305 mm (8–12 in.) in diameter and 2.4–9.1 m (8–30 ft) long. Virtually all construction logs are milled from softwoods such as the cedars and pines. They are made by passing tree-length logs or rough-sawn timbers through a four-sided cutterhead that machines the member to a circular or rectangular profile that is uniform along its length. A construction log's vertical faces, which are rounded or flat with beveled edges, become the exterior and interior surfaces of the wall. A system of tongues and grooves or grooves and splines is milled on the top and bottom faces so that construction logs interlock when stacked. Construction logs made from softwoods that lack natural decay resistance are treated by nonpressure dipping or spraying with a waterborne borate preservative to deter decay fungi and insects. Milled when green, construction logs shrink considerably in diameter after erection. Door and window openings in log buildings must be designed to accommodate this shortening of wall height.

Engineered Wood Products

During the last four decades of the twentieth century, traditional solid-sawn boards, dimension lumber, timbers, poles, piles, and construction logs were joined by numerous structural-engineered wood products made by gluing together small pieces of wood with a waterproof structural adhesive. The roster continues to expand as new products are introduced, but currently includes glue-laminated timber, laminated veneer lumber, wood I-joists, parallel strand lumber, laminated strand lumber, and panel products plywood and oriented strand board. Metal plate connected wood trusses are the nonglued exception.

Engineered wood products will eventually supplant the larger sizes of high-grade solid-sawn dimension lumber and timbers. A nonrenewable resource in truth, the old-growth forests from which large, high-grade dimension lumber and timbers were sawed are almost gone. Most of what is left has been set aside in national parks, wilderness areas, and other holdings that prohibit harvesting. Today's forest resources consist primarily of second- and third-generation trees managed under sustainable forestry practices for harvesting on 30–80-year rotations. Trees are thus smaller in diameter when felled, and the dimension lumber and timbers sawed from them contain more natural characteristics such as knots and juvenile wood that affect strength and in-service performance. While smaller sizes of dimension lumber (up to 51×254 mm (2×10 in.))

and timbers (up to 254×254 mm (10×10 in.)) will always be plentiful, the future availability of larger members, especially in the higher grades, is arguably uncertain. For these reasons, glue-laminated timber, laminated veneer lumber, wood I-joists, parallel strand lumber, laminated strand lumber, metal plate connected trusses, plywood, and oriented strand board represent the future of structural wood products. All of these engineered wood products can be made from trees no larger than 305 mm (12 in.) in diameter or from dimension lumber no wider than 102 mm (4 in.), and in lengths substantially longer than can be sawed from today's logs. Because knots and other natural strength-reducing characteristics are restricted to a single lamination, veneer, or strand, they are smaller and harmlessly dispersed throughout the product's volume. As a result, the range of stiffness and strength among individual pieces of engineered wood products is considerably narrower than that of solid-sawn dimension lumber and timbers. Allowable design values are consequently higher, as is the predictability of in-service performance.

Except for plywood and oriented strand board, which are commodity products, engineered wood products and their allowable design values are proprietary. This means that the allowable design values for an otherwise identical product made by two different manufacturers will almost certainly differ. As such, a wood I-joist fabricated by one manufacturer cannot necessarily be substituted for that made by another simply because both are the same depth. Because of the complications that arise from this present situation, some voices in the construction community have called for the production of commodity-engineered wood products that share the same allowable design values and are thus interchangeable. Whether this happens remains to be seen.

With the exception of trusses, engineered wood products are manufactured from wood kiln-dried to a moisture content of 12% or less, which is well below the 19% typical of boards and dimension lumber. Consequently, they shrink, warp, and split much less than solid-sawn boards, dimension lumber, and timbers after being installed. Fastener pops, floor squeaks, drywall cracks, and other shrinkage-related problems are virtually eliminated. Camber is routinely built in to nonpanel-engineered wood products to counter dead load deflection and creep (i.e., progressive sagging of a member under sustained load over a very long time).

Glue-laminated timber Glue-laminated timber or glulam is made by face-laminating softwood dimension lumber that has been finger-jointed end-to-end.

With this method, beams and columns that are longer, wider, and deeper than sawn timbers can be fabricated, as can curved members and arches. Lengths up to 30.5 m (100 ft) are common, as are depths and widths of 0.3 (1 ft) to several meters (feet). While small stock sizes are manufactured for residential use, the majority of glulams are custom-made. Efficient use of wood is made when designing glulams by strategically placing the highest-grade laminations where in-service stresses are highest, then filling out members with lower-grade laminations where stresses are lower. Glulams are used in structures where long, clear spans and/or appearance are of primary importance, such as factories, warehouses, sports arenas, aircraft hangars, churches, auditoriums, and large office, hotel, retail, and institutional buildings. Preservative-treated members are utilized in bridges, piers and other freshwater and marine structures, power transmission towers, and as the main vertical supports in postframe buildings. Due to their large size, connections between members are made with through-bolts and steel gusset plates and framing anchors. Because glulam is made from dimension lumber at 12% moisture content, initial shrinkage after installation is small. However, connections must be designed so that members can shrink and swell freely in-service without overstressing the surrounding wood (**Figure 1**).

Laminated veneer lumber Composed of multiple sheets of veneer bonded together such that the grain of each ply is parallel to the product's length, laminated veneer lumber (LVL) is essentially reconstituted

Figure 1 Glue-laminated timbers provide both structural support and pleasing aesthetics for this curling rink. Courtesy of APA – The Engineered Wood Association.

dimension lumber. Like glulam, veneers are graded for stiffness and strength, then strategically positioned within the product to maximize allowable design values. Manufactured in the same and slightly larger thicknesses as dimension lumber, but in greater widths and in lengths up to 24.4 m (80 ft), LVL is widely used in residential and commercial construction for beams, girders, headers, joists, purlins, posts, and columns. LVL is also used extensively for scaffold planks and for the flanges of wood I-joists. Most is made from high-density softwoods such as the hard pines and Douglas-fir, and medium-density hardwoods like yellow poplar. LVL pressure-treated with waterborne preservatives and fire retardants is available (**Figure 2**).

Wood I-joists   I-shaped in cross-section and light in weight, wood I-joists come in many depths and flange widths and in lengths up to 24.4 m (80 ft). Flanges are LVL or dimension lumber, while webs are plywood, oriented strand board, and sometimes, dimension lumber. As their name suggests, most I-joists are used for framing floors in houses and low-rise office, hotel, retail, and institutional buildings. The small mass and long span typical of an I-joist floor system occasionally interact to produce annoying vibrations underfoot. Blocking, cross-bracing, and strongbacks are needed to stiffen these floor systems and dampen vibrations. Increasingly, I-joists are being utilized as rafters and purlins in residential and commercial roofs. Because of their unique cross-section, the proper way of designing and building with wood I-joists may not be apparent to those

Figure 2 Engineered wood products such as wood I-joists (far left), laminated strand lumber (left, right), laminated veneer lumber (center), and parallel strand lumber (far right) are replacing the larger sizes and higher grades of solid-sawn dimension lumber. Courtesy of TrusJoist A Weyerhaeuser Business.

accustomed to using boards, dimension lumber, and timbers. As such, I-joist manufacturers supply design manuals and software to ensure their correct use (**Figure 2**).

Parallel strand lumber   Offering the highest allowable design values of today's engineered wood products, parallel strand lumber (PSL) competes for the same applications as timber and glulam. Because of its pleasing appearance, PSL beams, stringers, girders, headers, purlins, posts, and columns are typically left exposed. Composed of long, narrow strips of Douglas-fir, larch, hard pine, and yellow-poplar veneer bonded together and oriented parallel to the product's length, PSL is available in lengths up to 21.3 m (70 ft) and in widths and thicknesses ranging from 102 to 508 mm (4 to 20 in.). PSL readily treats with preservatives and fire retardants (**Figure 2**).

Laminated strand lumber   The most recent engineered wood innovation, laminated strand lumber (LSL) consists of short, thin strands of underutilized, fast-growing mixed softwoods and hardwoods consolidated with heat and pressure into dimension lumber-sized products. To date, its use is limited to rim joists, studs, blocking, and light-duty headers in residential construction (**Figure 2**).

Metal plate connected wood trusses   The dimension lumber chords and webs of metal plate connected wood trusses are joined not with adhesive, but with toothed metal plates pressed into the wood. Routinely used for framing roofs of virtually any shape in residential construction, trusses are commonly utilized in many types of commercial, industrial, and agricultural buildings as well. Lengths range from 4.6 to 24.4 m (15 to 80 ft) and more, with truss height dictated by roof pitch. Stock roof trusses are fabricated for residential use, but most trusses are designed to order using sophisticated engineering software. Because dimension lumber grade is matched to in-service stresses on a chord-by-chord and web-by-web basis, trusses make especially efficient use of wood. Where a conventionally framed roof might use 51×203 mm (2×8 in.) rafters spaced 406 mm (16 in.) on-center, for instance, trusses for the same roof, made from members 51×102 mm (2×4 in.) and spaced 610 mm (24 in.) apart, use 15–25% less wood. More and more, floors and low-slope roofs in nonresidential buildings are being built with parallel chord trusses whose open webs simplify and speed the placement of piping, ductwork, and wiring. Where spans and/or in-service loads are very large or appearance is important, heavy timber trusses are employed. Made from timber, glulam, or PSL, the chords and webs of these heavy-duty trusses are joined with through-bolts inserted into steel gusset plates, framing anchors, split-ring connectors or shear plate connectors. Depending upon their configuration, these massive trusses may span up to 90 m (300 ft) (**Figure 3**).

Plywood and oriented strand board Two structural panel products – plywood and oriented strand board – are routinely used in all types of wood-frame buildings. Most plywood is made from softwood veneer, while oriented strand board consists of small, thin strands of mixed softwoods and hardwoods. Both panels are cross-laminated such that the grain of each layer is perpendicular to that of adjacent layers. Most commonly manufactured in 1.2 × 2.4 m (4 × 8 ft) sheets 12.7–38.1 mm (0.5–1.5 in.) thick, plywood and oriented strand board are employed as roof and wall sheathing, subflooring, and under-layment. Special grades of both panels are made for use in engineered applications such as diaphragms and shearwalls in wind- and earthquake-resistant structures, as well as in stressed skin panels. Plywood is widely utilized for concrete formwork, while oriented strand board is the preferred facing for foam-core structural insulated panels. Plywood and oriented strand board panels intended for structural use are selected according to the span rating and exposure durability class found in the grade stamp. The span rating is a two-number code such as 812/406 (32/16). The number on the left is the maximum recommended on-center spacing in millimeters (inches) for framing when the panel is used as roof sheathing. The right-hand number is the maximum recommended on-center spacing of framing when the

panel is used as subflooring. In all cases, panels are to be installed with their long dimension perpendicular to framing and across three or more supports.

Exposure durability class indicates a panel's ability to resist the damaging effects of exposure to the weather or to moisture. Panels marked exterior or marine are the only choice for those that will be permanently exposed to the elements or to high moisture. Exposure 1 panels are intended for applications where long delays in construction or high moisture in service is possible. Interior panels are meant for dry, protected uses. Fire retardant-treated plywood is readily available, as is the preservative-treated plywood used in permanent wood foundations. Because treatment reduces ply-wood's stiffness and strength, the appropriate adjust-ment factors must be obtained from the formulator or treater. With oriented strand board, strands are treated before consolidation, so no adjustment is needed (**Figure 4**).

Wooden Structures

While the number of potential structural applications for wood is limited only by the imagination, the majority of structural wood products are used in constructing buildings and bridges. Wood-frame buildings are classified according to the size of the members used and the geometry of the structural skeleton they form. Five basic types are light-frame, log, post-frame, pole, and heavy timber. In addition, many very large, special-purpose buildings such as domed and arched sports arenas are constructed with solid-sawn and engineered wood products. The fundamental types of wooden bridges – beam, deck, truss, arch, and suspension – are named after the

Figure 3 Roofs of virtually any shape can be framed with metal plate connected wood trusses fabricated from dimension lumber. Courtesy of the Wood Truss Council of America.

Figure 4 Plywood and oriented strand board are routinely used for roof and wall sheathing in all types of residential and commercial construction. Courtesy of APA – The Engineered Wood Association.

configuration of their superstructure. Variations on these five archetypal designs abound.

Wood-Frame Buildings

Light-frame buildings By far the most common wood-frame structure, light-frame buildings are constructed largely from dimension lumber, wood I-joists, and roof and floor trusses spaced 406 or 610 mm (16 or 24 in.) on-center and sheathed with plywood or oriented strand board. Examples include single-family houses; garages and outbuildings; apartment and condominium buildings; and low-rise office, hotel, retail, and institutional buildings. The traditional method of stick-building – framing a structure on-site member-by-member – is gradually yielding to automated building in which structures are made from factory-fabricated subassemblies that are joined on-site. Leading this trend are panelized buildings made from preframed and sheathed wall, floor, and roof subassemblies and modular buildings consisting of three-dimensional boxes that are stacked on-site. Greater control over the quality of assembly, more efficient use of materials, freedom from the vagaries of weather, rapid on-site erection, and reduced on-site generation of construction waste are driving the switch (**Figure 5**).

Log buildings The walls of log buildings are made from construction logs, and sometimes profiled timbers, that are stacked vertically. Floors and roofs are framed with dimension lumber, wood I-joists, trusses, or exposed construction logs. Most log buildings are single-family dwellings, although many are park structures and retail shops where this rustic look is appropriate. Virtually all log buildings are sold as kits, with each log precut to length and marked for sequential stacking on-site. Typically, all

other materials needed to complete the shell such as roof framing, sheathing, shingles, and doors and windows are included (**Figure 6**).

Post-frame buildings Construction of a post-frame building begins with embedding in the ground preservative-treated nail-laminated dimension lumber, timber, or glulam posts, also known as wall columns. Horizontal wall girts of dimension lumber are then fastened to the posts, and plywood or oriented strand board sheathing and/or siding is affixed to the wall girts. This framework is capped with metal plate connected roof trusses installed on 1.2–3.6-m (4–12-ft) centers, with dimension lumber purlins spanning across or between trusses to support plywood or oriented strand board sheathing, and/or metal roofing. Formerly used only for livestock barns, equipment sheds and other agricultural structures, post-frame buildings are today erected for use as retail shops, warehouses, factories, fire stations, commercial garages, and recreational facilities (**Figure 7**).

Pole buildings The forerunner of post-frame buildings, pole buildings have declined markedly in popularity. Constructed in virtually the same manner as post-frame buildings, pole buildings are occasionally erected for agricultural use and as bulk storage sheds for road deicing chemicals. Structures supported by poles such as highway sound barriers and billboards, however, are common.

Heavy timber buildings

Timber frame buildings Timber frame construction represents the oldest formal use of wood as a

Figure 5 Light-frame buildings constructed from dimension lumber and plywood or oriented strand board sheathing such as these houses are the most common wood-frame structures. Courtesy of APA – The Engineered Wood Association.

Figure 6 Typically sold as kits, modern log buildings are increasingly complex in design. Courtesy of Original Lincoln Logs Ltd. and Craig Murphy Photography.

structural material. For over 20 centuries, timbers have been employed as the structural framework for all types of buildings. Members were connected with mortise and tenon joints pegged with wooden dowels called trunnels to prevent the tenon from pulling out. These same joints are still used today, especially where appearance is important, although mechanical fastening is increasingly common. While most timber frame buildings utilize timber, glulam usage is growing. The skeleton of a modern timber frame building differs little from that of its ancestors, but the walls and roof are now made of structural insulated panels. Applied to the outside of the timber frame, these energy-efficient panels have a foam core sandwiched between oriented strand board faces. Floor decks and interior partitions are typically built with dimension lumber. Although many types of modern buildings are of timber frame construction, including office, hotel and retail complexes, most are single-family residences (**Figure 8**).

Figure 7 Diagonal bracing holds the dimension lumber walls and roof trusses of this post-frame building plumb and square before sheathing is applied. Courtesy of National Frame Builders Association.

Figure 8 Diagonal braces lend rigidity to the timber frame of this future retail shop. Courtesy of Bensonwood Homes.

Mill buildings Infrequently constructed today, mill buildings have a masonry exterior and an interior framework of timber beams and columns. Floor and roof decking is usually tongue-and-groove dimension lumber. Originally built as factories and warehouses, thousands of nineteenth- and twentieth-century mill buildings have been renovated in the last few decades into retail and office complexes, and apartments and condominiums.

Wooden Bridges

Contemporary beam, deck, truss, arch, and suspension wooden bridges are used almost exclusively on secondary and rural roads where traffic volume and vehicular weights are relatively low. Components of the superstructure, which consists of the primary longitudinal supports, bracing, floor decking, railings, and other minor members, are preservative-treated timber or glulam. PSL and LVL are beginning to be used as well. Concrete abutments and intermediate supports of concrete or treated wooden piles form the underlying substructure. Beam bridges consist of longitudinal main carrying members with timber or glulam decking laid perpendicular to them. Spans are limited to about 7.6 m (25 ft) with timber supports, while 30 m (100 ft) or more can be achieved with glulam. The superstructure of a deck bridge is dimension lumber, timber, or glulam placed on edge and nail-laminated or, more commonly, drawn tightly together with threaded metal through-rods in a process known as stress-laminating, into a massive plate that doubles as both main support and decking. Because of the composite action that develops, deck bridges can span up to 11 m (36 ft). Parallel chord or bowstring trusses of timber or glulam form the sides and main supports of truss bridges. Bowstring trusses permit spans up to 30 m

Figure 9 Hinged glue-laminated timbers support the deck of this graceful arch bridge. Courtesy of APA – The Engineered Wood Association.

(100 ft), while 75 m (250 ft) is possible with parallel chord trusses. The familiar railroad trestle bridge is actually a beam, deck, or truss superstructure supported on wooden piles. Arch bridges have a timber or glulam deck that is supported by glulam arches. These graceful structures can span up to 60 m (200 ft) (**Figure 9**). The longest spans are achieved with suspension bridges, virtually all of which, however, are for pedestrian use only. Consisting of a timber or glulam deck hanging from wire rope cables, these bridges are up to 150 m (500 ft) long.

See also: **Solid Wood Products**: Construction; Logs, Poles, Piles, Sleepers (Crossties); Glued Structural Members; Lumber Production, Properties and Uses; Wood-based Composites and Panel Products. **Wood Use and Trade**: Environmental Benefits of Wood as a Building Material.

Further Reading

American Forest and Paper Association (1987) Permanent Wood Foundation System Design, Fabrication and Installation Manual. Washington, DC: AF&PA.

American Forest and Paper Association (1996) Load and Resistance Factor Design Manual for Engineered Wood Construction. Washington, DC: AF&PA.

American Forest and Paper Association (1997) National Design Specification for Wood Construction. Washington, DC: AF&PA.

American Forest and Paper Association (1997) Supplement National Design Specification for Wood Construction. Washington, DC: AF&PA.

American Institute of Timber Construction (1994) Timber Construction Manual., 4th edn. Englewood, CO: AITC.

Canadian Wood Council (1991) Wood Reference Handbook. Ottawa, Canada: CWC.

Canadian Wood Council (1993) Wood Building Technology. Ottawa, Canada: CWC.

Faherty K and Williamson T (1989) Wood Engineering and Construction Handbook. New York, NY: McGraw-Hill.

Forest Products Laboratory (1999) Wood Handbook. Wood as an Engineering Material. Madison, WI: Forest Products Society.

Goldstein E (1999) Timber Construction for Architects and Builders. New York, NY: McGraw-Hill.

Hoyle R and Woeste F (1989) Wood Technology in the Design of Structures., 5th edn. Ames, IA: Iowa State University Press.

National Frame Builders Association (2001) Post-Frame Building Design Manual. Lawrence, KS: NFBA.

National Institute of Standards and Technology (1999) American Softwood Lumber Standard DOC PS 20-99. Gaithersburg, MD: NIST.

Sherwood G and Stroh R (1989) *Wood-Frame House Construction*. USDA Forest Service Agriculture Handbook 73. Washington, DC: US Superintendent of Documents.

Smulski S (ed.) (1997). Engineered Wood Products. A Guide for Specifiers, Designers and Users. Madison, WI: PFS Research Foundation.

Williamson T (ed.) (2002) APA Engineered Wood Handbook. New York, NY: McGraw-Hill.

Wood Truss Council of America (1997) Metal Plate Connected Wood Truss Handbook. Madison, WI: WTCA.

Lumber Production, Properties and Uses

F G Wagner, University of Idaho, Moscow, ID, USA

Lumber production or sawmilling is the process of sawing and/or chipping logs to form rectangular pieces of wood (lumber, cants, or timbers) for buildings, packaging, furniture, and many other applications. Lumber production may have begun in Egypt as early as 6000 BC, where handsaws and planes were utilized to fashion small volumes of crude lumber. Today, facilities for lumber production (sawmills) range from those with one or two slow-simple machines powered by electric motors or internal-combustion engines to those with many high-speed computerized machines powered by electric motors and hydraulic pumps. Some modern high-speed sawmills are capable of producing as much as 2000 m³ (1 million board feet) of lumber per day. Sawmills often also include equipment for drying and shaping the sawn lumber into finished products. Properties important to lumber products include strength, stiffness, straightness, appearance, and proportion of clear wood. Standards have been established for grading lumber based on these properties.

Log Supply

Lumber manufacturing begins in the forest. Many large lumber-producing companies own forest land, and they obtain at least a portion of their log supply from that land. Other lumber-producing companies purchase logs or standing trees (stumpage) from private forest landowners or government agencies. Independent logging contractors are often hired to harvest and transport logs to the sawmill. In other cases, logs (gate wood) are purchased from individuals who deliver noncontracted logs to the sawmill. Logs may be cut to lumber lengths plus trim allowance, multiple lumber lengths (multisegment logs) plus trim allowance, or tree length. The trim allowance is a small amount of extra log length that allows lumber end trimming during manufacture. Logs may be as small as 10 cm in diameter, or they may be greater than 1 m in diameter.

Logs are purchased by weight or by log scale. If logs are purchased by weight, log trucks are weighed both loaded and empty to calculate the weight of the logs. Mathematical formulae are often used to convert weight to cubic or lumber volume.

Log scale is an estimate of the volume of lumber that is expected to be sawn from the logs. If logs are purchased by log scale, an experienced individual measures the diameter and length of logs, calculates gross lumber volume based on a scale stick or portable computer, and subtracts scale volume for defects that may reduce the volume of lumber sawn from the logs.

Logs are usually delivered to sawmills on log trucks or railcars. They are unloaded with large specially designed lift trucks or overhead cranes, and they are placed on a log yard. Logs are often sorted on the yard based upon species, species group, and diameter of the logs. It is important that enough logs be stored on the log yard to supply the sawmill during interruptions in log deliveries. Log deliveries may be interrupted because of wet weather, lags in log purchases, equipment breakdowns, or a number of other factors. Therefore, logs are sometimes stored for a year or more before they are sawn into lumber. If logs are stored for an extended period of time during warm weather (above 10°C), they must be protected from stain fungi, decay fungi, insects, and drying (see **Solid Wood Processing**: Protection of Wood against Biodeterioration. **Wood Formation and Properties**: Biological Deterioration of Wood). Protection is often accomplished by spraying the logs with water. The wet log surfaces provide an anaerobic environment in which most fungi and insects cannot survive, and it prevents drying of the logs. Environmental–government agencies often require that water sprayed on logs be captured at the sawmill site and reused. This prevents chemicals leached from the wood and bark of the logs from entering streams and other estuaries. If these chemicals enter streams and estuaries at high levels, they may be toxic to fish and other marine life.

Lumber Production

Stored logs are eventually transported to the sawmill by lift trucks or overhead cranes. Logs may then be moved by conveyor to a debarker where bark is detached from the logs. Debarkers are usually electrically powered machines that scrape or rub bark from the logs. Bark often contains soil and small rocks that become embedded during log harvest or storage. Thus, removing bark from logs helps prevent dulling of cutting tools in the sawmill. Removing bark from logs also separates bark from the outer portion of logs that often becomes pulp chips during the sawmill process. Bark and sawdust from the sawing processes are often burned to provide energy for lumber drying.

Either before or after the logs are debarked, multisegment logs and tree-length logs are crosscut (bucked) to lumber lengths plus trim allowance. Logs that were bucked to lumber lengths during the harvest process bypass this step. In large sawmills, logs are transported to the log-bucking station via conveyor where they are bucked to length with large circular saws or chainsaws powered by electric motors. At small sawmills, logs may be bucked to length with manually operated gasoline-powered chainsaws.

Logs are next processed by a machine called a headrig. A headrig is the first machine in a sawmill where longitudinal cuts are sawn or chipped on the log (see **Solid Wood Processing**: Machining). Every sawmill has one or more headrigs. Many different types of headrig are used worldwide, but most utilize one or more band saws, circular saws, and/or chipping heads to make longitudinal cuts. Logs may be completely sawn into lumber or timbers at the headrig, or they may be sawn into some combination of lumber, timbers, and cants. Cants are logs with one or more sawn or chipped faces. Some lumber may be produced with two sawn wide faces and wane (absence of wood) at the narrow faces (flitches). Flitches may be edged at an edger in the sawmill where the wane is sawn or chipped away. In the case of some hardwoods, flitches may also be sold to other manufacturers for further processing.

The speed of processing at headrigs is quite variable. At some small sawmills, only a few logs may be sawn on the headrig each hour. These are usually headrigs with many manual functions. At modern high-speed small-log sawmills, as many as 25 logs per minute may be processed. These are usually headrigs with scanners and computers that automatically determine the log size and shape, make sawing decisions, and perform many of the sawing functions. Many headrigs have chipping canters that chip a flat face on the side of logs. If the headrig does not have a chipping canter, flat faces are produced with the headrig saws, and the portion removed (slabs) is chipped at another location. Chips (small rectangular pieces of wood) produced at the headrig and at other machine centers in the sawmill are usually sold to pulp companies.

Various sawing methods may be used at headrigs and resaws. Sawn faces may be parallel to the log taper (follow the slope of the outside of the log from the small end to the large end of the log). This sawing method is termed 'taper sawing.' Logs may also be sawn parallel to the centerline of the log, which is termed split taper sawing. In addition, three different sawing patterns may be used. Logs may be completely sawn into lumber on the headrig with all saw lines parallel (live-sawing pattern). Alternatively, lumber and cants may be sawn on a headrig, and the cants may be transported to a resaw where sawn faces are made perpendicular to the sawn faces made at the headrig (cant-sawing pattern). A grade-sawing pattern is also sometimes used where the sawyer makes sawing decisions based upon defects in the log. In grade sawing, the sawyer attempts to improve the grade of the sawn lumber by first sawing the worst face. The log is then rotated to the best face, and the sawyer saws additional lumber from that face until grade declines. The sawyer then rotates the log 90° and continues to saw until the log is completely sawn into lumber.

If cants are produced at the headrig, they are further sawn into lumber at a resaw. Resaws often have multiple circular or band saws, and they may saw cants into lumber in one pass. Lumber produced at a headrig or resaw containing excess wane (absence of wood for any reason but usually due to sawing to the outside of the log) may be edged at an edger. An edger is a machine with saws or chipping heads that produce acceptably square narrow faces on each piece. Lumber is usually fed through an edger lengthwise. Typically some wane may be left on lumber if the amount of wane is not expected to lower the grade. Resaws and edgers may be operated manually, or they may be operated by scanning and computer systems. Chips are produced from the edges of wide faces.

At many sawmills, lumber trimsaws are used to trim one or both ends of lumber. Ends are trimmed to make the ends more square, to make the lumber consistent lengths for further processing, and to remove excess wane or other defects at one or both ends. Trimsaws typically have multiple circular saws that are set at specified distances apart. Lumber usually moves through trimsaws sidewise, and the appropriate saw is lowered to crosscut the lumber to length. Trimsaws may be operated manually, or they may be operated by scanning and computer systems. Short trim ends produced at the trimsaw may be chipped and sold to pulp companies.

Sawmill Performance

The principal measures of sawmill performance are lumber production and lumber recovery. Profitability of a sawmill is closely linked to lumber production. Because some costs at a sawmill are fixed (buildings, machines, and labor), higher lumber production results in lower fixed cost per unit of lumber. Many sawmills set goals or standards of production for a shift, day, week, month, or year. Sometimes bonuses are paid to sawmill workers if production standards are met or exceeded.

Lumber recovery is a measure of the proportion of lumber produced to the volume of logs processed. Lumber recovery is extremely important to the profitability of a sawmill because approximately 75% of the total manufacturing cost of lumber is the cost of logs. Therefore, even small improvements in recovery can greatly reduce manufacturing costs. Lumber recovery may be expressed in terms of percent cubic recovery, volume of lumber to cubic volume or weight of logs, or volume of lumber to log scale. When sawmill recovery is high, 50% or more of the log will become lumber. The rest of the log will become green sawdust and bark, which is often burned to produce energy for dry kilns, chips which are usually sold to pulp manufactures, and dry sawdust and planer shavings which are often sold to particleboard manufactures or burned to produce energy for the kilns. At most sawmills, 100% of the log is utilized.

One method of maintaining high lumber recovery is to have a quality-control program at the sawmill. Sawmill recovery is usually highest when log diameter is large, logs are straight with little taper, saw kerf (width of cut made by saws) is narrow, sawing variation (thick and thin lumber) is low, lumber products are wide and thick, equipment is well maintained, sawing decisions are good, and lumber is carefully dried to the correct moisture content. Therefore quality-control programs often collect and analyze data related to each of these factors. Measurements are taken on a regular basis within the sawmill, and statistics are used to determine whether established standards are being met and manufacturing processes are in control.

Lumber Drying

After trimming, lumber is sorted for thickness, width, and length to accommodate lumber drying and finishing. Lumber may be sorted manually by individuals who pull lumber from a slowly moving chain (green chain) and stack the lumber in an appropriate compartment. Lumber may also be sorted automatically by a large machine that drops lumber into compartments or slings according to thickness, width, and length. In these machines, sort decisions are often based upon limit switches placed along the length of the machine, or they may be based upon a scanning and computer system at the trimsaw.

Lumber may be sold in a rough-green condition, finished (planed) and sold in a dressed-green condition, dried and sold in a rough-dry condition, or dried, finished, and sold in a dry-dressed condition. Hardwood lumber is often sold in the rough-green or rough-dry conditions, and softwood lumber is often sold in the dressed-green or dressed-dry conditions. If lumber is dried at the sawmill, it is dried in an air-drying yard or in a dry kiln (see **Solid Wood Processing**: Drying). In the case of hardwoods, lumber may also be partially air-dried and then kiln-dried. Lumber is dried to reduce weight for shipping, to make the wood more dimensionally stable, and to comply with grade standards.

To prepare lumber for drying, it is usually stacked in layers with narrow pieces of lumber (stickers) placed perpendicular to the length of the lumber. This separates each layer of lumber in a stack, and allows air to flow through the stack and dry the lumber. Stacking may be done manually, or it may be done by machine. Softwood structural lumber is typically dried to 15% or 19% moisture content, and hardwood furniture lumber may be dried to 6–8% moisture content.

Lumber dried in an air-drying yard may take several months to reach desired moisture content. However, lumber may sometimes be dried in a dry kiln in as little as a few hours. A dry kiln is a chamber where temperature and relative humidity are closely monitored. Dry kilns are heated with steam or direct-combustion systems. As previously mentioned, heat is often produced by burning bark and sawdust. The heat provides energy for evaporation of water from the wood. Regulation of relative humidity helps control the rate of drying. It is important to control the rate of drying because some types of lumber may be damaged if dried too fast. Regulation of relative humidity within the kiln is achieved by opening vents to exhaust water vapor and reduce relative humidity and by spraying water or steam into the kiln to increase relative humidity. Temperatures within commercial dry kilns may be as high as 125°C.

After drying, lumber may be graded and packaged for sale. It may also be finished (planed) to a smooth surface, graded, and packaged for sale (see **Solid Wood Processing**: Machining). Lumber is often planed on four faces, and sometimes a pattern is machined into one or more faces. Lumber planers are usually composed of a lumber feed mechanism and planer heads with planning knives. As lumber is transported through a planer, the planing knives remove a small amount of wood on each planed surface. This provides a smooth surface, and it reduces variation in thickness and width.

Lumber Grading, Properties, and Uses

Lumber is then graded to separate lumber according to the level of quality needed for its intended use. Softwood structural lumber (lumber used for framing buildings) is usually graded based upon visual defects that detract from strength, stiffness, and utility. Structural lumber is graded on both faces for the presence of knots, excess wane, warp (deviation from straight), and other defects. It may also be machine stress-rated by passing each piece of lumber through a machine that bends the lumber flat-wise and measures resistance to bending. Almost all species of softwood trees are manufactured into structural lumber. However, where high strength and stiffness are needed, such as in roof trusses, those softwood species with high density (e.g., Douglas-fir: *Pseudotsuga menziesii*) are often preferred. Dry-dressed softwood structural lumber is typically 38–100 mm thick and 100–300 mm wide. Structural lumber thicker than 125 mm is often defined as timbers. Structural lumber and timbers often range in length from 2.4 to 6.1 m. However, longer lengths are sometimes produced.

Appearance-grade lumber (lumber used for trim and other nonstructural applications in building construction) is usually graded for appearance of the best face and for utility. Appearance lumber is graded on the best face, because often the best face is the only face that will be seen when the lumber is in service. This type of lumber may be painted or finished with a transparent material. Some defects that reduce the grade of appearance lumber are knots, stain, streaks, warp, and other defects. Since high strength is not required, low-density softwood species (e.g., Ponderosa pine (*Pinus ponderosa*) and spruce (*Picea* sp.)) are often preferred for appearance lumber. Dry-dressed appearance-grade lumber is often 19 mm thick and 100–300 mm wide. Lengths often range from 2.4 to 6.1 m.

Factory and shop lumber (lumber used for furniture and millwork) is graded based upon the proportion and size of clear area on the worst face of the lumber. This lumber is often sold to furniture or millwork plants where it will be sawn into parts for furniture, windows, doors, and other applications. Many species of hardwood logs are sawn into factory lumber for furniture production. However, the most popular species groups are white oak and red oak (*Quercus* spp.). Furniture manufacturers often prefer lumber produced from species with high strength and stiffness, attractive appearance, and good machining properties. Lower grades of hardwood factory lumber are sometimes used to manufacture pallets. Pallets are support structures used to ship numerous manufactured products. Rough (undressed)-dry hardwood factory lumber often ranges from 25 to 50 mm thick and may be almost any width 100 mm or greater. Lengths are usually from 2.4 to 4.9 m.

Softwood shop lumber is often used to manufacture furniture or millwork for wood doors and windows. As with hardwood factory lumber, softwood furniture and millwork lumber are often sawn into clear parts. Therefore, the size and proportion of clear-lumber area are important to the grade. Softwood furniture and millwork producers often prefer species with low density and good machining properties (e.g., Ponderosa pine and radiata pine (*Pinus radiata*)). Dry-dressed softwood shop lumber is usually 19 or 29 mm thick and 100–300 mm wide. Lengths often range from 2.4 to 6.1 m.

All types of lumber are graded by experienced sawmill employees who follow grade standards established by grade agencies. These grade standards specify the size, spacing, and/or volume of defects for each size and grade of lumber. Softwood structural lumber and softwood appearance lumber are stamped showing the grade, moisture content, supervising grade agency, and sawmill number. Supervising grade agencies provide training to sawmill graders, and inspect random packages of lumber for conformance to grade standards. They may also settle grade disputes between the sawmill and lumber customers. Hardwood factory lumber and softwood shop lumber usually do not carry a grade stamp. Rather, whole packages of lumber containing the same grade, species, and size are packaged and sold to experienced manufacturers of furniture, millwork, windows, doors, and other products.

Following grading, lumber is packaged and shipped to customers via truck, rail, barge, or ship. If lumber is to be transported over long distances and there is a chance that dry-lumber packages will encounter rain, the packages may be wrapped with a water-resistant covering. In other cases, packages are simply banded with steel bands and shipped without a covering.

See also: **Solid Wood Processing**: Drying; Machining; Protection of Wood against Biodeterioration. **Solid Wood Products**: Construction; Logs, Poles, Piles, Sleepers (Crossties); Structural Use of Wood. **Wood Formation and Properties**: Biological Deterioration of Wood; Formation and Structure of Wood.

Further Reading

Haygreen JG and Bowyer JL (1996) Lumber. In: *Forest Products and Wood Science*, 3rd edn, pp. 303–330. Ames, IA: Iowa State University Press.

Simpson WT (1991) *Dry Kiln Operators Manual*. Madison, WI: Forest Products Society.

Steele PH (1984) *Factors Determining Lumber Recovery in Sawmilling*. Madison, WI: USDA Forest Products Laboratory.

Williston EM (1981) *Small Log Sawmills: Profitable Product Selection, Process Design and Operation*. San Francisco, CA: Miller Freeman.

Williston EM (1988) *Lumber Manufacturing: The Design and Operation of Sawmills and Planer Mills*. San Francisco, CA: Miller Freeman.

Construction; Logs, Poles, Piles, Sleepers (Crossties)

J A Youngquist, Verona, WI, USA
R Youngs, Virginia Polytechnic Institute and State University, Blacksburg, VA, USA

Published by Elsevier Ltd., 2004

Introduction

The material in this article is adapted from the Forest Products Laboratory *Wood Handbook*, which is especially concerned with use of wood as an engineering material in the USA. However, the use of wood in log or timber form is common worldwide and the same principles apply. Such applications were among the first uses of wood by primitive people, because the material was available and could be used without further processing, except to cut to size. It was used to make homes, buildings of many types, and fortifications, as well as weapons and means of transport. The concepts developed through experience were carried on and improved over thousands of years, appearing today in homes, barns, bridges, and other structures of many kinds. Use of timber as sleepers (crossties) made possible the development of railroads in many parts of the world and continues as a major element in transportation systems. Poles for electric power transmission lines have developed with the industry and provide essential structures as electricity is generated and distributed to the far corners of the world.

Wood in the form of timbers and poles for construction has been an essential element in the development of civilization and continues in that role today.

Material Requirements

Round timber and tie material requirements vary with intended use. Most uses involve exposure to harsh environments. Thus, in addition to availability, form, and weight, durability is an important consideration for the use of round timbers and ties. Availability reflects the economic feasibility of procuring members of the required size and grade. Form or physical appearance refers to visual characteristics, such as straightness and occurrence of knots and spiral grain. Weight affects shipping and handling costs and is a function of volume, moisture content, and wood density. Durability is directly related to expected service life and is a function of treatability and natural decay resistance. Finally, regardless of the application, any structural member must be strong enough to resist imposed loads with a reasonable factor of safety. Material specifications available for most applications of round timbers and ties contain guidelines for evaluating these factors.

Availability

Material evaluation begins with an assessment of availability. For some applications, local species of timber may be readily available in an acceptable form and quality. However, this is not normally the case. Pole producers and tie mills are scattered throughout heavily forested regions. Their products are shipped to users throughout North America.

Most structural applications of poles require timbers that are relatively straight and free of large knots. Poles used to support electric utility distribution and transmission lines (**Figure 1**) range in length from 6 to 38 m (20–125 ft) and from 0.13 to 0.76 m (5–30 in.) in diameter, 1.8 m (6 ft) from the butt. Poles used to support local area distribution lines are normally <15 m (<50 ft) long and are predominantly southern pine.

Hardwood species can be used for poles when the trees are of suitable size and form; their use is limited, however, by their weight, by their excessive checking, and because of the lack of experience in preservative treatment of hardwoods. Thus, most poles are softwoods.

The southern pine lumber group (principally loblolly (*Pinus taeda*), longleaf (*P. palustris*), shortleaf (*P. echinata*), and slash (*P. elliottii*)) accounts for roughly 80% of poles treated in the USA. Three traits of these pines account for their extensive use: (1) thick and easily treated sapwood; (2) favorable strength properties and form; and (3) availability in popular pole sizes. In longer lengths, southern pine poles are in limited supply, so Douglas fir, and to

Figure 1 Round timber poles form the major structural element in these transmission structures. Courtesy of Koppers Co.

some extent western red cedar, Ponderosa pine, and western larch, are used to meet requirements for 15-m (50-ft) and longer transmission poles.

Douglas-fir (*Pseudotsuga menziesii*) is used throughout the USA for transmission poles and is used in the Pacific Coast region for distribution and building poles. Because the heartwood of Douglas fir is resistant to preservative penetration and has limited decay and termite resistance, serviceable poles need a well-treated shell of sapwood that is free of checking. To minimize checking after treatment, poles should be adequately seasoned or conditioned before treatment. With these precautions, the poles should compare favorably with treated southern pine poles in serviceability.

A small percentage of the poles treated in the USA are of western redcedar (*Thuja plicata*), mostly produced in British Columbia. The number of poles of this species used without treatment is not known but is considered to be small. Used primarily for utility lines in the northern and western USA, well-treated redcedar poles have a service life that compares favorably with poles made from other species and could be used effectively in pole-type buildings.

Lodgepole pine (*Pinus contorta*) is also used in small quantities for treated poles. This species is used for both utility lines and for pole-type buildings. It has a good service record when well treated. Special attention is necessary, however, to obtain poles with sufficient sapwood thickness to ensure adequate penetration of preservative, because the heartwood is not usually penetrated and is not decay-resistant. The poles must also be well seasoned prior to treatment to avoid checking and exposure of unpenetrated heartwood to attack by decay fungi.

Western larch (*Larix occidentalis*) poles produced in Montana and Idaho came into use after World War II because of their favorable size, shape, and strength properties. Western larch requires full-length preservative treatment for use in most areas and, as in the case of lodgepole pine poles, must be selected for adequate sapwood thickness and must be well seasoned prior to treatment. Other species occasionally used for poles are listed in the American National Standards Institute (ANSI) O5.1 standard. These minor species make up a very small portion of pole production and are used locally.

Glued-laminated, or glulam, poles are also available for use where special sizes or shapes are required. The ANSI standard O5.2 provides guidelines for specifying these poles.

Material available for timber piles is more restricted than that for poles. Most timber piles used in the eastern half of the USA are southern pine, while those used in western USA are coast Douglas fir. Oak, red pine, and cedar piles are also referenced in timber pile literature but are not as widely used as southern pine and Douglas fir.

Round timbers have been used in a variety of structures, including bridges, log cabins, and pole buildings. Log stringer bridges (**Figure 2**) are gene-rally designed for a limited life on logging roads intended to provide access to remote areas. In Alaska, where logs may exceed 1 m (3 ft) in diameter, bridge spans may exceed 9 m (30 ft). Building poles, on the other hand, are preservative-treated logs in the 0.15–0.25-m (6–10-in.) diameter range. These poles rarely exceed 9 m (30 ft) in length. Although poles sold for this application are predominantly southern pine, there is potential for competition from local species in this category. Finally, log cabin logs normally range from 0.2 to 0.25 m (8–10 in.) in diameter, and the availability of logs in this size range is not often a problem. However, because logs are not normally preservative-treated for this application, those species that offer moderate to high natural decay resistance, such as western red cedar, are preferred. Pole buildings, which incorporate round timbers as vertical columns and cantilever supports, require preservative-treated wood. Preservative-treated poles for this use may not be readily available.

The most important availability consideration for railroad crossties is quantity. Ties are produced from most native species of timber that yield log lengths > 2.4 m (8 ft) with diameters > 0.18 m (7 in.). The American Railway Engineering Association (AREA) lists 26 US species that may be used for ties. Thus, the tie market provides a use for many low-grade hardwood and softwood logs.

Form

Natural growth properties of trees play an important role in their use as structural round timbers. Three important form considerations are cross-sectional dimensions, straightness, and the presence of surface characteristics such as knots.

Standards for poles and piles have been written with the assumption that trees have a round cross-section with a circumference that decreases linearly with height. Thus, the shape of a pole or pile is often assumed to be that of the frustum of a cone. Actual measurements of tree shape indicate that taper is rarely linear and often varies with location along the height of the tree. Guidelines to account for the effect of taper on the location of the critical section above the groundline are given in ANSI O5.1. The standard also tabulates pole dimensions for up to 15 size classes of 11 major pole species.

Taper also affects construction detailing of pole buildings. Where siding or other exterior covering is applied, poles are generally set with the taper to the interior side of the structures to provide a vertical exterior surface (**Figure 3**).

Another common practice is to modify round poles by slabbing to provide a continuous flat face. The

Figure 2 Logs are used to construct logging bridges in remote forest areas.

Figure 3 Poles provide economical foundation and wall systems for agricultural and storage buildings.

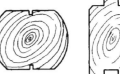

Figure 4 Construction logs can be formed in a variety of shapes for log homes. Vertical surfaces may be varied for aesthetic purposes, while the horizontal surfaces generally reflect structural and thermal considerations.

slabbed face permits more secure attachment of sheathing and framing members and facilitates the alignment and setting of intermediate wall and corner poles. The slabbing consists of a minimum cut to provide a single continuous flat face from the groundline to the top of intermediate wall poles and two continuous flat faces at right angles to one another from the groundline to the top of corner poles. However, preservative penetration is generally limited to the sapwood of most species; therefore slabbing, particularly in the groundline area of poles with thin sapwood, may result in somewhat less protection than that of an unslabbed pole. All cutting and sawing should be confined to that portion of the pole above the groundline and should be performed before treatment.

The American Society for Testing and Materials (ASTM) D25 standard provides tables of pile sizes for either friction piles or end-bearing piles. Friction piles rely on skin friction rather than tip area for support, whereas end-bearing piles resist compressive force at the tip. For this reason, a friction pile is specified by butt circumference and may have a smaller tip than an end-bearing pile. Conversely, end-bearing piles are specified by tip area and butt circumference is minimized.

Straightness of poles or piles is determined by two form properties: sweep and crook. Sweep is a measure of bow or gradual deviation from a straight line joining the ends of the pole or pile. Crook is an abrupt change in direction of the centroidal axis. Limits on these two properties are specified in both ANSI O5.1 and ASTM D25.

Logs used in construction are generally specified to meet the same criteria for straightness and knots as

poles and piles (ASTM D25). For log stringer bridges, the log selection criteria may vary with the experience of the person doing the selection but straightness, spiral grain, wind shake, and knots are limiting criteria. Although no consensus standard is available for specifying and designing log stringers, the *Design Guide for Native Log Stringer Bridges* was prepared by the US Department of Agriculture Forest Service.

Logs used for log cabins come in a wide variety of cross-sectional shapes (**Figure 4**). Commercial cabin logs are usually milled so that their shape is uniform along their length. The ASTM D3957 standard, a guide for establishing stress grades for building logs, recommends stress grading on the basis of the largest rectangular section that can be inscribed totally within the log section. The standard also provides commentary on the effects of knots and slope of grain.

Railroad ties are commonly shaped to a fairly uniform section along their length. The AREA publishes specifications for the sizes, which include seven size classes ranging from 0.13×0.13 m (5×5 in.) to 0.18×0.25 m (7×10 in.). These tie classes may be ordered in any of three standard lengths: 2.4 m (8 ft), 2.6 m (8.5 ft), or 2.7 m (9 ft).

Tables for round timber volume are given in the American Wood Preservers Association (AWPA) standard F3. The volume of a round timber differs little whether it is green or dry. Drying of round timbers causes checks to open, but there is little reduction of the gross diameter of the pole.

Wood density also differs with species, age, and growing conditions. It will even vary along the height of a single tree. Average values, tabulated by species, are normally expressed as specific gravity (SG), which is density expressed as a ratio of the density of water (*see* **Wood Formation and Properties: Physical Properties of Wood**). For commercial species grown in the USA, SG varies from 0.32 to 0.65. If you know the green volume of a round timber and its SG, its dry weight is a product of its SG, its volume, and the unit weight of water (1000 kg m^{-3} (62.4 lb ft^{-3})). Wood moisture content can also be highly variable. A pole cut in the spring when sap is flowing may have a moisture content (MC) exceeding 100% (the weight of the water it contains may exceed the weight of the dry wood substance). If you know the MC of the timber, multiply the dry weight by $(1 + MC/100)$ to get the wet weight.

Finally, in estimating the weight of a treated wood product such as a pole, pile, or tie, you must take into account the weight of the preservative. By knowing the volume, the preservative weight can be approximated by multiplying volume by the recommended preservative retention.

Durability

For most applications of round timbers and ties, durability is primarily a question of decay resistance. Some species are noted for their natural decay resistance; however, even these may require preservative treatment, depending upon the environmental conditions under which the material is used and the required service life. For some applications, natural decay resistance is sufficient. This is the case for temporary piles, marine piles in fresh water entirely below the permanent water level, and construction logs used in building construction. Any wood members used in ground contact should be pressure-treated, and the first two or three logs above a concrete foundation should be brush-treated with a preservative-sealer.

Federal Specification TT-W-571 (US Federal Supply Service (USFSS)) covers the inspection and treatment requirements for various wood products, including poles, piles, and ties. This specification refers to the AWPA standards C1 and C3 for pressure treatment, C2 and C6 for treatment of ties, C8 for full-length thermal (hot and cold) treatment of western red cedar poles, C10 for full-length thermal (hot and cold) treatment of lodgepole pine poles, and C23 for pressure treatment of construction poles. The AREA specifications for crossties and switch ties also cover preservative treatment. Inspection and treatment of poles in service has been effective in prolonging the useful life of untreated poles and those with inadequate preservative penetration or retention.

Service conditions for round timbers and ties vary from mild for construction logs to severe for crossties. Construction logs used in log homes may last indefinitely if kept dry and properly protected from insects. Most railroad ties, on the other hand, are continually in ground contact and are subject to mechanical damage.

The life of poles can vary within wide limits, depending upon properties of the pole, preservative treatments, service conditions, and maintenance practices. In distribution or transmission line supports,

however, service life is often limited by obsolescence of the line rather than the physical life of the pole.

It is common to report the average life of untreated or treated poles based on observations over a period of years. These average life values are useful as a rough guide to the service life to be expected from a group of poles, but it should be kept in mind that, within a given group, 60% of the poles will have failed before reaching an age equal to the average life.

Early or premature failure of treated poles can generally be attributed to one or more of three factors: (1) poor penetration and distribution of preservative; (2) an inadequate retention of preservative; or (3) use of a substandard preservative. Properly treated poles can last 35 years or longer.

Western red cedar is one species with a naturally decay-resistant heartwood. If used without treatment, however, the average life is somewhat less than 20 years.

The expected life of a pile is also determined by treatment and use. Wood that remains completely submerged in water does not decay although bacteria may cause some degradation; therefore, decay resistance is not necessary in all piles, but it is necessary in any part of the pile that may extend above the permanent water level. When piles that support the foundations of bridges or buildings are to be cut off above the permanent water level, they should be treated to conform to recognized specifications such as Federal Specification TT-W-571 and AWPA standards C1 and C3. The untreated surfaces exposed at the cut-offs should also be given protection by thoroughly brushing the cut surface with coal-tar creosote. A coat of pitch, asphalt, or similar material may then be applied over the creosote and a protective sheet material, such as metal, roofing felt, or saturated fabric, should be fitted over the pile cut-off in accordance with AWPA standard M4. Correct application and maintenance of these materials are critical in maintaining the integrity of piles.

Piles driven into earth that is not constantly wet are subject to about the same service conditions as apply to poles but are generally required to last longer. Preservative retention requirements for piles are therefore greater than for poles. Piles used in salt water are subject to destruction by marine borers, even though they do not decay below the waterline. The most effective practical protection against marine borers has been a treatment first with a waterborne preservative, followed by seasoning with a creosote treatment. Other preservative treatments of marine piles are covered in Federal Specification TT-W-571 and AWPA standard C3.

The life of ties in service depends on their ability to resist decay and mechanical destruction. Under sufficiently light traffic, heartwood ties of naturally durable wood, even if of low strength, may give 10 or 15 years of average service without preservative treatment; under heavy traffic without adequate mechanical protection, the same ties might fail in 2 or 3 years. Advances in preservatives and treatment processes, coupled with increasing loads, are shifting the primary cause of tie failure from decay to mechanical damage. Well-treated ties, properly designed to carry intended loads, should last 25–40 years on average. Records on life of treated and untreated ties are occasionally published in the annual proceedings of AREA and AWPA.

Strength Properties

Allowable strength properties of round timbers have been developed and published in several standards. In most cases, published values are based on the strength of small clear test samples. Allowable stresses are derived by adjusting small clear values for effects of growth characteristics, conditioning, shape, and load conditions, as discussed in applicable standards. In addition, published values for some species of poles and piles reflect the results of full-sized tests.

Most poles are used as structural members in support structures for distribution and transmission lines. For this application, poles may be designed as single-member or guyed cantilevers or as structural members of a more complex structure. Specifications for wood poles used in single-pole structures have been published by ANSI in standard O5.1. Guidelines for the design of pole structures are given in the ANSI National Electric Safety Code (NESC) (ANSI C2). The ANSI O5.1 standard gives values for fiber stress in bending for species commonly used as transmission or distribution poles. These values represent the near-ultimate fiber stress for poles used as cantilever beams. For most species, these values are based partly on full-sized pole tests and include adjustments for moisture content and pretreatment conditioning. The values in ANSI O5.1 are compatible with the ultimate strength design philosophy of the NESC, but they are not compatible with the working stress design philosophy of the National Design Specification (NDS). Reliability-based design techniques have been developed for the design of distribution–transmission line systems. This approach requires a strong database on the performance of pole structures. Supporting information for these design procedures is available in a series of reports published by the Electric Power Research Institute (EPRI).

Bearing loads on piles are sustained by earth friction along their surface (skin friction), by bearing of the tip on a solid stratum, or by a combination of these two methods. Wood piles, because of their tapered form, are particularly efficient in supporting loads by skin friction. Bearing values that depend upon friction are related to the stability of the soil and generally do not approach the ultimate strength of the pile. Where wood piles sustain foundation loads by bearing of the tip on a solid stratum, loads may be limited by the compressive strength of the wood parallel to the grain. If a large proportion of the length of a pile extends above ground, its bearing value may be limited by its strength as a long column. Side loads may also be applied to piles extending above ground. In such instances, however, bracing is often used to reduce the unsupported column length or to resist the side loads. The most critical loads on piles often occur during driving. Under hard driving conditions, piles that are too dry (<18% moisture content at a 51-mm (2-in.) depth) have literally exploded under the force of the driving hammers. Steel banding is recommended to increase resistance to splitting, and driving the piles into predrilled holes reduces driving stresses. The reduction in strength of a wood column resulting from crooks, eccentric loading, or any other condition that will result in combined bending and compression is not as great as would be predicted with the NDS interaction equations. This does not imply that crooks and eccentricity should be without restriction, but it should relieve anxiety as to the influence of crooks, such as those found in piles. There are several ways to determine the bearing capacity of piles. Engineering formulae can estimate bearing values from the penetration under blows of known energy from the driving hammer. Some engineers prefer to estimate bearing capacity from experience or observation of the behavior of pile foundations under similar conditions or from the results of static-load tests. Working stresses for piles are governed by building code requirements and by recommendations of ASTM D2899. This standard gives recommendations for adjusting small clear strength values listed in ASTM D2555 for use in the design of full-sized piles. In addition to adjustments for properties inherent to the full-sized pile, the ASTM D2899 standard also provides recommendations for adjusting allowable stresses for the effects of pretreatment conditioning. Design stresses for timber piles are tabulated in the NDS for wood construction. The NDS values include adjustments for the effects of moisture content, load duration, and preservative treatment. Recommendations are also given to adjust for lateral support conditions and factors of safety.

Design values for round timbers used as structural members in pole or log buildings may be determined following standards published by ASTM and the American Society of Agricultural Engineers (ASAE). The ASTM standard refers pole designers to the same standard used to derive design stresses for timber piles (D2899). The ASAE standard (EP388), which governed the derivation of construction poles for agricultural building applications, is being revised. The future revision will be designated EP560 and will only deal with round wood poles. Derivation of design stresses for construction logs used in log homes is covered in ASTM D3957, which provides a method of establishing stress grades for structural members of any of the more common log configurations. Manufacturers can use this standard to develop grading specifications and derive engineering design stresses for their construction logs.

Railroad cross and switch ties have historically been overdesigned from the standpoint of rail loads. Tie service life was largely limited by deterioration rather than mechanical damage. However, because of advances in decay-inhibiting treatment and increased axle loads, adequate structural design is becoming more important in increasing railroad tie service life. Rail loads induce stresses in bending and shear as well as in compression perpendicular to the grain in railroad ties. The AREA manual gives recommended limits on ballast bearing pressure and allowable stresses for crossties. This information may be used by the designer to determine adequate tie size and spacing to avoid premature failure due to mechanical damage. SG and compressive strength parallel to the grain are also important properties to consider in evaluating crosstie material. These properties indicate the resistance of the wood to both pull-out and lateral thrust of spikes.

See also: **Solid Wood Products**: Lumber Production, Properties and Uses. **Wood Formation and Properties**: Formation and Structure of Wood; Physical Properties of Wood.

Further Reading

ANSI (current edition). ANSI O5.1. *Specifications and Dimensions for Wood Poles*. ANSI C2. *National Electrical Safety Code*. ANSI O5.2. *Structural Glued Laminated Timber for Utility Structures*. New York, NY: American National Standards Institute.

AREA (1982) Ties and wood preservation. In: *Manual for Railway Engineering*. Washington, DC: American Railway Engineering Association.

AREA (1982) Timber structures. In: *Manual for Railway Engineering*. Washington, DC: American Railway Engineering Association.

Armstrong RM (1979) Structural properties of timber piles. In: *Behavior of Deep Foundations*, pp. 118–152.

ASTM STP670. Philadelphia, PA: American Society for Testing and Materials.

ASTM (current edition) *Standard Test Methods for Establishing Clear Wood Strength Values*. ASTM D2555. West Conshohocken, PA: American Society for Testing and Materials.

ASTM (current edition) ASTM D3200. *Standard Specification and Methods for Establishing Recommended Design Stresses for Round Timber Construction Poles*. ANSI/ASTM D1036-58. *Standard Methods of Static Tests of Wood Poles*. West Conshohocken, PA: American Society for Testing and Materials.

ASTM (current edition) ASTM D25. *Standard Specification for Round Timber Piles*. ASTM D2899. *Establishing Design Stresses for Round Timber Piles*. West Conshohocken, PA: American Society for Testing and Materials.

ASTM (current edition) *Standard Methods for Establishing Stress Grades for Structural Members Used in Log Buildings*. ASTM D3957. West Conshohocken, PA: American Society for Testing and Materials.

AWPA (current edition) *Book of Standards*. (American Wood-Preserver's Bureau official quality control standards.) Bethesda, MD: American Wood-Preservers' Association.

AWPI (1969) *Pile Foundations Know-How*. Washington, DC: American Wood Preservers Institute.

Carson JM and Dougherty M (eds) (1997) *Post-Frame Building Handbook: Materials, Design Considerations, Construction Procedures*. Ithaca, NY: Northeast Regional Agricultural Engineering Service.

Engineering Data Management and Colorado State University (1989–1998) *International Conference – Wood Poles and Piles*. Conference proceedings. Fort Collins, CO: Engineering Data Management and Colorado State University.

EPRI (1981) *Probability-Based Design of Wood Transmission Structures*, vols. 1–3. Palo Alto, CA: Electric Power Research Institute.

EPRI (1985) *Wood Pole Properties, vol. 1, Background and Southern Pine Data*. Palo Alto, CA: Electric Power Research Institute.

EPRI (1986) *Wood Pole Properties, vol. 2: Douglas Fir Data. vol. 3: Western Redcedar*. Palo Alto, CA: Electric Power Research Institute.

Forest Products Laboratory (1999) *Wood Handbook – Wood as an Engineering Material*. General Technical Report FPL-GTR-113. Madison, WI: US Department of Agriculture, Forest Service, Forest Products Laboratory.

Morrell JJ (1996) *Wood Pole Maintenance Manual*. Corvallis, OR: College of Forestry, Forest Research Laboratory, Oregon State University.

Muchmore FW (1977) *Design Guide for Native Log Stringer Bridges*. Juneau, AK: US Department of Agriculture, Forest Service, Region 10.

NFPA (current edition) *National Design Specification for Wood Construction*. Washington, DC: National Forest Products Association.

NRAES (1997) *Post-Frame Building Construction*. Ithaca, NY: Northeast Regional Agricultural Engineering Service.

USFSS (current edition) *Poles and Piles, Wood*. Federal specification MM-P-371c-ties, railroad (cross and switch); Federal Specification MM-T-371d-wood preservation: treating practice; Federal Specification TT-W-571. Washington, DC: US Federal Supply Service.

Wood-based Composites and Panel Products

F A Kamke, Virginia Polytechnic Institute and State University, Blacksburg, VA, USA

Introduction

Wood-based composites consist of wood elements, such as veneer, fibers, particles, or strands, which are bonded together to collectively perform some function. These wood elements may be bonded with natural adhesives (such as starch or protein from plant or animal sources) or synthetic adhesives (usually derived from petroleum). The classification of wood-based composites is inexact, but may be grouped as panels or composite lumber. The panels may be further divided into veneer (such as plywood) or particulate (such as particleboard) composites. Another means of categorizing the wood-based composites is by function, i.e., structural (building components) and nonstructural (furniture and cabinet applications). Examples of commercially available wood-based

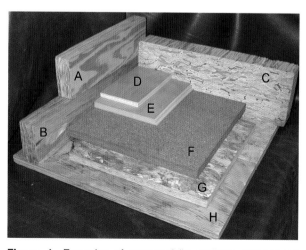

Figure 1 Examples of commercially available wood-based composites. (A) Laminated veneer lumber (LVL); (B) laminated strand lumber (LSL); (C) parallel strand lumber (PSL); (D) nonstructural plywood; (E) medium density fiberboard (MDF); (F) particleboard; (G) oriented strand board (OSB); (H) structural plywood.

composites are shown in **Figure 1**. While endless combinations of wood elements, and indeed wood and other materials, could be used to produce a vast array of products, this article will focus on the major wood-based composites produced commercially.

History

The event of the first composite produced from wood is probably unknown. The simple act of adhesively bonding together two or more pieces of wood is a composite manufacturing process. Paper is a composite of wood fibers, which utilizes the natural lignocellulosic compounds present in wood to bond the fibers. The Chinese, during the early second century, are believed to have produced the first paper from wood pulp. The ancient Egyptians, prior to 1400 BC, developed the art of bonding wood veneers for decorative articles. A type of wood fiberboard was patented in the USA by Lyman in 1858. This was followed by a high-density version of fiberboard, known today as hardboard, which was called Masonite by its inventor William Mason in 1924. Structural plywood was introduced to the USA in 1905 by the Portland Manufacturing Company in Oregon. Particleboard had its origin in Germany, with early references to Ernst Hubbard in 1887. The first commercial manufacturing facility for particleboard is thought to be one opened in Bremen, Germany in 1941. The growth of the modern wood-based composites industry was made possible with the development of synthetic adhesives during the 1930s. Thermosetting adhesives, such as urea-formaldehyde and phenol-formaldehyde, greatly accelerated the manufacturing process, improved performance, and reduced costs. The latter part of the twentieth century saw the development of structural lumber composites, including laminated veneer lumber, parallel strand lumber, and laminated strand lumber.

Manufacture of wood-based composites is now a worldwide industry. **Table 1** shows the world production of wood composite panels and laminated veneer lumber in 2001. Production has increased each year since the introduction of these products. Structural plywood, oriented strand board, and structural lumber composites are primarily North American products, due to preference for wood for building construction in this region. Europe and Japan are minor but growing producers and consumers of these products. The nonstructural panels are produced throughout the world, and find many applications in furniture, cabinets, and some building construction.

Table 1 World production of wood-based panels and laminated veneer lumber in 2001

Product	Production (1000 m³)
Fiberboard	33,277
Particleboard	60,723
Oriented strand board (OSB)	21,678
Plywood (structural and nonstructural)	55,528
Laminated veneer lumber (LVL)[a]	2,062

[a] Estimated from 2001 North American data and 1999 Europe and Asia data.
Data from FAO (2002) *Forest Products Statistics.* Timber Bulletin no. ECE/TIM/BULL/55/2. Rome: Food and Agricultural Organization. Available online at http://www.fao.org/. UNECE (2002) *Forest Products Annual Market Review 2001–2002.* Timber Bulletin LV ECE/TIM/BULL/2002/3. Rome: Food and Agricultural Organization. Available online at http://www.unece.org/trade/timber/.

Figure 2 Structural wood-based composites used in building construction; OSB floor sheathing, LSL rimboard, I-beams with LVL as flange stock and plywood webs, and LVL floor girder. Photograph courtesy of APA – Engineered Wood Association.

Products and Applications

Panels: Structural Plywood

Structural plywood is produced primarily from softwood species, although some hardwoods are also used. In North America the most commonly used species are southern pine (*Pinus* spp.) and Douglas-fir (*Pseudotsuga menziesii*). These species provide the proper combination of strength, stiffness, and ease of handling. The 2–5-mm thick veneer is produced by peeling logs on a rotary lathe. The veneers are arranged in layers, with the grain perpendicular in adjacent layers, and bonded together using a water-proof adhesive (usually phenol-formaldehyde). The veneer is visually graded, and sometimes machine graded, to eliminate severe defects. The highest-quality veneer is reserved for the highest-quality plywood. Lower-quality veneer can often be used as core plies, or on the backside of the panel.

Structural plywood is used principally in building construction as structural sheathing in floor, wall, and roof systems. Structural plywood has many other uses where strength, stiffness, and dimensional stability are important, such as furniture and cabinet frames, pallet bins, exterior siding, web stock for I-beams (**Figure 2**), and concrete forms. Structural plywood is manufactured in 1.2 × 2.4 m dimensions. The common thickness range is from 7 to 30 mm depending on the application.

Panels: Nonstructural Plywood

Nonstructural plywood, also called decorative plywood, is produced primarily from hardwood species, although many softwood species are used. In North America, oak (*Quercus* spp.), birch (*Betula* spp.), maple (*Acer* spp.), cherry (*Prunus* spp.), white pine (*Pinus strobus*), and lauan (*Shorea* spp.) are common species used for nonstructural plywood. The face veneer is the highest quality, since its function is decorative. Face veneers are often very thin, generally 0.8 mm and thinner, to provide the most efficient use of the best-quality wood. The back veneer is usually lower quality, although some grades require a good appearance on two sides. The core of nonstructural plywood may be comprised of lower-quality veneer or some other substrate, such as fiberboard, particleboard, or lumber.

Nonstructural plywood has numerous uses in consumer products, where appearance and dimensional stability, and some structural performance is required. Typical uses are furniture, cabinets, store fixtures, decorative paneling, and architectural woodwork. Since the adhesive that is used to manufacture nonstructural plywood is usually urea-formaldehyde, with a low water resistance, these products are limited to interior applications where the potential for moisture exposure is low.

Panels: Particleboard

Particleboard is comprised of wood elements bonded together with an adhesive under heat and pressure. The particles may be generated in a variety of ways starting with logs (rare) or wood residue (typical) from some other wood manufacturing operation. Mechanical devices break down the wood into particles. A clear classification of particleboard is not possible, as modern particleboard manufacturing processes sometimes employ pressure-refined wood fibers in the surface layers. A similar product made from 100% pressure-refined wood fibers is called fiberboard. Virtually any wood species could be used for particleboard, although softwoods and lower-density hardwoods are preferred. Lower-density wood allows for the production of lower-density particleboard without sacrificing strength and stiffness. The most common adhesive used in the manufacture of particleboard is urea-formaldehyde, although some melamine-formaldehyde is sometimes added to improve water resistance. Particleboard is intended for interior applications.

Particleboard is available in a wide variety of dimensions, limited only by the hot-press used in its manufacture. Thickness typically ranges from 12 to 38 mm. The panels are made up to 3.6 m in width and up to 18 m in length. Applications include core stock for furniture and cabinet panels, doors, counter tops, and floor underlayment.

Panels: Fiberboard

Fiberboard may be further classified into insulation board, medium density fiberboard (MDF), and hardboard. The primary difference between these panel types is density and the end-use application. All of these panels are produced from pressure-refined wood fibers. The fibers are individual wood cells or small bundles of cells. Both hardwood and softwood species may be used. Insulation board is a low-density product, less than 30 lb ft^3 (480 kg m^{-3}), with very little structural integrity. Its density is less than the density of the wood from which it was produced. MDF is similar to particleboard in its manufacture and end-used applications. MDF offers advantage over particleboard with smoother surfaces, void-free edges, and lower density. Hardboard is a high-density product, over 50 lb ft^3 (800 kg m^{-3}). Some hardboard is produced without adhesive, relying instead on lignocellulosic bonding imposed by extreme heat and pressure in the hot-press. Hardboard is typically produced in thickness ranging from 2.5 to 3.2 mm. Individual panels are sometimes bonded together to produce thicker panels. Synthetic or bio-based adhesives are often added to hardboard to improve properties, particularly water resistance.

Insulation board is used for nonstructural wall sheathing where thermal insulation is required. This product has been largely displaced by rigid, synthetic-foam panels. Insulation board is also used for accoustic tiles. MDF is used extensively as core stock in furniture and cabinet panels. It is also used for overlayed and powder-coated millwork. Hardboard is used for exterior siding, cabinets for electrical appliances, flooring, and overlayed decorative paneling.

Panels: Oriented Strand Board

Oriented strand board (OSB) is a structural panel designed for building construction. It is composed of slender wood strands, with the strand length parallel to the grain of the wood. The stranding process requires logs. Many wood species are used. Softwoods, such as the pines, and low-density hardwoods, such as aspen (*Populus* spp.), gum (*Nyssa* spp.), and yellow-poplar (*Liriodendron tulipifera*), are preferred. The strands are oriented and arranged into three layers in the panel. The two outer layers are parallel, and the core layer is either perpendicular to the face layers or not oriented. This cross-lamination concept is similar to plywood. Strength and stiffness is greater in the dimension parallel to the face layer, and the panel has good dimensional stability, with respect to moisture content changes, in both flat-wise directions. Thickness swell has been a problem with some OSB panels. A waterproof adhesive, either phenol-formaldehyde or polymeric methylene diphenyl diisocyanate (pMDI), is used to bond the strands together.

OSB was developed as a direct replacement for the more expensive structural plywood. It is used as structural sheathing for walls, roofs, and floors (**Figure 2**). OSB is also used as web stock in wood composite I-beams, shelving, pallets, and packaging. OSB is manufactured in thickness ranging from 6 to 28 mm. The panels are sold in 1.2 × 2.4 m dimensions, although the panels are produced in dimensions up to 3.6 × 18 m.

Structural Composite Lumber: Laminated Veneer Lumber

Laminated veneer lumber (LVL) is produced from veneer and intended for structural framing, where high strength and stiffness are required. Softwoods, such as Douglas-fir and southern pines, are typically used. Some hardwoods are also acceptable. As it is a structural product, only high-quality veneer with high strength and stiffness is acceptable. Unlike plywood, all of the veneer in an LVL billet is aligned in one direction to maximize strength and stiffness in that direction. An advantage of LVL over solid sawn lumber is the dispersion of defects, such as knots and pitch pockets, which greatly reduces the variability of the product. LVL is also more dimensionally stable than solid sawn lumber and it may be produced in large dimensions from small logs.

LVL is used for structural beams (**Figure 2**) and headers in building construction, as well as scaffold planks. Most of today's production is used as flange stock in wood composite I-beams (**Figure 2**). Some LVL is produced specifically for furniture and architectural woodwork, for which some hardwood species are used. LVL is produced in dimensions ranging from 38 to 90 mm thick, up to 1.2 m wide, and 24 m long. The billets are sawn into standard sizes that are compatible with dimension lumber.

Structural Composite Lumber: Parallel Strand Lumber

Parallel strand lumber (PSL) is produced from narrow veneer strips. Currently Douglas-fir, western hemlock (*Tsuga heterophylla*), southern pine, and yellow-poplar are the wood species used for PSL. The process permits veneer with many defects, as these defects will be eliminated or dispersed when the veneer is clipped into the narrow strips. A phenol-formaldehyde adhesive is used to provide excellent water resistance. The mechanical properties are similar to LVL. PSL is produced in large dimensions as a substitute for solid wood timbers.

PSL is intended for structural applications, including beams, columns, and headers. PSL is preferred over LVL for applications that require a large cross-section. When finished properly, PSL has a decorative appearance suitable for exposed timberframe construction.

Structural Composite Lumber: Laminated Strand Lumber

Laminated strand lumber (LSL) is a variation of OSB technology. LSL is produced from long wood strands. The strands are similar to OSB strands in width and thickness, but they are longer. Unlike OSB, all of the strands are oriented in the same direction. This high degree of orientation and long strands produces a structural lumber product with high strength and stiffness. Currently, aspen and yellow-poplar are used to produce LSL, but other low-density species could be used. Unlike OSB, LSL has a uniform density, which better simulates solid wood performance.

LSL is a structural product. It is used for truss cords, rim board in floor systems (**Figure 2**), headers, and columns. Because of its uniform density and good dimensional stability, LSL is also used for furniture and millwork.

Manufacturing Practices

Structural Plywood

All structural plywood is produced from rotary-peeled veneer. The peeler logs are debarked and cut to nominal 1.2 or 2.4 m long peeler blocks. The blocks are conditioned to soften the wood prior to peeling. This is done by soaking the blocks in hot water or spraying them with steam. The blocks are then electronically scanned and positioned in the rotary lathe. Scanning is a rapid and accurate means of maximizing the yield of the highest-quality veneer. The lathe rotates the block against a knife to peel veneer into a continuous sheet, much like paper pulled off a roll (**Figure 3**). The peeling speed is up to $240 \, \text{m} \, \text{min}^{-1}$. At the end of peeling, the remaining core, typically 50–100 mm in diameter, is ejected by the lathe operator and saved for other uses.

The continuous sheet of veneer, still wet, is again electronically scanned for defects and then automatically clipped into nominal $1.2 \times 2.4 \, \text{m}$ sheets, half sheets, or random widths. The veneer is visually

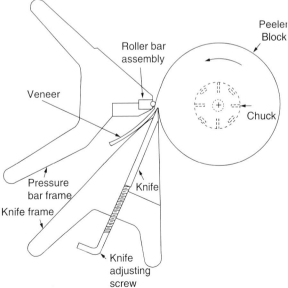

Figure 3 Rotary lathe used to produce veneer for structural plywood and laminated veneer lumber. Detail of peeling veneer from block shown at right. Photograph courtesy of COE Manufacturing.

graded and sorted. All veneer must be dried to the desired moisture content. The target moisture content depends on the adhesive system to be used, but typically is in the range of 5–10%. Electronic moisture detectors are used to identify wet or overdried veneer when it exits the dryer.

State-of-the-art plywood mills assemble full sheets of veneer from the half sheets and random width pieces. A thermoplastic 'string' is used to hold the sheets together loosely so that they may be handled by automated equipment. Adhesive is then applied to the dry veneer in precise amounts at the panel layup station. Roll coaters, curtain coaters, or extrusion coaters are used to apply the adhesive to the veneer. Adjacent veneer layers are arranged with the grain perpendicular to one another. The best grade of veneer is used for the face ply, a lower grade for the back ply, and the lowest grade for the core plies. The selection of the veneer grade depends on the desired finished plywood grade. The adhesive is almost always a phenol-formaldehyde formulation, which has a dark red–brown color. This adhesive has very good moisture resistance. Extenders and fillers are added to the resin to control flow and penetration characteristics. Many plywood mills still employ manual labor to assemble the panels at the layup station.

Prior to hot-pressing, the panels are cold-pressed to flatten the veneer and transfer the adhesive from one side of the bondline to the other. The panels are then loaded into a multi-opening heated press. A typical plywood press may process 20–50 panels simultaneously, with one panel per opening. Hot-press conditions are typically 100–200 psi (690–1380 kPa) pressure at 150°C. The time in the press depends on the thickness of the panel. Thicker panels require more time.

After the panels are removed from the hot-press, they are trimmed to the final dimensions, and visually graded. Some mills use ultrasonic detectors to examine each panel for hidden delaminations in the bondline. Some plywood grades are sanded. Secondary processing may include the addition of a tongue and groove on the edges, patches for aesthetic purpose, or overlays for water resistance. Quality assurance testing is routinely performed, and required, for grade stamp approval.

Nonstructural Plywood

There are many similarities between structural plywood and nonstructural plywood manufacturing processes. One major difference is the preparation of the veneer. Rotary peeled veneer is used for core stock and sometimes for face veneer. The fine face veneer is usually produced by slicing. Thin veneer,

often less than 1 mm thick, can be produced with a wide variety of grain patterns using any one of a number of slicing techniques. The log is first sawn into a flitch, which is cut to expose the desired grain pattern. Flat, quarter, or rift slicing are common flitch preparations. Prior to slicing, the flitch is conditioned to soften the wood. The flitch is then mounted on a veneer slicer, which moves the flitch in a linear, back and forth motion against a knife (**Figure 4**). With each stroke, a thin veneer, the length and width of the flitch, is removed. The carriage holding the flitch, or knife assembly, is then indexed a distance equal to the thickness of one veneer, and another veneer is cut. Each veneer is stacked in sequence as it is removed from the flitch, and remains together for further processing. This allows the veneer to be matched in panels to achieve interesting grain patterns.

The face veneer is gently dried to a moisture content of 5–10% in a forced-air dryer with restraints to keep the veneer flat. Core and back veneer may be dried more rigorously. The dry veneer is now precision clipped and edge-joined to create large sheets for further processing into plywood.

Nonstructural plywood is typically bonded with urea-formaldehyde adhesive. This is a near-colorless adhesive that produces a strong bond, but is not suitable for high humidity or water exposure. The decorative face veneer may be laid-up over core veneer, or some other substrate, such as particleboard or fiberboard. As with structural plywood, maintaining a balanced construction is important for preventing warp of the panel with subsequent moisture content changes. The remainder of the manufacturing process is similar to structural plywood processing.

Particleboard

Particleboard manufacture typically begins with some mill residue from some other wood processing

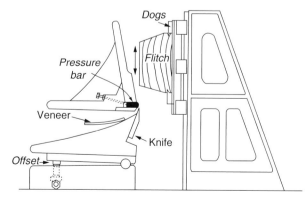

Figure 4 Veneer slicing machine used to produce high-quality face veneer for nonstructural plywood.

operation. Occasionally low-quality logs are used. Some residue, such as sawdust, is so small that no further processing is possible. Larger residue pieces are broken down into more uniform dimensions using various cutting devices, such as chippers, cutter mills, and knife-ring flakers. The desired particle geometry and size depend on the application. Higher strength and stiffness particleboard are achieved using long slender particles. Particleboard with a smooth surface can only be obtained with very small particles. Often fine particles are produced for the face layers of a multilayered particleboard, while the long slender particles are used in the core. Screens are used to separate the particles by size. Oversized particles are processed again, while undersized particles are burned for fuel.

The particles are dried in rotating drum dryers. The particles are tumbled inside the dryer to mix with heated air (200–400°C at the inlet) to achieve the desired particle moisture content, typically 3–6%. Air emissions from wood particle drying systems are a concern. Pollution abatement equipment is used to clean the air stream of particulates, volatile organic compounds, and other potentially hazardous compounds. Wet electrostatic precipitators or thermal oxidizers are commonly used to treat the exhaust air stream.

The dry particles are mixed with adhesive, usually urea-formaldehyde, in an amount of 6–10% based on dry weight. Some phenol-formaldehyde, melamine-formaldehyde, and pMDI are occasionally used. The low-cost urea-formaldehyde is preferred, and is quite suitable for particleboard applications. Wax is also added (1% or less) to impart some temporary resistance to liquid water absorption. Since the particles have a tremendous amount of surface area, and only a small amount of adhesive is added, the adhesive must be atomized and applied as tiny droplets.

The resinated particles are formed into loose mats by a device called a forming machine. Multiple layers are achieved by employing more forming machines. A uniform distribution of particles will provide a uniform density panel. The mats are formed continuously, and either pressed continuously, or the mat is cut and loaded into a multi-opening hot-press.

Continuous hot-presses are becoming more common. In a continuous press two moving metal belts are in direct contact with the mat. These belts run the full length of the press and are synchronized to move the mat slowly through the press. Mechanical pressure in the press creates intimate contact between the particles. Heat is applied to cure the thermosetting adhesive. The pressed panel may be cut to any length. In a multi-opening press the panel size is determined by the press size. Twelve to 16 press openings are typical. Current technology allows mats up to 3.7 m wide to be pressed.

After hot-pressing the raw panels are trimmed, cooled, and cut to size. Sanding is usually performed to achieve accurate thickness and to prepare the surface for bonding of overlay materials.

Fiberboard

The fiberboard manufacturing process begins with wood chips. Occasionally small mill residue may be used. The chips are washed, subjected to pressurized steam, and then fiberized in a device called a disk refiner. The disk refiner uses no knives, but rather two machined disks that rotate in opposing directions to shear the chips into fibers. The wet fibers are then pneumatically transported by steam through a blowline to the next manufacturing step.

Insulation board and wet-process hardboard employ a similar mat forming process to paper manufacture. The wet fiber is diluted to a very low consistency in water and then dispersed on a moving wire screen in a Fourdrinier machine. Water is quickly removed by vacuum suction and the fibers consolidate into a wet mat. Continuous rollers compress the mat and further remove water. Insulation board is then produced by simply drying the mat in an oven. Asphalt is added to insulation board as a binding agent prior to the forming machine. Wet-process hardboard is processed in a heated press. The mat enters the hot-press wet, thus generating a lot of steam when subjected to temperature in excess of 200°C. The mat is pressed on a wire screen to allow the steam to escape, which imparts a screen pattern on the back side of the panel. This hardboard panel is referred to as smooth-one-side (S1S). A variation in hardboard manufacture is to dry the mat prior to hot-pressing. In this case a wire screen is not needed, and the panel is smooth-two-sides (S2S). Hardboard uses little or no adhesive, relying instead on natural lignocellulosic bonding between the fibers. Consequently extreme pressure is needed in the press, resulting in a high-density panel.

Medium density fiberboard (MDF) is a more recent development. The fibers are produced as described above. Adhesive is typically added in the blowline, although separate blenders are sometimes employed. Blowline blending is a simple means of mixing adhesive with the fiber. It consists of a tube into which adhesive is injected and atomized. Turbulence inside the blowline thoroughly mixes the adhesive and fiber. The resinated fiber is then conveyed directly to a tube dryer, where drying to approximately 3–6% moisture content is achieved in a few seconds. This short drying time is not enough to cause the adhesive to cure. Mats are then formed from the dry resinated fibers, hot-pressed, and further processed in a manner similar to particleboard manufacture.

Oriented Strand Board

Oriented strand board (OSB) manufacture is a variation of particleboard manufacture. Certain process steps are modified to account for the long strands and the critical process of orientation. Wood strands are produced from debarked logs on either a disk or ring strander (**Figure 5**). Knives in these devices cut the strands to a precise thickness, width, and length (typically $0.7 \times 19 \times 100$ mm). The strands are dried in rotary dryers. Liquid phenol-formaldehyde or pMDI adhesive is added in a rotating blender using spinning disk atomizers to achieve a fine resin droplet coverage over the surface of the strands. Dry powder phenol-formaldehyde adhesive is sometimes used.

The resinated strands are formed into a three-layer mat. The strands in the face layers are oriented in the same direction, while the core strands are aligned perpendicular to the face, or randomized. Both continuous and multi-opening hot-presses are used by the industry. Secondary processing and testing is similar to that used for structural plywood manufacture.

Laminated Veneer Lumber

Laminated veneer lumber (LVL) manufacture is largely a variation on structural plywood technology. The major differences are in the lay-up of the veneer into billets and the hot-press. LVL has all of the veneer aligned in the same direction. The veneer sheets are overlapped or scarf-jointed to create continuous billets. The billet is then pressed in either a continuous hot-press, or a very long platen press is used. Since LVL is used for long structural members, the platen presses are 20–25 m in length. The pressed billet is then cut to length and ripped to the desired width.

As a critical structural component, LVL uses only the best-quality veneer. To insure adequate strength and stiffness, each sheet of veneer is nondestructively tested, then graded to its apparent modulus of elasticity. The LVL billet is engineered to the desired strength and stiffness by judiciously selecting the proper combination of veneer grades and placing them in the layers best suited for the grade.

Parallel Stand Lumber

The parallel strand lumber manufacturing process requires veneer, so the front end of this process resembles a structural plywood or LVL process. The dry, 3-mm thick veneer is sliced into strands of approximately 19 mm width. Partial sheets of veneer, or veneer with many defects, are well suited for this process because the strands may be random lengths down to a lower limit of about 35 cm. However, since the strands are not substantially compressed in the manufacturing process, the veneer must have acceptable strength and stiffness.

Strands are passed through a double-roll coater to apply a waterproof adhesive (phenol-formaldehyde) to both sides. The strands are then arranged in parallel with a billet-forming machine such that the ends of the strands are randomized in the billet. The unpressed billet is then drawn through a continuous press. The continuous press produces a pressed billet with cross section dimensions of approximately 30×45 cm. Due to the large cross-section, conventional heating is not feasible. Therefore, the continuous press employs a microwave heating section to cure the thermosetting adhesive. The resulting billet is then cross-cut to length and ripped to an appropriate width and thickness.

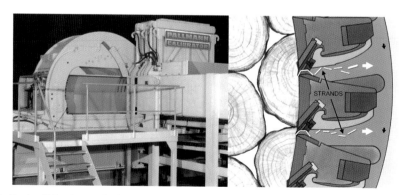

Figure 5 Long-log knife-ring flaker for producing strands for OSB and laminated strand lumber. Cutting action of the knives is shown at right. Photograph courtesy of Pallmann Pulverizers Co., Inc.

Laminated Strand Lumber

Laminated strand lumber manufacturing is a variation of the OSB process. The strands are longer than those found in OSB, and all of the strands are arranged parallel to each other to simulate solid-sawn lumber. The adhesive blending and mat forming are similar to OSB processes. LSL is produced in billets 5–12 cm thick, 2.4 m wide, and 15 m long. Due to its thickness, conventional heating in the press is not practical. An LSL press employs steam injection through the press platens into the mat of strands. The steam greatly accelerates the rate of heat transfer to the core of the mat, thus reducing the time in the press. The steam injection also serves to reduce the gradient in density through the thickness of LVL. Polymeric MDI adhesive is used for the manufacture of LSL due to the steam injection process. This waterproof, thermosetting adhesive requires water to polymerize, while steam interferes with the bond strength development of phenol-formaldehyde adhesives.

Further Reading

APA (1994) *PRP-108 Performance Standards and Policies for Structural Use Panels*. Tacoma, WA: APA – The Engineered Wood Association.

APA (1995) *PS1-95 Construction and Industrial Plywood*. Tacoma, WA: APA – The Engineered Wood Association.

APA (2000) *PRL-501 Performance Standard for APA EWS Laminated Veneer Lumber*. Tacoma, WA: APA – The Engineered Wood Association.

Baldwin RF (1995) *Plywood and Veneer-Based Products: Manufacturing Processes*. San Francisco, CA: Miller Freeman.

CPA (1996) *Particleboard from Start to Finish*. Gaithersburg, MD: Composite Panel Association.

CPA (1998) *MDF from Start to Finish*. Gaithersburg, MD: Composite Panel Association.

Haygreen JG and Bowyer JL (1996) *Forest Products and Wood Science: An Introduction*, 3rd edn. Ames, IA: Iowa State University Press.

HPVA (2000) *ANSI/HPVA HP-1-2000 American National Standard for Hardwood and Decorative Plywood*. Reston, VA: Hardwood Plywood and Veneer Association.

Maloney TM (1993) *Modern Particleboard and Dry-Process Fiberboard Manufacturing*. San Francisco, CA: Miller Freeman.

Sellers T Jr (1985) *Plywood and Adhesive Technology*. New York: Marcel Dekker.

Smulski S (ed.) (1997) *Engineered Wood Products: A Guide to Specifiers, Designers and Users*. Madison, WI: PFS Research Foundation.

Tichy RJ and Wolcott MP (eds) (published annually) *36th International Particleboard/Composite Materials Symposium Proceedings*. Pullman, WA: Washington State University.

US Department of Agriculture (1999) *Wood Handbook: Wood as an Engineering Material*. Gen. Tech. Rep. no. FPL-GTR-113. Madison, WI: US Department of Agriculture Forest Products Laboratory.

Streamflow *see* **Hydrology**: Hydrological Cycle; Impacts of Forest Conversion on Streamflow; Impacts of Forest Management on Streamflow; Impacts of Forest Management on Water Quality; Impacts of Forest Plantations on Streamflow.

SUSTAINABLE FOREST MANAGEMENT

Contents
Overview
Certification
Definitions, Good Practices and Certification
Causes of Deforestation and Forest Fragmentation

Overview

H Schanz, Wageningen University, Wageningen, The Netherlands

Introduction

Sustainable forest management (SFM) has become one of the core ideal concepts in the use and conservation of forest resources worldwide. Despite its uncontested appeal, a bewildering variety of interpretations of its meanings does exist, which makes discussions and implementation difficult. Underlying the concept is the ethical principle about how the relation between forests and people should be designed. Dependent on the interpretations, the aspect of continuation in the concept of SFM can include a wide range of different dimensions, including, for example, the maintenance of forest ecological characteristics, the maintenance of yields of forest products and services, as well as the sustenance of human institutions that are forest-dependent. Conflict among these is inherent and reflects other contested values in society. Consequently there cannot be an objective, universally agreed definition of SFM. The various understandings of SFM are outcomes of social or political processes, and are thus context-dependent as well as subject to continuous change. The international forest policy dialogue as well as market-driven certification approaches have provided major stimuli for such processes on national, regional, and local levels. There is widespread agreement that achievement of SFM requires adequate institutionalization as well as a widely shared understanding of the concept.

Bewildering Variety of Meanings

SFM is more and more frequently viewed as an ideal in managing forests worldwide. Numerous declarations have recently been published at national and international levels in which SFM is claimed to be the main objective of all future efforts in forestry. However, despite the long tradition of the term, there exists a virtual wilderness of meanings. The question already rises whether SFM is a mere constraint on forest management or whether it is a goal in itself. Depending on the answer to this question, the terms 'sustainable forest management,' 'forest sustainability,' 'sustainable forests' or 'sustainable development of forests' are interpreted as distinct, different concepts, or as at least partially overlapping synonyms. The discussion of what SFM means precisely has kept the forestry profession busy, probably since the term 'sustainable' was first mentioned explicitly with regard to forest management in 1713 by von Carlowitz in Central Europe. However, despite general agreement on the need to implement SFM, the term means different things to

different people. Nevertheless, there is consensus that SFM describes forest conservation practices, including their tools and techniques, that take into account the social, economic, and ecological dimensions of forests in the context of the needs of the present generation and future generations. In this respect SFM forms a strong unifying concept, with no one being conceptually against it.

Why Should Something Be Sustained?

The very core of discussions about the meanings of SFM are formed by the question of why something should be sustained with regard to forests or the relation between forests and people. SFM is thus not a natural characteristic of a forest or a technical issue in forest management planning. Rather, it is an ethical principle about how the relation between forests and people should be designed. History clearly shows that discussions about SFM always peaked in times of perceived or real crisis, such as timber shortages after war in the first half of the twentieth century or massive tropical forest destruction for whatever reason in the late twentieth century (overexploitation, forest fires, conflicting land uses, such as mining, etc.). In that respect also very early efforts such as religious obligations to replant for every tree that fell for whatever reason or to set aside certain forest patches as sacred groves, even though not termed 'sustainable forest management,' must be interpreted similarly. It is thus not a concept with origins limited to European forestry, as is often stated, even though it might have been there that the ethical core was explicitly designed over more than one generation and made an explicit technical science out of it.

What Should Be Sustained?

The second core question in discussions about the meaning of SFM is about the question of what should be sustained. This is well reflected by the etymology of the term 'sustainable,' which is described in dictionaries with synonyms such as continuous, perpetuated, constant, or durable. At first glance SFM therefore seems to show great affinity with concepts such as bag limits in wildlife management, carrying capacity in wilderness and recreation management, and recharge rates in aquifer management. Not surprisingly, discussions on SFM at the beginning of regular forest management often focused on aspects of sustained yield. Sustained yield in this respect was interpreted as constraining the periodic consumption of a renewable forest resource (timber and nontimber) not to exceed its periodic growth. However, the technical constraints for safeguarding continuous supply do not in themselves provide an answer to the question of what should be sustained on the demand side. Despite the voices of a few leaders in the forestry profession at the turn of the twentieth century, it is only more recently that the focus of discussion on SFM has broadened to include values on an ecological, social, and economical dimension similarly. The aspect of continuity in SFM can consequently refer to some quite different things, such as:

- maintenance of forest ecological characteristics, including the production capacity of forest soils, the vegetative renewal capacity, certain forest species and components, as well as biodiversity and natural forest ecological processes
- maintenance of yields of forest products and services
- sustenance of human institutions that are forest-dependent, including community stability, cultural integrity, and labor and income generation.

Reflection of Social Values

Accordingly, more than 14 different categories of definitions of SFM have been identified in literature depending on how the different dimensions are weighted. Even within one single dimension, be it the ecological, economical, or social one, weighting of values can differ greatly, leading to completely different interpretations of SFM. In the ecological dimension, for example, the question of whether ecological processes themselves (implying change and uncertainty) or the existence of individual species at a given time should be sustained has resulted in endless discussions. However, even if agreement about the relative weights of values can be achieved, their operational definition still remains vague and contested, because spatial and time scales often remain unidentified. On a spatial scale, different understandings of SFM are contested, depending on whether the achievement of norms and values is realized on forest stand levels, on district levels, or on regional levels. At a temporal scale a crucial point for discussion and different interpretations for SFM are formed by the way in which social and ecological changes are incorporated in different norms and values. For example, how do we deal with natural fluctuations (e.g., dry years) and disturbances (e.g., storms, forest fires)? The concept of SFM not only comprises three substantive dimensions – ecological, economical, and social – but also temporal and spatial dimensions.

Concept of Conflict

SFM is controversial for good reason: any one definition represents particular values on these five dimensions at others' expense. Inherent in the concept is conflict among the value systems that underlie these differences. SFM is thus a concept reflecting conflict rather than harmony, as it is often misinterpreted. SFM serves as the vehicle by which the underlying norms and values of these standards can be expressed. By supporting a certain understanding of SFM, participants' preferences and values are expressed, but nothing has been harmonized, no value conflicts have been resolved. The only thing that happens is that certain values are discussed so that social bargaining processes, e.g., concerning certification of SFM, may begin.

Thus, the achievement of SFM ultimately depends on the reconciliation of different social perspectives with respect to forest resources in social or political processes. The reasons behind differences in participants' values may be different interests, expertise, or knowledge levels but also different views of how the world works. Reconciliation processes are therefore not easy, and can become very easily corrupt or biased, where there is no right or wrong answer, only more or less appropriate ones.

Whereas in earlier times forest management planning was generally considered a technical issue and responsibility was exclusively dedicated to forest owners or forest professionals, it is increasingly recognized that SFM must integrate narrow private and broader public interests in forest resource utilization through adequate institutional designs of social or political processes. The challenge of SFM is to recognize, accommodate, and respond effectively to diverse and dynamic value perspectives about forest management in society. Achieving SMF is consequently in the first instance a social exercise and only secondarily a technical issue.

Context Dependency

There is widespread agreement between authors that the meaning of SFM is dependent on time and place and that there cannot be an objective, universal definition. What will be sustained, and for whom, is determined through social processes. Still, there are always predominant understandings in certain times and places, reflecting the prevailing social, economic, and political conditions. The understanding of SFM is thus not only context-dependent but also subject to continuous change. The question of which definition will predominate in a certain region and during a certain time period may also be one of political power, and not necessarily only of objective necessities, as is well reflected by the history of the 'sustained yield' principle in Europe and its adaptation when introduced in the USA.

With the age of enlightenment in the eighteenth century, central Europe was ripe for the development of scientific models for the use and conservation of forests, replacing practical and unsystematic approaches which had been predominating in European forestry until then. Based on the idea of continuous production, the aim of achieving, at the earliest practical time, an appropriate balance between growth and harvest was translated into mathematical formulae, which culminated in the ideal model of the 'normal forest.' Whereas initially sustained timber production with special attention to sustaining growing stock was central, the focus switched to sustaining net revenues and aspects of the ground rent when the predominant economic system of mercantilism was replaced by the free-market philosophy. In general, forest management for sustained yield in central Europe in the middle of the nineteenth century had as its objectives the production of annual timber crops of approximately equal size, maintenance of stable industrial communities, furnishing permanent income for forest owners, and purchasing power, and full use of the productive capacity of the forest lands. With the arrival of the first ideas on environmental conservation and the renaissance of a holistic perspective on nature at the turn of the twentieth century, sustained-yield forestry was brought into line with the productive power of the soil and the functioning of the forest as an organic community. With the increasing wealth of society in the twentieth century, when spare time and recreation became more important, the traditional sustained-yield concept gradually shifted to that of SFM for multiple benefits.

When the ideal of the normal forest and sustained-yield regulation necessary to maintain it were introduced from Europe to the USA at the turn of the twentieth century, the ignorance of the context dependencies of the concept gave rise to heavy criticism. The criticisms seemed to have two common elements: (1) perpetual output was perceived as inconsistent with the 'frontier' mentality of a young and still developing American society; and (2) the physical models bore little relation to the economic realities of the predominating liberal capitalism. Consequently, the idea of sustained yield as a production technique designed to ensure a sustained commodity flow over time was broadened to an understanding of SFM, encompassing the continuity of multiple benefit flows and ecological stability

while maintaining the potential to respond to evolving demands.

The context dependency of the understanding of SFM is also well illustrated by the rejection of the concept of SFM as being 'reactionary and capitalistic' under communistic sovereignty, as for example in the time of the Soviet Union. Forest resources there were instead interpreted as an important component in the development of a socialistic society, giving space to an alternative interpretation of the concept of extended reproduction.

Formal and Informal Processes

In the beginning of regular forest management, the idea of sustained yield was usually interpreted by the forestry profession and advocated by government and industry. Local communities themselves have not usually promoted sustained yield in such a scientific sense. However, in several cases they have undertaken measures to limit exploitation and protect forests. As the concept has been broadened from sustained yield to SFM, this has changed. The reconciliation of different social values in the respective understanding of SFM now takes place in the form of social processes which encompass socioeconomic impacts and the stakeholder participation. These processes usually began at national or regional level but more frequently became institutionalized at a local level. The character of these processes can be both formal and informal.

The United Nations Conference on Environment and Development (UNCED) in 1992 in Rio de Janeiro provided an important stimulus for discussion about SFM in all types of forest at a global level. Even though the conference did not result in a legally binding instrument on the conservation of forests, its follow-up processes resulted in a clear recognition of the importance of SFM. The issue of SFM was furthermore taken up by several regional political processes, in the follow-up, or parallel, to the United Nations' process, such as the so-called Montreal Process or the Ministerial Conference on the Protection of Forests in Europe – all provided important contributions to the discussions or even binding definitions of SFM for their member parties. These understandings have long departed from the classical understanding of SFM as sustained-yield regulation. The Ministerial Conference on the Protection of Forests in Europe, for example, defines SFM in their Helsinki resolution as 'the stewardship and use of forest lands in a way, and at a rate, that maintains their biodiversity, productivity, regeneration capacity, vitality and their potential to fulfill now and in the future, relevant ecological, economic and social functions, at local, national, and global levels, and that does not cause damage to other ecosystems.'

SFM has also emerged as a consideration in the international trade of forest products. Many consumers, individually and collectively, prefer to buy products obtained from sustainably managed forests and manufactured by environmentally acceptable processes. In response to this demand, several timber certification systems have been established at international as well as regional level, which concur with each other. At a global level, the Forest Stewardship Council (FSC) was founded by environmental non-government organizations in cooperation with the timber industry to promote the sustainable management of forests worldwide. By formulating principles, criteria, and indicators for SFM that are differentiated according to different regions of the world, the FSC acts as an accreditation body for certifying organizations, thereby guaranteeing certain minimum standards for SFM. However, given the impossibility of an objective, universally agreed definition of SFM, all certification schemes have also been the subject of conflict.

Another example of how the consumers' call is influencing discussions about SFM is reflected by the ambitious year-2000 objective of the International Tropical Timber Trade Organization (ITTO) which stated that 'ITTO members will progress towards achieving sustainable management of tropical forests and trade in tropical timber from sustainably managed resources by the year 2000.' Even though ITTO's own evaluation showed that only a few countries 'appear to be managing some of their forests sustainably,' it is nevertheless a good example for the many social and political processes which have been started all over the world in search of criteria and indicators for SFM. At the same time, the ITTO example clearly indicates that understanding of SFM needs to be adequately institutionalized, in order to become implemented.

Institutionalization

Experience from all over the world seems to indicate that one of the most important institutional prerequisites for SFM is legislation that establishes appropriate and reliable forms of forest tenure, including various forms of forest ownership and usage rights. There are furthermore clear indications that the political, economic, and ethical setting in which SFM is pursued will determine success or otherwise. As history and practical evidence show, SFM seems not to be feasible unless it benefits from a sound and stable context of consistent developments and converging strategies occurring in related

sectors. Implementing SFM thus involves policy action in forestry as well as in other policy fields, with cross-sectoral policy coordination being another crucial institutional device. In many countries the policies of several government ministries have an impact on forest lands.

Significant influential factors for the successful implementation of SFM include financial incentives, a clear sharing of costs and investments, as well as an active, informed civil society.

Symbolic Function

Yet, even if no consensus on criteria and indicators can be achieved, and implementation cannot be adequately institutionalized, the concept of SFM is not without importance for forestry. Critics of SFM have underestimated its emotional and symbolic significance. The bewildering variety of understandings and its multifaceted character is a weakness and a strength at the same time. The concept of SFM can also serve as a platform on which disparate actors can stand together – its ambiguity allows participants with seemingly irreconcilable positions to search for common solutions without appearing to compromise their principles. Furthermore, the informal, personal, and implicit properties of the concept should not be forgotten – its ability to provide a guideline for coping with uncertainty and ignorance in forest management decisions and to serve as an esprit de corps for the forestry profession.

See also: **Mensuration**: Yield Tables, Forecasting, Modeling and Simulation. **Plantation Silviculture**: Multiple-use Silviculture in Temperate Plantation Forestry; Sustainability of Forest Plantations. **Sustainable Forest Management**: Certification.

Further Reading

Aplet GH, Johnson N, Olson JT and Sample VA (eds) (1993) *Defining Sustainable Forestry*. Washington, DC: Covelo.

Clawson M and Sedjo R (1984) History of sustained yield concept and its application to developing countries. In: Steen HK (ed.) *History of Sustained Yield Forestry: A Symposium of the Forestry History Society*, pp. 3–15. Santa Cruz, CA: Forest History Society.

de Montalembert M-R and Schmithüsen F (1993) Policy and legal aspects of sustainable forest management. *Unasylva* 44(175): 3–8.

Lee RG (1982) The classical sustained yield concept: content and philosophical origins. In: LeMaster DC, Baumgartner DM, and Adams D (eds) *Sustained Yield – Proceedings of a Symposium, Spokane, Washington*, pp. 1–10. Washington, DC: Washington State University Cooperative Extension Pullman.

Lee RG (1990) Sustained yield and social order. In: Lee RG, Field DR, and Burch WRJ (eds) *Community and Forestry – Continuities in the Sociology of Natural Resources*, pp. 83–94. Boulder, CA: West View Press.

Romm J (1993) Sustainable forestry, an adaptive social process. In: Aplet GH, Johnson N, Olson JT, and Sample VA (eds) *Defining Sustainable Forestry*, pp. 280–293. Washington, DC: Covelo.

Schanz H (1996) 'Forstliche Nachhaltigkeit' – Sozialwissenschaftliche Analyse der Begriffsinhalte und -funktionen [Sustainable forest management – contents and functions of a central term in a social science perspective]. Dissertation. Schriften des Instituts für Forstökonomie, Band IV. Freiburg, Germany: Universität Freiburg.

Steen HK (ed.) (1984) *History of Sustained Yield Forestry.* IUFRO Symposium Western Forestry Center. Portland, OR: Forest History Society.

Wiersum KF (1995) 200 years of sustainability in forestry: lessons from history. *Journal of Environmental Management* 19(3): 321–329.

Zürcher U (1965) Die Idee der Nachhaltigkeit unter spezieller Berücksichtigung der Gesichtspunkte der Forsteinrichtung [The idea of sustainability in a forest planning perspective]. *Mitteilungen der schweizerischen Anstalt für das forstliche Versuchswesen, Zürich* 41: 87–218.

Certification

S Bass, Department for International Development, London, UK

Introduction

Certification provides a means by which the quality of forest management may be independently assessed to agreed standards. It offers credible evidence that enables the forest manager to obtain benefits, notably access to markets that demand sustainably-produced forest products. Several certification schemes have experienced rapid development and certification is now routine practice. This article reviews the process in general, the key players, and the early achievements of certification in light of its implicit assumptions.

Definitions and Description of Forest Certification Processes

Certification

Certification is the procedure by which a third party provides written assurance that a product, process or service conforms to specified standards, on the basis of an audit conducted to agreed procedures. Certification may be linked with product labeling for market communication purposes. It comprises a variety of mechanical tasks that aim to produce highly objective assessments. However, it tends to have market and political implications, because it results in a judgement of whether a product, process or service is acceptable or not. The International Organization for Standardization (ISO) has set precedents in the various tasks of certification, standardization, and accreditation that are outlined below, and most certification schemes in any sector have chosen to adhere to them. This is partly because ISO standards tend to be recognized by the World Trade Organization (WTO) as not creating unnecessary barriers to trade. Certification of social and environmental performance is already changing the rules of the game for many industries. It has occupied a key role in the 'organic' and 'fair trade' niches of food production for some time; it is emerging in fisheries and tourism; and it is being explored for mining. Certification has had a particularly rapid evolution in the forest sector, where it is becoming routine practice.

Forest Management Certification

Forest management certification is the process by which the performance of on-the-ground forestry operations is assessed against a predetermined set of standards. This is voluntary, at the request of the forest owner or manager. If the forestry operations are found to be in conformance with these standards, a certificate is issued, offering the owner/manager the potential to bring products from the certified forest to the market as certified products. This market potential is realized by a supplementary certification, which assesses the chain of custody of wood (see below). In this sense, forest certification is market driven – aiming to improve forest management through market-based incentives, and to improve market access and share for the products of such management. It addresses the quality of forest management, as opposed to the quality of forest products. In addition, systems for the certification of wood quality exist (see below).

Standards

Standards used in forest certification schemes are of two general types:

- performance standards
- management system standards.

Performance standards look for specified outcomes to be achieved, notably social, environmental, and economic outcomes: these may be expressed as thresholds. In contrast, management system standards look for specified elements in the management system, notably target setting, monitoring, and review, that ensure that performance continuously improves from whatever base. The latter are typified by ISO9000 quality management or ISO14000 environmental management standards. However, all forest certification schemes include some elements of both performance and management standards.

Procedures

Procedures for conducting forest certification can take several months from initial inquiry to issuance of the certificate. At the request of the forest owner or manager, typically the auditor conducts, in the following order:

- an (optional) preassessment or 'scoping' visit
- confirmation of the standard by which the forest will be certified or (if necessary) development of an interim standard
- consultation with stakeholders
- an independent formal audit of the quality of forest management in a specified forest area, under one management regime, against the specified standards, by assessing documents that prescribe and record management, together with checks in the forest and interviews with staff and stakeholders,
- writing the assessment report and, usually, peer review
- a decision to issue a certificate for a period

and/or

- corrective action requests (CARs) – a formal document which details noncompliances identified and remedial measures required within a specified time
- a public summary of the certificate placed on the certifier's website
- regular (annual) audits thereafter to ensure continued compliance and action on CARs, which process maintains the validity of the certificate.

Chain of Custody Certification

Chain of custody certification is a frequent supplement to forest management certification. It verifies the chain of responsibility through which a product passes, e.g., from the forest, through timber processor to manufacturer, to importer, to distributor, to retailer. The result is a certified origin of the forest product concerned.

Forest Product Labeling

Forest product labeling refers to the quality of forest management and the origin of the raw material of which the product is made. It is based on (1) certification of forest management, and (2) verification of the chain of custody. It may be displayed on the physical forest product itself. The same information can also be communicated off-product, i.e., in various promotional materials and communication media. Certification schemes operate strict rules regarding the use of on-product or advertising labels, which are usually trademarked.

Accreditation

Accreditation is the process of recognition – against published criteria of capability, competence, and impartiality – of a body involved in conformity assessment. Accreditation formally recognizes the competence and impartiality of the bodies involved in certification of forest management and the chain of custody, and results in licenses to operate a particular certification scheme. In effect, it 'certifies the certifiers.' With a few exceptions, accreditation is granted by national accreditation bodies, which can be governmental or private. A notable exception is an international body in the case of the Forest Stewardship Council (see below).

Provisions for Specific Circumstances

Acknowledging the specific issues affecting certain product types and producers, certification schemes tend to make provision for:

1. Multiple source chain of custody to enable certification for paper and composite wood products. This may allow processors a mix of certified and uncertified material where this reflects local supplies and so reduces cost. It may also favor mixture with recycled materials.
2. Group certification of smallholders, to allow for several small enterprises to be covered by one certificate, which is held by the group manager. This can reduce certification cost, provided group members are sufficiently similar to create scale economies.
3. Forest manager certification for similar reasons to the above, where a professional manager is responsible for several small areas.
4. Recycled wood certification which accords certified status to reclaimed or recycled wood where chain of custody is known.
5. Ecological zone harmonization of national standards, to ensure that standards covering similar ecological zones, if they were developed separately

by different (national) stakeholders, can be rationalized.

6. Other issues that emerge through reviewing the practice of, and problems faced by, certification schemes. Many schemes operate working groups to identify and respond to such needs.

Thus forest certification is not one single operation, but a mix of mechanical and political functions (**Figure 1**).

The Rationale for and Evolution of Forest Certification

Forest certification has developed in response to the interests and incentives facing many different interest groups. However, its origins lie largely with environmental nongovernmental organizations (NGOs) and the timber retail business. During the 1970s and 1980s, environmental NGOs grew increasingly disillusioned with the failure of government authorities and regulations to improve forest management in tropical regions, with the inadequacy of intergovernmental efforts to tackle deforestation, and with the forest products trade's lack of discrimination in where it sourced its products. By the late 1980s, NGOs had concluded that both the Tropical Forestry Action Plan and the International Tropical Timber Organization (ITTO) had failed to halt asset-stripping approaches to forestry. In Western Europe and North America in particular, NGO campaigns led to the emergence of consumer bans and boycotts against tropical timber, claiming that much of it

derived from deforestation. Many retailers could not make counterclaims as they had no idea where their wood came from.

The timber retailers' alarm was exploited constructively by some NGOs (notably the Worldwide Fund for Nature, WWF), who suggested the more attractive possibilities of developing markets for environmentally and socially sound forest products. This brought about one of the first alliances of environmental NGOs and businesses. They developed the idea of a mechanism to allow wood products to be traced back to their forest sources, to verify that the same forest was well managed, and to create market incentives that would make the mechanism viable. Forest owners and managers were then brought into the process. Like the retailers, they were motivated by the prospect that certification would offer a useful marketing tool in the face of consumer boycotts and competition with other materials. They expressed varied expectations ranged from premium prices, to reducing market risks, to maintaining or increasing market share, to product 'green branding' and differentiation to access further markets, to nonmarket motivations such as skills development and being recognized by forest authorities.

Thus the Forest Stewardship Council (FSC) emerged in 1993. (It was not the first forest certification scheme: in 1990 the Rainforest Alliance set up the Smart Wood forest certification program, which provided early lessons for, and is now accredited to, the FSC.) It has now certified forests in all continents, with an almost exponential increase in the area covered. However, numerous other

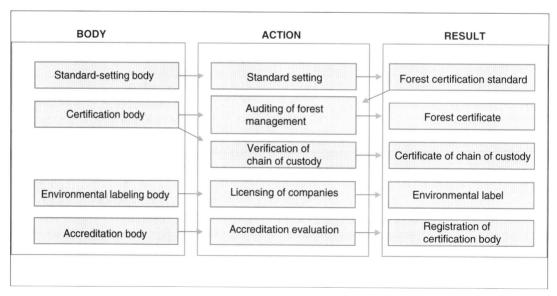

Figure 1 Elements of forest certification. From Bass S and Simula M (1999) Independent certification/verification of forest management. Background paper for WB/WWF Alliance Workshop, 8–9 November 1999, Washington, DC. http://www.worldbank.org/wwf/certwkshp.htm

international and national forest certification schemes have more recently emerged. Many local stakeholders wanted to take charge of the process of developing certification schemes, to ensure they were appropriate to their forest types, enterprise types and governance systems.

Whilst the problems of tropical deforestation were the main drivers of forest certification, certification is now commonplace in temperate and boreal forests as well. This was both in response to NGO and consumer worries about northern forests, and to the interest and opportunism of producers operating in these forests and retailers selling their products. Indeed, to date, more certificates have been awarded by FSC and other schemes to northern forests.

The Forest Stewardship Council

Until the introduction of the Pan-European Forest Certification Framework in 1999 (see below), the FSC was the only fully integrated, international system of forest certification. The FSC's objectives are to promote global standards of forest management, to accredit certifiers that certify forest operations according to such standards, and to encourage buyers to purchase certified products.

The FSC is a membership organization, with decisions made through meetings of a General Assembly, which is divided into three equal chambers: social, environmental, and economic. All three chambers have Northern and Southern subchambers, each with half of the total chamber votes. Governments are not entitled to participate in the FSC's governance, even as observers, although government employees have been very active participants in some FSC national initiatives.

The FSC has a set of ten principles and related criteria (P&C) of forest stewardship, which apply to all tropical, temperate, and boreal forests, both natural forests and plantations, with the tenth Principle being exclusively for plantations (**Table 1**). These P&C serve as a basis for the development of national and regional forest management standards. Certification standards that are consistent with both the P&C and with FSC's process guidelines for standards development are eligible for FSC endorsement. Such standards have been developed by both FSC-organized national working groups and by independent processes, e.g., that of Indonesia. The

Table 1 The Forest Stewardship Council's ten principles of forest stewardship

Principle 1: Compliance with laws and FSC principles
Forest management shall respect all applicable laws of the country in which they occur, and international treaties and agreements to which the country is a signatory, and comply with all FSC Principles and Criteria.
Principle 2: Tenure and use rights and responsibilities
Long-term tenure and use rights to the land and forest resources shall be clearly defined, documented, and legally established.
Principle 3: Indigenous peoples' rights
The legal and customary rights of indigenous peoples to own, use, and manage their lands, territories, and resources shall be recognized and respected.
Principle 4: Community relations and workers' rights
Forest management operations shall maintain or enhance the long-term social and economic well-being of forest workers and local communities.
Principle 5: Benefits from the forest
Forest management operations shall encourage the efficient use of the forest's multiple products and services to ensure economic viability and a wide range of environmental and social benefits.
Principle 6: Environmental impact
Forest management shall conserve biological diversity and its associated values, water resources, soils, and unique and fragile ecosystems and landscapes, and, by so doing, maintain the ecological functions and the integrity of the forest.
Principle 7: Management plan
A management plan – appropriate to the scale and intensity of the operations – shall be written, implemented, and kept up to date. The long-term objectives of management, and the means of achieving them, shall be clearly stated.
Principle 8: Monitoring and assessment
Monitoring shall be conducted – appropriate to the scale and intensity of forest management – to assess the condition of the forest, yields of forest products, chain of custody, management activities and their social and environmental impacts.
Principle 9: Maintenance of high conservation value forests
Management activities in high conservation value forests shall maintain or enhance the attributes which define such forests. Decisions regarding high conservation value forests shall always be considered in the context of a precautionary approach.
Principle 10: Plantations
Plantations shall be planned and managed in accordance with Principles and Criteria 1–9, and Principle 10 and its Criteria. While plantations can provide an array of social and economic benefits, and can contribute to satisfying the world's needs for forest products, they should complement the management of, reduce pressures on, and promote the restoration and conservation of natural forests.

FSC owns a trademark which may be used to label products from certified forests.

The Pan-European Forest Certification Framework

The Pan-European Forest Certification Framework (PEFC) is a voluntary private-sector initiative, designed to promote an internationally credible framework for forest certification schemes and initiatives. Its criteria are consistent with the intergovernmentally agreed Pan-European Criteria and Indicators for Sustainable Forest Management, thereby attracting considerable support from both European and national governments. National certification schemes that meet PEFC requirements can apply for endorsement and the right to use the PEFC trademark for product labeling. In contrast to accreditation by the FSC, PEFC leaves this function to national accreditation bodies. National PEFC governing bodies set standards and operate national schemes, and are represented on the PEFC Council Board.

The initiative was given strong impetus by Austrian, Finnish, French, German, Norwegian and Swedish forest owners, who wished to ensure that small woodland owners are not disadvantaged by certification, and that local conditions are catered for. It was supported by the national forest certification schemes that had been emerging in some of these countries yet which felt themselves to be individually too small to develop an adequate presence. The evolution of PEFC was rapid: it started in August 1998, and was launched in June 1999. Now there are many countries involved, extending into other continents. The rapid development of both country coverage and certified area has entrenched the position of some environmental NGOs; they believe that the ease of achieving PEFC certification, in countries which they perceive to have imperfect forest management, demonstrates that the scheme is not helping to improve forest management and thereby achieves little beyond attempts at market protection.

Regional and National Certification Schemes

At the level of individual countries, the number of certification schemes under development is increasing rapidly. They fall into three main groups:

1. Schemes aligned from the outset with either the FSC or PEFC.
2. Schemes that develop independently but aim for compatibility with the FSC and/or PEFC.
3. Schemes without any links to an umbrella scheme.

Where there is contention over any scheme, it tends to concern:

- the perceived dominance or exclusion of certain parties
- the lack of comparability between specific standards in a given region
- the degree of challenge or 'stretch' represented by the gap between normally applied legal standards and certification standards.

Observations on the Effectiveness of Certification

Forest certification schemes started on the basis of very little experience. Of necessity, they rested on a set of assumptions many of which have never really been made explicit. It is worth reviewing these assumptions in light of a good ten years of experience.

Assumption 1: One Set of Standards Can Apply to All Types of Forest

At the level of their basic principles, certification standards do seem to be applicable to many types of forest. Two observations support this: firstly, most certification schemes have been able to justify, develop, and apply one overarching standard; and secondly, there are considerable similarities in such standards between schemes. In many ways, therefore, certification has coped effectively with a tricky dilemma: how to deal with complexity (in standards and their interpretation) and yet also deliver a simple message to consumers and producers.

Assumption 2: One Set of Standards Can Apply to All Types of Forest Producer

In practice, larger producers find it easier to benefit from certification, as they have better access to information and markets, scale economies, formal management systems on simpler forest types, and an ability to bear risks and costs. The area of certified forest under community or small enterprise management is correspondingly much smaller. Recognizing this lack of uptake, many certification schemes have responded with special schemes for group certification of small growers. However, there are those who question why a small community group occasionally harvesting timber on its own land should be held as accountable as a major corporation harvesting 24 hours a day on leased public land. The fact that standards tend to be focused on performance forestry outcomes, and do not adequately recognize each step achieved in the process of getting there, prejudices against many developing country practices, in particular where there are often many steps to be undertaken. Part of the problem derives also from the next assumption.

Assumption 3: Forest Management Standards Should Be Based on Scientific Principles of Forest Management, with a Strong Emphasis on Records and Clear Business Strategy

Certification is largely document-based, and is predicated on formal means of planning and monitoring. In practice, this assumption has pre-judiced against the forestry norms and methods of traditional societies, and against part-time foresters. A national standard which may stretch to some 40 pages is intimidating to people with low literacy levels. Even if it is understood, some current certification standards and procedures cannot recognize good management in some of the complex land use systems of indigenous and community groups. Furthermore, the difficulties faced by certifiers in interpreting social standards in complex social contexts (or at least contexts which will be alien to the certifier) have meant that some inappropriate social CARs have been issued.

Assumption 4: Most Progress in Sustainable Forest Management Will Be Made through Focusing on the Forest Management Unit

It is true that, before certification, 'sustainability' was characterized by too much discussion and too little action. Certification has shifted energies to real forests and real enterprises. Yet some environmental and social services are often realized at the landscape level. Thus the forest unit plays only a partial role, and cannot be responsible for a complete role. Although certification must focus on what the enterprise (or other certified entity) does, it needs to be improved to account for critical sustainability issues at other levels (such as the landscape or the nation), which may not be under the control of that entity but which require its active engagement.

Assumption 5: Voluntary, Market-Based Certification Would Be a Cost-Effective Complement to Traditional Administrative Regulation in Improving Forest Management and Ensuring the Protection of Forest Environments

This assumption is proving to be valid. In some countries, state forest authorities support certifica-tion as a 'privatized' form of forest monitoring, and are making incentives available. In countries where

regulation and enforcement is weak, certification has ensured that at least some producers are meeting not only legal requirements but also higher standards, and that this is monitored. The presence of evidently good forest management and scrutiny has had useful knock-on benefits locally, notably by improving forest policy debates and provisions.

Assumption 6: By Involving Consumers, Producers, and other Forest Stakeholders in Standards Development, Certification Would Be More Credible than Traditional Regulatory Instruments

In many countries, certification has certainly become as significant as traditional instruments: stakeholders now tend to pay as much attention to developments in certification as they do to developments in national and intergovernmental law. Certification offers broader standards that tend to reflect more stakeholders' needs, improving credibility in many stakeholders' eyes. The key ingredients are: focused participation in defining standards, and verification by third parties using tried-and-tested mechanisms with precedents in other sectors. However, there are some tensions between the values that drive some protagonists of certification and the need for objective scrutiny. This mean that accreditation of certifiers is essential for objectivity but fraught with difficulties. A further problem is the proliferation of certification schemes, which is leading to consumer confusion and a reluctance of firms to be certified at all. Fears of proliferation have prompted consider-able efforts by the wood products industry to investigate the potential of mutual recognition or adjustment between schemes.

Assumption 7: By Being Voluntary and Not Involving Government, Certification Would Be Able to Avoid Charges of Trade Discrimination under WTO Rules, and Would Not Be Constrained by any Unprogressive Governmental Approaches to Forestry

In practice, there have been no serious challenges to certification under WTO; forests have been certified in countries where government controls and incen-tives are weak; and governments have been involved in some schemes. Indeed, the implications of a lack of government involvement in other schemes need serious consideration. This is because of the close relationship of certification standards to regulations, and the fact that some government bodies have direct interests as forest enterprises, as providers of environmental service, and as authorities concerned with the welfare of forest-dependent groups.

Assumption 8: Consumer Demand for Certified Products Will Be Strong Enough to Encourage Producers to Pay the Extra Costs of both Certification and the Necessary Forest Management Improvements

In practice, certified products command only a minority of the forest products market, with most market penetration in Western Europe. The market share of paper and construction timber/panels is particularly small. Consequently, only about 4% of commercial forestry is certified globally (as of 2003). However, all these figures are growing. Certified producers are gaining the benefit of market access, rather than a price premium (although a premium is available in some segments). More probably needs to be done to educate consumers about sustainable forestry and certification if the demand is to rise significantly. In addition, where market benefits have proven elusive, other incentives for certification might also be explored, e.g., access to resources such as land, finance, and insurance.

Assumption 9: Poor Forest Management and Deforestation Would Decline, as the Actors Involved Would Respond to the Incentive Effects of Market-Based Certification

In practice, the high threshold levels of certification standards (and FSC's in particular) have meant that certification has identified currently good practice, rather than improved bad practice. These 'good' producers now meet all current legal requirements, including those that they might normally not bother to meet. Most of them have also tightened management systems, especially for managing environmental impact. However, certification so far is only really inducing competition between excellent producers (just above the certified threshold), and good producers (just below the threshold). There are few incentives to cause the really bad producers to change behavior and be certified. Consequently, the worst forestry problems remain little affected by certification. The need for several thresholds (stepwise or phased approaches) is now being discussed, along with ways to complement certification with instruments to combat illegal logging.

Assumption 10: Certification Can Be a 'Magic Bullet' to Annihilate Multiple Forest Problems

Whilst it is clear that certification is an important innovation, there are many other prerequisites, complements, and alternatives that need to be considered in any given situation. For example, many certified community groups have expressed the opinion that better market information and

enterprise management capacity would have been higher priorities than certification – the latter having proven an inefficient means to acquire these assets. Further, policy prerequisites such as recognized forest and trade rights, and state protection of those rights, are necessary for the benefits of certification to be realized. Therefore the challenge is to understand and promote the right 'fit' of certification with other instruments for a given situation.

Conclusion

Because there are few surveys of what forest certification has achieved, the above observations are not definitive. Yet they point to some strengths and limitations that certification schemes, and their stakeholders, should keep under review. Perhaps the limits of the separate evolution of schemes have now been reached: it is important for all schemes to share the lessons and to develop responses together.

It is also important for all major government and multistakeholder initiatives to seriously consider what integral roles there might be for certification. Forest certification is based on concerns of both global and local imperatives for sustainable forest management and reflects the ongoing process of negotiation of the often conflicting ideas of what sustainable forest management is about. Where certification can manage these tensions creatively, it should certainly have an enduring role.

See also: **Genetics and Genetic Resources**: Forest Management for Conservation. **Harvesting**: Forest Operations in the Tropics, Reduced Impact Logging. **Operations**: Small-scale Forestry. **Plantation Silviculture**: Sustainability of Forest Plantations. **Social and Collaborative Forestry**: Forest and Tree Tenure and Ownership; Public Participation in Forest Decision Making. **Sustainable Forest Management**: Overview.

Further Reading

Bass S and Simula M (1999) Independent certification/verification of forest management. Background paper for WB/WWF Alliance Workshop, 8–9 November 1999, Washington, DC. http://www.worldbank.org/wwf/certwkshp.htm

Bass S, Thornber K, Markopoulos M, Roberts S, and Grieg-Gran M (2001) Certification's impacts on forests, stakeholders and supply chains. http://www.iied.org

Confederation of European Paper Industries (2002) Comparative matrix of forest certification schemes. http://www.cepi.org

de Camino R and Alfaro M (1998) Certification in Latin America: experience to date, Rural Development Forestry Network paper no. 23c. http://www.odi.org.uk

Eba'a Aryi R and Simula M (2002) *Forest Certification: Pending Challenges for Tropical Timber*, ITTO Technical Series no. 19. Yokohama, Japan: International Tropical Timber Organization.

Elliott C (2000) *Forest Certification: A Policy Perspective.* Bogor, Indonesia: Center for International Forestry Research.

FERN (2001) *Behind the Logo: An Environmental and Social Assessment of Forest Certification Schemes.* Moreton-in-Marsh, UK: FERN.

Higman S, Bass S, Judd N, Mayers J, and Nussbaum R (1999) *The Sustainable Forestry Handbook.* London: Earthscan.

Kanowski P, Sinclair D, Freeman B, and Bass S (2000) *Critical Elements for the Assessment of Forest Management Certification Schemes: Establishing Comparability and Equivalence amongst Schemes.* Canberra, ACT: Department of Agriculture, Fisheries and Forestry-Australia.

Meidengere E, Elliot C, and Oesten G (eds) (2003) Social and political dimensions of forest certification. http://www.forstbuch.de

Proforest (2001) *An Analysis of Current FSC Accreditation, Certification and Standard-Setting Procedures Identifying Elements which Create Constraints for Small Forest Owners.* Oxford: Proforest.

Upton C and Bass S (1995) *The Forest Certification Handbook.* London: Earthscan.

Worldwide Fund for Nature (2001) *The Forest Industry in the 21st Century.* Godalming, UK: WWF Forests for Life Campaign.

Definitions, Good Practices and Certification

M Karki, Medicinal and Aromatic Plants Program in Asia, New Delhi, India
R B S Rawat, National Medicinal Plants Board, New Delhi, India

Introduction

Non-wood forest products (NWFP) are found abundantly in tropical and temperate forests, range, and shrublands throughout the world. However, due to years of unwise use, the availability of certain NWFPs especially medicinal plants in desired quality, quantity, time, and place has become difficult. This raises serious doubts about their availability to meet both the local demand as healthcare products of local poor communities as well as growing demand of national and global phytomedicine industries. The sustainable production, conservation, and use of NWFPs are influenced by a number of factors, including those of a socioeconomic, technical, institutional, and policy nature. Unsustainable harvesting of the raw materials from the wild by untrained and poor collectors, mostly using primitive methods, and the lack of awareness of the real value of the resources are other important factors leading to widescale resource depletion. Rural people in developing countries derive a substantial portion of their income, and food and medicinal products for their basic needs from NWFPs gathered from forests.

This article presents conservation-through-use or sustainable conservation as a good practice to integrate biophysical and socioeconomic tools in the management of NWFP to reduce global poverty and enhance biodiversity conservation. The main premise is that NWFP resources are the natural capital of local people and their wise management can improve livelihoods of the rural people in the developing world who in turn will find incentives to conserve the global environment. However, this new approach to NWFP management needs to be properly and systematically monitored and linked to the prevailing national and global market conditions that permit the conversion of these natural resources into sources of gainful employment and the greater well-being of the local community. Mechanisms need to be developed and broadened to formalize the inclusion of market factors and good social and business behavior in the system of NWFP management. Procedures are needed for inspection of proper collection, cultivation, processing, packaging, marketing, maintaining market-demanded quality and schedules. These procedures should be governed by a certification system, which is scientific in operation and global in its acceptance. Central to this approach is the application of a value or commodity market chain method, which can be monitored by both the producers and consumers. Certification of quality product, good management, and fair trade based on the practices of good collection, cultivation, and management can lead to new and economic opportunities such as niche or green markets, price premiums for good social behavior, and a long-term producer–consumer relationship.

Definition, Scope, and Potential

Background

Non-wood forest products (NWFPs) are the other forest products apart from wood in its broadest sense. According to the Food and Agriculture Organization of the United Nations (FAO), NWFPs consist of goods of biological origin other than wood as well as services derived from forests and allied land uses. NWFPs are also understood as forest produce other than timber (construction wood), which can be harvested on a nondestructive basis from nature. More simply put, NWFPs include all goods of biological origin other than wood in all its forms as well as services derived from forests or similar lands. They include a number of goods such as fodder, fibers, flosses, food and food additives, fertilizer (biomass), medicinal plants and herbal potions, phytochemical and aromatic chemicals, fatty oils, latex, gum resin and other exudates, and different kinds of animal products (honey, wax, lac, silk, etc.). They also include services such as grazing, ecotourism, nature trekking, etc. as well as raw materials for different types of rural and cottage industries.

NWFPs are known by different names such as minor, special, nontraditional, and non-timber forest products. Medicinal and aromatic plants (MAPs) are the most prominent NWFP, which have potentialities to safeguard biodiversity, promote sustainable conservation, and help improve the local and national economies. Long-term and equitable economic development of poor NWFP-dependent communities is possible by promoting better protection of indigenous knowledge and providing direct pecuniary benefits to the local people through wise management of NWFPs. International policy documents such as Convention on Biodiversity (CBD), Trade Related Intellectual Property Rights (TRIPS), and Convention on International Trade in Endangered Species (CITES) provide the international legal platform over which different countries are building up their own system of NWFPS management, development, conservation, and commercialization.

NWFPs and People's Livelihoods

In many developing countries, millions of people residing in and around forests rely on NWFPs for their subsistence. More than half of the employment generated in the forestry sector is through NWFPs. Studies in the Rajasthan state of India have indicated that approximately 5 million indigenous populations sustain themselves through collection, processing, and marketing of NWFPs, which amounts to 50–80% of the total forest revenue in many countries. In the Gujarat state of India, 27% of adults and 72% of children and women collect NTFPs in forest regions, while in the Madhya Pradesh state more than 35% of the forest revenue is from NWFPs. In the NWFP-rich Northeast Himalayas, the contribution of the NWFPs to the local economy is up to 60% (**Table 1**).

Medicinal plants are among the most important NWFPs in poor developing countries. According to the World Health Organization (WHO), 80% of the people in developing countries rely on traditional

Table 1 Contribution of non-wood forest products in the rural economy of the northeast Himalayas (Assam and Meghalaya (ML) case studies)

Product	NC Hills, Assam	Karbianglong, Assam	W.K.Hills, ML	W.G.Hills, ML
Percent household involved in extraction of NWFPs				
Bamboo	50–60	45–50	100	100
Subsistence uses	2–3	3–4	0.5	0.7
Commercial uses				
Cane	10–12	12–15	—	—
Subsistence uses	3–4	5–6	0.15	—
Commercial uses				
Others	—	—	45	—
Subsistence uses	—	—	0.3	1
Commercial uses				
Quantity used/sold				
Bamboo				
Subsistence	0.25 t/yr	0.25 t/yr	0.45 t/yr	0.3 t/yr
Commercial	20–30 t/day	35–40 t/day	3–4 t/day	30–40 t/day
Cane				
Subsistence		10–15 kg	5–10 k/yr	—
Commercial	12–15 kg	215 kg/yr	225 kg/yr	—
Others	120–150 kg			
Subsistence			5 kg/yr	70–75 kg/yr
Commercial				
Contribution to household economy				
Bamboo	25–30%	25–30%	15–20%	50–60%
Canes	25–30%	30–35%	15–20%	—
Others	10–15%	15–20%	55–70%	30–35%

natural medicines and 85% of the traditional medicines involve the use of plant extracts. The ancient Indian Classical Ayurvedic texts, *Charaka Samhita*, *Susruth Samhita*, and *Ashtanga Hardaya Samhita*, mention of a large number of medicinal plants for curing different ailments. **Table 2** provides the most commonly used medicinal plants in primary health care. Medicinal plants grow in all kinds of lands throughout the world. A large number of these plants are found in tropical forests and temperate dry slopes, especially in dry and moist deciduous forests and mountainous grasslands. The coastal forests of India, the islands of Borneo and Madagascar, the rainforests of the Amazon and Congo basins, and the entire Hindu Kush, Himalayan and Andean mountain ranges are considered to be the treasure trove of the medicinal plants. Although fewer than 30% of medicinal plants are found in the temperate and dry alpine habitats, they include species of high medicinal value. **Figure 1** gives the distribution of medicinal plants by habits in the Indian subcontinent. One-third each of the medicinal plants are trees and shrubs/climbers and the remaining one-third are herbs/grasses (**Figure 2**). Among the rest of the NWFP species, again more than half are trees. As the demand of several medicinal plants has been increasing at a very fast rate, several species have become threatened or endangered. Threats to wild medicinal plant populations have been classified into seven categories: direct human interference (7.8%), fragmentation (5%), loss of habitat (18.7%), overexploitation (17%), harvest (19.8%), trade (24.6%), and others (7.9%). It may be noted that much of habitat loss and overexploitation are also human-induced.

System of Trade of NWFPs

NWFPs have been traded since the dawn of the exchange and barter system of trade in forest-based goods and services. The intercontinental trade in silk and black pepper dates back several centuries. Today, in most of the developing countries, the national Forest Department leases out the right to collect the NWFPs in designated areas every season or cutting cycle to the highest bidder through a system of auctions or through invitation of bids in a tender system. In this system, basically the state collects rent from the users of the NWFPs. In order to ensure

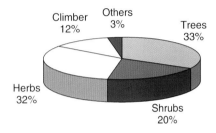

Figure 1   Distribution of medicinal plants by habits, in the Indian subcontinent.

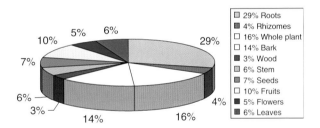

Figure 2   Break down of medicinal plants by their parts utilized, in the Indian subcontinent.

Table 2   Potential NWFP species in the Himalayan Mountains

Local name	Botanical name	Purpose/uses
Jatamansi	*Nardostachys grandifolora*	Medicine/aromatic oil
Sugandhawal	*Valeriana jatamansi*	Aromatic oils/medicine
Kutki	*Picrorhiza scrophulariflora*	Medicine
Chiraito	*Swertia chiraita*	Medicine/others
Guchichyau	*Morchella conica*	Food/medicine
Timur	*Zanthoxylum armatum*	Food/medicine
Dalchini	*Cinnamomum tamala*	Spice/medicine oil
Hathjadi/Panchaunle	*Dactylorhiza hatagirea*	Food/medicine
Atis	*A. heterophyllum*	Medicine
Pipla	*Piper longum*	Spice/medicine
Padamchal	*Rheum australe*	Medicine
Shikakai	*Acacia rugata*	Medicine
Neem	*Azadirachta indica*	Medicine/biopesticide
Amala	*Phyllanthus emblica*	Food/medicine/vitamin
Barro	*Terminalia bellirica*	Medicine
Haro	*Terminalia chebula*	Medicine
Talispatra	*Taxus wallichinana*	Anti-cancerous medicine
Satawari	*Asparagus racemosus*	Food/medicine

adequate and sustained supplies of NWFPs to local healers and village-based enterprises many countries and states have nationalized the trade in NWFPs. The government fixes minimum prices of select products and marketing is also done by the government on behalf of locals. This system is, however, highly inefficient and is on the decline. In many countries, collection, procurement, and marketing of select items of NWFPs especially medicinal plants, whether nationalized or not, is being undertaken through cooperatives of local peoples called community-based organizations.

Exploitative nature of trade The direction of trade in NWFPs is mostly from developing to developed nations, from rural to urban areas. The significant destinations are countries of the European Union (especially Germany), USA, and Japan. The import policies of these major players are increasingly becoming restrictive and are characterized by preference for standardized, organic, and certified produce. Poor nations who are hoping to conserve biodiversity through improved sales of value-added NWFPs are struggling to find stable markets for their NWFPs. However, there are many factors at their end that create market imperfections, price distortion, and sheer exploitation of collectors and small growers by traders and middlemen. In most of the developing as well as developed countries, there is no systematic national level comprehensive database on production, processing, and marketing-related information on NWFPs. In South Asia, countries like India, Nepal, Bhutan, Sri Lanka, and Pakistan are making some efforts in gathering and disseminating information. A number of sample studies have indicated that approximately 150 NWFPs, including 26 essential oils and a large number of botanicals (ranging between 4000 to 6000), enter national and international markets on a regular basis. The size of the global market for botanicals and homeopathic medicines was more than US$20 billion in 1999 and growing.

Environmental Consequences of NWFP Management

Most of the NWFP species including medicinal plants are used locally and information on supply and demand is often insufficient. It is not known whether the plants are abundant, scarce, or under extinction threat or not; if under cultivation then whether the techniques used are proper or not; what gaps exist in market linkages, and whether the species are endangered or threatened. If they are scarce, what conservation measures would be appropriate is also not clearly known. Undoubtedly, the conservation approach needs considerable policy

support, which in most countries is weak. Generally, product samples are not screened for quality, ineffective marketing methods are applied, packaging is of poor standard, and the products have a very limited shelf-life. The situation calls for effective regulatory frameworks both to control infringements of conservation laws and also to provide incentives to local people to use best practices. These are the reasons why NWFPs certification has a big role to play, as it can promote good sourcing, good field collection, good manufacturing, and good laboratory practices in the management of NWFP species.

NWFP Certification

Increasing global awareness of sustainable forest management and liberalized economic development along with the universal acceptance that market forces and consumer preferences dictate the quality of forestry products including NWFPs is necessitating a shift in the management paradigm that ensures the sustainable use of NWFP resources. There is also a need to ensure consumer acceptance and the creation of social and environmental accountability in the trading of natural forest produce. Certification of forests NWFPs is emerging as a widely accepted and effective instrument for possible solutions to these problems.

Evolution of Certification Concepts and Practices

Certification is a process by which the performance of on-the-ground production and handling operations is assessed against a set of predetermined set of standards and guidelines. Certification is a relatively new concept in marketing, which has been initiated to implement the provisions of WTO and other international agreements. In order to encourage sustainable forest management, the majority of timber-exporting countries have, on their own, initiated certification of their forest products. It has since become not only an important tool for conservation of rich forest flora and fauna, but also a promotional label to market forest products from sustainably managed forests. Developing countries, by using this tool wisely, can find their own niche in global NWFP markets and can thereby ensure a greater flow of benefits to the local communities through production of certified forestry products. Certification can create economic incentives to achieve and maintain high standards of forest and NWFP management worldwide.

Rationale for Certification

The certification process commenced with a strong focus on the goal of improving forest management standards, and in particular contributing strongly to reducing the rate of deforestation and degradation of the world's forests, with the initial focus heavily oriented to tropical forests. The aim has been to use market forces to encourage and enable improved management of the forests. Those promoting this new tool hope that buyers, especially in Western countries, will show a preference for certified products, which in turn will either encourage producers to improve their forest management in order to tap this demand, or force them to do so under the threat of losing markets if they do not. The focus has, however, changed considerably as the realities of what it might or might not be able to achieve have become recognized. It has also changed to reflect the interests of many different groups that have become involved with this process one way or another – environmentalists, forest managers, governments, industry, traders, retailers, certifying companies, consultants, investment firms, aid agencies, etc. As a market instrument, certification has both strengths and weaknesses, which vary with the specific circumstances of the producing country, the type of ownership of the NWFP resources, the social and institutional environment and, last but certainly not least, the markets served. A point that should be noted is that sustainable forest management is possible without certification, but the reverse is not.

Objectives of NWFP Certification

The basic objective of certification is to provide proof that all quality control criteria and standard specifications set for a particular production and marketing system have been complied with. The aim is to either increase market share, or at least avoid loss due to boycotts or restrictions such as are increasingly common in some parts of Europe and the USA. The idea is to discourage unethical and unsustainable commercialization of forest products, especially in NWFPs, which is rampant in trade with developing countries. The specifications encompass technical (raw materials, manufacturing process, etc.) as well as legal and financial compliance (environment laws, labor laws, taxes, etc.). The objective of NWFP certification should be to provide solutions towards a responsible trade of NWFPs following the principles of sustainable forest management. Its aim should be to fulfill the following objectives and criteria:

- control and ensure sustainable forest resource management techniques
- have a depth of science with a global scope and be carried out by an active and democratic organization

- manage NWFP resources economically and sustainably
- create a transparent and traceable system that addresses public concerns on environmental values
- manage resources holistically and equitably
- balance the need to extract resources from the environment with maintaining integrity of the ecosystem
- improve livelihood opportunities for local communities, especially women and marginalized groups.

Types of Certification

Basically there are three types of certification that are relevant to NWFPs:

1. Management certification as prescribed by organizations such as the Forest Stewardship Council.
2. Organic certification which complies with standards called as a set of 'Basic Standards for Organic Production and Processing' set by the International Federation of Organic Agriculture Movements (IFOAM). These have to be largely adopted with regional and local specifications throughout the world. IFOAM Basic Standards are also now recognized by the International Standards Organizations (ISO) as universal guidelines.
3. Fair Trade certification which ensures that the trade in NWFPs is done ethically and that proper mechanism of benefits flowing to the collectors and growers is in place.

Potential Advantages of NWFP Certification

Certification has an excellent potential to yield a variety of benefits reflected in the economic, environmental, and social spectrum.

Ecological benefits

- Maintenance and enhancement of forest resource productivity
- Improvement in conservation of biodiversity and its associated benefits such as the hydrological cycle of the area, forest ecosystems, soil fertility due to use of organic substances, and, subsequently, an increase in agricultural production
- Maintenance of ecological functions and integrity of forest ecosystems and their resultant benefits as NWFPs comprise a large and diverse floral vegetation.

Economic benefits

- Increased returns to the producers compared to uncertified forest produce, as certified NWFPs often are high-value low-volume products.

- Greater consumer preferences for certified products provide wider and larger market accessibility and competitive advantages.

Social benefits

- Development and improvement of the company's or producer's public image and workers' satisfaction.
- Improvement in the condition of workers, indigenous communities, and local people through participation of stakeholders in the development of NWFP-based forest/farm management standards.

Other advantages

- Increased market share or at least protection from the loss of the existing market share against the substitutes, such as forest and synthetic products.
- Market premium from selling 'green' products and greater market insurance.
- Long-term supply security because of the sustainability of the resource base, especially forests.
- Establish a basis for comparing different management practices and setting common standards, thus improving the image with a range of interest groups.

Possible disadvantages

- Initial high cost, both financial and managerial, due to initial investment.
- Reduced (short-term) revenue due to reduced output volumes.
- Loss of some control to other groups (e.g., to those developing the certification standards; those less close to the resource).
- Lack of consumer awareness making it hard to achieve an accelerated market penetration.

Components of Certification

Certification of either forest management or organic farms or fairly trading business comprises several activities, each of which has its own rules and guidelines: The main components are:

- certification
- standardization
- accreditation
- logo use (labeling).

Certification Certification is a potential market instrument that can contribute towards improving forest management and at the same time provide an assurance that a product or service is in conformity with certain specified standards. There are two main components of certification: (1) certifying the standards of NWFP-based forest management, and (2) certifying the products from these forests. The first involves an investigation of all the aspects relating to NWFP management including social, economic, and environmental conditions and assessment of how the management of these is being addressed. The process may then include the second component, that of product certification and the associated labeling.

Currently, a wide range of actions is under way concerning certification of NWFPs worldwide. The shift of emphasis from timber and timber products to NWFPs is a recent development. However, attention has mostly included pulp and paper and tea products. First, since a large number of NWFP species collected and transported are straight from the forests, it has been extremely difficult to trace the source of origin of the produce. It is still harder to find out whether or not the harvesting was done in an environmentally sound manner and that the produce available is not responsible for any damage done at the social, economic, or environmental levels. These gaps indicate that there is an urgent need for developing a certification process specifically targeted to the needs of NWFPs. Second, the present trend in management and trade does not lay any emphasis on the process of harvesting of NWFPs either from forested or agricultural lands. The primary forest produce gatherers go to the forests and harvest forest produce without giving much consideration to sustainable harvesting levels and techniques. They have little regard and information regarding the regeneration and health of the forests. Thus, there is a need to check the process of harvesting as well as building capacity of the forest produce collectors and farmers, at the same time as developing the framework for promoting certification of NWFPs including medicinal plants. Recently, several organizations especially the US-based Rainforest Alliance have started certifying NWFPs such as Brazil nuts, maple syrup, and chicle. However, there is considerable variation in what is being certified and some misunderstanding as to what certification of a NWFP actually means. A common assumption is that certification of a NWFP is a guarantee that it has been collected and/or produced in a sustainable way. This may not, in fact, be the case. There are three different certification approaches for NWFPs.

Certificate of origin This is used for a variety of products, including food and medicinal items. It guarantees only that a given product comes from a certain region or area – not necessarily that it has a certain standard of quality. An example is the Denomination of Controlled Origin (DOC) label used for wines, cheeses, and other products by many countries. Certain high-value edible NWFPs, such as truffles and morel mushrooms, are increasingly being certified through such documentation of origin systems.

Product quality standards Organic certification is being used for an increasing number of products, from food to textiles. It certifies that the full production sequence of a product (from the farm up to processing) has respected the criteria set by the competent authority for organic production and chain-of-custody protocols. The quality parameters are set by buyers or their organizations and may differ from market to market.

Social certification This involves documentation of certain social aspects of production, assuring that the labor conditions for production are acceptable, for example, or that the benefits are equitably distributed to those involved in production. Social-based certification schemes have existed for a long time for agricultural and manufacturing products (e.g., for soccer balls certified to have been produced without child labor).

Need for Generic Guidelines for NWFP Certification

As social and cultural issues are important in NWFP certification, there is a need to develop guidelines specifically covering this aspect. The solutions suggested need to be field-tested to determine the relative strengths and weaknesses during the implementation period in the following areas: (1) wider applications, (2) adequacy of plant indicators and verifiers, and (3) suitable species-specific indicators and verifiers. Field tests should be carried out at multiple locations to gather enough data to adequately assess and monitor sustainable NWFP management. In developing specific guidelines, there is a need to interact with a wide range of groups working on sustainable forest management and certification of products including workers engaged in fair trade and organic production and certification as well as the broader community practicing ecologically sustainable forest management. NWFPs do not appear to be adequately covered by any existing certification program, but most programs can make significant contributions to the process by which standards are developed and tested in the field. The work requires wider consultation and multistakeholder collaborations at all times. Certifiable NWFP management processes need to ensure long-term ecological viability of NWFP populations.

NWFP harvesting and management can have lower impacts on forest ecosystems than timber harvesting, but care must be taken that species are not overharvested, and appropriate protection must be provided for vulnerable species in residual stands. Assessments of the field conditions need to be completed prior to the commencement of production and collection activities based on the scale, type, and intensity of management operations.

Performance Indicators and Verifiers

NWFP species, in general, are no more or less susceptible to exploitation than trees. However, parameters to determine (1) the impact of harvest intensity and frequency, (2) the differential response to disturbances including invasion, (3) different regeneration and growth characteristics of different species, and (4) the degree to which the plant depends on animals for pollination and dispersal may need to be defined. Geographic and climatic variations, such as elevation, aspects, and moisture, may also influence production and desirable levels of harvest. Therefore there is a need to divide the broad category of NWFPs into classes, which are based upon the product or plant part harvested, in order to define the performance indicators and verifiers. The following classes of NWFPs has been suggested by the Rainforest Alliance:

- exudates
- vegetative structures: apical bud, bark, root, leaves
- reproductive propagules, fruit, seed.

The purpose is to achieve more effective field assessments by providing information necessary to define sustainability. Species-specific performance indicators, verifiers, and other guidance documents will be required for globally traded NWFPs. These indicators and verifiers can be based upon the general principle that the management plan, implementation activities, and monitoring need to ensure sustainable yield, ecological balance, and good soil/watershed health. Training, capacity building, and empowerment of the stakeholders, accompanied by the provision of information dissemination, are highly desirable activities to provide appropriate benefits to the various stakeholders involved in this sector.

Good Collection, Sourcing, and Manufacturing Practices

WHO has recognized the need to protect medicinal plants by promoting their sustainable use through a system of nondestructive harvesting and cultivation. In order to achieve this through the member countries, a series of good practices such as good agricultural and field collection practices (GAFCP) and good manufacturing practices (GMP) has been proposed. The purpose of GAFCP and GMP is to provide guidelines and set standards regarding the general strategies, basic methods, and simple rules of the game for both small- and large-scale field collections, harvesting, and postharvest handling of fresh NWFPs such as medicinal plant materials. Under these good practices rules, collection practices should ensure the long-term survival of wild populations and their associated habitats. Management plans for field collection should 'provide a rationale for setting harvest levels and describe the implementation of harvest practices that are suitable to each medicinal plant species and plant part used (root, leaves, fruits, etc.). Field collection of medicinal plants raises a number of complex environmental, technical, and social issues that vary widely from region to region and species to species. In many parts of the world, collection of medicinal plants is a cultural practice dating back many centuries, and which has been well recognized and documented as having a strong scientific basis as the practices were refined through years of trials and testing. It is acknowledged that these issues (some of which are outlined below) cannot be fully covered by the guidelines for good practices alone.

- The population density and geographic distribution of species must be identified and a harmony created between level of extraction and resource base to be maintained.
- Essential biological, social, and commercial information must be obtained and targets disseminated to the collectors, growers, processors, and local traders.
- Research on the morphology and variability of the plant must be undertaken in order to develop a 'search image' for the species and maintain authenticity of the plants.
- Training of personnel should be conducted on site or prior to departure so as to ensure quality maintenance across the chain of operations.
- Collection practices should ensure the long-term survival of wild populations and their associated habitats based on the biophysical requirement of each ecosystem and species.
- Medicinal plant parts should be collected during the appropriate season or time period to ensure both sustained yield and species survival.
- Mechanical instruments must be clean and kept in proper condition and operated correctly to ensure quality of the processed products.
- During collection, the crew should be trained to detect and remove nonmedicinal parts, foreign

matter, and damaged/decomposed medicinal plants from the lot.
- The collected raw medicinal plant materials should not come into direct contact with soil, and in case of roots, the attached soil should be washed off properly.
- After collecting and harvesting, the raw medicinal plant parts may be subjected to appropriate preliminary processing. The collected raw medicinal plant material should be protected from pests, rodents, and other animals and stored in proper sanitary conditions.
- Species that are designated as rare or scarce should not be collected from the wild. Collection of the oldest and youngest members of the population should be avoided to maintain ecological balance.
- Medicinal plants should not be collected in areas where pesticides or other possible contaminants are used or found.
- Only ecologically sound and nondestructive means of collection should be employed and collectors must be trained in such methods.
- Different plant species or plant materials should be packed and transferred in separate containers. Cross-contamination should be avoided at all times.
- Cultivation, collection, and harvesting of medicinal plants must be carried out respecting the laws of the land. The provision of national and international conventions such as the Convention on Biological Diversity (CBD) must be respected.
- Agreements on the return of immediate and/or long-term benefits and compensation for the use of sourced medicinal plant materials must be discussed and agreed to in writing prior to collection or cultivation.
- Medicinal plants that are protected by national and international laws such as Control of International Trade in Endangered Species (CITES) must not be collected illegally, and legal procedures must be followed.
- When medicinal plant materials are used from threatened/endangered/protected medicinal plant species through cultivation, the medical plant materials obtained should be given appropriate documentation to certify the source of origin according to national and international legislation, to demonstrate that no plants were collected from the wild population.

Constraints and Issues in Implementing Good Practices

There are a host of issues and constraints that need to be resolved to successfully implement good practices and certification of good practices, quality products, and fair trade. Among them policy and institutional issues are the most important.

NWFP policy issues   Critical review of the existing NWFP policies, legal framework, and institutional environment accompanied by justified revisions considering the above-mentioned issues are the most urgent tasks for achieving sustainable management of NWFP resources in developing countries. The policy and regulatory constraints are mainly of four types.

Regulatory policy issues   The regulatory policies are related to harvesting/collection, transport, and processing of NWFPs. Unsustainable harvesting of NWFPs from the wild is a serious issue which is also related to the principles and mechanism of appraising, monitoring, enforcing, and sanctioning rule-breakers in the sustainable management and harvesting of NWFPs. Various types of permits have been designed to implement regulatory policies, although no systematic and detailed inventory of NWFPs has so far been undertaken. The transaction cost of these instruments such as issuing permits, monitoring sustainable harvesting, enforcement of rules, etc. is a serious financial and economic issue. Moreover, the provision of these permits has encouraged rent-seeking behavior among various stakeholders.

Fiscal policy   Fiscal policies are related to the imposition of various types of taxes and subsidies that affect various agents involved in the collection, processing, and export of NWFPs. Revenue collection mechanisms such as royalties, and export and other informal taxes are included in this category. Some of the community forestry projects are now providing materials such as seeds and seedlings, and some block grants to promote the cultivation of NWFPs. Major fiscal policy constraints in the development of NWFP subsector are: (1) the system of royalty fixation and collection is irrational and (2) different forms of informal taxes are levied by various organizations which create various forms of disincentives.

Institutional and policy issues   The instruments and organizations using the rules and regulations to regulate NWFP trade and use comprise the institutions and organizations relevant to the NWFP policies. The revenue collection mechanisms used by the government are fundamental for the sustainable NWFP management, local addition, and generation of employment for the poor. Coordination

and cooperation among the NWFP stakeholders are the major policy issues having impacts on the conservation and sustainable use of the NWFP resources. The major institutional constraints in the development of the NWFP subsector remain the lack of coordination among different stakeholders for policy coordination and project implementation.

Marketing and trade issues   Many agents and institutions are involved in the collection, trade processing, and marketing of NWFPs. Marketing information on, and knowledge of, NWFPs is very weak among collectors, traders, and government officials. Similarly, the capital market is imperfect in rural areas. This has led to high interest rates being paid by NWFP collectors in the remote areas of the Himalayas. Input and output markets need to be made more effective and efficient for the growth of NWFPs.

A major issue in the marketing and trade of NWFPs is the lack of a system of transparent and accessible information collection, dissemination, and use by the collectors and growers so as to increase their bargaining power in negotiating the price of the NWFP. The nationalization or ban of collection and sales of many NWFP species has restricted the free and assured supply to the market resulting in a limited number of buyers who operate in monopsonic/monopolistic conditions.

General Opportunities in Implementing Good Management Practices

A large number of MAP species that are currently harvested from the wild are also possible to be regenerated *in situ* and cultivated *ex situ* by training and organizing traditional collectors and farmers. Different types of micro-enterprises, producer companies, and services agencies can be set up to produce quality raw materials, to insure that rural livelihoods are supported. Relevant factors for this type of development include:

- Existence of a high level of market demand, accessibility, and scope for reaching international, regional, national, and local markets with organic and certified products.
- Possibilities for augmenting raw material supplies through domestication, *ex situ* cultivation, and sustainable harvesting (many countries have large areas under forests, shrublands, and rangelands).
- Access to postharvest and processing technology, availability of skilled labor, infrastructure, and capital (e.g., the savings-to-loan ratio is quite low in South Asia and government budgets are not spent properly).

- Potential for decentralized production, processing, and marketing, and thereby downstreaming of the benefits to the local people as the supply chain of the quality MAP products link rural to urban areas.
- Economic viability of raw material collection, cultivation, primary processing, and marketing as the investment is low and returns are assured or have less risk.
- Availability of reliable markets for quality products, e.g., a buy-back guarantee to the collectors within the country and region.
- Possibility for creating MAP-based small and micro enterprises as well as organizing a viable enterprise support service, in the private sector, in order to provide credits, extension services, technical advice, plant management training, and market information on reliable terms and conditions.

Discussion

Sustainable and equitable commercialization of NWFPs holds a great promise in promoting economic growth and social equity in poverty-stricken but biodiversity-rich developing countries. The existing system of extraction and trade is exploitative, inequitable, and unsustainable. A certifiable system backed by implementation of good production, processing, and marketing practices using the commodity chain model is felt to be an answer, that can lead to better market access, product assessment, product development, and certification. Lessons learned from different parts of the world can provide us with in-depth knowledge of the diversity, complexity, and potentials of NWFPs in improving livelihoods and conserving biodiversity.

However, this article further suggests an approach of improved management practices and regulatory frameworks to contain NWFP resource misuse and environmental degradation. Training and capacity-building of local people are necessary prerequisites for implementing good management practices that can lead to income generation and local biodiversity conservation. When communities are provided with technical, financial, managerial, marketing, and training support, they will have better incentives to conserve the NWFP diversity of their forests. As community groups move from being only suppliers of raw materials to being processors and market players of those raw materials, they become aware of the greater values of the resources that can be realized by them, and thereby promote the conservation of those resources to assure a sustainable supply for their commercial operation. This in essence is the foundation for the institutionalization of good practices and of acquiring national and international certification.

See also: **Medicinal, Food and Aromatic Plants**: Edible Products from the Forest; Forest Biodiversity Prospecting; Medicinal and Aromatic Plants: Ethnobotany and Conservation Status; Medicinal Plants and Human Health; Tribal Medicine and Medicinal Plants. **Non-wood Products**: Resins, Latex and Palm Oil; Rubber Trees; Seasonal Greenery. **Silviculture**: Bamboos and their Role in Ecosystem Rehabilitation; Managing for Tropical Non-timber Forest Products.

Further Reading

Chamberlain J, Bush R, and Hammett AL (1998) Non-timber forest products: the OTHER forest products. *Forest Products Journal* 48: 11–19.

FAO (1995a) *Report of the International Expert Consultation on Non-Wood Forest Products, Yogyakarta, Indonesia.* FAO Technical Paper no. 3. Rome: Food and Agriculture Organization.

FAO (1995b) *Non-Wood Forest Products for Rural Income and Sustainable Forestry.* FAO Technical Paper no. 7. Rome: Food and Agriculture Organization.

FSC (1998) *Principles and Criteria for Forest Management.* London: Forest Stewardship Council.

GOI, Planning Commission (2000) *Report of the Task Force on Conservation and Sustainable Use of Medicinal Plants; Government of India.* New Delhi, India: Planning Commission, Yojana Bhawan.

IFOAM (2003) *Small Holder Group Certification: Compilation of Results.* IFOAM Compilation no. 03-03. Tholey-Theley, Germany: International Federation of Organic Agriculture Movements.

IIRR (2000) *Workshop on Shifting Cultivation for Sustainability and Resource Conservation in Asia,* August 14–27 2000, Manila, Philippines.

Karki M (2000a) Commercialization of natural resources for sustainable livelihoods: the case of forest products; In: *Growth, Poverty Alleviation and Sustainable Management in the Mountain Areas of South Asia.* pp. 293–320. Feldafing, Germany: German Foundation for International Development.

Karki M (2000b) Development of biopartnership for sustainable management of medicinal and aromatic plants in South Asia. In: *Proceedings of 21st IUFRO Congress,* August 6–12 2000, Kuala Lumpur, pp. 51–60.

Karki M (2001) Institutional and socioeconomic factors and enabling policies for non-timber forest products-based development in northeast India. In: *Pre-identification Workshop for NTFP-led Development in Northeast India,* February 22–23 2001, Rome, pp. 43–57(1–14).

Karki M (2002) Certification and marketing strategies for sustainable commercialization of medicinal and aromatic plants in Chhattisgarh. In: *Proceedings of National Research Seminar on Herbal Conservation, Cultivation, Marketing and Utilization with special emphasis on Chhattisgarh,* December 13–14 2001, Raipur, India, pp. 15–17.

Karki M (2003) Certification and marketing strategies for sustainable commercialization of medicinal and aromatic plants in South Asia. In: *Proceedings of IUFRO All Division 5 Forest Products Conference*, March 11–15 2003, Rotorua, New Zealand.

Karki M, Tiwari BK, Badoni AK, and Bhattarai NK (2003) Creating livelihoods and enhancing biodiversity-rich production systems based on medicinal and aromatic plants: preliminary lessons from South Asia. In: *Proceedings of 3rd World Congress on Medicinal and Aromatic Plants for Human Welfare*, February 3–7 2003, Chiang Mai, Thailand.

Kinhal GA (2003) Regulatory framework for harvest and trade in wild species of medicinal plants: principles, design and challenges. In: *Proceedings of the Workshop on Certification of Non-Wood Forest Produce Including Medicinal, Aromatic and Dye Plants*, pp. 10–12. 9 April, 2003, Raipur. Raipur, Chattisgarh, India: Chattisgarh Forest Department.

Pierce A and Laird SA (2003) Sustainable botanicals: in search of comprehensive standards for non-timber forest products in the botanicals trade. *International Forestry Review*.

Planning Commission, Government of India (2000) *Report of the Task Force on Conservation and Sustainable Use of Medicinal Plants*. New Delhi: Planning Commission, Government of India.

Rainforest Alliance (1988) *The Conservation Agriculture Program, Certification Criteria, 1998*. New York: Rainforest Alliance.

WHO (2002a) *WHO Traditional Medicine Strategy 2002–2005*. Geneva, Switzerland: World Health Organization.

WHO (2002b) *WHO Guidelines of Good Agricultural and Field Collection Practices (GACP) for Medicinal Plants* (Draft). Geneva, Switzerland: World Health Organization.

Causes of Deforestation and Forest Fragmentation

J Ghazoul and J Evans, Imperial College London, Ascot, UK

Introduction

At the close of the twentieth century there remained an estimated 1700 million ha of tropical forests and 1600 million ha of temperate forests worldwide. These figures represent about 60% of the original forest cover that is estimated to have existed some 8000 years ago. Much of this loss can be directly attributed to human impacts over the last three millennia, with increased clearance in recent centuries, and even more recently in tropical regions.

Forests provide important resources and a multitude of natural services and their recent rapid destruction is causing increasing concern due to environmental, social, and economic problems across the globe. However, developing solutions is proving to be a highly complex task due to the variety of causes of deforestation and conflicting stakeholder interests.

Deforestation is the complete or almost complete removal of tree cover and conversion of the land to other uses. Technically, deforestation may be defined as the semipermanent depletion of tree crown cover to less than 10%. In this respect a distinction needs to be made between deforestation and forest degradation, which is the significant damage to forest ecosystems but without the total elimination of forest cover.

This article begins by describing current deforestation trends. The present causes of deforestation in recent years are discussed, followed by the consequences of deforestation for a variety of environmental parameters. Solutions to the deforestation problem are presented, and potential future trends are described with a brief discussion of the impact of projected climate change.

Historical Deforestation and Land Clearance

At the advent of agriculture some 8000 years ago forests are thought to have covered approximately 40% of the world's land area, or about 6000 million ha. Up to 1500 AD the spread of agriculture across the globe resulted in the clearance of many forests, particularly those on the most accessible and fertile land. However, in the last 200 years deforestation rates have increased greatly. Between 1850 and 1980, 15% of the world's forests and woodlands were cleared. The world forest area has now shrunk to 3500 million ha as a consequence of human exploitation, most of which occurred in the latter half of the twentieth century.

Contemporary Deforestation

Deforestation and land clearance in the twentieth century increased greatly, with the highest rates of clearance occurring since 1960. Most current deforestation occurs in the tropical regions, while in temperate countries there has been a net increase of forest cover by 0.1% due to reforestation and regeneration policies. In Canada the area of land under tree cover increased by 1.4 million hectares to 417.6 million ha in the late 1980s. The Food and Agriculture Organization (FAO) has estimated annual rates of forest clearance in developing countries at 15.5 million ha for the period 1980–1990, and 12.3 million ha for 1990–2000. Thus, the total area of forest cleared during this 20-year period is approximately 280 million ha.

The causes of deforestation vary among regions. In Africa FAO reports that the major direct cause of deforestation is clearance by farmers driven by increasing population pressures. In Latin America settlement and infrastructure projects in forested areas result in clearance of land for cattle ranching and permanent agriculture, often combined with financial incentives such as subsidies and favorable tax policies. In Asia intensive timber harvesting and shifting cultivation as well as the expansion of large-scale agricultural projects and plantation crops such as oil palm and rubber and, to a lesser extent, transmigration projects, all contribute to deforestation. Forest land is often not suitable for sustainable agricultural development and, as soils become exhausted, new areas of forest have to be cleared. For example, 80% of the Amazon basin is ill-suited to sedentary farming. Desertification through unsustainable agricultural development has contributed to much deforestation in drier regions of Africa and Asia.

Most deforestation is concentrated in relatively few tropical countries. Fifty percent of global deforestation occurs in 10 developing countries (**Table 1**). Brazil is typical of tropical countries in that deforestation rates were low until the 1970s. Since then extensive spread of agriculture and ranching, encouraged by government subsidies, and clearance by landless farmers, has resulted in very rapid deforestation. Large-scale development and industrial projects such as mining and hydroelectric plants have contributed to these high deforestation rates in the tropics. Thus deforestation is largely a tropical issue (**Table 2**). As a large proportion of the world's biodiversity is found within tropical forests, tropical deforestation impacts also have very great relevance to global biodiversity.

In temperate countries there is no overall deforestation in terms of net area but a small increase in forest cover owing to policies of afforestation. However, this statement disguises a steady and continuing transition from natural forest formations to managed and plantation forests. In this sense there is some clearance of natural forest in temperate regions with the consequent loss of biodiversity. This trend is likely to decrease as conservation priorities assert themselves, except in eastern Europe and Russia where the importance of forest resources as an accessible and tradeable commodity takes priority. Nevertheless, in Europe as a whole there is very little natural forest undisturbed by human intervention, the forest of Bialowiezca in Poland being one of the few extensive examples of reasonably extant forest not dissimilar to the ancient 'wild wood.'

Causes of Deforestation

There is no single cause of deforestation but rather it is the result of the interaction of social, economic, political, and cultural forces with the environment. Several underlying socioeconomic causes create conditions that favor forest clearance by readily identifiable direct causes.

Underlying Causes of Deforestation

The underlying causes of deforestation are the factors that give rise to conditions in which forest clearance becomes a rational or necessary behavior. They may be local or national socioeconomic or political forces, or they may be external global forces such as the state of the global market economy. They are generally beyond the control of an individual but strongly influence the decisions individuals make regarding the management and use of forests and forest resources.

Table 1 'Top 10' deforesting countries in terms of annual rate of forest loss (1995)

Country	Ranking	Annual loss (hectares)
Brazil	1	2 550 000
Indonesia	2	1 080 000
Congo	3	740 000
Bolivia	4	580 000
Mexico	5	510 000
Venezuela	6	500 000
Malaysia	7	400 000
Myanmar	8	390 000
Sudan	9	350 000
Thailand	10	330 000

Reproduced with permission from FAO (1999) *State of the World's Forests 1999*. Rome, Italy: Food and Agriculture Organization of the United Nations.

Table 2 The rate of annual forest loss (1995) expressed as a percentage of forest area in 10 important deforesting countries and regions

Country	Ranking	Annual loss (%)
Philippines	1	− 3.5
Sierra Leone	2	− 3.0
Pakistan	3	− 2.9
Thailand	4	− 2.6
Paraguay	5	− 2.6
Central America	6	− 2.1
Caribbean Islands	7	− 1.7
Cambodia	8	− 1.6
Ecuador	9	− 1.6
Myanmar	10	− 1.6

Reproduced with permission from FAO (1999) *State of the World's Forests 1999*. Rome, Italy: Food and Agriculture Organization of the United Nations.

Population growth and poverty   Population growth is one of the most publicized but misleading underlying factors for tropical deforestation. Increasing populations place pressure on forests and the resources they supply. The rural poor have very few economic options and are often forced to seek short-term solutions to their economic problems. These solutions include clearing forested land to grow subsistence crops. Opportunities for improving livelihoods by other means are limited due to low political priority, the lack of rural capital, low capacity of subsistence farming to generate income, and the lack of infrastructure and education.

Development policies and tax incentives   Debt repayments constitute a large proportion of the national budget of many tropical countries, and structural adjustment programs introduced as a result often favor the maximization of foreign exchange through direct and unsustainable exploitation of forest capital, and by conversion of forests to agriculture for export crops. Large-scale extensive agricultural development, frequently at the expense of small farmers as well as forest cover, is further encouraged through the provision of state subsidies for agriculture and livestock expansion, reduction in income and corporate taxes, and tax breaks on imports of equipment for new industries. Expansion of agricultural crops for export or to satisfy national demands destroys forest directly, but it also causes the displacement of subsistence farmers who are forced to relocate and clear new and often marginal lands elsewhere.

The privatization of public resources, advocated by the World Bank and some bilateral donor agencies, favors management strategies that maximize the short-term economic gain for the new owners, while nonmonetary forest services, such as soil conservation and watershed protection, are not valued highly in a market-driven environment. Government incentives and subsidies have allowed some otherwise uneconomical industries to prosper at the expense of forest cover, while development projects often fail to account fully for the value of forest capital lost.

A failure to understand the real value of forests' goods and services results in the establishment of poor policies. The institutional weakness of the national forest department or corruption within the government can lead to policy decisions that favor private interests at the expense of the benefits to society as a whole. In recent years there has been an improvement in the reformulation of forest policies of several tropical countries. Subsidies that promote cattle ranching have been withdrawn in Brazil, while

Costa Rica is now beginning to account for the destruction of forest capital in its national economic accounts.

Tenurial policies   Much agricultural land in the tropics is owned by large landowners or corporations and improved agricultural production is obtained using chemical fertilizers and pesticides which, together with mechanization of labor, is most efficient on large-scale agricultural systems. This favors large farmers who have the capital to invest in such innovations and the land area to benefit from economies of scale. Small farmers who may not have legal title to their land are frequently displaced or forced to sell their land through mounting debts. These farmers often move to the forest frontier to clear a new plot of land, and it is usually politically easier for governments to ignore deforestation than to deal with the difficult issues of land redistribution or job creation.

Legal ownership of land has a great effect on the attitude people have to the land. Without legal land title there is little incentive to invest in increasing land productivity. It becomes economically logical to pursue short-term gain and to move on to clear new forest land once productivity declines. As most tropical forest lands are owned by the state, clearance is often illegal and governments are unwilling to grant legal title to small farmers for land acquired in this way. Lack of land ownership excludes farmers from obtaining credit to purchase seed or fertilizers and pesticides and discourages any long-term investment. In many Pacific-rim countries customary land ownership prevails. Precise boundaries are frequently unsurveyed and local communities and groups know only from tradition what is their land. Wholesale allocation of logging rights can be conveyed either by the local people themselves with relatively little outside control or, conversely, imposed from outside by governments that fail to account for local people's interests. In either case the land tenure system is a weak instrument in preventing unplanned deforestation and land clearance.

Market demands   As populations grow and become more affluent the demand for forest products rises, particularly for industrial timber and pulpwood for making paper. However, while it can be readily demonstrated that some countries have significant forest product exports (**Table 3**), the extent to which international markets contribute to deforestation varies greatly from country to country. In the top 10 deforesting countries it is the national demand for forest products that accounts for most industrial deforestation. Furthermore, there is not a strong link

Table 3 The importance of exports to the forest-based economies of the top 10 deforesting countries in 1996

Country	Timber products[a]			Paper and paperboard[b]			Charcoal and fuelwood			Total
	Production	Export	%	Production	Export	%	Production	Export	%	(%)
Brazil	107 360	5019	4.7	12 110	3396	28.0	135 652	63	0.05	3.3
Indonesia	64 711	9414	14.5	7021	2342	33.4	153 540	1039	0.7	5.7
Congo, DR	3554	227	6.4	3	0	0	45 142	0	0	0.5
Bolivia	1070	150	14.0	2	0	0	1419	0	0	6.0
Mexico	9063	557	6.1	3558	328	9.2	16 731	136	0.8	3.5
Venezuela	1790	52	2.9	900	50	5.6	918	0	0	2.8
Malaysia	50 923	16 143	31.7	777	41	5.3	10 035	186	1.9	26.5
Myanmar	3399	689	20.3	24	0	0	20 612	53	0.3	3.1
Sudan	2321	0	0	3	0	0	14 600	0	0	0
Thailand	3636	614	16.9	2744	335	12.2	36 894	53	0.1	2.3

All values in thousand m^3.
[a] Includes industrial roundwood, sawnwood, and wood-based panels.
[b] Includes pulp for paper.
Reproduced with permission from FAO (1999) *State of the World's Forests 1999*. Rome, Italy: Food and Agriculture Organization of the United Nations.

between rising international demand for forest products generally and deforestation. This is, first, because almost all pulp and paper comes from temperate forests or specially established tropical plantations, since paper manufactured from mixed tropical forest is generally expensive and has poor quality owing to the lack of wood uniformity. Second, much of the world's industrial-grade timber is softwood, i.e., coniferous, and tropical forests are overwhelmingly broad-leaved hardwoods. Supplies of industrial lumber in tropical countries increasingly come from tropical conifer plantations, notably of pines and cypress. Clearance of forest for agricultural production also appears to be driven by growing national demand for agricultural crops (over and above those for crops). All of the important deforesting countries listed in **Table 1**, except for Thailand, remain net importers of rice or maize and for many of these countries self-sufficiency in agricultural production has been a primary development goal that has led to policies that encourage conversion of forests to fields. Over the past decade, for example, the domestic demand for palm oil in Indonesia has led to the widespread establishment of plantations even though palm oil exports have remained at between 6% and 8% of the total production. Similarly, rising production of beef in Central and South America to feed a growing domestic market has resulted in extensive deforestation by ranchers, farmers, and land speculators.

Deforestation due to agricultural and livestock production is therefore largely due to the growth in the domestic markets and only partially attributable to markets in the developed world. Although the importance of export markets should not be underestimated, national market forces appear to be more important than international trade in determining the rates and extent of tropical deforestation. Consequently, it is likely that international trade offers only limited scope for reducing deforestation rates in most tropical countries.

Undervaluation of forests and forest products
Where logging has preceded wholesale land clearance, it is often because the value placed on the timber is no more than the cost of extraction and marketing. The value does not reflect cost of replacement nor cost of growing beyond what is often a nominal payment of royalty to the owner. If timber were valued to reflect its true cost of replacement, then growing trees to produce timber would become economically worthwhile and hence potentially a sustainable option. While it is not worthwhile, deforestation, especially in the tropics, is likely to continue because clearance and conversion are perceived as more profitable. However, undervaluation has a further dimension. The non-timber benefits and services trees and forests provide are often far more important than their timber products. Environmental benefits of soil protection, shelter, microclimate amelioration, and contribution to regional and global hydrological and carbon cycles all confer great benefits which are rarely quantified and hardly ever incorporated in economic assessments. Only when massive downstream flooding is traced back to wanton deforestation in the catchment are such connections made.

A major underlying cause of deforestation is this widespread failure to value sufficiently both forest products and the many environmental benefits forests bring. Regrettably, it is largely because simple and widely accepted approaches to such valuations in economic terms do not exist. For example, stumpage, the charges that governments demand from loggers for state-owned timber, often under-values the resource, which encourages waste and makes other land uses more economically attractive.

Weak government institutions While almost all countries have explicit forest laws and policies designed to conserve forest, two features of forest conditions in tropical countries exacerbate the risk of deforestation. First, extensive forests are likely to be remote from towns and cities and hence far from the rule of law. It is easy for illegal logging and clearance to continue unseen and unchecked. Second, forest services are frequently the 'Cinderella' organization of government, being viewed as inferior to agriculture and even wildlife and tourism. Few resources are attracted and poorly paid staff often have difficulty both in ensuring that sustainable management practices are implemented and in imposing their authority on perhaps large private-sector interests. Quite apart from the risk of corruption that these circumstances afford, many staff, once trained, simply dislike the remoteness of forest management and supervision and prefer the white-collar work of the city office.

Direct Causes of Deforestation

Shifting cultivation The contribution of small-scale shifting agriculture to tropical deforestation remains unresolved due to the widely variable agricultural practices that are encompassed by this term. Some types of small-scale agriculture undoubtedly cause deforestation, but the inherent stability and long-term viability of many shifting cultivation systems are unlikely to result in long-term forest clearance. The least destructive form of shifting cultivation is where land cultivated for 2–3 years is then left for a long fallow period. This long fallow shifting cultivation only occurs under conditions of very low human population density.

Expanding populations, land scarcity, and government policies have also created shifted cultivators who now form the typical slash-and-burn farmers of recent decades. Unlike the traditional farmers who have practiced shifting cultivation for decades, these shifted agriculturists have been forced by circumstances or government policy to cultivate habitats that are unfamiliar to them. Government resettlement and transmigration schemes such as those in Indonesia attract migrants for whom forest cultivation is an unfamiliar means of generating a livelihood and income. Similarly, in the Amazon, migrant cultivators are attracted to the forest frontier where they clear and cultivate land for a few years. This land quickly becomes exhausted due to unsuitable soils or farming techniques and the land is sold to

cattle ranchers while the 'farmers' move on to clear more land.

Commercial agriculture Large-scale commercial agriculture is most frequently practiced by large corporations or state enterprises. These large operations can dispossess local landowners and farmers of the best and most fertile agricultural land, indirectly leading to deforestation in areas to which the farmers relocate. The establishment of oil palm plantations in valleys of Honduras in the 1970s displaced thousands of farmers who were forced to clear forests from steep slopes to establish new farms.

Commercial agriculture often leads to direct conversion of large tracts of forest to plantation estates and rice fields. This has been particularly prevalent in Indonesia and other regions of Southeast Asia where oil palm, coconut, or rubber plantations have been established on cleared forest land. In Indonesia oil palm plantations have increased from about 4 million ha in 1980 to 5.8 million ha in 1995. Land clearance for agricultural development is often subsidized by governments and, because the owners of the agribusiness companies are politically well appointed, there is little interest in forest protection. Areas for conversion are frequently burnt as this is the least extensive method of clearance, and natural events such as the 1997–1998 El Niño are used as an opportunity to do so.

Cattle ranching and livestock grazing Intensive clearing of forest land in South and Central America has arisen from expansion of cattle ranching which was economically attractive due to low risk, little labor, well-established markets, and the availability of government subsidies. Cattle ranching expanded initially in response to the opening of large markets in North America, but has been sustained by the growing domestic markets for beef. Ranchers cleared forest land either by purchasing it directly and employing labor, or by purchasing land from slash-and-burn farmers and converted this land to grass-lands. The shifting cultivators would move deeper into the forest to repeat the cycle. The area of pasture in Central America is estimated to have increased from 3.9 million ha in 1955 to 13.4 million ha in 1995 and has been largely at the expense of the area's tropical forests. Thus, deforestation in Latin America due to ranching is also associated with slash-and-burn agriculture and land speculation.

Livestock grazing causes deforestation in Africa wherever herds exceed the carrying capacity of the area. Such pressure is acute in the drier tropics such as the Sahel region of Africa and in the Middle East where large flocks of sheep and goats are maintained.

The history of deforestation around the Mediterranean is linked to grazing regimes, especially by goats, but past simplistic assumptions have given way to the recognition that climatic, sociological, and agrarian factors have also contributed to forest clearance.

Infrastructural development Through the 1970s and early 1980s, development of the Amazon, which is illustrative of similar strategies throughout the tropics, was actively encouraged by the Brazilian government through the building of roads, tax incentives and subsidies, massive resettlement, and large-scale development programs. The Trans-Amazonian highway opened up millions of square kilometers of inaccessible forest to colonization and allowed further expansion of the cattle industry. Such roads improve access to poorly developed areas and therefore tend to increase the adjacent land value for nonforest uses and encourage land speculation and deforestation. Recent slowing of deforestation is due to Brazil's economic recession and has been aided by changes in government policies on tax incentives and subsidies, and increased enforcement of environmental regulations. Logging roads in Asia also facilitate deforestation by allowing access to farmers and illegal loggers who follow and deforest an area that is otherwise merely degraded through selective logging.

Plantations Much forest has been cleared for commercial plantation crops such as rubber, oil palm, and the beverage crops of cocoa, coffee, and tea. Huge areas of dipterocarp forest in peninsular Malaysia have been converted to oil palm or rubber plantations and, while such perennial woody crops offer some soil protection, the loss in biodiversity is enormous. Indeed, it can be argued that the great bulk of the world's tropical plantation crops, about 26.5 million ha, are on former forest land.

A key principle of good forest stewardship is that forest plantations for timber production are only located on already cut-over, abandoned, or waste land and in this way can actually help deflect pressure away from natural forest. However, the subject is not quite as simple since many forests have enjoyed enrichment by planting or have arisen through tree-planting operations, such as many 'natural' forests in France, Germany, and elsewhere.

Fuelwood collection and charcoal production Fuelwood accounts for over 50% of global wood use and for some 80% of all wood use in developing countries. Dependence on fuelwood is expected to decrease gradually with the introduction of electricity, kerosene, and propane, but heavy dependence on fuelwood by the rural poor is expected to continue well into the twenty-first century. Fuelwood collection as an agent of deforestation is particularly marked around urban centers and villages where continuous collection results in the gradual degradation and eventual deforestation of accessible areas. This is critical in the dry tropics along with domestic use of wood for other uses such as construction and fencing material.

Logging The most optimistic independent estimates of the amount of sustainably managed productive forest in the tropics are no more than 2% of the productive forest area. Most tropical logging consists of short-term exploitation of timber products with little concern for the future potential of the forest. This is largely due to insecurity of tenure and short concession periods. Although the intensity of logging in the tropics is usually low, removal of only 10% of the timber trees can result in damage to 55% or more of the remaining trees. Nevertheless, logging operations in the tropics usually result in degradation of the forest rather than its complete elimination. Deforestation does occur along logging roads, where forest is cleared for several meters either side, allowing the sun to dry the road surface. Poorly designed roads can result in severe erosion and landslides as well as facilitating movement into the area by illegal loggers and slash-and-burn cultivators, who often cause much greater damage than the initial logging operations. Logging continues to be one of the most important causes of forest degradation but not deforestation, although intensive logging in Southeast Asia has resulted in the conversion of thousands of hectares of forest to alang-alang (*Imperata cylindrica*) grassland that excludes almost all other vegetation.

Following industrial extraction of timber farmers, agribusinesses, ranchers, fuelwood collectors, and illegal loggers move in along logging roads to clear the land for other uses. Management plans and government policies oblige industrial foresters to prevent encroachment of this sort, but these rules are poorly enforced due to lack of will or staff.

The length of concessions is very often short, sometimes less than 10 years, and very rarely more than the rotation of the crop. In the absence of a long-term commitment the logging company has little incentive to invest in long-term forest management. Concessions are also granted for timber only with little regard for the other resources provided by the forest and the impact of the logging on local people.

Fire Serious losses in forest cover in Southeast Asia and South America have been reported as a result of forest fires in 1997 and 1998. The causes of these fires are new large-scale commercial agricultural projects (including plantations) and shifting cultivation. The fires were exacerbated by the dry coarse woody debris left after logging operations and the very dry climatic conditions caused by the El Niño phenomenon. The area of forest consumed by fires in 1997–1998 has not been accurately documented but estimates vary from 170 000 ha to over 2 million ha. Extensive fires in tropical moist forests have been previously associated with El Niño phenomenon, as in 1982, but the underlying causes are clearance of forest to establish plantations of oil palm, pulp wood, and rice and, in South America, cattle pastures and shifting cultivation.

Alternatives for Sustainable Development

Protection and Management of the Remaining Forests

Protected-area systems   Protected-area systems are needed to conserve habitat and biodiversity from encroachment and poaching. The majority of countries fall well short of placing 12% of their land surface within a protected area system as endorsed by the United Nations Conference on the Environment and Development (UNCED). To be effective, protected areas need to be sufficiently large to conserve all the biodiversity they contain and to include a broad range of naturally occurring forest types and all stages of natural succession. To be successful, protected-area systems need to be supported by adequate funding and legislation and managed by strong institutional departments. However, forest protection must be developed with the cooperation of the local communities that use forest resources, as alienation of them has led to failure or inadequate protection.

Joint forest management   New approaches to managing forest resources involve partnerships between local communities and local or national governments. These partnerships provide for sensitive management that acknowledges the needs of all stakeholders by providing a wide variety of benefits in a sustainable manner. Forest management decisions are made at a local level and are informed by state-supported science and developmental technologies. Providing local stakeholders with access to and benefits from forest resources and empowering them with the management of these resources encourages sustainable development and investment in forests.

Sustainable timber harvest procedures   Timber harvest practices that minimize damage to forests are well known but rarely implemented due to the perceived high cost. Indeed, over a short time scale, reduced impact logging procedures are more costly, but over the longer term they are cheaper due to increased efficiency of extraction (by eliminating extraction of low-value trees and damage to high-value timber) and reduced damage to the remaining forest stand. National standards for logging operations, where they exist, are often flouted and enforcement is weak.

To encourage sustainable timber production, most timber-producing countries have adopted criteria and indicator systems for sustainable forest management. These systems provide tools for assessing the state of forests which can be used to promote and inform sustainable forest management. Their development has been hampered by the complexities of definition of sustainable forest management and how to interpret the information generated. However, intergovernmental processes and market-led certification schemes seek to encourage wise and sustainable forest management.

Socioeconomic and Agricultural Development

Improving the productivity of subsistence agriculture and ranching   Greater productivity from and improved use of existing agricultural land, through intensification of agroforestry, will lessen the pressure for clearance of new forested lands and will promote private investment into currently occupied land which in turn encourages sustainable use. State-supported investment in deforested marginal lands, fair credit schemes, and educational development are all needed to provide extension services to improve the efficiency of land use.

An estimated 200 million ha of degraded lands exist in upland watersheds of tropical countries as a result of deforestation. Restoration of these lands through tree planting or for agricultural production will further alleviate the pressure on forest lands from agricultural expansion. Multiple-use species provide both benefits directly and additionally serve to renew a watershed's ability to regulate groundwater and reduce soil erosion (**Table 4**).

Tree plantations   Tree and forest plantations are not substitutes for natural forest but, appropriately sited, they can alleviate deforestation pressures. Plantations on already degraded land can be an excellent source of industrial-grade timber, pulpwood for paper-making, and fuel–solid firewood and charcoal. Thus they provide an alternative source of such products. In the tropics and subtropics there are estimated to be about 70 million ha of industrial plantations, of which probably 55 million ha are reasonably well stocked. This area is slowly increasing, is often more productive than temperate

Table 4 Soil erosion rates

	Rate (t ha^{-1} year^{-1})
Undisturbed natural forest	Negligible
Cut-over forest with litter and organic matter intact	1–5
Cut-over forest with litter and organic matter removed	30–100
Forest plantations with litter and undergrowth	0.5–3
Forest plantations with no undergrowth and litter removed	up to 100
Undisturbed or lightly grazed grassland	2–10
Cultivated arable land (depending on slope, terracing, and soil type)	20–400

Reproduced with permission from Evans J (1992) *Plantation Forestry in the Tropics*. Oxford, UK: Oxford University Press.

plantations, and represents a major new wood resource. Taking the world as a whole, nearly half of all industrial timber is likely to be sourced from plantations by about 2020.

Profitable plantations risk undermining the perceived value of natural forest and may accelerate conversion of these to plantations. If the primary cause behind deforestation is the conversion of land for agricultural development it is unlikely that plantations will reduce deforestation. However, tree plantations do offer an opportunity to reduce the pressure on natural forests if the latter are exploited primarily for wood products.

Policy and Institutional Reform

Forest valuation and the reformation of government policies and institutions National policies need to promote the necessary framework that encourages sustainable forest use before community-level projects can have an effect. However, undervaluation of forests by governments and people undermines forestry institutions nationally and internationally, making it difficult to enact the necessary changes. The lack of forest-user taxes and low stumpage fees discourage sustainable management of forests by undervaluing the resource. Subsidies to competing land uses should be removed and effective natural resource accounting should be established to reflect true forest values. Opportunity costs and externalities associated with conversion need to be factored into assessments of forest values. Thus, the value of the ecosystem services as well as alternative income-generating businesses, such as tourism, should be considered. Furthermore, forest land value can be greatly increased by more efficient use of a greater range of forest resources, and by improved marketing of them. The absence of clear

policy guidelines and trends in forests and forest resources lead to a confusion of strategies among national and international organizations. Strengthening of these institutions and developing mutually agreed frameworks that provide for more effective policy development and monitoring is needed if deforestation is to be arrested.

Provide education Educating the public as well as political and economic decision-makers about environmental and socioeconomic issues related to forests is crucial if policies promoting forest preservation through sustainable use are to be heeded. Education must be based on thorough and demonstrable arguments about the economic, social, environmental, and biological benefits of using forests wisely, and the costs associated with deforestation.

Conclusion

Deforestation is largely a tropical issue. The quality of data on deforestation rates has been improving but remains poor and a source of contention and debate. The causes of deforestation are complex and multifaceted, though socioeconomic factors and trade are foremost. Deforestation impacts on the environment through loss of biodiversity and disruption of ecosystem processes, as well as the economy by affecting ecosystem services and inefficient squandering of resources. Perhaps the most tragic consequence is the loss of traditional beliefs and customs and the displacement of forest-dependent communities. Solving the problem of deforestation requires a suite of strategies that include establishing an effective and global protected area network to preserve forest biodiversity, and the genuine implementation of good practice guidelines. Ultimately, a reformulation of policy and a change in the attitudes of decision-makers are needed to ensure that forests are correctly valued economically, socially, and biologically.

Acknowledgement

This contribution is adapted with permission from Ghazoul J and Evans J (2001) Deforestation and land clearing. In: *The Encyclopedia of Biodiversity*, Levin SA (ed.) Academic Press.

See also: **Ecology**: Biological Impacts of Deforestation and Fragmentation. **Environment**: Environmental Impacts. **Harvesting**: Forest Operations in the Tropics, Reduced Impact Logging. **Landscape and Planning**: Perceptions of Nature by Indigenous Communities. **Plantation Silviculture**: Forest Plantations. **Silviculture**: Managing for Tropical Non-timber Forest Products. **Wood Use and Trade**: History and Overview of Wood Use.

Further Reading

Brown K and Pearce D (1994) *The Causes of Tropical Deforestation*. Vancouver, Canada: University of British Columbia Press.

Brown D and Schreckenberg K (1998) *Shifting Cultivators as Agents of Deforestation: Assessing the Evidence*. Natural Resources Perspective Number no. 29. London: Overseas Development Institute.

Bryant D, Nielsen D, and Tangley L (1997) *The Last Frontier Forests: Ecosystems and Economies on the Edge*. Washington, DC: World Resources Institute.

Byron N and Shepherd G (1998) *Indonesia and the 1997–98 El Niño: Fire Problems and Long Term Solutions*. Natural Resource Perspective Number 28. London: Overseas Development Institute.

Downton MW (1995) Measuring tropical deforestation: development of the methods. *Environmental Conservation* 22: 229–240.

Evans J (1992) *Plantation Forestry in the Tropics*. Oxford, UK: Oxford University Press.

FAO (2001) *State of the World's Forests 1999*. Rome: Food and Agriculture Organization of the United Nations.

Fisher BS and de Fegely R (1999) *A Study on the Global Outlook for Plantations*. Technical Paper for the Intergovernmental Forum on Forests. Canberra, Australia: Commonwealth of Australia.

Myers N (1989) *Deforestation Rates in Tropical Forests and their Climatic Implications*. London: Friends of the Earth.

Rowe R, Sharma NP, and Browder J (1992) Deforestation: problems, causes and concerns. In: Sharma NP (ed.) *Managing the World's Forests: Looking for Balance between Conservation and Development*, pp. 33–45. Iowa: Kendall/Hunt.

WCFSD (1999) *Our Forests, Our Future*. World Commission on Forests and Sustainable Development. Cambridge, UK: Cambridge University Press.

T

TEMPERATE AND MEDITERRANEAN FORESTS

Contents

Northern Coniferous Forests

C D B Hawkins, University of Northern British
Columbia, Prince George, BC, Canada

Introduction

The northern coniferous forest or temperate needleleaf forest is restricted, essentially, to western North
America. It also occurs in small elevational bands on
mountain ranges of Europe, Asia, eastern North
America, Mexico, Mesoamerica, and the coastal
plains of the southeastern United States. The northern
coniferous forest is conventionally a synonym for the
boreal forest. Depending on the authority, the northern coniferous forest can be considered a southern
offshoot of the boreal forest on the Rocky, Coast,
Cascade, Appalachian, Alps, Carpathians, Urals, and
Himalaya mountain ranges, as well as mountains in
northern China, Korea, and Japan, or it can be
restricted to montane coniferous forest. Pinaceae
(pines, spruces, firs, and larches) are the major
northern coniferous forest family and account for its
economic importance. There are also mixed coniferous–deciduous stands in the western North American
northern coniferous forest with trembling aspen
(*Populus tremuloides*) and paper birch (*Betula papyrifera*). Compared to the boreal forest, the northern
coniferous forest is warmer and more productive:
mature trees ≥ 25 m compared to ≤ 23 m. This article
focuses on western North America because compared
to other areas of the world, there are still large areas
of natural northern coniferous forest.

Generally mountains become wetter, colder, and
windier with increasing elevation. This results in
distinct zones or bands of vegetation. A given
vegetation zone tends to be found at higher elevations on drier sites compared to wetter, on south
aspects compared to north, and at southern latitudes
compared to northern. Low to mid elevation northern coniferous forests are rich in species diversity
while the upper northern coniferous forest is less
complex. The upper northern coniferous forest and
lower subalpine have similar species composition
and they are transitional to one another.

Distribution

Western North America

The northern coniferous forest includes the central
plateaux of British Columbia and isolated Intermountain, mountain ranges between the Cascade–Sierra
ranges as well as the Rocky Mountains. In the Rocky
Mountains, it extends from the southern Yukon to
south central New Mexico. Some consider it to
include the Madrean (Mexican) section of the Rocky
Mountains and the Coastal, Cascade, and Sierra
Nevada ranges while others consider the Madrean
and Sierra Nevada to be part of the southern
coniferous forest. The Sierra Nevada is excluded
from the northern coniferous forest as: (1) true
coniferous forests are relatively rare in the northern
hemisphere south of 40° N latitude; and (2) giant
sequoias (*Sequoiadendron giganteum*) are present in
the Sierra Nevada, which some authors consider to be
members of the subtropical mountain system.

Rocky Mountains The Rocky Mountain ($19–65^{\circ}$ N
latitude) northern coniferous forest has a subalpine
forest above, characterized by subalpine fir (*Abies
lasiocarpa*), white or Engelmann spruce (*Picea glauca*,

P. engelmannii), and depending on latitude other conifer species. Species diversity increases moving south from the boreal forest.

In the Boreal Rocky Mountains (53–65° N latitude), the northern coniferous forest is above the boreal forest dominated by aspen, balsam fir (*Abies balsamea*), white spruce, and jackpine (*Pinus banksiana*), with black spruce (*Picea mariana*) and tamarack (*Larix laricina*) in wetter areas (**Figure 1**). The northern coniferous forest is not complex having both boreal and subalpine species plus lodgepole pine (*Pinus contorta* var. *latifolia*). White spruce dominates at low and mid elevations. Common broadleaf trees are birch hybrids (*Betula* spp.), aspen, and balsam poplar (*Populus balsamifera*). The northern limit is marked by the absence of lodgepole pine and subalpine fir. The southern boundary is the transition between the Peace and Fraser River drainages. This roughly corresponds to Engelmann spruce and Douglas-fir's (*Pseudotsuga menziesii* var. *glauca*) northern distribution limit.

The Central Rocky Mountain (45–53° N latitude) northern coniferous forest is a rich productive forest

rising to 1800 m in elevation above Rocky Mountain (western) juniper–ponderosa pine (*Juniperus scopulorum–Pinus ponderosa*) woodlands from 800 to 1500 m. It is dominated by cedar (*Thuja plicata*), western hemlock (*Tsuga heterophylla*), grand fir (*Abies grandis*), and Douglas-fir on the western slopes. Western white pine (*P. monticola*) and western larch (*Larix occidentalis*) are common on mesic and drier sites as are white–Engelmann (interior) spruce hybrids on wetter ecosystems (**Figure 2**). This is the most productive complex of the northern coniferous forest with site indices at 100 years (SI_{100}) of 40 m for spruce and 38 m for white pine and Douglas-fir. The eastern slopes are less diverse and not as productive. Aspen and paper birch are the dominant broadleaf species and are usually found in seral mixed species stands. The subalpine forest, in addition to *Abies* and *Picea*, has whitebark pine (*Pinus albicaulis*), limber pine (*P. flexilis*), mountain hemlock (*Tsuga mertensiana*), and subalpine larch (*Larix lyallii*). The Central sector is defined by the distribution of whitebark pine.

Ponderosa pine parklands in the Southern Rocky Mountains (33–45° N latitude) are below two northern coniferous forest zones. The lower is a Douglas-fir forest with white fir (*Abies concolor*) and Colorado blue spruce (*Picea pungens*) and the upper is a lodgepole pine forest. Aspen is the primary broadleaf species. The subalpine, in addition to spruce and fir, has bristlecone pine (*Pinus aristata*).

The Madrean (19–35° N latitude) northern coniferous forest has complex topography and flora. About half of the world's pine species occur in Mexico. Fir forests (*Abies concolor, A. religiosa*, and *A. guatemalensis*) with codominant *Pinus, Quercus, Pseudotsuga*, and *Cupressus* species usually occur below *Pinus hartwegii* forests. Douglas-fir associated with *P. flexilis* and *Abies concolor* occurs below the fir-dominated forests. A ponderosa pine parkland is

Figure 1 Boreal Rocky Mountain northern coniferous forest rising above the boreal forest at 59° N.

Figure 2 Central Rocky Mountain northern coniferous forest at 54° N; mixed wood stands dominate recent cutovers.

below the Douglas-fir forest and above a mixed pine–oak (*P. edulis*, *P. cembroides–Quercus arizonica*, *Q. gambelii*) chaparral in southern regions and a pinyon–juniper (*P. edulis–Juniperus* spp.) pygmy conifer woodland in northern regions.

Plateau   The Nechako and Fraser Plateaux comprise much of central British Columbia. The western portions are in the rainshadow of the Coast Mountains and are less productive than more easterly portions (**Figure 3**). Rain shadow areas are dominated by lodgepole pine with interior spruce occurring on rich, moist soils. The primary species, moving east away from the rainshadow, are interior spruce and subalpine fir with Douglas-fir occurring on drier sites. Lodgepole pine is a seral species on much of the plateau but it may be the climax species of the rainshadow region.

Intermountain   From 37° to 45° N latitude, between the Rocky Mountains and the Cascade–Sierra complex are mountain chains, isolated like islands, in an otherwise very arid, high elevation environment. Above a pinyon–juniper woodland from 1500 to 2500 m is the northern coniferous forest. A white fir montane forest with lodgepole pine, ponderosa pine, and Douglas-fir on mesic sites characterizes the region. The subalpine is dominated by limber pine, subalpine fir, and the intermountain bristlecone pine (*Pinus longaeva*). On very arid ranges, the subalpine is absent and pinyon pine covers the slope.

Mesoamerica   Low mountain pine forests of Guatemala, Belize, Honduras, and Nicaragua are usually stands of *Pinus oocarpa* although *P. caribaea* may be present. *Pinus hartwegii* and *Juniperus standleyi* are the major species of high mountain humid forests in northern Mesoamerica. *Abies guatemalensis* and *A. religiosa* continue southwards from Mexico and dominate the high mountain, perhumid forests of northern Mesoamerica.

Coast and Cascade Mountains   In the Coast and Cascade Ranges (43–49.5° N latitude), the northern coniferous forest starts immediately above the temperate coniferous forest. Along the western slope of the Cascades and in the Coast Range, the northern coniferous forest has a lower amabilis fir (*A. amabilis*) zone and an upper mountain hemlock zone. These forests are nearly as productive as those of the Central Rocky Mountains. The northern coniferous forest consists of a ponderosa pine forest often with Douglas-fir, and a mesic *Abies* or mountain hemlock forest above 1500 m, but below the subalpine on the eastern Cascade slopes.

Other Northern Coniferous Forests

Appalachians   Above the elevational limit of the deciduous forest along the Appalachian chain are dense, even-aged, red spruce (*Picea rubens*) stands. *Abies* increases in abundance with elevation (*A. balsamea* in the north, *A. fraseri* in the south). Pure subalpine stands can form if the mountain has sufficient elevation. In mixed spruce–fir stands, fir is shorter-lived and faster-growing than spruce. The Appalachian northern coniferous forest has been severely impacted by acid rain, woolly aphid, and unknown mortality agents over the past 25 years.

Southeastern USA   Pre-European settlement pine forests were old and open, and contained a two-layered canopy and diverse groundcover. Upland pine forest of the southeastern USA can be classified into three general communities: northern pine barrens, xeric sand communities, and mesic pine communities. Pine–oak forests (*Pinus serotina–Quercus stellata*, *Q. marilandica*) of the northern pine barrens are confined to Delaware Bay. Longleaf pine (*P. palustris*) dominates the xeric, well-drained coarse sands of the southern coastal plain. Historically fire return intervals of 3–6 years maintained the open nature and facilitated reproduction of this forest. Mesic pine communities are generally dominated by an even-aged, closed canopy of longleaf, loblolly (*P. taeda*), pond (*P. serotina*), and/or slash (*P. elliottii*) pine. Species composition depends on site quality and disturbance frequency. Today's pine forest is young, dense, dominated by loblolly pine with a substantial hardwood component, has little or no groundcover, and accounts for nearly 60% of the USA's wood production.

Europe   The northern coniferous forest is a significant component of mountain forests in France,

Figure 3   Northern coniferous forest on the rolling eastern Fraser Plateau; interior spruce and subalpine fir dominate on mesic and wetter sites.

Germany, and Switzerland. Generally it is found above a beech–conifer (*Fagus sylvatica*–conifer) mixed wood, and is typified by a spruce–fir (*Abies alba–Picea abies*) forest below a pine–larch (*Pinus cembra, P. nigra, P. sylvestris–Larix decidua*) forest. In the Carpathian Mountains, a spruce northern coniferous forest lies above a broadleaf forest and below a mixed beech–fir forest. The northern coniferous forest of the Ural Mountains is a spruce–fir (*Picea obovata–Abies sibirica*) forest below a spruce–fir–Siberian stone pine (*Pinus sibirica*) forest.

Asian subcontinent The northern coniferous forest in northern and northwest Pakistan is diverse. It contains deodar (*Cedrus deodara*), kail (*Pinus wallichiana*), spruce (*Picea smithiana*), and silver fir (*Abies pindrow*), with chir (*Pinus longifolia*) at lower elevations and on hot southerly aspects. A subalpine spruce–fir forest again lies above the northern coniferous forest. The northern coniferous forest of the Himalayas continues eastward from Pakistan to Sikkim at high elevations: 1500–3300 m in the west, 2750–3350 m in Sikkim. Pencil juniper (*Juniperus macropoda*) and pine (*Pinus gerardiana*) are found throughout Kashmir while in moister valleys there are deodar and silver fir. In Nepal or the central Himalayas, northern coniferous forest species include silver fir, *Picea smithiana*, cedar, hemlock (*Tsuga dumosa*), and kail. Kail, *Picea spinulosa, Juniperus wallichiana*, hemlock, and *Larix griffithii* are the northern coniferous forest species at the eastern end of the Himalayas.

East Asia In China, the northern coniferous forest is a spruce–fir (*Picea brachytyla–Abies fabri*) forest with hemlock (*Tsuga chinensis*). Eastward to Korea, the northern coniferous forest is north of 40° N latitude. Species include *Picea jezoensis, Abies nephrolepis, Larix koreanna, Picea koyamae, Pinus koraiensis*, and *A. holophylla*. The northern coniferous forest decreases in elevation moving north along the Japanese island chain. The forest is fir–spruce (*A. homolepis–Picea jezoensis*) with a yew (*Taxus cuspidata*) component.

History of the Northern Coniferous Forest in Western North America and Europe

Expansion of high montane and mixed coniferous forest at high latitudes and high elevations began 35 to 11 million years before present (BP). This coincided with a significant drop in North American temperature. Cooling continued from 10 to 2 million years BP concomitant with a retreat in hardwood forests from mid and high latitudes and a continental expansion

of coniferous forest. The present day Boreal and Central Rocky Mountain northern coniferous forest regions were covered with ice when the Cordilleran and Laurentide ice sheets joined at the last glacial maximum (LGM) about 18 000 years BP. The LGM defined present North American distributions of plant communities. Glacial refugia existed in the Queen Charlotte Islands, the exposed Coastal Plain, and areas to the south of the ice sheet (e.g., Clearwater River drainage in Idaho). The ice sheets separated and retreated from 13 500 to 11 000 years BP. This resulted in a corridor, the Rocky Mountain Trench, for northern coniferous forest species migration from refugia. It is predicted that with climate change the northern coniferous forest will expand into boreal and subalpine forests in coming centuries.

Much of northern Europe was covered by large ice sheets at the LGM, about 22 000 to 14 000 years BP. Forests and woodlands were nonexistent except for isolated pockets of woody vegetation in southern European mountains. Birch and conifers (open woodland) were present in European Russia 13 000 years BP. Open woodland returned to much of Europe by 12 000 years BP. Open woodland retreated during the younger Dryas and forest returned to much of Europe by 9000 to 8000 years BP. A warm period persisted from 7000 to 5000 years BP and forests spread northward. Present-day northern coniferous forest was established about 4500 years BP.

Environment

Climate

Climate is the most important determinant of natural terrestrial ecosystems. In western North America, the northern coniferous forest has a continental climate with a moderating maritime influence. Similar to the boreal forest, winters are cold and summers are short: growing degree days average about 90 in the north to more than 120 in the south. Mean annual temperature ranges from 0.5°C in the north and at high elevations to 9°C in the south. The average temperature drops below 0°C for approximately 4 months (range 1–5) of the year, and rises above 10°C for 2–5 months. Generally, frost can occur in any month. Precipitation varies by locality; it is least in valleys and increases with slope position. It ranges from 300 to 1650 mm, of which 25–50% falls as snow.

Soils

Over time, soils develop as a function of parent material, climate, biota, and topography. Generally northern coniferous forest soils are young. In the Central Rocky Mountains, mesic soils are humo–feric podzols and brunisolic or orthic gray luvisols. Podzolic soils are typical of the northern coniferous forest but given the complex topography and variety of parent materials, many soil types can develop. Podzols are well drained and are leached of clay and organic matter. The lack of calcium in these soils makes them susceptible to erosion and weathering. Brunisolic soils result from slow weathering and/or restricted development due to long winters and low temperatures in cold climates and lack of soil moisture in dry climates. Brunisols are found primarily in forested areas such as lodgepole pine forests. Luvisolic soils are characterized by a horizon of clay in the subsoil resulting from leaching which may restrict root penetration. Luvisols form under forest cover having either high rainfall or low temperature. The northern coniferous forest organic soil layer arises through slow humification of forest litter low in nutrients and high in resins, waxes, and lignins. Climate warming may promote a change in soil type due to increased respiration and accelerated loss of organic matter.

Disturbance

Historically, fire has been the most important and conspicuous disturbance agent of the Rocky Mountains. European settlement and fire suppression reduced fire frequency in the northern coniferous forest in the twentieth century. Consequences include altered species composition, increased insect and pathogen epidemics, and enhanced probability of catastrophic fires due to increased fuel loading. The fire cycle or fire return interval lengthens with increased elevation. Fire intensity decreases with increased fire frequency: low-intensity fires every 5–12 years in ponderosa pine woodlands versus stand-replacing fires every 100 years in lodgepole pine forests to every 200–400 years in higher elevation forests.

Insect and pathogen outbreaks are also primary northern coniferous forest disturbance agents. The spruce beetle (*Dendroctonus rufipennis*) killed virtually all spruce in northwestern Colorado during the 1940s. The mountain pine beetle (*D. ponderosae*) infested 2 million ha in the western USA from 1979 to 1983. On the Fraser and Nechako plateaux in British Columbia, in excess of 5 million ha of the northern coniferous forest were infested with mountain pine beetle in the spring of 2003. Many have attributed serious pest outbreaks in the northern coniferous forest to the success of wildfire control programs and climate change. Fungal pathogens such as *Armillaria*, *Phellinus*, and *Tomentosis* can also be significant disturbance agents.

There are other northern coniferous forest disturbance agents. Wind destroys patches of old, high-elevation stands with increased bole rot. Avalanches can be significant disturbance events on a local scale. In some areas, indiscriminate grazing by native and domestic ungulates can impact regenerating vegetation or lead to forest degradation.

Global Warming

Past changes in climate were natural processes that probably drove species extinction as well as speciation. The current concern surrounding climate change is relevant because (1) the rate of change appears to be greater than most previous changes, (2) ecosystems are often more fragmented, except perhaps in the boreal forest, resulting in barriers to species migration, and (3) most ecosystems serve multiple needs and loss – damage to forests will have significant environmental, economic, and social impacts.

Warming is expected to be more significant at higher latitudes. To accommodate changing climate patterns, species will shift to more northern latitudes and higher elevations. This will alter the northern coniferous forest distribution. In addition to increased temperature and precipitation, frequency of extreme weather events will increase.

Temperature is hypothesized to increase by 1° to 4.5°C within the present century. With a temperature change of 3°C, species would have to move about 250 km in latitude or 500 m in elevation to maintain the same temperature. Tree species have variable rates of migration, 1 to 45 km per century. Predicted temperature shifts requiring migrations of over 100 km per century are beyond the dispersal abilities of coniferous species. If species cannot migrate, they will: (1) exist at current locations with reduced productivity and presence, (2) adapt slowly to changing conditions, or (3) become extinct. Where there are obligate community relationships, e.g., deer and forest type, deer will only be able to migrate at the same speed as the tree species unless an alternate forest type is found. This could lead to local extinctions.

Forest Dynamics, Management, and Utilization

Stand Dynamics

Stand development following disturbance is a function of local elevation, moisture gradients, and soil. Mesic stands in the northern coniferous forest exhibit developmental stages widely encountered in boreal and montane conifer forests. The first stage or establishment stage is characterized by little competition and significant seedling establishment and growth. The second, stem exclusion stage is typified by competition among trees resulting in mortality and increased tree size. Little, if any, recruitment occurs. The third, understory reinitiation stage results when gaps occur in the canopy allowing new regeneration. The fourth, equilibrium or old-growth stage is when, simplistically, tree mortality is balanced by tree recruitment. Due to frequent disturbances, stands rarely reach the equilibrium stage in the northern coniferous forest; a noted exception is the Central Rocky Mountain's hemlock–cedar-dominated forests.

Where competition is minimal and seed supply is abundant, establishment occurs in 10 years. However, establishment is typically prolonged, 40–70 years, particularly on severe or very good sites where herbs can overtop seedlings. At higher elevations, tree establishment is slower and results in multiple age classes. Consequently the stem exclusion stage is bypassed, and tree mortality and recruitment of the third stage follow stand establishment. At lower elevations where fires are not detrimental to the canopy trees, seedling regeneration occurs in waves assisted by a good seed year, favorable weather, and no fire. Stand dynamics can also vary along environmental gradients: on a mesic north-facing slope an even-aged Douglas-fir stand will develop while on the adjacent south-facing slope an uneven-aged, open Douglas-fir stand will establish with understory lodgepole pine.

Productivity

In the Rocky Mountain northern coniferous forest, biomass peaks early in stem exclusion, declines as mortality increases and then increases as recruitment proceeds. Species diversity tends to track resource availability, dropping dramatically at the start of stem exclusion and staying low until understory reinitiating. The northern coniferous forest is a moderate carbon store compared to temperate rainforest and boreal forests. The northern coniferous forest produces 6–18 tonnes ha^{-1} $year^{-1}$ compared to 4–12 tonnes ha^{-1} $year^{-1}$ on upland boreal sites and 15–25 tonnes ha^{-1} $year^{-1}$ in the temperate rainforest.

Nontimber forest products and environmental services can be classified as being market or nonmarket regulated. Market products and services include grazing, medicinal plants, edible products (mushrooms, wild rice), decorative products, trapping, and outfitting. Nonmarket items include traditional first nation's uses, hunting, fishing, birdwatching, and ecotourism. In order to provide timber, nontimber forest products, and environmental services, northern coniferous forest seral stage diversity must be maintained.

Environmental Services

The northern coniferous forest provides many important values or services in addition to fiber production for subsistence and industrial uses. Watershed quality and water production is a function of a healthy, intact forest cover. Forest cover regulates snow storage and snowmelting rates by snow interception, shading, and wind amelioration. Peak flow and soil erosion are reduced by intact forest cover. Erosion is further reduced when groundcover vegetation is present. Maintenance of northern coniferous forest forested slopes helps regulate stream temperature and stabilize steep slopes.

Wildlife species diversity is a function of the complexity of tree species and associated understory vegetation. Wildlife is directly linked to seral stages of the northern coniferous forest (or any plant community). As wildlife species have different preferences for different plant species, they have different life or stand developmental stage (seral) needs. Time of year (season) may also result in different habitat needs for a species. Maintenance of riparian areas is crucial for fish survival and mature forest habitat is critical to some species' survival. Therefore, it is important to have seral stage (structural) diversity, including standing and fallen dead wood, to maintain northern coniferous forest species diversity.

Forests in the northern coniferous forest are increasingly managed to provide leisure and recreational services. They include hiking, photography, birdwatching, hunting, and fishing. This places leisure and recreational management in conflict with traditional forest product management. In addition to parks and wilderness areas for recreational services, managing for northern coniferous forest seral stage diversity will provide ongoing recreational opportunities.

Management and Utilization

Industrial activity in the northern coniferous forest varies by locale. About half of the world's pulp comes from the northern coniferous forest. In Canada, there is significant harvesting activity as the northern coniferous forest is second in productivity only to the northern temperate coastal forest. In the western USA, logging activities have fallen during the 1990s due to a focus on forest services rather than forest products: 57 million m^3 were cut on US National Forests in 1986 and 23 million m^3 were cut in 1996. The northern coniferous forest is part of the industrial forest of Europe while on the Asian subcontinent it provides fuel and subsistence for local peoples as well as industrial wood.

Depending on northern coniferous forest locale, even- or uneven-aged management may be utilized.

Silvicultural system selection dictates harvesting systems and equipment (if any). Steep slopes in much of the northern coniferous forest also influence equipment selection. In general, cable systems are required on steeper ground while ground-based systems can be used if slopes do not exceed 30–50%. Soils of the northern coniferous forest are young and often thin, which influences equipment selection. The risk of soil degradation is generally greater with ground-based systems. Harvesting is highly mechanized on large-scale western North American operations whereas in Eastern and Central Europe, power saws and small tractors are used in small-scale forestry operations. In Asia, past forestry practices have significantly compromised the productivity of the northern coniferous forest due to flooding and erosion. Small-scale fuelwood collection and mechanized harvesting are both practiced in the Asian northern coniferous forest.

Significance

The northern coniferous forest provides a significant proportion of the world's industrial forest products as well as nontimber forest products and environmental services. It helps to maintain the social fabric of indigenous peoples and preserve aboriginal culture. The northern coniferous forest also provides services such as watershed integrity, habitat, and recreational and leisure opportunities. Compared to boreal and subalpine forest, the northern coniferous forest is diverse and productive. A challenge for northern coniferous forest managers, worldwide, is to maintain structural and species diversity without compromising the potential of the northern coniferous forest to provide its products and environmental services.

See also: **Operations**: Forest Operations Management. **Temperate and Mediterranean Forests**: Southern Coniferous Forests; Subalpine and Boreal Forests; Temperate Broadleaved Deciduous Forest. **Temperate Ecosystems**: Pines; Spruces, Firs and Larches

Further Reading

Barbour MG and Christensen NL (1993) Vegetation of North America north of Mexico. In: Flora of North America Editorial Committee (ed.) *Flora of North America, Introduction*, Vol. 1, pp. 97–129. New York: Oxford University Press.
Christensen NL (2000) Vegetation of the southeastern coastal plain. In: Barbour MG and Billings WD (eds) *North American Terrestrial Vegetation*, 2nd edn, pp. 396–448. New York: Cambridge University Press.
Delcourt PA and Delcourt HR (1993) Paleoclimate, paleovegetation, and paleofloras of North America north of Mexico during the Late Quaternary. In: Flora of North America Editorial Committee (ed.) *Flora of North America, Introduction*, Vol. 1, pp. 71–94. New York: Oxford University Press.
Farjon A (1998) *World Checklist and Bibliography of Conifers*. Kew, UK: Royal Botanic Garden.
Haden-Guest S, Wright JK, and Tecloff EM (eds) (1956) *A World Geography of Forest Resources*. New York: Ronald Press.
Hartshorn GS (2000) Tropical and subtropical vegetation of Mesoamerica. In: Barbour MG and Billings WD (eds) *North American Terrestrial Vegetation*, 2nd edn, pp. 623–659. New York: Cambridge University Press.
Meidinger D and Pojar J (1991) *Ecosystems of British Columbia*. Victoria, Canada: Province of British Columbia.
Oliver CD and Larson BC (1996) *Forest Stand Dynamics*, updated edn. New York: John Wiley.
Peet RK (2000) Forests and meadows of the Rocky Mountains. In: Barbour MG and Billings WD (eds) *North American Terrestrial Vegetation*, 2nd edn, pp. 75–121. New York: Cambridge University Press.
Veláquez A, Toledo VM, and Luna I (2000) Mexican temperate vegetation. In: Barbour MG and Billings WD (eds) *North American Terrestrial Vegetation*, 2nd edn, pp. 573–592. New York: Cambridge University Press.

Southern Coniferous Forests

I R Smith, University of Queensland, St Lucia, Australia

Introduction

When referring to coniferous forests, an image comes to mind of the great boreal forests of the northern hemisphere or carefully managed and regular pine plantations. The native conifer forests of the southern hemisphere rarely conform to this image. In fact, except in a few cases, the term 'coniferous forest' is a misnomer and most of the associations described in this section might more properly be called 'forests with a coniferous element.' Most of the southern hemisphere conifers are of exclusively southern hemisphere families or, in the case of those families which are represented in both hemispheres, are of genera which are represented only in the southern hemisphere. In a total of 67 conifer genera and 557 species worldwide, 31 genera and some 200 species are largely southern and 160 species are totally southern. Of those genera that are found in both hemispheres only one 'northern' genus is found in the southern hemisphere while 12 'southern' species extend into the northern hemisphere mainly into closely adjacent areas such as Malesia, the Philippines and northern South America. The Pinaceae, which dominate northern forests, are not represented in the southern hemisphere except in extensive plantations or as naturalized exotics.

Conifer forests in the northern hemisphere tend to dominate in more extreme climates where the ability of conifers to compete with angiosperms is enhanced. Thus, they are most abundant at high altitude, high latitude, and in other cold, high rainfall areas. These areas are more extensive in the north, with the great high latitude land-dominated boreal region having no southern analog since the break-up of Gondwana.

The other factor that has a bearing on the differences between the northern and southern conifer forests is the relatively greater oceanic effects on the climate of the southern hemisphere. Annual seasonal effects are less extreme than in the large continental masses of the north, but conversely there are greater, and less regular, year to year climatic changes under the influence of such phenomena as the El Niño Southern Oscillation.

The southern conifers tend to occupy similar niches to their northern cousins, but the geographic extent of the niches is much smaller and as a result, many species of southern conifer have small geographical ranges. There is fossil evidence that southern conifer diversity was much higher at times in the past.

There are close analogs in both conifer genera and forest types across the southern lands as a result of their common Gondwanan heritage. Fossil records indicate that Antarctica once shared a similar coniferous flora. South Africa, which has only a limited conifer flora, is the exception to this and there are puzzling aspects to both its present-day and fossil coniferous flora.

Little study has been carried out on the ecological associates of the southern conifers, especially fungal associations. The Araucariaceae, Podocarpaceae and *Callitris* spp. (Cupressaceae) in Australia have vesicular–arbuscular mycorrhizae (VAM). *Wollemia nobilis* (Araucariaceae) also has ecto-endomycorrhiza. VAM mycorrhizae have been associated with Araucariaceae and Podocarpaceae since the Jurassic.

There is a range of particular insects associated with the Araucariaceae, including weevils, chrysomelid leaf beetles, and scolytid bark beetles. The first two araucarian beetle groups have been associated since the early Jurassic while the bark beetles colonized them at the end of the Cretaceous.

As with the northern conifers, many of the southern conifers are very desirable timber species and were heavily exploited (and overexploited) for timber. As will be discussed later, several species have been plantation grown and natural stands have been managed for silviculture. In addition *Araucaria araucana* and *A. angustifolia* in South America and *A. bidwillii* in Australia were valued for their edible nuts and played an important part in indigenous culture in two continents.

Coniferous Forest Types in the Southern Hemisphere

To cover the diversity of those forests containing southern conifers in a brief treatment such as this is best done using a simple classification drawing on the similarity between southern forests. The following classification is introduced:

1. Tropical and subtropical rainforests with coniferous elements, with or without coniferous emergents.
2. Warm temperate rainforest with coniferous emergents.
3. Temperate rainforests containing conifers.
4. Arid zone coniferous forests and woodlands.
5. Heathland and shrubland with coniferous emergents/components.
6. Alpine and subalpine shrubland and forest with conifers.

Some clarification is required for these terms. Tropical and subtropical rainforests are complex forests with multiple layers and characterized by large numbers of lianas and epiphytes. The complexity and leaf sizes generally reduce from tropics to subtropics and with increasing altitude and/or soil fertility. Warm temperate rainforests are found only in Australia and are much simpler rainforests (often dominated by older Gondwanan elements) on less fertile soils. The cool temperate rainforests are the classic fern/southern beech/conifer forests of southern Australia, Chile and Argentina, and New Zealand.

Often these forests can overlap. On the central coast of New South Wales the three types are found at the same latitude but separated by soil/moisture/altitude gradients.

In using such a classification, there is a range of species with specialist niches, which will be omitted, e.g., *Microstrobos fitzgeraldii* with a specialized niche in the spray zone of waterfalls in the Blue Mountains of New South Wales, Australia. There are also likely to be oversimplifications and omissions in dealing with such a complex subject in such a brief treatment. For instance the monkey-puzzle (*Araucaria araucana*) in Chile and Argentina exists in forest types (3), (4), (5), and (6) but is only dealt with below in (5). Further reading will be necessary to elaborate such a complex subject.

1. Tropical and Subtropical Rainforests with Coniferous Elements, with or without Coniferous Emergents

Forests of this type are represented in Australia, New Caledonia and other Pacific Islands, New Guinea, and South America. With *Agathis* spp. as an emergent they also extend into Malesia. It is important to note that while conifers are emergent they are not the only emergents as in many parts of the forest large angiosperms such as *Ficus* spp. are also important. While the lower forest layers are normally dominated by angiosperms, conifers especially Podocarpaceae and Cupressaceae can also form an important part of both the canopy and understory.

The most developed of these types of forest are found in New Caledonia, especially on the 'Grand Terre' or Main Island. New Caledonia has a total of 43 conifer species of which 26 are found in rainforest associations. The high diversity of conifers and the survival of many primitive angiosperms on New Caledonia is attributed to the dominance (but not exclusivity) of ultramafic soils on the island which acted as a barrier to many modern species. However, the ultramafics are an intrusion that postdates the Gondwanan geology of New Caledonia so the conifers have radiated since the ultramafics were put in place. The ultramafics may have been a barrier to the movement of some angiosperm groups on to these areas (e.g., Poaceae does not occur on New Caledonian ultramafics), so making radiation and survival more likely. Where this forest occurs there is often a gradient from a lowland rainforest to an evergreen cloud forest. Overall 14 species of Araucariaceae, 11 species of Podocarpeaceae, two Cupressaceae and a single species of Taxaceae occupy niches in these forests. The araucarians (*Araucaria* and *Agathis* species) plus *Retrophyllum comptonii* and *Dacrydium araucarioides* form both the canopy and emergent layers (however, these latter two form an emergent layer only on 'cuirasse' boulder fields that are largely unvegetated), and *Austrotaxus spicatus*, *Libocedrus austrocaledonica*, and the majority of the Podocarpaceae are found in the understory. Angiosperms such as *Metrosideros* (Myrtaceae) and *Quintinia* (Saxifragaceae), and primitive groups such as Winteraceae are also found in the understory and canopy. Most species have strong Gondwanan associations. In some areas unusual, almost pure tree layer stands occur, such as *Agathis montana* on several mountain tops and *Neocallitropsis* in some wetlands in the south of the main island, and *Araucaria columnaris* in a pure narrow band on calcareous rocks on the seashore on the main island, the Isle of Pines, and the Loyalty Islands.

Through the Pacific Islands between New Guinea and Fiji similar associations of conifers occur. These rainforests are often more complex and diverse than New Caledonia, but the number of conifer species is lower, with one coniferous emergent (*Agathis macrophylla*) and from one to seven species of podocarps. The isolated South Pacific island Norfolk Island has one emergent araucarian, Norfolk Island pine (*Araucaria heterophylla*) which now dominates foreshore ornamental plantings in warmer parts of the world.

New Guinea has variants of the same structure but once again with high diversity with four species of Araucariaceae, 29 species of Podocarpeaceae, and two Cupresseaceae. As with New Caledonia, the araucarians tend to be emergent with the other conifers mixed with angiosperms in the canopy and understory. The podocarps are rare at low altitude (mostly *Podocarpus*, some *Falcatifolium*, etc.) but increase with altitude and may dominate mid and upper altitude forests (mostly *Dacrycarpus* and *Dacrydium*). The Araucariaceae have a patchy distribution in the forests. There is little information on the ecology of *Agathis macrophylla* and the threatened *A. spathulata*, but more is known of the biology of hoop pine (*Araucaria cunninghamii* var. *papuana*) and klinki pine (*A. hunsteinii*). Both are mast seeders and occur in lower to mid montane forests with overlapping ranges. They can form mixed stands but normally either one or the other is found with klinki most common from 700 to 1000 m above sea level and hoop more common above 1000 m. In these forests the tall emergent *Araucaria* spp. appear to exhibit additive basal area, where the presence of emergents does not tend to subtract from the total basal area of the remainder of the stand. This phenomenon has also been reported from the temperate kauri forests of New Zealand.

In Australia, this type of forest extends from Cape York in Queensland to south of Sydney but only one podocarp species is present in the southern part of the range, south of Coffs Harbour. North of Coffs Harbour, on the New South Wales north coast, emergent Araucariaceae become a feature and other conifer species gradually increase. Overall there are five Araucariaceae, six Podocarpaceae, and one Cupresseaceae (*Callitris macleayana*) present in these forests. Araucarian emergents are most commonly found in drier types of rainforest or on poorer substrates. The most common is *Araucaria cunninghamii*, which has a discontinuous distribution from Dorrigo (near Coffs Harbour) to Cape York. *Araucaria bidwillii* has a restricted distribution (which appears to be an interglacial refugium) north and west of Brisbane and in two relict areas north and south of Cairns. *Agathis robusta* is found in a small area in South Queensland and the wet tropics while *A. atropurpurea* and *A. microstachya* are confined to scattered areas of the wet tropics. The forests containing Araucariaceae are normally known as Araucarian vine forests (in several variants). Extensive plantations of *Araucaria cunninghamii* have been planted in Queensland as well as a small area of *A. bidwillii*.

In tropical and subtropical South America two Araucariaceae and up to seven podocarps occur in tropical montane forests. The podocarps follow a similar pattern to Australia as part of a generally angiosperm dominated forest, with seven species in Peru declining to one in northeast Argentina. In southeast Brazil and northeast Argentina they form part of the canopy under the emergent Parana pine (*Araucaria angustifolia*) in an association known as Araucarian moist forest, which in the past formed extensive stands. It is interesting to note the structural similarities of many of these forests in different continents (**Figures 1** and **2**). Extensive plantations of *A. angustifolia* have been established in Brazil, as well as *A. araucana* in Andes of Chile and Argentina, from wet forests including

Figure 1 *Araucaria angustifolia* forest, Brazil. Courtesy of Rudi Seitz.

Nothofagus at high altitude, to dry open forests on the Argentinean side.

In South Africa, three of the four podocarp species may be considered to be part of a subtropical evergreen forest, although the forest is not strictly analogous to any of the other southern conifer forests in this group and has structural similarity to some of the simpler subtropical rainforest types of Australia.

Status In Australia and New Caledonia these forests, while heavily cleared and logged in the past, are generally well protected although some minor clearing on private land still occurs. In South America and New Guinea clearing for agriculture and illegal or poorly controlled logging remains a continuing threat.

2. Warm Temperate Rainforest with Coniferous Emergents

This is one of the most restricted types and is found only in Australia from Victoria to the Queensland on poorer soils derived from rhyolite, trachyte, and metasediments in the northern part and on the more fertile eutrophic rocks in southern cooler regions. It requires rainfall over 1300 mm per year. It is characterized by a two-strata layer with a more limited range of species than the above type, with stranglers, palms, woody vines, and buttressing rare or absent. The tree trunks tend to be slender and uniform in appearance. Tree and ground ferns are frequent, and epiphytes can be common but are not generally abundant in the numbers or species present. Angiosperms are such species as coachwood (*Ceratopetalum apetalum*), sassafras (*Doryphora sassafras*), and scentless rosewood (*Synoum glandulosum*). Hoop pine (*Araucaria cunninghamii*) is found in some patches north of Dorrigo, but its main claim to fame is that it is in this association that Wollemi pine (*Wollemia nobilis*), representing a third araucarian genus (previously only known from fossils) was found in 1994, with a tiny distribution in two stands in deep sandstone gorges just north of Sydney.

Status Most of this type is found in protected areas, but smaller patches embedded in sclerophyll forest may be vulnerable to wildfire. *Wollemia nobilis* has adapted to wildfire by strong coppicing mechanisms. The main threat to *W. nobilis* is considered to be introduction of pathogens by illegal visitors to the site.

3. Temperate Rainforests Containing Conifers

These forests are the dominant vegetation of the wetter coastal and montane areas of Chile and Argentina, New Zealand, and Tasmania. In only a

Figure 2 *Araucaria bidwillii* forest, Bunya Mountains, Queensland, Australia.

few parts of this forest type are conifers as dominant as they are in the equivalent forest types of the North American Pacific coast, but there are also few areas where conifers are not part of this forest.

The conifer families present are Araucariaceae, Cupressaceae, Podocarpaceae, and, in Tasmania only, Taxodiaceae (although Taxodiaceae is now generally included in the Cupressaceae). The most common angiosperms associated with such species are old Gondwanan families such as the family Winteraceae and species of *Nothofagus*, *Metrosideros*, *Quintinia*, *Weinmannia*, etc.

Conifer dominated forests of alerce (*Fitzroya cupressoides*) and *Pilgerodendron uviferum* once dominated the wet soils of the valley between the Chilean coastal ranges and the Andes but were cleared by early Spanish settlers restricting this forest type to less conifer dominated montane forests, although *P. uviferum* is still present in large stands in the Chiloe archipelago.

Conifer dominated forests are also present on the west coast of New Zealand's South Island, on wet river terraces. These forests are dominated by the podocarps *Dacrydium cupressinum*, *Prumnopitys ferruginea*, *P. taxifolia*, *Dacrycarpus dacryioides*, and *Manoao colensoi*. These forests are associated with the angiosperms *Metrosideros*, *Knightia*, *Quintinia*, and *Weinmannia*. There is a great variation in the dominance of conifers in other areas of New Zealand. *Nothofagus* species tend to dominate the

forests closer to the treeline but *Libocedrus* is a major component sometimes dominating stands. Other conifers also occur in these beech forests. There appears to be a long-term dynamic interaction between *Nothofagus* and conifers depending on large- and small-scale disturbance. Indeed disturbance is a major factor in most forests with a high conifer component. In Westland, the river terrace forest probably results from periodic flooding, while in the central North Island the large podocarp stands appear to have been associated with the enormous Taupo eruption that occurred about 1800 years ago. There is evidence that over time the podocarps decline until angiosperms dominate the canopy, but podocarps remain as emergents and enough survive to maintain a population until the next catastrophic disturbance.

In New Zealand's northland, the kauri (*Agathis australis*) is added to the forest mix to form some of New Zealand's most famous forests with some existing kauris up to 50 m tall and up to 4.5 m in diameter. While not tall by world standards, this tree has little taper until the crown so the kauri appears as a solid block of timber. There is evidence that the kauri as a component of mixed angiosperm coniferous forests has expanded and retreated with long-term climatic variation.

In Tasmania, conifers are a less dominant feature of the forests but podocarps such as celery top pine (*Phyllocladus aspeniifolius*) and King Billy pine

(*Athrotaxis selaginoides*) occur in rainforests dominated by *Nothofagus* and sassafras (*Atherosperma moschatum*). Probably one of the main reasons for the nondominance of conifers is the dynamic, fire-mediated relationship between rainforest and wet tall eucalypt forest. The other important rainforest species, a podocarp, Huon pine (*Lagarstrobos franklinii*), is virtually confined to riparian forests of the south and southwest with the exception of a few stands away from the river systems.

Status In Chile, this forest is not secure particularly in the northern part of the forested region. Although a reasonable percentage is in protected areas, not all forest types are represented. Much clearing occurred during early European settlement especially in the valley between the coastal range and the Andes. A variety of pressures still exists including clearing, selective legal and illegal logging affecting forest structure and replacement by exotic plantations. In New Zealand much of the original forest was cleared for agriculture, grazing, and exotic plantation. Much remains in mountainous areas and in the Westland area of the South Island. Remnant areas in the North Island are now generally secure. In Tasmania, large areas are preserved in the World Heritage area, but in large areas where eucalypt is logged the cyclical progression to rainforest has been halted by silviculture practice.

4. Arid Zone Coniferous Forests and Woodlands

The *Callitris* forests and woodlands of Australia, and the drier forests of cipré (*Austrocedrus chilensis*) in Chile and Argentina form an unusual and distinctive coniferous forest type and one where the forest ecology is most sensitive to human interference. The almost extinct drier mountain forests of Clanwilliam cedar (*Widdringtonia cedarbergensis*) and *W. schwartzii* with an asteraceous understory of the South African Cape region also fit into this group. In dense stands of these species, fire has an extreme behavior with high rate of spread, crown fire, and spotting. Even in more open woodland with these species, fire can be intense due to dry grass and shrub understory. The Pilliga Scrub in New South Wales, one of the largest cypress forests, has been referred to as 'big fire country' with up to 100 000 ha of a total of 500 000 ha being burnt in one fire.

The forests have contrasting post-European fire histories. The cipré forests originally covered a vast area of the drier foothills and lower slope area of the Andes in Chile and Argentina. It is a long-lived species which existed in an environment of infrequent catastrophic disturbance (e.g., volcanic activity) and requires a time period of over a 100 years to regenerate. With more frequent fires since European settlement a large area of its former range has been converted to shrubland. Fire and overexploitation have also reduced the South African cedar forests (*Juniperus* extends in to southern hemisphere in Africa, but is northern in relationship) to small remnants, although there is now a strong conservation push to preserve and extend these.

The *Callitris* forests have had a more complex history. The most common forest consists of *Callitris glaucophylla* as a codominant with a number of *Eucalyptus*, *Angophora* and *Casuarina* species. This forest type extends from southern Queensland into northern Victoria. Other species such as *Callitris priessii* and *C. endlicheri* also form similar, but more geographically restricted forests. *Callitris intratropica* forms small stands in savanna vegetation in northern Australia and several species also form similar associations in sandy soils of some coastal areas. Early records and analysis of stumps indicates that under Aboriginal land management practices the *C. glaucophylla* forest was more an open woodland with a grassy understory (**Figure 3**).

Cessation of Aboriginal burning following European settlement combined with a series of good seasons resulted in a dense but fire-prone forest dominated by cypress. This forest has since been modified and diminished by a variety of factors.

Most important has been clearing for grazing and agriculture, with large areas cleared particularly since 1945. Grazing by rabbits and severe drought has also impacted on populations with some populations not recovering from extreme droughts. Although wildfire often stimulates 'wheatfield' regeneration, overfrequent fire can cause loss of this ecosystem. A large number of forests can no longer be considered natural (however that may be defined in this complex system), as they are silviculturally manipulated production forests.

Status The Australian *Callitris* forests, although under pressure, can be regarded as secure due to their large area and management as a timber resource.

The cedar forests of South Africa and the cipré forests of South America are threatened. The following are listed by the IUCN (World Conservation Union) as threats to the cipré forests. They could be repeated almost exactly for *Widdringtonia* in southern Africa:

- Habitat loss/degradation – agriculture – livestock (ongoing);
- Habitat loss/degradation – land management of non-agricultural areas (ongoing);
- Habitat loss/degradation – extraction – wood – clear-cutting (ongoing);

Figure 3 *Callitris glaucophylla* woodland in New South Wales, circa 1910. Reproduced with permission from Baker RT and Smith HG (1910) *A Research on the Pines of Australia*, Technical Education Series no. 16. Sydney, Australia: New South Wales Department of Education, Technical Education Branch, Government Printer.

- Habitat loss/degradation – infrastructure development – human settlement (ongoing);
- Habitat loss/degradation – fires (ongoing);
- Invasive alien species (directly affecting the species) – pathogens/parasites (ongoing)
- Changes in native species dynamics – predators.

5. Heathland and Shrubland with Coniferous Emergents/Components

These are interesting associations and are found in four widely dispersed forms: *Araucaria araucana* in southern South America, *Widdringtonia* in 'fynbos' heathland in South Africa, 'maquis' with araucarian emergents in New Caledonia, and 'kwongan' (heathlands) with *Actinostrobus* species in southwest Australia.

As previously discussed the *Araucaria araucana* forests in drier high altitude sites could be regarded as part of a number of associations, but it has been included here as fire interactions form a common component of these associations. *Araucaria araucana* has a range of fire adaptations including basal epicormic buds, protected terminal buds and thick bark. The trees grow over a shrub canopy made up primarily of *Nothofagus* species (the structure differs at lower altitudes and higher moisture areas and can vary in height). Some of these higher altitude stands of *A. araucana* in many ways appear to provide a structural analog to high-latitude southern hemisphere Cretaceous forests.

In New Caledonia, araucarians exist in most forest types, but the most interesting are emergent araucarians of a number of species up to 7–8 m high overtopping a shrub layer to 2.5 m on ultrabasic substrates. Other conifers may also occur in the shrub to small tree layer (*Dacrydium*, *Podocarpus*, *Neocallitropsis*).

In the Cape Province of South Africa *Widdringtonia* spp. are small tree emergents above a heath layer of Proteaceae, Restionaceae, and ericoid shrubs. All species are to some degree fire dependent, seeding after fire from retained cones. *Widdringtonia whytei* has fire resistant bark, and *W. cupressoides* resprouts after fire from underground tubers, an unusual habit in conifers. All species have suffered badly under a regime of overfrequent fires.

Interestingly, a similar habit is found in southwest Western Australia in kwongan where one of the two *Actinostrobus* species is also a resprouter. In nearby tall eucalypt forests (and extending on to adjacent heaths) is the only fire-adapted podocarp, *Podocarpus drouynianus*, which resprouts after fire.

Status The *A. araucana* forests are protected but still vulnerable to the wide range of human impacts including illegal logging. In New Caledonia, the maquis areas are not suitable for agriculture, but are subject to human-induced wildfires. In South Africa the communities containing *Widdringtonia* are badly affected by wildfire, alien species invasion, and overexploitation of *Widdringtonia* for timber. However, active conservation activities are targeting preservation of all the species but particularly *W. cedarbergensis*. In Western Australia the kwongan has been affected by overclearing, overfrequent fire, and infection by the exotic root fungus *Phytophthora cinnamomi*.

6. Alpine and Subalpine Shrubland and Forest with Conifers

In South America, South Africa, New Guinea, and New Zealand there is a range of montane and subalpine forest types that are typical of these areas. Generally these tend to be part of an altitudinal gradation, e.g., afromontane forest contains *Widdringtonia* species that are also common at lower altitudes and *Librocedrus* in New Zealand also forms a distinctive subalpine forest type.

Only in Australia has a distinctive alpine conifer flora developed (or persisted). Two Tasmanian podocarps, *Microcachrys tetragona* and *Microstrobos niphophilus*, occur as shrubs above the eucalypt treeline. A Tasmanian Cupresseaceae, *Diselma archeri*, although most common as a shrub in the alpine and subalpine zone, also extends below the treeline. *Podocarpus lawrencei* occurs as a pioneer shrub on alpine scree slopes in Tasmania, New South Wales, and Victoria but is also found as a small tree below the treeline. In Tasmania, King Billy pine (*Athrotaxis selaginoides*) can exist as a low twisted 'krummholz' tree in subalpine shrubland. The second true species, *A. cupressoides* (pencil pine) occurs at higher altitudes than *A. selaginoides*, although there is overlap between the two. It has more compact foliage and does not grow to such a large tree.

Status The Australian alpine zone is very small and fragile by world standards and is vulnerable to climate change. Warmer temperatures could effectively eliminate Australian alpine areas or reduce them to tiny remnants. Wildfires can invade alpine and subalpine areas and recovery is slow. Human-induced changes could prevent recovery after climate change cycles.

Conclusion

The conifers of the southern hemisphere are a distinctive group occurring in a large range of forms and occupying a large range of ecological niches from tropical rainforest to alpine shrublands and semi-arid woodlands. They have a distinctive place in the paleobotanical history of conifers and have been used (and have great potential) for silvicultural and horticultural use. In the past they have been little studied but this is beginning to change and further study is likely to lead to both a greater understanding of the group and a greater utilization of their unique characteristics.

See also: **Biodiversity**: Endangered Species of Trees. **Entomology**: Bark Beetles. **Medicinal, Food and Aromatic Plants**: Edible Products from the Forest. **Temperate Ecosystems**: Fagaceae; Pines. **Tree Breeding, Practices**: Southern Pine Breeding and Genetic Resources. **Tree Physiology**: Mycorrhizae. **Tropical Ecosystems**: Southern Hemisphere Conifers; Tropical Pine Ecosystems and Genetic Resources.

Further Reading

Bieleski R (ed.) (in press) *Proceedings of the International Araucariaceae Symposium*, (2003) Auckland. Auckland, Australia: International Dendrology Society.

Bowman DM (2000) *Australian Rainforests: Islands of Green in a Land of Fire*. Cambridge: Cambridge University Press.

Dargavel J, Hart D, and Libbis B (2001) *Perfumed Pineries: Environmental History of Australia's Callitris Forests*. Canberra, ACT: Australian National University.

Enright NJ and Hill RS (eds) (1995) *Ecology of the Southern Conifers*. Melbourne Victoria: Melbourne University Press.

Enright NJ, Ogden J, and Rigg LS (1999) Dynamics of forests with Araucariaceae in the Western Pacific. *Journal of Vegetation Science* 10: 792–804.

Haebich A (2002) *On the Bunya Trail*, Queensland Review Special Edition vol. 9.2. Brisbane, Queensland: University of Queensland Press.

Hill RS (ed.) (1994) *History of the Australian Vegetation: Cretaceous to Recent*, p. Cambridge. UK: Cambridge University Press.

Hill RS and Brodribb TJ (1999) Southern conifers in time and space. *Australian Journal of Botany* 47: 639–696.

Hueck K (1966) *Die Wälder Südamerikas*. Stuttgart, Germany: Gustav Fischer Verlag.

Klein RM (1960) O aspecto dinâmico do pinheiro Brasileiro. *Sellowia* 12: 17–44.

Lowry PP (1996) Diversity, endemism, and extinction in the flora of New Caledonia: a review. In: Peng CI and Lowry PP (eds) *Rare, Threatened, and Endangered Floras of the Pacific Rim*, pp. 181–206. Taipei: Institute of Botany, Academica Sinica.

Neira E, Verscheure H, and Revenga C (2002) *Chile's Frontier Forests: Conserving a Global Treasure*. Washington, DC: World Research Institute.

Reitz R and Klein RM (1966) *Araucariaceae*. Flora Ilustrada Catarinense.

Specht RL, Dettman ME, and Jarzen DM (1992) Community associations and structures in the late Cretaceous vegetation of southeast Australia and Antarctica. *Paleogeography, Paleoentology, Paleoecology* 94: 283–309.

Stockey RA (1994) Mesozoic Araucariaceae: morphology and systematic relationships. *Journal of Plant Research* 155(6): 806–815.

Taylor TN and Taylor EL (1990) *Antarctic Palaeobiology: Its Role in the Reconstruction of Gondwana*. New York: Springer-Verlag.

Worldwide Fund for Nature (2003a) *South Malawi Montane Forest Grassland Mosaic: Ecoregion Profile*. Stellensboch, South Africa: Worldwide Fund for Nature.

Worldwide Fund for Nature (2003b) *Drakensberg Montane Grasslands, Woodlands and Forests: Ecoregion Profile*. Stellensboch, South Africa: Worldwide Fund for Nature.

Subalpine and Boreal Forests

N A Balliet and C D B Hawkins, University of Northern British Columbia, Prince George, BC, Canada

Table 1 Some species commonly occurring in subalpine and boreal forests, with their common names

Species	Common name
Abies balsamea	Balsam fir
Abies lasiocarpa	Subalpine fir
Abies sibirica	Siberian fir
Betula papyrifera	Paper birch
Juniperus spp.	Juniper spp.
Larix dahurica	Dahurian larch
Larix laricina	Tamarack
Larix lyallii	Subalpine larch
Larix sibirica	Siberian larch
Picea abies	Norway spruce
Picea engelmannii	Engelmann spruce
Picea glauca	White spruce
Picea mariana	Black spruce
Pinus albicaulis	Whitebark pine
Pinus aristata	Bristlecone pine
Pinus banksiana	Jack pine
Pinus contorta	Lodgepole pine
Pinus flexilis	Limber pine
Pinus sibirica	Siberian pine
Pinus sylvestris	Scots pine
Populus balsamifera	Balsam poplar
Populus tremuloides	Trembling aspen
Salix spp.	Willow spp.
Taxus spp.	Yew spp.
Thuja plicata	Western red cedar
Tsuga heterophylla	Western hemlock
Tsuga mertensiana	Mountain hemlock

Introduction

Many biogeographers consider boreal and subalpine forests as one biome, others separate them because, although boreal and subalpine forests share many similar attributes with respect to climate, vegetation, and soil, there are significant differences between the two. In this article the two will be treated separately.

Subalpine forests are high-elevation forests that occur in mountainous regions around the world. Coniferous subalpine forests, however, are largely limited to the northern hemisphere. These forests are found immediately above the northern coniferous forest in the European Alps, the mountains of east-central Europe, the Urals, the Himalayas, the mountains of northeast China, and the Appalachians, the Sierra Nevada, Cascade and Coastal Ranges and the Rocky Mountains of North America.

The majority of subalpine forests are dominated by *Picea*, *Abies*, *Pinus*, and *Larix* species; however, some variation does occur among regions (see **Table 1** for common names of these species). Subalpine forests of the European Alps are characterized by *Picea–Abies* forests at lower elevations and *Larix–Pinus* forests at higher elevations. The mountainous regions of Romania, Yugoslavia, and Bulgaria are characterized by *Abies*, *Larix*, *Picea*, and *Pinus* species, whereas the Urals are dominated by *Abies*, *Picea*, and *Pinus* species. The subalpine forests of the Himalayas are characterized by *Abies* and *Picea* at lower elevations and *Juniperus*, *Larix*, *Pinus*, and *Taxus* species at higher elevations, whereas the mountainous regions of northeast China support *Picea–Abies* species at elevations between 2500 m and 3500 m.

Due to distinct differences in species, climate, and soils, the subalpine forests of the Sierra Nevada and Cascade and Coastal Ranges in North America will be excluded from this description (*see* **Temperate and Mediterranean Forests**: Southern Coniferous Forests; Temperate Broadleaved Deciduous Forest). Additionally, because the Appalachians are often considered temperate and because subalpine forests are only found on the highest peaks, these forests will be covered elsewhere (*see* **Temperate and Mediterranean Forests**: Temperate Broadleaved Deciduous Forest).

In western North America, subalpine forests occur along the entire length of the Rocky Mountains. These subalpine forests will be the focus of this article, where, owing to their similarities with the boreal forest, they are often referred to as mountain, taiga, or boreal forests.

The boreal forest (separate from the subalpine forest) is commonly referred to as taiga (a Russian term), or northern coniferous forest. Although it is restricted to the northern hemisphere, it forms nearly a continuous belt of coniferous trees across portions of North America and Eurasia. In Canada, it extends from coast to coast. It is bordered by the northern coniferous forest, temperate forest, or prairie to the south and tundra to the north. In Eurasia, it extends across Norway, Sweden, Finland, Russia, and Siberia, where it is bordered by tundra to the north and steppe or northern temperate forest to the south.

The boreal forest is characterized by a mosaic of coniferous genera including *Abies*, *Larix*, *Picea*, and *Pinus*, and broadleaf genera including *Betula*, *Populus*, and *Salix*. These genera occur as both pure and mixed stands across the landscape.

Subalpine Forests

While the following description focuses on subalpine forests of the Rocky Mountains, many of the characteristics are common to subalpine forests around the world.

Distribution

In Western North America, subalpine forests are found along the Rocky Mountains from as far south as Mexico to north of the Arctic Circle. The subalpine forests of the Rocky Mountains can be divided into four regional groups: Boreal, Central,

Southern, and Mexican. The most northerly section, the Boreal Rocky Mountain forest (**Figure 1**), extends from Alaska south to the Peace River in Northern British Columbia. The Central Rocky Mountain forest extend south from the Peace River to Wyoming. The Southern Rocky Mountain forest extend south from Wyoming to New Mexico. The most southerly group, the Mexican Rocky Mountain forest (also sometimes called the Madrean Rocky Mountain forest), extend south from New Mexico into southern Mexico and even into the mountains of Guatemala. Most consider the Mexican or Madrean Rocky Mountain forest to be part of the southern coniferous forest, however (*see* **Temperate and Mediterranean Forests**: Southern Coniferous Forests).

Postglacial Development

Currently there is very little information on the postglacial development of subalpine forests. Although pollen cores taken from lakes reveal that pioneer species such as *Betula*, *Juniperus*, *Populus*, and *Salix* were followed after glaciation by coniferous species such as *Abies*, *Larix*, *Picea*, and *Pinus*, it is unknown whether the present forest is a recent development or has been in existence for some time. It is believed the subalpine forest reached its modern state between 6000 and 5000 years ago.

With the retreat of glaciers, *Betula* and *Picea* spp. migrated west and northwest across Canada from refugia south and southeast of the continental ice sheet. *Larix* and *Populus* spp. may have followed the

Figure 1 Subalpine forests of the Boreal Rocky Mountains.

same migration pattern. In the west, *Pinus* spp. migrated from refugia south of the ice up the Rocky Mountain Trench as the Cordilleran and Laurentide ice sheets separated. Today, the Rocky Mountain subalpine forest occurs in the steep mountainous terrain of western North America above the northern coniferous forest.

Climate

The subalpine forest is characterized by a short growing season (less than 90 growing degree days); winters are generally long with heavy snow, while summers are short, dry, and cool. The climate varies somewhat with elevation and slope position (i.e., windward versus leeward slopes); temperatures drop while precipitation, solar radiation, wind, and snow depth and duration increase with increasing elevation. As such, the subalpine forest is often divided into two subzones: the lower subalpine area (1200–1800 m elevation), which is defined by a closed forest and a relatively favorable climate, and the upper subalpine area (1800–2300 m), which is characterized by open parkland or woodland and a harsher climate. These zones are found at lower elevations in the north and at higher elevations in the south.

Soil

Subalpine forests are most frequently associated with luvisols, brunisols, and regosols. Luvisols are characterized by an accumulation of clay; conversely, brunisols and regosols are poorly developed soils. Soils of the subalpine forest are typically shallow and generally poor in nutrients. They can also be acidic, and erosion is common due to frost heaving and steep slopes.

Vegetation

Rocky Mountain subalpine forests consist mainly of conifers with a few hardy deciduous species. These forests are often viewed as a southern extension of the boreal forest, particularly in the most northerly zone, the Boreal Rocky Mountain Forest, where it is often difficult to separate the boreal forest from the subalpine forest and the northern coniferous forest. Although vegetation varies somewhat with elevation, slope position, and soil, particularly from north to south and east to west, the Rocky Mountain coniferous forests are remarkably similar in species composition and stand structure along their entire length.

The lower subalpine area is typified by a closed forest of productive *Picea engelmannii* (south of 54°N), *P. glauca* (north of 54°N), *Abies lasiocarpa*, *Pinus contorta*, and *Populus tremuloides*, whereas the upper subalpine area is typified by shorter, open grown *Abies lasiocarpa*, *Picea engelmannii*, and *P. glauca*. *Picea* and *Abies* species tend to dominate the mature forests, whereas *Pinus contorta* dominates in the drier parts of the zone where fire disturbance has occurred. At the timberline, harsh climatic conditions affect tree growth. These trees grow in clumps and are often stunted, flagged or krummholz. In the Northern Rockies, the treeline is dominated by *Larix lyallii*, whereas in the Central Rockies *P. albicaulis* and *Pinus flexilis* dominate. This area is dominated by *P. aristata* in the Southern Rockies.

Ecosystem Dynamics

Subalpine forests are disturbance driven, with a mean disturbance return interval of 150 to 350 years. Although fire is the most important form of natural disturbance in these forests, wind, insects, disease, ungulate browsing, avalanches, landslides, extreme weather, and volcanism also play a role.

Successional patterns vary from north to south along the Rocky Mountains. In the Boreal Rocky Mountain Forest, *Betula papyrifera*, *P. balsamifera*, and *Populus tremuloides* are successional following fire disturbance. *Abies* spp and *Picea glauca*. follow. The Central Rocky Mountain Forest is somewhat more variable. In general, *Pinus contorta*, *Populus tremuloides*, and *P. balsamifera* are successional following fire, whereas, *Picea engelmannii* dominates older forests, although *Abies lasiocarpa*, *Betula papyrifera*, *Larix* spp., and *P. mariana*, and are also present. *Picea engelmannii* appears on the south eastern slopes of the Central Rocky Mountain forest, while *Larix lyallii*, *Pinus albicaulis*, and *P. flexilis* appear near the timberline. On the southwestern slopes of the Central Rocky Mountain Forest, *Abies* spp., *Tsuga heterophylla*, and *Thuja plicata* are associated with *Larix lyallii*, *Picea* spp., *Pinus albicaulis*, and *Tsuga mertensiana* appear at higher elevations. The subalpine forests of the Southern Rocky Mountain forest are dominated by *Abies lasiocarpa* and *Picea engelmannii*.

Damaging Agents

Insects and disease Many species of insect and disease impact trees in the subalpine forest. Although insects such as spruce budworm (*Choristoneura* spp.), bark beetles (*Dendroctonus* spp.) and white pine weevil (*Pissodes strobi*), are the major pests to conifers of the subalpine forest, diseases such as mistletoe (*Arceuthobium* spp.), western gall rust (*Endocronartium harkenssii*), and broom rusts are also present.

Fire and wind Fires in the subalpine forest are infrequent but tend to be stand destroying, making them an important part of the successional pattern in these forests. Shallow soils are common in the subalpine forest, which make for a poor rooting medium leaving trees susceptible to windthrow.

Avalanche paths Avalanche paths are common in the subalpine forest. Recurrent slides leave many of these paths devoid of trees and dense with shrubs and herbaceous species.

Climate change Global climate change may have serious implications for subalpine forests. Although temperatures are not expected to rise higher than they have historically, the rate of change appears to be much faster than it has been in the past. Global warming of 1.0–4.5°C over the next 100 years is anticipated. It is likely that changes in precipitation patterns and carbon dioxide levels will also accompany changes in temperature. All of these changes may result in latitudinal or, to a limited extent, elevational shift in species ranges. Differences in dispersal ability may also result in changes in plant communities and competition between 'exotic' species, which could result in extinction for some species. Extinction may also occur because species cannot adapt or move fast enough under the changing conditions.

Forest management Forests in the lower subalpine area are highly productive. *Abies lasiocarpa*, *Picea glauca*, *P. engelmannii*, and *Pinus contorta* are the largest and most productive species in the subalpine forest. As such, these species are a highly valuable resource where timber harvesting is the major economic activity. These large, nature forests, however, are also highly valuable caribou habitat. In recent years, efforts have been made through alternative silviculture systems such as variable retention, shelterwoods, or group selection, to protect the structural and functional integrity of caribou habitat in these high elevation forests.

Boreal Forests

Distribution

The boreal forest (**Figure 2**) forms a circumpolar forest belt in the northern hemisphere and as such it is one of the world's largest forested areas, and a major carbon reservoir.

Postglacial Development

The majority of the area covered by the boreal forest today was once completely covered by ice. As the ice sheets melted, the land was slowly invaded by herbaceous plants and shrubs, followed by conifers. Although the distribution of boreal species was

Figure 2 The boreal forest in northeastern British Columbia.

largely a response to climate and soil, species dispersal rates and locations of refugia played a large role following glaciation. In North America, refugia existed south, west, and east of the ice. Species migration in the boreal region was similar to that of the subalpine region, with *Picea*, *Betula*, *Populus*, and *Larix* spp. migrating west and northwest across Canada and *Pinus* spp. migrating north up the Rocky Mountain Trench as the Cordilleran and Laurentide ice sheets separated. Due to the lingering ice sheets, the boreal forest in eastern Canada is believed to be younger than the boreal forest in western Canada.

Climate

The climate of the boreal forest varies somewhat between coastal and continental regions. In continental regions, winters are long, cold, and dry, while summers are short, moderately warm, and moist, whereas in coastal regions, such as eastern Canada and Scandinavia, the climate tends to be warmer and moister. In general, however, an average of 100–900 mm of precipitation falls annually and the mean annual temperature does not rise above −0.5 °C.

Terrain and Soil

The terrain of the boreal forest is diverse. Rolling uplands are interspersed with lakes of varying sizes, bogs, and wetland communities. Bogs or peatlands are thick deposits of peat and organic soils often saturated with water that cover vast areas of the boreal forest. Bedrock outcrops, eskers, and moraines are also common.

Boreal forests are most frequently associated with podzols (spodosols). These soils are characterized by an accumulation of organic matter as well as iron and aluminum deposits. They are acidic and have low nutrient status. Other soil types commonly found in the boreal include luvisols and organics. Luvisols are defined by an accumulation of clay, whereas organic soils are composed largely of organic matter and tend to be poorly drained. Pockets of continuous and discontinuous permafrost exist throughout the boreal forest, chilling the soil above and slowing decomposition. Permafrost also forms an impenetrable layer, retarding drainage.

Vegetation

Coniferous trees dominate the boreal forest; however, hardy deciduous species such as *Betula papyrifera*, *Populus balsamifera*, and *P. tremuloides* are also common. Shrub willow (*Salix* spp.) is also very common on the wetter areas. In western North America, *Picea glauca*, *P. mariana*, *Larix laricina*, *P. banksiana*, *P. contorta*, *A. lasiocarpa*, and *A. balsamea* dominate the boreal forest, whereas, in eastern North America, *A. balsamea* forms the climax species. In Scandinavia and western Russia, *Picea abies* and *Pinus sylvestris* dominate, whereas *Abies sibirica*, *L. dahurica*, *Larix sibirica*, and *Pinus sibirica* dominate in Siberia.

The boreal forest is often divided into three latitudinal zones: closed forest, lichen woodland, and forest–tundra. The closed forest at lower latitudes is characterized by continuous northern coniferous forest with *Betula* and *Populus* spp. intermixed. Maximum tree height in these forests is about 23 m. The trees of the lichen woodland at mid latitudes are shorter and more open than those of the closed forest; however, they are not as scattered as the trees of the forest–tundra. The treeline is often found at the northern limit of the forest–tundra zone and is analogous to the treeline above subalpine forests. Temperature appears to regulate the northern and southern bounds of the boreal forest: respectively, the boundaries correspond roughly to 13 °C and 18 °C July mean temperatures.

The mosaic of forest communities found in the boreal forest is largely due to a response to climate, topography, the presence or absence of permafrost, soils, fire activity, as well as the reproductive capacity, vigor, and distribution of boreal tree species.

Productivity Productivity of the boreal forest is limited by low atmospheric temperatures, the presence of permafrost and low soil temperatures, thick organic layers with slow rates of decomposition, and poorly drained acidic soils with low nutrient availability. This is why it is one of the major carbon reservoirs on earth. Consequently, productivity of the boreal forest varies widely with latitude, proximity to the coast, topography, and seral stage. In general, however, productivity differs greatly from the lowlands to the uplands. The most productive sites are the lowland floodplains. These sites are dominated by *Populus balsamifera*. In contrast, *Picea mariana* sites are the least productive.

Ecosystem Dynamics

The boreal forest is disturbance driven with a mean disturbance return interval of 50–200 years in North America and 50–270 years in Sweden. Although fire is the main disturbance factor, insect outbreaks and windthrow also play a key role. These frequent and diverse disturbance regimes in conjunction with a varied environment are thought to contribute to the diversity of forest types and the range in stand productivity typical of the boreal forest.

Most boreal species have evolved with fire and have adapted their growth and reproductive strategies accordingly. These diverse responses have led to a variety of successional pathways, and a diverse landscape.

Many boreal species have adapted an even-aged growth strategy. For instance, *Pinus banksiana* and *P. contorta* have adapted to poor dry sites, whereas *Picea mariana* has adapted to poor wet sites. In both cases, the extreme environmental conditions under which these species grow and reproduce leaves them relatively free of interspecific competition.

Boreal species also vary widely in their shade tolerance, longevity, and regeneration strategies. For example, *Betula papyrifera*, *Populus balsamifera*, and *P. tremuloides* are early successional species, regenerating quickly following disturbance. As a result, however, these species are short-lived and shade-intolerant. Conversely, *Picea glauca* and *Abies* spp. are long-lived and shade-tolerant, making them keystone species in late successional and climax boreal forest types.

Indigenous Use

The indigenous people of Canada's boreal forest region have been harvesting a wide variety of natural products from the forest, to maintain their culture, for thousands of years. These products were used for a wide variety of purposes including (but not limited to) medicine, food (e.g., berries, roots, bark, small and large mammals), shelter, baskets, and clothing.

Damaging Agents

Insects and disease   Insects and disease, are important components of forest ecosystem dynamics in the boreal forest. For boreal conifer species, the major pests include spruce budworm (*Choristoneura* spp.), bark beetles (*Dendroctonus* spp.), and Siberian silkworm (*Dendrolimus sibericus*), all of which can cause widespread damage. For instance, the spruce budworm has been an extensive and extended problem in northeastern British Columbia as well as in eastern Canada. White pine weevil (*Pissodes strobi*), mistletoe (*Arceuthobium* spp.), western gall rust (*Endocronartium harkenssii*), and broom rusts are also present; however, these are minor pests compared to those mentioned above.

Fire and wind   Fire is an important aspect of ecosystem dynamics in the boreal forest. Fires destroy mature and overmature forests which are then replaced by new forests. Although stand-destroying fires are frequent, they tend to be small. Due to shallow rooting, boreal trees tend to be susceptible to windthrow, which opens up small gaps allowing species to regenerate in the openings.

Pollution and climate change   The boreal forests of eastern North America and Europe have been severely impacted by acid deposition (i.e., acid rain). Acid rain acidifies the soil which makes it toxic to plant roots, leaving the trees more susceptible to damage from insects and disease.

As discussed for subalpine forests, global climate change may also have serious implications for boreal forests. Change may result in a northward latitudinal shift in species ranges. However, in some areas, barriers such as urban areas may limit migration. The increase in temperature could enhance soil respiration and accelerate carbon emissions from the vast stored pool of the boreal forest.

Changes in temperature and precipitation will also have an impact on disturbance mechanisms such as insects, drought, and fire, influencing their occurrence, timing, frequency, duration, extent, and intensity. For example, extended periods of drought may result in fires burning more frequently, over larger areas, and at higher intensity, further reducing carbon storage in the boreal forest.

Industrial activities   Historically, boreal forests have played an important role in the economic development of northern countries. Resource extraction (e.g., trapping and forestry activities) began in the nineteenth century in Scandinavia and the twentieth century in Canada. Today, the boreal forests of North America and Europe continue to be an important region for the production of minerals, petroleum, hydroelectricity, and timber. The Siberian boreal forest is currently undergoing rapid development.

Although the majority of the boreal forest is suitable for sustainable resource extraction, industrial activities can result in the destruction of permafrost and the surrounding landscape. In Scandinavia, for example, large-scale forestry operations have transformed virtually all forested land into intensively managed secondary forests.

This emphasis on large-scale industrial resource extraction has resulted in conflicts between traditional resource users and industrial users world wide. The Temagami region of Ontario, for example, has been in dispute since the mid nineteenth century. The Teme-Augama Anishnabai people seek land claim settlements, the government seeks to establish industrial logging and mining operations in the area, and environmental groups seek to protect old-growth forests.

Subalpine and Boreal Forests: A Comparison

There are some distinct differences between subalpine and boreal forests even though in many ways they are similar. Subalpine and boreal forests both occur in the northern hemisphere, but subalpine forests are restricted to high elevation mountainous regions, while boreal forests occur at northerly latitudes. Subalpine and boreal forests likely shared similar postglacial development patterns. As the ice sheets retracted, species migrated northward and upward with continued warming and species migration from southern refugia; the northern coniferous forest established below the subalpine forest. Subalpine and boreal forests both have short growing seasons due to long winters. As the boreal is a cold biome, organic matter decays slowly and it is a major carbon sink along with the coastal temperate forest.

Subalpine forests are characterized by dry summers and snowy winters, whereas boreal forests are characterized by warm moist summers and cold dry winters. Subalpine forests occur in mountainous terrain, where soils tend to be shallow and low in nutrients. Boreal forests occur in rolling terrain with many lakes, bogs, and wetlands interspersed. Soils are also low in nutrients and permafrost can be continuous or discontinuous. This too contributes to the slow decay processes in the boreal forest. Both subalpine and boreal forests are dominated by coniferous trees with some hardy deciduous species. *Abies* and *Picea* species dominate the subalpine forest with *Pinus* species occupying the higher elevations near timberline and drier microsites. The boreal forest is characterized by a mosaic of *Abies*, *Betula*, *Larix*, *Picea*, *Pinus*, and *Populus* species. Subalpine forests become more open with increasing elevation as boreal forests do with increasing latitude. Both subalpine and boreal forests are disturbance driven, largely by fire which occurs at intervals of 150–350 years in subalpine forests and at slightly shorter intervals of 50–270 years in boreal forests. Insects, diseases, and wind also play a role in the ecosystem dynamics of both forests. Climate change is also a concern for both forest types. Changes in temperature, precipitation, and carbon dioxide levels may lead to shifts in species ranges, either latitudinally or elevationally.

Both forests are valued for their timber resources, while the boreal forest region is also valued for minerals, petroleum, and hydroelectricity, as well as for indigenous peoples' needs. Consequently, environmental groups are increasingly interested in protecting the boreal forest from such industrial activity as well as implementing actions to minimize the effects of global warming. Loss of the boreal forest could have serious global consequences, including impacts on the economy, the atmosphere, and the water supply.

See also: **Ecology**: Natural Disturbance in Forest Environments. **Environment**: Impacts of Elevated CO_2 and Climate Change. **Temperate and Mediterranean Forests**: Northern Coniferous Forests. **Temperate and Mediterranean Forests**: Southern Coniferous Forests; Temperate Broadleaved Deciduous Forest. **Temperate Ecosystems**: Alders, Birches and Willows; Pines; Spruces, Firs and Larches.

Further Reading

Billings WD (1990) The mountain forests of North America and their environments. In: Osmond CB, Pitelka LF, and Hidy GM (eds) *Plant Biology of the Basin and Range*, pp. 17–86. New York: Springer-Verlag.

Bonnan GB (1992) Processes in boreal forests. In: Shugart HH, Leemans R, and Bonan GB (eds) *A Systems Analysis of the Global Boreal Forest*, pp. 9–12. New York: Cambridge University Press.

Brown S (1990) Structure and dynamics of basin forested wetlands in North America. In: *Ecosystems of the World*, vol. 15, *Forested Wetlands*, pp. 171–199. New York: Elsevier.

Critchfield WB (1985) The late Quaternary history of lodgepole and jack pines. *Canadian Journal of Forest Research* 15: 749–768.

Elliott-Fisk DL (2000) The taiga and boreal forest. In: Barbour MG and Billings WD (eds) *North American Terrestrial Vegetation*, 2nd edn, pp. 41–73. New York: Cambridge University Press.

Gawthrop D (1999) *Vanishing Halo*. Vancouver, Canada: Greystone Books.

Henry JD (2002) *Canada's Boreal Forest*. Washington, DC: Smithsonian Institution Press.

Larsen JA (1980) *The Boreal Ecosystem*. New York: Academic Press.

MacDonald GM (1987) Postglacial development of the subalpine–boreal transition forest of western Canada. *Journal of Ecology* 75: 303–320.

Peet RK (2000) Forests and meadows of the Rocky Mountains. In: Barbour MG and Billings WD (eds) *North American Terrestrial Vegetation*, 2nd edn, pp. 75–121. New York: Cambridge University Press.

Pielou EC (1988) *The World of Northern Evergreens*. Ithaca, NY: Cornell University Press.

Pielou EC (1991) *After the Ice Age*. Chicago, IL: University of Chicago Press.

Pojar J (1996) Environment and biogeography of the western boreal forest. *Forestry Chronicle* 72(1): 51–57.

Temperate Broadleaved Deciduous Forest

P S Savill, University of Oxford, Oxford, UK

Introduction

Deciduous temperate forests (sometimes called summer-green forests) are dominated by broadleaved trees which lose their leaves during winter. They constitute the main potential natural vegetation over much of temperate Europe, eastern Asia, and north-eastern North America, and also appear in some climatically comparable, but much smaller, regions in the southern hemisphere. Owing to the deciduous habit of the main dominants and the characteristic dying-down of many of the associated plants as the trees come into leaf, these forests look entirely different in spring, summer, autumn, and winter. The deciduous habit is a strategy to deal with the lack of sunlight and cold temperatures in winter.

The regions potentially occupied by temperate broadleaved deciduous forest are among the most densely populated on earth and much of the original forest has been cleared. Only patches remain, few of which approach a truly natural condition, but many retain a seminatural character. Most of the earliest civilizations emerged in places with Mediterranean climates, and this led to early large-scale destruction of their forests. By the Middle Ages, the most important forest left in Europe was the broadleaved deciduous one. However, clearance of this was already widespread and more was lost or altered over the ensuing centuries. The fertile former forest ground was ideal for agricultural use as arable or pasture land. In some cases, the depredations of domestic animals were sufficient to prevent trees from regenerating and transformed these forests to grasslands.

Distribution

Temperate broadleaved deciduous forests occur in three major zones. In western and central Europe they extend across Poland and central Russia, down the mountain chains of southern Europe and into Asia minor; eastern Asia, including eastern China, Korea and Japan; and eastern North America. There is a smaller zone in South America (**Figure 1**).

1. In western and central Europe the temperate deciduous forests occur from the Atlantic coast, northwards to almost 60° N, eastwards to the Ural mountains of central Russia and down into the Caucasus and Elburz mountains of northern Iran, and southwards at higher altitudes in central Spain, southern Italy, and Greece. The tree and shrub composition is relatively poor to the north, with many species having failed to return after past glaciations. In many parts of Europe (e.g., the

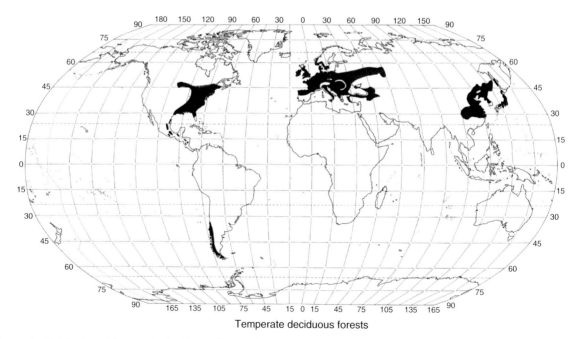

Temperate deciduous forests

Figure 1 Distribution of temperate deciduous forests. Reproduced with permission from Röhrig E and Ulrich B (eds) (1991) *Ecosystems of the World*, vol. 7, *Temperate Deciduous Forests*. London: Elsevier.

UK and Ireland), no truly natural woodland at all has survived. As elsewhere, prehistoric people cleared the majority of the original natural forests.

2. In northern Japan and adjacent parts of eastern continental Asia, the forests lie mostly between 30° and 50° N, extending to 125° E in the northwest, and 115° E in the southwest. In China intensive agriculture has caused this region to be largely cleared of natural vegetation for at least 4000 years.

3. In eastern North America, the forests lie in a belt from the coast, northwards to between around 35–48° N, and to the Great Lakes, and west to beyond the Mississippi. Almost all the forests of eastern North America are second growth, the original forest having been cleared by early settlers, but they contain a great diversity of flora and fauna. This is especially true of the Appalachian plateau of eastern Kentucky and Tennessee which was never glaciated, and western North Carolina and Virginia. The Great Smoky mountains have been designated a world biosphere reserve to help protect the rich assortment of species.

4. In the southern hemisphere, there is a small area of temperate deciduous forest in Chile and southwestern Argentina between 35° and 55° S, and in Tasmania. The majority of southern deciduous forests are located in Chile where they extend from higher altitudes on the Coastal and Andean mountain ranges of central–southern Chile to temperate cold-humid climates in Patagonia and Tierra del Fuego. Since colonial times the forests of central–southern Chile have been under intense pressure for transformation to agricultural and pasture uses and, more recently, for the establishment of fast-growing exotic forest plantations.

Climate and Seasonal Changes in the Forest

Most temperate deciduous forests have mild, damp climates, with average temperatures in the coldest months of between 18° and − 30°C. Monthly average temperatures in the warmest months are greater than 10°C, but seldom exceed 22°C. Precipitation is reasonably well distributed throughout the year, totaling 750–1500 mm or more. The growing season is about 6 months or a little longer, and never less than 4 months.

No other ecosystem is characterized by such marked seasonal changes as the temperate deciduous forest. It has four distinct seasons, spring, summer, autumn, and winter (**Figures 2–5**). In the autumn (late August to early October) the leaves change

Figure 2 Beech (*Fagus crenata*) in Ishikawa Prefecture, Japan, in autumn. The dark-green evergreen trees are *Cryptomeria japonica* and *Pinus parvifiora*. Courtesy of Koso Saito.

Figure 3 Beech (*Fagus sylvatica*) woodland in winter in Belgium. The trees are leafless, and no green ground vegetation can be seen. Even in summer it is sparse in this type of woodland where the trees cast a very heavy shade.

Figure 4 Walnut (*Juglans regia*) forest in summer in Kyrgyzstan. All the canopy trees in this picture are walnuts. The lower shrub/small tree stratum consists of fruit trees, including apples (the ancestors of many cultivated apples), plums and *Crataegus* species. Courtesy of Gabriel Hemery.

Figure 5 Spring in oak (*Quercus robur*) woodland in southern England. Spectacular displays of bluebells (*Hyacinthoides non-scripta*) are characteristic of many of these woods.

color and fall off the trees. During the winter months nearly all the trees are leafless; only a few species (e.g., holly – *Ilex aquifolium*) retain their foliage.

In spring, the ground vegetation becomes active first, including many herbs with perennial bulbs, tubers, or corms. They exhibit a distinct seasonality, taking advantage of the brief period of maximum light to flower very early in spring, before the leaves of the trees expand and cut most of it off. They flower and fruit rapidly and die down soon afterwards, as in the case of the lesser celandine (*Ranunculus ficaria*), and bluebell (*Hyacinthoides non-scripta*). Other species such as yellow archangel (*Lamiastrum galeobdolon*) appear somewhat later while the trees' leaves are expanding. Activity in the ground vegetation is followed by the shrubs, and then the trees. Buds burst and the leaves expand quickly, as soon as temperatures become suitable. In Europe and North America, bud burst progresses from the south to the north and from the more maritime to the more continental regions. The foliage is fully developed early in the season, so little photosynthetic time is lost. Flowering of trees also tends to be completed early, giving ample time for the development and ripening of the fruit. In a few species, the flowers open before the leaves expand (e.g., *Corylus* and *Populus*), allowing freer access for the wind and insects for pollination. Most trees flower at the time the leaves begin to expand in spring; very few (like *Tilia*) flower in summer. Spring also sees many insects, and in America a few mammals emerge from hibernation; many birds breed in deciduous woodlands, and later various summer-migrant birds arrive.

During summer the leaves of the trees are fully grown and form a dense canopy that keeps the forest interior shady but cooler and more humid than in the open. Various shade-bearing lower plants are adapted to tolerate the low level of light, and make use of occasional sun flecks (e.g., wood sorrel (*Oxalis acetosella*)). Insect life is abundant, with plant leaves, nectar, and sap providing rich supplies of food – in turn, these provide food for resident and migrant birds and mammals.

Autumn can be the most visually striking season of all in some regions, offering brilliant displays of leaves: reds of maples, yellows of birches, and oranges of various other species. The change in color, triggered by shortening day length, is caused by the cessation of chlorophyll synthesis (the green pigment in leaves), and breakdown of existing chlorophyll. This unmasks the other colored pigments in the leaves which are phenolic compounds that are present all the time. They have two functions: (1) being unpalatable and relatively indigestible, they provide leaves with a partial means of resistance to attacks by damaging fungi and leaf-eating insects; and (2) they act as filters to ultraviolet light and prevent damage to the leaves from it. The main pigments are anthocyanin, which gives the glowing reddish colors (bluish purple to scarlet), depending on the acidity of the cell sap, and carotene and xanthophyll, which give the orange and yellow colors.

The actual colors particular trees assume depend upon the mixture of the particular pigments in the leaves. The variety of colors both between and within species is due to the slightly varying strategies trees adopt to provide protection from potential predators and fungi. Some species are dependable in producing good colors almost every year; others are spectacular quite irregularly. Some species change to only one color (e.g., birches and some maples turn yellow; *Acer palmatum* red). Others show every tint from purple to yellow (e.g., cherry).

Autumn is also the time when most trees and shrubs produce fruit. Some species, especially oaks, have 'mast' years. These occur periodically in, say, one year in 4 or 5 when vast numbers of acorns are produced. This glut of food is conserved by squirrels, woodpeckers, and jays by burial in the soil or in holes in trees.

Winter is a period of dormancy for many species of trees and also ground vegetation, insects, and some mammals. Some species of birds migrate instead.

Why be Deciduous?

In comparison with the evergreen leaves of conifers, deciduous leaves are very efficient users of solar energy. They have higher photosynthetic rates per unit dry weight of leaf than the perennial evergreen leaves found on many conifers (about 10–14 mg $CO_2\,g^{-1}\,h^{-1}$ compared to 4–6 mg $CO_2\,g^{-1}\,h^{-1}$ in conifers). They are also much less expensively constructed in terms of content of assimilated carbon so that a proportionally larger part of the carbon gain by the tree, due to photosynthesis, is available for the growth of the nonphotosynthetic stems, roots, and fruits. A deciduous habit is very effective at making trees competitive if the growing season is at least 4 months in duration, where the climate is relatively humid, and where soil water and nutrients are readily available. In such environments the trees can produce sufficient photosynthate for at least the year's maintenance, growth, and reproduction, and they are competitive with evergreens. Shedding thin deciduous leaves in winter and the protection of meristems from water loss represents a considerable energy saving compared to maintaining a mass of thick evergreen leaves over winter. However, when the growing season becomes unduly restricted by winter cold or a long dry season, and on soils with low mineral resources, evergreen leaves can be an advantage.

This is because they are retained for several years. The evergreen habit enables leaves that are already on the tree to contribute to photosynthetic gain as soon as environmental conditions are suitable, even if the new leaves flush relatively late. They can also store nutrients in excess of current requirements for later use. The disadvantage of being evergreen is that the carbon input, or cost of constructing the leaves, is much higher than for deciduous leaves. It takes several years for a substantial leaf biomass to accumulate. The high structural cost provides protection against heat, cold, desiccation, and possibly predation and can be justified if the leaves serve for long periods but the trees have to accumulate leaf biomass over several years before fast rates of growth are achieved. Some evergreen trees are more competitive than deciduous ones in temperate deciduous climates where soils have few mineral resources and are drought-prone. Thus pines are often found on sandy soils in these regions. For example, *Pinus rigida* is the dominant pine in the New Jersey Pine Barrens, and Scots pine (*P. sylvestris*) is found on the heathlands in much of western Europe. Evergreens also predominate in boreal climates and can be very productive in climates with prolonged droughts such as in tropical monsoon and Mediterranean regions.

Because of leaf retention, there is often a much greater leaf biomass, or leaf area index (LAI), in evergreen forests. (LAI indicates the area of leaves per unit area of ground, and is indicated in units of square meters of leaf per square meter of ground.) For example, the LAIs in deciduous forests are typically between 4 and 7 whereas among evergreen conifers they can range up to 20.

Soil

Brown forest soils (alfisols, in the American soil taxonomy) develop under temperate broadleaved deciduous forests. These are among the most fertile, most easily worked, and most easily cleared of the temperate zone soils. Many have been under continuous cultivation since Neolithic times. Some of the world's major agricultural regions are found in the temperate deciduous forest zone, which is why there are so few of the original deciduous forests left. Part of the reason for their fertility is that most soils in the temperate deciduous forest zones are relatively young, having started to develop (in North America and Europe) after the last glaciation, about 12 000 years ago. They are therefore relatively rich in nutrient elements compared with, for example, most tropical rainforest soils, which are much older.

The leaves of deciduous broadleaved trees retain the major nutrient bases when they drop in the autumn. Thus the litter under this forest is not as acidic as under evergreen trees and aluminum and iron are not mobilized from the A horizon. The autumn leaf fall provides an abundant and rich organic matter which begins to decay rapidly in spring just as the growing season begins. The organic content gives both the A and B horizons a brown color.

Ultisols replace alfisols in the southeastern USA, where the older soils of unglaciated regions have been weathered to a much greater degree and are more completely leached than the younger soils to the north. Distinctive red or yellow subsoils have developed under the warmer climate. Ultisols are generally less fertile than alfisols.

Productivity

The productivity of temperate deciduous forests tends to be higher in the southern part of its range (in the northern hemisphere), and generally at lower elevations. However, since climate and light levels are broadly similar, net productivity is controlled primarily by local variations in nutrient and moisture regimes, as well as the inherent capacities of the various species to grow.

Productivity of the trees in stable temperate deciduous forests is usually quoted as around $10–12$ dry $t\,ha^{-1}\,year^{-1}$. Young stands on productive sites can achieve as much as $25\,t\,ha^{-1}\,year^{-1}$. The average usable production of wood is usually considered to be about 40% of net primary production, giving levels of $4–5$ dry $t\,ha^{-1}\,year^{-1}$. Total above-ground biomass in mature forests is $150–400\,t\,ha^{-1}$. In addition, in unmanaged forests, there may be about 20% of this volume lying as dead wood on the forest floor.

Strata

Most temperate deciduous forests have closed canopies, but open stands occur as well, particularly where the climate is dry and/or large grazing animals are abundant. Trees usually form only a single main stratum, story, or layer, though there may be an understory of shrubs, medium-sized trees, and saplings below.

These forests are among the most intensively managed in the world, so often they comprise only a single layer of developing overstory trees. Although natural temperate deciduous forests are more structured, they still tend to be far less luxuriant than moist tropical forests. Typically they consist of:

1. An overstory tree stratum, 20–35 m high, dominated regionally by various combinations of a rather limited number of genera.
2. A moderately developed subcanopy, mixed with but below the overstory and containing dying light-demanding trees and suppressed shade-tolerant trees; the latter can include younger specimens of the tall trees, but also medium-sized species such as (in Virginia, northeast USA) the Allegheny serviceberry (*Amelanchier arborea* var. *laevis*) and (in western Europe) the wild service tree (*Sorbus torminalis*) or field maple (*Acer campestre*).
3. An understory or shrub layer, including shrubs, smaller species of trees, and/or saplings of the taller trees. Species usually limited to this layer include (in Europe) hazel (*Corylus avellana*), hawthorn (*Crataegus monogyna*), and holly (*Ilex aquifolium*). This stratum is most noticeable when the tree stratum is not well developed; when it is, the development of shrubs and regeneration beneath it is scanty and may be missing altogether.
4. A low-growing herb layer of perennial forbs that flower in early spring; and sometimes, a ground layer mainly of mosses; lichens and mosses also grow on the trunks of trees.

The tree stratum occasionally consists of pure or nearly pure stands, with only slight differences in age (e.g., *Fagus sylvatica* in Europe). Mixed-species stands that are more or less even-aged and composed predominantly of late successional species (e.g., *Acer saccharum*, *Betula alleghaniensis*, *Fagus grandifolia* and *Tilia americana*) are common in northeastern North America. More mixed-age forests occur, for example, in the oak-dominated forests of Europe, with hornbeam (*Carpinus betulus*) and other species as an understory. Truly all-aged forests are found where a strongly continental climate or very moist or very dry soils prevent the dominance of any species with a high degree of shade tolerance.

Climbers such as ivy (*Hedera helix*), honeysuckle (*Lonicera periclymenum*) in Europe, and wild grape (*Vitis* spp.), poison ivy (*Rhus* spp.), and Virginia creeper (*Parthenocissus quinquefolia*) in North America climb the trees to flower and fruit high in the forest canopy. However, they are relatively few in number.

Tree Flora

Many tree genera are common to all three of the northern hemisphere temperate deciduous forest zones. Included among them are *Acer* (maple), *Castanea* (chestnut), *Fagus* (beech), *Juglans* (walnut), *Quercus* (oak), *Tilia* (basswood or lime), and *Ulmus* (elm). Different species of the genera occur on each continent. In South America, *Nothofagus* is a common genus (**Figure 6**).

In other respects, the climatic changes and successive glaciations during the Pleistocene, which gave rise to repeated migrations of the flora, have

Figure 6 Dense and apparently undisturbed *Nothofagus pumilio* forest in autumn, Tierra del Fuego, Chile. Courtesy of Franz-E Arnold.

resulted in substantial differences in the floras of deciduous forests. In North America and eastern Asia migrations were relatively unaffected by the large north–south mountain ranges (e.g., the Rocky Mountains and Appalachians), whereas the east–west ranges in Europe reduced the opportunities for plants to retreat to warmer regions and recolonize during interglacial periods. As a result, there are far fewer genera and species in Europe compared with eastern Asia and North America and, because of this, the relatively few European species tend to be more dominant due to the lack of competitors.

Although they naturally intergrade, as well as vary in detail, a number of main types of deciduous temperate forests are usually recognized:

- Western and central European oakwoods tend to be relatively open and light. The dominant species are the pedunculate and sessile oaks (*Quercus robur* and *Q. petraea*). Associated trees that are more or less common according to the nature of the soil include ash (*Fraxinus excelsior*), hornbeam (*Carpinus betulus*), birch (*Betula pendula* and *B. pubescens*), elm (*Ulmus glabra*, *U. procera*, *U. carpinifolia*), lime (*Tilia cordata*, *T. platyphyllos*), cherry (*Prunus avium*), alder (*Alnus glutinosa*), and aspen (*Populus tremula*). Small trees and large shrubs include hazel (*Corylus avellana*), hawthorn (*Crataegus monogyna*), field maple (*Acer campestre*), crab apple (*Malus sylvestris*), and three species of *Sorbus* (rowan, wild service tree, and whitebeam). There are also two evergreens, yew (*Taxus baccata*) and holly (*Ilex aquifolium*).
- The more luxuriant forests of eastern North America, eastern Asia, and southeastern Europe/Asia minor differ in species composition but are similar in appearance. The principal species usually include various oaks (*Quercus* spp.), beeches (*Fagus* spp.), birches (*Betula* spp.), hickories (*Carya* spp.), walnuts (*Juglans* spp.), maples (*Acer* spp.), limes (*Tilia* spp.), elms (*Ulmus* spp.), ash (*Fraxinus* spp.), tulip trees (*Liriodendron* spp.), sweet chestnuts (*Castanea* spp.), and hornbeams (*Carpinus* spp.). The lower stories are normally more luxuriant and varied than in the western and central European forests. In the colder eastern and more northern parts of North America, conifers such as *Pinus strobus* begin to appear with the deciduous trees.
- Beech forests which, especially in Europe, with the very shade-tolerant *Fagus sylvatica* form almost uniform, closed canopies and cast such dense shade that few shrubs or herbs can grow. Similar types, though on a smaller scale, are found with *F. orientalis* in Turkey and other parts of its range,

and with *F. crenata* in Japan. In the higher mountains of central and southern Europe, the conifers *Abies alba* and *Picea abies* become admixed.
- Southern beech, especially *Nothofagus nervosa* (syn. *N. procera*) and *N. obliqua*, usually with associated evergreens such as *Laureliopsis philippiana*, *Laurelia sempervirens*, and *Persea lingua*. Numerous ferns and bryophytes are features of these forests.
- The damper deciduous woodlands, especially those on marshy ground, are dominated by alders (*Alnus* spp.), willows (*Salix* spp.), poplars (*Populus* spp.) and birches (*Betula* spp.). The understories may be dense, and climbers and epiphytes numerous.

See also: **Forest Ecosystems**: Fagaceae (Oaks, Beeches, Hickories and Nothofagus); Juglandaceae (The Walnut Family: Walnuts, Hickories, Pecans). **Plant Diversity in Forests**. **Genetics of Oaks**.

Further Reading

Ford Robertson FC (ed.) (1971) *Terminology of Forest Science, Technology, Practice and Products*. Washington, DC: Society of American Foresters.

Helms JA (ed.) (1988) *The Dictionary of Forestry*. Bethesda, MD: Society of American Foresters; and Wallingford, UK: CABI Publishing.

Packham JR, Harding DJL, Hilton GM, and Stuttard RA (1992) *Functional Ecology of Woodlands and Forests*. London: Chapman & Hall.

Peterken GF (1996) *Natural Woodland: Ecology and Conservation in Northern Temperate Regions*. Cambridge, UK: Cambridge University Press.

Polunin N (1960) *Introduction to Plant Geography and Some Related Sciences*. London: Longman.

Röhrig E and Ulrich B (eds) (1991) *Ecosystems of the World*, vol. 7, *Temperate Deciduous Forests*. London: Elsevier.

Walter H (1979) *Vegetation of the Earth and Ecological Systems of the Geo-Biosphere*. New York: Springer-Verlag.

Mediterranean Forest Ecosystems

B Fady, Institut National de la Recherche Agronomique, Avignon, France
F Médail, Université d'Aix–Marseille III, Aix-en-Provence, France

Introduction

Occupying only 2% of the world's surface area, the Mediterranean biome contains nearly 20% of the earth's total plant diversity, making the five regions of the world under a Mediterranean climate (the Mediterranean Basin, California, the South African Cape Province, south and southwestern Australia, and parts of central Chile) a very significant biodiversity hot spot, second only to tropical regions (**Figure 1**). Strong biogeographical, environmental and human-made constraints have shaped this structural and functional diversity. The most typical characteristics of Mediterranean forests, compared to temperate or boreal forests, are their spatial and temporal complexity and heterogeneity, not only in terms of the physical factors (geography, geology, geomorphology, pedology, and bioclimate) that prevail where they grow, but also in terms of their biological components and attributes: functional dynamics at local and landscape levels, floristic and faunistic composition, richness and biogeographic origins.

Mediterranean forests represent 1.8% of world forest area. In this article, we will focus our attention on forests of the largest Mediterranean region of the world, the Mediterranean basin, where historical and paleogeographical episodes, long-term human influence, and current geographical and climatic contrasts have created both high species and ecosystemic diversity and heterogeneity. A short comparative overview of all world Mediterranean forests will also be presented.

Definition of Mediterranean Forests

The Mediterranean Climate: A Strong Driver for Forest Type Diversity

The Mediterranean region *sensu stricto* is usually defined by its climate, which in turn is responsible for its flora. It stretches between the northern latitudes of

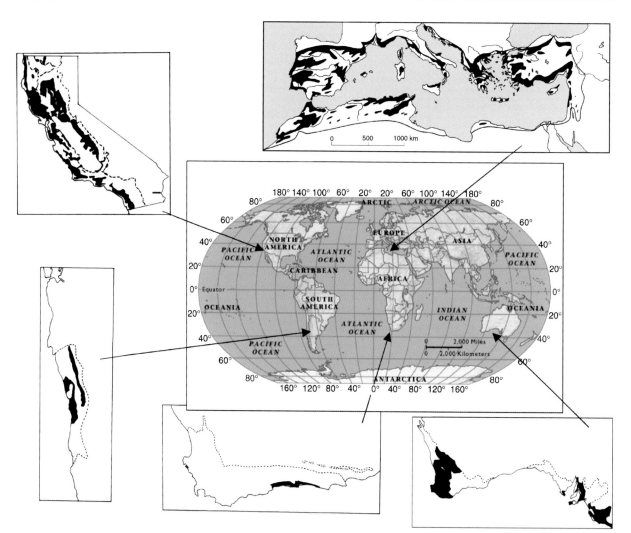

Figure 1 The world's Mediterranean regions. Plain or dotted lines indicate the limits of Mediterranean type ecosystems. Dark areas represent the extent of forest ecosystems. Modified from Quézel P and Médail F (2003) *Ecologie et Biogéographie des Forêts du Bassin Méditerranéen*. Paris: Elsevier and Dalmann PR (1998) *Plant Life in the World Mediterranean Climates*. Oxford, UK: Oxford University Press.

25° and 45° over approximately $2\,300\,000\,km^2$. The originality of the Mediterranean climate, which is transitional between temperate and dry tropical climates, lies in the existence of a combined dry and hot summer period of variable length, which imposes a strong water stress on the vegetation during its growing season.

Mean minimum temperatures of the coldest month (m) are often used to define climatic subdivisions (**Table 1**). These values are correlated with elevation and to a lesser extent with increased latitude and continentality. In most places, m is between 0 and $+3^{\circ}C$ although extremes can reach $+8$ to $+9^{\circ}C$ in desert margins and -8 to $-10^{\circ}C$ on the highest mountains. This large-scale potential gradient is often locally modified by rainfall, soil type, and millennia-long human impact which has durably affected ecological equilibrium. The distribution of Mediterranean forest species is also shaped by irregular events such as late spring below freezing temperatures and absolute minimum temperatures. For example, the extremely cold winters of 1956 and 1985 contributed to determine the distribution of the olive tree (*Olea europaea*), Aleppo pine (*Pinus halepensis*), and holm oak (*Quercus ilex*) in the northern Mediterranean.

Rainfall is extremely variable among the Mediterranean regions, with mean annual values ranging from 100 to 2000 mm. The lowest values are found at desert margins especially in North Africa and the Near East. Below 100 mm per year is the borderline between the Mediterranean and the desert climates. Rainfalls higher than 1500 mm are mostly found on coastal mountain ranges. Rainfall plays an essential role in the organization of Mediterranean forests and can be used to define six different bioclimatic types (**Table 2**). Rainfall can also be extremely variable

from year to year, which increases vegetation water stress, especially south of the Mediterranean.

Main Characteristics and Functional Definition

In the Mediterranean region, both open and closed canopy tree populations are considered to be forests. Closed canopy forests are similar in structure to temperate forests, such as those most common in Europe, where the undergrowth is limited and contains mostly shade-tolerant herbaceous species. Open canopy forests have few trees and their undergrowth is limited to a few or no forest-type herbaceous species. For ecological and functional reasons (see 'Current vegetation types' below), all Mediterranean ecosystems of more than 0.5 ha, where tree density is over 10% and tree height can reach over 5 m, are considered to be forests by the Food and Agriculture Organization (FAO) of the United Nations.

Mediterranean forests are less productive than the average world forests. The most productive ones are located in southern Europe, which contains more than 80% of total Mediterranean tree standing volume (**Table 3**).

Most comparative ecological and ecophysiological studies have shown that plant communities in the five Mediterranean regions of the world demonstrate similar strategies to resist climatic and edaphic stress as well as natural and human disturbances, such as wild fires. Sclerophylly (evergreen leaves coated with a thick cuticle) is one such common and widespread strategy. Other strategies include resprouting after disturbance, disturbance-dependent seed production and germination, complex root systems, cellular tolerance to low water potentials or high secondary compound production (e.g., terpenes).

Table 1 Vegetation levels showing the correspondence between temperature variants and dominant (and frequent) woody types of the Mediterranean basin

Vegetation level	Temperature variant	m (°C)	T (°C)	Dominant woody species
Infra-Mediterranean	Very hot	$> +7^{\circ}C$	$> +17^{\circ}C$	*Argania*, *Acacia gummifera*
Thermo-Mediterranean	Hot	$+3$ to $+7^{\circ}C$	$> +17^{\circ}C$	*Olea*, *Ceratonia*, *Pinus halepensis* and *P. brutia*, *Tetraclinis* (*Quercus*)
Meso-Mediterranean	Temperate	0 to $+3^{\circ}C$	$+13$ to $+17^{\circ}C$	Sclerophyll *Quercus*, *Pinus halepensis* and *P. brutia*
Supra-Mediterranean	Cool	-3 to $0^{\circ}C$	$+8$ to $+13^{\circ}C$	Deciduous *Quercus*, *Ostrya*, *Carpinus orientalis* (*Pinus brutia*)
Mountain-Mediterranean	Cold	-7 to $-3^{\circ}C$	$+4$ to $+8^{\circ}C$	*Pinus nigra*, *Cedrus*, *Abies*, *Fagus*, *Juniperus*
Oro-Mediterranean	Very cold	$< -7^{\circ}C$	$< +4^{\circ}C$	*Juniperus*, prostrate spiny xerophytes

m, mean minimum temperatures of the coldest month; T, mean annual temperature.
Data from Quézel P and Médail F (2003) *Ecologie et Biogéographie des Forêts du Bassin Méditerranéen*. Paris: Elsevier.

Table 2 Types of bioclimates and their theoretical correspondence with the main vegetation types of the Mediterranean basin

Bioclimate	Mean annual rainfall (for m = 0°C)	Number of months without rainfall	Main vegetation type
Per-arid	<100 mm	11 to 12	Saharan
Arid	100 to 400 mm	7 to 10	Steppe and pre-steppe (Juniperus turbinata, Pinus halepensis, Pistacia atlantica)
Semi-arid	400 to 600 mm	5 to 7	Pre-forest (Pinus halepensis, P. brutia, Juniperus spp., Quercus)
Subhumid	600 to 800 mm	3 to 5	Forest (mostly sclerophyll Quercus, Pinus halepensis, P. brutia, P. pinaster, P. pinea, P. nigra, Cedrus)
Humid	800 to 1000 mm	1 to 3	Forest (mostly deciduous Quercus, Pinus brutia, P. pinaster, P. nigra, Cedrus, Abies, Fagus)
Perhumid	>1000 mm	less than 1	Forest (deciduous Quercus, Cedrus, Abies, Fagus)

m, mean minimum temperatures of the coldest month.
Data from Quézel P and Médail F (2003) *Ecologie et Biogéographie des Forêts du Bassin Méditerranéen*. Paris: Elsevier.

Table 3 Distribution of forest volume and surface area among the three ecoregions of the Mediterranean basin

Region	Mean biomass volume ($m^3 ha^{-1}$)	Surface area, in 2000 ($ha \times 10^6$)	Forest area in the major forested countries of each region (%)
Middle East	66	11	Turkey (90%)
North Africa	35	6.1	Morocco (50%)
			Algeria (35%)
Southern Europe	100	30	Spain (30%)
			Italy (25%)
			Greece (10%)

Data from Food and Agriculture Organization.

Forest Paleoecology: Current Biodiversity Explained by History

Pre-Pleistocene History: The Mixing of Floras of Different Origins

The current flora of the Mediterranean region arises from several biogeographic origins. Its coniferous flora diversified during the Cretaceous. Its angiosperm flora diversified during the early Tertiary, when the Mediterranean region was situated at the crossroads between Laurasia and the remains of Gondwana. Thus it includes tropical elements, mostly of African and Asian lineages, as well as extratropical elements, of autochthonous and northern lineages. This complex geological-scale paleogeography is one of the reasons that the Mediterranean has such a high plant biodiversity and woody species endemism. Two different lineage groups can be described for angiosperms:

1. A **pre-Pliocene group**, consisting of mostly sclerophyll taxa which resprout from stumps after disturbance (fire, clearance) and are often found in the most complex stages of ecosystem dynamics (e.g., *Arbutus unedo*, *Olea* spp., *Quercus* spp.).

2. A **post-Pliocene group**, including nonsclerophyll taxa which are obligate seeders after disturbance and are mostly found in the less advanced stages of ecosystem dynamics (e.g., *Cistus* spp., *Lavandula* spp.). These taxa successfully diversified and competed with taxa of the pre-Pliocene group due to their short life cycle, high seed production, and ecological plasticity towards the highly fluctuating Mediterranean bioclimatic cycles.

Strategies considered as typically Mediterranean could thus have emerged at the end of the Tertiary under a tropical climatic regime well before the advent of the Mediterranean climate, at the beginning of the Quaternary. Similarity between Mediterranean woody plants could be due more to phylogenetic inertia than to common adaptive strategies. The ability of Mediterranean woody species to resprout after fire, for example, does not originate from an adaptation to recurrent fires, but rather from an older adaptation to herbivory.

From Glacial Refugia to Current Distribution: Holocene Recolonization Pathways around the Mediterranean

In the more recent past, Mediterranean glacial refugia have played a key role in shaping the current genetic diversity of woody species and the spatial distribution of the main forest ecosystems around the Mediterranean and in Europe. Refugia are territories somewhat sheltered from the climatic disturbance of the most recent ice age (Würm) where plants survived the effects of the last glacial maximum (about 20 000 years ago). They contributed to the forest recolonization process that started approximately 13 000 years ago and lasted throughout the Holocene. They are responsible for the high floristic diversity of Mediterranean forests (compared to that of temperate European forests). Glacial refugium distribution estimated using paleoecological and phylogeographical data matches that of current high floristic richness and high endemism

and rare woody species hot spots around the Mediterranean.

The main regions where temperate and thermophilous forest species survived around the Mediterranean are the Iberian, Italian, and Balkan peninsulas, the Black Sea region, some areas in North Africa, and the largest Mediterranean islands. Territories that link these primary refugia, such as the south of France and the borders of the Adriatic Sea (Slovenia and Croatia), possibly acted as secondary refugia. These refugia were characterized by high species richness. Once climatic conditions became truly favorable, the expansion of a highly diversified deciduous forest could happen rapidly over large territories, such as in the Pindos mountains in northwestern Greece where over 20 deciduous woody species could already be found in the early Preboreal (about 10 000 years ago). Some tree genera such as *Pinus*, *Quercus*, and *Corylus* seem to have been present in all southern European refugia, although others had a clear geographic distribution, e.g., *Abies alba*, *Fagus sylvatica* and *Carpinus* in the Italian and Balkan refugia (possibly in Spain as well), and *Tilia* and *Ulmus* in the eastern Mediterranean (**Figure 2**).

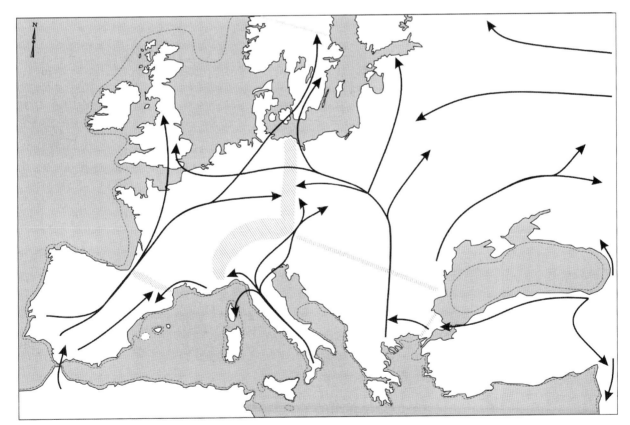

Figure 2 Main Holocene recolonization routes from glacial refugia in Europe. Dotted lines indicate the extent of land masses during Late Glacial maximum. Large shaded areas represent main hybrid zones and smaller ones represent secondary hybrid zones. Reproduced with permission from Quézel P and Médail F (2003) *Ecologie et Biogéographie des Forêts du Bassin Méditerranéen*. Paris: Elsevier.

Current Vegetation Types

Structural and Regional Typology

The current diversity of Mediterranean forest structures can be organized into three major structural types based on bioclimatic and/or human impact criteria.

True forest vegetation types These are made of metastable equilibrium vegetation structures. Shade-tolerant plant species growing on evolved soils are dominant (**Figure 3**). These true forests constitute what were previously considered to be 'climax' forests; they are in fact the potential structures at the end of a dynamic ecological cycle that can be achieved where soil and climate conditions are favorable and where the impact of humans is not too strong.

Preforest types These can be divided into two categories. Under perhumid, humid, and subhumid bioclimates, they consist of vegetation structures that have undergone severe human impact, although their soil is still relatively well preserved (**Figure 4**). They are transitory structures from true forests to more open systems. Under semi-arid bioclimatic conditions, or under particularly stressful conditions (e.g., ultramafic substrates) in any bioclimate, preforests are composed of shrub-dominated vegetation structures with scattered trees (matorrals) under equilibrium (or close to equilibrium) at the human timescale. Conifer species play an important role in these structures.

Presteppic forest types Very frequent in southern and eastern Mediterranean, these consist of open-vegetation structures dominated by nonforest plant species under scattered trees. Nonforest species are steppe-type perennial species that can eventually be replaced by ruderal annual species when grazing occurs. Soils are usually poor and topsoil is frequently missing. Presteppes are most frequent under warm and hot temperature variants of arid (and sometimes semi-arid) bioclimates. They gradually merge into steppes under hotter and drier conditions. On mountains, presteppes are a transitional vegetation structure from forests (or preforests) to high elevation steppes dominated by low and scattered cushionlike spiny xerophytes.

These three main structural forest types are found in the four major geographical subdivisions of the Mediterranean basin (**Table 4**).

Current Evolution: Sclerophyllous Trees Replaced by Deciduous Trees

Traditional agriculture and grazing have been decreasing since the mid-twentieth century on low to medium elevation mountain ranges in the northern Mediterranean. This has led to a dramatic increase in forest cover and a change in forest composition. Concurrently, atmospheric CO_2 has been increasing because of industrial activity, thus increasing the productivity of many Mediterranean trees such as *Quercus ilex* and *Q. pubescens*.

One of the results of these changes is the physiognomical convergence of Mediterranean and non-Mediterranean forests when dominated by the same deciduous tree species (*Quercus, Fagus, Acer, Sorbus*). Areas where woody sclerophyll plants and heliophyllous conifers (*Pinus halepensis, P. sylvestris*) used to be the dominant species are now colonized by these deciduous trees, along with some mesophilic conifers (*Abies, Taxus*) and laurophyllous trees (*Ilex aquifolium, Laurus nobilis*). Deciduous *Quercus* around the Mediterranean and in California, and *Nothofagus* in Chile, currently play an extremely

Figure 3 Example of a true forest vegetation type: the Mediterranean *Fagus–Abies* mixed forest of Mont Ventoux, southeastern France.

Figure 4 Example of a true preforest vegetation type: cattle grazing in the Algerian Aures *Cedrus atlantica* forest.

Table 4 Main forest types of the four major geographical subdivisions of the Mediterranean basin, arranged according to vegetation level (see Table 1). Species names for each community refer to the dominant woody species

Vegetation level	Northwestern Mediterranean communities	Southwestern Mediterranean communities	Northeastern Mediterranean communities	Southeastern Mediterranean communities
Infra-Mediterranean		Argania spinosa and Acacia gummifera; Acacia raddiana		
Thermo-Mediterranean	Olea europaea, Ceratonia and Chamaerops; Quercus ilex and Q. suber; Pinus halepensis, P. pinaster, P. pinea; Juniperus turbinata, J. phoenicea; Quercus coccifera	Olea europaea, Ceratonia and Chamaerops; Q. ilex subsp. rotundifolia, Q. suber; Pinus halepensis and P. pinaster; Juniperus turbinata, J. phoenicea; Quercus fruticosa; Pistacia atlantica; Tetraclinis articulata, Cupressus atlantica	Olea europaea and Ceratonia; Quercus ilex; Pinus halepensis, P. brutia, P. pinea; Cupressus sempervirens; Quercus coccifera subsp. calliprinos; Formations with Quercus ithaburensis and Q. pubescens	Olea europaea and Ceratonia; Quercus ilex; Pinus halepensis or P. brutia; Cupressus sempervirens; Quercus infectoria and Q. coccifera subsp. calliprinos; Quercus pubescens, Q. ithaburensis
Meso-Mediterranean	Quercus ilex, Q. suber; Quercus pubescens; Quercus coccifera; Quercus petraea subsp. broteroi; Pinus halepensis; Quercus canariensis, Q. pyrenaica	Olea europaea, Ceratonia and Chamaerops; Quercus ilex subsp. Rotundifolia, Q. suber; Quercus canariensis; Pistacia atlantica; Tetraclinis articulata	Quercus ilex; Quercus coccifera subsp. calliprinos; Quercus ithaburensis; Q. brachyphylla, Q. pubescens; Pinus halepensis, P. brutia; Cupressus sempervirens	Quercus ilex; Quercus coccifera subsp. calliprinos; Quercus ithaburensis; Quercus infectoria, Q. cerris subsp. pseudocerris; Pinus brutia, P. halepensis, P. pinea; Cupressus sempervirens; Cedrus brevifolia and Quercus alnifolia (Cyprus)
Supra-Mediterranean	Quercus pubescens, Q. cerris, Q.petraea; Quercus faginea; Abies alba, A. pinsapo; Quercus robur, Q. petraea and Q. pyrenaica; Ostrya carpinifolia and Carpinus betulus; Pinus sylvestris; Castanea sativa	Quercus canariensis, Q. faginea, Q. afares; Quercus ilex subsp. rotundifolia, Q. suber; Cedrus atlantica and Abies marocana	Quercus frainetto and Q. cerris; Quercus pubescens, Q. ithaburensis; Abies cephalonica; Cupressus sempervirens; Ostrya carpinifolia and Carpinus orientalis; Quercus petraea and Castanea sativa; Quercus pubescens subsp. anatolica	Quercus frainetto and Q. cerris; Quercus infectoria; Pinus brutia; Pinus nigra subsp. pallasiana; Carpinus orientalis and Ostrya carpinifolia; Cupressus sempervirens; Quercus macranthera subsp. syspirensis
Mountain-Mediterranean	Pinus sylvestris; Pinus nigra (subsp. salzmannii or laricio); Abies alba or A. pinsapo; Juniperus thurifera subsp. thurifera; Fagus sylvatica subsp. sylvatica; Pinus uncinata and P. mugo	Pinus nigra subsp. mauretanica; Cedrus atlantica; Abies marocana or A. numidica; Juniperus thurifera subsp. africana; Quercus ilex subsp. rotundifolia	Pinus nigra subsp. pallasiana; Pinus heldreichii; Abies cephalonica, A. borisii-regis; Abies nordamanniana, Abies bornmuelleriana and Juniperus excelsa; Fagus sylvatica sensu lato; Quercus petraea	Pinus nigra subsp. pallasiana; Cedrus libani; Abies cilicica; Juniperus foetidissima and J. excelsa; Fagus sylvatica subsp. orientalis; Quercus petraea; Quercus brantii, Q. ithaburensis subsp. look
Oro-Mediterranean	Juniperus thurifera subsp. Thurifera	Juniperus thurifera subsp. africana; Quercus ilex subsp. rotundifolia	Juniperus excelsa	Juniperus excelsa

important role in the forest recruitment dynamics of previously traditionally cultivated or grazed lands. In forests least affected by humans, structures are shifting towards old-growth forest types where vertebrate seed dispersal plays a crucial role, and floristic and faunistic compositions are shifting towards medio-European or Euro-Asian dominated assemblages. Using sclerophylly to define Mediterranean forests is thus now an oversimplification.

Human Impact

Although human impact may have been already significant when people lived as hunter–gatherers, for example in increasing seed dispersal though seasonal migrations, it became truly significant for Mediterranean forests with the advent of domestication, about 10 000 years ago in the Near East. Because of an ever-increasing need for arable land for crop cultivation and grazing, the area of forest declined over the centuries, first sporadically around the main human settlements during the Atlantic period (about 4700 to 4500 years ago), then systematically during the Bronze Age and throughout Antiquity. Wood was then also used on a large scale for shipbuilding, carpentry, and many areas of human social life. Although it often slowed down during the Middle Ages as demographic pressure lessened, deforestation re-increased during the Renaissance. By the end of the nineteenth century, after the Industrial Revolution, the Mediterranean forest had lost three-fourths of its initial postglacial area. The consequences of this millennia-long impact have affected both vegetation structures and biodiversity.

Vegetation Structures

In areas where agricultural and grazing effects are the strongest, i.e., North Africa and most semi-arid and arid Eastern Mediterranean zones, forest ecosystems are no longer resilient, and a degradation cycle (often irreversible) starts as soil structure and water, nutrient, and carbon cycles are also affected, with often spectacular and dramatic effects (e.g. floods, landslides).

Four levels of increasing severity on forest structures can be described:

1. Transformation of forests and preforests into matorrals with scattered trees ('matorralization').
2. Transformation of woody matorrals dominated by resprouters into secondary, lower, matorrals mainly composed by seeders ('dematorralization').
3. In semi-arid bioclimates, replacement of matorrals by steppes dominated by non-woody perrenial species or low chamaephytes ('steppization').

4. Invasion of forest ecosystems by annual, often ruderal, or low-palatability species ('therophytization').

Biodiversity

Human impact on forest ecosystems can significantly modify all natural processes that regulate biodiversity at population, species, and ecosystem levels. Three categories of human impacts can be recognized, from strongest to probably least consequential.

Habitat destruction and fragmentation   Traditionally the longest standing impact on forests over time, in relation to human settlements, habitat destruction has been driven by agriculture and grazing, wars and industrial activities, and carried out with tools such as wildfires and clear-cutting. It has led to the disappearance of ecosystems and species, as well as isolation of those that have remained. The main impacts on genetic processes for isolated populations are (1) reduction of long-distance gene flow, (2) increase of genetic drift and of consanguineous mating, leading to (3) loss of adaptive potential and eventually, (4) disappearance when the number of reproducing individuals is too small or when deleterious genes have accumulated.

Species introduction   Exotic forest genetic resources have often been transported by humans throughout historical times because they were a potential food supply (e.g., *Pinus pinea*, *Olea europaea*), had landscape or religious value (*Cupressus sempervirens*), or were able to stop degradation processes and yield more wood than the local resource (e.g., in France, *Pinus nigra* subsp. *nigra* and *Cedrus atlantica* during the nineteeth century). More recently, with the advent of tree breeding, selected varieties have been planted extensively. Introduction of new taxa has led to the creation of completely new ecosystems, thus increasing biodiversity locally. However, phytosanitary risks are high in these artificial forests as they usually lack a complete biologically functional structure. Risks of hybridization are high when the exotic resource is genetically close to the local resource (e.g., subspecies of *Pinus nigra*), with potential reduction of fitness for the local resource.

Forestry practice   Forests have been managed since the Middle Ages in Europe. Loss of biodiversity cannot be positively linked to forestry practice, except in the case of seed transfer over regions with very different ecological requirements (e.g., in southern France, Aleppo pines imported from Sicily died from frost during the winters of 1984 and 1985). However, recent studies indicate that reforestation reduces genetic diversity because of plant material selection in the nursery. When a stand is prepared for natural regeneration, a significant part of the sexually mature trees is removed, and thus part of the genetic diversity is eliminated from the original population, which may disturb mating systems, increase consanguineous mating and genetic drift, and impact the selective value of the future stand. Due to their long life cycle (long juvenile and long sexual maturity phases) and overlapping generations, trees may be able to compensate efficiently for these genetic impacts in their long-term adaptation.

Different Recent Human Impacts around the Mediterranean Basin

Although human impact was broadly similar during the Holocene, it diverged sharply among the different Mediterranean ecogeographic regions during the twentieth century.

In the northern Mediterranean, after the Industrial Revolution, the least productive agricultural and grazed lands were abandoned and became progressively colonized by expansionist (mostly conifer) species. Open lands have progressively changed into non human-impacted (except for some large-scale wildfires) preforest and forest structures. The FAO reported an annual increase of 0.3–0.9% in forest cover in the 1990s. There is a growing concern over loss of human-made biodiversity because of the disappearance of open grass and shrub ecosystems. Although habitat destruction remains a concern, especially along the coast because of urban extension, the main risks for forest genetic resources come from forest management, with the introduction of species and improved varieties and seed transfer, and their corollaries, hybridization and gene flow from cultivated to wild compartments.

In the southern Mediterranean, the use of forest resources is generally not sustained, although the FAO reported positive forest cover increase (from 0.2% to 1.4%) in the 1990s. Habitat destruction for agriculture, grazing, fuel wood, construction, etc. remains the major type of human impact. In North Africa, forest area per capita is less than 0.1 ha although it is 0.2–0.4 ha in the northern Mediterranean. In the past 30 years, forest product use has dramatically increased due to human demography. Illegal cuttings, forest clearing, overgrazing, and fuelwood exploitation are rapidly destroying forests and their associated biological resources. Low socioeconomic standards of rural populations are thus also a significant cause of habitat destruction.

In the eastern Mediterranean, the trend is somewhat similar to that of North Africa. Habitat destruction remains a high risk in countries where forest cover is already very limited and forest resources not sustained (e.g., Syria, Lebanon). In other countries, forest cover has grown tremendously (+ 4.9% in Israel) or steadily (+ 0.2% in Turkey) in the 1990s because of active reforestation and conservation programs.

Conservation of Mediterranean Forest Biodiversity: An International Effort

The need to conserve forests and their biodiversity has been internationally recognized since the United Nations Conference on Environment and Development (UNCED) in Rio during 1992. Conservation of biodiversity needs to be undertaken at three complementary levels:

- genes, where evolution can occur
- species and populations, where reproduction and gene flow can occur
- ecosystems (habitats), where organisms are sustained.

Ecosystems are usually preserved separately from genes. Species and populations can be a means to sustain gene diversity and future adaptation (forestry approach to conservation) or the primary target to protect through diversified and functional habitats (ecological approach to conservation).

Forest genes and populations Many forest conservation and sustainable management strategies designed globally can apply to the Mediterranean. Such is the case of the *in situ* and *ex situ* conservation networks advocated by the European Forest Genetic Resource Conservation Program (EUFORGEN), although they are still rare around the Mediterranean. *In situ* networks concern species of high ecological, patrimonial, and/or economic value that are not threatened with short-term extinction in their natural environment (e.g., *Pinus brutia* in Turkey, *Abies alba* in France). They are designed to make genetic evolution possible under current ecological constraints. *Ex situ* networks generally concern rare and endangered forest species. They are made of collections of selected or remaining genotypes conserved outside their normal ecological conditions. One current sustainable management strategy is the control of the origin and commerce of forest reproductive material (in Europe, see European Union directives 66/404/CEE and 71/161/CEE), which must come from certified seed stands and seed orchards and whose transfer from one ecological zone to another is under strict control. Other initiatives, sponsored by the FAO and the UN Environmental Program, have produced sets of indicators and guidelines for replacing yield-oriented forest management practice by the sustainable management of forest resources in Mediterranean countries.

Forest species and ecosystems (habitats) Species and ecological diversity are typically conserved and managed in natural parks and reserves. Many of such structures exist around the Mediterranean. However, out of 425 Man and Biosphere Reserves worldwide, only 32 shelter significant Mediterranean forest areas. Eastern Mediterranean forests are notably underprotected. Particularly, conservation of potential and old-growth sclerophyll and deciduous Mediterranean forests remains extremely limited as less than 2% have been included in natural parks or reserves. Old-growth Mediterranean forests contain many typical species that are rare because linked to large, non-fragmented, and undisturbed forest areas. Some of these species are functionally primordial, e.g., those related to organic matter decomposition. Because Mediterranean biodiversity arises from a high spatial and temporal heterogeneity, natural parks and reserves designed for Mediterranean forests must be large enough to include disturbance cycles (open and closed canopy structures, large vertebrate populations, fires, etc.) which can guarantee the maintenance of this typical biodiversity. They must also be large enough to include a complex mosaic of functionally diversified ecological structures, at equilibrium. Such requirements have guided the European Natura 2000 (European Union habitats directive 92/43/CEE) initiative for habitat conservation and the international efforts of the World Parks Congresses sponsored by the World Conservation Union (IUCN). Ideally, these guidelines should be included into forest practice, thus linking gene and ecosystem-oriented approaches to sustainable resource management.

A Global Comparative Assessment of the World Mediterranean-Type Forests

Species richness and diversity, which are the most frequently used parameters to describe and assess biodiversity, are scale-dependent. Three main types of spatial scales are generally recognized (**Table 5**). This partitioning of biodiversity makes it possible to compare ecosystem types. At the local scale (less than 0.1 ha), Mediterranean biodiversity is two times lower than that of tropical regions. Mean local (alpha) floristic diversity of the world Mediterranean forests is between 10 species m^{-2} and 25 to 110 species 1000 m^{-2}. At this spatial scale, woody plant communities of the Mediterranean basin are both very heterogeneous and also among the richest types, ahead of the alpha diversity found in the western

Cape Province. However, habitat (beta) and regional (epsilon) scale diversities are much higher in the western Cape Province than around the Mediterranean, although they concern mainly matorral type (fynbos) vegetation.

From a biogeographic and ecological point of view, several forest types of the Mediterranean basin are relatively similar to those of the California Floristic Province, due to a pre-Atlantic ocean land connection which lasted until the Eocene (Madro-Tethysian flora) and explain the existence of some common tree genera (*Pinus, Quercus, Arbutus, Cupressus, Juniperus*). At low and medium altitudes, physiognomical similarities exist for sclerophyll oak forests. The existence of thermophilous coniferous at the thermo- and meso-Mediterranean (*Pinus halepensis, P. brutia, P. pinaster*) and thermo- and meso-Californian (*Pinus attenuata, P. sabiniana, Cupressus macrocarpa*) levels, but also of several mesophilous coniferous (*Abies, Pinus*) at higher altitude constitutes another key feature. A recent survey indicates that the Mediterranean region harbors a higher tree richness (290 indigenous trees with 201 endemics) than the California Floristic Province (173 trees with 77 endemics), although its area is seven times larger.

Northern hemisphere Mediterranean forests show a higher structural and species diversity than those of the southern hemisphere, because the latter cover less extensive areas and, as in South Africa, may be completely outside the range of Mediterranean bioclimate. The Southern Cape forests are very patchy and scarce, mainly made up of plants of a cool and humid Afromontane origin, with warm subtropical elements; sclerophyll trees and conifers (*Afrocarpus, Podocarpus*) predominate. Forests of Mediterranean Chile are more diverse due to the strong latitudinal gradient and the increase in rainfall from north to south; semi-arid *Acacia caven* and *Prosopis chilensis* forests in the north are succeeded by subtropical broadleaved and sclerophyll forests in the central region, and by deciduous *Nothofagus* forests farther south. Together with species-rich sclerophyll matorrals (kwongan and mallee), the woodlands of Mediterranean Australia are dominated by *Eucalyptus, Acacia*, and *Casuarina* on relatively fertile soils where mean annual rainfall exceeds 400 mm.

Outlook for the Future

The originality of the Mediterranean biome is dependent upon the interaction of complex ecological factors. However these ecosystems are fragile and global warming will undoubtedly soon be a major source of disturbance. Research and long-term monitoring of biodiversity and ecosystem functioning

Table 5 Main patterns of forest biodiversity in the five Mediterranean regions of the world in relation to spatial scale, species composition and level of disturbance

Major biodiversity drivers	Mediterranean Basin (2 300 000 km²)	California Floristic Province (324 000 km²)	Mediterranean Chile (140 000 km²)	South and southwestern Australia (112 000 km²)	Western Cape Region (90 000 km²)
Patterns of plant diversity					
Local within habitat (alpha diversity)	Medium to very high	Low to medium	Medium	Low to high	Medium to high
Differentiation among habitats (beta diversity)	Medium	Medium	Low to medium ?	High	Medium to high
Regional (epsilon diversity) Total plant species richness	Medium ~30 000	Medium ~4450	Low ~2540	High ~8000	High ~9000
Major forest trees					
Sclerophyll	Arbutus unedo, A. andrachne, Olea europaea, Ceratonia siliqua, Erica arborea, Phillyrea latifolia, Quercus ilex, Q. suber, Q. coccifera	Arbutus menziesii, Heteromeles arbutifolia, Lithocarpus densiflora, Quercus agrifolia, Q. chrysolepis, Q. wislizenii, Umbellularia californica	Colliguaja odorifera, Cryptocarya alba, Drimys winteri, Jubaea chilensis, Kageneckia angustifolia, Lithraea caustica, Peumus boldus, Maytenus boaria, Nothofagus dombeyii, Quillaja saponaria	Eucalyptus spp. (E. marginata, E. diversi-sicolor, E. incrassata, E. oleosa, E. wandoo, E. camaldulensis, E. calophylla, E. baxteri), Melaleuca spp., Acacia spp., Leptospermum spp., Banksia spp.	Maytenus spp., Olea capensis, Ocotea bullata, Virgilia divaricata, V. oroboides, Ilex mitis, Cunonia capensis, Pittosporum viridiflorum, Platylophus trifoliatus, Pterocelastrus rostratus, Schefflera jumbellifera, Sideroxylon inerme
Broadleaved and semibroadleaved	Castanea sativa, Fagus sylvatica, Carpinus orientalis, Fraxinus ornus, Ostrya carpinifolia, Platanus orientalis, Quercus pubescens, Q. canariensis, Q. afares, Q. ithaburensis, Q. pyrenaica, Q. frainetto	Aesculus californica, Quercus lobata, Q. douglasii, Q. engelmannii, Q. kelloggii, Q. garryana	Acacia caven, Nothofagus obliqua		Celtis africana, Ficus sur, Calodendron capense
Coniferous and Casuarina (coniferous-like leaves)[a]	Abies alba, A. borisii-regis, A. cephalonica, A. cilicica, Cedrus atlantica, C. libani, Cupressus sempervirens, Juniperus excelsa, J. thurifera, J. turbinata, Pinus brutia, P. halepensis, P. nigra, P. pinaster, P. pinea, P. sylvestris, Tetraclinis articulata	Abies bracteata, A. concolor, A. magnifica, Calocedrus decurrens, Cupressus macrocarpa, Pinus attenuata, P. contorta, P. coulteri, P. edulis, P. juarezensis, P. jeffreyi, P. lambertiana, P. monophylla, P. torreyana, Pseudotsuga menziesii, P. macrocarpa, Sequoia sempervirens, Sequoiadendron giganteum	Araucaria araucana, Austrocedrus chilensis, Fitzroya cupressoides	Casuarina spp. (e.g., C. pusilla, C. muellerana)	Afrocarpus falcatus, Podocarpus latifolius, P. elongatus, Widdringtonia cedarbergensis
Impact of forest fires	Strong impact of anthropogenic fires; natural fires very rare	Predominance and high frequency of natural fires	Rarity of natural fires; anthropogenic fires uncommon	Frequent natural and anthropogenic fires	Frequent natural and anthropogenic fires
Other disturbances	Destruction and fragmentation, overgrazing, clear-cutting	Destruction and fragmentation, biological invasions	Destruction and fragmentation, overgrazing	Destruction and fragmentation, biological invasions	Destruction and fragmentation, afforestation, biological invasions

[a] Total plant richness refers to angiosperms, gymnosperms, and pteridophytes.

at a cross-continental Mediterranean scale must be combined with public awareness strategies and international policy-making, not only to understand but also to protect Mediterranean ecosystems effectively and use them efficiently, now and in the future.

See also: **Biodiversity**: Biodiversity in Forests; Endangered Species of Trees; Plant Diversity in Forests. **Ecology**: Biological Impacts of Deforestation and Fragmentation; Human Influences on Tropical Forest Wildlife. **Environment**: Environmental Impacts; Impacts of Elevated CO_2 and Climate Change. **Genetics and Genetic Resources**: Forest Management for Conservation; Population, Conservation and Ecological Genetics. **Landscape and Planning**: Landscape Ecology, the Concepts. **Silviculture**: Forest Dynamics. **Sustainable Forest Management**: Causes of Deforestation and Forest Fragmentation. **Temperate and Mediterranean Forests**: Southern Coniferous Forests. **Temperate Ecosystems**: Fagaceae; Pines; Spruces, Firs and Larches. **Tropical Ecosystems**: Acacias; Eucalypts.

Further Reading

Arroyo MTK, Zedler PH, and Fox MD (eds) (1995) *Ecology and Biogeography of Mediterranean Ecosystems in Chile, California and Australia*. New York: Springer-Verlag.

Dalmann PR (1998) *Plant Life in the World's Mediterranean climates*. Oxford: Oxford University Press.

Davis GW and Richardson DM (eds) (1995) *Biodiversity and Ecosystem Function in Mediterranean-Type Ecosystems*. New York: Springer-Verlag.

Di Castri F and Mooney HA (eds) (1973) *Mediterranean-type ecosystems*. New York: Springer-Verlag.

FAO (2001). *State of the World's Forests 2001*. Rome: Food and Agriculture Organization of the United Nations.

Johnston VR (1994) *California Forests and Woodlands: A Natural History*. Berkeley, CA: California University Press.

Moreno JM and Oechel WC (eds) (1994) *The Role of Fire in Mediterranean-type Ecosystems*. New York: Springer-Verlag.

Oldeman RAA (1990) *Forests: Elements of Sylvology*. Berlin: Springer-Verlag.

Quézel P and Médail F (2003) *Ecologie et Biogéographie des Forêts du Bassin Méditerranéen*. Paris: Elsevier.

Teissier du Cros E (ed.) (2001) *Forest Genetic Resources Management and Conservation: France as a Case Study*. Paris: Ministry of Agriculture and Fisheries, Bureau of Genetic Resources, Commission of Forest Genetic Resources, INRA DIC.

TEMPERATE ECOSYSTEMS

Contents
Alders, Birches and Willows
Fagaceae
Juglandaceae
Pines
Poplars
Spruces, Firs and Larches

Alders, Birches and Willows

S Harris, University of Oxford, Oxford, UK

Early botanists considered the alders (*Alnus*), birches (*Betula*), and willows (*Salix*) part of a large, closely related group of catkin-producing, woody species, known as the Amentiferae. This group was presumed to have a single origin, and also included the walnuts, oaks, figs, and elms. We now know, based on detailed morphological and molecular analyses, that many of these families are not closely related and that superficial resemblance based on catkins is due to convergence. In addition to sharing catkins, alders, birches, and willows are ecologically similar since they are important pioneer species of the northern temperate region. Furthermore, they have a diverse array of similar uses, especially gunpowder production.

Alnus and *Betula* comprise the monophyletic subfamily Betuloideae of the family Betulaceae, whilst the other four members (*Carpinus*, *Corylus*, *Ostrya*, and *Ostryopsis*) comprise subfamily Coryloideae. Traditionally, *Salix* and the genus *Populus* have comprised the family Salicaceae. However, using molecular data it has been proposed that the family Salicaceae should also encompass other genera, most notably the acyanogenic genera of the Flacourtiaceae.

The biology and ecology of alders, birches, and willows are briefly described and then the diverse uses of these important trees and shrubs are presented.

Alnus

The genus *Alnus* comprises approximately 25 species of small to large trees or shrubs of the temperate and boreal zones of the northern hemisphere and Central America to the high elevations of South America, although the genus is poorly understood in Central America and China. Members of the genus are often associated with wet sites, swamps, and stream margins, and their ability to fix nitrogen means *Alnus* species are important early successional species. For example, *A. viridis* is an important pioneer, whilst others are important components of mature forest (e.g., *A. rubra* in the floodplain forests of the North American Pacific North-west). Alders, as with other Betulaceae, have male and female flowers separated into different catkins. Alders are wind-pollinated, producing large amounts of pollen. Pollen release occurs before (subgenus *Alnus*) or at the same time (subgenus *Alnobetula*) as the new leaves unfold or in late summer (subgenus *Clethropsis*), just after the new catkins mature. The woody alder infructesences produce small, abundant, winged fruits that are carried primarily by wind but also by water. In some species (e.g., *A. serrulata*), the wings are reduced to ridges, and the fruits are dispersed primarily by water. *Alnus* species form a polyploid group ($2n = 14-56$; $2x-8x$). Fossil material attributable to the genera *Alnus* and *Betula* appears earlier in the fossil record than other Betulaceae, whilst *Alnus* fossils are known from as early as the Miocene.

Furthermore, analyses of chloroplast DNA and pollen data have enabled the postglacial history of *A. glutinosa* to be reconstructed and glacial refugia to be identified.

The genus is divided into four subgenera: *Alnus*, *Alnobetula*, *Clethropsis*, and *Cremastogyne* (**Table 1**), although these have also been recognized as separate genera. *Alnus* nomenclature is complicated by morphological variation and hybridization. For example, in subgenus *Alnobetula*, numerous subspecies are described in the circumpolar species *A. viridis*. Alder hybrids form readily when species grow together; for example, in North America, *A. incana* subsp. *rugosa* hybridizes with *A. serrulata*, leading to extensive hybrid swarms that complicate the differentiation of the taxa. However, most species are either geographically or ecologically differentiated.

Seed is an effective way of raising alder, although many species can be vegetatively propagated. Large areas of alder growth may give the impression of extensive clonal population growth. However, allozyme studies indicate that populations of *A. incana* subsp. *rugosa* and *A. viridis* subsp. *crispa* are the result of sexual reproduction. Furthermore, inbreeding is very low and gene flow is high. For best growth, alders (e.g., *A. glutinosa*, *A. rubra*, *A. cordata*) must be symbiotically associated with the nitrogen-fixing actinomycete *Frankia*, which leads to formation of root nodules. Few pests and diseases appear to affect alders, although scale insects can be a problem in *A. serrulata* in North America. However, in recent years in the UK, natural populations of *A. glutinosa* have been lethally affected by the fungal pathogen *Phytophthora cambivora*. In North America, *Fomes ignarius* is the most significant fungal pathogen of

Table 1 Characteristics of the main grouping within the genus *Alnus*

	Subgenus Alnus	*Subgenus* Alnobetula	*Subgenus* Clethropsis	*Subgenus* Cremastogyne
Distribution	Temperate and boreal northern hemisphere, Central and South America	Temperate and boreal northern hemisphere	Eastern North America, eastern Asia	South-central Asia
Habit	Small trees to medium-sized shrubs	Small trees to shrubs	Small trees	Small to medium-sized trees
Fruits	Wingless or narrow wings	Two large lateral membranaceous wings	Wingless	Broad hyaline wings
Infructesence	Short pedunculate	Long pedunculate	Short pedunculate	Long pedunculate
Catkins	Catkins racemose, develop during growing season before anthesis and exposed during winter	Catkins racemose, develop during growing season before anthesis and only male exposed during winter	Catkins solitary or racemose clusters	Catkins solitary
Flowering	Spring	Spring	Fall	Spring
Buds	Stipitate, two-scaled	Subsessile, several imbricate scales	Naked	Stipitate, two-scaled
Examples	*A. incana A. serrulata*	*A. viridis A. sieboldiana*	*A. maritima A. nepalensis*	*A. cremastogyne*

trees older than 40 years, whilst *Taphrina* species may affect female catkins.

Betula

The genus *Betula* comprises approximately 35 species of small to large trees or shrubs of the temperate and boreal zones of the northern hemisphere. The genus occupies a wide range of habitats, including peat lands, stream banks, lake shores, damp woods, ruderal habitats (including road and rail margins), and alpine and tundra sites. In addition, the genus reaches the northern limit of tree growth. Birches are wind-pollinated, producing large amounts of pollen, and the achenes are wind-dispersed. The female catkins appear with the new growth, whilst anthesis occurs as the leaves unfold. However, ovule fertilization occurs much later than pollination. *Betula* species form a polyploid group ($2n = 28$–112; $2x$–$8x$), whilst some hybrids are aneuploid. Fossil material attributable to the genus *Betula* has been found in deposits from the Upper Cretaceous and appears to have been highly diversified by the Middle Eocene.

The genus is divided into four series, Albae, Costatae, Acuminatae and Humiles (**Table 2**), although some species (e.g., *B. utilis*, *B. nigra*) are difficult to place in these series. *Betula* nomenclature is complex due to the patterns of morphological variation, the wide ecogeographic range of some species (e.g., *B. pubescens*) and the existence of hybridization and introgression within and between the series. In northern Europe, there has been considerable discussion as to whether *B. pendula* and *B. pubescens* are separate species or intraspecific variants. In many cases across their ranges, the two species are readily distinguished. However, morphological intermediates do occur, although these are rarely sterile, triploid hybrids, as might be expected (*B. pendula* ($2n = 2x = 28$), *B. pubescens* ($2n = (4x) = 56$)), which suggests that there is a complex interaction between the morphological and cytogenetic variation. Areas where introgression is important include Kamchatka (e.g., *B. platyphylla* introgresses with *B. ermanii*) and north-east North America (e.g., *B. populifera* introgresses with *B. cordifolia*), whilst in northern Europe *B. pubescens* hybridizes with *B. nana*.

Series Albae and Costatae contain the most important forestry species. Seed is an effective way of raising birch although, when seed is collected from natural or cultivated specimens, the possibility that it may be of hybrid origin must be considered. Birch seed is orthodox, and if dried and stored in cool conditions it will remain viable for many years. Many *Betula* species can be vegetatively propagated from soft or semiripe side shoots, whilst grafting is important if particular genotypes are to be maintained. In the case of grafting, the scion and rootstock should come from the same series of the genus, although in practice *B. pendula* is very commonly used.

The leaves of birches are often rich in resins, whilst the barks, particularly of white-barked birches, are rich in phenolics. Furthermore, the bark of series Albae species contains granules of the triterpenoid betulin, which makes the bark waterproof. These compounds are thought to be important antifeedants, especially effective against browsing mammals, in the winter months. Many insect species feed

Table 2 Characteristics of the main grouping within the genus *Betula*

	Series Albae	Series Costatae	Series Acuminatae	Series Humiles
Distribution	Circumpolar	North America, Transcaucasia, temperate Far East	Japan, Sino-Himalayas	Circumpolar
Habit	Small to medium-sized trees	Large trees	Medium-sized trees	Shrubs
Leaves	Thin, weakly veined with long petiole	Strongly and deeply veined, most with single-toothed margin	Strongly and deeply veined, double-toothed margin	Small, rounded, with few veins
Stem	Bark white (due to betulin), peeling in sheets	Bark dark, most lack betulin	Bark dark, most lack betulin	Bark dark, lack betulin
Catkins	Pendulous, long, fragile, and break up readily in the fall	Upright, short (even globose), persistent, often until early spring	Pendulous, long	Upright, male catkins borne laterally
Ecology	Pioneer species. Fast-growing, relatively short-lived, requiring high light intensity. Not adversely affected by wind exposure	Mixed mesophytic forests. Shade-tolerant, wind-shy	Mesophytic forests	Montane and alpine regions. Peat lands, bogs, tundra
Examples	*B. papyrifera B. populifolia*	*B. alleghaniensis B. lenta*	*B. maximowicziana*	*B. nana B. glandulosa*

on birch, of which one of the most economically important in North America is the bronze birch borer (*Agrilus anxius*), although others include the gypsy moth (*Lymantria dispar*), tent caterpillars, leaf miners, and scale insects. Fungal diseases may also be significant, especially the heartwood rots, caused by *Fomes* and *Poria* species, e.g., *F. ignarius*, and nectria canker (*Nectria galligena*).

Salix

The genus *Salix* comprises approximately 400 species of dwarf or procumbent shrubs to large trees and is found in most parts of the world, particularly the temperate and boreal regions, although there are tropical and subtropical species (e.g., *S. humboldtiana*). One species *S. mucronata*, crosses the equator in Kenya. The genus is very diverse, but poorly known, in western China. Willows occupy a wide range of habitats and climatic zones; the majority of species are pioneers and shade-intolerant (e.g., *S. repens*). Most willows are scrub, marginal, or riverine species, although some are forest-dominants; the association of willows with water is reflected in the origin of the generic name (derived from Celtic, meaning 'near water'). Willows become increasingly important on upland and northward from the boreal forest into the arctic, where they are the most important woody species (e.g., vegetation succession on glacial moraines). In such habitats, willows tend to have underground branches and act as herbaceous perennials. *Salix* species are almost all dioecious, having separate male and female plants, and produce catkins in the spring. Willows, except subgenus *Chosenia*, are usually insect-pollinated (Hymenoptera and Lepidoptera), and the seeds have tufts of hair that aid in wind dispersal. *Salix* species form a polyploid group ($2n = 38–224$; base numbers 11, 12, 19), although aneuploidy appears to be common in some species and hybrids. Fossil material attributable to the genus *Salix* has been found in deposits from as early as the Miocene.

The genus is conveniently divided into four subgenera: *Salix, Caprisalix, Chamaetia*, and *Chosenia* (**Table 3**); subgenus *Chosenia* is sometimes regarded as a distinct genus. However, the intrageneric division of *Salix* is controversial and numerous alternative schemes have been published. Subgenus *Salix* species are commonly called the true willows, whilst the members of subgenus *Caprisalix* are the sallows and osiers. The accurate identification of *Salix* species is difficult since it is often necessary to have mature flowers and leaves, structures that are usually not available at the same time. *Salix* nomenclature is complex due to the patterns of morphological variation and hybridization, although most species of subgenus *Salix* do not hybridize with those of the other two sections. Most hybrids are fertile, hence it is possible for individual plants to have complex hybrid parentages, e.g., artificial hybrids have been created involving up to 14 *Salix* species, whilst hybrids of three or more species are frequently found in the UK. This means that in areas where there are numerous interfertile species it may be difficult to establish accurately the identity of individual trees. Furthermore, many hybrids are clones of a single sex, e.g., *S.* × *calodendron* is known only from female plants. Furthermore, natural hybridization is complicated by the separation of the sexes and interspecific differences in flowering periods.

Subgenera *Salix* and *Caprisalix* contain the most important forestry species, although subgenus *Chamaetia* contains some of the most important high-latitude species. In natural populations, *Salix* produces large amounts of easily germinated, very short-lived seed, whilst some species form extensive clonal stands (e.g., *S. repens, S. herbacea*). In

Table 3 Characteristics of the main grouping within the genus *Salix*

	Subgenus Salix	*Subgenus* Caprisalix	*Subgenus* Chamaetia	*Subgenus* Chosenia
Distribution	Temperate and boreal, plus few tropical and subtropical Old and New World	Temperate and boreal, plus few tropical and subtropical Old and New World	Temperate and boreal	North-East Asia
Habit	Medium-sized trees, large shrubs	Small trees, shrubs	Dwarf, creeping shrubs	Large trees
Floral nectaries	2 + nectaries in male flowers, 1–2 nectaries in female flowers	1 nectary	Nectaries fused	Absent
Male flowers	3–10(12) stamens	2 stamens	(1–)2 stamens	Five stamens
Catkins	Erect; stalked on leafy shoots	Erect; sessile or subsessile, precocious	Erect; on leafy shoots	Pendulous
Pollination	Insect	Insect	Insect	Wind
Examples	*S. alba S. babylonica*	*S. caprea S. viminalis*	*S. herbacea S. polaris*	*S. arbutifolia*

cultivation, *Salix* species are readily propagated from seed, although more generally they are vegetatively propagated from hardwood cuttings; some species, e.g., *S. caprea*, are difficult to root from cuttings. Vegetative reproduction has the advantage that particular cultivars can be maintained, and it is essential for the propagation of male clones. The economic importance of the genus has led to the selection of many local *Salix* genotypes, all of which are maintained through clonal propagation. For established lowland species, coppicing and pollarding are effective forms of management for wood products, although large amounts of organic material must be available in the soil.

Willows are the hosts of many insect species. Willows are prone to fungal diseases (e.g., *Melampsora* leaf rusts and *Armillaria*), and the planting of single areas with single clones may make disease control difficult. The bacterium *Erwinia salicis* is an important threat to the production of high-quality cricket bats from *S. alba*.

Utilization

Timber

Betula species (e.g., *B. alleghaniensis*, *B. lenta*, *B. pubescens*) are important hardwoods for the production of veneers and plywoods. *Alnus* species produce soft, fine-grained woods used for pilings, beams, and shipbuilding (e.g., *A. acuminata*, *A. jorullensis*). The wood of larger *Salix* species is used for building purposes, whilst female clones of *S. alba* var. *caerulea* are the sole source of wood for cricket bats. *Alnus*, *Betula* and *Salix* species are important pulpwood sources.

Wood Products

Salix is an important raw material of rural crafts (e.g., hurdles, coracles, baskets) in both the New and Old Worlds. Basketry is an example where particular species produce different qualities of products, e.g., *S. triandra* (rods), *S. purpurea* (thin withies for fine basketry), and *S. viminalis* (withies for basketry). Furthermore, male and female clones produce different qualities of rods and withies. Birch bark (e.g., *B. papyrifera*) is used for canoe and roof construction. Furthermore, birch bark has been used as writing material, e.g., the oldest (*c.* 1800 years old) known Buddhist manuscripts. Birch branches have also been used for brush construction and administering corporal punishment (the name *Betula* is derived from the Latin 'to beat'). *Betula* and *Salix* species are used as short-rotation biomass crops.

Fuelwood

Alnus, *Betula*, and *Salix* species are important fuelwood sources, e.g., *Salix* woodchips in Sweden. All three genera have been widely used for charcoal production and are important in gunpowder manufacture.

Medicines, Food, Chemicals

Alder, birch, and willow have limited food value, although *Salix* species are important pollen and nectar sources for bees early in the year. In the northern Appalachians, *B. lenta* sap is tapped in spring and fermented to produce birch beer, tea is made by infusing birch bark and twigs, and birch bark (rich in oil and starch) is a famine food. Medicinally, salicin has been extracted for centuries from willow bark and used as a febrifuge and analgesic, although this has been superseded by salicylic acid (aspirin), and wintergreen (methyl salicylate) is extracted from *B. lenta* and *B. alleghaniensis*. The astringent properties of alder bark are used for the treatment of burns and infections, whilst the triterpenes betulin and lupeol, extracted from bark and wood of *A. rubra*, have some *in vitro* antitumor activity. Birch and alder pollens are important sources of hayfever allergens, whilst birch sap may cause contact dermatitis. Distillation of *B. pendula* bark and wood is used to produce pyroligneous oil for the preparation of leather, and *B. pubescens* and *B. pendula* leaves produce a green dye.

Habitat Amelioration

Salix species are often planted along riverbanks, subject to extensive flooding, to minimize soil erosion, whilst others (*S. purpurea*, *S. interior*) are used for estuarine land reclamation. *Salix* species are also important as windbreaks and for the treatment of wastewater. *Betula* species are used as heavy-metal bioindicators (e.g., *B. populifolia* for lead in Wisconsin, USA), whilst alder leaves accumulate gold.

Ornamentals

Alnus and white-barked *Betula* species have wide-ranging horticultural uses. Many *Salix* species and selected cultivars (particularly males) are grown (e.g., for stem color), whilst weeping (e.g., *S. babylonica*) types are popular in riverine situations.

See also: **Biodiversity**: Plant Diversity in Forests. **Ecology**: Reproductive Ecology of Forest Trees. **Genetics and Genetic Resources**: Cytogenetics of Forest Tree Species; Genecology and Adaptation of Forest

Trees; Genetic Systems of Forest Trees; Population, Conservation and Ecological Genetics. **Temperate and Mediterranean Forests**: Subalpine and Boreal Forests; Temperate Broadleaved Deciduous Forest. **Tree Physiology**: Physiology of Sexual Reproduction in Trees.

Further Reading

Argus GW (1973) *The genus Salix in Alaska and the Yukon*. Ottawa: National Museums of Canada.

Chase MW, Zmarzty S, Lledo MD, *et al.* (2002) When in doubt, put it in Flacourtiaceae: a molecular phylogenetic analysis based on plastid *rbc*L DNA sequences. *Kew Bulletin* 57: 141–181.

Chen ZD, Manchester SR, and Sun HY (1999) Phylogeny and evolution of the Betulaceae as inferred from DNA sequences, morphology, and paleobotany. *American Journal of Botany* 86: 1168–1181.

Furlow JJ (1990) The genera of the Betulaceae in the Southeastern United States. *Journal of the Arnold Arboretum* 71: 1–67.

Hibbs DE, DeBell DS, and Tarrant RF (1994) *The Biology and Management of Red Alder*. Corvallis, OR: Oregon State University Press.

Newsholme C (1992) *Willows. The Genus Salix*. Portland, OR: Timber Press.

Savill PS (1991) *The Silviculture of Trees used in British Forestry*. Wallingford, UK: CAB International.

Fagaceae

R Rogers, University of Wisconsin–Stevens Point, Stevens Point, WI, USA

Introduction

The following sections characterize members of the beech family (Fagaceae) in relation to their taxonomy, distribution, ecology, and silviculture. Also included is information about their botanical importance as well as their significance in meeting human needs.

The beech family contains some of the world's most important trees to human culture. Uses are myriad and include such things as woven baskets, toys, storage containers, ship timbers, and food sources. However, members of the beech family are generally acknowledged as most important sources of hardwood timber (oak (*Quercus*), beech (*Fagus*), and chestnut (*Castanea*)), chestnut, and cork and tannins from the oaks (**Figure 1**).

Figure 1 Cork oak (*Quercus suber*) plantation in Portugal showing tree trunks whose bark has been stripped for cork. Photograph courtesy of Heinrich Speicker, Institut für Waldwachstum, Albert-Ludwigs-Universität Freiburg, Freiburg, Germany.

Taxonomy

The beech family contains from six to nine genera (*Fagus*, *Nothofagus*, *Lithocarpus*, *Castanopsis*, *Colombobalanus*, *Castanea*, *Chrysolepis*, *Quercus*, and *Trigonobalanus*) and includes between 600 and 900 species, although numerous classification issues exist which accounts for the variation in the number of genera (**Table 1**). Perhaps the best-known members of the beech family are the oaks which are recognized by their distinctive fruit, the acorn (**Figure 2**). The genera of Fagaceae as we know them probably became established about 60 million years ago during the late Cretaceous period in geologic history following migration from areas centered in tropical mountains.

Characteristics that unite members of the family include leaves with a single blade that are either persistent or deciduous and which often remain on the tree after withering and dying. Leaflike appendages (stipules) are present at the base of a relatively short leaf stem (petiole). Leaves are arranged in an alternate pattern on the stem. Veins of the leaves are featherlike and have branches that are laterally connected to a central stem.

Male and female flowers are found within the same tree. Female flowers are wind pollinated. Male flowers are pendulous spikelike structures while female flowers are on short spikes with few flowers or may be grouped in clusters near the base of the male flowers. Although female flowers may contain one or two ovules, only one develops to maturity.

The fruit is distinctive and consists of a nut that is surrounded by an outer somewhat firm yet elastic coat that is partially or completely enclosed by a cluster of bracts (**Figure 3**). The nut contains only one seed which lacks food reserves associated with the embryo but which has large, fleshy primary

Table 1 Distribution of the beech family (Fagacaeae)

Genus	Number of species	Range
Beech (Fagus)	10	Northern hemisphere
Oak (Quercus)	400	Northern hemisphere; red oak group (Lobatae) restricted to North America
Southern beech (Nothofagus)	40	Australia, Chile, Argentina, New Zealand, New Guinea, and New Caledonia
Chestnut (Castanea)	10	Southern Europe, northern Africa, southwestern and eastern Asia, and eastern United States
Chinkapin (Castanopsis)	150	North America, China, India, and Malayan archipelago
Tanoak Lithocarpus	100–200	North America (1 species), Asia
Chinquapin (Chrysolepis)	2	Western United States
Colombobalanus	1	Columbia, South America
Trigonobalanus	2	China, Malaysia

Figure 2 Acorns of northern red oak (*Quercus rubra*).

Figure 3 Fruit of tanoak (*Lithocarpus densiflorus*).

leaves that it uses for its initial nourishment upon germination. The fruit matures in one or two seasons. A botanic comparison of the well known genera is given in **Table 2**.

Beech (*Fagus*)

There are 10 species of beeches all of which are found in the northern hemisphere. One species is found in North America, one is European, one is found in the Caucasus Mountains on the border between Europe and Asia, and the rest are found within the temperate regions of eastern Asia. Although the beech genus is relatively small, the European beech has been used extensively for ornamental purposes and many horticultural varieties exist which display a vast array of morphological characteristics such as coloration and form (**Figure 4**).

Oak (*Quercus*)

Worldwide there are about 400 species of oaks, and they are taxonomically divided into three groups: (1) the red oak group (*Quercus* section *Lobatae*), (2) the white oak group (*Quercus* section *Quercus*), and (3) the intermediate group (*Quercus* section *Protobalanus*). All three groups include tree and shrub species. The red oaks and white oaks include evergreen and deciduous species, whereas the intermediate oaks are all evergreen. The red oaks are found only in the western hemisphere where their north–south range extends from Canada to Colombia. In contrast, the white oaks are widely distributed across the northern hemisphere. The intermediate group comprises only five species, all of which occur within southwestern USA and northwestern Mexico. Many of the world's oaks occur in regions with arid climates, including Mexico, North Africa, and Eurasia, where they are often limited in stature to shrubs and small trees. About 80% of oaks occur below 35° N latitude and fewer than 2% (six or seven species) reach 50° N.

The most reliable distinction between the white oaks and red oaks is the inner surface of the acorn shell. In the white oaks it is hairless or nearly so, whereas in the red oaks it is conspicuously hairy or velvety. In the intermediate group, this characteristic is not consistent among species. The

Table 2 Summary of characteristics of the more common genera in the beech family

Genus	Leaves	Flowers	Fruit
Beech (*Fagus*)	Deciduous	Male are in heads, female are in short spikes with two to four flowers	A triangular nut occurring in twos enclosed by a bur covered by weak unbranched spines; matures in one season
Chestnut (*Castanea*)	Deciduous	Male, female, or both borne on erect many-flowered apetalous spikes	A rounded nut occurring singly or in twos or threes covered by a bur having sharp, rigid, branched spines; matures in one season
Chinkapin (*Castanopsis*)	Persistent	Similar to chestnut	The same as chestnut but takes 2 years to mature
Tanoak (*Lithocarpus*)	Persistent	Similar to chestnut	An acorn which matures in 2 years
Oak (*Quercus*)	Deciduous or persistent	Male are borne in many-flowered apetalous spikes; female are borne in several-flowered spikes	An acorn which matures in 1 or 2 years
Southern beech (*Nothofagus*)	Deciduous or persistent which are small, oval, and have finely toothed edges	Male are bell-shaped of varying numbers; female are generally few in number and borne on stalks	Similar to beech
Chinquapin (*Chrysolepis*)	Persistent	Chestnutlike spikes of creamy-white; male flowers are borne in the leaf axils; female flowers usually occur in a cluster at the base of male spikes	Spine-covered bur which encloses from one to three nuts

Figure 4 Leaves of copper beech (*Fagus sylvatica* 'Purpurea'). Photograph courtesy of Heinrich Speicker, Institut für Waldwachstum, Albert-Ludwigs-Universität Freiburg, Freiburg, Germany.

Figure 5 Leaves of white oak (*Quercus alba*). Note absence of bristles at the ends of the leaf lobes.

leaves of the white oaks are usually rounded and without bristle tips (**Figure 5**), whereas the leaf lobes of the red oaks are usually pointed and often bristle-tipped (**Figure 6**). To many botanists and others, the most important difference between the white oaks and red oaks is the length of the acorn maturation period. Acorns of species in the white oak group require one season to mature whereas species in the intermediate and most of the red oak group require two seasons. The white oaks and intermediate oaks are characterized by the presence of tyloses (occlusions) in the latewood vessels (water-conducting cells) of the xylem whereas tyloses are usually absent in the red oaks. These vessel-plugging materials confer greater decay resistance to the wood of the white and intermediate oaks than the red oaks. Other morphological features that differentiate the three groups and species within them are presented in various taxonomic treatments.

Figure 6 Leaves of northern pin oak (*Quercus ellipsoidalis*) showing bristle-tipped leaves.

Of the more than 250 oak species occurring in the western hemisphere, the largest number occur in Mexico and Central America. About 10 species occur in Canada while 90 species of oaks are native to the continental USA. Oak hybrids are not uncommon where species ranges overlap as evidenced by the more than 80 hybrids recognized in the USA alone.

The oaks are distinguished from other members of the beech family (e.g., the beeches and chestnuts) by their fruit, the acorn. With one exception, all plants that produce acorns are oaks. The exception is the genus *Lithocarpus*, which includes the tanoak of Oregon and California. Although represented by only one North American species, *Lithocarpus* is represented by 100 to 200 species in Asia. Some taxonomists think *Lithocarpus* may be an evolutionary link between the chestnut and the oak.

Southern Beech (*Nothofagus*)

Southern beech or *Nothofagus* is a genus of some 40 species that only occur in the temperate regions of the southern hemisphere. The name *Nothofagus* means 'false beech'; however, *Notofagus* meaning 'southern beech' might have been more appropriate and in fact the original intent of the nomenclature. Some plant historians have suggested that the original name was mis-spelled by inserting the *h*. Nine species of *Nothofagus* occur in South America while three occur in Australia. The importance of their timber is second only to that of the eucalypts.

Besides Australia, Chile, and Argentina, *Nothofagus* is also represented in New Zealand, New Guinea, and New Caledonia. Paleobotanists believe the current distribution of *Nothofagus* species resulted from the continental drift that occurred following the break-up of the Great Southern land. Forests of *Nothofagus* were noted as early as the mid-nineteenth century by the botanist Sir Joseph Hooker who accompanied James Ross on exploratory trips to the Southern Ocean between 1839 and 1843.

Chestnut (*Castanea*)

Castanea is the generic name for the chestnuts whose alternate name is chinkapin, not to be confused with *Castanopsis* and *Chrysolepis*, genera whose species are also commonly referred to as chinkapins or chinquapins. *Castanea* is a relatively small genus consisting of 10 species distributed across southern Europe, northern Africa, southwestern and eastern Asia, and the eastern United States. Prior to the 1930s in the eastern USA, the American chestnut (*Castanea dentata*) was prized for its high-quality, durable wood and sweet fruit but it is now relegated to a shrubby form because of its susceptibility to a pathogenic organism, the chestnut blight (*Endothia parasitica*). The blight eventually kills the stem but the root system is resistant to infection and results in sprout growth which is in turn killed back in a never-ending cycle.

Chinkapin (*Castanopsis*)

Most botanists agree that the taxonomy of *Castanopsis* is poorly understood. Only two of about 150 species of *Castanopsis* are found in North America whereas the rest are found in the forests of China, India, and the Malayan archipelago. These two are distinct from their Asian relatives, and systematists have created a new genus for them called *Chrysolepis*. The American species have a flower structure that is intermediate between *Castanopsis* and *Lithocarpus* suggesting a more primitive form within the family Fagaceae. The new scientific names for the American species, with the older names in parentheses, are *Chrysolepis chrysophylla* (Dougl.) Hjelmqvist (*Castanopsis chrysophylla* (Dougl.) A. DC.) for giant chinkapin and *Chrysolepis sempervirens* (Kell.) Hjelmqvist (*Castanopsis sempervirens* Dudl.) for evergreen chinkapin.

Ecology

Beech (*Fagus*)

Approximately 12% of all species in Fagaceae appear in the 2003 IUCN *Red List of Threatened Plants*.

Beech is found mixed with other temperate deciduous species and requires a site with a well-drained soil with good moisture holding capacity; it is more particular in that regard than many of the species it associates with. However, it does not tolerate soils that experience either prolonged flooding or dry periods. Beeches are extremely tolerant of shade and can persist under the shade of other species for decades.

European beech (*Fagus sylvatica*) is a dominant species in the broadleaved forests of Europe located principally in the foothills of mountainous areas. It was once more extensive in its distribution and composition than nowadays because of forest exploitation practices of past centuries which resulted in reforesting former broadleaved forests with faster growing species such as Scots pine (*Pinus sylvestris*) and Norway spruce (*Picea abies*). Efforts are under way to increase the proportion of broadleaved forests in Europe and in Germany in particular in order to return to the 'more natural' forest conditions of former times. Sessile oak (*Quercus petraea*), English oak (*Q. robur*), and European hornbeam (*Carpinus betulus*) are frequent associates.

Similarly, the American species, American beech (*F. grandifolia*) enjoys a wide range covering all of the eastern part of the USA on mesic sites and is associated with a large number of trees in a number of forest types. Like its European cousin, it has a distinctive smooth light-gray bark that remains so until maturity. Some of its principal associates include sugar maple (*Acer saccharum*), red maple (*A. rubrum*), yellow birch (*Betula alleghaniensis*), American basswood (*Tilia americana*), black cherry (*Prunus serotina*), eastern white pine (*Pinus strobus*), and red spruce (*Picea rubra*), as well as several hickories and numerous oaks and, in the southern part of its range, southern magnolia (*Magnolia grandiflora*). Beech is an important component of 20 forest cover types in eastern US forests and is one of the dominant species in three types; sugar maple–beech–yellow birch, red spruce–sugar maple–beech, and beech–sugar maple. It is found in lesser amounts in 17 other types.

American beech reproduces by seed which germinates on mineral soils but is best on forest soils containing humus. It is prevalent on podzolic soils. The largest species are found on alluvial bottom lands of Ohio and the lower Mississippi River valleys, and along the western slopes of the southern Appalachian Mountains. American beech also reproduces by root sprouts which can develop into desirable trees. Root systems are generally shallow compared to species with which it associates. Beech are long-lived trees only being exceeded by white oak (*Q. alba*) and sugar maple. Crown spread typically is wide compared to its associates. However, they can prune themselves well provided that stand density is not too low.

Southern Beech (*Nothofagus*)

The temperate regions of the southern hemisphere do not have direct counterparts of the northern temperate broadleaf deciduous forest. Instead the humid subtropical climate regions have a mixed (broadleaf and needleleaf) evergreen forest whose biogeographic interest stems from the occurrence of Gondwanan relicts: *Araucaria* pines (South America and Australia), *Podocarpus* pines (South America, Africa, and Australia), and the evergreen southern beech *Nothofagus* (South America, Australia, and New Zealand).

In general, southern beeches are slow-growing trees found in temperate rainforests of the southern hemisphere whose origins are believed to have been derived from a time when there was a single primordial landmass in the southern hemisphere called Gondwana. Continental drift is presumed to be the reason for the widespread occurrence of the genus across the southern hemisphere in essentially similar habitats in such places as South America, Australia, New Zealand, New Caledonia, and Papua New Guinea. Trees of some species can be quite large and may reach a height of 30 m or more with diameter at 1.3 m above the ground (diameter at breast height, dbh) of 1 m and occasionally up to 2 m. The strong similarity of form and the persistence of these trees in comparable habitats across southern hemisphere landmasses supports other evidence that these trees have survived largely unchanged since continental separation. In fact, fossil *Nothofagus* leaves have even been found on the Antarctic continent. Interestingly, other plant and animal species exclusively associated with southern beech forests also have close relatives associated with the comparable trees all across the southern landmasses. Beech orange fungus and the Peloridiidae bugs are good examples.

The extent of southern beech forests has been reduced in certain places. Southern beech forests in Australia were once far more widespread, when the climate was wetter and fire was less frequent.

The subantarctic forests of evergreen southern beech in Patagonia are threatened with extinction. They occupy a 60-km wide strip along the base of the Andes and extend, in pockets, 1500 km from the Province of Neuquén south to Tierra del Fuego. Two indigenous species – the lenga (*Nothofagus dombeyi*) and ñire (*N. procera*) trees – dominate the forest, which serves as home to pumas, guanacos, southern river otters, geese, Andean condors, and huemul deer. Logging and forest clearing have been extensive in the region's northerly latitudes, and now threaten the southern forests of lenga and ñire. However, the boundaries of Perito Moreno National Park in Patagonia are being expanded through land donated by the Patagonian Land Trust in an effort to preserve these forests of evergreen southern beech.

The American Chinquapins (*Chrysolepis*)

The uniqueness of the two species of the American genus *Chrysolepis* in relation to the species within *Castanopsis* level does not translate to differences between the American species. The ranges of the shrub form of giant chinkapin and of evergreen chinkapin overlap from northern coastal California into the Cascade Range of Oregon. The two species probably hybridize where they co-exist. An apparently continuous intergradation of characters can be found in the Cascades in southern Oregon and in the Siskiyou Mountains.

The two growth forms of giant chinkapin are probably not the result of plastic phenotypic response to site conditions, although they may be in portions of the species range. In the northern Coast Ranges of California, the tree form occupies relatively moist conditions; the shrub form grows on dry, sterile ridgetops in chaparral communities. In the central part of the Cascades of Oregon, the pattern is reversed – the tree form is found primarily in relatively open and dry ridgetop forest communities, and the shrub form is spread through the more mesic forest stands. Only the shrub form is found at high elevations in the Cascade Range.

This variation is due to the probable existence of at least three ecotypes of giant chinkapin: (1) a dry-site chaparral shrub ecotype of southwestern Oregon and northwestern California which probably matches the taxonomic category of *Castanopsis chrysophylla* var. *minor*; (2) a high-elevation ecotype adapted to heavy snowpack, cool temperatures, and short growing seasons found along the Oregon Cascades and in eastern Oregon; and (3) a tree form that occurs in forest stands at lower elevations. The latter ecotype seems well adapted to dry, relatively infertile sites but can and does do well in more mesic conditions that have a history of disturbance by fire.

Oaks (*Quercus*)

It is an understatement to say that oaks are found on a wide variety of sites, soil conditions and landforms throughout its range in the northern hemisphere. It is worth noting that one species (*Quercus humboldtii*) crosses the equator and is found in Ecuador.

Located between 5900 and 8600 feet (1800 and 2600 meters) above sea level, the Cachalú Biological Reserve in Colombia features one of the last remnants of pristine oak forests of this species. The 2000-acre (800-hectare) reserve is in northern Colombia in the Eastern Cordillera Montane Forest and is part of a 'globally outstanding' ecoregion. Oak prefers high altitudes, 1000–2600 m above sea level, with annual precipitation of 1500–2500 mm and temperatures of 16–24°C. Ecologically very plastic, it can be found both in moderately fertile and deep soils and in degraded, almost barren soils. Nevertheless, it grows better on shallow soils with a thick layer of humus, and relatively loose soils with good drainage and a pH between 5.8 and 7.0. It is intolerant of shade and will dominate competing species.

The oaks are widely distributed throughout the temperate regions of the northern hemisphere. Generalizing about the ecological relations of the genus is dangerous at best given the enormous number of species and their genetic, morphological, and life history diversity. The reader is directed to local or regional guides to the various species.

The oaks of the Mediterranean region of southern Europe and northern Africa typically are shrubby or low-growing trees that are adapted to dry growing conditions. They typically are found in savanna like environments and may co-exist with various agricultural crops. The world's cork supply comes chiefly from cork oak growing in Portugal, Spain, and north Africa.

Conversely, oaks can be found on extremely dry sites to those inundated by flood waters and span the shade tolerance spectrum from intolerant to moderately tolerant. Oaks have been known to reproduce by seed and by sprouting from stumps, seedlings, and rhizomes. Regeneration strategies are largely species-site dependent and the anomalies in regeneration strategy among the oaks emphasize the difficulty of generalizing their regeneration ecology across species and habitats. Different oaks have solved their regeneration problems in different ways and some are more flexible than others in reaching a successful establishment. Each species, environment, physiology, and genetics determine its ability to regenerate successfully.

Oaks are one of the most, if not the most, important hardwood species of the USA. The genus is represented throughout the USA except for the Great Plains area to the west of the Mississippi and east of the Rocky Mountains. The greatest variety of oaks occurs in the eastern deciduous forest most of which is classified as the oak-hickory forest region. Of the 145 forest cover types defined by the Society of American Foresters in the USA 31 contain oak in the name or are included as part of a species list defining a name. Of these, 23 oak types are found east of the Mississippi River. In addition, many of the non-oak types have oak as a common associate.

Although oaks are relatively intolerant of shade, species vary considerably in this regard. In some habitats, oaks are vulnerable to replacement by more tolerant species such as maples and beeches. Compared to other competitors, oak seedlings grow more slowly during the years following establishment. When young oaks are overtopped and heavily shaded few survive for very long. However, oaks tend to be relatively drought tolerant and often survive on sites that limit the establishment and development of associated species with less drought tolerance. On droughty sites oak stems and shoots often die back but have a remarkable capacity to sprout from the roots when growing conditions become favorable again. These sprouts often have the capacity to outgrow competitors. Oaks tend to accumulate on these dry sites and may eventually dominate the overstory vegetation.

Most forest ecologists class oaks as a genus whose species for the most part become established following disturbances to the forest overstory. These disturbances may be natural such as fire and windstorm, extensive or intensive, or may result from harvesting activities. Much of the current oak forest in the USA is the result of early forest exploitation and fires used to clear land for agriculture during settlement times. Oak opportunistically occupied sites in the Appalachian Mountains following the destruction of the American chestnut (*C. dentata*) by the chestnut blight in the 1930s.

Silviculture

Beech (*Fagus*)

Beech is classed as very tolerant of shade and hence possesses the ability to regenerate beneath tree canopies. However, on very poor soils or in very cold climates, beech may be less tolerant. This suggests silvicultural systems that retain an overstory component such as individual tree selection or group selection methods of harvesting. Beech prune themselves in well-stocked stands but open-grown trees tend to have wide crowns and lower limbs close to the ground. Often other species are purposely introduced into beech stands to increase stand density and act as 'trainers' in order to promote self-pruning. For example, European hornbeam is used to 'train' European beech in order to promote straight stems and encourage early self-pruning of lower branches. Beech responds readily to thinnings even at late ages and rapidly expands its crown following thinning. Thus beech is capable of producing high volume increment even to relatively old ages (130–150 years). When grown for high-quality wood the silvicultural target is to grow beech to

60 cm dbh in 110–140 years at a density of 80–110 trees per hectare. Thinnings are restricted to these 'crop trees' to keep their crowns in a free-to-grow condition. This sometimes means that thinnings must be from above (i.e., removing some dominant trees).

Southern Beech (*Nothofagus*)

Clear-felling has been the common way of harvesting southern beech in New Zealand and other areas across its distribution in the southern hemisphere. However, research is ongoing in New Zealand to find out if group selection (an uneven-aged silvicultural method) could be used to sustain southern beech forests. The group selection method is a modification of the single-tree selection method whereby openings larger than the crowns of the largest trees are made in the forest canopy. Typical openings range from 0.1 to 0.25 hectare. In large part, this method requires adequate advance regeneration to successfully regenerate the stand.

Oak (*Quercus*)

As a genus, oak has a wide ecological amplitude, that is it has a wide range of habitat conditions that individual species can tolerate. Therefore making silvicultural generalizations is difficult at best and an interested reader is best advised to seek regional or local information about the oak species and the location in which it is found.

Having said that, the potential exists for applying both even-aged and uneven-aged silvicultural methods to stands dominated by oak. In order for uneven-aged silvicultural methods to succeed there must be a sustained, periodic recruitment of oak reproduction into the overstory. This is a necessary prerequiste to create and maintain a negative exponential diameter distribution, a stand structure characteristic of uneven-aged stands. Although it may be possible, through thinning, to create the requisite diameter distribution without adequate regeneration, it cannot be sustained. Any event, natural or otherwise, that interrupts this process, will disrupt the recruitment of stems into succeeding size classes. The single-tree selection method is one way of creating this type of stand structure. From outward appearances, the single-tree selection method may seem to represent the most 'natural' of the silvicultural systems. The naturalness of the method nevertheless may be deceptive because there must be silvicultural control of the rate of natural reproduction, stand structure, and density. For all but the most shade-tolerant species, greater silvicultural control is obtained through single-tree selection than any other silvicultural method. Applying this method to the relatively shade-intolerant oaks with their erratic seed production cycles, seedling establishment, and other regeneration uncertainties is problematic. However, despite these problems, there is evidence that the method is suited to some oak forests.

Stands that are managed using even-aged silvicultural methods are regenerated naturally at the end of their rotation by one of three techniques: (1) clear-cutting, (2) shelterwood, or (3) seed tree. Although all three methods can be used to regenerate the spectrum of shade tolerant to shade intolerant oaks, they are most suited to the intolerant to mid-tolerant species. If clear-cutting is contemplated one should consider the suitability of the ecosystem for meeting oak reproduction requirements, the likelihood of regeneration success, and economic, social, and ecological implications. Clear-cutting is successful if oak regeneration of sufficient size is present in the stand before it is harvested.

The shelterwood method is employed principally to create conditions suitable for the establishment and development of tree reproduction. Typically, there is a preparatory cut to facilitate crown expansion and seed production, an establishment cut to prepare a seedbed, and a removal cut to release the newly established regeneration. There are several variants of this system in the way the cuts are carried out and how long trees are retained. The key to using shelterwood successfully to establish and maintain oak stands is in manipulating stand density in order to control light and competition on the forest floor. This may entail controlling the understory vegetation in addition to manipulating the overstory.

The seed tree method leaves 20 or fewer seed trees per hectare. Although applied successfully in certain locations, the seed tree method generally provides too little regeneration too late. However, it could be useful in providing mast for wildlife and may have a greater visual appeal than a clear-cut.

Tree diameter growth is sensitive to stand density. If the goal of a forest management program is to produce large diameter trees in the shortest time possible, then stand density needs to be reduced as early as 15 years for some species to provide the maximum amount of growing space needed by the average tree. However, this approach may not be economically feasible. Thinning only around a smaller number of 'crop' trees ensuring that they have sufficient growing space may be a more cost effective solution.

Special situations require special considerations. The leaves of Mongolian oak (*Q. mongolica*) furnish food for the silk worm in northeastern China. The silviculture of these stands aims to create large crowns with nutritious leaves and to manage the density of silkworms that feed on the leaves. In the cork oak forests of Portugal and Spain, silvicultural techniques focus on the timing, method, and intensity of stripping bark from the trees.

Chinkapin, Chinquapin

Chinquapins are vigorous sprouters and most trees originate as root crown sprouts. Mature trees tend to have straight boles and narrow crowns. They exist singly or in small groves. Natural regeneration is usually sparse or lacking. The best evidence suggests that the greatest success in regenerating chinquapin is achieved by covering seed in partially shaded, moist conditions.

Utilization

A small market exists for chinkapin wood for furniture and cabinet stock and decorative veneer. However, it is difficult to dry without the wood checking (splits and cracks). Southern beech is noted for its high-quality timber that is used for fine woodwork. The genus is second only to the eucalypts in wood production in the southern hemisphere. Beech is excellent for turning and steam bending. It wears well, is easily treated with preservatives, and is used for flooring, furniture, veneer, and containers. The nut is eaten by people and is an important source of food for wildlife. European beech has many horticultural varieties used in cultivated landscapes. Similar uses can be described for oak. Other well-known uses of oak include staves for barrels used for whiskey and wine, and cork for wine and other stoppers. The wood of tanoak (*Lithocarpus*) is hard, strong, and fine-grained but is mostly used for pulp and firewood. Tannin is extracted from tanoak bark (as well as oak) and used for tanning leather.

See also: **Non-wood Products**: Cork Oak. **Silviculture**: Coppice Silviculture Practiced in Temperate Regions; Natural Stand Regeneration; Silvicultural Systems; Unevenaged Silviculture. **Temperate and Mediterranean Forests**: Mediterranean Forest Ecosystems; Southern Coniferous Forests; Temperate Broadleaved Deciduous Forest. **Tree Breeding, Practices**: Genetics of Oaks. **Tropical Forests**: Tropical Montane Forests.

Further Reading

Burns RM and Honkala BH (tech. coords.) (1990) *Silvics of North America*, vol. 2, *Hardwoods*. Agriculture Handbook no. 654. Washington, DC: US Department of Agriculture Forest Service.

Eyre FH (ed.) (1980) *Forest Cover Types of the United States and Canada*. Washington, DC: Society of American Foresters.

Faculty of Forestry, University of Zagreb (1996) *Pedunculate Oak in Croatia*. Zagreb, Croatia: Vinkovci. (In Croatian with English summaries and articles.)

Johnson PS, Shifley SR, and Rogers R (2002) *The Ecology and Silviculture of Oaks*. Wallingford, UK: CAB International.

Royal Botanic Gardens, Kew (2002) *Electronic Plant Information Centre*. Available online at http://www.kew.org/epic/

Spiecker H, Mielikainen K, Kohl M, and Skovsgaard J (eds.) (1996) *Growth Trends in European Forests*. European Forest Institute Research Report no. 5. Berlin, Germany: Springer-Verlag.

van den Berg AKJ, Matos AP, Ferreira A, *et al.* (1979–2001) *Investigacao em Sobreiro e Cortica*. Lisbon, Portugal: Centro de Estudos Florestais, Instituto Superior de Agronomia, Tapada da Ajuda. (CD Rom.) Available online at http://www.isa.utl.pt/def/cef/

Watson L and Dallwitz MJ (1992) *The Families of Flowering Plants: Descriptions, Illustrations, Identification, and Information Retrieval*. Available online at http://biodiversity.uno.edu/delta/

Juglandaceae

R Rogers, University of Wisconsin–Stevens Point, Stevens Point, WI, USA

Introduction

The following sections characterize members of the walnut family (Juglandaceae) in relation to their taxonomy, distribution, ecology, and silviculture. Also included is information about their botanical importance as well as their significance in meeting human needs.

The walnut family contains tree species that produce some of the world's finest high-quality hardwood that is used to manufacture cabinets and fine furniture (walnut). Moreover, there are species in this family that are important sources of edible nuts (walnut and pecan). Members of the family are found in the north temperate and subtropical regions of the world, extending to India, Indochina, Malaysia, and Andean South America. The family is not present in Africa and Australia.

The walnut family originated during the Eocene epoch of the Tertiary period of geologic time about 65 to 55 million years ago. The climate of Eocene times was subtropical and moist throughout North America and Europe. Palm trees and alligators were found as far north as the Dakotas in the USA, while at high northern latitudes in Greenland and Siberia, moist temperate zone forests were dominated by giant redwoods and deciduous trees such as beech, chestnut, and elm, while cycads, magnolias, and fig trees flourished in Alaska. The walnut family reached its greatest extent in numbers and distribution at that time after which it has steadily declined.

Taxonomy

The most recent taxonomic information indicates that the walnut family (Juglandaceae) comprises eight genera (*Alfaroa, Carya, Cyclocarya, Engelhardtia, Juglans, Oreomunnea, Platycarya,* and *Pterocarya*) with about 50 species (**Table 1**). However, some taxonomists report as few as seven genera (*Cyclocarya* omitted) and as many as nine genera (*Annamocarya* added) that include 60 species.

Members of the walnut family are mostly trees (often resinous), but a few are shrubs. All family members have more or less aromatic leaves which are mostly deciduous and consist of individual leaflets arranged like a feather with a central axis and lateral branches (pinnate) or arranged similar to pinnately compound leaves but leaflets are arranged groups of three (ternate). The leaves of the majority of the species are spirally arranged on twigs but they are oppositely arranged in two genera, *Alfaroa* and *Oreomunnea*. Superposed buds are common (bud found above lateral bud).

Male and female flowers are usually found on the same tree although occasionally sexes are found on separate trees. Flowers are wind pollinated and are mostly in the form of catkins.

Fruit is a nut encased within a husk (drupe-like) or a disk-winged nutlet. A drupe is usually a one-seeded fleshy fruit with the outer layer (husk) fleshy and the inner layer bony. Husks may split to release

Table 1 Distribution of the genera of the walnut family (Juglandaceae)

Genus	Number of species	Range
Juglans	20	North, Central, South America; Europe, and Asia
Carya	16	North America (13) and Asia (3)
Platycarya	1	China, Japan, Korea, and Vietnam
Englehardia	7	Southern and southeastern Asia, and northern India
Cyclocarya	1	China
Pterocarya	6	Eastern and southwestern Asia
Alfaroa	5	Central and South America
Oreomunnea	3	Mexico, Central and South America

the nut or may remain whole. The botanic characteristics of some of the more common genera are shown in **Table 2**.

There are about 20 species of walnut (*Juglans*) which are found mainly in the temperate and subtropical areas of the northern hemisphere. These species are distributed in North, Central, and South America, Eastern Europe, and Asia. Six species are native to the USA while three are native to Asia. The best-known is eastern black walnut (*Juglans nigra*), a native of eastern North America, for its use in the manufacture of fine furniture. The eastern European species, English or Persian walnut (*J. regia*), is important in the production of nuts for human consumption.

At one time, prior to glaciation, Europe, Asia, and North America were home to many species of hickories (*Carya*); however, many of them were driven to extinction by the advance of the glaciers, especially in Europe. Today about 16 species remain. Three are native to Asia while the rest are found in North America. One species is restricted to Mexico.

The hickories are subdivided into two groups: the true hickories and the pecan hickories. The true hickories are distinguished from the pecan hickories by differences in leaves, fruit husks, and bud scales. True hickories usually have seven or fewer leaflets per leaf while pecan hickories have more than seven leaflets. Fruit husks are unwinged (although they may have ribs) in the true hickories while the husks are broadly winged at the sutures in the pecan hickories. The buds of true hickories consist of more than six overlapping scales while the pecan hickories have buds that consists of from four to six scales that are valvate (non-overlapping).

The genus *Platycarya* consists of only one species (*P. strobilacea*) found in China, Japan, Korea, and Vietnam. There are about seven species in the genus *Engelhardtia* widely distributed in southern and southeastern Asia and northern India. There is one species in the genus (*Cyclocarya*, *C. paliurus*) and it

is found in China. The genus *Pterocarya* has six species distributed across eastern and southwestern Asia. Five species are listed for the genus *Alfaroa* located primarily in Central America. The members of this genus are unusual in the walnut family because the leaves are arranged oppositely on the stem. This leaf arrangement is also the case for the genus *Oreomunnea* which contains three species distributed through Mexico and Central America.

Ecology

Walnut (*Juglans*)

Black walnut (*J. nigra*) typically grows as scattered individual trees or in small groups throughout the central and eastern parts of the USA (**Figure 1**). Black walnut grows best on good sites in sheltered areas on well-drained bottomland sites in the Appalachians and the Midwest. Black walnut is sensitive to soil conditions and develops best on deep, well-drained, nearly neutral soils that are generally moist and fertile. Walnut grows best on sandy loam, loam, or silt loams. Walnut is common on limestone soils and grows especially well on deep loams, windblown soils, and fertile water deposited soils.

Black walnut grows in many of the mixed mesophytic forests but is seldom abundant. Usually it is found scattered among other trees and pure stands are rare, small, and usually located on the forest edge. An antagonism between black walnut and other plants growing within the root zone has been documented and attributed to juglone, a toxic substance found in the leaves, bark, nut husks, and roots of walnut trees. Some species are immune but others are not such as paper birch (*Betula papyrifera*), red pine (*Pinus resinos*), eastern white pine (*P. strobus*), Scotch pine (*P. sylvestris*), and apple (*Malus pumila*). Tomato (*Lycopersicon esculenta*) plants are especially susceptible. Root system is deep and wide-spreading and black walnut is smoderately tolerant of flooding. However, it is intolerant of

Table 2 Summary of characteristics of the more common genera in the walnut family

Genus	Leaves	Twigs	Fruit
Juglans (walnut)	Deciduous, odd-pinnate, alternate	Pith chambered	Nut encased in husk which may or may not split
Carya (hickory)	Deciduous, odd-pinnate, alternate	Pith solid	Nut surrounded by husk most split on maturity
Platycarya	Deciduous, odd-pinnate, alternate	Pith solid	Small flattened narrowly two-winged nutlet
Engelhardia	Deciduous, semievergreen or evergreen, even-pinnate, alternate	Pith solid	Three-winged nutlet
Cyclocarya	Deciduous, odd-pinnate, alternate	Pith chambered	Disk-winged nutlet
Pterocarya	Deciduous, odd or even pinnate, alternate	Pith chambered	Two-winged nutlet
Alfaroa	Opposite	Pith solid	Nut enclosed in husk
Oreomunnea	Opposite	Pith solid	Three-winged nutlet

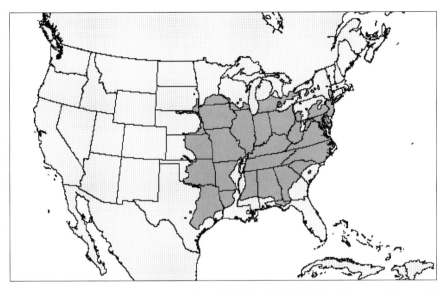

Figure 1   Range of black walnut (*Juglans nigra*). Adapted from Little EL, Jr (2003) *Digital Representations of Tree Species Range Maps. Atlas of United States Trees*. http://climchange.cr.usgs.gov/data/atlas/little/.

shade and in mixed species forests it must be in dominant or codominant canopy position if it is to survive.

Black walnut contains great genetic variation for growth and survival. More than 400 black walnut cultivars have been named and released over the last 100 years. However, hybridization is not common among species of walnuts. In fact, crossing between black walnut and butternut (*J. cinerea*) is difficult or impossible.

Ranging from cool temperate steppe to wet through subtropical thorn to moist forest life zones, English Walnut (*J. regia*) is reported to tolerate annual precipitation of 310–1470 mm, annual temperature of 7.0–21.1°C, and pH of 4.5–8.2. It thrives on rich, sandy loam, well-drained, slightly acid or neutral soils. English walnut responds well to cultivation and fertilization. In areas where hardiness is a problem, trees should not be forced into excessive vegetative growth and minimum temperature should not go below −29°C. If growth begins early in spring crop and foliage may be damaged by late frosts. When fully dormant, trees can withstand temperatures from −24°C to −27°C without serious damage.

Most true hickories are found on medium to dry sites and are often found in association with oaks (*Quercus* spp.). In fact, the largest forest region in the USA is situated in the eastern USA and is named the Oak–Hickory Forest because of the close association between the two genera. Most hickories are classed as moderately tolerant of shade and are considered to be relatively slow growing compared to its associates. There are exceptions however. Shellbark

hickory (*Carya laciniosa*) is very shade tolerant, exceeded only by sugar maple and beech.

The pecan hickories, on the other hand, are found on moist but well-drained ridge bottoms in river bottoms with other bottomland hardwoods. The exception is bitternut hickory (*C. cordiformis*) which is found on a wide variety of sites including dry, gravelly uplands. Pecan (*C. illinoinensis*) is the largest of the hickories and attains a height of 35–40 m and a diameter (at breast height, dbh) of 60–120 cm or more.

The other six genera are typically found in semitropical forests characterized by mixed species forests in relatively high rainfall areas on mountain slopes and in valleys. Some, like *Oreomunnea*, are found in cloud forests. Cloud forests are usually found in humid areas 1000 m above sea level. In such forests, trees usually reach more than 20 m. Here the mean annual temperature varies from 12°C to 23°C and the annual mean precipitation is always higher than 1000 mm and sometimes exceeds 3000 mm. In many cases the forests are enshrouded in semipermanent mist, giving rise to the term cloud forest. Cloud forests harbor many species that can be found in the rain forests, but are typically rich in epiphytes, parasitic plants, bromeliads, vines, etc.

Silviculture

Walnuts are generally a minor tree species in most landscapes and as a consequence not cultured in a natural setting. If an individual tree is encountered in a forest stand its growing space requirements are assessed and the individual is released from competition as required. Release is necessary in high-density stands because stem diameter growth of walnut is extremely sensitive to the degree of crowding in a stand. Trees have been mechanically pruned to increase stem quality. Research and experience has shown that with proper thinning and pruning it is possible to produce 40 cm saw logs in 30–35 years and veneer logs (50 cm) in 40–50 years. Given a silvicultural objective of veneer logs, the recommended stocking and spacing for an average stand diameter of 50 cm dbh should be 62 trees per hectare at a spacing of 13 m between trees.

Pecans should be grown on sites that have well-drained, deep soils (1.2–2 m) with moderate soil moisture holding capacity. Pecan trees are native to river valley soils and have a relatively high water requirement. They do best on sandy loam soils but also can be grown on heavier soils such as clay loams if the soils are well drained. In areas where the soil is lighter and relatively dry, irrigation is required. When pecan trees are fully mature, approximately 20 years after planting, tree spacing should be approximately 20–25 m between rows and also between trees within rows, or 15–22 trees per hectare.

Utilization

English walnut (*Juglans regia*) is native to the region in Eurasia extending from the Near East through to the Himalayas and on to Western China. This single species is known by various names: Persian, French, Turkish, Italian, Circassian, and Carpathian walnut. Walnuts must have been harvested from earliest times but the earliest records of growing of orchards of walnut trees go back to classical Greek and Roman times. Besides the nuts, trees are also a source of high-quality wood used for furniture and gunstocks. Growing of walnuts in Europe began in the 1500s; but by the 1600s walnut was replaced by mahogany as the wood most favored for furniture. They are now grown worldwide and the largest production is from California. Black walnut and other walnuts are used in much the same way as European walnut.

Hickories produce heavy, strong, shock-resistant wood with a high fuel value. These characteristics make hickory suitable for handles used in axes, hammers, and other striking instruments. Pecan is not only valuable as a fine furniture wood but the nut is prized for food. Species in the *Engelhardtia* and *Pterocarya* also produce fine cabinet woods.

See also: **Temperate and Mediterranean Forests**: Temperate Broadleaved Deciduous Forest. **Temperate**

Ecosystems: Fagaceae. **Tropical Forests**: Tropical Montane Forests.

Further Reading

Burns RM and Honkala BH (tech. coords.) (1990) *Silvics of North America*, vol. 2, *Hardwoods*. Agriculture Handbook no. 654. Washington, DC: US Department of Agriculture Forest Service.

Eyre FH (ed.) (1980) *Forest Cover Types of the United States and Canada*. Washington, DC: Society of American Foresters.

Royal Botanic Gardens (2002) *Plant Information Centre*. Available online at http://www.kew.org/epic/

VanSambeek JW (ed.) (1997) *Knowledge for the Future of Black Walnut*: Proceedings of the 5th Black Walnut Symposium, July 28–31 1996, Springfield, MO. Gen. Tech. Rep. no. NC-191. St Paul, MN: US Department of Agriculture Forest Service, North Central Forest Experiment Station.

Watson L and Dallwitz MJ (1992) *The Families of Flowering Plants: Descriptions, Illustrations, Identification, and Information Retrieval*. Available online at http://biodiversity.uno.edu/delta/

Pines

P W Rundel, University of California, Los Angeles, CA, USA
D M Richardson, University of Cape Town, Cape Town, South Africa

Introduction

Pines clearly form the most ecologically and economically significant tree group in the world. The genus *Pinus* contains 110 species (**Table 1**), comprising more than half the species in the Pinaceae and almost 20% of all gymnosperm species. Ecologically, pines also influence the structure and function of many forest ecosystems. They affect biogeochemical processes, hydrological and fire regimes, and provide food and create habitats for animals. Pines are important, and very often dominant, components of the vegetation over large parts of the northern hemisphere (**Figure 1**). Economically, pines play a major role as sources of timber, pulp, resin, nuts, and other products. Pines have also been cultivated in many parts of the world, both within and well outside their natural range, and they form the foundation of exotic forestry enterprises in many southern hemisphere countries. Moreover, pines have featured in ancient myths and rituals throughout human history, and have been celebrated in visual art, prose, poetry, and music.

Pines are found in a remarkably wide range of environments, from above the arctic circle where winters are very cold and growing seasons are short, to the tropics where frost never occurs and growth continues through the year. Pines are the dominant trees over large parts of the boreal forest, or taiga, which covers about 12 million km^2 of the northern hemisphere. In temperate latitudes of the northern hemisphere they occur abundantly in high mountains, in Mediterranean-climate regions, and mixed with junipers over extensive semi-arid woodlands. Some pine species form virtually monospecific forests over very large areas whereas others form mixed forests with other conifers (notably spruce and fir species) and broadleaved trees (notably oak, poplar, birch, and alder species), or form subtropical savannas or open woodlands. In temperate regions, and even more so in the tropics, pines are usually associated with acidic, nutrient-poor soils. Pines possess a range of specialized mechanisms that enable them to thrive (and usually attain dominance) in these harsh environments. That pines are not restricted to such sites is clearly shown by their ability to spread into more productive sites, both within and outside their natural ranges, following disturbance that reduces the competitive superiority of vigorous angiosperms. The disturbance regime is thus an important determinant of pine distribution and abundance in the landscape. Fire is the driving force in succession in nearly all pine habitats.

The Origin and Evolution of Pines

The expansion of angiosperms and the concurrent decline of gymnosperms in the late Mesozoic had a significant impact on the phytogeographic history of the earth. The earliest-known angiosperms arose in the Early Cretaceous (130–90 million years ago), and there are now between 250 000 and 300 000 extant species. The first gymnosperms arose in the Middle Devonian (365 million years ago), much earlier than the angiosperms, but the group never achieved a high diversity of species. Evidence from fossilized cones shows that ancestors of the Pinaceae had evolved by the mid-Jurassic, and that pines themselves had evolved by the Early Cretaceous. Most of the other modern genera of the pine family appeared only in the Early Tertiary or later.

By the end of the Mesozoic (65 million years ago), pines had diversified into two major groups, or subgenera (**Table 2**); the subgenus *Pinus* (diploxylon or hard pines, with two fibrovascular bundles in each

needle) and subgenus *Strobus* (haploxylon or soft pines, with one fibrovascular bundle in each needle). At this stage, pines had migrated throughout the middle latitudes of the supercontinent Laurasia. However, as major environmental changes occurred in the Early Cretaceous (between 130 and 90 million years ago), the diversification and rapid spread of angiosperms throughout middle latitudes pushed most conifers to small, cool or dry refugia in polar latitudes and scattered upland refugia at middle latitudes.

Intensive mountain-building events in the Tertiary created the environmental heterogeneity that drove the radiation of pine taxa in secondary centers of diversification, notably Mexico and northeastern Asia. Angiosperms that were best adapted at that time to tropical and subtropical conditions declined dramatically throughout middle latitudes following climatic deterioration at the end of the Eocene, allowing pines to expand their ranges.

Like the Eocene, the Pleistocene was also characterized by profound environmental changes that influenced the evolution of pines. However, whereas events in the Eocene completely reshuffled elements of the genus, Pleistocene changes caused pine species and populations to shift first toward the equator, then poleward (and to lower, then higher elevations), following the cycle of glacial and interglacial periods. Such migrations had important influences on the genetic diversity of pines. In some areas, such as the Pacific Northwest of North America, pine distributions were not so much split into distinct ranges by glaciations, as fragmented into small, semidisjunct populations. Such migrations served to promote intraspecific diversity while not necessarily promoting speciation. Although geographic conditions prevented pines from migrating south of the Sahara Desert, Nicaragua in Central America, or Java and Sumatra in Asia, the success of planted pines in the southern hemisphere shows that large parts of this hemisphere are highly suitable for pine growth.

Many significant changes in the abundance and geographic ranges of pines have occurred since the end of the last glacial period as pines rapidly expanded their ranges into deglaciated regions of North American and Europe. Wood rat middens preserved over the past 40 000 years at many sites in the Great Basin and other parts of the southwestern United States show a replacement of pinyon–juniper woodland by desert scrub in the Great Basin with warming at the end of Pleistocene.

Why Are Pines so Successful?

It is in the role of aggressive postdisturbance colonizers that pines are most clearly differentiated

Table 1 List of *Pinus* taxa, with common names, selected morphological features, and biogeographic region and habitat; figures relate to conditions regularly observed in the field (figures in brackets indicate exceptional dimensions)

Pinus taxon	Common name	Needle number	Needle length (cm)	Needle longevity (years)	Cone length (cm)	Height (m)	Biogeographic region	Habitat
P. albicaulis	Whitebark pine	5	3–7	5–8	4–8	5–10(30)	Western North America	Subalpine
P. aristata	Colorado or Rocky Mountain bristlecone pine	5	3–4	10–20	5–6(11)	5–15(30)	Rocky Mts, North America	Subalpine
P. armandii	Chinese white, Armand('s), or David's pine	5	8–15(18)	2–3	8–14	20–30	West and central China, Taiwan	Temperate montane
P. attenuata	Knobcone pine	3	9–15	4–5	8–15	10–20	Baja California, California, southwest Oregon	Mediterranean coastal
P. ayacahuite	Mexican white pine	5	8–15(22)	3	25–45	35–50	Mexico, Central America, Arizona, New Mexico	Tropical montane
P. balfouriana	Foxtail pine	5	(1.5)3–4	10–30	6–9(12)	10–22	California	Subalpine
P. banksiana	Jack pine	2	2–5	2–4	3–3.5	10–18(20)	Canada, northern USA	Boreal forest
P. bhutanica	Bhutan white pine	5	12–28	2–3	12–20	25	Himalayas	Temperate montane
P. brutia	Eastern Mediterranean or Calabrian pine	2	8–15	?	6–9	10–25	Eastern Mediterranean Basin	Mediterranean coastal
P. bungeana	Lacebark pine	3	6–8	3–4	5–6	15(30)	Central and north China	Temperate montane
P. canariensis	Canary Island pine	3	20–30	2–3	10–20(25)	30	Canary Islands	Mediterranean
P. caribaea	Caribbean pine	(2)3(4–5)	15–25	2	5–12	20–30	Caribbean area, Central America	Tropical/savanna
P. cembra	Swiss stone or Arolla pine	5	7–9	3–12	4–10	8–20(25)	Central Europe	Subalpine
P. cembroides	Mexican pinyon	(2)3(4)	2–6(7)	3–4	1–3.5	5–10(15)	Northwest Mexico, southwest USA	Arid/montane
P. chiapensis	Chiapas white pine	5	10–12	?	7–16	40	South-central to south Mexico, Guatemala	Tropical
P. clausa	Sand pine	2	6–9	2–3	3(4–8)	6(10)	Southeastern USA	Subtropical
P. contorta	Lodgepole pine	2	2–8	3–8	2–6	3–46(50)	Western USA	Temperate montane/subalpine
P. c. subsp. bolanderi	Bolander pine	2	2–5	?	?	6–15	California	Temperate
P. c. subsp. contorta	Shore or beach pine	2	2–7	?	2–5	3–10(16)	Coastal north California to British Columbia	Temperate
P. c. subsp. latifolia	(Rocky Mountain) lodgepole pine	2	(4)5–8	5–18	?	40–46	Rocky Mts, North America	Temperate montane
P. c. subsp. murrayana	Sierra (Nevada) lodgepole pine	2	(5–8)	?	2–5	15–40(50)	Sierra Nevada to Baja California	Temperate montane/subalpine
P. cooperi	Cooper pine	5(6–8)	8–10	?	6–10	30–35	Western Mexico	Tropical montane
P. coulteri	Coulter or bigcone pine	3	16–30	3–4	20–35	15–25	California, Baja California	Mediterranean coastal
P. cubensis	Cuban pine	3	10–14	?	4.5	?	Cuba	Tropical/savanna

Species	Common name						Region	Climate
P. culminicola	Potosí pinyon	(3–4)5(6)	5–6	?	3–5	1–5	Northeast Mexico	Tropical
P. dabeshenensis	Dabie Shan white pine	5	5–14	?	11–14	20–30	Eastern China	Temperate
P. dalatensis	Dalat or Vietnamese white pine	5	4–10	?	5–10	?	Vietnam	Tropical
P. densata	Sikang or Gaoshan pine	2(3)	8–14	3	4–6	30	China	Temperate montane
P. densiflora	Japanese red pine	2	(6)9–12	2–3	3–5	20–30 (36)	Japan, Korea, China	Temperate
P. devoniana	Michoacán pine	5	20–35	?	20–30	20–30	Mexico, Guatemala	Tropical
P. discolor	Border pinyon	3	2–6	?	2–3	5–10	Southwest USA, central and northwest Mexico	Arid/montane
P. donnell-smithii	Donnell Smith pine	5–6(7–8)	5–22	?	10–13	25	Guatemala	Tropical/subalpine
P. douglasiana	Douglas pine	5	20–35	?	7–10	20–35	West Mexico	Tropical
P. durangensis	Durango pine	6(7–8)	12–20	?	7–10	30–40	Northern and central Mexico	Tropical
P. echinata	Shortleaf pine	2	7–11	3–5	4–7	15–30(35)	Southeastern USA	Subtropical
P. edulis	Colorado pinyon	2	2–4	4–6	3–6	5–15	Western USA	Arid
P. elliottii	Slash pine	2–3	15(–30)	2	8–18	25–30	Southeastern USA	Subtropical
P. engelmannii	Apache pine	(2)3(4–5)	25–35	?	(10)–15	25(– 30)	West Mexico, Arizona, New Mexico	Temperate/montane
P. fenzeliana	Fenzel pine	5	4–18	?	6–10	13–50	South China to central Vietnam	Temperate
P. flexilis	Limber or Rocky Mountain white pine	5	3–8	5–6	7–15	7–15 (24?)	Western North America	Subalpine
P. gerardiana	Chilgoza or Gerard's pine	3	6–10	?	12–20	10–20(25)	Punjab, Afghanistan, Pakistan	Temperate montane
P. glabra	Spruce pine	2	(4)6–8	2–3	4–9	22–35	Southeastern USA	Temperate
P. greggii	Gregg's pine	3	8–15	2–3	8–14	10 – 15(25)	East Mexico	Tropical
P. halepensis	Aleppo pine	2(3)	6–12(15)	2	5–12	10–20(25)	Mediterranean Basin	Mediterranean coastal
P. hartwegii	Hartweg pine	3	8–16	?	8–14	20–30	Mexico, Guatemala	Tropical/subalpine
P. heldreichii	Heldreich whitebark or Bosnian pine	2	6–10	2–3(6?)	7–8	20(30)	Balkan peninsula, Greece	Temperate montane/subalpine
P. herrerai	Herrera pine	3	10(10–25)	?	2–3(4)	20–25(35)	West Mexico	Tropical
P. hwangshanensis	Hwangshan (Huangshan) pine	2	5–9	?	4–6	25	Central and eastern China	Temperate
P. jaliscana	Jalisco pine	4–5	12–16	?	4–8	20–30	West Mexico	Tropical
P. jeffreyi	Jeffrey pine	3	12–15(23)	4–6	15–30	25–50(60)	California, Baja California	Temperate montane
P. johannis	Zacatecas pinyon (pine)	3	3–5	?	3–4	2–4	Northeast Mexico	Arid/montane
P. kesiya	Khasi or Khasya pine	3	12–20(22)	2	5–7(10)	20–35(45)	Southeast Asia	Tropical
P. koraiensis	Korean stone pine	5	(6)8–13	2	9–20	20–35	Korea, Japan, northeast China, Siberia	Temperate montane
P. krempfii	Krempf pine	2	3–7	?	7–9	12–30	Vietnam	Tropical
P. lambertiana	Sugar pine	5	(5)8–10	2–4	25–50(60)	75	Baja California, California, Oregon	Temperate montane
P. lawsonii	Lawson's pine	3–5	15–20	?	6–8	25–30	South Mexico	Tropical

continued

Table 1 Continued

Pinus taxon	Common name	Needle number	Needle length (cm)	Needle longevity (years)	Cone length (cm)	Height (m)	Biogeographic region	Habitat
P. leiophylla	Smooth-leaved or Chihauhuan pine	5	5–9(15)	2	4–6.5(8)	20–25(30)	Mexico, Arizona, North Mexico	Temperate montane
P. longaeva	Western, Great Basin, or Intermountain bristlecone pine	5	1.5–3	10–33(45)	6–9.5	16	Western USA	Subalpine
P. luchuensis	Luchu pine	2	15–20	?	<5	<20	Japan, Ryukyu (Luchu) Islands	Temperate
P. lumholtzii	Lumholtz pine	3	(15)20–30	?	4–5(7)	10–20	Central Mexico	Tropical
P. massoniana	Masson, or Chinese red pine	2	15–20	?	5–6	8–25(30)	Central and eastern China, Taiwan	Temperate montane
P. maximartinezii	Martínez or Maxi pinyon	5	7–11	?	15–23	6–10	South Mexico	Arid/montane
P. maximinoi	Maximino pine	5	15–28	?	5–8	20–35	Mexico, Central America	Tropical
P. merkusii	Merkus or Tenasserim pine	2	17–25	1.5–2	5–9	20–30	Southeast Asia	Tropical/savanna
P. montezumae	Montezuma or roughbranched pine	(3–4)5(6–8)	15–25	3	(6)12–15	20–30(35)	Mexico, Guatemala	Tropical
P. monophylla	Singleleaf pinyon	1(2)	3–6	4–12	5–8	5–10	Southwestern USA to northern Baja California	Arid
P. monticola	Western white pine	5	(4)7–13	3–4	14–25(30)	50–55(70)	Western North America	Temperate montane
P. morrisonicola	Taiwan white pine	5	4–10	?	7–11	25(30)	Taiwan	Temperate
P. mugo	Dwarf mountain pine	2	3–8	5+	3–5(6)	2–6	Europe	Subalpine
P. muricata	Bishop pine	2	7–15	2–3	4–9	10–15(25)	California, Baja California	Mediterranean coastal
P. nelsonii	Nelson pinyon (pine)	3	5–10	?	7–12	5–10	Northeast Mexico	Arid
P. nigra	European black or Austrian pine	2	8–16	4(8)	3–10	20–40	Europe, Mediterranean Basin	Temperate
P. nubicola	Perry's pine	5–6(7–8)	25–43	?	10–15	25–30	South Mexico, Central America	Tropical
P. occidentalis	Hispaniolan pine	(3)4–5	11–18	?	5–7(8)	18	Caribbean Islands	Tropical montane/savanna
P. oocarpa	Eggcone pine	(3–4)5	20–25	?	6–10	15–30	Mexico and Central America	Tropical
P. palustris	Longleaf pine	3(5?)	20–45	2	15–25	25–30	Southeastern USA	Subtropical
P. parviflora	Japanese white pine	5	5–8	3–4	5–10	20–30	Japan	Subalpine
P. patula	Mexican weeping pine	3(4–5)	15–25(30)	3–4	7–10	30–35	East Mexico	Tropical
P. peuce	Macedonian or Balkan (white) pine	5	6–12	?	8–15	20–30	Balkan Peninsula	Temperate montane
P. pinaster	Maritime or cluster pine	2	(10)15–20(25)	3	10–22	20–35(40)	Western Mediterranean Basin	Mediterranean coastal
P. pinceana	Weeping or Pince pinyon	3	6–8(14)	?	5–10	4–10	Northeast Mexico	Arid/montane

Species	Common name							
P. pinea	Mediterranean stone, Italian stone, or umbrella pine	2	(8)12–15(20)	2–3	10–15	15–30	Mediterranean Basin	Mediterranean coastal
P. ponderosa	Ponderosa or western yellow pine	(2)3(4–5)	17–25	4–6	5–15	10–50(72)	Western USA	Temperate montane
P. praetermissa	Styles's pine	5	8–16	?	3–5	15	West Mexico	Tropical
P. pringlei	Pringle's pine	3(4–5)	15–25	?	5–8	15–30	South Mexico	Tropical
P. pseudostrobus	False Weymouth pine	5(6–8)	20–25	?	8–15	30–40	Mexico, Guatemala	Tropical
P. pumila	Dwarf stone pine	5	4–6	5	3–5(6)	1–4	East Asia	Boreal forest, subalpine
P. pungens	Table Mountain pine	2	5–7(9)	3	6–10	15–20	Northeastern USA	Temperate
P. quadrifolia	Parry pinyon	4–5	1.5–5	?	3.5–6	5–15	South California Baja California	Arid/montane
P. remota	Texas or paper-shell pinyon	2	3–5	?	2.5–3.5	3–8	Texas, northeast Mexico	Arid
P. resinosa	Red pine	2	12–18	4–5	3.5–6	20–30(40)	Northeastern USA, Canada	Temperate
P. rigida	Pitch pine	(2)3	5–10(12)	2–3	3–4(5–10)	10–25(30)	Northeastern USA	Temperate
P. roxburghii	Chir pine	3	20–30	1–3	10–15(20)	40–50+	Himalayas	Temperate montane
P. rzedowskii	Rzedowski pinyon	(3)4(5)	6–10	?	10–15	15–30	Southwest Mexico	Tropical
P. sabiniana	Foothill or digger pine	3	15–25(30)	3–4	15–25	15–25	California	Mediterranean coastal
P. serotina	Pond pine	3	15–20	2–3	5–8	20	Southeastern USA	Temperate
P. sibirica	Siberian stone pine	5	(5)10–13	?	6–12	20–35	Central Asia	Boreal forest
P. squamata	Qiaojia pine	5	9–17	?	9	?	Southwest China	Subtropical montane
P. strobus	Eastern white pine	5	6–10(12)	2–3	8–20	25–30(40)	Northeastern USA and Canada	Temperate
P. sylvestris	Scots pine	2	3–7	2–8	3–6	30(35)	Europe, central Asia	Boreal forest, temperate, subalpine
P. tabuliformis	Chinese red pine	2–3	10–12(13–17)	?	4–9	25(30)	North and west central China	Temperate montane
P. taeda	Loblolly pine	3	12–22	3–4	6–12(15)	20–30	Southeastern USA	Temperate
P. taiwanensis	Taiwan red or Formosa pine	2	8–12	?	4–8	20–25(35)	Taiwan	Tropical montane
P. tecunumanii	Tecun Umán pine	4–5	14–21	?	4–7	50	Central America	Tropical
P. teocote	Twisted-leaved or Aztec pine	(2)3(4–5)	8–15	3	4–7	8–25(30)	Mexico, Guatemala	Tropical
P. thunbergii	Japanese black pine	2	7–12	3–4	4–6	30–40	Japan, Korea	Temperate
P. torreyana	Torrey pine	5	15–30	3–4	10–15	5–10(15)	California	Mediterranean coastal
P. tropicalis	Tropical pine	2(3)	15–30	?	?	?	Cuba	Tropical/savanna
P. uncinata	Swiss mountain pine	2	(3)5–6	5+	4–6	10–20	Europe	Temperate montane
P. virginiana	Virginia or scrub pine	2	4–8	3–4	3–7	8–15(30)	Eastern USA	Temperate montane
P. wallichiana	Himalayan blue pine	5	11–18(20)	3–4	20–30	50+	Himalayas	Temperate montane
P. wangii	Wang pine	5	2.5–6	?	4.5–9	20	Southwest China	Temperate
P. washoensis	Washoe pine	3	10–15	4–6	7–10	35(70)	Sierra Nevada	Temperate montane
P. yunnanensis	Yunnan (white) pine	2–3	15–20(30)	?	3–7(10)	15–30	China	Temperate montane

Adapted from Richardson D (ed.) (1998) *Ecology and Biogeography of Pinus*. Cambridge, UK: Cambridge University Press.

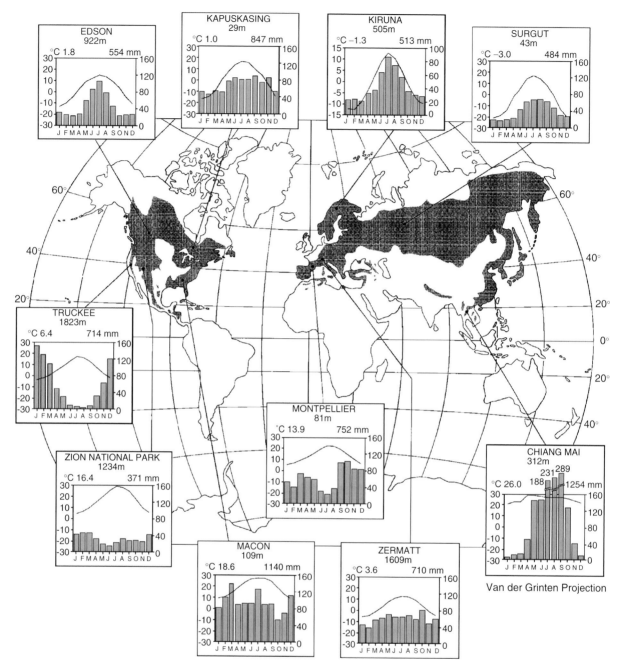

Figure 1 The worldwide distribution of the genus *Pinus* with examples of the varied climate regimes in which pines occur. Reproduced with permission of Cambridge University Press from Richardson D (ed.) (1998) *Ecology and Biogeography* of Pinus. Cambridge, UK: Cambridge University Press.

from firs, spruces, other conifers, and from angiosperm trees. An idealized 'pine prototype' would conform with the following profile: a light-demanding, fast-growing tree that regenerates as even-aged cohorts following landscape-scale disturbance, and retains its position in the landscape by exploiting aspects of its regeneration biology. This is an oversimplification, however, when one considers the wide range of habitats in which pines occur,

and the range of life history syndromes evident in the genus.

Among the factors that have contributed to the ecological success of pines are their abundant output of seeds from an early age, their effective mechanisms for long-distance seed dispersal, their ability to colonize nutrient-poor and disturbed sites, and their mating system that permits inbreeding and selfing in isolated trees and confers resilience at

Table 2 Systematic relationships within the genus *Pinus*. Subgeneric categories are based on data in Richardson (1998) and personal communications from Aaron Liston (Oregon State University)

Genus *Pinus*
  Subgenus *Pinus*
    Section *Pinus*
      Subsection *Pinus* (Eurasia, North Africa, northeastern North America, Cuba):
        P. densata, *P. densiflora*, *P. hwangshanensis*, *P. kesiya*, *P. luchuensis*,
        P. massoniana, *P. merkusii*, *P. mugo*, *P. nigra*, *P. resinosa*, *P. sylvestris*,
        P. tabuliformis, *P. taiwanensis*, *P. thunbergii*, *P. tropicalis*, *P. uncinata*, *P. yunnanensis*
      Subsection *Pinaster* (Canary Islands, southern Europe, North Africa, West Asia, Himalayas):
        P. brutia, *P. canariensis*, *P. halepensis*, *P. heldreichii*, *P. pinaster*,
        P. pinea, *P. roxburghii*
    Section *Trifolius*
      Subsection *Contortae* (North America):
        P. banksiana, *P. clausa*, *P. contorta*, *P. virginiana*
      Subsection *Australes* (Eastern USA, Caribbean, Central America):
        P. caribaea, *P. cubensis*, *P. echinata*, *P. elliotii*, *P. glabra*, *P. occidentalis*, *P. palustris*,
        P. pungens, *P. rigida*, *P. serotina*, *P. taeda*
      Subsection *Ponderosae* (Western North America to Central America):
        P. cooperi, *P. coulteri*, *P. devoniana*, *P. donnell-smithii*, *P. douglasiana*,
        P. durangensis, *P. engelmannii*, *P. hartwegii*, *P. jeffreyi*, *P. maximinoi*,
        P. montezumae, *P. nubicola*, *P. ponderosa*, *P. psudostrobus*, *P. sabiniana*,
        P. torreyana, *P. washoensis*
      Subsection *Attenuatae* (Western USA, adjacent to Mexico):
        P. attenuata, *P. muricata*, *P. radiata*
      Subsection Oocarpae (Mexico, Central America):
        P. greggii, *P. herrerae*, *P. jaliscana*, *P. lawsonii*, *P. oocarpa*, *P. patula*,
        P. praetermissa, *P. pringlei*, *P. tecunumanii*, *P. teocote*
      Subsection *Leiophyllae* (Mexico and southwestern USA):
        P. leiophylla, *P. lumholtzii*
  Subgenus *Strobus*
    Section *Parrya*
      Subsection *Balfourianae* (Western USA):
        P. aristata, *P. balfouriana*, *P. longaeva*
      Subsection *Cembroides* (Southwestern USA, Mexico):
        P. cembroides, *P. culminicola*, *P. discolor*, *P. edulis*, *P. johannis*,
        P. maximartinezii, *P. monophylla*, *P. pinceana*, *P. quadrifolia*, *P. remota*, *P. rzedowskii*
      Subsection *Nelsoniae* (Mexico):
        P. nelsonii
    Section *Strobus*
      Subsection *Gerardianae* (East Asia, Himalayas):
        P. bungeana, *P. gerardiana*, *P. squamata*
      Subsection *Kremfianae*
        P. krempfii
      Subsection *Quinquefolius* (North and central America, southeast Europe, Asia):
        P. albicaulis, *P. armandii*, *P. ayachuite*, *P. bhutanica*, *P. cembra*,
        P. chiapensis, *P. dabeshanensis*, *P. dalatensis*, *P. fenzeliana*, *P. flexilis*,
        P. koraiensis, *P. lambertiana*, *P. monticola*, *P. morrisonicola*, *P. parviflora*,
        P. peuce, *P. pumila*, *P. sibirica*, *P. strobus*, *P. wallichiana*, *P. wangii*

the population level under a wide range of disturbance regimes.

Morphological Traits of Pines

Pines, like many other conifers, typically have a main trunk which can grow to a large size. The largest species of pines in the world are found in California and the Pacific Northwest of the USA. Growth conditions in these regions favor immense size in many conifer genera, including *Abies*, *Picea*, *Pseudotsuga*, *Thuja*, *Tsuga*, *Sequoia*, and *Sequoiadendron*. The largest species of pine in both height and girth is *Pinus lambertiana* which reaches over 75 m in height and more than 5 m in diameter in the Sierra Nevada of California. Three other pines from the western USA, *P. jeffreyi*, *P. monticola*, and *P. ponderosa*, all reach heights of 60 m or more.

Pines can, however, be quite short in stature in more extreme habitats. The pinyon pines usually attain heights of no more than 5–10 m when mature. Timberline pines also may be low growing, particularly when they occur as multistemmed krummholz shrubs at the upper limits of tree distribution. Most of these timberline species have the genetic potential for taller growth, and may reach 10–20 m in height under more favorable conditions.

Many pines are very long-lived, and the two bristlecone pines, *Pinus aristata* and *P. longaeva*, are the oldest living organisms in the world, with the latter reaching documented ages of nearly 5000 years. *Pinus albicaulis*, *P. balfouriana*, and *P. flexilis* may live for more than 2000 years, while others such as *P. jeffreyi*, *P. monticola*, and *P. ponderosa* can reach ages beyond 1000 years. All of these are montane or timberline species from western North America.

Because of their great ages, pines have played a fundamental role in the development of the modern science of dendrochronology, beginning with the pioneering work of Andrew Douglas in the American Southwest. Douglas developed the concept of cross-dating to compare and extend tree ring measures over broad regional areas to identify year-to-year variation in climate. It was this research that led to the establishment of the Laboratory of Tree Ring Research at the University of Arizona in 1906. Collaborative work with anthropologists soon led to what were then revolutionary approaches to dating the construction of Indian dwellings in Chaco Canyon and Mesa Verde in the Southwest. These studies allowed the earliest measurement and linkages of floating chronologies to develop long-term records over more than 2000 years, and had profound impacts in the field of anthropology.

The field of dendrochronology has expanded greatly in scope and depth in recent decades. Chronologies of living *P. longaeva* tied to floating records in logs show promise of developing a 10 000-year record across the Holocene. Tree ring chronologies are also proving to be valuable records of alteration of typical forest growth regimes resulting from fires and from atmospheric pollution or other causes.

Although all pines share the defining morphological trait of possessing pine needles, there is a wide variation in the size and manner of needle display. Needles are arranged in bundles (generally termed fascicles or needle clusters), with the number of needles per fascicle being a reasonably constant and species-specific characteristic in many taxa. Most pine species have two, three, or five needles per fascicle, but other numbers are also present. Only one species has one needle per fascicle: *P. monophylla*, the singleleaf pinyon of the southwestern USA. At the other extreme, four species of typically five-needled Mexican pines (*P. cooperi*, *P. donnell-smithii*, *P. durangensis*, and *P. pseudostrobus*) frequently have six needles per fascicle, and sometimes up to eight.

Needle number does not have any established ecological correlation. Adaptive radiation within specific subsections of the genus *Pinus* has taken place, both with and without modifications of needle number per fascicle. For example, almost all of the 24 Old World pines of the subsections *Pinus* and *Pinaster* have two needles per fascicle (**Table 2**) – this despite the wide range of habitats occupied by taxa in this group (e.g., *P. resinosa* and *P. sylvestris* in boreal-type forest; *P. nigra* and *P. pinaster* in lower-elevation sites in the Mediterranean Basin; *P. heldreichii*, *P. mugo*, and *P. uncinata* at high-elevation sites in the Mediterranean Basin; *P. kesiya* and *P. merkusii* in tropical savannas; and a set of eastern Asian species that occupy a wide range of habitats). The white pines occupying varied montane and subalpine habitats all typically have five needles per fascicle. At the other extreme are the pinyon species of North America which include taxa with one to five needles per fascicle, despite the arid environments in which all these species occur.

The length and form of pine needles varies greatly among pine species. The longest needles of any pine species are those of the appropriately named longleaf pine, *P. palustris*, in the southeastern USA (up to 45 cm), and *P. nubicola* in Mexico which also reach lengths of over 40 cm. At the other extreme are many pines with very short needles in the 2–8 cm range of maximum lengths. These short-needled species are almost entirely confined to the arid-adapted pinyon pines, high-elevation, or timberline pines, and pines on low nutrient sites, suggesting a relationship with environmental stress.

There are other interesting needle traits in pines that have not been studied to assess ecological significance. Several Mexican pine species have drooping, or 'weeping', needles that hang downward, and there are intermediate morphologies in other species with relatively flexible needles. Such long, fine needles may aid the condensation and drip of fog moisture in tropical mountain areas or in coastal fog zones, as with *P. lumholtzii*, *P. nubicola* and *P. patula* in Mexico, *P. radiata* on Cedros Island and the coast of California, and *P. canariensis* in the Canary Islands. Such hypotheses remain conjectural, however. Another unusual needle morphology in pine is that of flattened needles which are characteristic of the rare *P. krempfii* from the central highlands of Vietnam.

One strong environmental correlate of needle traits in pines does exist. Needle longevity is strongly correlated with habitat water availability and nutrient relations and/or stress. Tropical pines such as *P. caribaea* and the southern USA species *P. palustris* keep needles for no more than 2–3 years, and the Indian species *P. roxburghii* usually sheds its needles every year. Temperate forest pines commonly retain their needles for intermediate periods of 4–6 years. Pinyon pine leaves have relatively greater longevities of up to 10 years. Subalpine pines such as *P. longaeva* retain their leaves for up to 30 years or more, and even 45 years in extreme circumstances at the timberline in the White Mountains of California. This is the greatest needle longevity recorded for any conifer.

The form and morphology of pine cones is highly variable, with obvious relationships to the reproductive biology of individual species. The greatest length of cone in any pine occurs in *P. lambertiana*, where cones reach up to 50 cm in length. In terms of fresh cone weight, *P. coulteri* from California holds the record, with large globular cones 20–35 cm in diameter weighing as much as 2.3 kg. Large cones are also present in the Mexican taxa *P. ayacahuite*, *P. devoniana*, and *P. maximartinezii*. About one-third of pine species typically bear cones that are less than 5 cm long. As a broad generalization, it appears that taxa associated with stressful environments have smaller cones. *Pinus* is far more diverse in the morphology of its seeds than all other Pinaceae combined, a fact that certainly contributes to the wide range of habitats in which pines flourish. While most pines have wind-dispersed seed, the pinyon pines and many subalpine pines have large seeds dispersed by birds. It is intuitive to expect the largest seeds in species with the largest cones, but correlations between cone size and seed size is poor.

Ecophysiological Traits of Pines

Coniferous forest trees characteristically utilize a very different strategy of canopy carbon gain than do hardwood trees. Compared to deciduous hardwoods, conifers generally show a relatively low level of carbon gain per unit of leaf area, but a far higher leaf area index (LAI). Needles are retained for several to many years, and a clustered arrangement of foliage and regular canopy architecture has evolved to allow maximum irradiance of older foliage. Thus, the net primary productivity of conifer forests with high LAI is typically as great or greater than that of deciduous hardwood forests in the same climatic regime despite the lower photosynthetic rates. However, most conifers are inherently slow in becoming established in successional sequences where environmental stress is not extreme because it takes them multiple years to attain a full canopy. Under these conditions, deciduous hardwood saplings which can attain a full canopy in a single year are much more competitive.

Pines differ from the typical conifer strategy in several respects. Typical ranges of LAI in field populations of pines are only 2–4 m^2 m^{-2}, compared with values of 9–11 m^2 m^{-2} in the more shade-tolerant genera *Abies*, *Picea*, and *Pseudotsuga*. The low LAI in pines largely results from the fact that many species carry relatively few years of needles compared to other conifers. Except in pines characteristic of environments of extreme cold or drought stress, 2–5 years of needles in the canopy at any time is typical. Thus, despite their relatively low LAI, pines are inherently more effective colonizers than many other conifers because they can attain a full canopy of foliage more rapidly early in succession. Many pines, however, can be selected for a higher LAI under plantation conditions where resources are not limiting. Highly productive plantations of commercial pine species such as *P. radiata* owe much of their productivity to LAIs two or three times those found under natural conditions.

It is interesting to speculate on the potential similarities of the rapid growth and colonizing abilities of many pines and the traits of early successional hardwood trees. The relatively low LAI of pines and their generally poor shade-tolerance are shared by such hardwoods as temperate *Eucalyptus* and many tropical pioneer trees. Shade-tolerant conifers such as *Abies*, *Picea*, *Pseudotsuga*, and *Sequoia* not only have high LAIs, but share a typical architectural form characterized by growth cycles that produce regular whorls of branches at levels determined by the height of the trunk meristem. In contrast to this pattern, most pines and many tropical colonizers (e.g., *Cecropia*, *Macaranga*, and *Musanga* spp.) are shade-intolerant and possess a canopy architecture with the cyclical addition of tiers of branches which are structurally identical to the trunk.

Considering the wide range of ecological habitats in which pines occur, it is noteworthy that there is relatively little variation in their photosynthetic characteristics. Maximum rates of photosynthetic capacity under field conditions within ecologically plastic species such as *P. contorta* and *P. sylvestris* appear to vary as much as within pines as a group. When grown under common garden conditions under nonlimiting conditions, pines from very different environments exhibit quite similar photosynthetic responses to irradiance, suggesting a considerable degree of phenotypic plasticity. This is equally true both for ecotypes of the same species and different species. Thus, variation in net primary production rates of pines in different environments is less a function of differences in photosynthetic capacity than of climatic factors of cold or drought that limit the period of positive net carbon gain throughout the year.

Seasonal patterns of low temperatures in autumn and winter are clearly important components of the potential net primary production of pine species. Thus pines in cold-temperate environments or timberline habitats have high levels of positive canopy photosynthesis limited to relatively few months of the year. Subtropical and tropical species grow throughout the year, with light, LAI, and nutrient availability as the primary factors controlling net primary production. Although pine species may tolerate habitats over a wide range of annual precipitation, the response of individual species to limited water availability is surprisingly consistent, as with almost all conifers. Net photosynthesis in pines typically falls to zero at relatively modest tissue water stress, thereby limiting the growth potential of pines in semi-arid environments.

Other aspects of the ecophysiology of pines show highly adapted traits between species that adapt them to specific climatic or environmental conditions. As logic would suggest, pines of cold habitats commonly have much lower temperature optima for photosynthesis than do species of warm climates. A stomatal response to environmental water vapour deficit is another trait showing adaptive selection. Species of semi-arid environments are highly sensitive to small changes in vapor pressure, thereby regulating summer water loss, while subtropical species are quite insensitive to such changes. Clear differences in tolerance of low nutrient conditions are also apparent in pine species whose ranges overlap.

Human Impacts on Pines and Pine Forests

Human-induced changes to pine forests have had significant impacts on the structure, dynamics, and biodiversity of these ecosystems for centuries. The consequences of human activities likely extend back thousands of years in the Mediterranean Basin where marked changes in human population numbers and far-reaching changes in land use practices have exerted major influences. Human impacts have come from logging and deforestation, land use practices that increase or decrease natural frequencies of fire, grazing, and plantation establishment outside of normal species ranges.

There is a massive literature on the history, policies, politics, and practices of logging in different parts of the range of pines. Logging takes place in natural pine forests around the world for construction-grade lumber, with varying levels of sustainability. Additionally, the need for fuelwood in many

parts of the natural range of pines in the developing world still accounts for a large part of the total area of pine forest cleared every year. While pines are important lumber sources, logging of hardwood forests has often led to a stimulation of pine establishment and dominance. For example, past clearing of broadleaved forests in the southeastern USA and areas of Asia has created suitable conditions for pines. Human-induced changes to natural fire regimes have had a particularly dramatic effect on pine ecosystems. This impact has been seen most strongly where human activities have led to increased fire frequency. In Central America, Mexico, and Southeast Asia this has often arisen through the agency of slash-and-burn agriculture. However, the opposite condition of reduced fire frequencies has also been widespread and has affected pine establishment. Heavy grazing of rangelands has reduced fire frequency in many parts of the American West by reducing fuel loads, and this has had a major impact on vegetation dynamics. Fire exclusion has allowed pines to spread into some areas where the natural fire regime excluded them, and has changed the forest composition in areas where the natural fire regime allowed pines to grow, but where changed fire characteristics have altered processes affecting vegetation dynamics. Some impacts of fire suppression in pine forests through the disruption of the relationships between pines, fire, pathogens and insects are complex.

Changes in grazing pressure have triggered changes in pine distribution in many regions, but the phenomenon has been best studied in North America. Grazing facilitates pine establishment in abandoned fields by reducing the cover of vigorous grasses and thus competition with pine seedlings. Areas subjected to heavy grazing often remain susceptible to colonization by pines long after grazing pressure has been greatly reduced or eliminated. Such effects have been documented for pine forests adjoining mesic subalpine meadows and mixed grass and brush in more arid regions.

Humans have harvested pines and their products for thousands of years. There are 29 pine species whose seeds are harvested for human consumption. In some societies, pine seeds harvested from natural forests are still important economic resources, as in Pakistan, India, China, and Mexico.

Pines have been widely planted in the Mediterranean Basin since prehistoric times, and more recently throughout the world. Some pines have proved highly successful for use in plantations outside their natural ranges where there is a shortage of coniferous species to produce fibers and solid wood products. This is particularly true of temperate areas in the southern hemisphere where there are massive plantations of *Pinus radiata* and other pine species. Reasons for the widespread use of pines in exotic forestry plantations include their simple design with straight trunks and geometrical branching habitat that makes them ideal for timber production. Moreover, pines grow faster than many other potential species, are easy to manage in plantations, have easily collected seeds, and are ideally suited for planting in marginal forest lands where most plantations are desired. Many pine species – *P. caribaea*, *P. elliottii*, *P. kesiya*, *P. oocarpa*, *P. patula*, *P. radiata* and *P. taeda* – are widely grown in plantations in the tropics and subtropics.

Threats to Pine Species

One-third of all pine species are either threatened in their entirety, or have subspecies or varieties that are threatened. This includes species with naturally restricted ranges and small population sizes as well as others that owe their threatened status to human activities. Even among pine taxa that occupy large ranges, large portions of their genetic diversity have been lost; this may have reduced their ability to respond to changing environmental conditions.

See also: **Biodiversity**: Biodiversity in Forests. **Ecology**: Plant-Animal Interactions in Forest Ecosystems. **Environment**: Environmental Impacts. **Genetics and Genetic Resources**: Population, Conservation and Ecological Genetics. **Hydrology**: Hydrological Cycle. **Landscape and Planning**: Perceptions of Forest Landscapes. **Mensuration**: Tree-Ring Analysis. **Plantation Silviculture**: Forest Plantations. **Temperate and Mediterranean Forests**: Mediterranean Forest Ecosystems; Northern Coniferous Forests; Southern Coniferous Forests; Subalpine and Boreal Forests; Temperate Broadleaved Deciduous Forest. **Tree Breeding, Practices**: *Pinus Radiata* Genetics. **Tree Physiology**: Canopy Processes. **Tropical Ecosystems**: Tropical Pine Ecosystems and Genetic Resources.

Further Reading

Burns RM and Honkala BH (eds) (1990) *Silvics of North America*, vol. 1, *Conifers*, Agriculture Handbook no. 654. Washington, DC: US Department of Agriculture Forest Service.

Critchfield WB and Little EL (1966) *Geographic Distribution of Pines of the World*, US Department of Agriculture Forest Service Miscellaneous Publication no. 991. Washington, DC: US Department of Agriculture Forest Service.

Farjon A, Page CN, and Schellevis N (1993) A preliminary world list of threatened conifer taxa. *Biodiversity and Conservation* 2: 304–326.

Lanner RM (1981) *The Piñon Pine: A Natural and Cultural History*. Reno, NV: University of Nevada Press.

Lanner RM (1996) *Made for Each Other: A Symbiosis of Birds and Pines*. New York: Oxford University Press.

Millar CI (1993) Impact of the Eocene on the evolution of *Pinus* L. *Annals of the Missouri Botanical Garden* 80: 471–498.

Perry JP (1991) *The Pines of Mexico and Central America*. Portland, OR: Timber Press.

Richardson D (ed.) (1998) *Ecology and Biogeography of* Pinus. Cambridge, UK: Cambridge University Press.

Thirgood JV (1981) *Man and the Mediterranean Forest: A History of Resource Depletion*. London: Academic Press.

Van Pelt R (2001) *Forest Giants of the Pacific Coast*. Seattle, WA: University of Washington Press.

Poplars

B Stanton, GreenWood Resources, Clatskanie, OR, USA

Introduction

The genus *Populus* (family Salicaceae) comprises 29 diverse species found almost exclusively in forests of the northern hemisphere. Considered as a whole, *Populus* covers an impressive ecological amplitude from the tropics to the boreal forests. In China alone, an extraordinary number of species are found in the cold northeast, the arid northwest, and the subtropical Qinghai–Tibetan plateau. No less impressive is the close association between *Populus* forests and the development of humankind that has included their cultivation for shelterbelts, fuel, animal feed and forage, pulp, veneer, lumber, and more lately, engineered wood products. Moreover, this group of trees has lately assumed a vital ecological role in forestalling desertification in Asia and in restoring and maintaining many of the world's degraded rivers and floodplains (**Figure 1**). In the latter regard, conserving the genetic resources embodied in the natural stands of many *Populus* species is critically important. These genetic resources are also an indispensable foundation for many breeding programs that support ongoing *Populus* domestication efforts. As the global forest plantation industry becomes inexorably associated with high-yield plantations of the tropical and subtropical regions, such applied genetics programs will help to sustain *Populus* plantations as the only temperate-zone tree that can be managed for near-comparable yields.

This article is an overview of the genus *Populus* and its members, where they occur, examples of how

Figure 1 *Populus* frequently grows in riparian habitats that are also the base for much of society's agricultural and industrial sectors. The conservation of *Populus* stands in the riparian zone is an integral component of the restoration of such ecologically important habitats.

they have adapted to their environment, the particulars of their genetic recombination systems that allow for future adaptive changes, the needs inherent in their conservation, and the current genetic improvement strategies being used to domesticate *Populus* to meet the demands of a growing world population.

The *Populus* Genus

Populus is mainly found in the northern hemisphere's boreal and temperate forests but is also an inhabitant of the world's tropical and subtropical forests. The genus is divided into six sections. Three sections contain nearly all of the commercial species: section *Populus*, the aspens and white poplars (formerly known as section *Leuce*), section *Aigeiros*, the cottonwoods, and section *Tacamahaca*, the balsam poplars. Section *Populus* is distributed throughout North America, Europe, and Asia. Section *Aigeiros* is best known in North America and Europe, while section *Tacamahaca* has a North American and Asian distribution. Three less economically important sections (*Abaso*, *Leucoides*, and *Turanga*) have less extensive botanical ranges, but include species that greatly extend the class of sites occupied by *Populus* (**Table 1**).

Populus has a pioneering habit, colonizing sites after disturbances; fire and floods are often a prerequisite for good establishment. They are fairly unique among forest trees in their capacity for impressive reproduction by both sexual and asexual means. Very rapid growth rates during the juvenile phase are often exhibited. However, lifespans do not extend much beyond 100 years. In some cases, succession to ensuing seral stages may be postponed by fire or other disturbances; spruce budworm

Table 1 Sections and species of the genus *Populus* according to Eckenwalder (1996)

Section	Species
Abaso	P. mexicana
Aigeiros	P. deltoides
	P. fremontii
	P. nigra
Leucoides	P. glauca
	P. heterophylla
	P. lasiocarpa
Populus	P. adenopoda
	P. alba
	P. gamblei
	P. grandidentata
	P. guzmanantlensis
	P. monticola
	P. sieboldii
	P. simaroa
	P. tremula[a]
	P. tremuloides
Tacamahaca	P. angustifolia
	P. balsamifera
	P. ciliata
	P. laurifolia
	P. simonii
	P. suaveolens[b]
	P. szechuanica
	P. trichocarpa
	P. yunnanensis
Turanga	P. euphratica
	P. ilicifolia
	P. pruinosa

[a] *Populus. tremula* includes *P. davidiana*.
[b] *Populus suaveolens* includes *P. cathayna, P. korena, P. maximowiczii*.
Source: Eckenwalder JE (1996) Systematics and evolution of *Populus*. In: Stettler RF, Bradshaw HD Jr, Heilman PE, and Hinckley TM (eds) *Biology of Populus and its Implications for Management and Conservation*, pp. 7–32. Ottawa, Canada: NRC Research Press.

outbreaks in eastern Canada maintain the presence of *P. tremuloides*, preventing its replacement by *Abies* and *Picea*.

The species are deciduous in all but a few cases. Their growth habit is indeterminate with the production of neo-formed leaves occurring until growth cessation occurs, triggered in many species by diminishing day length. They are largely shade-intolerant, although there are noticeable differences within the genus ranging from the intolerant (*P. balsamifera, P. trichocarpa*) to the very intolerant (*P. tremuloides, P. deltoides*). The white wood is diffuse–porous with indistinct annual growth rings and comparatively soft and light quality.

The major sections of the genus can also be broadly characterized according to the general class of sites on which they are commonly found. Sections *Aigeiros* and *Tacamahaca* are prominently adapted to lowland riparian zones along major river systems with broad floodplains, but not exclusively; *P. balsamifera* (section *Tacamahaca*) and *P. deltoides* (section *Aigeiros*) have been found respectively, on grasslands and abandoned farm fields and *P. ciliata* (section *Tacamahaca*) is found at higher elevations in the Himalayan foothills. By comparison, the aspens of section *Populus* are more frequently found on drier, less fertile, upland and montane sites; *P. tremuloides* is found at elevations of 3000 m in western North America and *P. tremula* at 3300 m in Mongolia. *Populus euphratica* (section *Turanga*) is typically found in the arid, desertlike environments of Asia, often growing on saline soils, while *P. heterophylla* (section *Leucoides*) is well adapted to prolonged inundation in swamps along the southeastern seaboard of North America.

Botanical ranges in *Populus* typically cover exceedingly wide geographic areas. For example, in section *Populus*, the range of *P. tremuloides* spans approximately 110° of longitude and over 50° of latitude in North America. Even more outstanding is *P. tremula* which grows throughout Europe and Asia, from the Atlantic to the Pacific Oceans, ranging from 70° N latitude in Norway and the tundra in Russia, south to the Mediterranean basin. Similarly, *P. alba* is distributed throughout central and southern Europe and extends southward into Afghanistan, Iran, Iraq, and Syria. In section *Tacamahaca*, *P. balsamifera* has a transcontinental range covering much of Canada, Alaska, and the Great Lakes Region of the United States. *Populus trichocarpa* spans approximately 30° of latitude from southeastern Alaska south to Baja California. The Asian *Tacamahaca* species of widest distribution, *P. suaveolens*, is found from central Asia eastward to the Japanese islands. In section *Aigeiros*, *P. nigra* spans all of Europe, northwestern Africa, western Asia, the Caucasus, and western Siberia. *Populus deltoides* ranges from the Canadian prairie southward to the coast of the Gulf of Mexico and east to the Atlantic seaboard. *Populus euphratica* (section *Turanga*) occurs over an area from North Africa and the Mediterranean through central Asia and northwestern China.

Other species have more limited or disjunct ranges. *Populus ilicifolia* (section *Turanga*) is found growing along four rivers in Kenya between 1° N and 3° S latitudes. *Populus heterophylla* (section *Leucoides*) is endemic to the coastal plain of the southeastern USA and then further inland in the Mississippi and Ohio River valleys. Separate populations of the tropical species *P. mexicana* (section *Abaso*) are located along the Pacific and Gulf coasts of Mexico.

Adaptation

The genus *Populus* has successfully adapted to the world's climatic variations. This adaptation may be expressed in a differentiation among populations and its expression is critical to the ecological and evolutionary functioning of individual species and the genus as a whole. One example, adaptive variation in phenology, is of primary importance and is often associated with a population's geographic source. The association is keyed to environmental stimuli, including temperature, photoperiod, and precipitation. In species of the temperate and boreal forests, spring growth takes place only after sufficient winter chilling has occurred which allows a response to warming temperatures, while a reduction in day length towards the end of the growing season cues the process of winter dormancy. Similarly, above-freezing cold temperatures bring about leaf abscission. Populations of *P. balsamifera*, *P. deltoides*, *P. tremuloides*, and *P. trichocarpa* from different latitudes differ in the timing of these spring and autumnal events. Northern populations typically have a lower temperature threshold required for spring growth initiation than their more southerly counterparts. Northern populations also enter the dormant phase under the influence of a longer day length than southern sources of the same species. The synchronization of these growth cycles with the change of seasons has allowed *Populus* species to achieve their characteristically wide geographic distributions.

Other examples of adaptive population variation include:

1. *Populus trichocarpa* from coastal and inland regions of the North American Pacific Northwest are differentiated in their tolerance of winter temperatures. *Populus trichocarpa* populations sampled from contrasting elevations within the same river drainage are differentially adapted to growing season length.
2. *Populus deltoides* from the lower Mississippi River valley has greater chilling requirements for flowering than more northerly populations.
3. *Populus deltoides* populations in southwest North America exhibit differences in drought tolerance that are associated with local precipitation.
4. Differences in crown architecture of Italian *P. alba* populations are correlated with latitude, from which an adaptive strategy for light interception has been inferred.

Adaptations to temperature, photoperiod, light intensity, and precipitation are sufficiently precise that populations of the same species originating from contrasting environments can be differentiated in their response to these environmental cues when tested in a single locale. In nearly all cases, the pattern of adaptive variation in studies sampling populations from latitudinal ranges has been continuous, suggesting the existence of clines. Population differences notwithstanding, genetic systems are such that the larger source of variation in most studies has been found within populations among the individual members; appreciable gene flow between populations partially counters the effects of natural selection. This reservoir of variation allows populations to accommodate yearly variations in climate as well as long-term climatic changes that alter the future adaptive landscape (**Figure 2**).

Next to the importance of climatic adaptations, the resistance to foliar, shoot, and stem diseases also plays a major role in the adaptive strategies of *Populus*. The pathogens of most significant ecological and commercial impact include *Melampsora* leaf

Figure 2 The timing of spring growth initiation in *Populus trichocarpa* is of critical importance to the adaptation of populations to their environment. The adaptive strategy includes differences in the earliness with which individuals of a population initiate growth, perhaps in response to yearly variation in warming spring temperature patterns.

rust, *Marssonina* leaf spot, *Venturia* shoot blight, *Septoria* canker, *Hypoxylon* canker, *Dothiciza* canker, and *Xanthomonous* bacterial canker. Pathogenic variation encompasses a range in both virulence and aggressiveness. *Populus* genetic systems have coevolved mechanisms of resistance to both as their pathogens undergo mutation and sexual recombination.

Host–pathogen interactions of *Melampsora* leaf rust have been extensively studied in *Populus*. Resistance involves both major and minor gene systems. Qualitative resistance is expressed in the isolation of the infection by the host's hypersensitive response. If qualitative resistance is lacking and the infection moves throughout the leaf tissue, the rate at which the pathogen spreads and sporulates is controlled by the host's rate-limiting quantitative resistance mechanism. Pathogen interspecific hybridization has been observed and may progress to advanced generations with the formation of hybrid swarms potentially adding a new dimension to the range of variability and virulence; in *Melampsora* leaf rusts, there have been two occurrences of interspecific hybridization.

The strategy of disease adaptation in *Populus* is oftentimes tied to environmental conditions that determine selection pressure. *Populus trichocarpa* populations from mesic, low-elevation environments typically exhibit significantly higher overall levels of *Melampsora* resistance, compared with populations native to arid regions that lack rust populations that act as a force of natural selection to heighten host resistance levels. A similar pattern has been observed in *P. deltoides*; populations from the drier portion of the range show lower levels of rust resistance in comparison with populations sampled from more humid, wetter environments.

Recombination System

The *Populus* recombination system is efficient in both the creation of new phenotypes in succeeding generations to allow for adaptation to changing environments, and in preserving the standing adaptability of the parental generation. The recombination system is characterized by mostly dioecious species and is thus outcrossing. Staminate and pistillate flowers are grouped in unisexual inflorescences (hermaphroditism is rare but has been reported in sections *Aigeiros*, *Populus*, and *Tacamahaca*). Sex ratios are balanced in most cases, thereby maximizing the effective population breeding number (sex ratios may shift in favor of females on higher-quality sites). A higher proportion of recombinant progeny is promoted by outcrossing and a large effective breeding number. The following characteristics of *Populus* reproductive biology further promote open recombination (**Figure 3**):

1. Full reproductive maturity is achieved after 10–15 years, ensuring wide participation in the breeding population before individuals are eliminated by stand competition.
2. Periodicity seems to be an unknown in sections *Aigeiros* and *Tacamahaca* with fruiting occurring every year (production of sizable seed crops in section *Populus* occurs on 4- or 5-year intervals).
3. Pollination is anemophilous, achieving wide distribution of male gametes.
4. Each pistillate inflorescence may contain 30–40 flowers, each of which develops into a two- to four-carpelary capsule that can contain upwards of 30 ovules leading to impressive seed production by individual female trees.
5. Seeds are capable of long-distance transport by virtue of their small size and attached cotton fibers that facilitate movement by air and water. Germination is epigenous; stand establishment is prompt and fairly complete when seeds germinate on a moist mineral soil (dormancy is incomplete and stratification is not required).
6. The basic chromosome number of 19 is high in comparison to other dicotyledonous forest trees. Triploids are known in section *Populus* and probably occur in *Tacamahaca* although polyploidy is the exception rather than the rule throughout the genus. The relatively high basic number and the distinctiveness of a diploid chromosome set allows for a higher rate of recombinant gametes during reduction division.

7. The F_2 *P. trichocarpa* × *P. deltoides* generation typically displays large segregation variation for growth and phenology with a relatively high frequency of intermediate types as well as transgressive segregants. This may indicate a loose linkage system that furthers open recombination. Conversely, a physical clustering of genes controlling *Melampsora* leaf rust resistance may lead to an increase in parental phenotypes.

Vegetative reproduction is also highly developed in *Populus* which along with stabilizing selection counterbalances the open recombination system of *Populus* preserving the parent generation's refined adaptations. Clonal propagation from roots, stumps, and twigs commonly occurs. Extensive clonal stands of *P. tremuloides* have been established by suckering from root sprouts on upland sites. Similarly, grasslands have been colonized by *P. balsamifera* by suckering from roots of trees growing in surrounding forests. *Populus trichocarpa* reproduces clonally along riparian corridors by a process of cladoptosis. *Populus nigra* establishes along river courses by sprouting from limbs and stems buried in alluvium. Apomixis is also known to occur in the genus, although the frequency of apomictic offspring is probably low and does not significantly restrict the recombination system.

Introgression and the Recombination System

Introgression can alter the genetic composition of populations of the participating parental species. Although phenological barriers to the cross-pollination of distinct *Populus* species appear to be insubstantial in most instances, the reproduction of interspecific crosses usually functions at a lower level than their intraspecific counterparts owing to problems with either prezygotic (pollen–stigma interactions) or postzygotic (embryo abortion, low seed germination, seedling mortality) effects. Nevertheless, interspecific hybridization is known to occur in the wild between members of the same section. *Populus × canescens*, the hybrid offspring of *P. alba* and *P. tremula*, is widely distributed throughout Europe. *Populus grandidentata* hybridizes with *P. tremuloides* (*P. × smithii*) in the upper Midwest of North America. Furthermore, intersectional hybridization between *Aigeiros* and *Tacamahaca* has been observed; in California and Nevada, hybridization between *P. fremontii* and *P. trichocarpa* (*P. × parryi*) occurs, whilst *P. deltoides* reproduces with *P. trichocarpa* (*P. × generosa*) at the western limit of its range in Washington and Idaho where the two species come into contact. Hybrids of *P. deltoides* and *P. balsamifera* (*P. × jackii*) are found in Ontario and Alberta.

Figure 3 Whilst *Populus* is normally dioecious and outcrossing, departures occur in many species. Shown here is *Populus trichocarpa* cv. PS-53-97 bearing pistillate (center), staminate (upper) and two hermaphroditic inflorescences (left and right) along one long and one short shoot.

A quite large hybrid swarm involving *P. trichocarpa*, *P. balsamifera*, *P. angustifolia*, and *P. deltoides* is being studied along several rivers in southern Alberta.

Although interspecific hybrids have largely formed the foundation of commercial *Populus* plantations with vigorous growth rates and substantial disease and insect resistances, they are often less disease-resistant, less tolerant of herbaceous competition, and more palatable as herbivore browse when grown in the wild without benefit of cultivation, a phenomenon known as hybrid breakdown. But despite their reduced fitness, barriers to continuous backcrossing and introgression are not absolute. Persistent hybrid swarms are a force that opens the recombination system of the participating species, especially at the fringes of their ranges, where the pressure to adapt may be greatest. Natural hybrid zones are also of ecological significance to the degree that they foster an extensive diversity of associated plant and animal species.

Conservation

Sections *Aigeiros* and *Tacamahaca* are commonly found occupying floodplain and riparian habitats, at times growing in large contiguous, pure stands. The construction of dams, revetments, levees, and channelization projects along many of the world's rivers has reduced the frequency with which their banks are scoured and gravel bars created, both of which are essential to the establishment of a next generation of *Populus* stands. Construction of levees along the Mississippi River has eliminated much of the natural cycle of flooding and meandrous flow and, consequently, a noticeable decline in the regeneration of *P. deltoides*. The same can be said of many river systems in Europe and Asia.

The conservation of the genetic resource contained in riparian *Populus* species include *ex situ* preservation of wild *Populus* collections in cultivated arboretums. Some arboretums may incorporate a multiple population breeding system to direct and enhance within-species genetic variation. The European Forest Genetic Resources (EUFORGEN) Program to conserve *P. nigra* is perhaps the most advanced *ex situ* effort today with a collection of nearly 2800 clones from 19 countries. Similarly, an *ex situ* collection of *P. trichocarpa* from 100 stands has been assembled in the Pacific Northwest of the USA by GreenWood Resources in response to the loss of riparian forests along the Columbia and Willamette Rivers and their tributaries. Alternatively, *in situ* conservation efforts secure native *Populus* populations in large nature reserves and, in some cases, may include efforts to restore degraded habitats. A major *in situ* effort has been initiated in China's Xinjiang Autonomous Region with the establishment of the Tarim River nature reserve; a critical component is the conservation of *P. euphratica* riparian forests that have shrunk in area by nearly two-thirds.

Other conservation examples include a long-standing effort to preserve *P. nigra* in the Netherlands where it has been replaced *Populus* hybrid plantations. Similarly, the conservation of Italian *P. alba* populations has been proposed in view of the loss of native germplasm in the wake of expanding agriculture. Finally, the Indian government with support from the International Poplar Commission and the United Nations Development Program has surveyed *P. ciliata* populations in the Himalayan foothills as the first step in implementation of its conservation.

Relatively recent changes in air quality are now known to have impacted *Populus* genetic resources. A well-documented example is *P. tremuloides* in North America; populations sampled from regions with a history of chronic exposure to polluted air show significantly higher tolerances to ozone, as natural selection has eliminated sensitive individual phenotypes. The long-term effect of this narrowing of the *P. tremuloides* genetic resource is not known but no less an important concern. Natural selection and loss of diversity is likely to be occurring in polluted areas of Europe and Asia. Conservation efforts here are worthwhile to the extent that populations undergoing selection may also be losing potentially valuable alleles.

The Conservation Role of Commercial *Populus* Plantations

Production plantations established with highly selected interspecific hybrid varieties and intensive agronomic-style tending practices, are among the highest-yielding crop trees in the temperate zone. For example, growth rates of $21–33 \, m^3 \, ha^{-1}$ have been achieved at age 7 in *P. $\times$ generosa* plantations in the Pacific Northwest. High-yield plantations allow for the preservation of natural forested lands while meeting the fiber and fuel needs of a growing world population.

Beyond North American *P. $\times$ generosa* plantations, other worldwide plantations programs include cultivation of *P. $\times$ canadensis* (*P. deltoides $\times$ P. nigra*) in France's Loire River Valley and the Po Valley of Italy, *P. simonii $\times$ P. nigra* in northeastern China, *P. $\times$ tomentosa* (*P. alba $\times$ P. adenopoda*) in the northern plains of China, and *P. tremuloides $\times$ P. tremula* in western boreal Canada. Plantations of *P. deltoides* have been established in the southeastern USA, southern Brazil, Argentina, northern India, and southern China. These plantations are managed for a range of products including fuelwood, chips for paper, and logs for veneer and sawnwood products. Intercropping with soya, ryegrass, and corn during the first several years of a *Populus* rotation is practiced in agroforestry programs in China, India, and elsewhere where labor costs are low and arable land is scarce.

A reduction in soil erosion and an increase in water quality are often claimed as environmental benefits of *Populus* cultivation. *Populus* plantations have also been used extensively in various afforestation projects in India and China to address wood shortages while also slowing desertification. Over 1 million ha of *Populus* plantings were established during the 1970s as part of China's 'Green Great Wall' project to slow the spread of the northern deserts (**Figure 4**).

Their environmental benefit notwithstanding, the degree of gene flow between plantations of exotic species or interspecific hybrids and neighboring wild *Populus* populations is an important question in the context of native species conservation. Low levels of gene flow between *P. × generosa* plantations and native *P. trichocarpa* stands in the Pacific Northwest have been observed. The level of gene flow between *P. × canadensis* plantations and *P. nigra* stands in France may be higher, however.

Domestication

As high-yield plantations become ever more important in meeting the world demand for wood and fiber, novel genetic improvement strategies become

Figure 4 *Populus simonii × P. nigra* hybrid plantation Shanxi Province, China along the Inner Mongolian frontier. *Populus* stands are being used to reduce the severity of sandstorms and to contain the spread of China's northern deserts. Courtesy of Dave Austin.

an integral component of intensive plantation management practices. A unique combination of classical plant breeding methods and contemporary molecular approaches is used in *Populus*.

Classical *Populus* breeding strategies

Breeding and selection of *Populus* has a lengthy and distinguished history among trees, beginning with a large-scale commercial improvement program conducted in North America in the late 1920s. Successful breeding programs have since been initiated in Europe, Asia, and North America in many cases relying upon nonrecurrent, first-generation (F_1) interspecific hybridization. Hybridization brings the variation encompassed by separate species into a single generation that often exhibits heterosis for yield. Although controlled reproduction may be difficult when some species are hybridized, the ease with which superior individual selections can be vegetatively propagated promotes F_1 hybridization as a popular breeding method (**Table 2**). Advanced generation breeding into the second generation (F_2) is sometimes accompanied by diminished vigor most likely due to the disruption of coadapted linkage groups that occurs during F_1 gametogenesis or to a reduction in overdominant gene action, although transgressive segregants are occasionally found. Backcross breeding is used to introduce a single, highly heritable trait from a donor species to improve an otherwise suitable recurrent parent. For example, in the North Central region of the USA, *P. deltoides × P. suaveolens* F_1 hybrids are crossed (back) to unrelated *P. deltoides* selections in an attempt to introduce the strong adventitious rooting ability of *P. suaveolens* into the recurrent *P. deltoides* parent that shows superior resistance to *Septoria* canker (F_1 *P. deltoides × P. suaveolens* hybrids are themselves highly canker susceptible).

Given that the entire range of genetic variation can be exploited by clonal selection, a very significant advantage compared to other species that rely upon seedling-based family selection programs, *Populus* programs have frequently focused solely on the selection of superior individuals as opposed to efforts to improve the average performance of whole populations. A complete strategy incorporates recurrent breeding of parental populations so as to improve their hybridizing quality thereby more fully guaranteeing future genetic gains. The ideal is a reciprocal recurrent breeding program. But this has often proved too expensive to implement. Moreover, a lack of full reproductive compatibility between species can greatly complicate the estimation of parental hybrid breeding values required by a reciprocal recurrent

Table 2 Examples of applied *Populus* genetic improvement programs

Pedigree	Breeding centers
Populus alba × P. adenopoda	China[b]
Populus alba × P. alba	Italy[u]
Populus alba × P. deltoides	Spain[j]
Populus alba × P. grandidentata	Canada,[d] Serbia[f]
Populus alba × P. tremula	China,[c] Italy,[u] Korea[o]
Populus alba × P. euphratica	Iran[t]
Populus ciliata × P. deltoides	India[e]
Populus ciliata × P. suaveolens	India[e]
Populus ciliata × P. yunnanensis	India[e]
Populus deltoides × P. deltoides	Argentina,[k] Beligum,[m] Canada,[d] USA,[h,n,p,q] France[j]
Populus deltoides × P. balsamifera	Canada[d,r]
Populus deltoides × P. nigra	Belgium,[m] Canada,[d] France,[j] Italy,[l] Serbia,[f] USA[q]
Populus deltoides × P. suaveolens	Canada,[d,r] China,[c] USA[h,q]
Populus deltoides × P. trichocarpa	Belgium,[m] France,[j] USA[h,q]
Populus nigra × P. nigra	Belgium,[m] Italy[l,u]
Populus nigra × P. suaveolens	Canada,[d,r] China,[c] Korea[o]
Populus simonii × P. nigra	China[c,s]
Populus tremula × P. tremuloides	Canada,[a,d] Finland,[g] Serbia[f]
Populus tremuloides × P. tremuloides	Canada[d]

[a] Alberta-Pacific Forest Industries, Inc., Boyle, Alberta, Canada.
[b] Beijing Forestry University, Beijing, People's Republic of China.
[c] Datong Poplar Bureau, Jinshatan, People's Republic of China.
[d] Direction de la Recherche Forestière, Sainte-Foy, Québec.
[e] Dr. Y. S. Parmar University of Horticulture and Forestry, Solan, India.
[f] Faculty of Agriculture, Poplar Research Institute, Novi Sad, Serbia.
[g] Finnish Forest Research Institute, Vantaa, Finland.
[h] GreenWood Resources, Portland, OR, USA.
[i] Institut National de la Recherche Agronomique, Ardon, France.
[j] Instituto Nacional de Investigación y Tecnologia Agraria y Alimentaria, Madrid, Spain.
[k] Instituto Nacional de Tecnologia Agropecuaria, Buenos Aires, Argentina.
[l] Istituto di Sperimentazione per la Pioppicoltura, Casala Monferrato, Italy.
[m] Instituut voor Bosbouw en Wildbeheer, Geraardsbergen, Belgium.
[n] Iowa State University, Department of Forestry, Ames, IA, USA.
[o] Korea Forest Research Institute, Kyunggi-do, Korea.
[p] MeadWestvaco, Corporation, Wickliffe, KY, USA.
[q] Natural Resources Research Institute, University of Minnesota, Duluth, MN, USA.
[r] Prairie Farm Rehabilitation Administration, Indian Head, Saskatchewan, Canada.
[s] Poplar Research Institute of Liaoning Province, Gai, People's Republic of China.
[t] Research Institute of Forests and Rangelands, Tehran, Iran.
[u] Università della Tuscia, Viterbo, Italy.

breeding. Consequently, many *Populus* programs substitute intraspecific breeding values as a guide for the manner in which parental populations are refined for interspecific hybridization.

The traits targeted for *Populus* improvement are usually the agronomic ones of yield, stem form, pest resistance, tolerance of cold and drought, wind firmness, and adventitious rooting. All have exhibited pronounced rates of genetic variation and have responded well to clonal selection programs. Field evaluations typically involve a multistage process to sequentially refine large populations until a group of elite selections has been identified. Other selection criteria may include wood and fiber properties for the veneer and sawnwood industries and the calorific quality of biomass for the heat- and power-conversion industries.

An imperative for production programs that incorporate clonal stands is a diverse pool of operational selections to help minimize the risk of plantation failures due to unforeseen climatic and biotic events. Most plantation programs are therefore allied with an ongoing hybridization program that continuously feeds new selections into production use. Continuous turnover of the commercial pool of clones is a safeguard against catastrophic failures due to coevolution of associated pests.

Application of Molecular Tools to Tree Improvement

Populus, by virtue of its relatively small genome, ease of cloning, and use of interspecific hybridization, has emerged as the model species for the application of molecular tools (genomic mapping and genetic engineering) to more traditional tree improvement approaches. Genomic markers associated with quantitative trait loci could lead to new approaches to the evaluation of full-sib seedling populations for superior selections that normally would not be revealed until conventional field tests are conducted for a half rotation or longer. Genomics could eventually lead to map-based cloning of important genes that are then used in transformation projects. The Joint Poplar Genome project is scheduled to complete sequencing of the *Populus* genome by the end of 2003.

Genetic transformation methodologies are well developed in *Populus*. Transformation can improve existing varieties for desired traits that otherwise are unavailable to conventional hybridization programs using recombinant DNA. *Populus* varieties have been modified for herbicide resistance, altered lignin content, and leaf beetle resistance. Currently field trials of genetically modified varieties have been conducted in North America with *P. deltoides* and *P. trichocarpa × P. deltoides* hybrids. In Europe, more than 20 field trials have been established using genetically modified *P. tremula*, *P. tremuloides*, *P. deltoides*, and *P. alba* × *P. tremula* selected varieties. The use of genetically modified plants has raised concerns over the risk posed to the fitness or future adaptability of wild relatives with whom transgenic plantations might reproduce. Consequently, a major ongoing effort has been sterility transformation that would prevent completely the sexual reproduction of transgenic plantations.

See also: **Genetics and Genetic Resources**: Propagation Technology for Forest Trees. **Tree Breeding, Practices**: Breeding for Disease and Insect Resistance; Genetics and Improvement of Wood Properties. **Tree Breeding, Principles**: A Historical Overview of Forest Tree Improvement; Breeding Theory and Genetic Testing; Conifer Breeding Principles and Processes; Economic Returns from Tree Breeding; Forest Genetics and Tree Breeding; Current and Future Signposts.

Further Reading

Dickmann DI and Stuart KW (1983) *The Culture of Poplars in Eastern North America*. MI: East Lansing: Michigan State University Press.

Dickmann DI, Isebrands JG, Eckenwalder JE, and Richardson J (eds) (2001) *Poplar Culture in North America*. Ottawa, Canada: NRC Research Press.

Grant V (1975) Genetics of flowering plants. New York: Columbia University Press.

International Union of Forest Research Organizations (1995) *International Poplar Symposium*, abstracts. Seattle, WA: University of Washington.

International Union of Forest Research Organizations (1999) *International Poplar Symposium II*, abstracts. Orleans, France: INRA, Station d'Amélioration des Arbres Forestiers.

International Union of Forest Research Organizations (2002) *International Poplar Symposium III*, abstracts. Uppsala: Swedish University of Agricultural Sciences.

Isebrands JG and Richardson J (comps.) (2000) *21st Session of the International Poplar Commission (IPC-2000): Poplar and Willow Culture: Meeting the Needs of Society and the Environment*, 24–28 September 2000, Vancouver. Gen. Tech. Rep. no. NC-215. St. Paul, MN: US Department of Agriculture Forest Service, North Central Research Station.

Lefevre, F. (2001) Managing the dynamic conservation networks. In: Teissier du Cros, E. (ed.), *Forest Genetic Resources Management and Conservation: France as a Case Study*, pp. 23-27. Paris: Ministry of Agriculture and Fisheries, Bureau of Genetic Resources, Commission of Forest Genetic Resources.

Stettler RF, Bradshaw HD Jr, Heilman PE, and Hinckley TM (eds) *Biology of* Populus *and its Implications for Management and Conservation*. Ottawa, Canada: NRC Research Press.

Spruces, Firs and Larches

H Wolf, State Board for Forestry (Saxony), Pirna, Germany

Introduction

Together with the genera *Pinus* (subfamily Pinoideae), *Cathaya*, *Pseudotsuga* (subfamily Laricoideae), and *Cedrus*, *Keteleeria*, *Nothotsuga*, *Pseudolarix*, *Tsuga* (subfamily Abietoideae), the genera *Picea* (subfamily Piceoideae), *Abies* (subfamily Abietoideae), and *Larix* (subfamily Laricoideae) belong to the family Pinaceae. The subfamilies are distinguished by cone and seed characters like the existence of an umbo or the existence of resin vesicles on the seed.

Species of the genera *Picea* (spruce), *Abies* (fir), and *Larix* (larch) are exclusively distributed in the northern hemisphere from 22°N in the south to 73°N forming the polar borderline of trees. Several species of these genera cover wide areas in boreal Eurasia and North America. They contribute to a major extent to the northern coniferous forests which stretch from coast to coast across these latitudes and form the greatest expanses of continuous forests. Many species of these genera are also found in mountainous regions of the more temperate zones often forming the alpine tree border line.

Picea, *Abies*, and *Larix* species occur in a wide range of habitats with very different soil and climate conditions. They are associated with various tree species depending on certain site conditions but they can also be found in pure stands under extreme site conditions. Mainly reproducing sexually by wind pollination, vegetative reproduction is the dominant mode of propagation if sexual reproduction is limited due to climatic limitations.

The lifetime of *Picea*, *Abies*, and *Larix* species ranges variously from 150 to 900 years. Under favorable conditions they grow to tall trees often forming dense forests with considerable growing stocks. Among populations of most species genetic differences can be observed in various traits. Due to their wood characteristics, the timber of spruces, firs, and larches can be used for a wide variety of purposes and is therefore of high economical importance.

Spruces

The genus *Picea* (subfamily Piceoideae) is related most closely to the genus *Pinus* (subfamily Pinoideae), but differs significantly by, e.g., cone and seed characteristics, the absence of short shoots, or the period of cone maturing. *Picea* is a very uniform genus, showing no significant differences within the genus allowing the delineation of subgenera. The genus *Picea* includes 34 species of cone-bearing, tall evergreen trees with straight stems and regularly constructed crowns with columnar or pyramidal habit. The horizontally arranged and usually rather short branches are whorled. On young trees, the bark is rather thin, on old trees scaly. The buds are conical or ovate, resinous or without resin. The spirally arranged needles are either four-sided or flat on a short petiole which remains on the shoot after needle fall. Stomatal bands can be found on all four sides or in the case of flat needles on the lower surface.

Natural Distribution

Out of the 34 species of *Picea*, eight species occur naturally in North and Central America, and 26 species are distributed in Eurasia (**Table 1**). The greatest species diversity is found in China and the Himalayas often in single species stands.

Picea species are mainly distributed in the boreal and subboreal zones of the northern hemisphere as well as to a minor extent in the mountainous regions of the more southerly zones where *Picea* can be found up to the subalpine range forming the treeline (**Figure 1**). The species of the genus *Picea* can be divided in a northern and a southern group, the differences between the groups are important from the ecological and genetical point of view. *Picea* species of the northern group occur mainly in large, often overlapping natural distribution areas either from east to west only interrupted by the Atlantic Ocean and the Bering Sea like *Picea abies*, *P. glauca*, and *P. obovata* or from north to south like *P. engelmannii* (**Figure 1**). In contrast, the species of the southern group grow in small, often isolated natural occurrences, for example *P. omorika*.

The northern limit of distribution of *Picea* is reached at about 69° N in Norway (*P. abies*) and the Northwest Territory of Canada (*P. glauca*, *P. mariana*). In the south, *Picea* stands can be found up to 23° to 27° N at the eastern (*P. morrisonicola*) and up to 23° to 25° N at the western hemisphere (*P. chihuahuana*) (**Figure 1**). In warmer regions, the water supply is the limiting factor of distribution.

In the northern part of the distribution area, the vertical occurrence of *Picea* reaches from sea level in North America and Eurasia to 2250 m above sea level in the Central Alps (*P. abies*) and about 3700 m in the southern Rocky Mountains (*P. engelmannii*). In the southern part, *Picea* species with upright growth can be found in altitudes up to 4700 m in the

Table 1 The intragenetic classification and distribution of species of the genus *Picea*

Distribution	Botanical name	Common name
North America	P. breweriana	Brewer spruce
	P. chihuahuana	—
	P. engelmannii	Engelmann spruce
	P. glauca	White spruce
	P. mariana	Black spruce
	P. pungens	Blue spruce, Colorado spruce
	P. rubens	Red spruce
	P. sitchensis	Sitka spruce
Europe and Northern Asia	P. abies	Norway spruce
	P. obovata	Siberian spruce
	P. omorika	Serbian spruce
	P. orientalis	Oriental spruce
Central Asia and Himalayas	P. schrenkiana	Schrenk spruce
	P. smithiana	Himalayan spruce
	P. spinulosa	—
East Asia including islands	P. alcoquiana	Alcock spruce
	P. glehnii	Sakhalin spruce
	P. jezoensis	Hondo spruce, Yezo spruce
	P. koraiensis	—
	P. koyamae	Koyama spruce
	P. maximowiczii	—
	P. morrisonicola	—
	P. torano	Japanese spruce
Central China and South Asia	P. asperata	Chinese spruce
	P. aurantiaca	—
	P. brachytyla	—
	P. crassifolia	—
	P. farreri	—
	P. likiangensis	Purple spruce
	P. meyeri	—
	P. neoveitchii	—
	P. purpurea	—
	P. retroflexa	—
	P. wilsonii	—

Himalayas forming the most upper limit of closed forests in the world (*P. asperata*).

Climate and Soils

Picea species can withstand extremely cold temperatures down to $-60°C$. The amplitude of temperature varies from $-60°C$ to $35°C$. The mean annual precipitation ranges from 230 to 4000 mm with the maximum falling outside the vegetation period. The vegetation period ranges from 26 to 175 days, the shorter growing season in the north counterbalanced by longer periods of daylight and the ability of spruces to assimilate down to temperatures of -6 to $-7°C$.

Picea species are not very demanding of soil conditions with the exception of the water supply.

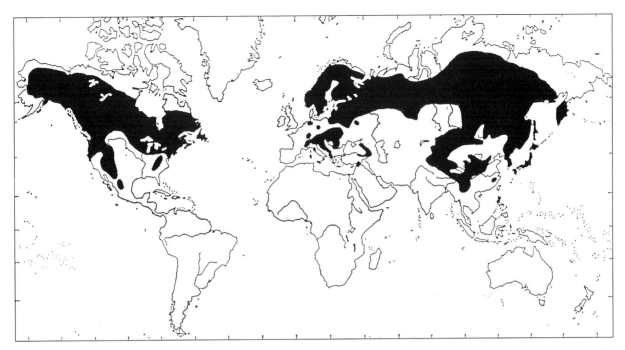

Figure 1 Natural distribution area of spruces (*Picea* spp.) Adapted with permission from Kruessmann G (1983) *Handbuch der Nadelgehoelze*. Berlin: Parey-Verlag.

In the northern part of the distribution area, *Picea* species occur on all soils showing the best growth on well-aerated, deep, acidic to slight alkaline soils with an intermediate nutrient supply and water supply over average. In the southern part, they are restricted to wet, cold or shallow soils of bogs.

Associated Forest Cover

Growing at extreme site conditions, *Picea* species can be found in pure, often uneven-aged stands. Under more favorable conditions, however, *Picea* species are associated with species of the genera *Abies*, *Chamaecyparis*, *Larix*, *Pinus*, *Pseudotsuga*, *Thuja*, and *Tsuga* as well as *Acer*, *Alnus*, *Betula*, *Populus*, *Prunus*, *Quercus*, and *Salix* in North America. In Eurasia, the species admixed to *Picea* belong to the genera *Abies*, *Juniperus*, *Larix*, *Pinus*, *Taxus*, *Thuja*, and *Tsuga* as well as *Betula*, *Fagus*, *Quercus*, *Populus*, and other deciduous broadleaved species.

Reproduction and Growth

Flowering starts between the age of 10–50 years. Male and female flowers are inserted in axils of needles of the previous year's shoots on different branches of the same tree, the female flowers inserted upright in the upper part of the crown. The flowering period varies from April to July. Peak flowering can be observed from every second year to every 13th year, in average from the third to the sixth year.

Pollination is by wind over long distances due to the light weight and the low falling speed of the pollen grains which contain air vesicles. The yellowish green, crimson, or purple-colored cones ripen in the same year turning color during ripening. A ripe cone consists of brownish, woody scales, each bearing two brown to black seeds at the base. The ovate seeds are winged and mainly dispersed by wind during autumn and winter. The empty cones do not disintegrate and remain on the trees for about 1 year. Germination capacity varies from 75% to 95%. The weight of spruce seeds shows a big variation and ranges from 60 000 (*Picea torano*) to 890 000 (*P. mariana*) cleaned seeds kg^{-1}.

Seeds of most *Picea* species show no dormancy and germinate promptly without stratification. However, seeds of some species may require light for germination but prechilling will usually overcome the light requirement. Under natural conditions, seeds germinate on almost any seedbeds including rotten wood, but survival may be low. The germination is most successful on a mineral or mixed mineral and organic soil seedbed, especially under light shade, as long as drainage is adequate and the soil provides sufficient nutrients. The germination is epigeal, the four to 15 cotyledons rising above the ground.

If sexual reproduction is limited or nonexistent due to climatic limitations at the arctic or alpine tree line, vegetative reproduction of *Picea* species by layering is apparently the dominant mode of propagation.

Roots are also known to produce shoots. Artificially, vegetative propagation is easily possible by rooting of softwood cuttings from juvenile material or grafting.

Similar to that of *Abies* and *Pseudotsuga*, the root growth of *Picea* species starts before the shoot growth. The development of the root system is generally influenced by the existing soil conditions of which the oxygen supply may play an important role. Growing at sites with unfavorable soil conditions (e.g., near surface water table, clay-containing or compacted soil), *Picea* species develop an extremely shallow lateral root system near to the surface. On deep, porous, and well-drained soils, the lateral root system penetrates the soil by layer roots to a depth of 2.5 m and more.

The average age of *Picea* species varies from 250 to 800 years (*P. sitchensis*). Under favorable conditions, the average height of mature trees ranges from 25 to 40 m, some species reaching heights between 50 and 60 m (*P. sitchensis*). The mean diameter at breast height (dbh) of mature spruces ranges from 50 to 150 cm. Under favorable conditions, *Picea* forests produce timber volumes between 190 and 690 m^3 ha^{-1}, and at exceptionally good sites between 870 and 1200 m^3 ha^{-1} (*P. abies, P. sitchensis*).

Species of the genus *Picea* have intermediate tolerance of shade, the tolerance decreasing with increasing age. Height growth is slow in the first few years but increases rapidly thereafter. When mixed with other species, *Picea* species can also survive and grow in the understory using occasional stand disturbances to rise up in the overstory.

Silviculture

Depending on the site conditions, even-aged as well as uneven-aged silvicultural systems are appropriate for the regeneration of *Picea* forests. The even-aged methods include clear-cutting and shelterwood cutting. Seed tree cuttings are not suitable for the regeneration of spruce due to its susceptibility to windthrow. Appropriate uneven-aged cutting methods are individual tree and group selection cuttings and their modifications. Thinning in young *Picea* stands enhances the growth of diameter and the crown development improving the stability of spruces.

In deep shade, lower branches soon die, decay, and break off, the resinous stubs remaining for many years. *Picea* species only exceptionally develop sprouts from adventitious buds along the stem related to light intensity, e.g., after thinning.

Pests and Diseases

Picea species are subject to damage from abiotic agents, pathogens, insects, and animals. Among abiotic agents windthrow is the most serious especially after initial or partial cuttings in old-growth stands. Species of the genus *Picea* are also sensitive to air pollution. However, most common diseases of spruces are caused by wood-rotting fungi resulting in loss of volume and predisposition of trees to windthrow and wind break. In pure stands, the mass propagation of bark beetles can cause serious damage. Due to their thin bark, *Picea* species can also be damaged by game animals that peel the bark.

Genetics

Compared to *Picea* species growing in the northern part of the distribution area, the species from the southern part show a greater systematic uniformity. Most of the *Picea* species of the northern part can be separated into geographical races or systematic varieties indicating genetic differences. The differences can be seen in phenological, morphological, quantitative, and qualitative characters as well as in resistance against pest and diseases influencing the suitability of the provenance in question for cultivation out of its natural distribution area. In North America and Asia, spontaneous hybridization between *Picea* species can be observed in common growing zones of the species in question. In Germany, the UK, and Scandinavia, *P. abies* and *P. sitchensis* in particular are the subjects of intense breeding programmes for commercial plantation forestry.

Uses

The strong, lightweight, light-colored, fine-grained, even-textured, and long-fibered wood makes most spruce species useful timber trees. The timber can be used as lumber, construction wood, rotary-cut veneer, furniture timber, posts, poles, and mine timber as well as plywood, pulpwood, and fuelwood. The high strength-to-weight ratio and the resonant qualities make the wood suitable for the construction of aircraft parts and musical instruments. Due to its wood qualities and yield, *Picea* is one of the most important commercial genus in the boreal forest. Several species like *P. abies, P. glauca, P. sitchensis,* or *P. omorika* are planted commercially outside their natural distribution area. Most *Picea* species are also important watershed protectors because of their occurrence at high elevations and on steep slopes.

Firs

Compared to the genus *Picea*, the genus *Abies* (subfamily Abietoideae) is a very heterogenous genus allowing the delineation of 10 sections with several subsections. The genus *Abies* includes 49 species of cone-bearing, tall evergreen trees with straight stems and regularly built-up crowns with pyramidal habit (**Table 2**). The horizontally arranged branches are distinctly whorled. On young trees, the bark is thin and smooth, often with resin blisters, in old trees often thick and fissured. The buds are usually resinous, globose, or ovate to fusiform. The linear–lanceolate, flat, singly borne needles are dark green above with two bluish or silvery-white stomatal bands on the lower surface. The needles which are widened like a shield at the base are inserted on long shoots usually in two ranks leaving a rounded scar after fall or removal.

Natural Distribution

Out of the 49 species of *Abies*, 15 species occur naturally in North and Central America, and 33 species are distributed in Eurasia (**Figure 2**). In contrast to *Picea* and *Larix*, one *Abies* species is found exclusively in northern Africa (**Table 2**). Similar to *Picea*, the greatest species diversity in *Abies* can be observed in China and the Himalayas.

Abies species occur from sea level to the timberline but the majority are found at middle to high elevations in mountainous areas. However, in North America as well as in North Asia, *Abies* species are found as components of boreal forests. Few species of the genus *Abies* grow as components of low-elevation, temperate forests. In North America, *Abies* species can be found from 64°30′ N in Yukon Territory, Canada (*Abies lasiocarpa*) to 14°49′ N in Central America (*A. guatemalensis*) and from 53° W in Newfoundland (*A. balsamea*) to 140° W parallel to the borderline between Alaska and Canada (*A. lasiocarpa*). The vertical distribution ranges from sea level to about 3600 m. In Eurasia and Africa, the distribution area extends from 67° 40′ N in the north (*A. sibirica*) to about 22° N in the south (*A. kawakamii*) and from 6° W in the west (*A. alba*) to 160° E in the east (*A. sachalinensis*). Vertically, firs grow at elevations from about 300 m to 4700 m in the Himalayas (*A. squamata*).

Climate and Soils

Since *Abies* species occur in very different regions of the northern hemisphere, the requirements of the climate also vary accordingly. The mean annual temperature ranges from −4°C to 11°C within the distribution area with an amplitude of temperature from −45°C to 41°C. The mean annual precipitation varies from 510 to 2540 mm with extremes between 390 and 6650 mm. In mountainous regions, between 50% and over 80% of the annual precipitation is snow and sleet. Snow packs between 3 and 12.7 m are

Table 2 The intragenetic classification and distribution of species of the genus *Abies*

Distribution	Botanical name	Common name
North America	A. amabilis	Pacific silver fir
	A. balsamea	Balsam fir
	A. bracteata	—
	A. concolor	White fir
	A. durangensis	—
	A. fraseri	Fraser fir
	A. grandis	Grand fir
	A. hickelii	—
	A. hidalgensis	—
	A. lasiocarpa	Subalpine fir
	A. magnifica	California red fir
	A. procera	Noble fir
	A. religiosa	—
	A. vejarii	—
Central America	A. guatemalensis	—
Europe and West Asia	A. alba	European silver fir
	A. borisii-regis	King Boris fir
	A. cephalonica	Greek fir
	A. cilicica	Cilician fir
	A. nebrodensis	Silician fir
	A. nordmanniana	Nordmann fir
Europe and North Africa	A. pinsapo	Spanish fir
North Africa	A. numidica	Algerian fir
Northern and Central Asia	A. sibirica	Siberian fir
Central Asia and Himalayas	A. densa	—
	A. pindrow	Pindrow fir
	A. spectabilis	Himalayan fir
Central China and South Asia	A. chengii	—
	A. chensiensis	—
	A. delavayi	—
	A. fabri	—
	A. fanjingshanensis	—
	A. fansipanensis	—
	A. fargesii	—
	A. forrestii	—
	A. recurvata	—
	A. squamata	—
	A. yuanbaoshanensis	—
	A. ziyuanensis	—
East Asia including islands	A. beshanzuensis	—
	A. firma	Japanese fir, Momi fir
	A. holophylla	Manchurian fir
	A. homolepis	Nikko fir
	A. kawakamii	—
	A. koreana	Korean fir
	A. mariesii	Maries fir, Shasta red fir
	A. nephrolepis	—
	A. sachalinensis	Sakhalin fir
	A. veitchii	Veitch fir, Veitch's silver fir

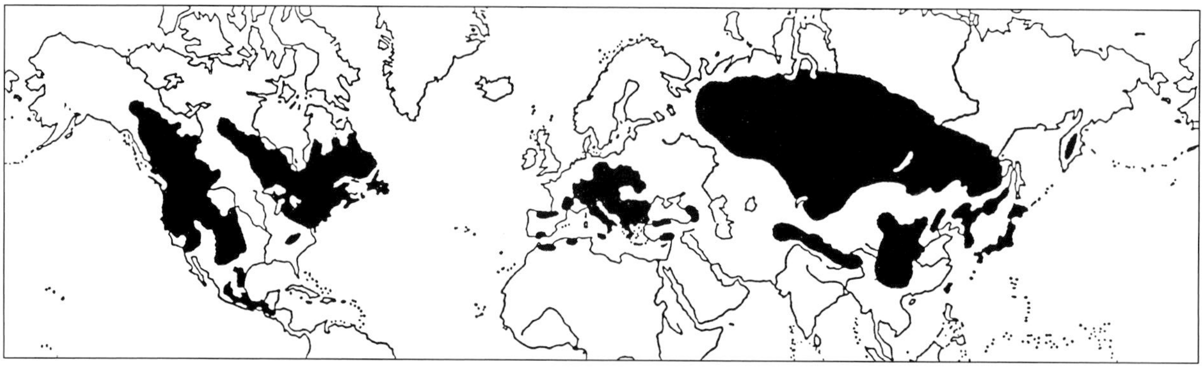

Figure 2 Natural distribution area of firs (*Abies* spp.) Adapted with permission from Kruessmann G (1983) *Handbuch der Nadelgehoelze*. Berlin: Parey-Verlag.

reported. The vegetation period ranges from 40 to 250 days, the shorter growing season in higher elevations being compensated by the ability of some fir species to assimilate down to a temperature of $-5°C$.

Due to its large distribution area with very different geological bedrocks, *Abies* species grow on a wide variety of soils developed from almost every kind of parent material. *Abies* species are tolerant of a wide range of soil conditions, nutrient content and availability as well as pH values. Species of the genus *Abies* are more dependent on moisture availability and temperature. However, the best growth of *Abies* species can be expected on deep, nutrient rich, fine to medium textured and well-drained soils.

Associated Forest Cover

Abies species seldom grow in pure, uneven-aged stands. Mainly, they can be found in mixed forests also under extreme site conditions. In North America, *Abies* species are associated more or less with the same species as *Picea* species. In Eurasia and Africa, the species mixed with *Abies* belong to the genera *Cedrus*, *Chamaecyparis*, *Juniperus*, *Larix*, *Picea*, *Pinus*, *Taxus*, *Thuja*, and *Tsuga* as well as *Acer*, *Betula*, *Fagus*, *Fraxinus*, *Quercus*, *Populus*, and other deciduous broadleaved species.

Reproduction and Growth

Flowering starts between the ages of 20 to 50 years. Male and female flowers occur separately on the same tree. The female flowers are typically inserted highly in the crown on the upper side of the previous year's shoot, the male flowers generally lower in the crown than female flowers densely along the undersides of 1-year-old twigs. The flowering period varies from April to July. Peak flowering can be observed from every second to every eighth year, on average from the second to the fourth year.

Pollination by wind takes place mostly among neighboring trees due to the heavy weight and the fast sinking speed of the pollen despite the existence of air vesicles. The red or greenish conspicuous cones ripen the first year; a ripe cone consists of brownish, woody scales, each bearing two winged and typically ovate to irregularly triangular seeds at the base. The seeds with conspicuous resin blisters are mainly dispersed by wind from August to November. In contrast to other conifers, the erect cones disintegrate leaving only the spikelike cone axis on the tree. Germination capacity varies from 25% to 70% but it is very often low, around 30%. The weight of the comparatively heavy fir seeds ranges from 10 000 (*Abies cilicica*) to 200 000 (*A. koreana*) cleaned seeds kg^{-1}.

Since *Abies* seeds are disseminated in autumn under conditions which may allow an early germination, the germination is hampered by resins stored in the seed coat. Under forest conditions the dormancy is broken by evaporation of the resins during the winter after seed fall. The germination is most successful on a warm seedbed with moist mineral soil. The germination is epigeal, the three to 14 well-differentiated cotyledons rising above the ground.

Under natural conditions, most *Abies* species do not reproduce vegetatively either by sprouting or layering. Layering can be observed in few species growing in extreme conditions of the more northern and mountainous regions, e.g., *A. balsamea* or *A. lasiocarpa*. Artificially, vegetative propagation is possible by grafting or rooting of cuttings from juvenile material.

The root systems of *Abies* vary from shallow and widespread where the effective soil depth is limited by rocks or seasonable water tables, through relatively deep lateral root systems under more favorable conditions, to a deep and intensive taproot system which also develops under less favorable soil conditions.

The average age of *Abies* species varies from 150 to 500 years, exceptionally to 700 years (*A. procera*). Under favorable conditions, the average height of mature trees ranges from 20 to 50 m, several species reaching heights between 60 and 90 m (e.g., *A. alba, A. amabilis, A. grandis, A. procera, A. spectabilis*). The mean dbh of mature *Abies* trees ranges from 30 to 300 cm (*A. spectabilis*). Due to their capacity to maintain a high level of stand density and due to the generally low taper of *Abies* trees, a considerable growing stock can be observed between 450 and 600 $m^3 ha^{-1}$ on average sites. Under favorable conditions, *Abies* forests produce timber volumes between 1000 and 1600 $m^3 ha^{-1}$ (e.g., *A. alba, A. amabilis, A. concolor, A. grandis, A. procera*), and in exceptional cases up to 2300 $m^3 ha^{-1}$ (*A. magnifica*).

Although *Abies* species grow well in full sunlight, most species can survive and grow for long periods in relatively dense shade and therefore they are classified as shade tolerant. However, some species are not too tolerant of shade especially if regeneration under a closed forest canopy is considered. Due to their shade tolerance over average compared to other tree species, *Abies* species can be found in mixed coniferous and conifer–broadleaved forests as well as in pure stands.

Silviculture

For most *Abies* species, uneven-aged silvicultural systems are the most appropriate way for regeneration. Appropriate uneven-aged cutting methods are individual tree and group selection cuttings and their modifications providing the necessary growth advantage several species need in front of competing species due to their slow growth in the juvenile stage.

Pests and Diseases

Abies species are subject to damage from abiotic agents, pathogens, insects, and animals. *Abies* species are very sensitive to air pollution. Due to their thin bark, *Abies* species are susceptible to severe damages and fire. Among pathogens, mistletoe causes major damage. In old-growth trees, wood rotting fungi cause major losses. Species of the genus *Abies* are also very sensitive to browsing and bark peeling by game.

Genetics

Several *Abies* species show a high self-fertility, up to 70% and more of sound seeds being produced by outcross pollination. Since the range in elevation and latitude is large in various *Abies* species and due to different evolutionary processes, differences among populations of several species can be observed in morphology, phenology, growth rate, monoterpenes, or isozyme patterns. In North America and Eurasia, spontaneous hybridization between *Abies* species is reported in common growing zones of the species in question. In the USA, selective breeding programs are practiced, particularly for the improvement of shape, size, and color of Christmas trees.

Uses

With the exception of the absence of primary resin canals, the characteristics and uses of fir wood are similar to them of spruce wood. Young trees of most *Abies* species are preferred Christmas trees. *Abies* species growing at high elevations and on steep slopes are also important for the protection of watersheds. Only few species of the genus *Abies* are planted commercially outside their natural distribution area, for example *A. grandis* or *A. nordmanniana*.

Larches

The genus *Larix* (subfamily Laricoideae) is the type genus of the subfamily mentioned before. The genus is divided into two groups separated by the position of the bracts (exserted or nonexserted). The genus *Larix* includes 11 species of cone-bearing, tall deciduous trees with straight stems and narrow, sometimes broad, mostly regularly built-up crowns. The horizontally arranged branches are not whorled. The bark is fissured, reddish-brown to gray-brown in color. The buds are small and ovate with a little number of short and imbricate scales. The soft and thin needles are inserted in bunches on short shoots and spirally on long shoots.

Natural Distribution

Out of the 11 species of the larches, three species occur naturally in North America, and eight species are distributed in Eurasia (**Table 3**). The conifer forests around the Arctic Circle are mainly formed by

Table 3 Intrageneric classification and distribution of species of the genus *Larix*

Distribution	Botanical name	Common name
North America	*L. laricina*	Tamarack
	L. lyallii	Alpine larch
	L. occidentalis	Western larch
Central Europe	*L. decidua*	European larch
North Eurasia	*L. czekanowskii*	—
	L. gmelinii	Dahurian larch
	L. sibirica	Siberian larch
China and Himalayas	*L. griffithii*	Sikkim larch
	L. mastersiana	—
	L. potaninii	Chinese larch
Japan	*L. kaempferi*	Japanese larch

Larix laricina, L. sibirica, and *L. gmelinii* with largely extended distribution areas. Other larches occur in the mountainous regions of more temperate latitudes, distributed in smaller and more scattered areas with extreme vertically extension.

In North America, species like *L. laricina* extend from 53° W in Newfoundland to 140° W parallel to the border of Alaska and Canada and from 40° N in the south to 67° N forming the northern treeline. The vertical distribution reaches from sea level to 1220 m above sea level in eastern North America (*L. laricina*) and from 180 to 3020 m (*L. lyallii*) in the west of North America.

In Eurasia, the distribution area of *Larix* species reaches from 68° N to 73° N (*L. gmelinii*), its northern limit forming the polar treeline. The southern limit can be found at about 22° N in the Himalayas and China (*L. griffithii, L. potaninii*). The west–east distribution reaches from 5° E in the western Alps (*L. decidua*) to about 170° E in East Siberia (*L. gmelinii*) (**Figure 3**). The vertical extent varies among the different parts of the natural distribution area. In Europe and North Asia, the genus ranges from the riverine lowlands of the north (*L. sibirica, L. gmelinii*) to elevations of 2400 m forming the alpine treeline in the western Alps (*L. decidua*) or in the Manchurian Mountains (*L. gmelinii*). *Larix* species grow in altitudes between 1000 and 2700 m on the island of Hondo in Japan (*L. kaempferi*), and they can be found between 2500 and 4000 m in the Himalayas and China (*L. griffithii, L. potaninii*).

Climate and Soils

Larix species can withstand extremely cold temperatures down to − 70°C as well as a large range of temperatures from − 70°C to 35°C. The mean annual precipitation varies from 180 to 2500 mm. In mountainous regions, about 75–80% of the annual precipitation is snow and sleet. The vegetation period ranges from 50 to 230 days, the shorter growing season in the north being counterbalanced by longer periods of daylight.

Species of the genus *Larix* can tolerate a wide range of soil conditions. Species forming the forests at the Arctic Circle grow most commonly on wet to moist organic, boggy, and acidic sites with a shallow layer of peat or soil over permafrost. The best growth of *Larix* species can be observed on moist and deep soils rich in nutrients with high water storage capacity.

Associated Forest Cover

Growing in extreme site conditions, species of the genus *Larix* can be found mainly in pure, often even-aged stands. Under more favorable conditions, however, *Larix* species are associated with species of the genera *Abies, Picea, Pinus, Pseudotsuga, Thuja,* and *Tsuga* as well as *Acer, Betula, Fraxinus, Populus,* and *Ulmus* in North America. In Eurasia, the species associated with larch belong to the genera *Abies, Picea,* and *Pinus* as well as *Betula, Fagus,* and *Populus*.

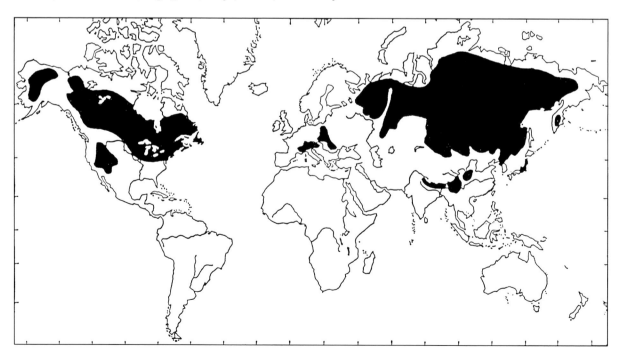

Figure 3 Natural distribution area of larches (*Larix* spp.) Adapted with permission from Kruessmann G (1983) *Handbuch der Nadelgehoelze*. Berlin: Parey-Verlag.

Reproduction and Growth

Flowering starts between the ages of 10 and 40 years. Male and female flowers occurring separately on the same tree open a few days before needle elongation or appear with the needles. The flowering period varies from March to June. Peak flowering can be observed from every year to every 10th year, on average from the third to the sixth year. Pollination by wind takes place mostly among neighboring trees due to the heavy weight and the fast falling speed of the pollen grains which lack air vesicles. The red or greenish cones ripen the first year; a ripe cone consists of brownish, woody scales, each bearing two seeds at the base. The winged and nearly triangular seeds are mainly dispersed by wind from September to spring. The empty cones do not disintegrate and remain on the trees for an indefinite period. Germination capacity varies from 15% to 50%. The small and lightweight *Larix* seeds range from 100 000 (*L. sibirica*) to 700 000 (*L. laricina*) cleaned seeds kg^{-1}.

With few exceptions internal seed dormancy ranges from none to mild. Under forest conditions any existing dormancy is broken during the winter after seed fall. The germination is most successful on a warm seedbed with moist mineral soil. Germination is epigeal, the five to seven cotyledons rising above the ground.

If sexual reproduction is limited or nonexistent due to climatic conditions along the northern limit of *Larix* species, e.g., in Canada and Alaska, layering is apparently the dominant mode of propagation. Roots are also known to produce shoots. Artificially, vegetative propagation is easily possible by rooting of softwood cuttings of juvenile material or grafting.

Species of the genus *Larix* have a very adaptable root system, coping with permafrost soil, rocky substrate, or deep and well-drained soils. Under favorable conditions, most *Larix* species develop a deep taproot with extensive and large lateral roots.

The average age of *Larix* species varies from 150 to 900 years (*L. occidentalis*). Under favorable conditions, the average height of mature trees ranges from 15 to 55 m, occasionally exceeding 60 m (*L. occidentalis*). The mean dbh of mature *Larix* trees ranges from 35 to 230 cm. In the most northern parts of the distribution area, a growing stock can be observed from 30 to 50 m^3 ha^{-1}. Under favorable conditions, larch forests produce timber volumes between 300 and 550 m^3 ha^{-1} (*L. occidentalis*).

Larix species are highly intolerant of shade. Compared to other conifers, most *Larix* species show rapid juvenile growth, giving larches the height advantage they need to survive. When mixed with other species, *Larix* must be in the overstory and they are practically never found in the understory.

Silviculture

The requirements of *Larix* forests are best met by even-aged silvicultural systems of shelterwoods, seed tree cuttings, and clear-cuts. Thinning in young *Larix* stands enhances the growth of diameter and height during the juvenile years when response potential is greatest.

Compared to other conifers, *Larix* trees are good self-pruners, and boles of 25–30-year-old trees may be clear of branches for one-half or two-thirds their length. Older *Larix* sometimes produce sprouts from adventitious buds after thinning, the amount of sprouting increasing with the severity of thinning.

In natural forest stands located in the boreal zone, fire is essential for the maintenance of *Larix* forests. Fires thin stands, reduce fuels, regenerate the undergrowth, and prepare seed beds.

Pests and Diseases

Larix species are more resistant than other conifers to air pollution, mechanical damage or soil compaction. Some species with thin bark have low resistance to surface fire. In mountainous areas, snow avalanches and snow slides can cause serious damages. Outside the natural distribution area, *Larix* trees are very often subject to damage from pathogens and insects.

Genetics

Within *Larix* species growing over a wide range of sites as well as within species with a distribution area divided into different parts, significant differences of traits can be observed among provenances. The traits include morphological, quantitative, and qualitative characters as well as resistance against pests and diseases, influencing the suitability of the provenance in question for cultivation out of the natural distribution area. In North America and Asia, spontaneous hybridization between *Larix* species is reported in common growing zones of the species in question. In Europe, hybrids between *L. decidua* and *L. kaempferi* are planted commercially providing exceptional growth and resistance to canker.

Uses

Larix timber consists of a narrow, bright yellow sapwood and a reddish-brown heartwood which is hard, heavy, durable, and tough as well as fungi and acid resistant. The timber can be used as lumber, construction wood, fine veneer, furniture timber, posts, poles, and mine timber as well as pulpwood and fuel wood. Several species including

L. decidua, L. kaempferi, L. laricina, and *L. sibirica* are planted commercially outside their natural distribution areas.

See also: **Silviculture**: Natural Stand Regeneration. **Temperate and Mediterranean Forests**: Northern Coniferous Forests.

Further Reading

Burns RM and Honkala BH (1990) *Silvics of North America*, vol. 1, *Conifers*. Washington, DC: US Department of Agriculture, Forest Department.

Earle CJ (2002) *Gymnosperm Database*. Bonn, Germany: Rheinische Friedrich-Wilhelms-University, Department of Botany. Available online at http://www.conifers.org.

Farjon A (1998) *World Checklist and Bibliography of Conifers*. Kew, UK: Royal Botanic Gardens.

Kruessmann G (1983) *Handbuch der Nadelgehoelze*. Berlin, Germany: Parey-Verlag.

Maydell HJ and Cejchan S (1994) *Forst- und Holzwirtschaft der gemeinschaft unabhaengiger Staaten—GUS (ehemals Sowjetunion)*, Teil 5, *Die Russische Foederation*. Hamburg, Germany: Wiedebusch-Verlag.

Schmidt-Vogt H (1986) *Die Fichte: Ein Handbuch in 2 Baenden*. Berlin, Germany: Parey-Verlag.

Schuett P, Schuck HJ, and Stimm B (1992) *Lexikon der Forstbotanik*. Landsberg/Lech, Germany: ecomed Publishers.

Young JA and Young CG (1992) *Seeds of Woody Plants in North America*. Portland, OR: Dioscorides Press.

Vidaković M (1991) *Conifers: Morphology and Variation*. Zagreb, Croatia: Grafički zavod Hrvatske.

Thinning *see* **Plantation Silviculture**: Forest plantations; Rotations; Stand Density and Stocking in Plantations; Tending; Thinning. **Silviculture**: Silvicultural Systems.

TREE BREEDING, PRACTICES

Contents
Biological Improvement of Wood Properties
Genetics and Improvement of Wood Properties
Breeding for Disease and Insect Resistance
Genetic Improvement of Eucalypts
Nitrogen-fixing Tree Improvement and Culture
Genetics of Oaks
***Pinus Radiata* Genetics**
Breeding and Genetic Resources of Scots Pine
Southern Pine Breeding and Genetic Resources
Tropical Hardwoods Breeding and Genetic Resources

Biological Improvement of Wood Properties

B Zobel, North Carolina State University, Raleigh, NC, USA

Introduction

The objective of this article is to discuss how wood can be changed either naturally or by manipulation and how these changes might affect the final product.

All wood characteristics are the result of physiological effects (controls) on growth. When the physiological controls are determined by genetic or other within-plant influences, they are referred as internal. These are difficult to manipulate and require activities such as breeding to obtain the desired kind of wood. When the physiological controls are primarily influenced by forces outside the tree, such as weather, nutrient availability or other, one refers to them as external controls.

A good example of a wood property strongly controlled internally is wood density or wood specific gravity. This makes possible the development of high or low wood density races of trees within a species, when selective breeding is used. When the wood of the tree is primarily influenced by outside factors such as weather or wind, external control is indicated. If, for example, a southern yellow pine has been affected by ice or tip moth so that it is no longer straight, the reaction wood resulting will differ a great deal from wood that will result under normal growth conditions no matter what the genetic situation is.

The control of wood formation is certainly not simple or clear-cut as a definition might imply. For example, tree straightness is the result of genetic control but is also affected by environmental factors. Thus, no matter what genetic controls are acting, major environmental differences can result in wood of differing kinds. However, the simplistic way to assess what the wood in a tree will be, is to consider the result of the interaction of both internal and external influences.

General Concepts

Wood is a very pliable and variable substance and can be changed in numerous ways as described below. In the past, when a lot of old, or virgin, timber was available, there was not much need, or effort, to change the wood quality available for use. As the practice of forestry has become more widespread and important, especially since plantation forests have become a major supplier of wood, it has been necessary to grow wood most suitable for given final products; this means methods must be developed to change wood qualities to meet the needs of the intended product.

I will use the southern pine forests in the USA and eucalypt plantations in Brazil as examples of the changes and needs to modify wood properties. Initially, almost all harvesting of softwoods in the southern USA was from quite mature pine trees, from 30 to 70 years of age. There was little concern about wood variation and wood quality as the wood harvested was mature and there was little concern about variation affecting its utilization. After more intensive forestry was practiced, wood quality has become variable enough to have a major effect on its utilization. Different products were found to require different kinds of wood to make the desired product efficiently. A personal example will illustrate this:

> In 1951, I gave a talk to the pulp mill managers and executives from the southern USA about wood, how it varied, and what this variation could mean to the industry. The audience was polite enough to listen but it was evident during the talk that the attendees did not think wood variation was a very important problem since they had good wood to work with which varied only a little. After my talk, the manager of the largest group of mills in the South came to the podium, put his arm around my shoulders and said: 'Son, your talk was interesting but we do not have to worry about wood variation. We are chemists; just grow us any kind of wood and we can make usable paper from it.'

Of course, in reality, this was true, but with the changes in wood from intensive forestry, it has become neither operationally nor economically correct. The differences in wood quality with shorter rotations (harvest age) and more intensive utilization of the trees available has resulted in a large proportion of juvenile wood being used. This, along with more intensive silviculture, has resulted in the costs, quality, and expected yields of the desired products changing. Because of this, the production of substandard products sometimes has been rather dramatic. Currently, wood quality has become recognized as of key importance for efficient production of the kind and quality of product to be produced. The properties of the wood used has become of major interest for pulp as well as for lumber, in both the conifers and hardwoods.

Although the emphasis here will be on wood quality and how it affects the final product, it is necessary not to underestimate the ability of the industry to alter methodologies to adapt to differing woods. Great progress has been made in this area; methods of sawing, methods of curing timber, particleboard construction, pulping technologies, and paper manufacture have all been altered to better use the younger, different-quality wood that is becoming available. Sometimes the changes have been reasonably efficient but too often they have resulted in increased costs and/or poorer-quality final products. The first need for an industry making a given product is to have the raw material it uses reasonably uniform. When this is so, it can develop the best methods of manufacture for a reliable and stable product.

It is necessary to note that the emphasis here is on solid wood and fiber production, used in construction and for paper products. However, there are other major uses for wood; reports are available that show that more than half the wood used on a world basis is for energy production. For example, until recently, a great proportion of the hardwood produced in Brazil was for charcoal, much being utilized for energy in the steel industry. (I worked for several steel companies in this area for a number of years, with the directive to develop wood most desirable for charcoal. This was done by changing species and selecting and breeding for fast-growing trees that had the genetic potential to produce the high-density wood best used for charcoal.) It has been well proven that the *Eucalyptus* wood ideal for tissue production differs greatly from that needed to make good charcoal. Because of the large basic variation in wood properties in the eucalypts, it has been possible to develop wood in the eucalypts most suitable for charcoal, or ideal for pulp, diverse as the needs for these products are. The details as to how such changes can be made will not be covered in this article (but see my books listed in the Further Reading section).

Important Wood Properties

Before one can consider changing wood, it is essential to know which properties are the most important. Although many wood properties can be altered, only a few are of key importance; five of these are listed below:

Wood Density

Wood density, or wood specific gravity, is by far the most important wood property, affecting nearly all products. Wood density and specific gravity measure the same thing – the solid wood substance in a given volume of wood – but they are expressed somewhat differently. (They are the ratio of the dry weight of wood in a given green volume of wood; this can be expressed as dry weight/green volume. The higher the ratio the denser the wood. In pine, a specific gravity of 0.41 is low density while one with a ratio of 0.62 is considered to be very high.) Wood density is normally the term used in the industrial area, while specific gravity is more commonly used by researchers. They can easily be determined from each other. They affect strength, stability, and appearance of solid wood products and grossly affect the kind and quality of paper produced. For example, low-density wood is best for quality paper products like writing papers and tissues, while high-density wood gives the best yields when pulped and is most suitable for fiberboard containers and paper that needs good tear strength.

Wood density is easily measured and can even be roughly estimated when looking at a piece of wood. It can be altered both through silvicultural and genetic manipulation.

Spiral Grain

Spiral grain is of primary importance for stability in solid wood products such as boards while it plays only a small role in its effect on pulp. Most spiral grain is found near the center of the tree; it varies from species to species and from individual to individual. Commonly, it is considered to be im-

portant if it exceeds 4 degrees, so is not important in some species with low spiral. Some species, especially in the tropics and sometimes in those like sweet gum (*Liquidambar styraciflua*) have an extreme spirality called interlocked grain. Such wood is extremely variable and not suited for solid wood products. However, there is a reasonable genetic component so a selection program will help.

Fibril Angle

Fibril angle (correctly called microfibrillar angle) is of increasing importance as its effects become better known and methods for its measurement are improved. The wall of a wood cell is not solid, it is made up of numerous microfibrills. The orientation of these in the wall is very important to the stability and quality of the products produced. Fibril angle is greatest near the tree center; it also varies greatly from tree to tree. It has a major effect on the stability of solid wood products and can have an influence on the quality of paper produced.

Wood Uniformity

Uniformity is of great concern to the manufacturer of wood products. The more uniform the wood, the better the product produced and the greater the efficiency in manufacture. As harvest periods for trees become shorter, a greater amount of juvenile wood is obtained, resulting in increased nonuniformity of the raw material available. Currently, there is much effort to change wood properties to obtain greater uniformity, and organizations that have been successful have benefited greatly economically.

Wood uniformity can be improved by controlling the time of harvest as well as growth conditions and silvicultural treatments such as fertilization and site preparation. We have found, in species such as loblolly pine (*Pinus taeda*), that a heavy nitrogen fertilization will usually result in low-density wood being formed for a few years but normally the use of phosphorus fertilizer has only a minor effect on wood density.

General Wood Properties

If space were available, one could list many other wood qualities that can be changed by external or internal means. Some of these can be of considerable importance under certain circumstances, such as the necessity for thin-walled cells and larger cell lumina in the manufacture of tissue papers or straight grain in quality boards. Other characteristics that may be of importance are cell length, resin content of the wood, amount of heartwood present, and numerous things depending on the product desired and the species of trees being used.

Methods of Making Changes in Wood

Wood can be altered in two major ways which will be described separately below: these are external and internal. The external one includes such things as altering tree form, differences in silviculture, and choosing the most desirable species and provenances within species. Internal changes can be obtained by controlling the amount and use of juvenile wood and through genetic manipulation and silvicultural control.

External Control of Wood Properties

Tree form is the most important tree characteristic that affects wood quality. Two major aspects of tree form are straightness of the bole and limb characteristics.

Straightness of bole   Straightness of the tree bole is most important. Any time a tree is not straight, it forms a kind of wood called reaction wood. One can reduce the amount and severity of reaction wood by growing straighter trees, either through silvicultural manipulation or control of parentage using a breeding program.

Reaction wood in most conifers is called compression wood. It is formed on the inside of a 'bend' in the trunk of the tree or in the underside of limbs. Its main function appears to be to straighten the tree or push up the limb by pressure on the nonstraight area.

Compression wood has many unique anatomical and chemical characteristics, most of which are adverse to good wood quality. For example, it contains an excess of lignin, often as much as 9% more than the more normal wood; this results in low cellulose yields when pulped. The cells in compression wood have fissures that cause the cell to fragment into small segments not good for the manufacture of paper. The cell walls of compression wood are often unusually thick, resulting in a coarse fiber which is not suitable when making fine papers or absorbing tissues and which result in a nonuniform surface of the paper.

The cells of compression wood have flat fibril angles so it shrinks an exceptional amount longitudinally when dried (up to 9% or more). This makes for unstable boards. Quality is especially adversely affected when a board consists partially of regular wood and partially of compression wood; the result is that one part of the board shrinks longitudinally more than another portion which causes warping, cracking, and checking in the board.

In the hardwoods, reaction wood is called tension wood. It is formed on the outside of the curve in the tree bole. Its function is to pull the tree bole straighter. Opposite to compression wood, tension wood has an excess of cellulose, otherwise the short cells and other abnormalities in compression wood such as adverse fibril angles, are present. (Since paper is made from cellulose, years ago some industrialists suggested that we breed crooked hardwoods which would increase the amount of cellulose and reduce the lignin formed. However, the cellulose in tension wood is different than that in normal wood and, when pulped, gives low yields and inferior paper qualities.)

When tension wood is used for solid wood products, the boards often have a weak plane in them (high cellulose and low lignin) causing the boards to break easily. Also, because of the flat fibril angle, it is difficult to finish the boards by planing or use of sanding, because the angle of the fibrils prevents formation of a smooth surface.

One of the most interesting things relative to the biology of wood in trees is how such opposite methods (compression wood and tension wood) have developed in the conifers and in the hardwoods, both to straighten the tree. The wood properties resulting from the two methods differ greatly. The amount of reaction wood can be reduced by producing straighter trees. This can be partially done through the use of selection and breeding straight trees since the genetic control of straightness is usually moderate to high. Natural variability in straightness is large so the combination of that plus moderately high heritability results in dramatic improvement in the population resulting from a breeding program which emphasizes tree straightness. (Put roughly, gain is the product of variability in the characteristic times its genetic control.)

Straightness can also be improved through the use of good forest management. Uniform and well-spaced, well-established plantations will result in straighter trees. As one example, if a pine tree is planted poorly so the stem of the seedling is not above the root, the resulting tree will grow crookedly, with an excess of compression wood, for the rest of its life. Planting using machines often creates serious problems when the foot of the planting machine is too shallow, resulting in the planted tree's having trailing roots. Trees from such plantations have excessive crook in their stems causing a major degrade in their wood quality. Based on my experience, the fastest and best method to improve wood quality is to develop straight trees. Frequently, detailed studies as to the cause of crookedness have been made, blaming such things as seed source, when the act of good planting would have avoided the trouble.

Limb Characteristics

Altering limb characteristics can have a major effect on the type of wood product produced. Smaller and more horizontal limbs are most suitable for the quality of both solidwood and the strength and yields of pulp. These characteristics are influenced both by the knotwood itself and by the reaction wood which is associated with the knots. Limb size can best be controlled via tree spacing in the plantation; genetic control of limb size is relatively small. However, limb angle has a much stronger genetic control, and can be improved by a breeding program. When excessively limby trees are used, limb size and angle has an effect on product quality, especially on the stability of boards and the tear strength of the paper produced. Changes in limb characteristics are not as easy to obtain or as large as for wood density, but they can be very important for certain products.

Forest Management Approaches

Variation in methods of forest management can result in differences in wood. All management activities must be done carefully if wood quality is to be as desired.

Silviculture

Silvicultural treatments that change nutrients via fertilization can have a major effect on wood properties. Especially in the conifers, but also for some hardwoods, heavy fertilization, using a high nitrogen content, often causes a considerable lowering in wood density. In the hard pines, the wood produced when a heavy nitrogen fertilization is used is somewhat similar to juvenile wood with thin cell walls resulting in lower wood density and usually in shorter cells. The response to nitrogen rarely continues for more than 5 years. As a result, there will be excessive longitudinal shrinkage in the affected annual rings of boards made from this kind of wood which will be unstable when dried. Although detailed studies on the effect of fertilization on fibril angle have not been made, I predict that the wood from heavily nitrogen-fertilized trees will have flatter fibril angles than normal, making the wood similar to juvenile wood.

Phosphorus content of the soil usually has little effect on wood density, although a shortage of phosphorus sometimes results in higher wood density. Here, the addition of this substance will reduce the higher density to that of normal wood.

Fertilization Fertilization, especially in the tropics, is often mandatory if suitable growth is to be obtained;

when this is so nitrogen fertilizer should be applied slowly in small quantities at each treatment, not in large amounts at one time during the midterm of the rotation. This is especially true in the pines; when a heavy application of nitrogen is made, the trees will form a band of wood in the tree trunk that is similar to juvenile wood, resulting in unsatisfactory lumber which is difficult to cure and stabilize.

Stand density A variation in normal stand density among trees will have little effect on wood other than the width of the annual rings; this can be very important for some products and species.

Species and provenance choice Matching species and provenance to site is of key importance. Normally, reasonably small site differences, or somewhat poor adaptability to the site, do not result in unusual wood but extreme site differences can result in wood so varied that it is not usable. For example, when *Pinus caribaea var. hondurensis* is grown in certain especially good environments the wood produced can be of very low density, making it undesirable for either solid wood products or pulp. The movement of slash pine (*Pinus elliottii*) to the same environment has resulted in very dense wood, with characteristics much like that of oak, making suitability for utilization very limited.

Pruning For most species, pruning is necessary if good solidwood products are desired, especially for conifers grown in the tropics. Under the environments there, limbs will hang on and not shed for many years and become almost like little steel rods; this results in degrade of the final product. Pruning is also usually necessary for quality tropical hardwoods but there are exceptions, like some of the best eucalypts, where the limbs die early and shed naturally. Caution is necessary when pruning; if done poorly leaving stubs, or if the bark is cut into the cambium when pruning, as almost always happens when machetes or axes are the tools used, pruning becomes adverse to quality. When the cambium is cut in the conifers, the result is pitch pockets and undesirable abnormal wood grain formation. In certain of the quality hardwoods, rot will occur which ruins the pruned log for quality products when harvested.

Pest Control

Both insects and diseases can cause major changes in wood properties. An example is fusiform rust on pine which results in a high resin content (double or more of the normal) and abnormally short, and sometimes forked, cell formation. Pulp yields from rust infected wood will be reduced as much as 50%; additionally, the wood will not be suitable for production of lumber. Eucalypt canker is similar to fusiform rust in that it affects both pulp yield and quality. Suitable boards cannot be sawn from the infected stem. Until brought under control genetically by the use of rooted cuttings from disease-free parents, the eucalypt canker had a major effect on the utility of wood from disease-sensitive species. There was considerable talk in the late 1970s of not growing eucalypts in parts of Brazil because of the high incidence of the canker and its effect on wood. It is important to control insect damage and disease in the tree trunks if normal wood quality is to be obtained. Additionally, supplemental nutrients, such as nitrogen, must be used carefully or there will be a degrade in wood quality.

Effectiveness of Forest Management

A good summary relative to the effect of forest management on wood is that anything that can cause growth differences in trees can also result in changes in wood properties. Such a reaction is especially obtained in the conifers, often less than for many hardwoods.

Internal Control of Wood Properties

There are two major causes affecting the internal wood properties of a tree. The first is the time of formation and location of the wood produced, generally subdivided as juvenile and mature wood. The second is the genetic and physiological control of the anatomy and morphology of the cells produced; these can be affected by breeding, as well as by some of the external controls outlined above.

Juvenile and Mature Wood

The quality and ratio of juvenile and mature wood are key to the determination of wood quality within the bole of the tree. All trees have a zone near the tree center (the pith) where there is a change, often rapid, in wood quality from the center of the tree outward. After a number of annual rings, the changes become smaller and more or less constant, sometimes with little change from ring to ring. This is mature wood; in juvenile wood, the variation is related to the number of rings from the pith, regardless of the height in the tree or the age of the tree. This results in a juvenile wood zone that has rapid changes followed by a mature wood zone with minor changes in wood properties, regardless of height in the tree. For example, a 30-year-old loblolly pine with 30 annual rings near the base of the tree will have about the first

10 rings from the pith as juvenile wood, the next 20 as mature wood. Therefore, a log from the base of the tree will consist largely of mature wood, while a log from the upper part of the tree is predominantly juvenile wood. Closer to the top of the same tree, where there might be only 12 annual rings; the first 10 will be juvenile wood with only the last 2 rings being mature wood. Although not strictly correct, the juvenile wood of a loblolly pine tree can be considered as being in a cylinder made up of the 10 rings from the pith. The wood qualities of this core will be essentially the same regardless of the height in the tree where they are measured. Differences in wood quality of each log is therefore dependent on the proportion of juvenile wood to mature wood. The age of the tree is not relevant to the presence of juvenile wood; it is determined at any height by the location of the cambium and by the number of rings from the pith, regardless of tree age.

Juvenile wood qualities vary from the pith outward. In the conifers the wood density becomes greater, the cell length increases, and spiral grain decreases and fibril angle decreases in wood produced from the older cambium as ring number becomes greater from the pith. Juvenile wood in most conifers has low density, short cells, a high spiral grain, and high fibril angle. Such wood gives low yields of pulp with weak tear strength. It is overall considered to be of poor quality related to strength and stability for boards when compared to the mature wood in the same tree. This pattern is usual for the hard pines and some diffuse porous (soft) hardwoods like sweetgum. Many of the hard hardwoods (like oak (*Quercus* spp.) and hickory (*Carya* spp.)) have a different pattern with high wood density near the tree center but with other wood properties that follow the same pattern as described for the pines. There are some diffuse porous hardwood species, like the eucalypts or poplars, whose juvenile wood is very similar to their mature wood.

There are many other wood properties that vary between juvenile and mature wood such as extractive content, or cell size. There are so many of these that they will not be dealt with in detail in this section.

Although often considered to be of low quality, juvenile wood is preferred for some products, like printing papers and tissues, where thin-walled cells are best. Such wood produces strong mullin (bursting strength) but the tearing strength is low. Juvenile wood of some conifers is somewhat similar to mature wood of the diffuse porous hardwoods and is sometimes used to supplement the need for hardwood fibers, such as when hardwoods are in short supply or are costly to obtain.

Wood from thinnings of pine in young plantations or tops from older trees is predominantly juvenile since mature wood has not yet has a chance to be formed. In some hardwoods like the eucalypts, the effect of juvenile wood is minor since the differences between juvenile and mature wood are quite small; this enables the use of short rotations without a major sacrifice in wood quality such as one finds in the conifers.

A major effect on wood and product quality differences within a tree relate to the ratio of juvenile wood present. One major control of the effect of juvenile wood is by varying the age of harvest or the part of the tree from which the wood is obtained.

Young plantations have a large proportion of juvenile wood; despite this, the economic importance of early harvest is often assessed without a proper consideration as to the kind of wood being obtained when there is a large amount of juvenile wood present.

There have been some studies on the genetic control of the amount and kind of juvenile wood. We have found considerable genetic control in loblolly pine but little has been done with this operationally since the effect of juvenile wood can be modified by changing rotation age or by use of the part of the tree bole with the desired percentage of juvenile wood.

Genetic Control of Wood Properties

The genetic control of wood properties is usually strong to moderate and the kind of wood can be influenced using selection and breeding. A strong additive genetic control is found for wood density but there is essentially none in cellulose yield. Strong additive genetic control along with a large suitable variation pattern makes possible the changing of important wood qualities in the desired direction when a selection and breeding program is followed. There are two major categories of genetic control, generally called additive and nonadditive. When the genetic variation is largely of the additive type, and where suitably large variation occurs, improvement by selection and breeding is relatively large and quick. The amount of additive genetic variation is usually represented by the term narrow-sense heritability (h^2) (common in the literature). This is a ratio indicating how much of the characteristic is controlled by additive genetic variation and how much results from other causes, including the environment and nonadditive variation. Thus, wood density has a high narrow-sense heritability (h^2) of 0.6–0.7, straightness of the tree of 0.3–0.5, and limb size shows a heritability of about 0.1–0.2.

Although a more exact formula is used by researchers, a working relation for estimating gain from selection is

$$\text{gain} = \text{SD} \times h^2$$

In this formula SD is the selection differential which is related to the variation in the wood property and the intensity of selection used to obtain the parents which give the desirable gain. Gain in a genetics program with a wood property is dependent on the variability present within the property, the intensity of selection used, and the heritability of that wood characteristic.

Only a few wood properties, like cellulose yield per unit weight of wood, have very little additive variation, but they have considerable non-additive variation. Gains from a selection program with them will be very small. When low additive variation is present, as for cellulose yield, the use of vegetative propagation (or a complex breeding system) is necessary to capture genetic variation in the new plantation trees. (A reduction or change in the amount of juvenile wood is difficult to achieve using a genetic breeding program, because the heritabilities are low).

Wood density   Wood density is a characteristic that can be improved quickly and significantly through breeding because its genetic variation is large and consists mostly of the additive type. Other wood properties that are easy to change by selection are resin content of wood and cell length. Some of the more important wood characters like spiral grain and fibril angle (along with tree straightness) have intermediate inheritance and gains through selection will be less.

Operationally, then, when a high wood density tree with high heritability is crossed with another high density tree, its progeny will have relatively high density. If a high cellulose yielder tree (with very low heritability) is crossed with a similar tree, one cannot predict the cellulose yields of the progeny, because cellulose yield is inherited nonadditively. Many wood properties are intermediate, where about half the genetic variation is of the additive type, half nonadditive. When this occurs, a selection program is not fully efficient and is dependent on the amount of variation present.

Vegetative Propagation

Although genetic gain is more difficult to obtain when the genetic control is nonadditive, the use of vegetative propagation will enable good improvement. Vegetative propagation will result in the new plant having the characteristics of the donor parent, since the new plant (propagule), usually a rooted cutting, contains all the additive as well as the nonadditive genetic variation present in the donor tree. The use of vegetative propagation in producing trees for operational planting is becoming much more widely used as methodologies for successful vegetative propagation are being improved.

The simplest way of producing improved wood for characters with a large portion of nonadditive variation is to use vegetative propagation to produce plantable trees.

Wood Uniformity

Wood uniformity, both within a tree and among trees, is a most important characteristic. When wood used in a manufacturing operation is reasonably uniform, efficiency in manufacture and quality of the final product will be greatly improved. Conversely, however, if juvenile and mature woods are both included in the same mix or board, and are treated similarly in manufacture, the final product will be variable and the efficiency and the value of the manufactured product will drop considerably.

The best way to obtain uniformity among plantation trees is to use vegetative propagation since the wood of the propagules from a given tree will all have wood similar to its donor tree. This methodology is now being much used in operational programs; one of the best examples is for the eucalypts when their wood is intended to be used for tissues. The mills have determined the best wood for making tissues and then rooted cuttings from the donor trees with these characteristics are used in establishing plantations. Both the quality and yields of tissues made from such plantations are greatly improved. This method of producing planted trees is now being applied to many other species as techniques for developing the propagules improves; in the future a great proportion of the wood available from plantations will have the desired wood uniformity and properties suited for the final product.

For the long term, the major improvement in wood, both through external and internal sources, will be to develop wood that is uniform and ideal for a given product line. Both the internal and external methodologies of changing wood must be used it such a goal is to be achieved.

See also: **Tree Breeding, Practices**: Breeding for Disease and Insect Resistance; Genetics and Improvement of Wood Properties. **Wood Formation and Properties**: Formation and Structure of Wood; Mechanical Properties of Wood; Physical Properties of Wood; Wood Quality.

Further Reading

Allen PJ (1985) *Estimation of Genetic Parameters for Wood Properties in Slash Pine in Southeast Queensland.* Research Note no. 41. Brisbane, Australia: Queensland Department of Forestry.

Baas P (1982) *New Perspectives in Wood Anatomy.* The Hague, The Netherlands: Dr W Junk.

Bamber RK and Burley J (1983) *The Wood Properties of Radiata Pine.* Slough, UK: Commonwealth Agricultural Bureau.

Barefoot AC, Hitchings RG, Ellwood EL, and Wilson E (1970) *The Relationship between Loblolly Pine Morphology and Kraft Paper Properties.* Technical Bulletin no. 202. Raleigh, NC: North Carolina State University.

Bendtsen BA (1978) Properties of wood from improved and intensively managed trees. *Forest Products Journal* 28(10): 61–72.

Blair RL, Zobel BJ, Franklin EC, and Mendel JM (1974) The effect of tree form and rust infection on wood and pulp properties of loblolly pine. *TAPPI* 57(7): 46–50.

Burdon RD (1975) Compression wood in *Pinus radiata* clones on four different sites. *New Zealand Journal of Forest Science* 5: 152–164.

Burley J and Nikles DG (1973) *Selection and Breeding to Improve some Tropical Conifers.* Brisbane, Australia: Queensland Department of Forestry.

Campinhos E (1980) More wood of better quality through intensive silviculture with rapid-growth improved Brazilian *Eucalyptus*. *TAPPI* 63(11): 145–147.

Cown DJ (1973) Effects of severe thinning and pruning treatments on the intrinsic wood properties of young radiata pine. *New Zealand Journal of Forest Science* 3: 379–389.

Falkenhagen ER (1979) *Provenance Variation in Growth, Timber and Pulp Properties in* Pinus caribaea *in South Africa.* Technical Bulletin no. 59. City, South Africa: Department of Forestry.

Foelkel CE, Barrichelo LE, Garcia W, and Brito JO (1976) Kraft cellulose of juvenile and adult wood of *Pinus elliottii*. *IPEF* 12: 127–142.

Megraw RA (1985) *Wood Quality Factors in Loblolly Pine: The Influence of Tree Age, Position in the Tree and Cultural Practices on Wood Specific Gravity, Fiber Length, and Fibril Angle.* Atlanta, GA: TAPPI Press.

Saucier JR (1990) Forest management and wood quality. In: *Proceedings of the South Plant Wood Quality Workshop*, Athens, GA, pp. 47–56.

Senft JF, Bendtsen BA, and Galligan WL (1985) Weak wood. *Journal of Forestry* 83: 476–485.

Taylor FW (1972) Anatomical wood properties of South African-grown *Eucalyptus grandis*. *South African Forestry Journal* 80: 20–24.

van Buijtenen JP (1963) Heritability of wood properties and their relations to growth rate in *Pinus taeda*. 1st World Consul For Gen Tree Improv., Stockholm, Sweden.

van Buijtenen JP (1969) Controlling wood properties by forest management. *TAPPI* 52(2): 257–259.

Wright JA (1991) Impact of wood quality assessments on future fiber resources in the pulp and paper-making industry. *South African Forestry Journal* 157: 96–99.

Yang KC (1994) Impact of spacing on width and basal area of juvenile and mature wood in *Picea mariana* and *Picea glauca*. *Wood Fiber Science* 26: 479–488.

Zobel BJ and Talbert J (1984) *Applied Forest Tree Improvement*. New York: John Wiley.

Zobel BJ and Jett JB (1995) *The Genetics of Wood Production*. New York: Springer-Verlag.

Zobel BJ and Sprague JR (1998) *Juvenile Wood in Forest Trees*. New York: Springer-Verlag.

Zobel BJ and van Buijtenen JP (1989) *Wood Variation: Its Causes and Control*. New York: Springer-Verlag.

Genetics and Improvement of Wood Properties

J P van Buijtenen, Texas A&M University, College Station, TX, USA

Introduction

Wood quality must be defined in terms of the end product: what is good for linerboard is not necessarily good for newsprint. The most critical properties for breeding programs are usually wood specific gravity, tracheid length and microfibril angle, although many other properties are also important. In general, wood properties are strongly inherited, with heritabilities of 0.5 and up. This would make breeding for wood properties easy if they could be determined easily and cheaply. Unfortunately this is true only for wood specific gravity. Therefore, much effort has gone into developing assay methods suitable for small wood samples which can be taken from the tree with little damage.

Wood quality can be improved by silviculture and by breeding. Spacing, thinning, and fertilization all have major effects on the growth of the tree and the properties of its wood. Selective breeding also has a major impact. Traditionally, the selected trees are grafted into seed orchards, progeny tested, and rogued. The time between the start of the program and the harvest of the first trees is typically 50 years making it appropriate to breed for a general purpose tree. For species that can be vegetatively propagated another approach is feasible: clonal forestry. Using it with shorter rotations allows development of trees suitable for specific products.

What is Wood Quality?

This is a difficult question to answer. Many years ago some of the pioneers in forest tree improvement asked managers of the local paper mills what wood properties they considered desirable, and were unable to obtain helpful answers. It was not until the 1970s that breeders started to ask the right questions. The quality of any raw material is defined as its suitability for use and quality is affected by many properties. There is a wide range of products made out of wood and it is therefore necessary to define wood quality in terms of the end product. What is good for linerboard is not necessarily good for multiwall sack paper and might be disastrous for newsprint. This is the most important point to keep in mind when considering wood quality.

What Are the Important Products?

Wood products belong in two major groups: solid-wood products, and pulp and paper products. Solid-wood products include not only lumber, but also plywood, oriented strand board and particle board. They can be used for construction as well as furniture. Pulp and paper products can be produced by three major processes: the sulfite process, the kraft process, and mechanical pulping. The sulfite process is used extensively for spruces and firs. The kraft process is more flexible and can be used for most species, including almost any pine. Mechanical pulping is often used for lighter woods such as poplars, but can be used successfully for some pines. The sulfite process is very suitable for producing high quality writing papers. Unbleached kraft is used extensively for the production of linerboard and sack paper, while bleached kraft can be used for writing papers, computer paper and paper used in copy machines. Mechanical pulps are primarily used for newsprint.

What Are the Important Wood Properties?

First we must distinguish between the wood of two major groups of trees: hardwoods (essentially broad-leaved trees) and conifers. The two groups have distinctly different wood. That of hardwoods is more complex, and its most distinguishing feature is the presence of vessels the elements of which are connected to each other through large pores. Other elements include fibers, tracheids, and parenchyma. The hardwoods are further divided into ring-porous and diffuse-porous species (**Figure 1**). Conifers have tracheids, ray parenchyma, and resin ducts. The tracheids are much longer than those in hardwoods.

The wood in conifers usually has distinct spring-wood and summerwood, also called earlywood and latewood. Springwood has large-diameter tracheids

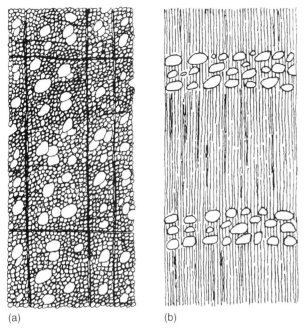

(a)   (b)

Figure 1 Cross-sections of (a) diffuse-porous and (b) ring-porous wood. From Zobel BJ and van Buijtenen JP (1989) *Wood Variation: Its Causes and Control*. New York: Springer-Verlag.

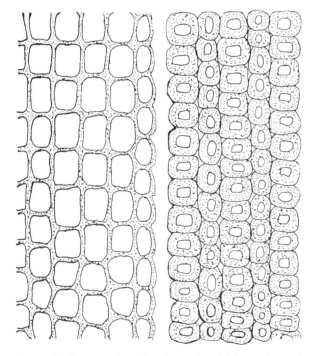

Figure 2 Cross-section of earlywood and latewood, clearly showing the difference in the cell diameter and wall thickness of the tracheids. From Zobel BJ and van Buijtenen JP (1989) *Wood Variation: Its Causes and Control*. New York: Springer-Verlag.

with thin walls and looks light on a cross-section of wood, while summerwood has narrow, thick-walled tracheids and looks dark (**Figure 2**). The most important wood properties are wood specific gravity

(dry weight divided by green volume), latewood percentage, tracheid length, tracheid diameter and wall thickness, microfibril angle (the angle of inclination of the cellulose microfibrils to the long axis of the tracheid), grain spirality (the angle of the tracheids to the vertical axis of the stem), and the chemical composition of the wood.

Techniques for Determining Wood Properties Using Small Samples

In a breeding program it is most important to evaluate wood quality without destroying the tree, and much effort has been expended over the years to develop techniques to make determinations on small wood samples. The favorite method is to remove one or more small radial cores (increment cores, ≤ 10 mm diameter) from the tree, which can be used for determinations. Methods have also been developed to pulp these on a very small scale and determine the pulp and papermaking properties. It is also relatively easy to determine anatomical properties on these samples. Almost all the important properties listed earlier can be determined from an increment core. Also, new high-throughput techniques have been developed recently such as near infrared (NIR) spectroscopy, image analysis, computer tomography, X-ray densitometry, X-ray diffraction, and pyrolysis molecular beam mass-spectrometry which allow very large numbers of chemical analyses on these small samples. Several techniques have been incorporated in the Silviscan equipment developed by Robert Evans at CSIRO, Australia (**Figure 3**). These approaches are ideal for a breeding program where large numbers of individuals must be screened quickly and cheaply.

Silvicultural Improvement of Wood Properties

Spacing

The initial spacing in plantations usually has no direct effect on specific gravity and tracheid length. A wider spacing results in larger juvenile cores. In spruce closer spacing results in better pulp yield and sometimes in greater strength. On sites where water availability is a problem, wider spacing may lead to a higher wood specific gravity.

Thinning

Thinning removes the poorer quality trees and therefore increases the quality of the timber left for the final harvest. Thinning removes trees that contain little of the higher quality wood (outerwood) that is formed after the first few rings from the pith, and

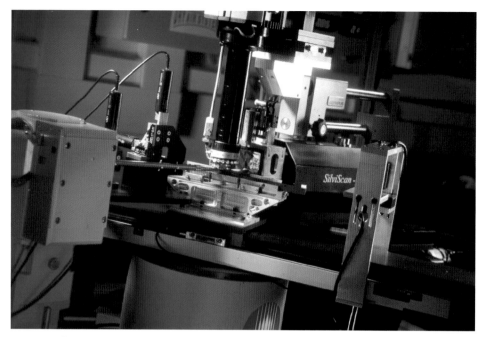

Figure 3 The SilviScan® instrument combines X-ray densitometry, diffractometry and image analysis to measure a variety of properties in a single wood sample. Photograph courtesy of CSIRO.

enhances production of such wood in the remaining crop. The effect of thinning is greatest in ring-porous species, less in diffuse-porous species, and least in conifers. Specific gravity and tracheid length are not much affected.

Fertilization

In general, soil fertilization has more effect on wood of conifers than of hardwoods. In particular, nitrogen fertilization decreases wood specific gravity in conifers and its effect may last 5–10 years. It also decreases tracheid length and increases earlywood production. To get the benefits of increased growth, while minimizing the adverse effects on wood properties, nitrogen fertilization should be light and frequent. The overall effect of fertilization both in hardwoods and conifers is beneficial, since the increase in volume more than offsets the loss in wood specific gravity. The effects of phosphorus and potassium are less pronounced than that of nitrogen. One should note that the effect of fertilization depends greatly on soil conditions. Obviously the effect is greatest when there is a nutrient deficiency.

Genetic Control of Wood Specific Gravity

The Components of Wood Specific Gravity

Wood specific gravity is a complex trait with many contributing factors. The major factor is usually the latewood percentage. Another important component is the cell wall thickness in the earlywood and the latewood. The diameter of earlywood tracheids is also important, but the diameter of the latewood tracheids is less so. The packing density, which is the specific gravity of the cell wall material itself, contributes to the actual density, but not to the variation among trees, since it is rather constant at $1.54\,\mathrm{g\,cm^{-3}}$. Extractives and insoluble deposits are the final components, which are particularly important in the heartwood.

Inheritance of Wood Specific Gravity in Conifers

Genetic variation among provenances Trends in genetic variation among provenances, if present at all, are usually weak. Specific gravity tends to be lower with increasing latitude and altitude. In the southern pines in natural stands wood specific gravity increases from the northwest to the southeast following the rainfall patterns in the southern USA. Genetic trends, determined by growing different provenances in the same location, are in the opposite direction. Clinal patterns are expected in the southern USA, the northeastern USA, and the boreal regions. This is not true, however, in the western USA with its mountainous topography. There, broad trends are expected to be less common except for elevational differences.

Tree-to-tree variation in wood specific gravity The literature on genetic differences among trees is abundant and is only outlined here. Narrow-sense heritabilities for wood specific gravity range from 0.4 to 0.7 in both corewood and outerwood. Low specific gravity species, such as Virginia pine, spruce, and silver fir, tend to have somewhat lower heritabilities than high specific gravity species such as the hard pines, larch and Douglas-fir. In general, the specific gravity of corewood and outerwood are well correlated, with genetic correlations frequently above 0.7. This makes it possible to select for specific gravity at an early age. For species that can be vegetatively propagated, the broad-sense heritability can be substantially higher than the narrow-sense heritability, which can be important for clonal forestry.

Inheritance of Wood Specific Gravity in Hardwoods

Not as much is published on the inheritance of specific gravity in hardwoods as in conifers, but the information is still substantial. Most of the work was done on eucalypts and poplars, with some on other species. In general, wood specific gravity is inherited quite as strongly in hardwoods as in conifers. In the eucalypts and poplars the heritability of specific gravity tends to range from 0.6 to 0.8, while in oak it ranges from a little below 0.4 to almost 0.6. In sycamore reported values range from 0.7 to 0.8. Juvenile–mature correlations in hardwoods are as high as in conifers.

Genetic Control of Other Wood Properties

Latewood Percentage

Differences between earlywood and latewood are so strong that they should often be evaluated separately. A fair amount of information is available on the relationship between latewood percentage and specific gravity, but far less on the genetics of it. There is no general trend in the earlywood : latewood ratio, although the higher latewood percentage is usually associated with high wood specific gravity. The heritability of latewood percentage is rather variable with reported values ranging from 0.25 to over 0.9. The narrow-sense heritability is often around 0.5, while the broad-sense heritability may be around 0.8. One should note that latewood percentage is related to other factors such as fertilization and it also affects the average cross-sectional tracheid dimensions which are very important for pulp and papermaking. On the average, latewood cells are slightly longer than earlywood cells.

Cell Dimensions

Tracheid length is moderately to strongly heritable, but information is somewhat limited, particularly in hardwoods. Most of the work in hardwoods has been with eucalypts and poplars. Estimated heritabilities ranged from 0.36 to 0.86. It has also emerged that polyploidy has a major effect on fiber length in both natural and artificially produced polyploids, increasing fiber length by 21% to 26%. Reported narrow-sense heritabilities in conifers range from 0.28 to 0.9 and broad-sense heritabilities from 0.56 to 0.86. In some species such as Scots pine (*Pinus sylvestris*), lodgepole pine (*P. contorta*), and shortleaf pine (*P. echinata*) differences among provenances have been reported.

Tracheid diameter and wall thickness are in general fairly strongly inherited, but information is quite limited. In loblolly pine (*Pinus taeda*) heritabilities up to 0.8 were reported. Inheritance in *Eucalyptus viminalis* was equally strong.

Spiral Grain

Spiral grain is probably related to wind resistance, but is difficult to measure accurately. If severe it can be a problem for solid-wood products, but generally it is not economically important. It has been intensively studied in *P. radiata* where it can cause problems. Heritability is strong enough to make genetic improvement feasible. There are also some data for eucalypts and beech indicating the same situation. Some species, such as sweetgum (*Liquidambar styraciflua*), have interlocking grain, which can be very troublesome but is also amenable to genetic improvement.

Chemical Properties

Genetic control of wood chemistry is topical, for two reasons. Much work is going on with control, at the molecular level, of lignin synthesis, and new techniques have been developed to analyze small wood samples in large numbers.

Traditionally the lignin, cellulose, and extractives content have been studied most extensively. Lignin content is very strongly inherited but its range of variation is small, indicating that it is very important and natural selection maintains it in a very narrow range. It can be determined extremely accurately. Cellulose cannot be measured as accurately; this lowers the heritability and makes genetic improvement more difficult. In eucalypts, however, considerable progress has been made in increasing cellulose content in clonally propagated trees.

Oleoresin components are quite often under the control of individual genes of large effect, and could be manipulated readily. There has been limited interest, with the exception of overall resin yield in pines, and the presence of limonene, which conveys insect resistance. In the decade 1970–80 some terpenes were used as a form of early genetic marker in studies of forest tree populations.

Other Wood Properties

Compression wood is rather strongly inherited both in loblolly pine and radiata pine. Surprisingly the relationship with form is rather weak, so factors other than straightness must play a major role. Another important property is heartwood formation, but its heritability is rather low.

A trait that is currently of major interest is microfibril angle. It is inherited rather strongly and is related to the strength of individual fibers as well as solid-wood stiffness. Bark percentage is rather variable in loblolly pine, being very important in young trees, where it can occupy as much as 50% of their volume. It is much less so in mature trees and it has a strong geographic component.

Finally, in eucalypts it has been found that collapse during drying, a rather common defect, is highly heritable.

Interrelationships among Traits

Interrelationships among traits are of great importance to the breeder. To select for one trait, but accidentally cause an adverse change in another, may be fruitless. For instance, if wood specific gravity and volume growth were negatively correlated, then selection just for wood specific gravity would decrease growth. This could be good or bad. Selection for low wood specific gravity could result in increased volume and wood that is more suitable for newsprint. On the other hand, selection for increased growth could result in wood less suitable for sack paper. In principle, one copes with this by using a selection index. Knowing the economic value of the traits under selection and their genetic and phenotypic relationships, one can assign a weight to each trait, to give a best estimate of the overall genetic value. A way to show the interrelationships among traits is by use of the so-called coefficient of genetic prediction. This shows the purely incidental change in trait 2 from a change of one standard deviation in trait 1. An example is given in **Table 1**.

Specific Gravity and Growth Traits

In general, there tends to be a weak negative correlation between specific gravity and height and diameter growth. Since in general the correlations between specific gravity and growth are not strong, it is usually not difficult to find individuals with desirable combinations for both traits. Specific gravity and date of bud break have a noteworthy correlation based on research done in Norway spruce. Early flushing is associated with less latewood, lower wood specific gravity, and greater ring width.

Wood Specific Gravity and its Components

Because of the totally different anatomy of the wood of conifers and hardwoods, they will be discussed separately. In loblolly pine latewood percentage, latewood specific gravity, earlywood specific gravity, and latewood tangential tracheid width showed the strongest genetic relationships to overall wood specific gravity. The first three factors have a positive association, while the tangential tracheid width has a negative relationship to overall wood specific gravity. Compression wood has a strong positive relationship with specific gravity.

In hardwoods little is known about the genetic relationships among the proportions of different cell types, but the important cell types are tracheids, libriform fibers, vessel elements, and medullary ray parenchyma.

Relationships among Other Wood Properties

In a few conifers tracheid length has a negative genetic correlation with wood specific gravity and growth rate and positive correlations with other

Table 1 Coefficients of genetic prediction (CGP). Selecting a population of parents one standard deviation above or below the average for a trait listed in one of the columns, will change the genotypic values of the progeny traits by the CGP times one standard deviation (based on data from the Western Gulf Forest Tree Improvement Program). The CGP is calculated as the phenotypic covariance of trait 1 and trait 2 divided by the product of their genetic standard deviations

	25-year height	25-year DBH	25-year volume	Juvenile SG	Mature SG	Average SG
25-year height	0.22	0.16	0.18	− 0.06	− 0.06	− 0.08
25-year DBH		0.25	0.26	− 0.12	− 0.11	− 0.14
25-year volume			0.26	− 0.12	− 0.11	− 0.13
Juvenile SG				0.19	0.16	0.21
Mature SG					0.36	0.30
Average SG						0.30

DBH, diameter at breast height; SG, specific gravity.

fiber dimensions such as lumen diameter, tangential and radial width, and wall thickness in the latewood.

In loblolly pine the microfibril angle in the earlywood is greater than in the latewood. It is fairly constant in the earlywood, but decreases from the pith to the cambium in the latewood.

In loblolly pine and eucalypts moisture content is negatively correlated with wood specific gravity. Hence, while wood specific gravity increases, the green weight stays relatively constant, since water is replaced with wood substance.

Controlling Wood Properties by Breeding

First one should consider the breeding objectives in terms of the end product. Since the trees will be harvested 50 to 75 years after the selections are made, it seems advisable to breed for properties that are generally desirable, because future wood technology is so uncertain. Increased specific gravity would be particularly suitable, since the use of thinnings and shorter rotations associated with plantation management depresses wood specific gravity (along with other components of wood quality), and it will be important to compensate for this, especially in corewood, which will make up a larger portion of the wood harvested. Another useful strategy is to try to reduce wastage and/or processing costs, e.g., by reducing lignin or by modifying lignin so it can be more easily removed by pulping. Significant reductions in lignin content probably cannot be achieved without major modifications in the system of growing, harvesting, and processing the trees. Wood uniformity within and between trees is also of great importance to the users of wood.

When designing a long-term breeding program for wood quality two key decisions must be made: (1) how to cope with the correlations among traits and (2) how to deal with the selection and progeny test phases. Index selection is, in principle, the best way to deal with adversely correlated traits. In order to cope with the negative correlations between specific gravity and growth, a multiple-population breeding strategy may be considered as an alternative to simultaneous improvement within a single population. Differentiated 'breeds' may be used for different end products or even for different categories of site.

Progeny testing is actually not necessary for traits as highly inherited as wood properties. Just selecting the individuals with the most desirable wood properties would suffice. Since selection for wood properties is generally combined with selection for other properties, such as growth rate, form, and disease resistance, progeny tests will be available anyway, and thus one only has to evaluate the best individuals already selected for other reasons. The age of testing is another major consideration. Since juvenile and mature wood properties are highly correlated, early selection is desirable. Another possibility is to use selection for wood properties in a stepwise screening program, where trees are evaluated first for the traits that can be measured easily and cheaply and are subsequently tested for properties that are progressively more expensive to determine.

Breeding for Wood Specific Gravity

A main consideration when breeding for wood specific gravity is whether wood specific gravity is a main objective or a secondary trait. Most breeding programs opt for the second alternative. One needs to consider, however, that it has a high economic worth, and the fact that an increase in quality generally means higher economic returns than increases in yield. Specific gravity should therefore be a high priority. An additional attractive feature of high wood specific gravity is that in the production of pulp and paper it allows a better combination of tensile strength and tear factor, which is desirable for some products such as multiwall sack paper. The economic effect of per-hectare fiber yield can vary according to the ownership. Since the weight of the green wood is not affected by wood specific gravity and pulpwood is often sold by weight, there is little incentive for a small private landowner to increase wood specific gravity. On the other hand, a company that grows wood on its own holdings has several incentives: increased dry matter production, increased quality, and reduced transportation cost.

Breeding for Other Wood Properties

This is not often done, because they are more expensive to evaluate and often less important. Tracheid length and microfibril angle are the two traits sometimes considered. However, owing to recently developed methods for high-throughput analysis of wood properties the situation is rapidly changing. There is an increased interest in microfibril angle, because of its effect on wood stiffness and pulp properties. Many chemical properties can be determined by the same methods as well.

Chemical properties can also be modified indirectly through improvement in stem straightness and branch size. This results in a reduction in reaction wood, which in conifers reduces lignin content and microfibril angle.

How Are Genetic Gains Obtained Operationally?

There are two major approaches: the seed orchard approach and clonal forestry. The seed orchard approach involves selecting the best individuals, grafting them in seed orchards, progeny testing the orchard to remove the less desirable clones and providing a new generation to select in. Operational plantations are generated from the seed produced by the orchards.

Clonal forestry depends on the availability of efficient vegetative propagation methods, usually rooted cuttings, sometimes tissue culture. A few highly selected individuals can than be propagated to reforest substantial acreages. Because of the cost involved this is most economical on the best sites, located close to manufacturing facilities. Because the time to deployment is shortened this method lends itself to tailor-making trees for specific products. For example the Aracruz company in Brazil has achieved rotations of 6 to 7 years with eucalypts. With *Gmelina arborea* 4 year rotations are possible. With blocks of well characterized clones, it is possible to fine-tune processing to the individual clones.

See also: **Genetics and Genetic Resources**: Molecular Biology of Forest Trees. **Papermaking**: Overview; World Paper Industry Overview. **Pulping**: Chemical Pulping; Mechanical Pulping. **Tree Breeding, Practices**: Biological Improvement of Wood Properties. **Tree Breeding, Principles**: A Historical Overview of Forest Tree Improvement; Conifer Breeding Principles and Processes; Forest Genetics and Tree Breeding; Current and Future Signposts. **Wood Formation and Properties**: Formation and Structure of Wood.

Further Reading

Helms JA (ed.) (1998) *The Dictionary of Forestry.* Bethesda, MD: Society of American Foresters.

Tuskan GA, West D, Bradshaw HD, *et al.* (1999) Two high-throughput techniques for determining wood properties as part of a molecular genetics analysis of loblolly pine and hybrid poplar. *Applied Biochemistry and Biotechnology* 77–79: 1–11.

Zobel BJ and Jett JB (1995) *Genetics of Wood Production.* New York: Springer-Verlag.

Zobel BJ and Sprague JR (1998) *Juvenile Wood in Forest Trees.* New York: Springer-Verlag.

Zobel BJ and Talbert J (1984) *Applied Forest Tree Improvement.* New York: John Wiley.

Zobel BJ and van Buijtenen JP (1989) *Wood Variation: Its Causes and Control.* New York: Springer-Verlag.

Zobel BJ, van Wyk G, and Stahl P (1987) *Growing Exotic Forests.* New York: John Wiley.

Breeding for Disease and Insect Resistance

B B Kinloch, Institute of Forest Genetics, Berkeley, CA, USA

Introduction

Pest resistance historically has been the single most important trait in crop breeding, reflecting the vast number of biotic agents that challenge domesticated plants. The number of diseases and insects that afflict forest trees may be even greater than their agricultural counterparts, but no comparable investment to combat them has been made, in spite of the fact that some forest trees have been victims of some of the most spectacular and disastrous epidemics known. Virtual elimination of American chestnut to chestnut blight and extirpation of large populations of American and European species of elm to Dutch elm disease, and white pines to white pine blister rust are textbook examples, as are the depredations of gypsy moth on North American hardwoods. Other important epidemics that started in the last century, some recently, include dogwood anthracnose, butternut canker, Port-Orford cedar root rot, pitch canker of pines, sudden oak death in North America, and the pinewood nematode in Japan. Almost all, of course, are the result of introduced pests. More will undoubtedly follow.

Exotic pests have caused immense economic and ecological damage, and, with few exceptions, are the only ones that merit serious attention. A few pathosystems that exhibit properties of both endemic and exotic diseases are often disturbed, or 'degenerate,' as a result of human intervention (for example, offsite planting, narrow genetic base, dysgenic selection). The same applies to insect pests. The far greater number of endemic forest pests has been regulated by natural selection over epochs of mutual adaptation through coevolution with their hosts.

While much basic understanding of pest resistance and breeding strategies have come from agronomic crops, distinctive properties of tree populations make the former incomplete models. The most important of these properties is the extension of trees in space and time. This has several important biological and practical consequences, especially for disease resistance. Great size projects a tree's parts into different microenvironments above and below ground, providing diversity of niches and habitats, while great longevity provides a perennial source of energy for different forest organisms, including pathogens and predators. Ontogenetic changes occur in morphology, physiology, and susceptibility to pests. Extension also imposes great logistical constraints to the breeder in time required for trees to reach sexual maturity, as well as access to flowers high in the crown. Great diversity (heterozygosity) of wild tree populations provides an abundant resource of variability, but is accompanied by high genetic load and inbreeding depression. This inhibits use of conventional agronomic breeding tools of selfing and backcrossing, complicating analysis of heritable traits, including resistance.

Mechanisms and Inheritance of Resistance

In comparison with crop pathosystems, relatively little is known about mechanisms and inheritance of resistance in trees to specific pests, especially insects, but several general characteristics are shared, such as hypersensitivity, partial resistance, ontogenetic (age-related) resistance, and tolerance. Morphological traits (e.g., leaf toughness, bark or cuticle thickness, trichomes, hairs) that impede pest feeding or ingress, or phenological traits that put host tissues out of synchrony with the life cycle of the pest are particularly important in host–insect interactions. Constitutive products of secondary metabolism (e.g., phenolics, tannins, monoterpenes) protect against herbivory. Behavioral characteristics (e.g., host preference, apparency, predator attraction) add a dimension of complexity to insect–tree interactions.

Genetic resistance is conditional: it depends as much on the genotype of the pathogen as it does on that of the host. The same is true of pathogen virulence and aggressiveness. Although emphasis is most often placed on host resistance, as if it were independent of the pathogen, it is the interaction phenotype that is inherited, and this is a property of both symbionts. This is made especially clear in gene-for-gene systems.

Hypersensitive reactions (HR) are often controlled by single, dominant, major resistance genes (R genes) in gene-for-gene systems. These systems exhibit precise specificity between interacting gene loci of host and pathogen, in which the resistant interaction phenotype is conditioned by an R allele in the host and a complementary allele for avirulence (AVR) in the pathogen. R alleles function in pathogen recognition and activation of host defenses, often leading to HR. HR causes necrosis in host cells immediately surrounding the lesion, effectively arresting further pathogenesis.

The outcome is virtual immunity for the host. Virulence (vR) alleles function to avoid or suppress this recognition, thus genetically restoring a compatible (i.e., susceptible) interaction phenotype. R genes can impose intense selection pressure on pathogen vR genes, which may cause them to increase exponentially in frequency until the usefulness of the R genes deployed in the host population is nullified. However, except when selected for by R genes, vR genes are thought to be less fit than AVR genes, which may explain why they do not become fixed in natural pathosystems. HR and R genes are more likely to be found in specialized, biotrophic pathosystems, such as leaf rusts of poplars and stem rusts of pine. HR is also common in tree–insect interactions, but the genetic basis has not been determined.

Partial resistance (PR), as the name implies, restrains pathogen development and/or reproduction without entirely excluding disease. Epidemiologically, PR functions to reduce the rate of infection, and has often assumed names more descriptive of particular kinds of diseases (e.g., 'slow rusting,' 'slow mildewing'). The degree of protection PR affords ranges widely, but can be highly effective in ensuring survival and mitigating damage. It is usually more complexly inherited than major gene resistance (MGR), and may involve several to many genes. Although much less dramatic than MGR, resistance conferred by PR is likely to be more stable, because it is not vulnerable to pathogen races with specific virulence to it. MGR and PR can exist together and act synergistically.

Ontogenetic resistance (OGR) and tolerance are the least understood mechanisms, but may be the most widespread and important in regulating forest diseases and predators in natural ecosystems. These two mechanisms may represent the greatest contrasts with annual plants in disease interactions. OGR is resistance that increases with age (occasionally decreases, but not to be confused with senescence). It has both a seasonal component, similar to annuals, wherein tissues become morphologically or physiologically less susceptible to pathogenesis or herbivory, and a perennial component that extends over the tree's lifetime. Tolerance implies the ability of a tree to survive, grow, and reproduce despite harboring the pest. Although conceptually clear, it is often difficult in practice to separate tolerance from low levels of resistance.

Unique to woody perennials is the inherent capacity to create barriers that wall off and compartmentalize invading pathogens in living sapwood. Upon injury, parenchyma tissues in rays react, synthesizing phenolic and other toxic compounds that discolor wood in a zone surrounding the site of infection and confine spread of invading microorganisms to the limits of the reaction zone. Trees also protect living bark from injury from abiotic or biotic origin by formation of a nonsuberized impervious layer of cells in phloem and cortex tissues at the site of the lesion, temporarily isolating invaders from water and nutrients. Necrophyllactic periderms are then laid down behind the injury site which seal the wound. Although both of these reactions are non-specific, reaction rates are genetically determined and amenable to selection.

General Considerations

Because tree breeding is expensive, there must be a clear economic benefit to justify a program. Usually, only pests of severe epidemic potential will justify the effort, and these are usually ones that have been introduced to a susceptible host population (or vice versa), although in some circumstances, such as widespread off-site planting, dysgenic selection, or crowded monocultures, endemic pests can become epidemic.

There should be some indication that selection and breeding for resistance to the pest will work. Addressing some of the following questions should assist in making a determination:

1. Is there a pattern of infection? Natural stands under strong epidemic pressure from the pest may reveal resistant phenotypes that are unlikely to be chance escapes. Provenance or family trials in established plantations may also show clear genetic differences that can be exploited.
2. Is there an efficient screening technique in place to evaluate candidate parental genotypes? Criteria for resistance should be clear, and expression of the traits selected for unambiguous. Most important, if artificial inoculation/infestation techniques are used, results should be consistent with field performance throughout the length of the rotation.
3. Is the pest more or less specialized in its host range? Usually, there are better chances of finding host genetic variation in resistance to specialists than generalists, and to biotrophs than heterotrophs.
4. Do exotic relatives of the host exist, especially at the pest's gene center, with resistance to the same or related pest? These may be able to be used as resistance donors in interspecific hybridization and backcross breeding.
5. How well is the genetic structure of the pest population known, both in its places of origin and introduction? Is its breeding behavior pre-

dominantly outcrossing or inbreeding (or clonal)? The amount of diversity and its potential for recombination will suggest the level of risk to races of wider virulence.

The goal of selection and breeding should always be for durable resistance. R genes, while highly effective in the short term, can be completely overcome by virulence genes with the appropriate specificity. Developing pyramids ('stacking') of different R genes in breeding lines, or buffering MGR with PR, are alternative breeding strategies to prevent or dampen exponential increases in pathogen virulence frequencies.

As detailed an understanding as possible of mechanisms and inheritance of resistance/virulence will always assist in making gene deployment strategies more effective. Nevertheless, resistance can still be used without such knowledge.

A clear distinction must be kept between breeding for production and for information. For example, if it is deemed necessary to understand the inheritance of resistance mechanisms, strict genetic control of both inoculum source and host material must be exercised in an appropriate mating design. If on the other hand the objective is simply to 'pick the winners' with as broad a base of resistance possible, bulk inoculum from throughout the range of intended deployment is more appropriate for screening candidates.

Maintaining as broad a genetic base as possible is probably the most essential requirement of any breeding program. Selection, by definition, narrows the genetic base. But sufficient diversity in either program breeding or archival populations is necessary as a hedge against the risk of new pests arising, or races of the same one with wider virulence. How much diversity is enough is a difficult and controversial issue, and will depend on the specific circumstances. Gene frequencies for resistance to exotic pests can be extremely rare, as for example those that confer resistance to white pine blister rust and root rot of Port-Orford cedar in North America. In such situations, availability of large, wild populations are the best solution, especially if natural selection is being imposed by the pest.

Examples of Active Resistance Breeding Programs

Table 1 lists seven major forest tree disease or insect epidemics that have motivated breeding programs. These include canker diseases, a vascular wilt,

Table 1 Examples of major pests with active breeding programs

Disease/pest	Host	Pathogen/pest	Type of disease	Origin	Type of resistance (parameter)
Chestnut blight	Castanea dentata	Cryphonectria parasitica	Canker	Exotic	PR (canker size)
Dutch elm disease	Ulmus americana	Ophiostoma ulmi, O. novo-ulmi	Vascular wilt	Exotic	Tolerance (% crown damage)
White pine blister rust	Pinus (subsect. Strobi)	Cronartium ribicola	Canker	Exotic	MGR, PR (infection frequency; canker abortion, size)
Leaf rusts	Populus, Salix	Melampsora spp.	Leaf rust	Exotic, Indigenous	MGR, PR (slow rusting)
Fusiform rust	Pinus taeda, P. elliottii	Cronartium quercuum f.sp. fusiforme	Canker	Indigenous (degenerate)	MGR, PR (% infection, canker size)
Port-Orford cedar root rot	Chamaecyparis lawsonia	Phytophthora lateralis	Root rot	Exotic	MGR?
White pine weevil	Picea sitchensis, P. glauca	Pissodes strobi	Shoot feeder	Exotic, indigenous	PR (% infested)

foliage rusts, a root rot, and a shoot-feeding insect. Thumbnail sketches of problems and progress in four of these follow, illustrating some of the general principles discussed above. Some are also covered in other articles in this volume (*see* **Pathology:** Vascular Wilt Diseases; Leaf and Needle Diseases; Stem Canker Diseases; Pine Wilt and the Pine Wood Nematode; Rust Diseases; Insect Associated Tree Diseases).

Chestnut Blight

Chestnut blight is responsible for one of the worst epidemics of trees, if not all plants, in history, having destroyed the dominant species (*Castanea dentata*) of an entire ecosystem that reached from Maine to Georgia. Caused by *Cryphonectria parasitica*, introduced from Asia, the disease also severely impacted European chestnuts (*Castanea sativa*). After a century of frustrated efforts, the biological tools and knowledge seem to be in place to make restoration of the American chestnut a real possibility. Critical elements consist of high crossability of American chestnut with Asian congeners; simple inheritance of effective partial resistance; a reliable and consistent screening technique; and sexual precocity enabling short intervals (5–6 years) between breeding cycles. It will nevertheless be a long-term endeavor.

No silviculturally useful variation in resistance was found in native chestnut stands, and early breeding efforts sought to exploit the inherent resistance of chestnuts from Asia, where the disease is endemic. The Chinese chestnut (*C. mollissima*), the

most wide-ranging and resistant species, was used as the principal source of resistance. Although significant resistance was observed in F_1 hybrids in early trials, it was not adequate for deployment. Further backcrossing to the Chinese parent could increase resistance, but only exacerbate the problem of undesirable growth and form inherited from the Chinese parent.

However, early analysis of certain F_1 and backcross progenies suggested the possibility of relatively simply inherited resistance. Subsequent quantitative trail loci (QTL) mapping with molecular markers of progeny of an F_2 cross confirmed this, and indicated the presence of two or three partially dominant, independently inherited genes responsible for the phenotypic resistance observed. Resistance was expressed as a marked reduction in canker growth rate following artificial inoculation of stem bark with defined cultures of the pathogen. Now the stage was set for a new breeding approach: backcrossing could be done on the recurrent susceptible American parent, to introgress the few genes for resistance from the *C. mollissima* donor, while continually purging remaining Chinese background genes affecting the desired American phenotype. After three backcross (BC) generations from the F_1, only one-sixteenth of the genome, on average, remains Chinese. Each BC generation is screened in field inoculations, using uniform blight cultures placed in drill holes in the bark. Partial resistance is measured by the area of canker expansion after 9–11 months. After the most resistant offspring are selected in each round, a final cross between two BC3 trees ('BC3 F_2s') with partial resistance should theoretically result in one of 16 trees having two copies of both resistance genes, making them as resistant as the Chinese parents in their pedigree.

Diversity for local adaptation will be provided by including at least 20 different American parents in the BC3 breeding population for any given area. This model, currently being tested and implemented in Virginia, could eventually be applied to a large portion of American chestnut's range. It would involve pollinating American chestnut flowers on sprouting stumps in the wild to produce F_1 seed before they become lethally infected.

Dutch Elm Disease

The impact of Dutch elm disease on American elms has been almost as severe as chestnut blight on American chestnut, and has affected many more species worldwide. It is a more difficult and insidious disease to deal with, because of its complexity. It is a systemic vascular wilt, caused by a species complex of at least two fungal pathogens (*Ophiostoma ulmi*, *O. novo-ulmi*) from uncertain origin in Asia, each with different races spanning a wide range of virulence; it has a saprophytic stage, extending survival of the fungus beyond the disease cycle; it is vectored by several different species of elm bark beetles (Scolytidae), with all the problems of host preference, resistance, and environmental interactions that they entail; and resistance mechanisms and inheritance are difficult to assess and interpret. It is a breeder's nightmare, and were it not for the extremely high aesthetic and amenity value of some elm species for urban and landscape forestry, the nearly century-long effort to develop resistance might never have been attempted. Success has been elusive in both North America and Europe, yet some significant progress has been made.

The American elm (*Ulmus americana*) is the most susceptible of over 40 species in the genus, and over 40 million trees are estimated to have been killed by the disease, including 70% of landscape elms. Sources of resistance are abundant in Asia, especially in populations of *U. pumila*, *U. parviflora*, and *U. japonica*. However, the relative ease with which resistance genes can be introgressed from Asian chestnuts into American chestnut does not apply to the corresponding elms, because *U. americana* is tetraploid, resulting in severe barriers to breeding with potential Asian donors. Additionally, Asian species tend to be highly susceptible to other diseases and insects, can be climatically maladapted, and generally lack the irreplaceable vaselike architecture

that defines American elm. Nevertheless, a few promising *U. parviflora* × *U. americana* hybrids have been made in the University of Wisconsin program that seem to combine resistance traits of the Asian parent with morphological features of the American. Many more such hybrids from diverse sources will be needed for a successful breeding program, but these results are encouraging.

Like the experience with chestnut blight, early selection and testing of American elm were disappointing. Of many thousands of candidate phenotypes tested, only a handful survived for further breeding. These are usually referred to as having tolerance, rather than resistance, and perhaps only 1 in 100 000 American elms have this in useful amounts. To efficiently screen selections, the University of Wisconsin program uses artificially inoculated seedlings or rooted cuttings and measures the volume of discoloration in stems as an index of relative tolerance. Seedlings with less than 50% discoloration, with or without foliar symptoms, usually correlate well with field performance. The criterion for acceptable tolerance in the field was <20% crown damage. A few long-term survivors, intercrossed with each other and susceptible controls, have produced up to 50% of offspring with less than 20% crown damage after 1 year in the field. Recent results of tests conducted by the National Arboretum showed the ability of a few earlier as well as new selections to respond and then recover from heavy artificial inoculation in the field, equaling performance of some non-American tolerant clones. This suggests that extended evaluation of candidates in the field may be more rewarding in the long term than relying completely on artificial inoculation.

White Pine Blister Rust

The nine white pine species native to North America are highly susceptible to blister rust, and most have been severely damaged in parts of their native range since the disease was introduced over a century ago. All species have important ecological functions, but breeding has been focused on the tall timber species, western white pine (*Pinus monticola*) and sugar pine (*P. lambertiana*).

Unlike most other exotic diseases, a surprising number of resistance mechanisms have been found in white pines to blister rust, even though hosts and pathogen have not coevolved. Three general types of resistance are recognized:

1. MGR, causing classic hypersensitive necrosis in needles on challenge by the pathogen. R genes have been found in several white pines, and exist in a gene-for-gene relationship with cognate genes

for avirulence in the rust. Thus, virulence gene *vcr1* in *Cronartium ribicola* neutralizes resistance gene *Cr1* in sugar pine but not *Cr2* in western white pine, and vice versa for *vcr2*. Single recessive genes are also thought to contribute high levels of resistance in western white pine.

2. PR has two main components in white pines: reduced infection frequency, and different kinds of bark reactions that abort infections after they establish in stem tissues. These mechanisms are more complexly inherited, but can still give effective, if incomplete, resistance. Most important, they are not specifically vulnerable to major virulence genes in the rust.

3. OGR is recognized in adult trees that are free of rust when surrounded by heavily infected cohorts, either in natural stands or seed orchards, but which produce highly susceptible offspring. It is genotype specific, and appears to be very strong and stable. OGR would be useful in stabilizing a crop in later parts of a rotation, but is the least understood and probably most difficult of all the mechanisms to develop.

The problem for breeding is how to recognize, concentrate, and deploy these different mechanisms and the genes that control them into synthetic populations to effect durable resistance. Dominant R genes are easy to breed with and confer immunity to all rust biotypes that lack specific virulence to them. But they place severe selection pressure on the rust for these virulent mutants, which are usually rare in natural populations. When this happens, the selected virulence alleles increase exponentially in frequency in the ambient inoculum, nullifying the protection conferred by populations deployed with only R gene resistance. A strategy devised for sugar pine is to prevent or dampen sudden increases in virulence gene frequency by buffering MGR with different PR mechanisms. This is accomplished in a two-stage process. Seedlings are screened first for MGR by artificial inoculation. Those selected are then outplanted in a field location where the frequency of virulence has been maintained at high levels by continuous natural selection from planted MGR. Since MGR is neutralized in this environment, seedlings surviving have both PR and MGR, and by forward selection will constitute the new parental generation when they mature. Concentration of both MGR and PR genes are effected and increased in subsequent generations (**Figures 1–3**).

Phytophthora Root Rot of Port-Orford Cedar

Phytophthora lateralis was introduced into western North America from an unknown source over half a

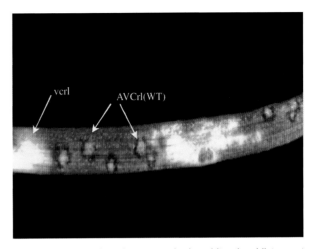

Figure 1 Interaction phenotypes in the white pine–blister rust pathosystem: needle symptoms on sugar pine with the Cr1 gene express as hypersensitive necrotic spots to inoculum carrying avirulence allele AVCr1 (wild type), but as normal yellow spots to inoculum with virulence allele vcr1.

Figure 2 Sugar pine families susceptible and resistant to white pine blister rust in a field trial. The resistant family (far right) has the major gene Cr1 in homozygous condition.

century ago, and has since caused widespread mortality in Port-Orford cedar (*Chamaecyparis lawsonia*), a narrow but valuable endemic of northwest California and southwest Oregon. Spread by motile zoospores is rapid and unstoppable – by water coursing through infested stands, or carried by vehicles, people, or animals passing through. Roots are the main infection courts, but foliage can also serve. Environmental variance is high, with low areas being most vulnerable, but root grafts extend infection foci uphill more gradually. The resulting pattern is a mosaic, making assessment of phenotypic resistance ambiguous and difficult.

Figure 3 Partial resistance in sugar pine to white pine blister rust. (a–c) Bark reactions of varying size; (d) low infection frequency. Both trees have Cr1, but have been exposed to natural inoculum with a high frequency of vcr1. b–d reproduced with permission from Kinloch BB Jr. and Davis D (1996) Mechanisms and inheritance of blister rust resistance in sugar pine. In: Kinloch BB Jr., Marosy M, and Huddleston M (eds) *Sugar Pine: Status, Values, and Role in Ecosystems*, pp. 125–132. Davis, CA: University of California, Division of Agriculture and Natural Resources.

Yet, this seemingly intractable problem has recently been overcome by exploiting Port-Orford cedar's unusual reproductive characteristics: precocious flowering (2–4 years) enables rapid turnover of generations compared with other conifers; breeding can be done in containerized orchards in greenhouses; seed is produced abundantly in the same season as pollination; and ease of vegetative propagation by rooted cuttings, even of older trees, permits establishment of ramets of selected candidates, or rapid multiplication of selected progeny genotypes.

Efficient screening is accomplished in two stages. Candidate trees are prescreened by dipping detached branches into zoospore suspensions, then measuring the length of the lesion formed under the bark after a few weeks. The most promising candidates are then rooted, dip inoculated in the same way, planted in nursery beds, and monitored for survival. Most mortality occurs within a year.

The high throughput enabled by these techniques has uncovered rare but highly effective resistance. Although the exact mechanism is not known, progeny of controlled crosses among a few highly selected parents have shown Mendelian segregation of healthy/living : dead offspring, implicating a single dominant gene for resistance. This will greatly facilitate deploying resistant genotypes for restoration of this species. Whether or not the pathogen harbors virulence capable of overcoming this resistance is unknown, but its overall diversity, based on molecular markers, is very low. Partial resistance or tolerance may also be found in the host that could be combined with MGR to mitigate the effect of wider virulence arising. The distribution of MGR is not known, and its rarity could be an impediment to restoring locally adapted, resistant Port-Orford cedar throughout its range. However, the ability to rapidly turnover breeding generations in Port-Orford cedar renders this problem soluble by introgressing nonlocal sources of resistance into local populations through backcrossing.

See also: **Ecology**: Plant-Animal Interactions in Forest Ecosystems. **Entomology**: Bark Beetles; Defoliators; Foliage Feeders in Temperate and Boreal Forests; Population Dynamics of Forest Insects; Sapsuckers. **Pathology**: *Phytophthora* Root Rot of Forest Trees; Diseases of Forest Trees; Insect Associated Tree Diseases; Leaf and Needle Diseases; Pine Wilt and the Pine Wood Nematode; Rust Diseases; Stem Canker Diseases; Vascular Wilt Diseases.

Further Reading

Alfaro RI, Borden JH, King JN, *et al.* (2002) Mechanisms of resistance in conifers against shoot infesting insects. In: Wagner MR, Clancy KM, Lieutier F, and Paine TD (eds) *Mechanisms and Deployment of Resistance in Trees to Insects*, pp. 101–126. London: Kluwer Academic Publishers.

Anagnostakis SL (1999) Chestnut research in Connecticut: breeding and biological control. *Acta Horticulturae* 494: 391–394.

Bingham RT (1983) *Blister Rust Resistant Western White Pine for the Inland Empire: The Story of the First 25 Years of the Research and Development Program*. US Department of Agriculture Forest Service General Technical Report no. INT-146. Ogden, UT: US Department of Agriculture, Intermountain Forest and Range Experiment Station.

Brasier CM (2001) Rapid evolution of introduced plant pathogens via interspecific hybridization. *BioScience* 51: 123–133.

Burdon RD (2002) Genetic diversity and disease resistance: some considerations for research, breeding, and deployment. *Canadian Journal of Forest Research* 31: 596–606.

Carson SD and Carson MJ (1989) Breeding for resistance in forest trees: a quantitative genetic approach. *Annual Review of Phytopathology* 27: 373–395.

Crute IR (1997) *The Gene-for-Gene Relationship in Plant–Parasite Interactions*. Oxford, UK: Oxford University Press.

Guries RP and Smalley EB (2000) Once and future elms: classical and molecular approaches to Dutch Elm Disease resistance. In: Dunn CP (ed.) *The Elms: Breeding, Conservation, and Disease Management*, pp. 231–248. Boston, MA: Kluwer Academic Publishers.

Hansen EM and Sutton W (eds) (2000) *Phytophthora Diseases of Forest Trees*, Proceedings from the 1st International Meetings on Phytophthoras in Forest and Wildland Ecosystems. Corvallis, OR: Forest Research Laboratory, Oregon State University.

Heybroek HM, Stephan BR, and Weissenberg K (eds) (1982) *Resistance To Diseases and Pests of Forest Trees*, Proceedings of the 3rd International Workshop on the Genetics of Host–Parasite Interactions in Forestry, Pudoc, Wageningen, The Netherlands.

Kinloch BB Jr. and Davis D (1996) Mechanisms and inheritance of blister rust resistance in sugar pine. In: Kinloch BB Jr., Marosy M, and Huddleston M (eds) *Sugar Pine: Status, Values, and Role in Ecosystems*, pp. 125–132. Davis, CA: University of California, Division of Agriculture and Natural Resources.

Namkoong G (1991) Maintaining genetic diversity in breeding for resistance in forest trees. *Annual Review of Phytopathology* 29: 325–342.

Shigo AL (1984) Compartmentalization: a conceptual framework for understanding how trees grow and defend themselves. *Annual Review of Phytopathology* 22: 189–214.

Zobel BJ and Talbert JT (1984) *Applied Forest Tree Improvement*. New York: John Wiley.

Genetic Improvement of Eucalypts

B M Potts, University of Tasmania, Hobart, Tasmania, Australia

Introduction

Eucalypts are virtually endemic to Australia; they are the tallest flowering plants on earth and the most widely grown hardwood plantation species. No sector of world forestry has expanded as rapidly as the industrial use of eucalypts and, while they are still at the early stages of domestication compared with crop species, they are fast becoming amongst the most advanced genetic material in forestry. This article overviews (1) the unique biological features of the genus, including its distribution and taxonomy, breeding systems, and natural regeneration mechanisms; (2) the history of its domestication, from its first discovery in the late eighteenth century, through its rapid dispersal around the world in the nineteenth century to its prominent role in the industrial plantations of the late twentieth century for the pulp and paper markets; (3) the genetic improvement of species, from provenance selection to advanced generation breeding strategies, including definition of breeding objectives and large-scale assessment of key biological traits affecting profitability; (4) the important role played by eucalypt hybrids, particularly in tropical and subtropical zones; (5) deployment options through seed and clonal propagation systems; and (6) progress towards molecular breeding and genetic engineering.

The Genus

Eucalypts are generally long-lived, evergreen hardwood species belonging to the predominantly southern hemisphere, angiosperm family Myrtaceae. They range in habit from shrubs and multistemmed mallees to enormous trees some which include the tallest flowering plants on earth (*Eucalyptus regnans*, up to 96 m). Most species are endemic to Australia but five tropical species are confined to islands north of Australia (e.g., *E. urophylla* and *E. deglupta*). A small group of species also extends outside of Australia into Papua New Guinea (e.g., *E. alba* and *E. tereticornis*). Eucalypts are the dominant species in open forests and woodlands throughout Australia but extend into a great diversity of habitats. They occur naturally from sea level to the alpine treeline, from high rainfall to semi-arid zones, and from the tropics to latitudes as high as 44° S, but they are absent from true arid and rainforest environments in Australia.

In the broad sense, eucalypts include the genera *Eucalyptus*, *Corymbia*, and *Angophora*. A key feature of the majority of eucalypts is the fusion of either the petals and/or sepals to form an operculum from which the eucalypts derive their name (from a Greek root *eu* – well and *calyptos* – covered). The operculum appears to have evolved independently in different eucalypt lineages and has not evolved in *Angophora*. There is some debate as to whether the *Corymbia* and *Angophora* genera (bloodwood taxa) warrant separation from the genus *Eucalyptus* in the strict sense (non-bloodwood taxa), but this split is supported by several independent DNA studies and is adopted herein. This dichotomy appears to be associated with differences in the structure of raised oil glands (termed bristle glands), wood properties (the bloodwood lineage for example only has solitary vessels in the xylem), leaf venation, and ovule arrangement. The latest taxonomic revision of the eucalypts recognizes just over 700 species that belong to 13 main evolutionary lineages (**Table 1**) but still treats the bloodwood eucalypts as subgenera of *Eucalyptus*. Most species belong to the subgenus *Symphyomyrtus*, and it is mainly species from three sections of this subgenus that are used in plantation forestry.

Eucalypts have several noteworthy biological features. Many species are heteroblastic, with leaves changing from a sessile, horizontally orientated juvenile form to a petiolate, vertically orientated adult form. This is also accompanied by changes in leaf anatomy, physiology, and chemistry. The timing of this heteroblastic transition is under strong genetic control and susceptibility to many pests is dependent upon the leaf type present in the canopy. Eucalypts also have well-developed mechanisms for vegetative recovery from defoliation arising from factors such as fire, drought, frost, or herbivory. The bark often protects numerous dormant vegetative buds that sprout to form epicormic shoots after defoliation. If the whole stem is killed by, for example fire, many species also have the possibility of resprouting from lignotubers. Lignotubers are organs that develop as swellings in the axils of the cotyledonary and early seedling nodes and comprise a mass of vegetative buds, vascular tissue, and food reserves. They usually become buried and allow the plant to regenerate after the death of the main stem. Epicormic or coppice shoots exhibit varying degrees of reversion to the juvenile leaf form. Other vegetative regeneration mechanisms such as rhizomes or root suckering have been reported in *Corymbia*. Regeneration usually occurs by seed that is stored in woody capsules, 5–30 mm in diameter, and often held on the

Table 1 Major evolutionary lineages[a] within the eucalypts

Pryor and Johnson's subgenera/genera	Brooker's subgenera	Number of species	Examples of well-known forestry species
Angophora (genus)	Angophora	7	
Blakella	Blakella	15	
Corymbia	Corymbia	67	C. torelliana, C. citridora, C. maculata
Eudesmia	Eudesmia	19	
Gaubaea	Acerosa	1	
Gaubaea	Cuboidea	1	
Idiogenes	Idiogenes	1	E. cloeziana
Monocalyptus	Primitiva	1	
Monocalyptus	Eucalyptus	110	E. regnans, E. delegatensis, E. obliqua, E. marginata, E. fastigata
Symphyomyrtus	Cruciformes	1	E. guilfoylei
Symphyomyrtus	Alveolata	1	E. microcorys
Symphyomyrtus	Symphyomyrtus	474	E. camaldulensis, E. exserta, E. globulus, E. grandis, E. nitens, E. paniculata, E. robusta, E. saligna, E. tereticornis, E. urophylla, E. viminalis
Telocalyptus	Minutifructus	4	E. deglupta

[a]The alignment of Pryor and Johnson's (1971) genera and subgenera with Brooker's (2000) subgenera. Pryor and Johnson's classification was informal, but widely used for 30 years. The number of species in each of Brooker's subgenera is indicated and examples of well-known forestry species are given. The subgenera *Blakella* and *Corymbia* had previously been treated as a separate genus *Corymbia* Hill and Johnson (Hill and Johnson 1995) and the subgenus *Angophora* treated as a genus and this treatment has been adopted in the text.
Sources: Pryor LD and Johnson LAS (1971) *A Classification of the Eucalypts*. Canberra: Australian National University Press; Brooker MIH (2000) A new classification of the genus *Eucalyptus* L'Her. (Myrtaceae). *Australian Systematic Botany* 13: 79–148; Hill KD and Johnson LAS (1995) Systematic studies in the eucalypts 7. A revision of the bloodwoods, genus *Corymbia* (Myrtaceae). *Telopea* 6: 185–504.

tree for several years. In good years, large numbers of seed are shed, particularly following wildfire. The seeds generally have no special adaptation for dispersal and, with the exception of a few cases of water dispersal (e.g., *E. camaldulensis*), seed dispersal is mainly by wind and normally occurs over short distances. Eucalypt seed is short-lived in the soil seed bank.

Eucalypt flowers are occasionally solitary (e.g., *E. globulus*), but often occur in clusters of three or more in umbels (**Figure 1**) or terminal inflorescences. The eucalypt flower is normally bisexual, with numerous stamens that expand outwards after the operculum is shed to form the conspicuous floral display. Eucalypts are predominantly animal-pollinated, with vectors encompassing a wide variety of insects, birds, and marsupials, and a few bat species. They have a mixed mating system, but are generally preferential outcrossers, with high levels of outcrossing maintained by protandry and various incomplete pre- and postzygotic barriers to self-fertilization. The postzygotic barriers include intense selection against the products of inbreeding. For example, inbreeding depression for growth in selfed *E. globulus* is nearly 50%, and this is quite typical. Consistent with most myrtaceous genera, eucalypts are diploids with virtually all having a chromosome

Figure 1 Flowers and flower buds of *Eucalyptus nitens*. *Eucalyptus nitens* bears its flowers in umbels of up to seven flowers. The figure shows buds just about to shed their inner operculum and those from which the operculum has been shed. In this group of eucalypts, the inner operculum is derived from fused petals and shed just before the anthers expand and shed pollen. The outer operculum is derived from the fused sepals and is shed early in bud development. The stigma of this species becomes receptive 5–7 days after operculum shed, at a stage when most pollen has been released from the anthers. Photograph courtesy of Dean Williams.

number of $2n = 22$. While the major eucalypt subgenera do not hybridize, reproductive barriers between species within subgenera are often weak. Hybridization and intergradation between recognized taxa are common in nature, often making delineation of species difficult. Many artificial hybrid combinations have been produced. In general, hybrid inviability tends to increase with increasing taxonomic distance between the parents, but there are exceptions.

History of Domestication

Eucalypts are the most planted hardwood trees in the world. Following their discovery in the late eighteenth century, they were spread rapidly around the world and were early introduced into countries such as India (c. 1790), France (c. 1804), Chile (1823), Brazil (1825), South Africa (1828), and Portugal (1829). Initially they were introduced as botanical curiosities but, as the potential for some species to grow fast was quickly recognized, they were grown for windbreaks, land reclamation, and leaf-oil production, but mainly for fuel wood and timber production. Plantations were established, for example, to provide railway crossties and fuel for wood-burning locomotives in Brazil and South Africa, mine props in Chile and South Africa, and charcoal in Brazil for iron and steel production. One factor causing their rapid early spread appears to be the belief that growing eucalypts could banish diseases such as malaria, and they became known as 'fever gums' in the latter half of the nineteenth century.

Eucalypts became renowned for species with fast growth, straight form, valuable wood properties, wide adaptability to soils and climates, and ease of management through coppicing. They are now found in more than 90 countries where the various species are grown for products as diverse as sawn timber, mine props, poles, firewood, pulp, charcoal, essential oils, honey, and tannin as well as for shade, shelter, and soil reclamation. The exotic eucalypts became an important source of fuel and building material in rural communities in countries such as India, China, Ethiopia, Peru, and Vietnam. However, it was the great global demand for short-fiber pulp that drove the massive expansion of eucalypt plantations throughout the world during the twentieth century. Their high fiber count relative to other wood components, coupled with the uniformity of fibers relative to other angiosperm species, has caused high demand for eucalypt pulp for coated and uncoated free-sheet paper, bleach board, sanitary products (fluff pulp), and secondarily for top liner on cardboard boxes, corrugating medium, and as a filler in long-fiber conifer products such as newsprint and containerboard. New technologies are also increasing interest in the use of plantation eucalypts for sawnwood, veneer, medium density fiberboard, and as extenders in plastic and molded timber.

No sector of world forestry has expanded as rapidly as the industrial use of eucalypts. While precise global figures are difficult to obtain, it is estimated there were 9.5 million ha of industrial eucalypt plantations in the world in 1999 (**Table 2**), with the vast majority of these established since the 1950s. This area is predicted to reach 11.6 million ha in 2010 (**Table 2**). Other less conservative global estimates suggest that there were nearly 16 million ha of general eucalypt plantations by the 1990s which would reach 20 million ha by 2010. These figures compare with the estimated 30 million ha of tall (> 30 m tall) and 240 million ha of open (10–30 m tall) native eucalypt forest in Australia in 2001. The majority of plantations consist of only a few eucalypt species and hybrids. The most important plantation eucalypts around the world are *E. grandis*, *E. globulus*, and *E. camaldulensis*, which together with their hybrids account for about 80% of the plantation area; these are followed by *E. nitens*, *E. saligna*, *E. deglupta*, *E. urophylla*, *E. pilularis*, *Corymbia citriodora*, and *E. tereticornis*. In the case of pulpwood, the market favorites are *E. grandis*, *E. urophylla*, and their hybrids in tropical and subtropical regions and *E. globulus* in temperate regions. However, eucalypt plantations of the traditional pulpwood species as well as other species (e.g., *C. citriodora*, *C. maculata*, *E. cloeziana*, and *E. nitens*) are increasingly being managed for solidwood production. While there are reports of eucalypt plantations achieving growth rates of over $60 \, \text{m}^3 \, \text{ha}^{-1} \, \text{year}^{-1}$, with intensive management, typical growth rates reported for the *E. grandis* plantations in Brazil and South Africa are $40 \, \text{m}^3 \, \text{ha}^{-1} \, \text{year}^{-1}$ with a harvest age of 6–8 years,

Table 2 Area of industrial plantations of eucalypts (millions of hectares)

Region	1999	2010	Change
Africa	1.08	1.00	−7%
Asia	2.43	3.20	32%
Europe	1.32	1.40	6%
North and Central America	0.08	0.10	30%
South America	4.09	5.00	22%
Oceania	0.48	0.90	89%
Total	9.48	11.60	22%

Source: Wood resources international cited in Raga FR (2001) Perspectiva para el eucalipto chileno. In *Developing the Eucalypt of the Future*, IUFRO International Symposium, 10–15 September 2001, pp. 13. Valdivia, Chile: INFOR.

and 20–22 $m^3 ha^{-1} year^{-1}$ for *E. globulus* plantations in Portugal and Chile with a harvest age of 8–10 years. The world average is suggested to be more like 20 $m^3 ha^{-1} year^{-1}$, but it is anticipated that this could reach 25–30 $m^3 ha^{-1} year^{-1}$ in the future with better silviculture and breeding.

Initially, the botanical gardens of southern Europe played a major role in the introduction of eucalypts to other parts of the world, including Africa and South America. Later in the nineteenth century eucalypts were introduced directly from Australia with, for example, large quantities of seed being sent out of Australia by Ferdinand von Mueller, a government botanist and eucalypt specialist. These early introductions were often used as the base to establish large-scale plantings, resulting in narrow, potentially inbred, genetic bases in some cases (e.g., *E. globulus* in South Africa and Ecuador). In other cases, seed for plantation establishment was collected from ornamentals or multispecies plantings, and appears to have contained high frequencies of interspecific hybrids. In the latter case, F_1 generation hybrids may have performed well but subsequent seed collection from these hybrid plantations resulted in F_2 and subsequent generations with poor growth and form as well as extreme variation (e.g., those derived from the Rio Claro *E. urophylla* hybrids in Brazil 'Brazil alba,' or Mysore *E. tereticornis* hybrid in India). In many countries where eucalypts have been introduced for a long time and continually reproduced from local seed sources, they have formed landraces that are adapted to the specific environment of the country. However, there are many examples where the initial use of a limited sample of the genetic diversity in the native gene pools, the use of suboptimal provenances, inbreeding, or hybrid breakdown have led to landraces being outperformed in field trials by seedlots from some native-stand provenance collections (e.g., *E. globulus* in Argentina, *E. grandis* in South Africa). The planting of suboptimal germplasm is particularly problematic in rural communities where seed obtained for new plantings has been collected with no or only little phenotypic selection from local plantings, generation after generation. In a few cases, where more active breeding has occurred the local landrace has outperformed newly imported native stand seedlots (e.g., *E. grandis* in Florida).

Some of the earliest breeding of eucalypts was undertaken by French foresters in Morocco in 1954–1955. Coincident with the increasing interest in industrial plantations of eucalypts, the 1960s saw a more formal approach to genetic improvement with, for example, the commencement of the Florida *E. grandis* breeding program in 1961, *E. globulus*

breeding in Portugal in 1965, and establishment of large provenance tests of *E. camaldulensis* in many countries. Major advances in domestication of the genus occurred in the 1970s with, for example, the first commercial plantings of selected clones derived from hardwood cuttings at Pointe Noir in the Congo followed by Aracruz in Brazil (many of which were spontaneous hybrids), and the establishment in many countries of the first large base-population trials of species such as *E. urophylla* and *E. globulus*. These trials were established from open-pollinated seedlots collected from range-wide provenance collections and formed the bases for deployment and breeding populations in many countries. Many other major international base-population trials were established through the 1980s for species such as *E. grandis*, *E. tereticornis*, and *E. viminalis*, and using more intensive collections of elite provenances identified in earlier collections.

While eucalypts are still at the early stages of domestication compared to crop species, they are fast becoming amongst the most advanced genetic material in forestry, with stock originating from the *E. grandis* program in Florida already in its sixth generation. In Brazil, around 500 000 ha of plantation were apparently established with 'Brazil alba' seed between 1940 and 1970 before it was realized that the quality of the new plantations was much inferior to earlier plantations and *E. grandis* due to hybrid breakdown. The company Aracruz Celulose S.A. has subsequently doubled yields from its Brazilian plantations through species and provenance selection, breeding, and the use of proven clones. Domestication of eucalypts has proceeded faster in countries like Brazil that rely on plantations for their eucalypt wood than in Australia, where up until the 1990s wood products of eucalypts were derived almost entirely from native forests. However, major provenance trials of species such as *E. regnans*, *E. delegatensis*, *E. globulus*, and *E. nitens* were established in Australia in the late 1970s, and major breeding programs for *E. globulus* and *E. nitens* were started in the 1980s.

Species Improvement

A key feature of eucalypt species is the great diversity of the native gene pools. Large, genetic differences between provenances are the rule rather than the exception. In some cases, provenances of a single species may vary from tall forest forms to small trees and even shrubs when grown in common environment trials (e.g., *E. globulus*). This diversity may occur for all traits of interest to breeders such as growth and survival, pest resistance, and wood properties, as well as flowering season and precocity. Such provenance variation makes it important that, firstly, species-elimination trials are based on adequate provenance representation and, secondly, when establishing base populations for breeding the full range of genetic diversity is assessed. This is further complicated by the large provenance × environment interactions that have been revealed in multisite field trials of species such as *E. camaldulensis*, *E. deglupta*, *E. delegatensis*, *E. nitens*, *E. urophylla*, and *E. viminalis*. Increasing information is available for environmental matching of species and provenances to sites through comparison of local environmental profiles with native ranges in Australia as well as exotic environments where they have been successfully grown. However, a traditional approach for formation of base populations for breeding has been the establishment of large range-wide provenance trials, supplemented with more intensive collection from elite provenances in a second stage. While early provenance trials pooled individual-tree seedlots, later trials have tended to maintain family identity to allow better pedigree control and conversion of trials to seed orchards. Increasing international exchange of eucalypt germplasm amongst breeding programs now means that base populations are comprising not only seedlots from native stand collections in Australia but also material from landraces and more advanced breeding programs.

A focus of eucalypt breeding in recent years has been the clear definition of breeding objectives and identification of relevant selection traits. Major developments were made in the 1990s in clarifying breeding objectives for kraft and mechanical pulpwood production using eucalypt wood. Wood density, pulp yield, and volume per hectare were identified as the key biological traits influencing the economics of pulpwood production. Economic weights have been determined to allow estimation of total breeding value in terms of monetary value to the industry sector. Wood density and pulp yield were rarely considered in earlier selection programs, yet they can account for over 70% of the benefits from breeding for pulp production. Approaches have now been developed for the quick, cheap, and nondestructive measurement of many key wood properties (e.g., pilodyn, mechanized coring (**Figure 2**) and near-infrared reflectance analysis (NIRA)), allowing their widespread application in breeding programs. Extending such work beyond pulp to paper is the next step. There is increasing work being undertaken on identifying breeding objectives and selection traits for solidwood products; however, this is complicated by the greater range of products

Figure 2 Coring *Eucalyptus globulus* for wood density assessment using a mechanized coring machine. Photograph courtesy of Carolyn Raymond, Cooperative Research Centre for Sustainable Production Forestry.

involved from sawn timber, composites, and veneer, and changing technologies, as well as the fact that plantations may be required for multiple products through thinning or changes in product pricing.

The amount of genetic variation and intercorrelation among selection traits in the breeding population has a major effect on genetic progress. The genetic correlation between growth and wood density, for example, is probably slightly adverse in species such as *E. globulus* and *E. nitens*, but estimates are variable ranging from zero to significantly adverse. Most genetic parameters such as heritabilities and genetic correlations published for eucalypts to date refer to the additive genetic variation within provenances and have been calculated based on open-pollinated progeny trials. As eucalypts have a mixed mating system and the male parent is unknown, the accuracy of these genetic parameter estimates is questionable, particularly from native-stand seed collections where outcrossing rates may vary markedly. In *E. globulus*, for example, no correlation has been observed between open-pollinated and control-pollinated breeding value estimates for growth traits, but the correlation is significant for traits of higher heritability such as wood density and disease-resistance traits. The other types of heritability often reported include additive and nonadditive components of genetic variation and are the clonal and family heritability (or repeatabilities of their means). This is a measure of the relative differentiation between genotypes or families and is a measure of the repeatability of performance for clonal or family deployment respectively.

Traditionally, eucalypt breeding has involved open-pollinated breeding strategies using single populations or sublines, possibly coupled with open- or controlled-pollinated nucleus populations of the most elite selections or specialized breeds (**Figure 3**). In programs where clones are deployed, the standard approach has involved progeny testing, and phenotypic or genetic selection of elite genotypes, followed by various stages of selection on cloning potential and clonal elimination trials. Selected clones are frequently used as parents in the subsequent generations. Traditionally, breeding programs have involved dis-

crete generations. However, programs in Australia and Portugal are now implementing a 'rolling front' breeding strategy that has overlapping generations with selection, crossing, and trial planting done each year. This strategy is believed to be more flexible in the face of changing breeding objectives, technologies, resource allocation, and industry reorganization, which are becoming increasingly common. In this scheme, decisions are defined in terms of dynamic rules, where a general objective function guides the

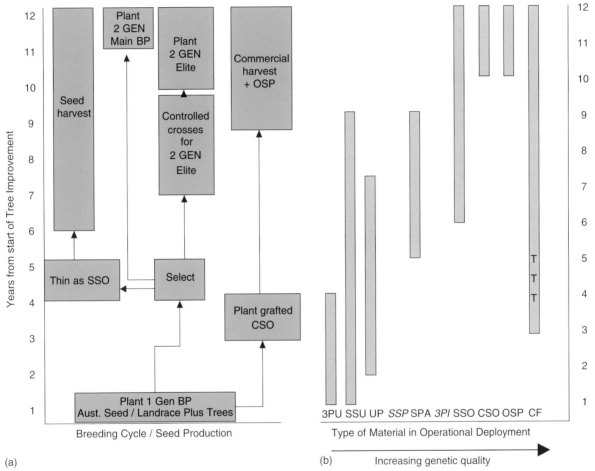

Figure 3 Elapsed time for first generation breeding and take-up of deployment options for *Eucalyptus globulus* in the company Forestal y Agricola Monteaguila S.A. in Chile (year 1 = 1990). (a) The type of genetic material deployed. The breeding population contained two sublines, a large Australian native stand collection and the other the Chilean landrace. The breeding populations (BP) were planted on multiple sites, the majority of the landrace selections from which seed was collected were also grafted and used to develop a clonal seed orchard (CSO) and a mass controlled pollination system based on 'one-stop pollination' (OSP). One site of the Australian subline was converted to a seedling seed orchard (SSO). (b) Planting started with importation of Australian seed (3PU), supplemented by harvests from the best trees in the plantations of the Chilean landrace (SSU). Within 3 years the superiority of the Jeeralang provenance in Australia (UP) was demonstrated and imported native stand seed formed a main component of the plantations established for the next 5 years until SSO and CSO seed came on stream. In 2000, backward and forward selected families from OSP contributed 30% of plantings and was expected to yield 30% volume improvement relative to Jeeralangs (UP). A clonal program (CF; T, test scale) was commenced in 1991, with cloning high rooting, selected families from the landrace and cold tolerant selection and later selections from the first generation breeding population (1GEN BP) trails. Commercial planting started in year 6 and by year 11, 20% of the total planting used clonal stock. Seed stands derived from plantations of selected provenance (SSP) or third party improved seed (3PI) were not utilized. From Griffin AR (2001) Deployment decisions: capturing the benefits of tree improvement with clones and seedlings. In *Developing the Eucalypt of the Future*, IUFRO International Symposium, 10–15 September 2001, pp. 16. Valdivia, Chile: INFOR.

selection and crossing done each year. Such a strategy exploits advances in genetic evaluation through best linear unbiased prediction (BLUP) methodology using individual-tree models that allow for overlapping generations, and complex pedigree- and field-trial structures. The costs of controlled pollination of many eucalypts have now been reduced substantially, through the development of techniques requiring only a single visit as opposed to three visits to the flower. Such reductions in costs have now made controlled crossing of the breeding population viable in species such as the large-flowered *E. globulus*, allowing improved accuracy of genetic evaluation over open-pollination where the male parent is unknown and breeding values could be biased by selfing and nonadditive genetic effects. Other major advances in genetic evaluation have come through improved trial designs such as incomplete-block and row–column designs, as well as including clonal information into evaluation models.

Interspecific Hybridization

Interspecific eucalypt hybrids have been used in forestry for decades and are a significant component of eucalypt plantation forestry, particularly in the tropics and subtropics. While some multiclonal seed orchards are used for F_1 hybrid production, cost-efficient clonal propagation is the key to their successful exploitation. Failures to develop such systems has limited deployment and hence reduced use of many desirable species combinations, particularly in temperate regions.

Clones of *E. urophylla* × *E. grandis* are easy to propagate and are widely planted in Brazil and Congo (**Figure 4**). Most eucalypt hybrids tested or deployed are either F_1s or composites derived from spontaneous hybridization (e.g., 'Brazil alba,' or Mysore hybrid in India) or more recently manipulated F_1 hybrids. The main hybrids used in industrial plantations are *E. grandis* × *E. urophylla*, *E. grandis* × *E. camaldulensis* (**Figure 5**), and cultivars including at least one of *E. saligna*, *E. pellita*, *E. exserta*, and *E. tereticornis*. Such hybrids are planted on a relatively large scale in Brazil and Congo, although sizeable plantations also occur in China, Indonesia, and South Africa. While hybrids are less utilized in more temperate zones, eucalypt hybridization programs involving controlled crossing were undertaken early in countries such as Russia and France, but hybrid development was curtailed by extreme frosts. Such artificial hybridization was undertaken early in temperate Australia, mainly aimed at understanding trait inheritance and the reproductive barriers between species. Hybrid development has

Figure 4 Clonal plantation of an elite *Eucalyptus urophylla* × *E. grandis* hybrid at Pointe Noire, Congo. Photograph courtesy of Rod Griffin, Shell Forestry.

focused on F_1 hybrids and has aimed to combine species with complementary attributes. However, as most traits are inherited in a more or less intermediate manner in the F_1s there is increasing interest in backcross and other advanced generation eucalypt hybrids to provide desirable combinations of traits. Some desirable species combinations produce high proportions of inviable/uncompetitive hybrids (e.g., *E. grandis* × *E. globulus*, *E. camaldulensis* × *E. globulus*, *E. urophylla* × *E. dunnii*, *E. dunnii* × *E. grandis*) and the key to hybrid selection appears to be rapid production and testing of large populations and application of high selection intensities. There are also advantages in selecting seed parents for both sexual and vegetative propagation traits.

Deployment

Seedlings

In rural communities outside Australia, eucalypts have historically been propagated from the most accessible seed that is often derived from ornamentals or local plantations, with little attention paid to its

Figure 5 A phenotypically outstanding *Eucalyptus grandis* × *E. camaldulensis* F₁ hybrid in a family trial in Guangxi Dongmen Forest Farm, China. At 10 years the diameter at breast height of this tree was 32 cm compared with the adjacent tree in the foreground that measured only 11.3 cm. Such individuals are damaged at the base to cause coppice shoots that are multiplied by tissue culture to provide sufficient stock plants for production of hardwood cuttings for clonal tests.

genetic quality. However, seed with varying levels of improvement has been obtained for deployment in industrial plantings from the best native-stand provenances in Australia, seed production areas (**Figure 6**), seed orchards, and more recently, mass controlled or supplementary pollination. The main problem with collection of seed from native stands is that genetic gain, from even the best provenances, may be limited due to varying degrees of inbreeding from selfing or crossing between related individuals which often grow in close proximity in the forest owing to limited seed dispersal. Self-fertilization is particularly a problem when seed is collected from isolated trees. Nevertheless such an approach has been a means of rapidly obtaining genetic gain in plantations during the early stages of domestication (**Figure 3**). Similarly, seed-production areas were often established early by visually thinning even-aged exotic plantations to

Figure 6 Seed production stand of landrace *Eucalyptus globulus* near Lota, Chile after seed-bearing branches were harvested by climbers.

leave large trees of good form for seed collection in subsequent years (**Figure 6**). While this will avoid the problem of the neighborhood inbreeding that may occur in native forests, it does not avoid problems of inbreeding due to selfing or a narrow genetic base, and genetic gain may also be limited by the low heritability of growth and some tree-form traits.

A large component of improved seed for the main plantation species is now available from open-pollinated seedling or clonal seed orchards established in many countries (**Figure 3**). Seedling seed orchards can be rapidly obtained by thinning pre-established progeny tests based on phenotypic selection, or preferably breeding-value estimates. In species such as *E. globulus*, large genetically based differences in the season and age of flowering may limit outcrossing and the number of effective pollen parents. To improve flowering synchrony, specialized thinning or planting designs are often employed. Higher genetic gains are expected from the more expensive, clonal seed orchards established by either forwards or backwards selection of elite genotypes. Mature scion wood of most commercial eucalypt species can be grafted onto seedling rootstocks using a variety of techniques including bottle-, top-cleft-, patch-, and micrografting, but the success rate is variable at the species and genotype level. Loss of trees due to late-acting graft incompatibility can be a significant cost with such clonal orchards and can be overcome by the use of cuttings or micropropagated clones.

Two major advances have occurred in the production of improved eucalypt seed in the last decade. One was through the discovery that the gibberellin inhibitor paclobutrazol could be used not only to reduce tree growth and allow easier canopy management, but also to enhance flowering. The other advance has been the discovery that the stigma is not necessary for successful pollination and that the pollen will germinate on the surface of the style when it has been cut either just after or even just prior to operculum shed, which often occurs about a week before stigma receptivity. This development has enabled pollination to be undertaken at the same time as emasculation and, coupled with single-flower or style-isolation procedures, has allowed controlled pollination to be undertaken in a single visit to the flower (termed 'single-visit pollination' (SVP) or 'one-stop pollination' (OSP)) (**Figure 7**). The traditional approach involved three visits – emasculation and isolation at operculum shed, pollination at stigma receptivity, and then removal of isolation bags. In the large-flowered species, *E. globulus*, orchards are now established for the manual production of elite full-sib families for deployment using SVP, with or without style isolation and emasculation (**Figure 8**). This approach is also being widely adopted with small-flowered species such as

E. grandis, for the large-scale production of interspecific hybrids for clonal testing.

Vegetative Propagation

Industrial-scale clonal propagation of eucalypts is widespread, particularly in the tropics and subtropics. Selected eucalypt clones are now used routinely in countries such as Brazil, Congo (**Figure 4**), Morocco, and South Africa. Most clonal systems use hardwood (ripened-shoot) cuttings. Micropropagation is mainly used to rejuvenate adult material or rapidly bulking up mother plants for hardwood cutting production. Embryogenesis is still in the research stage with eucalypts. Cuttings can be obtained relatively easily from seedlings or from basal coppice of most eucalypts, but the ability of shoots to produce roots rapidly declines with tree age and with a few exceptions (e.g., *E. deglupta*), adult shoots will not root. Maturation usually occurs rapidly and appears to be due to the production of a rooting inhibitor in mature apical or epicormic leaves. However, rejuvenation of shoots from the crown of mature trees is possible through rapid, 'cascade' grafting (including micrografting) on juvenile rootstocks or micropropagation (five to six transfers are usually required). Felling mature

Figure 7 One-stop pollination of *Eucalyptus globulus*. (a) Emasculation of the flower just prior to operculum shed before pollen is released; (b) isolation of the style after it has been cut transversely just below the stigma and pollen applied. Photograph courtesy of Dean Williams.

Figure 8 Grafted seed orchard of *Eucalyptus globulus* of Bosques Arauco S.A., Chile. The orchard is being used for the production of controlled cross seed using one-stop pollination procedures similar to those shown in **Figure 7**.

trees will usually result in stumps producing juvenile coppice shoots from which cuttings can be obtained and used to establish mother plants for subsequent harvesting. The rooting potential of cuttings is generally increased in the next phase when shoots are harvested directly from well-maintained mother plants. Rapid multiplication is often achieved by using sequential generations of cuttings for mother plants. Clone banks of mother plants from which basal shoots are regularly harvested are either maintained in containers or in field plots.

Cuttings are usually obtained by dipping stem cuttings of one or two nodes into 1–3% indole butyric acid (IBA) rooting hormone. Rooting is usually obtained within 6–12 days and aided by high humidy (e.g., misting) and bottom heating. However, species vary in their propensity to form well-rooted cuttings and the conditions to achieve their maximum rooting potential, particularly mother-plant environment and handling. Species such as *E. globulus*, *E. nitens*, and *E. regnans* have a reputation for being difficult to root, whereas *E. camaldulensis*, *E. deglupta*, *E. grandis*, and *E. robusta* are easy. Even within species, there is considerable variation between families and genotypes. Genotypes of a species may vary in the proportion of cuttings that root from 0% to 90%. For example, in *E. globulus* only 25% of selections have been reported to root at rates of over 75%. In *E. deglupta*, the mean success is between 85–90%. However, good rooting does not ensure high growth rates and there are many examples of good rooting clones which have below-average growth rates. High rooting ability is essential for the successful exploitation of eucalypt hybrids, and most indications to date suggest that it will be inherited in a predominantly additive manner in most interspecific combinations. For economic production of clones, rooting success greater than 70–80% is usually required, which often results in a large number of individuals initially selected on breeding-objective traits being discarded.

Recent advances in technology for industrial-scale clonal propagation of eucalypts have occurred with the development of intensive micro- and minicutting systems in Brazil. Microcuttings use apices obtained from micropropagated plantlets, while the minicutting is based on the rooting of axillary shoots derived from rooted stem-cuttings. In both systems, field clonal hedges are replaced by intensively managed minihedges grown indoors using hydroponic systems (**Figure 9**). This reduces costs and can also make the propagation cycle less dependent on weather conditions.

Figure 9 Indoor hydroponic, minicutting systems developed at Klabin Riocell, Brazil. Mother plants (left bottom) are grown indoors in hydroponic beds (left top) from where shoots are harvested for minicuttings. Cuttings are set in indoor rooting facilities (right top) and well-rooted cuttings obtained by 30 days (right bottom). Photograph courtesy of Teotônio Francisco de Assis.

Genetic Modification and Molecular Breeding

Development of genetically modified (GM) eucalypts has been slow compared with *Populus* species. Traits being considered for modification are no different from those being examined in other forest tree genera. Most transformation has involved marker genes, although genes of commercial significance including herbicide and insect resistance have been stably inserted. Genetic engineering of sexual sterility has been a major focus of research in Australia where eucalypts are native. Transgenic plantlets have been recovered from species such as *E. grandis*, *E. camaldulensis*, *E. globulus*, *E. saligna*, *E. urophylla*, *E. dunnii*, and various hybrids of these species. Field trials were established in the UK in 1995 and in Spain, Portugal, and South Africa in 1997. However, the development of fully tested GM clones to the stage of large-scale planting is likely to be a slow process, taking up to 12 years, and owing to regulatory problems research has, for the moment, shifted more towards molecular breeding through marker- or gene-assisted selection.

The first eucalypt gene sequenced was the important lignin gene CAD of *E. gunnii*, published in 1993 by French researchers working at the University of Toulouse. The first genomic maps of *Eucalyptus* appeared in the early 1990s and were based on random amplified polymorphic DNA (RAPDs) which are dominant polymerase chain reaction (PCR) markers or codominant restriction fragment length polymorphisms (RFLPs), and were used to study the genetic control of quantitative traits in species such as *E. grandis, E. urophylla, E. nitens,* and *E. globulus.* There are now hundreds of codominant (more informative) microsatellite loci developed for eucalypts that are transferable across species and have allowed alignment of genome maps from different studies and species. High consistency in marker order (synteny) is being revealed, and generic maps are emerging with candidate genes (e.g., for flowering and wood properties) positioned. Considerable progress has been made toward identifying genomic regions and markers associated with variation in quantitative traits (quantitative trait loci, QTL). QTL have been detected for numerous traits of economic significance including growth, propagation and wood properties, and in several cases these have been shown to colocate with candidate genes (e.g., *cinnamoyl* CoA reductase (CCR) gene with pulp yield, cellulose yield, and lignin quality (S/G ratio)). Research is now focusing on identifying genes and alleles responsible for the variation in traits of economic significance, particularly the highly heritable and expensive-to-measure wood property traits, through QTL and association studies. The next decade will see major advances in our understanding of the eucalypt genome and molecular breeding. There are now several privately owned databases containing partial sequences of many of the genes expressed in various tissues (e.g., cambium) of *Eucalyptus,* microchips have recently been produced to study eucalypt gene expression, and there is growing interest in large-scale sequencing of the eucalypt genome.

See also: **Genetics and Genetic Resources**: Genetic Systems of Forest Trees; Propagation Technology for Forest Trees. **Tree Breeding, Practices**: Genetics and Improvement of Wood Properties. **Tree Breeding, Principles**: Breeding Theory and Genetic Testing; Forest Genetics and Tree Breeding; Current and Future Signposts. **Tropical Ecosystems**: Eucalypts.

Further Reading

Boland DJ, Brooker MIH, Chippendale GM, *et al.* (1985) *Forest Trees of Australia.* Melbourne, Australia: Australian Government Publishing Service.

Borralho NMG, Cotterill PP, and Kanowski PJ (1993) Breeding objectives for pulp production of *Eucalyptus globulus* under different industrial cost structures. *Canadian Journal of Forest Research* 23: 648–656.

Doughty RW (2000) *The Eucalyptus: A Natural and Commercial History of the Gum Tree.* Baltimore, MD: John Hopkins University Press.

Downes GM, Hudson IL, Raymond CA, *et al.* (1997) *Sampling Plantation Eucalypts for Wood and Fiber Properties.* Melbourne, Australia: CSIRO.

Eldridge K, Davidson J, Harwood C, and van Wyk G (1993) *Eucalypt Domestication and Breeding.* Oxford, UK: Clarendon Press.

Grattapaglia D (2000) Molecular breeding of *Eucalyptus*: State of the art, operational applications and technical challenges. In: Jain SM and Minocha SC (eds) *Molecular Biology of Woody Plants,* pp. 451–474. Dordrecht, The Netherlands: Kluwer Academic Publishers.

Griffin AR, Burgess IP, and Wolf L (1988) Patterns of natural and manipulated hybridization in the genus *Eucalyptus* L'Herit: a review. *Australian Journal of Botany* 36: 41–66.

Jacobs MR (1979) *Eucalypts for Planting.* Rome: Food and Agriculture Organization.

Keane PJ, Kile GA, Podger FD, and Brown BN (eds) (2000) *Diseases and Pathogens of Eucalypts.* Melbourne, Australia: CSIRO.

Moran GF, Thamarus KA, Raymond CA, *et al.* (2002) Genomics of *Eucalyptus* wood traits. *Annales des Sciences Forestières (Paris)* 59: 645–650.

Potts BM and Dungey HS (2004) Interspecific hybridization of eucalypts: key issues for breeders and geneticists. *New Forests* 27: 115–138.

Potts BM, Borralho NMG, Reid JB, *et al.* (eds) (1995) *Eucalypt Plantations: Improving Fibre Yield and Quality,* Proceedings CRCTHF-IUFRO Conference, 19-24 February, Hobart, Tasmania.

Potts BM, Barbour RC, Hingston A, and Vaillancourt RE (2003) Turner Review no. 6. Genetic pollution of native eucalypt gene pools: identifying the risks. *Australian Journal of Botany* 51: 1–25.

Turnbull J (1999) Eucalypt plantations. *New Forests* 17: 37–52.

Williams JE and Woinarski JCZ (eds) (1997) *Eucalypt Ecology: Individuals to Ecosystems.* Cambridge, UK: Cambridge University Press.

Nitrogen-fixing Tree Improvement and Culture

J L Brewbaker, University of Hawaii, Honolulu, Hawaii, USA

Introduction

This review focuses on the genetic improvement and culture of important tree species that fix nitrogen. About 700 tree species are known to fix nitrogen, among approximately 3000 suspected to do so. They represent 11 plant families. Most N-fixing trees (NFTs) are multipurpose and tropical in origin. They are often as valuable as fuelwood, green manure, or forage as they are for lumber or craftwood, and they are cultivated in a great diversity of agroforestry systems. A majority are legumes nodulated by *Rhizobia* or *Bradyrhizobia* bacterial species. However, 10 dicotyledonous families fix nitrogen with the aid of actinomycetes of the genus *Frankia*. Legume trees that fail to fix nitrogen are primarily in the subfamily Caesalpinioideae and include highly selected tropical ornamentals, commonly grown as clones, in genera such as *Bauhinia*, *Caesalpinia*, *Cassia*, *Delonix*, *Haematoxylon*, and *Parkinsonia*. The great majority of significant NFT species can be thought of as newly domesticated. Only a few NFT genera (e.g., *Acacia*, *Casuarina*, *Erythrina*, *Leucaena*, *Prosopis*, and *Robinia*) have attracted the investment of provenance collections and strategic plant improvement. The review is in alphabetical order by genus, and within genera by species. An especially useful reference is the book by K.G. MacDicken (see further reading list).

The Genus *Acacia* (Mimosoideae: Leguminosae)

This large genus dominates NFT literature and embraces three great groups of species – about 850 Australian (now assigned by some authors to a genus *Racosperma*), 200 African, and 200 American. Most American species are shrubs and most African species are thorny trees. Diploid species are largely outcrossing, often due to self-sterility, but about one-third of acacias studied are polyploid, and polyploidy in legumes is often associated with self-fertility. Many species of great forestry potential are in early phases of domestication, provenance collection, and evaluation, among them the moist tropical species *A. aulacocarpa*, *A. cincinnata*, *A. crassicarpa*, *A. holosericea*, *A. leptocarpa*, and *A. polystachya*. Only limited provenance studies or genetic improvement is reported for many important acacias, including the following:

- *A. albida* ($2n = 26$) (= Faidherbia albida): this large, slow-growing tree of dry African tropics is widely distributed for its use as shade and forage on arid lands.
- *A. confusa* ($2n = 26$): 'Formosan koa,' a native of the Philippines and Taiwan, is a small tree grown as fuelwood and as an ornamental and soil-stabilizer, especially on wetter, acid soils. As with many other acacias, some selection has occurred for ornamental use.
- *A. farnesiana* ($2n = 52$): as with other polyploid legume trees, this small, thorny, tropical American tree is widely adapted, self-fertilizing, and often weedy. It has been grown for fuelwood and forage, and provides gum for glue and black dye

for ink. It was planted and selected for flowering in France, as the 'cassie' flowers yield a pleasant perfume.
- *A. nilotica* ($2n = 52, 104$): 'Babul' is a thorny Indian and African tree used as firewood, fodder, charcoal, gum, and tannin. A polyploid, it is extremely variable genetically, and several varieties are recognized commercially. These probably include both self-fertile and self-sterile types.
- *A. saligna* ($2n = 26$): this small tree of south-west Australia is highly variable and grows rapidly in a wide range of ecosystems. It provides fodder and fuel and has been planted widely for sand-dune and mine-dump stabilization.
- *A. senegal* ($2n = 26$): this slow-growing, thorny African tree is the source of gum arabic and can be used for fuel, charcoal, and feed. Limited selection has been made to optimize productivity of gum under severe harvest stress conditions.
- *A. tortilis* ($2n = ?$): this thorny, polymorphic African tree (**Figure 1**) provides firewood and fodder in the dry, hot tropics. It tolerates alkaline soils and is often shrubby in growth.

Widely cultivated acacias that have been the subject of provenance and family evaluations and of other genetic improvement include the following species.

Acacia auriculiformis and *A. mangium*

These are related, rapidly growing trees from Australia to New Guinea, whose hybrid is of increasing genetic interest. The former is a smaller, rather crooked tree widely adapted and grown since 1900 throughout the tropics for shade, fuelwood, furniture, and pulpwood. The latter is taller but less forked and has large phyllodes and branches with much fluting; wood is lower in specific gravity. Both are diploids ($2n = 26$) that can be selfed and show low isozymic heterozygosity values, although outcrossing by bees

Figure 1 Naturalized stand of *Acacia tortilis* in Kenya, often coppiced for fuelwood and fodder.

Figure 2 *Acacia mangium* trial in Chumphon, Thailand, age 3 years.

Figure 3 High-value hardwood trials of *Acacia koa* in Hamakua, Hawaii, age 8 years.

occurs (pollen is in polyads). Both can be cloned from cuttings, and both thrive on acidic soils. *A. mangium* (**Figure 2**) was introduced into Malaysia for pulpwood in 1967 (to 25 000 ha) as seeds from a single tree. A broader sample of germplasm was introduced in the 1980s to overcome the loss of form and vigor that occurred due to inbreeding. Extensive provenance collections have been made and evaluated throughout the world for both species. Vigorous hybrids of good form among the two species were then observed and came to dominate scientific interest. As yet the marketing of hybrid seeds or clonal propagules from hybrids is not economic. Provenances from Papua New Guinea have generally dominated yield trials, and growth habit shows startling differences on different sites. Related, interfertile species of interest include *A. aulacocarpa*, *A. crassicarpa*, and *A. leptocarpa*.

Acacia koa Gray (2n = 52)

Koa (**Figure 3**) is a high-value hardwood that is endemic to Hawaii, polyploid, and largely or completely self-sterile. Among 700 accessions eval-

uated since 1989 in Hawaii, 40 were chosen as parents for seed orchards. Genetic advance through selection was seen in degree of forking, improved bole form, tolerance of koa wilt (*Fusarium oxysporum*), and high wood yield. Seed orchards began bearing in 3–4 years. Genetic advance is sought particularly for tolerance of wilt, a limiting factor in growing koa at lower elevations.

Acacia mearnsii (2n = 26)

Australia's black wattle is a temperate tree now found worldwide as a source of tannin (35–40% recovery from bark), fuelwood, charcoal, poles, windbreaks, and other benefits. This self-sterile species is aggressive, however, and can become weedy. Provenance selections in the mid-1900s for high bark tannin contents at the Wattle Research Institute in South Africa (now the Institute for Commercial Forestry) and in Zimbabwe's Rhodesian Wattle Co. led to varieties preferred for production of tannins. Trees were felled after approximately 10 years, selection focusing on rapid growth. Provenance evaluations and plantations for wood also developed extensively in China. Selected provenances also proved of major value in the reforestation of Korea after the Korean war. With the advent of synthetic tannins and leather substitutes, bark tannin production greatly declined. It is agreed that genetic diversity is great and selection for wood productivity could be profitable, but limited investment is currently made in improvement. Related wattle species of less value for tannins include the green wattle (*A. decurrens*) and silver wattle (*A. dealbata*) that have also been planted widely in the tropics.

Acacia melanoxylon ($2n = 26$)

Australian blackwood is a fine hardwood of the quality of kauri or walnut that occurs over a wide latitudinal range on the east coast of Australia. It is noted for its environmental plasticity and for the importance of locally adapted provenance evaluations. It was introduced widely into East Africa and Sri Lanka in the 1950s.

The Genus *Albizia* (Mimosoideae: Leguminosae)

This is a genus of 150 tropical species of trees, shrubs, and lianas. Many have been domesticated and widely planted but little studied for genetic improvement (e.g., *Albizia chinensis* of the Himalayas, *A. odoratissima* and *A. procera* from South and Southeast Asia). Also important but little bred is *A. lebbek* ($2n = 26$), the 'siris tree,' a widely adapted tree evidently native from Africa to Australia. Limited variation among local and very seedy populations suggests that it is self-pollinated, with abundant dried pods that rattle 'like a woman's tongue.' It is used as an ornamental, for timber and fuelwood, and for fodder. The following species have been the subject of some provenance evaluation, selection and improvement.

Albizia falcataria ($2n = 26$)

Also known as *Paraserianthes falcataria*, albizia (**Figure 4**) is one of the fastest-growing trees of the world. This Southeast Asian tree is planted widely in the tropics as a shade tree and favors moist and acid to neutral soils. Its wood is of low density and of low caloric value, but it is used for pulpwood, boxes, and particle board. Varieties have been selected for use as matchsticks and other products in the Philippines, where plantations are harvested on 10–15-year cycles.

Albizia saman ($2n = 26$) (= Samanea saman)

The classic parasol-shaped 'raintree' or 'monkeypod' shares with many legumes a host of Latin and

Figure 4 Naturalized stand of *Albizia falcataria* on acid soils in Hawaii.

common names. It was distributed worldwide from its Central American center of origin as an ornamental, timber tree, craftwood, and shade tree. It was distributed throughout the tropics from unknown sources and from narrow gene bases, not unlike most tropical trees. Almost no genetic variation occurs, for example, among Hawaii's beautiful, spreading raintrees, that appear to be highly self-pollinated and abundantly seedy in our fuelwood trials. Several accessions of the raintree were included in the gene conservation program of Oxford Forestry Institute.

The Genus *Alnus* (Betulaceae)

This amazingly widespread genus of alders is largely temperate. It includes 35 species, all NFT through association with *Frankia* actinomycetes. They grow rapidly and aggressively (to 30 m in 10 years), and are often considered weeds, although they provide significant soil improvement for forests. Most are $2n = 28$ and outcrossing. Like many NFTs, the alders are widely planted, fully domesticated, poorly represented by forest genetic resources, and managed with little view to genetic improvement. Among these are:

- *A. acuminata*: a Central and South American species planted extensively throughout Latin America for timber and fuelwood.
- *A. glutinosa*: black alder, a widely distributed European species that provided wood for early violins and that is grown as a fuelwood and craftwood and as a stabilizing tree along rivers and roadsides.
- *A. nepalensis*: the Nepal alder of Himalayan origin, planted extensively worldwide for timber, forage, and firewood.
- *A. rubra*: the red alder of northwest North America, a tree up to 40 m tall that is used for construction and furniture, as fuel and in pulpwood mixtures. It can become annoyingly weedy in young stands of pines. As with other alders, the red alder varies greatly in ecosystem adaptability (latitudinal, elevational).

The Genus *Calliandra* (Mimosoideae: Leguminosae)

Most of the 132 species of this predominantly American genus are shrubby, and few enter commerce, but the genus is noted for growth on acid tropical soils. Several are common as ornamental shrubs or trees selected for red, pink, or white flowers, including *C. inaequilatera* and *C. haematoma*.

Calliandra calothyrsus (2n = 22)

Calliandra is a small, clonable, rapidly growing tree used less in its native America than in countries like Indonesia, where it serves as fuelwood, green manure, and fodder. It is sparsely seedy due to its nocturnal flowering habit and cross-pollination largely by bats and moths. The US National Academy of Science supported an early publication on calliandra, and Oxford Forestry Institute provided seed collections for >120 international trials of different seedlots and species. Wide variations were recorded in wood yield, branching, and growth habits. Selection in Australia and Costa Rica has focused on variations in fodder utility and digestibility, which are very low in fresh foliage due to high condensed tannin contents.

The Genus *Casuarina* (Casuarinaceae)

This Australian genus is now recognized to include 17 tree species, with about 70 related polymorphic species assigned to the genera *Allocasuarina*,

Ceuthostoma, and *Gymnostoma*. The true casuarinas are noted for hardwood, fuelwood, and shade on tropical beaches and waterways. Major shelterbelts occur along coastlines in China and in Pacific islands. N fixation is by *Frankia*, pollination is by wind, and some species are dioecious. The species below have been hybridized and evaluated widely in China.

Casuarina cunninghamiana and the related (and cross-fertile) C. glauca (2n = 18)

These are of less significance as plantation species than *C. equisetifolia*, but their genetic variation is much better studied. *C. glauca* can be weedy due to root-sprouting. These species have a broad ecological range as riverine species of eastern Australia, and extensive provenance collections have been made and studied, e.g., in California, China, and Egypt. Genetic diversity was similar to that of other tropical wood species (0.2–0.3, probabilities that any two alleles are different) with unusually large between-provenance variations. Significant variations are reported in traits like freezing survival, tree height, and diameter. Clinal variations by latitude were very significant. Selected families and species hybrids dominate modern plantings.

Casuarina equisetifolia (2n = 18)

The 'ironwood' is the most extensively planted casuarina, noted for fuelwood, pulp, and timber, and as a shade tree. Provenance collections are somewhat limited and significant variations occur among them. Clones based on its stately hybrid with *C. junghuniana* (= *C. montana*) are prominent in Thailand and India (**Figure 5**).

The Genus *Dalbergia* (Papilionoideae: Leguminosae)

The 'rosewoods' of fame occur among the 100 species of this tropical papilionoid genus of trees, shrubs, and lianas. Many species are known for their high-value hardwood and widely planted, but have been the subject of no major genetic improvement. These include *D. decipularis* (Brazilian tulipwood), *D. latifolia* (Indian rosewood, blackwood), *D. melanoxylon* (African blackwood), and *D. nigra* (Brazilian rosewood). The rosewoods are often endangered by deforestation and major genetic erosion.

Dalbergia sissoo Roxb. (2n = 20)

'Sissoo, shisham' is a widely planted high-value hardwood endemic to the Himalayas (**Figure 6**). It is also recognized for shade, soil enrichment,

Figure 7 Hawaii's largest tree is the Costa Rican earpod, *Enterolobium cyclocarpum*.

temperatures. Sissoo is self-fertile but appears to be partially outcrossed in nature and provenance variations are large. Like most legume trees, sissoo is light-seeking and invariably crooked, and genetic variability is high for stem form and growth habit. Estimates of heritability for stem form are high (40–50%) but these assume complete outcrossing. They have led to optimistic projections for expanded use of genetically improved sissoo throughout the tropics, despite its relatively slow growth and lack of institutional investment.

The Genus *Elaeagnus* (Elaeagnaceae)

This European genus includes 40 species of shrubs and trees that fix nitrogen through association with the actinomycete *Frankia*. Similar American NFTs occur in the genera *Shepherdia* and *Hippophae*, often noted as fodder trees but 'armed' with spines for protection. *Elaeagnus angustifolia*, the Russian olive, is commonly cultivated as an ornamental and has been planted widely as a shelterbelt companion of trees that do not fix nitrogen. Selected cultivars and clones are reportedly of better form and appearance.

The Genus *Enterolobium* (Mimosoideae: Leguminosae)

A small genus of five tropical American species, this is related to the genus *Albizia*. A widely cultivated rapidly growing ornamental (**Figure 7**) is the giant, spreading *Enterolobium cyclocarpum*, known as 'guanacaste' or 'elephant's ear.' Like *Albizia saman*, its roots are often superficial and it is undesirable as a street tree. The wood ranges widely in density and quality, and the wood dust causes allergies. Foresters favor trees with dark walnut-like wood, but there is no evidence that these selections are prominent in

Figure 5 Three years' growth of hybrid *Casuarina equisetifolia × C. junghuniana* in Chumphon, Thailand.

Figure 6 Logs of *Dalbergia sissoo* with Director C. Sheikh of Pakistan Forest Institute.

fuelwood and charcoal, honey, and traditional medicines. While it thrives on gravelly outcroppings in the terai at the foot of the Himalayas, it also grows under a wide range of stressing environmental factors, including aridity, mild frost, and very high plantations. Fuelwood plantings in Hawaii (1×1 m spacing) yielded well but showed great intraprovenance variations.

The Genus *Erythrina* (Papilionoideae: Leguminosae)

The 112 species of 'coral trees' are tropical and worldwide in origin, with *E. fusca* native to three continents, its seeds surviving in sea water. Most are small thorny trees with soft wood and high alkaloid contents in leaves. Truly multipurpose but low in value, their uses range from fodder, food, and medicinal to fencepost, shade tree, green manure, and ornamental. Interspecific hybrids were evaluated widely and proved highly interfertile. All appear to be $2n = 42$ and outcrossed by hummingbirds. Many are American in origin, with one endemic to Hawaii, *E. sandwicensis*. *E. abyssinica* and *E. cristagalli* are grown as ornamentals worldwide. Erythrinas are easily cloned from stakes or cuttings. Centro Agronomico Tropical de Investigacion y Enseñanza (CATIE) in Costa Rica maintains a clonal and provenance collection, and the following species are largely grown as locally adapted clones selected for specific use.

- *E. berteroana*: a coral tree that is highly tolerant of aluminous clays, and is often cloned to serve as fence posts in its native tropical America.
- *E. fusca*: the most international species, a classic multipurpose tree. It often serves as shade and green manure for coffee and cocoa and as fenceposts.
- *E. poeppigiana*: a tall South American tree that serves widely as a shade or nurse tree for coffee and as fodder (despite high alkaloid contents).
- *E. variegata* ($= E.$ *indica*): used as a thorny living fence, ornamental, shade for coffee, and support for viny crops. A fastigial, erect cultivar is widely cultivated throughout the Pacific as hedgerows.

The Genus *Gliricidia* (Papilionoideae: Leguminosae)

This small meso-American genus (four species) is known primarily for the species *G. sepium*.

Gliricidia sepium ($2n = 20$)

Gliricidia (**Figure 8**) is a small, rapidly growing, and thornless tree with bright pink flowers in the spring that appear to be entirely outcrossing. It has been spread internationally as an ornamental, green manure, fodder, and firewood tree. The trees clone easily from stem cuttings but develop better roots

Figure 8 *Gliricidia sepium* managed for alley farming trials at Ibadan, Nigeria.

from seedlings. Planting of gliricidia clones as living fences, as support trees for peppers and yams, and as shade for cacao and coffee, often involves 'seat of the pants' selection of erect, less-forked types. A joint series of provenance collections was made in the 1980s, with inputs from International Livestock Center of Africa, University of Hawaii, Nitrogen Fixing Tree Association, Oxford Forestry Institute, Food and Agriculture Organization of the UN and other organizations. Genetic variations were great both between and within provenances. An outstanding provenance, Tequisate, from Guatemala, was observed in trials from Hawaii and the Philippines to Nigeria. Its superior growth was evident in both fodder and total biomass. Extensive studies were conducted in Nigeria of gliricidia in alley farming systems with crops like maize, and as a leguminous fodder supplement in animal diets. The fresh fodder was not palatable to animals, but palatability increased upon drying, and digestibility of the pure legume was relatively low (55%) but increased when in grass mixtures. Improvement in forage quality with selection was predicted among gliricidia provenances and clones.

The Genus *Inga* (Papilionoideae: Leguminosae)

Over 200 species of tropical American origin are in this genus of woody shrubs and trees, studied taxonomically by the Oxford Forest Institute. The species *Inga laurina* ('icecream bean') is used as a food and shade tree in Latin America, *I. vera*, *I. edulis*, and others serve variously as shade, fuelwood, and food (sweet pulp), notably on acid soils in humid tropics. Seeds are recalcitrant, restricting the cultivation and improvement of these species.

The Genus *Intsia* (Caesalpinioideae: Leguminosae)

This tropical Asian genus of three species includes *Intsia bijuga* ($2n = 24$), a handsome timber tree called 'ipil' in the Philippines. The hard, rot-resistant timber of this and *I. palembanica* (Borneo teak) are noted for use in decking and truck bodies. Ipil is believed to be highly variable genetically in the Philippines but there is little evidence of selection and breeding. Debate also exists about its ability to fix nitrogen.

The Genus *Leucaena* (Mimosoideae: Leguminosae)

No NFT genus has been selected or bred more extensively than this American genus of 22 species ranging from Peru to Texas, from sea level to 3000 m. Among the fastest-growing trees, all are woody and most will flower the first year. All are polyploids, ranging from $2n = 52$ to $2n = 112$. The predominant diploid species ($2n = 52, 56$) are self-sterile, while three of the four polyploids ($2n = 104$, 112) are self-fertilized. A single self-pollinated variety of the $2n = 104$ species, *Leucaena leucocephala*, circumnavigated the world four centuries ago, accounting for early interest in this model multipurpose tree for agroforestry systems. Cultivation and management systems differ greatly for leucaenas; some are maintained as shrubs for fodder, some as trees for a wide variety of uses. All species have been included in >2500 seed collections made by University of Hawaii, Oxford Forestry Institute and Commonwealth Scientific and Industrial Organization (CSIRO) of Australia, with evaluations in Hawaii, Queensland, and Nicaragua. In Hawaii, 232 interspecific hybrids were made among 16 species, resulting in 77% interfertility. Many of the 73 hybrids grown were heterotic for growth rate and involved attractive combinations of parental traits. Many species are widespread, at least partially domesticated and of use as fodder or fuelwood, e.g., *L. collinsii*, *L. lanceolata*, *L. macrophylla*, *L. shannonii*, and *L. trichandra*. Much current breeding is based on populations from interspecific hybrids, involving taxa such as *L. pallida* ($2n = 104$), *L. diversifolia* ($2n = 104$), and *L. pulverulenta* ($2n = 56$). Species fully domesticated and of breeding interest include the following:

- *L. diversifolia* ($2n = 104$): self-fertile tree of highland Mexico, now widespread, used as coffee shade, fuelwood, and green manure. Fertile hybrids with *L. leucocephala* are being evaluated for timber and fuelwood.
- *L. esculenta* ($2n = 52$): widely grown outcrossing food tree (edible pods) of highland Mexico, also used as shade. Seedless hybrids with *L. leucocephala* are attractive as high-value hardwood, widely adapted in elevation and resistant to psyllid insects.

Leucaena leucocephala ($2n = 104$)

Leucaena leucocephala is the familiar leucaena throughout the lowland tropics on less acid soils, known by a hundred vernacular names. Among 700 international collections of this self-fertile species grown in Hawaii, most were identical seedy shrubs, the 'common type' widely used for fodder and fuelwood in warm tropics. In contrast, seed collections in its native Mexico and Central America range widely in ideotype, including arboreal types from which 'giant' cultivars have been bred and are now international in use. These are distributed largely as pure lines, e.g., K8, Cunningham, K636, and Tarramba, for fodder and wood uses, and are not inclined to be weedy. Hybrids among pure lines show some heterosis, and one F_2 population (K636 × K584) is marketed. However, interspecific hybrids with highland species are of great commercial interest. KX2 derives from the fifth cycle of recurrent selection following the crossing of *L. leucocephala* with a small Mexican tree, *L. pallida*, a self-sterile polyploid that confers resistance to psyllids and to cold weather. Another, KX3 (**Figure 9**), is from hybrids with *L. diversifolia*, described above. An attractive, clonable, seedless triploid hybrid is K1000 (**Figure 10**) showing impressive hardwood quality and growth rate derived from the cross with *L. esculenta*.

Figure 9 High-value hardwood from 12-year old hybrid, *Leucaena leucocephala × L. diversifolia*, in Waimanalo, Hawaii.

Figure 10 Seedless triploid clone K1000, *Leucaena esculenta* × *L. leucocephala*, age 7 years, Waimanalo, Hawaii.

The Genus *Millettia* (Papilionoideae: Leguminosae)

This genus of 90 African and East Asian species now embraces the genera *Pongamia* and *Derris*, and includes a number of lesser-known fuelwood and timber trees. The pongam or Indian beech is *Millettia* spp., formerly known as *Pongamia pinnata* and as *Derris indica*. It is a native of East Asia that is now widespread and used in many ways, providing a seed oil as fuel and medicinal, fuelwood, postwood, shade, and ornamental. Profuse root suckers and weediness limit its use.

The Genus *Mimosa* (Mimosoideae: Leguminosae)

Few arboreal species occur in this large genus of 400 species, and these are often thorny and shrubby. *Mimosa scabrella* ($2n = ??$), bracatinga, is an exception. It is a fast-growing Brazilian legume of good form with diverse use as fuelwood, lumber, charcoal, ornamental, pulpwood, and shade for coffee. It is believed to be outcrossing and one study showed wide provenance variations.

Figure 11 Variegated-leaf clone of *Pithecellobium dulce* as ornamental, Honolulu, Hawaii.

The Genus *Parkia* (Mimosoideae: Leguminosae)

Forty species of this genus range from Africa to Southeast Asia, and a few are now worldwide. They are bat-pollinated and probably self-sterile, and have recalcitrant seeds. They are observed to vary genetically, but with no evidence for breeding and selection. Two species are outstanding:

- *P. javanica* (= *P. roxburghii*): an imposing tree to 40 m with umbrella crown, used as ornamental or timber tree, with seeds used medicinally.
- *P. speciosa*: a source of food in Southeast Asia (seeds, from the large pods), known to produce hybrids with *P. javanica*.

The Genus *Pithecellobium* (Mimosoideae: Leguminosae)

The 20 tropical American trees of this genus are largely thorny and best known as sources of sweet fruit. It was earlier treated by early botanists as a much broader taxon, including genera like *Albizia*.

Pithecellobium dulce ($2n = 26$)

Manila tamarind is a thorny American tree up to 15 m tall that can be found throughout the drier tropics (**Figure 11**). Its multiple roles include food use of the pods and seeds, honey, postwood, fuelwood, shade, and ornamental. It is alternately planted and cursed, as its thorns and weediness (seeds are spread by birds) reduce its utility and attractiveness. Variegated mutants are selected as ornamental trees, and thornless mutants (as in *Prosopis*) are known to occur.

The Genus *Prosopis* (Mimosoideae: Leguminosae)

The 44 species of this genus are American in origin, and most are drought- and salt-tolerant, thorny,

$2n = 28$ and self-sterile. They include the mesquites of fuelwood and charcoal fame (*Prosopis glandulosa* in North America) that add flavors to many a grill. They are also known as honey and fodder trees and occasionally provide high-value hardwood. Among species that are fully domesticated and widely planted but little studied genetically are *P. cineraria* (= *P. spicigera*), a widespread Indian tree of the hot tropics used as firewood, fodder, green manure, and charcoal. It segregates for thorns, and thorny trees are favored for goat-proof fences. Also of fame is *P. tamarugo*, a slow-growing Chilean species widely planted locally for its saline tolerance under annual rainfall < 100 mm. It has not been adapted effectively outside of Chile. The following two species complexes have been more widely evaluated as provenances or localized selections. However, as with most NFTs, expert panels routinely recommend the increased availability of genetically improved materials, if research money could accompany the recommendations.

Prosopis alba ($2n = 28$) and *P. chilensis*

These are algaroba trees from a related complex largely found in highland subtropics that also includes *P. flexuosa* and *P. nigra*. All serve as sources of honey, firewood, and charcoal, and the sweet succulent pods are used for food and cattle fodder. Seedlot variations are reported for growth rate, limbiness, stem form, and thorniness. Phenotypic selection in natural stands was declared ineffective, due to environmental plasticity, a phenomenon with which all NFT breeders are familiar.

Prosopis pallida ($2n = 28$) and *P. juliflora*

These ($2n = 28$, 56) are two closely related mesquites from Peru north into Central America that are now abundant worldwide; their awkwardly forking trees often dominate arid landscapes and seascapes (**Figure 12**). Known best for their excellent charcoal and dense fuelwood, they were also planted internationally as animal fodder (pods). The wood has very high calorific value (4200–4800 kcal kg^{-1}), and the relatively slow-growing trees offer a durable postwood and an excellent source of honey. *Prosopis pallida* in Hawaii segregates about 1/8 thornless, suggesting single-gene control based on the presumed two-tree origin (introduced from Paris Botanical Garden in 1828). Such a narrow gene base is undoubtedly common in many countries. Trees are coppiceable and cuttings and grafts take fairly well, permitting some use of clones. Thornless trees are universally favored for tropical beaches but do not breed true due to self-sterility. Some selection

Figure 12 The Peruvian *Prosopis pallida* dominates Pacific beaches, such as this in Molokai, Hawaii.

has also occurred for pod yields, tree form, and growth, but serious genetic improvement awaits financial support.

The Genus *Pterocarpus* (Mimosoideae: Leguminosae)

Many fine timbers (bloodwood, narra, padouk, Philippine mahogany, vermilion wood) derive from the 20 species of this tropical Indian and African genus of tall leguminous trees. Narra is probably the best known and most widely cultivated. Timber, dye, and shade use are also made of many other taxa, notably *Pterocarpus erinaceus* (kino, Burmese rosewood), also referred to as *P. angolensis* and *P. echinatus*. Other important species include *P. dalbergioides* (Andaman padauk), *P. macrocarpus* (Burma padauk), *P. marsupium* (malabar kino, source of astringent resin), *P. santalinus* (red sandalwood), and *P. soyauxii* (West African padauk). All are characterized by winged pods, presumed outcrossing, clonability, and extensive natural variability.

Pterocarpus indicus ($2n = 22$)

This majestic spreading tree (up to 40 m tall) is known as narra, Burmese rosewood, and Andaman redwood, and is native over a wide ecological range from Myanmar to Borneo and the Philippines. It is cultivated as an ornamental and street tree and is harvested as a choice timber for furniture and flooring. Flowering occurs in short intervals and pod set appears to be due to self-pollination. Much variation is seen in tree form, fluting, forking, and growth rates of narra. Cuttings root easily from trees of all ages and clones have been selected for adaptability to location, ecology, and use. It responds well to deep, high-quality soils of reduced acidity.

The Genus *Robinia* (Papilionoideae: Leguminosae)

Four interfertile species make up this North American temperate genus, a relict of tropical origin related to gliricidia and sesbania that becomes deciduous only upon frost. Like sesbania, it has a unique N-fixing spectrum of rhizobia. The shrubby species *Robinia hispida*, rose acacia, is planted as an ornamental but has little selection history. In contrast, the black locust is among the most intensively studied and bred NFTs.

Robinia pseudoacacia (2*n* = 20)

The black locust (or false acacia) is widely naturalized throughout North America, where the borer *Megacyllene robiniae* has restricted commercial plantings to erosion control, land stabilization, and as postwood. It is nodulated by both *Rhizobium* and *Bradyrhizobium* bacteria and can become weedy. Away from the borer, black locusts have been planted worldwide and cultivated intensively in Eastern Europe as a pulpwood, postwood, and fuelwood tree. Its outcrossed papilionoid flowers also serve as a bee pasture for honey and cultivars have been selected for use as an ornamental. It was introduced to Europe in the 1700s, where 'shipmast locust' arboreal types were selected and grown intensively (250 000 ha in Hungary) as a timber tree on a 30-year harvest cycle. Great genetic variability (average heterozygosity 0.30) and breeding progress were recorded for height, yield, spinelessness, and coppiceability. In contrast, much less variation was observed in specific gravity (average 0.62 at age 20 years). Intensive studies have been made to accelerate planting of uniform clones from vegetative and root cuttings, tissue cultures, and from grafts.

The Genus *Sesbania* (Papilionoideae: Leguminosae)

This genus includes 50 species of shrubs and small trees in the section Robinieae, now scattered worldwide. Most species are annuals, of which many are important as fodder (**Figure 13**) and ornamental. All nodulate aggressively, some having nodules on the stems. A very fast-growing fodder and multipurpose species is *Sesbania sesban* (= *S. aegyptica*; 2*n* = 12) a short-lived shrub or tree now planted worldwide, and a similar shrub called 'ohai' is native to Hawaii, *S. tomentosa*.

Sesbania grandiflora (2*n* = 24)

S. grandiflora, called 'agati,' is a small polyploid tree from Southeast Asia or Indonesia with showy flowers

Figure 13 Forage trials in Maseno, Kenya, of several arboreal and shrubby species of the genus *Sesbania*.

that are self-fertile but largely outcrossed. It is planted internationally as a multipurpose tree for fodder, fuelwood, ornamental use and often for food (flowers, young pods, and leaves). It is recognized by farmers as a source of fixed nitrogen and green manure. It coppices vigorously for use as fodder or fuel (fast-burning), and selections have been made for ornamental or food use, e.g., with larger flowers or with red (versus white) flowers.

The Genus *Sophora* (Papilionoideae: Leguminosae)

This genus includes 52 species of temperate and tropical origin, several noted as ornamentals or as source of hardwood and of toxic or medicinal chemicals. *Sophora japonica* (2*n* = 28; Japanese pagoda tree) is a large deciduous tree native to China and Korea that has been cultivated for more than 30 centuries in China as an ornamental, dye, and medicinal plant. Flowering begins only on very old trees and the outcrossed flowers cause stains to form where they fall. Genetic variations exploited by horticulturists include weeping, fastigiate, and variegated-leaf trees, and cloning or grafting is common.

The Genus *Tipuana* (Papilionoideae: Leguminosae)

This is a monotypic South American genus with *Tipuana tipu* (2*n* = 20) as the sole species. The 'pride of Bolivia' is a fine timber (rosewood) and ornamental, and is widely planted for fodder, windbreak, and as a street tree to 20 m height in Argentina and Bolivia (to 3000 m elevation). The outcrossed large yellow flowers produce winged one-seeded pods, and it can be weedy. It has an irregular bole similar to most legume trees and it is coppiceable and clonable. Limited studies suggest major provenance variations in ecosystem adaptability (elevation and cold tolerance).

See also: **Genetics and Genetic Resources**: Cytogenetics of Forest Tree Species; Propagation Technology for Forest Trees. **Tree Breeding, Practices**: Tropical Hardwoods Breeding and Genetic Resources; A Historical Overview of Forest Tree Improvement; Forest Genetics and Tree Breeding; Current and Future Signposts.

Further Reading

Awang K and Taylor DA (eds) (1993) Acacias for rural, industrial, and environmental development. In *Proceedings of 2nd Meeting of the Consultative Group for Research and Development of Acacias*, Udorn Thani, Thailand.

Brewbaker JL and Sorensson CT (1994) Domestication of lesser-known species of the genus *Leucaena*. In: *Tropical Trees: The Potential for Domestication and Rebuilding of Forest Resources*, pp. 195–204. Institute of Terrestrial Ecology Symposium no. 29. Edinburgh Centre for Tropical Forests. London, UK: HMSO.

Carron LT and Aken KM (eds) (1992) Breeding technologies for tropical acacias. In: *Proceedings of a Workshop*, July 1991, Tawau, Sabah, Malaysia, July 1991. ACIAR proceedings no. 37.

El-Lakany MH, Turnbull JW, and Brewbaker JL (eds) (1990) Advances in Casuarina research and utilization. In *Proceedings of the 2nd International Casuarina Workshop*, January 1990, Cairo, Egypt.

Evans DO (ed.) (1996) International workshop on the genus *Calliandra*. In *Proceedings of a Workshop*, January, 1996, Bogor, Indonesia.

Gutteridge RC and Shelton HM (eds) (1994) *Forage Tree Legumes in Tropical Agriculture*. Wallingford, UK: CAB International.

Hughes CE (1998) *Leucaena, A Genetic Resources Handbook*. Oxford, UK: Oxford Forestry Institute, Department of Plant Sciences.

MacDicken KG (1994) *Selection and Management of Nitrogen-Fixing Trees*. Morrilton, AR: Winrock International Institute of Agricultural Development.

Pasiecznik NM, Felker P, Harris PJC, *et al.* (2001) *The Prosopis juliflora–Prosopis pallida complex: A Monograph*. Coventry, UK: Henry Doubleday Research Association.

Roshetko JM (ed.) (2001) *Agroforestry Species and Technologies: A Compilation of the Highlights and Factsheets Published by NFTA and FACT Net 1985–1999*. Taiwan: Taiwan Forestry Research Institute and Council of Agriculture; Morrilton, AR: Winrock International.

Shelton HM, Piggin CM, and Brewbaker JL (eds) (1995) Leucaena–opportunities and limitations. In *Proceedings of a Workshop*, January 1994, Bogor, Indonesia.

Turnbull JW (ed.) (1987) Australian acacias in developing countries. In *Proceedings of an International Workshop*, August 1986, Gympie, Australia.

Westley SB and Roshetko JM (eds) (1994) Dalbergia. In *Proceedings of an International Workshop*, Winrock International, Morrilton, AR.

Withington D, Glover N, and Brewbaker JL (eds) (1987) *Gliricidia sepium* (Jacq.) Walp.; management and improvement. In *Proceedings of a Workshop*, June 1987, CATIE, Turrialba, Costa Rica.

Genetics of Oaks

A Kremer, L A Xu, and A Ducousso, INRA, UMR Biodiversité Gènes et Ecosystèmes, Cestas, France
L A Xu, Nanjing Forestry University, Nanjing, Jiangsu, China

Introduction

Oaks (*Quercus* spp.) belong to the most widely distributed genus of forest trees. Besides their economic and ecologic importance, oaks are also considered in many countries as cultural and patrimonial resources. Despite their value, they have received very little and spasmodic attention in genetic research in comparison to other forest trees. They were some of the earliest species that were investigated for inheritance studies in Europe, but were neglected in genetics for almost a century. The first international conference on oak genetics was organized in 1991, whereas international working groups in conifers had been well established for decades. This conference synthesized the state of knowledge in oak genetics. Over the past 10 years, significant contributions have been made in population and evolutionary genetics of oaks. This contribution adds to the 1991 synthesis the genetic knowledge of oaks that has accumulated over the past decade.

Biogeography

The genus *Quercus* is distributed over the northern hemisphere in Asia, North America, Europe, and Africa. There are more American than Eurasian species. The highest oak species diversity exists at 15–30° N, in Central America and Mexico and in Southeast Asia (Yunnan province in China). Species richness decreases northward and southward from both Mexico and southern China. The northern limit of distribution is at 50° N, except for the European *Q. petraea* and *Q. robur*, which extend up to 60° N. The southern limit of the genus is reached in the southern hemisphere in Colombia and Indonesia, where oak species exist at higher altitudes. Oak species grow from sea level to very high altitudes, up to 4000 m in Yunnan province in China.

Throughout its natural range, the genus has differentiated into numerous species adapted to extremely variable habitats, from swamps to deserts. For example, evergreen species have differentiated under Mediterranean climates as *Q. agrifolia* and *Q. wislizenii* in California, and *Q. coccifera* and *Q. ilex* in southern Europe. Typical examples of extremely wide distribution are *Q. rubra* and *Q. alba* in North America, *Q. acutissima* and *Q. mongolica* in Asia, and *Q. robur* and *Q. petraea* in Europe. In most cases the widely distributed species are those that have received the most intensive genetic studies.

Taxonomy and Phylogeny

Depending on the authors, there are between 300 and 600 reported oak species. Since the beginning of Linnaean taxonomy, classification within the genus *Quercus* has been controversial, and more than 20 classifications have been proposed. Disagreements involve the characters to be used for the classification, the infrageneric subdivisions adopted (subgenera or sections), and species delineation. There is so much variation within some species that several authors have questioned the concept of species, and further complications in taxonomy are due to frequent interspecific hybridization. The most complete classification is that proposed by Camus (1936–1954), which has recently been supported by molecular approaches. Classification criteria are mostly based on foliar and fruit characteristics. In Camus' classification, the genus *Quercus* (*sensu lato*) is subdivided into two subgenera: *Euquercus* (*Q. sensu stricto*) and *Cyclobalanopsis*. About 150 species belong to *Cyclobalanopsis*; these only exist in South Asia, whereas species belonging to *Euquercus* are the more familiar oak species. The subgenus *Euquercus* (now called subg. *Quercus*) has been further subdivided into six different sections by Camus, and into three sections in a more recent review based on phylogenetic inferences of morphological characters. Earlier taxonomists considered *Cyclobalanopsis* and *Quercus* (*sensu stricto*) as two separate genera. Recently taxonomy in the genus *Quercus* has benefited from phylogenetic approaches based on molecular data. Analysis of nuclear and chloroplast DNA sequences showed that the genus was composed of three major clades: *Cyclobalanopis*, *Cerris*, and the remaining three main sections that form one monophyletic group (*Protobalanus*, *Erythrobalanus* (red oaks), and *Lepidobalanus* (white oaks) *sensu* Camus). A major finding of the DNA data in comparison to previous morphological data was the ancient evolutionary separation of *Cerris*.

Genomics

Although a few cases of naturally occurring triploids have been mentioned in the literature, oaks are diploid species, bearing $2n = 24$ chromosomes. Extra chromosomes ($2n = 24 + 1$, 2, or 3) have been reported as consequences of irregular segregation in mitoses. The diploid DNA content per cell is remarkably homogeneous across species and botanical sections, as reported values only vary between 1.88 and 2.00 pg ($= 10^{-12}$ g per cell). The DNA content of two widely separated sections was 1.88 pg for *Lepidobalanus* (*Q. petraea* and *Q. robur*) and 1.91 pg for section *Cerris* (*Q. cerris* and *Q. suber*), and these species are representative of the most widely separated sections (*Lepidobalanus* and *Cerris*). The genome of oak species contains 40% guanine + cytosine (G + C) base composition, which is similar to most higher plants. Genetic mapping in *Q. robur* resulted in 12 linkage groups and a total map length ranging between 1200 and 1800 cM. The map length of the different linkage groups in *Q. robur* varies between 10 and 200 cM. Eighteen percent of the genetic markers used in the mapping study deviated from Mendelian segregation as a result of a high genetic load in the species. The physical characteristics of the oak genome (number of chromosomes, physical and genetic size, genetic map length) are similar to tomato (*Lycopersicon*)! The oak genome is six times larger in physical size and three times larger in genetic size than *Arabidopsis*, the prime model species in plant genomics.

Genomic research has further addressed the molecular differentiation among species and gene discovery. Phylogenetically closely related oak species exhibit limited molecular variation among species, as a result of their interfertility. In the case of *Q. robur* and *Q. petraea*, the interspecific differentiation, regardless of the molecular markers used, is only slightly larger than the intraspecific variation. Hence genomic regions responsible for species variation are extremely rare. As a result of the similarity between genomes, molecular markers as microsatellites could easily be transferred across species and botanical sections.

Evolutionary Biology

Origin and Diversification

Fossil remains of oaks are common and have been discovered on the three continents. Earliest remains found in China, Europe, and North America come from the Eocene. The almost simultaneous appearance of the genus on the three continents has raised the question of its geographic origin and radiation.

Two scenarios were proposed to reconstruct the history of the species. In the first, the genus appeared in Southeast Asia, deriving from a sister genus *Trigonobalanus* during the Palaeocene, and migrated in two directions: to Europe and America via the North Atlantic land bridge before the Eocene, and via the Bering strait after the Miocene. In the second scenario, the genus *Quercus* derived from the widely distributed boreal–tropical deciduous forest that occupied the northern hemisphere at the beginning of the Tertiary. The genus further differentiated as the continents separated further. As a result, oak species arose 'simultaneously' on the different continents and differentiated from the ancestral group composing the boreal–tropical forest. Between the Oligocene and Miocene, oaks diversified extremely rapidly as a response to important climatic changes. Most fossil remains of that period are similar to extant samples. Hence it is believed that most of the extant species already existed at the mid-Miocene.

Postglacial Migration

During the Quaternary, oaks underwent important migrations in response to climatic changes. There were about 17 Milankovitch climate oscillations (alternation of glacial and interglacial periods) when oak species, like other plants, were subjected to successive contractions and expansions of their distributions. A glacial period lasted 50–100 thousand years, whereas interglacial periods were much shorter and lasted 10–20 thousand years. Climatic oscillations were strong selective forces, favoring species that were vagile enough to track their moving habitats. They were most likely responsible for the selection of a reduced number of species that occupy today large continental distributions (*Q. robur* in Europe, *Q. alba* in America, or *Q. acutissima* in Asia). These movements have profoundly influenced the genetic diversity of the species, but in rather different ways between North America and Europe. A large survey conducted recently in Europe comparing the remaining historical footprints (pollen deposits) with genetic fingerprints (chloroplast DNA (cpDNA) polymorphisms) demonstrated how the extant distribution of genetic diversity was shaped by the dynamics of postglacial colonization. At the end of the last glaciations, European oaks were restricted to three major refugia (southern Iberian peninsula, central Italy, and southern Balkan peninsula). As glacial periods lasted up to 100 000 years, species were most likely genetically differentiated among these refugial zones, as shown by the completely different haplotype lineages (= cpDNA variant) occupying these regions. In less than 7000

years (from 13 000 to 6000 years ago), oaks recolonized the majority of their modern ranges. On average, the migration was extremely rapid (300–500 m year^{-1}). Rare long-distance dispersal events contributed significantly to the rapid spread of the species. These dynamics had various consequences for the diversity of the species. Despite the strong founder effects that accompanied the recolonization, oaks were able to maintain high levels of genetic diversity. Although the highest neutral diversity is restricted to the southern areas of Europe, the level of diversity is still important in the central part of Europe, where the different migration fronts originating from the refugial zones merged. However, today's distribution of adaptive diversity is not correlated with neutral diversity; there is no footprint left by the maternal origin on the variation of adaptive traits. Genetic variation for adaptive traits resulted from more recent local selection pressures. Interspecific hybridization was a key migration mechanism as it facilitated the introgression of late-successional species (*Q. petraea*) into the pioneer species (*Q. robur*). The systematic sharing of the same cpDNA haplotype by different white oak species occupying the same stands indicates that hybridization was extremely important during recolonization. Postglacial colonization dynamics in North America were quite different from Europe. Species were not restricted to genetically separated refugial zones. Furthermore, oak stands persisted as low-density populations close to the Laurentide ice sheet. Hence postglacial recolonization was more diffuse than in Europe.

Reproduction and Mating System

Reproduction in oaks can be either vegetative or sexual. Coppicing has been a widely used vegetative system to regenerate oak stands. Stump sprouting is also a natural way of propagation for oaks after forest fires and, when repeated over generations, creates clonal structures in natural stands. The production of root suckers is a less frequent natural means of propagation, but has been reported in *Q. pyrenaica* and *Q. ilex*. Oaks are predominantly monoecious species with distinct male and female flowers, although cases of floral hermaphroditism have been reported. *Quercus* is anemophilous (wind-pollinated) whereas other genera of Fagaceae (except *Fagus* and *Nothofagus*) are entomophilous. There are important differences among species groups in the lag between pollination and fertilization. In the *Lepidobalanus* section (white oaks), acorns mature at the end of the growing season in which the pistillate flower is pollinated. In contrast, in the

Erythrobalanus and *Cerris* sections, fertilization occurs more than 12 months after pollination.

Oaks are also predominantly outcrossing species. All reported values of effective outcrossing rates using the mixed-mating model exceed 0.90. Hence it has often been suggested that a self-incompatibility mechanism existed in oaks, although no experimental data have yet been published on the subject. Mating studies have also indicated that crosses among related trees are rare.

Hybridization

There is much literature on oak hybridization. Hybridization was first investigated by using morphological traits as diagnostic markers, but this has raised controversy as the range of within-species variation of morphological features remains largely unknown. During the past 10 years, gene markers have been applied to study introgression that provided new interpretations on the ecological and evolutionary role of hybridization in sympatric oak species. In two examples, one in European oaks (*Q. petraea* and *Q. robur*) and one in North American oaks (*Q. grisea* and *Q. gambellii*), hybridization was shown to be asymmetric. In the European example, *Q. petraea* preferentially pollinated *Q. robur*, whereas in the other example *Q. grisea* was the predominant male parent. As indicated earlier, asymmetric hybridization can reinforce the succession of species replacing the pioneer species (*Q. robur*) by a late successional species (*Q. petraea*) and is thought to have facilitated the dispersal of species during the postglacial recolonization. The use of molecular markers also permitted estimation of the level of introgression and revisiting of former interpretations of the geographic distribution of hybrids. Occurrence of hybrids has been reported more frequently at the margins of the natural distributions of sympatric species where typical parental habitats are less frequent. The hypothesis of higher fitness of hybrids under nonparental habitats has recently been challenged by an alternative interpretation. In the *Q. grisea*/*Q. gambellii* example, it was suggested that the mate-recognition systems can be impaired under stress conditions prevailing at the margin of a species' range. It was found in this example that the formation of a hybrid zone resulted from the diminishing male function due to environmental stress.

Hybridization in natural stands was further confirmed by artificial crossings. Extensive controlled crossing was done within and between species belonging to the three sections *Lepidobalanus*, *Erythrobalanus*, and *Cerris*. Among the 75 intersec-

tional crosses, only three resulted in viable seedlings (*Q. turbinella* (section *lepidobabanus*) × *Q. cerris* (section *cerris*), *Q. turbinella* (section *lepidobabanus*) × *Q. suber* (section *cerris*), and *Q. turbinella* (section *lepidobabanus*) × *Q. marilandica* (section *erythrobabalnus*)), and were confirmed by segregation analysis of the progeny. Hence hybridization is mostly intrasectional, as has been extensively reported in the *Lepidobalanus* section. Artificial controlled crosses also confirmed the preferential asymmetric crosses between *Q. petraea* and *Q. robur*, and challenged the use of morphological features for hybrid identification. Hybrids resulting from controlled crosses between *Q. petraea* and *Q. robur* exhibited foliar characteristics that were not intermediate between the parental forms, as they resemble more the female parent.

Gene Flow in Natural Populations and Neighborhood Size

Oaks have small pollen grains that can be physically transported over long distances. Physical models of oak pollen dispersal pointed to maximum theoretical distances of several hundreds of kilometers. Investigations on oak pollen production and dispersal in California indicated that pollen grains can be transported at least 16 km. In Finland, at the northern margin of *Q. robur*, pollen grain capture on traps along a gradient was recorded at 7 km from the source stand. However, pollen may lose viability quite rapidly. Effective pollen dispersal has recently been measured using parentage analysis with microsatellite fingerprinting obtained in *Q. macrocarpa* and in *Q. petraea* with *Q. robur*. In both examples, it was shown that more than half of the male parents contributing to pollination of female parents on a 5-ha study stand were actually located outside the stand, and that the mean distance of pollen dispersal exceeded several hundred meters. Although nearest neighbors contributed preferentially to pollination in these two examples, pollen dispersion curves are clearly composed of both a short- and a long-distance contribution, most likely related to different wind-transport mechanisms. These data were obtained in rather dense stands (10–100 trees ha^{-1}), and contrasted sharply with those obtained in a savanna landscape where oak trees are more sparsely distributed. In a pollen-dispersal study of the Californian *Q. lobata* (1–2 trees ha^{-1}), effective pollen flow was much more limited (mean dispersal distance = 65 m) as a result of the low density of trees. There is an important asymmetry between pollen and seed dispersal: the ratio of the number of gene migrants by pollen and seed between populations amounts to several hundreds, even though parentage analysis has indicated that long-distance seed dispersal can also occur. Based on dispersal curves from gene-flow data, attempts were made to estimate neighborhood sizes. In dense stands (100–200 trees ha^{-1}), as with *Q. petraea* and *Q. robur*, the neighborhood size was estimated at 12–20 ha, representing 1200–4000 trees. However, these numbers are lower for more sparsely distributed species, as for *Q. lobata* where a male neighborhood size of 3 ha was inferred.

Genetic Diversity

Genetic variation for morphological and adaptive traits has been investigated in oaks for more than a century. Provenance tests were established in Europe at the end of the nineteenth century, and progeny tests in the 1950s. Similar efforts were made in North America in the second part of the twentieth century. During the past 15 years, genetic surveys have been conducted in many oak species to monitor the level and the distribution of genetic diversity with various molecular tools in response to conservation issues. While investigations of phenotypic traits were mostly concentrated on economic important species for which provenance tests were established, molecular diversity was assessed for a greater range of species.

Diversity of Phenotypic and Adaptive Traits

Levels of diversity   Phenotypic and adaptive traits exhibit extremely high levels of diversity, even for fitness-related traits. Heritability values (h^2) were estimated by many authors in progeny and clonal tests for the commercially important species (*Q. petraea, Q. robur, Q. rubra,* and *Q. acutissima*). The highest estimated heritabilities were for phenological characters like bud burst (0.35–0.80) and leaf retention (0.35–0.65), and for wood quality (0.15–0.87). Genetic variability for height growth is extremely variable among species and case studies (in *Q. petraea* estimated h^2 ranges from 0.15 to 0.78, in *Q. acutissima* from 0.43 to 0.44, and in *Q. rubra* from 0.15 to 0.25). Most of the crown-architecture characters of oaks have given low estimates of heritability (<0.05) except for the presence of epicormic shoots (0.38). These heritability values are statistical estimates and their range of variation does not correspond to confidence intervals but rather variation between estimates made among different experiments.

Geographic distribution of diversity   Phenotypic traits exhibit important population differentiation but not as much as for the chloroplast genome.

However, differentiation values (Q_{st}) reach 0.06–0.6 for height and phenological traits in *Q. petraea*. Geographic trends of variation exist for phenological growth, and form traits. Geographic gradients are, however, most evident in phenological traits (dates of bud break and growth cessation). In the European species, *Q. petraea*, there is a clinal trend of variation with latitude and altitude, with southern origins flushing earlier than northern origins; these trends are consistent across the different, widely scattered provenance tests that were established. In the widely distributed American species, *Q. rubra*, there are contrasting patterns depending on the site where the provenance test was established. Longitudinal clines were observed in tests planted in Nebraska whereas an altitudinal cline was found in tests established in Tennessee. These trends are different from those observed in widely distributed north temperate conifers, suggesting that not only climatic factors may impose selection pressures, but most likely also biotic factors, such as defoliating insects. For other traits such as growth and form, no consistent geographic gradient of variation was observed in either American or European species.

DNA and Protein Diversity

Levels of diversity   There is now evidence that, in respect of their DNA features, oaks are among the most diverse species of forest trees. This is particularly so for species with large continental distributions, such as *Q. robur* and *Q. petraea* in Europe, *Q. macrocarpa* in North America, or *Q. acutissima* in Asia. These can exhibit high levels of heterozygosity both within a population and throughout their ranges. For microsatellites, the number of identifiable alleles present at a locus within a population can frequently exceed 20. There is also evidence that levels of diversity differ between the two major botanical sections: white oaks (section *Lepidobalanus*) are more variable than red oaks (section *Erythrobalanus*), as shown by a comparative allozyme analysis between these two sections. High levels of diversity are most likely due to the maintenance of large population sizes, the ability for long-distance gene flow, and prevalent interspecific hybridization. Long generation intervals may be advocated for managing oak populations, to minimize the allele losses associated with genetic drift.

Geographic distribution of diversity   Most nuclear genetic diversity resides within populations, as is usual for wind-pollinated species. With a few exceptions, genetic differentiation among populations (F_{st} or G_{st}, which are analogs of Q_{st}) is less than 10%. Earlier results obtained with allozymes were confirmed by other molecular markers, random amplified polymorphic DNA (RAPD), amplified fragment length polymorphisms (AFLPs), or microsatellites (simple sequence repeats). As for the level of diversity, substantial pollen flow, large populations, and long generation intervals may account for these results. The geographic distribution of genetic diversity of chloroplast genomes is strikingly different from those of nuclear markers. Oak stands tend to be completely fixed within populations for the chloroplast genome but fully differentiated among stands. Hence differentiation values (F_{st} or G_{st}) in most cases exceed 0.80. The discrepancy between nuclear and chloroplast genome differentiation is due to their different inheritance. As chloroplast genomes are maternally inherited, and as seed exhibits restricted dispersal, diversity within a stand rapidly becomes eroded as a result of stochastic effects. These trends are facilitated during the initial establishment of the stand, which is often associated with low population sizes due to founder effects. Fixation of chloroplast genomes is enhanced by the limited number of founder individuals and the restricted dispersal of seed. When these mechanisms are extended to larger geographic scales, they lead to strong geographic patterns of cpDNA diversity that reflect the colonization dynamics of the species, resulting in strong phylogeographic structures. In conjunction with historical records gathered from fossil pollen, phylogeography of cpDNA permitted reconstruction of postglacial colonization pathways of oaks throughout Europe.

Genetic Improvement

Oaks have several features that limit operational breeding. Besides the biological constraints of longevity, such as delays in the onset of flowering, and the impossibility of seed storage, the uncertainty of long-term breeding objectives makes the implementation of improvement programs economically questionable. Hence research in breeding and improvement has been much less intensive than in shorter-rotation species, even for highly valuable tree species. The general understanding is that tree improvement would be a rather risky initiative for such long-lived species and that research in genetics should be oriented towards a sustainable management of oak stands rather than to the improvement of the existing resources by breeding and selection methods. Hence objectives of tree improvement initiatives were limited to the selection of seed stands, or the installation of first-generation seed orchards.

Europe

There is a long tradition of oak improvement in Europe, although it has not taken the typical form of a modern tree-breeding program. In the Netherlands, it was traditional to raise Q. robur for several years in the nursery and to select for stem form. These procedures resulted in the selection of various cultivars that were used in horticulture. Classical tree breeding started in the early 1950s in Germany, and even earlier in Eastern European countries when the earliest plus-tree selection was done and clonal seed orchards were established. Ongoing activities in tree improvement are being conducted on three species: Q. petraea, Q. robur, and Q. suber. For these species, European countries have selected seed stands which are clustered in provenance regions following European Community regulations on reproductive material. For Q. petraea and Q. robur, progeny tests associated with seed orchards were installed in Belgium, Croatia, Denmark, Hungary, Germany, Ireland, Lithuania, Netherlands, Slovakia, Ukraine, and the UK. Objectives of improvement are wood quality (including the quality of cork for Q. suber), stem form, and adaptation to the site. Research to solve the problems posed by the poor storage ability of seed was also pursued. Besides improvement of seed-storage protocols, techniques were developed for vegetative reproduction either by traditional cutting propagation or by using in vitro techniques and somatic embryogenesis.

North America

At the first international conference on oak genetics held in 1991, 27 ongoing oak improvement programs were reported on a total of nine species (Q. alba, Q. falcata, Q. macrocarpa, Q. nigra, Q. phellos, Q. prinus, Q. robur, Q. rubra, and Q. velutina). These programs were mainly conducted by public agencies and institutions in the eastern USA, whereas two projects in Canada were mentioned. In this period, some of the oldest provenance and progeny tests were established for Q. rubra. Objectives of breeding programs were timber and veneer for Q. rubra but more generally, juvenile growth and plantation success. Other objectives were also pulp production or use as shelterbelts (for Q. macrocarpa in the Great Plains). Breeding efforts varied from only plus-tree selection (in about half of the programs) to also producing seedlings or clonal seed orchards. However, owing to the decline of oak plantations and to reduced public budgets (national or state agencies), these projects have all been reduced in the past 10 years. Recent initiatives have, however, revitalized tree improvement activities in northern red oak, such as the creation of the Hardwood Tree Improvement and Regeneration Center (HTIRC) in Purdue (Indiana). HTIRC aims to improve the genetic quality and regeneration of *Q. rubra* through application of classical breeding, genomics, and advanced propagation technology.

Exotics

Oaks have been transferred to various regions in the world. Red oaks from the eastern USA have been introduced in Europe, and *Q. rubra* is currently used throughout western Europe, not only as an ornamental tree but also as a plantation species for veneer or timber production. Hence tree improvement activities in *Q. rubra* were implemented in France, Germany, and the UK, starting with the installation of combined provenance and progeny tests. As the introduction in Europe began at the end of the eighteenth century, there have been only a few generations since the species was introduced in Europe but landraces (a landrace is a population that became adapted in a new environment to which it was transferred) have already been genetically differentiated in Europe. Similarly, *Q. robur* was introduced in many countries throughout the world, but no genetic improvement program has been reported outside its natural range and Europe.

See also: **Genetics and Genetic Resources**: Cytogenetics of Forest Tree Species; Genecology and Adaptation of Forest Trees; Genetic Systems of Forest Trees. **Genetics and Genetic Resources**: Molecular Biology of Forest Trees; Population, Conservation and Ecological Genetics. **Temperate Ecosystems**: Fagaceae. **Tree Breeding, Principles**: Breeding Theory and Genetic Testing; Conifer Breeding Principles and Processes.

Further Reading

Axelrod DI (1983) Biogeography of oaks in the Arcto-Tertiary province. *Annals of the Missouri Botanical Gardens* 70: 629–657.

Camus A (1936–1954) Les chênes, Monographie du genre *Quercus* et Monographie du genre *Lithocarpus*. Encyclopédie Economique de Sylviculture. Paris, France: Editions Le Chevallier.

Guttman SI and Weight LA (1989) Electrophoretic evidence of relationships among *Quercus* (oaks) of eastern North America. *Canadian Journal of Botany* 67: 339–351.

Kremer A (ed.) (2002) Range wide distribution of chloroplast DNA diversity and pollen deposits in European oaks: inferences about colonisation routes and management of oak genetic resources. *Forest Ecology and Management*, Special issue, 156(1–3): 224.

Kremer A, Savill PS, and Steiner KC (eds) (1993) Genetics of oaks. *Annales des Sciences Forestières* 50(1): 1s–469s.

Manos PS, Doyle JJ, and Nixon KC (1999) Phylogeny, biogeography, and processes of molecular differentiation in *Quercus* subgenus *Quercus* (Fagaceae). *Molecular Phylogenetics Evolution* 12: 333–349.

Turok J, Kremer A, and de Vries S (eds) (1998) *Proceedings of the first EUFORGEN meeting on Social Broadleaves*. Rome, Italy: IPGRI.

Pinus radiata Genetics

R D Burdon, New Zealand Forest Research Institute, Rotorua, New Zealand

Introduction

Pinus radiata is arguably the most domesticated of all forest trees. It is grown in exotic plantations occupying over 4 million ha, an area roughly 500 times its natural extent. Overall these plantations are highly productive, and many are intensively managed. Associated with the intensive management, several large-scale, intensive genetic improvement programs have developed, which have prompted a large volume of genetic research on the species. Indeed, this genetic research, and commercially motivated research on most other aspects of the species' biology, have led to the species assuming the role of a model species for research into forest trees. The genetics of the species are of twofold interest. On the one hand, the story typifies that of many conifers, and pines in particular, in respect of karyotype, genomic characteristics, and genetic system in general. On the other hand, there are a number of features that are highly distinctive of the species. Notable among these are the biogeography, with five discrete natural populations that are differentiated by a combination of adaptive features and apparent founder effects, and the conspicuously high level of functional genetic variation from tree to tree. Intensive genetic improvement began from around 1950, and is now being pursued at varying levels of sophistication in at least five countries. It has delivered major genetic gains, in growth rate, tree form, and disease resistance. Improvement work is shifting in emphasis towards improving wood properties, while differentiated breeds are being developed. Challenges remain in the management of gene resources.

The Genetic System

Breeding System

Like almost all pines (*Pinus* spp.), *P. radiata* is an outbreeder. Effective self-fertility, reflected in filled seed produced upon selfing, is very incomplete, but highly variable from tree to tree. This is consistent with the postulated mechanism of a fairly high 'load' of recessive embryo lethal genes, combined with the archegonial polyembryony – with this polyembryony, the set of viable seed can be much higher than the percentage incidence of viable zygotes resulting from inbreeding.

The viable offspring produced by self-pollination show, on average, marked inbreeding depression, with poorer growth and competitive ability than outcross progeny. This inbreeding depression reflects sublethal deleterious recessive genes. It varies markedly according to parents and individual offspring. This variability, in both effective self-fertility and inbreeding depression in viable offspring, is consistent with random variation among parents in the load of deleterious recessive genes.

Matings between relatives that are less extreme than selfing also cause inbreeding depression, roughly in proportion to the relatedness between the seed- and pollen parents.

Seed collections made from natural stands show appreciable inbreeding depression, resulting from neighborhood inbreeding whereby neighboring trees tend both to be related to each other and to interpollinate. In plantations, the natural neighborhood structures are typically broken down, and seed collections from plantations show negligible signs of inbreeding. Self-thinning evidently eliminates inbred individuals preferentially during the life of a natural stand.

Genomic Characteristics

Pinus radiata is strictly diploid with a haploid chromosome number of 12. Any departure from the diploid state evidently reduces natural fitness to zero. Regarding the karyotype, the chromosomes are extremely large, all of similar size and metacentric, with only subtle distinguishing features. In these respects the species is typical of pines (*Pinus* spp.) in general, and also of most other conifer genera.

In keeping with the size of the chromosomes, the genome is enormous, around 2×10^{10} basepairs, but over 95% noncoding. However, despite the extremely stable karyotype, it appears that there is a relatively high mutation rate, judging from the level of the genetic load and the general sensitivity of pines to gamma rays. In keeping with the genomic stability, DNA analysis has revealed a very high level of homologies, in respect of functional genes and their loci within chromosomes, between *P. radiata* and *P. taeda*, which has become another main 'model-species' pine.

Crossing-over of chromosomes in meiosis is high – estimated map length is around 1800–2000 centi-Morgans – and is evidently slightly higher in male than female meiosis.

Genetic Architecture

Taxonomic Position and Crossability

Pinus radiata belongs within the subgenus *Pinus* (syn. *Diploxylon*) or the 'hard pines.' It has recently been assigned to a section Attenuatae van der Burgh (the 'California closed-cone pines') which has recently been separated from the section Oocarpae, which now comprises a group from Mexico–Central America. Within the Attenuatae, it is readily crossable with *P. attenuata* and moderately crossable with some southern populations of *P. muricata*, but tends to be reproductively isolated from both species by pollination season and distance. However, there is one area where hybrids with *P. attenuata* occur naturally, but without conclusive signs of long-term introgression. *Pinus radiata* is also known to be weakly crossable with three or four members of the Oocarpae.

Population Differences

The pattern of natural population differences reflects the distinctive natural distribution. The species occurs in just five discrete natural populations (**Figure 1**). While all populations exist in a particular variant of a Mediterranean climate, created by a cold ocean current reducing summer temperatures and causing summer sea fogs, the habitats of the populations differ significantly (**Table 1**). In addition, the geographic separation between populations varies widely. In keeping with that, the degree of taxonomic separation varies. The southernmost populations, from Cedros and Guadalupe Islands, are recognized as separate varieties, vars *cedrosensis* and *binata* respectively, both having their needles usually in pairs rather than threes. The three northern populations, on the mainland, are assigned to var. *radiata*; that from Cambria is apparently the most distinct.

Chemotaxonomic information is very incomplete, but it serves to reinforce a picture of highly multidimensional differentiation among the various natural populations. In this pattern, the apparent affinities between individual populations can depend greatly on the trait in question, such that many traits have to be considered simultaneously, preferably in common-garden experiments, for the overall pattern to become clear. However, immunoassay techniques have been used to give a measure of genetic distances between populations, with results that generally match the classical taxonomic picture.

The populations differ not only in traditional taxonomic traits and phytochemistry but also in tree morphology, growth rate, site tolerances, and pest and disease resistance (which are often the effective manifestations of site tolerances).

Some population differences for morphological traits, turpentine composition, and wood density are summarized in **Table 2**. Corresponding differences in growth rate, site tolerances and disease and pest

resistance are summarized in **Table 3**. In some morphological features, such as cone size and branching pattern, marked population differences are superimposed upon large tree-to-tree differences. However, for needles per fascicle (except on vigorous shoots of young trees) and bark thickness (except in old trees), tree-to-tree differences are totally subordinate to population differences.

The pattern of population differences can in part be interpreted in terms of adaptation to the different environments. For example, the strong taproot development of the Cedros population, and to a lesser extent the Guadalupe population, are presumably an adaptation to more intense drought on the islands. The greater palatability of Guadalupe to browsing animals can be readily interpreted as reflecting a lack of browsing mammals on the island. However, there are other population differences that are difficult to interpret as being adaptive. It therefore appears that some of the differences reflect founder effects and genetic drift occurring in the processes of colonizations, local extirpations, and coalescences that evidently resulted from climatic fluctuations and eustatic sea-level changes that have occurred since the Pleiocene.

Marker and Genomic Differentiation

Some strong population differences exist within *P. radiata* with respect to the standard isozyme systems, in contrast to the norm of isozyme variation within species being almost entirely among individuals within populations. Indeed, there are electromorphs that represent high-frequency private alleles for some of the populations. Actual DNA marker differentiation has not been studied thoroughly. Markers (simple sequence repeats or SSRs) have been developed that give excellent 'fingerprinting' of individual genotypes and pedigree verification, but such markers, because they are so polymorphic within populations, are inherently unsuited to differentiating among populations. Thus, while populations will surely be differentiated by DNA markers,

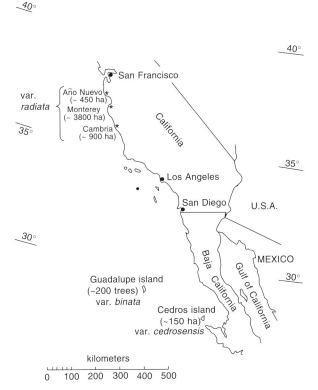

Figure 1 Map showing natural distribution of *Pinus radiata*. Current extent is shown for each population, being reduced by urbanization at Monterey and Cambria and grossly reduced on Guadalupe island. Adapted with permission from Burdon RD (2000) *Pinus radiata*. In: Last FT (ed.) *Ecosystems of the World*, vol. 19. *Tree Crop Ecosystems*. Amsterdam, The Netherlands: Elsevier.

Table 1   Natural occurrence and habitats of *Pinus radiata*

Population	Latitude (°N)	Altitude (m)	Exposure	Rainfall (mm)	Geology/soil	Extent (ha)	
						Historic	Current
Año Nuevo	37	0–330	Very varied	675–900?	Argillite-derived, slightly calcareous	450	450
Monterey	$36\frac{1}{2}$	0–420	Generally moderate	400–650?	Very varied geology and soils	7400	3800
Cambria	$35\frac{1}{2}$	0–180	Varied	450–575?	From single sandstone formation	1400	900
Guadalupe	29	330–1200	Severe	150–500?	Basaltic, rocky	250?	200 trees
Cedros	28	380–640	Locally severe	150–250?	Skeletal, old sediments and metamorphics	150	150

Adapted from Burdon RD (2000) *Pinus radiata*. In: Last FT (ed.) *Ecosystems of the World*, vol. 19: *Tree Crop Ecosystems*, pp. 99–161. Amsterdam, The Netherlands: Elsevier.

Table 2 Native-population differences within *Pinus radiata* in some morphological traits, turpentine composition, and corewood density

Trait	Population				
	Año Nuevo	Monterey	Cambria	Guadalupe	Cedros
Bark thickness (young trees)	Thinnish	Thickish	Medium	Thin	Thin
Cone length (cm)	8–15	5.5–13	10–19	5–11.5	3.5–9.5
Mean seed weight (mg)	42	23	48	29	29
Needles per fascicle	3	3	3	2	2
Persistence of juvenile features	Low	High	Very high	Very low	Low
α-pinene (% pinenes) in wood turpentine	23	35	34	21	14
Inner corewood density (site-dependent)	325	330	320	360	360
Sinker root development	Medium	Medium	Least	Strong	Greatest

(Adapted from Burdon RD (2000) *Pinus radiata*. In: Last FT (ed.) *Ecosystems of the World*, vol. 19: *Tree Crop Ecosystems*, pp. 99–161. Amsterdam, The Netherlands: Elsevier.)

Table 3 Differences between natural populations of *Pinus radiata* in growth potential, site tolerances, and resistance to pests and pathogens

Feature	Grade of evidence	Population				
		Año Nuevo	Monterey	Cambria	Guadalupe	Cedros
Growth potential	a	+	+	+	−	− −
Ease of transplanting	bc	+	o	−	+ (+)	− −
Resistance to/tolerance of:						
Frost	b	+ +	+	−	o?	− −
Snow damage	c	+	o	−	n.d.	n.d.
Boron deficiency	b	+	+	+	−	− −
Phosphorus deficiency	b	−	+ +	+ +	− ?	n.d.
Soil salinity	bc	o	+	+ +	− −	−
Damage by pathogens						
Dothistroma pini	ab	+ +	+ +	− −	o	− −
Cyclaneusma minus	a	+	+ +	− −	−	− ?
Sphaeropsis sapiniea	b	+ +	+ +	− −	− −	−
Phytophthora cinnamomi	b	− −	+	+ +	n.d.	n.d.
Endocronartium harknesii	b	o	−	− −	+ +	+
Damage by invertebrates						
Pineus pini	c	+	+	− −	− −	+
Damage by mammals						
Deer/rabbit browse	bc	o	o	o	−	+
Deer browse	b	−	o	+	n.d.	n.d.
Porcupines	b	+	+	− −	n.d.	n.d.

o, average; +, better than average; + +, markedly better than average; −, worse than average; − −, markedly worse than average; n.d., no firm data available.
a–c denote decreasing weight of evidence.
(Reproduced with permission from Burdon RD (2000) *Pinus radiata*. In: Last FT (ed.) *Ecosystems of the World*, vol. 19: *Tree Crop Ecosystems*, pp. 99–161. Amsterdam, The Netherlands: Elsevier.)

there are not yet the markers identified whereby a tree can be assigned unequivocally to a single native population, let alone to its correct hybrid ancestry.

Within-Population Genetic Variation

Tree-to-tree genetic variation, both visible and cryptic, is a striking feature of *P. radiata*, which has led to much past confusion among taxonomists. Cone size and shape show much variability, which is superimposed upon the considerable population differences. Dramatic variation exists in branching pattern (**Figure 2**), with neighboring trees often ranging from being monocyclic or uninodal (with only one cluster of branches produced in a year's growth on the leader) to highly polycyclic (with up to six such clusters); this variability is of profound importance for breeding programs and wood utilization. Considerable tree-to-tree genetic variation is also evident for growth rate, resistance to some diseases, stem straightness, a wide range of wood properties, turpentine composition, rate of onset of

(a)   (b)

Figure 2 *Pinus radiata* trees of contrasting branching patterns. (a) This tree has a highly polycyclic (or multinodal or short-internode) branching habit, producing several quite closely spaced branch clusters on each year's growth of the leader. In consequence, the branches are relatively small, giving a dispersed pattern of knots in timber, which favors producing structural grades. It is usually associated with less susceptibility to malformation and often better straightness and faster growth, at least early in the rotation. This sort of habit has been favored for the main breeding programs of New Zealand and Chile. Preferable for structural timber, it requires pruning in order to produce clear timber, which has been widely practiced in New Zealand. (b) This tree has an essentially monocyclic (or uninodal or long-internode) branching habit. The branches are large and steep-angled, but clearcuttings can be obtained between branch clusters without pruning. Prone to malformation and general poor form on many sites, this habit has been pursued in a subsidiary breeding program in New Zealand to produce a long-internode breed. This variation is strongly heritable, with the two trees representing extremes of an essentially normal distribution. For many sites, the ideal might be two co-equal branch clusters per year's leader growth, but that can only be expected reliably through mass propagation of well-proven clones. Courtesy of New Zealand Forest Research Institute Ltd.

some adult characteristics, and soil tolerances. Soil tolerances can generate substantial genotype–site interactions among phosphorus-deficient sites and elsewhere.

Estimated heritabilities and additive genetic coefficients of variation (which between them encapsulate the scope for genetic improvement) are shown for a range of traits in **Table 4**. While some of the values relating to branching pattern and cone characteristics may be exceptional, those for other traits seem fairly typical for the genus. For many additional wood properties only broad-sense estimates are available; while generally very high, they are unlikely greatly to

exceed narrow-sense heritabilities. Some of the wood properties, e.g., grain spirality and percentage heartwood, can show very high coefficients of variation, but such figures need to be interpreted with caution. As always, heritabilities for individual traits can depend, to varying degrees, on both the populations and the environments.

Relatively few between-trait genetic correlations are known at all well (**Table 5**), although, as with heritabilities, the values may vary according to both population and environment. Those best known involve positive associations between growth rate, frequency of branch clusters, light, wide-angled

Table 4 Estimated heritabilities and phenotypic coefficients of variation among individuals within base populations in *Pinus radiata* for different traits, together with likely economic significance for genetic improvement

Trait	Heritability	Coefficient of variation (%)[a]	Economic significance
Turpentine composition	>0.9		Negligible
Wood density (cores or disks)	0.7	7	Sometimes major
Cone characters[b]			
Volume, seed weight	>0.5	20–35	Minimal
Length, shape, scale no.	>0.5	12–18	Minimal
Grain spirality	0.3–0.7	~45	Sometimes major
Branch clusters on bole	>0.5	20–30	Often high, but indirect
Stem sinuosity[c]	0.4		Not major (− ve)
Wood density (penetrometer or torsiometer measurements)	0.3–0.4		As for wood density
Branching habit overall[c]	0.3		Generally high
Height to first cone	0.3	20–30	Little direct importance
Dothistroma attack[c]	0.3		Locally major
Cyclaneusma needle cast[c]	0.1–0.35		Considerable (− ve)
Branch angle (steepness)[c]	≤0.2		Considerable (− ve)
Height	0.2	12	Limited in itself
Stem diameter	0.1–0.3	15	Major
Stem volume	0.1–0.3	30	Major
General stem straightness[c]	0.1–0.3		Generally major
Branch diameter	0.2		Major (− ve)
Frost resistance (growth room)	0.2		Minor overall
Butt sweep[c]	0.1–0.2		Often major (− ve)
Forking, etc.	0.05–0.1		Major (− ve)
Wind damage	0.05		Locally major (− ve)
Leader dieback	0.05		Sometimes important

[a] Where measurement scale allows valid estimate.
[b] Broad-sense heritability, instead of narrow-sense, but unlikely to be much greater than narrow-sense.
[c] Based on visual scores, with observer error depressing effective heritability values.
Reproduced from Burdon RD (1992) Genetic survey of *Pinus radiata*. Part 9. *New Zealand Journal of Forestry Science* 22: 275–298, with permission.

Table 5 Approximate values of the better-estimated between-trait genetic correlations in *Pinus radiata*

	Height	Wood density	Stem straightness	Branching frequency	Forking (incidence)	Branch diameter	Branch angle
Stem diameter	0.7	− 0.2 to −0.4	0.1	0.15–0.45	0.1		0.1
Height		0.15	0.2	0.2–0.45	0.35		0.25
Wood density			0	− 0.05	0		
Stem straightness				0.4	0.5		0.15
Branching frequency					0.3–0.5	0.75	0.6
Forking						0.3	0.4
Branch diameter							0.65

Note: Positive signs denote favorable genetic correlations in relation to ideal of fast growth, high wood density, small, wide-angled branches, zero forking, and polycyclic (multinodal or short-internode) branching habit. Hence there are a number of adverse correlations in relation to an ideal of long internodes that would allow significant clear cuttings without pruning, more so on some sites than others.
After Burdon RD (1992) Genetic survey of *Pinus radiata*. Parts 1–9. *New Zealand Journal of Forestry Science* 22: 275–298.

branching, stem straightness, and freedom from malformation, and a negative association between wood density and stem diameter. Significant constraints therefore face the breeder in trying to pursue long internodes (which offer clear cuttings without pruning) along with improved growth and form, or both increased wood density and volume production.

Genotype–environment interactions are evident in respect of both variation among sites in expression of

genetic variation and rank changes among sites in performance of genotypes. Differences in tree form can be more strongly expressed on fertile sites. Rank changes are strongly evident between phosphorus-deficient sites and elsewhere (pointing to genetic variation in tolerance of this deficiency) but otherwise tend to be limited.

Within-population variation in genetic markers (isozymes, restriction fragment length polymorphisms

(RFLPs), randomly amplified polymorphic DNA (RAPDs), amplified fragment length polymorphisms (AFLPs), SSRs) is significant, but it does not stand out from other conifer species in the way that much of the morphological variation does.

Early Domestication Genetics

Domesticated stocks of the species have arisen since the species was first introduced as an exotic, around 1850–1860 for South Africa, Australia, New Zealand, and Spain, and in 1885 for Chile. New Zealand evidently became self-sufficient for seed by the early 1880s, and made significant exports of unimproved seed to South Africa at least in the 1920s and to Australia until the middle of the twentieth century. Documentation of follow-up seed importations by Chile and Spain has not been traced. It appears that the two northernmost of the natural populations, Año Nuevo and Monterey, have been the progenitors of almost all the domesticated stocks, with a disproportionate contribution from the small Año Nuevo population. For many purposes these are the natural populations that are best adapted to the exotic environments, but even broader adaptation can presumably be obtained from drawing germplasm from the other populations.

While domesticated stocks may have come from a very incomplete and unbalanced representation of the natural range, seed importation records for New Zealand and genetic evidence indicate a fairly broad ancestral base in terms of numbers of individuals.

Even before intensive breeding began, some genetic improvement occurred in a process of landrace development. Release from the 'neighborhood inbreeding' of natural stands has evidently been a positive factor. There have also been some genetic shifts in response to pressures of natural and silvicultural selection in the adoptive environments, although it is difficult to quantify these shifts accurately. Heterosis, or hybrid vigor, from crossing between two natural populations, has been postulated but not proven.

Intensive Genetic Improvement

General History

Pioneering research on genetic variation in *P. radiata* began in Australia during the 1930s, under the auspices of the (Commonwealth) Forestry and Timber Bureau, Canberra. Intensive breeding programs began in New Zealand, Australia, and South Africa in the 1950s. These were based on local stocks, in the belief that provenance variation would not be important. This decision was put to the test in parallel or subsequent provenance or provenance/progeny trials. In fact, it proved to be justified, despite initial underestimation of provenance variation and the likelihood that additional germplasm from the natural range could bring long-term benefits. However, some of these benefits may only be realizable in segregating generations, after the F_1.

Improvement began with very intensive selection of 'plus trees,' mainly in commercial stands (**Figure 3**). Selection criteria varied significantly among agencies according to perceptions of whether growth rate or form was the higher priority for improvement. The plus trees were grafted into archives prior to establishing grafted clonal seed orchards. This put tree breeders on a long 'learning curve' in the siting, establishment, and management of the orchards. Difficulties arose with delayed incompatibility of grafts (or else obtaining cuttings from postjuvenile trees), achieving good pollen isolation, and with seed yields.

An interim improvement measure, pending self-sufficiency for orchard seed, has been collection of seed from the best trees in stands, either at felling or on standing trees. This was much helped by the serotinous cones which could store several years' seed crops on the trees. In addition, progeny trials were available as back-up seed sources.

Figure 3 One of the original *Pinus radiata* plus trees selected in a closed stand in New Zealand, shown well after the selection age. The outstanding vigor of this parent ('Clone 55') characterizes almost all its progeny. The wood of the progeny, while of low density, has some very desirable technical properties. Courtesy of New Zealand Forest Research Institute Ltd.

Progeny testing was embarked upon from the outset, with varying thoroughness and success. However, it became appreciated, by the late 1960s, that the extremely intensive selection of plus trees left little scope for reselection on the basis of progeny-test information, and severely restricted the genetic base for long-term breeding. Further selection of first-generation plus trees was done, making vastly more selections.

Despite the technical problems, clonal seed orchards came close to meeting planting requirements, and actually exceeded them in some areas. However, the slow and incomplete capture of genetic gain prompted the development of new delivery systems. Selection of orchard sites was greatly improved. Hedged seed orchards were adopted in some quarters, which allowed controlled pollination with full capture of genetic gain and greater flexibility, and they are easier and safer to manage and harvest. Other types of orchard that allow controlled pollination have also been developed (**Figure 4**). Vegetative multiplication of small amounts of top-quality seed is a slightly more recent development that can further speed up the capture of genetic gain. It is being done on a large operational scale using nursery cuttings, and on a smaller scale using tissue-culture plantlets, while embryogenesis from seed embryos is being pursued. Embryogenesis, while more difficult to achieve in pine than in spruces (*Picea* spp.), offers a platform for future genetic transformation. Clonal forestry, based on mass propagation of well-characterized, intensively select clones, is being pursued by a few agencies, and is close to being fully developed, although there still remain some problems of long-term storage of clones to retain full vigor and ease of propagation.

As befits the species' commercial importance and its model-species status, it is the subject of a full-scale genomic sequencing project, but the information is proprietary.

Early improvement work was directed mainly at improving growth rate and tree form, in varying emphasis on the two. Genetic gains achieved have generally been large (**Figure 5**), typically reflecting

Figure 5 Trees of *Pinus radiata* produced by early pair-crossing between intensively select parents on a very high-quality site in New Zealand. Tree form is strikingly good for the site and stocking. Planted at 750 stems ha^{-1} in pasture, and thinned at age 8 to 215 stems ha^{-1}, 18-year predominant mean height was 33.5 m, mean breast height diameter 54 cm, with 480 m^3 stemwood ha^{-1}. The better pair-crosses of similar material, kept at higher stockings but on a similar site, gave mean annual increments approaching 50 m^3 ha^{-1} year^{-1} at age 27, compared with an expected value of 30–35 m^3 ha^{-1} year^{-1} for unimproved stock. With large genetic gains achieved in growth and tree form, attention is shifting to improving wood properties to help produce high-quality raw material on short rotations. Courtesy of New Zealand Forest Research Institute Ltd.

Figure 4 Clonal seed orchard of *Pinus radiata* designed to produce seed of superior genetic quality by controlled pollination. This is one of several types of orchard that has been developed to avoid the operational problems of producing seed on tall, tree-form grafts or cuttings, and is an adaptation of the meadow orchard system of producing apples. A site has been chosen that favors early and profuse seed production on the grafts. Often such seed is now produced in limited quantities for mass vegetative multiplication, still mainly by nursery cuttings. Courtesy of New Zealand Forest Research Institute Ltd.

the relative emphasis on growth and form respectively. Since then there has been some focus on resistance to needle-cast diseases, with local or sporadic efforts directed at resistance to some other diseases. More recently has come increasing emphasis on improving wood properties (**Figure 6**), to offset the impacts of various measures that cut effective growing costs, viz. shorter rotations, fertilizer use, heavier thinning regimes.

Genetic Improvement in Individual Countries

New Zealand   The breeding program was initiated by the Forest Research Institute (FRI) within the New Zealand Forest Service. FRI also conducted associated research, gathering up some earlier work. A national program was effectively operated until 1987, when the Forest Service was dissolved. Following that, the New Zealand Radiata Pine Breeding Cooperative was created, with FRI doing the breeding and genetic research, but with increasing in-kind contributions from member companies after corporatization and then privatization of Forest Service plantations. Cooperative members have come to include some from Australia, the Forestry Commission of New South Wales and some smaller concerns. During 2000–2002, the Cooperative became a limited-liability company. In the meantime, some companies have developed their own propagation and clonal programs as their own intellectual property. In 2003 a decision was made to terminate state funding of breeding and gene-resource work and immediately associated research.

Intensive plus-tree selection began in the early 1950s, for establishing regional seed orchards, although the regionalization proved to be unnecessary.

Figure 6   Sampling a *Pinus radiata* candidate for selection for determining several key wood properties by taking a core of 12 mm diameter. Courtesy of New Zealand Forest Research Institute Ltd.

The first block of orchard was planted in 1958, to start producing seed in 1968. Orchards produced enough seed for the whole country by 1986. Since then, control-pollinated orchards have become predominant, with considerable vegetative multiplication. Fully clonal systems, while still hampered by imperfect control of maturation, are being implemented on a significant scale by two companies.

Following the initial round of plus-tree selection, many more first-generation plus trees were selected in 1968–1970, to give a broadly based breeding population, with a further round during 1984–1987.

Selection was initially for growth and form, arriving at a strongly polycyclic (or multinodal or short-internode) ideotype (**Figure 2a**), although a side-program pursued a long-internode ideotype (**Figure 2b**) as an insurance. Recently a portfolio of differentiated breeds has been created, to serve different sites and end-uses as well as addressing market uncertainties.

Australia   Although the federal organization (Forest and Timber Bureau, later the Division of Forestry and then Forestry and Forest Products) of the Commonwealth Scientific and Industrial Research Organisation (of Australia) (CSIRO) started the research, breeding programs began under the auspices of individual states and Australian Capital Territory (ACT). Of the states, New South Wales, Victoria, and South Australia had a major involvement in the species, with lesser involvements on the part of Western Australia, ACT, Tasmania, and Queensland. All the states and ACT began intensive breeding by 1960 or soon after, with two programs in Victoria, although some programs have effectively lapsed or been absorbed. Lack of coordination among the states, and the consequent thin spread of expertise, hampered progress, but some coordinated efforts were eventually achieved under the auspices of the Australian Forestry Council. The Council established a research working group that met biennially to address forest genetic improvement in general, and New Zealand participants were eventually admitted.

Selection emphasis has been more on growth rate and less on tree form than in New Zealand, but some shifts towards establishing new plantations on more fertile ex-pasture sites call for greater emphasis on improving tree form.

In 1978 CSIRO led a major initiative to collect seed from natural stands for *ex situ* gene resources. Numerous plantings resulted from that, but are in need of active management. Further seed collection was done on Guadalupe island in 1991.

In 1983, after disastrous fires in South Australia, the Southern Tree Breeding Association was formed, initially to address a crisis of availability of seed of acceptable genetic quality. Members now include, in addition to various South Australian agencies, ones from Victoria, Western Australia, and Tasmania.

South Africa Despite an early start with breeding, in the 1950s, activity has been limited by the restricted areas over which the species succeeds.

Chile An abortive start by Instituto Forestal in the early 1970s was followed by the successful establishment of a Cooperative (initially Convenio) between the Southern University of Chile and industry parties. Established along the lines of the Industry/North Carolina University Tree Improvement Cooperative, it began with individual members setting up their own seed-orchard programs. However, it appears not to have led to a coordinated national program based upon free exchange of genetic material, although some interregional integration has occurred within large corporate structures.

Initial plus-tree selection was intensive, aimed at much the same short-internode ideotype as in New Zealand. Each member company established a 42-clone grafted seed orchard. Choice of orchard site was guided by experience in New Zealand and Australia, and was mostly very successful, leading to orchards meeting most members' seed requirements in about 10 years.

Among major member companies there have been separate developments, pursuing vegetative multiplication, and sophisticated biotechnology for appropriating intellectual property.

Spain In the late 1980s a breeding program was set up for the Basque autonomous region, on the northern coast just west of the Pyrenees, based in Vitoria. By far the main emphasis has been on breeding for diameter growth. Problems in finding a suitable seed-orchard site within the region have led to the establishment of an orchard far to the south, in Andalusia.

Hybridization

Experimental hybridization of *P. radiata* was undertaken as early as the 1930s, the main success being crossing with *P. attenuata*. While this hybrid had advantages, difficulties of mass production, and limited availability of sites where it had a decisive advantage prevented its large-scale planting. Interest in interspecific hybrids has been rekindled by a combination of availability of technology for vegetative multiplication of seeds or seedling stock, combined with a desire to extend site tolerances and/or improve resistance to diseases that are threats.

Genetic Transformation

Genetic transformation is being researched in *P. radiata*, initially as proof of concept, with current emphasis on control of reproduction and herbicide resistance, but with a view to other goals, notably manipulating wood properties. It is serving as a research tool. Operational use is envisaged as being in the context of clonal forestry.

See also: **Genetics and Genetic Resources**: Cytogenetics of Forest Tree Species; Genetic Systems of Forest Trees; Molecular Biology of Forest Trees; Population, Conservation and Ecological Genetics; Propagation Technology for Forest Trees. **Tree Breeding, Practices**: Genetics and Improvement of Wood Properties. **Tree Breeding, Principles**: A Historical Overview of Forest Tree Improvement; Conifer Breeding Principles and Processes; Forest Genetics and Tree Breeding; Current and Future Signposts.

Further Reading

Burdon RD (2000) *Pinus radiata*. In: Last FT (ed.) *Ecosystems of the World*, vol. 19: *Tree Crop Ecosystems*, pp. 99–161. Amsterdam, The Netherlands: Elsevier.

Burdon RD (2001) *Pinus radiata*. In: CAB International (compil.) *Pines of Silvicultural Importance*, pp. 359–379. Wallingford, UK: CAB International.

Burdon RD and Moore JM (eds) (1997) *IUFRO '97 Genetics of Radiata Pine*. Proceedings of NZFRI-IUFRO conference 1–4 December and workshop 5 December, Rotorua, New Zealand. FRI Bulletin no. 203.

Burdon RD (1992) Genetic survey of *Pinus radiata*. Parts 1–9. *New Zealand Journal of Forestry Science* 22: 275–298.

Burdon RD, Hong SO, Shelbourne CJA, *et al.* (1997) International gene pool experiments in *Pinus radiata*: patterns of genotype–site interaction. *New Zealand Journal of Forestry Science* 27: 101–125.

Burdon RD, Firth A, Low CB, and Miller MA (1998) *Multi-site Provenance Trials of* Pinus radiata *in New Zealand*. Forest Genetic Resources no. 26, pp. 3–8. Rome: FAO.

Jayawickrama KJ and Carson MJ (2000) A breeding strategy for the New Zealand Radiata Pine Breeding Cooperative. *Silvae Genetica* 40: 82–90.

Millar CI (2000) Evolution and biogeography of *Pinus radiata* with a proposed revision of quaternary history. *New Zealand Journal of Forestry Science* 29: 335–365.

Moran GF, Bell JC, and Eldridge KG (1988) The genetic structure and conservation of the five natural populations of *Pinus radiata*. *Canadian Journal of Forest Research* 18: 506–514.

Rogers DL (2002) *In situ* conservation of Monterey pine (*Pinus radiata* D. Don): information and recommendations. Report no. 26. Davis, CA, USA: University of California Division of Agriculture and Natural Resources, Genetic Resources Conservation Program.